CONCRETE DESIGN HANDBOOK

4TH EDITION

Cement Association of Canada

Association Canadienne du Ciment

1105 – 350 Sparks St.
Ottawa, Ontario, Canada
K1R 7S8

4th Edition
Second Printing December 2017

ISBN 978-1-896553-23-8

CAC Concrete Design Handbook
Printed in Canada

Table of Contents

Chapter 13 — Tilt-up Concrete Wall Panels

FOREWORD

This Handbook supersedes the third edition of the Concrete Design Handbook, published by the Cement Association of Canada in 2006.

The Concrete Design Handbook addresses the analysis and design of reinforced concrete structural elements in accordance with the CSA Group standard A23.3-14, Design of concrete structures and the 2015 National Building Code of Canada. This Standard, henceforth referred to as "CSA A23.3", contains significant revisions to the content of the previous edition. Major changes include:

- revised provisions for determining the resistance of compression members in Clause 10,

- new provisions on the termination of longitudinal reinforcement in flexural tension zones, revised provisions for determining the critical shear section near supports and refined strut-and-tie models in Clause 11,

- a complete reorganisation of Clause 21 with new provisions for shear walls, tilt-up walls and frames, foundations and members not considered part of the seismic force resisting system, and

- new provisions for adhesive anchors and revised earthquake provisions in Annex D on anchorage.

The preface of the CSA Group standard A23.3 contains a more exhaustive list of changes to the Standard.

Material explaining the intent and application of these revisions is included in this Handbook.

A reproduction of the Standard appears in the Handbook, together with explanatory notes on its provisions in Part I. This material is followed by a total of thirteen chapters in Part II covering many aspects of the structural design of conventionally reinforced and prestressed concrete buildings. Basic information on design for fire resistance and design recommendations for structures which will be exposed to corrosive environments are also included.

The format of this Handbook was selected to aid designers in a systematic manner. Following the CSA Group standard and its explanatory notes, each chapter contains informative text and background information on its subject. Design aids covering a broad range of practical applications are provided for design efficiency. Chapters have been prepared by different authors and therefore differ somewhat in the style of presentation. Some authors emphasize reviews of design requirements or trace the background of new provisions, while others concentrate on numerical examples to illustrate applications. Every effort has been made to ensure that a chapter format which best illustrates practical use of the material under consideration has been adopted in all cases. In all example problems, unless otherwise noted, reference to a 'section', 'table' or 'figure' is an implied reference to the Handbook. A reference to a 'clause' is an implied reference to the CSA Group standard A23.3.

In order to keep the volume of the Handbook to a reasonable size, several design aids which form part of this Handbook are not included in the printed version but are available for download from the www.cement.ca website.

PRÉFACE

L'Association Canadienne du Ciment a mis à jour son manuel de calcul de structures de bâtiments en béton (Concrete Design Handbook) suite à la publication de la norme Groupe CSA A23.3-14 et du Code national du bâtiment du Canada 2015.

Ce manuel contient la norme Groupe CSA A23.3-14 avec des notes explicatives en partie I, suivie de 13 chapitres dans la partie II. Chacun de ces chapitres contient du texte explicatif, des exemples ainsi que des graphiques et des tableaux couvrant une vaste gamme d'applications pratiques, le tout tenant compte des commentaires reçus des utilisateurs de la version précédente.

Le manuel "Concrete Design Handbook" est disponible en anglais seulement. Le personnel technique de l'Association Canadienne du Ciment peut toutefois répondre aux questions qui lui seront posées dans les deux langues officielles du Canada.

DISCLAIMER

This publication has been prepared by the Cement Association of Canada (CAC) to aid in the design of reinforced concrete building structures. It has been the intent of the CAC to present information in a manner which will serve as an extension to the CSA Group standard A23.3-14, Design of concrete structures, and the other documents referenced herein. While every attempt has been made to present information that is factual and in a useable format, none of the references to the CSA Group standard or the National Building Code of Canada should be construed as an endorsement of the material appearing in the Handbook by the agencies responsible for the referenced material.

This publication is intended SOLELY for the use of PROFESSIONAL PERSONNEL who are competent to evaluate the significance and limitations of the information provided herein, and who will accept total responsibility for the application of this information. The authors and the Cement Association of Canada disclaim any and all RESPONSIBILITY and LIABILITY for the application of the stated principles and for the accuracy of any of the material contained in this publication to the full extent permitted by law.

AVIS DE NON-RESPONSABILITÉ

Cette publication a été préparée par l'Association Canadienne du Ciment (ACC) pour aider à la conception de structures de bâtiments en béton armé. L'intention de l'ACC est d'y présenter de l'information qui complémente la norme Groupe CSA A23.3-14, Calcul des ouvrages en béton, et d'autres documents de référence ci-inclus. Bien que tous les soins aient été pris pour présenter des informations factuelles et dans un format utilisable, aucune des références à la norme Groupe CSA ou au Code national du bâtiment du Canada ne doit être interprétée comme une approbation du contenu figurant dans le Manuel par les organismes responsables du matériel de référence.

Cette publication a été conçue UNIQUEMENT à l'intention d'un PERSONNEL PROFESSIONNEL qui détient les compétences nécessaires pour évaluer la signification et les limitations de l'information contenue dans ce Manuel, et qui acceptera l'entière responsabilité de l'usage de cette information. Les auteurs et l'Association Canadienne du Ciment se dégagent de toute RESPONSABILITÉ pour l'application des principes énoncés et de l'exactitude de l'information contenue dans cette publication à la pleine mesure permise par la loi.

ACKNOWLEDGEMENT

The Cement Association of Canada wishes to express its deepest gratitude to the experts who spent countless hours of effort in updating this publication. This edition of the Handbook would not have been possible without the dedication and hard work of these individuals.

The fourth edition of the Concrete Design Handbook was prepared by a team of authors, many of whom are members of the CSA Group standard A23.3 Technical Committee on Reinforced Concrete Design. These authors are:

Perry Adebar	University of British Columbia
Scott Alexander	COWI
C. Michael Allen	Adjeleain Allen Rubeli Ltd.
F. Michael Bartlett	Western University
Evan C. Bentz	University of Toronto
Michael P. Collins	Univesity of Toronto
Ronald H. DeVall	Read Jones Christoffersen Ltd.
Hélène Dutrisac	Cement Association of Canada
Wayne Kassian	Kassian Dyck and Associates
Tibor Kokai	Read Jones Christoffersen Ltd.
Kevin Lemieux	Weiler Smith Bowers
Robert E. Loov	Consultant
Richard J. McGrath	Cement Association of Canada
Denis Mitchell	McGill University
Jim Mutrie	Consultant
Patrick Paultre	Université de Sherbrooke
Murat Saatcioglu	University of Ottawa

In addition to several of the current edition authors, the following authors contributed to previous editions of the Concrete Design Handbook: A. Abdel-Akher, Paul Breeze, T. Ivan Campbell, Stan Cumming, Walter Dilger, Gordon A. Fenton, John Fowler, N. John Gardner, Noel Nathan, Tel Rezanoff, Andrew Scanlon, Sid H. Simmonds, Gary T. Suter and Gerry Weiler.

Permission has kindly been granted by the Canadian Standards Association to reproduce the CSA Group standard A23.3-14, Design of concrete structures, in this Handbook. The permission of the Canadian Commission on Building and Fire Codes to reproduce portions and selected extracts from the National Building Code of Canada 2015 is gratefully acknowledged.

The review of this Handbook's chapters and design examples by Adjeleian Allen Rubeli Ltd, more specifically Michael D'Costa, Farrokh Fazileh and Greg Woltman, is also gratefully acknowledged.

A23.3-14

CSA
Group

Design of concrete structures

REVISED DECEMBER 2015

Legal Notice for Standards

PART I

CSA Group standard A23.3-14 – Design of concrete structures
Explanatory Notes on the CSA Group standard A23.3-14
Index

With the permission of the Canadian Standards Association (operating as CSA Group), CSA Group standard **"A23.3-14 - Design of concrete structures"** which is copyrighted by CSA Group, 178 Rexdale Blvd., Toronto, ON, M9W1R3, has been reproduced in its entirety. All content of the CSA Group standard **"A23.3-14, Design of concrete structures"**, and all copyrights, ownership and other rights are the sole and exclusive property of CSA Group. Reproduction of this standard in any form is prohibited without the written permission of CSA Group.

For more information or to purchase standards from CSA Group, please visit shop.csa.ca or call 1-800-463-6727.

The Explanatory Notes on the CSA Group standard A23.3-14 are copyrighted by the Cement Association of Canada.

Note:
The copy of the CSA Group standard A23.3-14 included with the Concrete Design Handbook will not be updated to reflect amendments made to the original content by CSA Group. For up-to-date information, see the **Standards Update Service** page in the standard included in this document and follow the instructions on how to register for e-mail notifications about any updates to the standard.

Revision History

A23.3-14, Design of concrete structures

Update No. 1 — December 2015	Revision symbol (in margin)
Clause D.4.3.5.3	①

Errata — October 2015	Revision symbol (in margin)
Clauses 3.1, 12.3.1, 13.3.6.2, 21.10.3.3.2, 22.8.5, 23.2.4, 23.2.10, 23.3.1.3, 23.3.2, C.1.2.7, D.6.1.1, D.6.2.4, D.7.2.1, and D.7.2.5 Figures 23.2, D.4B, and D.6	Δ

Standards Update Service

A23.3-14
June 2014

Title: *Design of concrete structures*

To register for e-mail notification about any updates to this publication
- go to shop.csa.ca
- click on **CSA Update Service**

The **List ID** that you will need to register for updates to this publication is **2422755**.

If you require assistance, please e-mail **techsupport@csagroup.org** or call 416-747-2233.

Visit CSA Group's policy on privacy at **www.csagroup.org/legal** to find out how we protect your personal information.

A23.3-14
Design of concrete structures

™*A trade-mark of the Canadian Standards Association, operating as "CSA Group"*

Published in June 2014 by CSA Group
A not-for-profit private sector organization
178 Rexdale Boulevard, Toronto, Ontario, Canada M9W 1R3

To purchase standards and related publications, visit our Online Store at shop.csa.ca
or call toll-free 1-800-463-6727 or 416-747-4044.

ISBN 978-1-77139-390-4

Contents

Technical Committee on Reinforced Concrete Design

M. Ghabrial   HGS Limited Consulting Engineers,
                        Windsor, Ontario
                        Representing Producer Interest

W. Kassian   Kassian Dyck & Associates,
                        Calgary, Alberta
                        Representing Producer Interest

T. Kokai   Read Jones Christoffersen Consulting Engineers,
                        Toronto, Ontario
                        Representing User Interest

K.L. Lemieux   Weiler Smith Bowers Consultants,
                        Burnaby, British Columbia
                        Representing Producer Interest

R.E. Loov   Calgary, Alberta
                        Representing General Interest

J.G. Mutrie   Jones Kwong Kishi Consulting Engineers,
                        North Vancouver, British Columbia
                        Representing User Interest

J.A. Patrick   Alberta Infrastructure,
                        Edmonton, Alberta
                        *Representing Government and/or Regulatory
                        Authority*

C.R. Taraschuk   National Research Council Canada,
                        Ottawa, Ontario
                        *Representing Government and/or Regulatory
                        Authority*

S. Vézina   Groupe SMi,
                        Montréal, Québec
                        Representing User Interest

C.M. Wang   Grande Cache Coal,
                        Calgary, Alberta
                        Representing User Interest

P. Gulletson   CSA Group,   *Project Manager*
                        Mississauga, Ontario

L. Jula Zadeh   CSA Group,   *Project Manager*
                        Mississauga, Ontario

In addition to the members of the Committee, the following individuals made significant contributions to the development of this Standard:

E.C. Bentz   University of Toronto,
                         Toronto, Ontario

R.H. DeVall   Read Jones Christoffersen Consulting Engineers,
                         Vancouver, British Columbia

K. Truderung   Tower Engineering Group,
                         Winnipeg, Manitoba

In addition, the members of the Structural Engineers Association of BC Technical Committee on Concrete Design made contributions to the development of this Standard.

Preface

This is the sixth edition of CSA A23.3, *Design of concrete structures.* It supersedes the previous editions published in 2004, 1994, 1984, 1977 (metric), and 1973 (imperial), and 1959.

This Standard is intended for use in the design of concrete structures for buildings in conjunction with CSA A23.1/A23.2, *Concrete materials and methods of concrete construction/Methods of test and standard practices for concrete,* and CSA A23.4, *Precast concrete — Materials and construction.*

Changes in this edition include the following:
a) Clause 3.1 contains new definitions for conventional construction, moderately ductile wall systems, different types of tilt-up construction, and gravity-load resisting frames.
b) Clause 7.4.3.1 contains new requirements for the clear distance between pretensioning wires or strands at the ends of members. Clause 7.6.5 contains new requirements for additional column ties in column-slab connections over the slab depth where the slab is discontinuous. In Clause 7.6.4, the minimum diameter of spiral reinforced has been changed to 10 mm and the limit of one-sixth of the core diameter for the clear spacing between successive turns in a spiral has been removed. Clause 7.7.3 has new requirements for column ties in beam-column joints.
c) Clause 9.2.1.2 gives guidance on stiffnesses to be used in members of lateral load resisting systems for wind loading. Clause 9.8 provides cautionary notes on member minimum thickness requirements and accounting for construction stages and early loading in computing deflections.
d) Clause 10.9.4 contains a new requirement for the required ratio of spiral reinforcement. Clause 10.10.4 has increased the maximum factored axial load resistance of spirally reinforced columns and contains new provisions for the resistance of compression members as a function of wall thickness. Clause 10.16.3 provides a new factor for determining the amplitude of sway moments.
e) Changes to the shear design provisions in Clause 11 include the following: the need to account for cover spalling for members subjected to high shear stress; new requirement for sections near supports; definition of special member types; accounting for effect of bars terminated in the flexural tension zone; and increased spacing limit for transverse reinforcement for special cases. Changes to the strut-and-tie design provisions of Clause 11.4 include the following: introduction of refined strut-and-tie models; modelling of members subjected to uniform loads; revised strut dimensions for struts anchored by reinforcement and for struts in narrow part of fanning compression regions; simplified expression for limiting compressive stress in struts; new detailing requirements for anchorage of ties; and provisions accounting for confinement of bearing in nodal regions.
f) Clause 13 on two-way slab systems has been revised to include the following: the use of d_v in determining the one-way shear resistance; new details for bottom bars in column strips of slabs with drop panels (see Figure 13.1); and a change in the definition of V_{se} for the design of structural integrity reinforcement (see Clauses 13.10.6.1 and 3.2).
g) Clause 14 contains a new requirement to account for strong axis bending in bearing walls and new wall thickness requirements and slenderness requirements for flexural shear walls.
h) Clause 18.3.1 permits a higher compressive stress limit in the concrete at transfer at the ends of simply supported members.
i) Clause 21 on special provisions for seismic design has a number of significant changes. This Clause has been reorganized so that all the requirements for ductile frames are in Clause 21.3, while all the requirements for moderately ductile frames are in Clause 21.4. New dimensional limitations for moderately ductile moment-resisting frames have been added in Clause 21.4.2. The requirements

for moderately ductile shear walls have been spelled out in greater detail, and because of the significant overlap with the requirements for ductile shear walls, the requirements for moderately ductile and ductile shear walls are presented together in Clause 21.5. All shear wall design requirements that were redundant with Clause 14 have been removed from Clause 21. Thus, the designer of seismic shear walls must look to Clause 14 for important requirements such as dimensional limitations, transfer of forces across construction joints, and many other requirements. The requirements for strength and ductility over the height of shear walls in Clause 21.5.2 have been expanded. New requirements have been added for the design for bending moment and shear force below the plastic hinge at the base, and for the increased shear force in walls due to the inelastic effects of higher modes. New requirements have been added in Clause 21.5.5 for the anchorage of horizontal reinforcement at the ends of walls depending on the level of ductility. New requirements have been added in Clause 21.5.7 to ensure that walls have adequate ductility to tolerate some yielding near mid-height due to higher mode bending moments. The design requirements for two new types of reinforced concrete SFRS — moderately ductile coupled walls and moderately ductile partially coupled walls — have been added in Clause . The requirements for squat shear walls in Clause 21.5.10 have been relaxed where the walls are longer than needed. The requirements for conventional construction shear walls in Clause 21.6.3 have been expanded. New requirements for the design and detailing of tilt-up construction, including moderately ductile and limited ductility tilt-up walls and frames, are presented in Clause 21.7. New requirements for the design of foundations are presented in Clause 21.10, including the requirement to consider foundation movements. New requirements are presented in Clause 21.11 to ensure that all members not considered part of the seismic-force-resisting system have adequate displacement capacity.

j) Clause 23.2.9 provides revised design provisions for structural integrity of tilt-up construction. The effective area of reinforcement used to calculate the factored resisting moment has been modified.

k) Annex D on anchorage has been modified to include changes to the requirements specified in Appendix D of ACI 318M-11/318RM-11, *Building Code Requirements for Structural Concrete* and *Commentary*. Annex D provides new provisions for the bond strength of adhesive anchors in tension; installation of horizontal and upwardly inclined adhesive anchors; the bond strength of adhesive anchors in tension; the resistance of anchors for load cases involving earthquake effects; revised breakout resistance in shear for an anchor in cracked concrete; and new requirements for the installation of anchors.

This Standard was prepared by the Technical Committee on Reinforced Concrete Design, under the jurisdiction of the Strategic Steering Committee on Construction and Civil Infrastructure, and has been formally approved by the Technical Committee.

Notes:
1) *Use of the singular does not exclude the plural (and vice versa) when the sense allows.*
2) *Although the intended primary application of this Standard is stated in its Scope, it is important to note that it remains the responsibility of the users of the Standard to judge its suitability for their particular purpose.*
3) *This Standard was developed by consensus, which is defined by CSA Policy governing standardization — Code of good practice for standardization as "substantial agreement. Consensus implies much more than a simple majority, but not necessarily unanimity". It is consistent with this definition that a member may be included in the Technical Committee list and yet not be in full agreement with all clauses of this Standard.*
4) *To submit a request for interpretation of this Standard, please send the following information to inquiries@csagroup.org and include "Request for interpretation" in the subject line:*
   a) *define the problem, making reference to the specific clause, and, where appropriate, include an illustrative sketch;*
   b) *provide an explanation of circumstances surrounding the actual field condition; and*
   c) *where possible, phrase the request in such a way that a specific "yes" or "no" answer will address the issue.*

Committee interpretations are processed in accordance with the CSA Directives and guidelines governing standardization and are available on the Current Standards Activities page at standardsactivities.csa.ca.

5) This Standard is subject to review five years from the date of publication and suggestions for its improvement will be referred to the appropriate committee. To submit a proposal for change, please send the following information to **inquiries@csagroup.org** and include "Proposal for change" in the subject line:

    a)   Standard designation (number);

    b)   relevant clause, table, and/or figure number;

    c)   wording of the proposed change; and

    d)   rationale for the change.

A23.3-14
Design of concrete structures

1 Scope

1.1 General

This Standard specifies requirements, in accordance with the *National Building Code of Canada,* for the design and strength evaluation of
a)   structures of reinforced and prestressed concrete;
b)   plain concrete elements; and
c)   special structures such as parking structures, arches, tanks, reservoirs, bins and silos, towers, water towers, blast-resistant structures, and chimneys.

Note: *Special requirements for parking structures are specified in CSA S413.*

1.2 Fire resistance

This Standard requires designs to be carried out in accordance with the fire resistance requirements of the applicable building code (see Clause 8.1.2).

1.3 Alternative design procedures

Designs that use procedures that are not covered by this Standard but are carried out by a person qualified in the methods applied and provide a level of safety and performance equivalent to designs complying with this Standard are acceptable if carried out by one of the following methods:
a)   analysis based on generally established theory;
b)   evaluation of a full-scale structure or a prototype by a loading test; or
c)   studies of model analogues.

1.4 Terminology

In this Standard, "shall" is used to express a requirement, i.e., a provision that the user is obliged to satisfy in order to comply with the standard; "should" is used to express a recommendation or that which is advised but not required; and "may" is used to express an option or that which is permissible within the limits of the standard.

Notes accompanying clauses do not include requirements or alternative requirements; the purpose of a note accompanying a clause is to separate from the text explanatory or informative material.

Notes to tables and figures are considered part of the table or figure and may be written as requirements.

Annexes are designated normative (mandatory) or informative (non-mandatory) to define their application.

1.5 Units of measurement

Equations appearing in this Standard are compatible with the following units:
a)   area: mm^2 (square millimetres);
b)   force: N (newtons);
c)   length: mm (millimetres);

d)   moment: N·mm (newton millimetres); and

e)   stress: MPa (megapascals).

Whenever the square root of the concrete strength is determined, the concrete strength and the square root of the concrete strength are both expressed in megapascals.

Other dimensionally consistent combinations of units may be used, provided that appropriate adjustments are made to constants in non-homogeneous equations.

Note: *Some examples of non-homogeneous equations are found in Clauses 12.2.2 and 12.8.*

2 Reference publications

This Standard refers to the following publications, and where such reference is made, it shall be to the edition listed below, including all amendments published thereto.

CSA (Canadian Standards Association)

A23.1-14/A23.2-14
Concrete materials and methods of concrete construction/Test Methods and standard practices for concrete

A23.4-09
Precast concrete — Materials and construction

G30.18-09
Billet-steel bars for concrete reinforcement

G40.20-04/G40.21-13
General requirements for rolled or welded structural quality steel/Structural quality steel

S16-14
Design of steel structures

S413-07 (R2012)
Parking structures

W59-13
Welded steel construction (metal arc welding)

W186-M1990 (R2012)
Welding of reinforcing bars in reinforced concrete construction

ACI (American Concrete Institute)

302.1R-04
Guide for Concrete Floor and Slab Construction

302.2R-06
Guide for Concrete Slabs that Receive Moisture – Sensitive Flooring Materials

318M-11/318RM-11
Metric Building Code Requirements for Structural Concrete and Commentary

336.3R-93 (R2006)
Design and Construction of Drilled Piers

355.2-07/355.2R-07
Qualification of Post-Installed Mechanical Anchors in Concrete and Commentary

355.4-11
Qualification of Post-Installed Adhesive Anchors in Concrete and Commentary

360R-06
Design of Slabs on Grade

374.1-05
Acceptance criteria for moment frames based on structural testing and commentary

T1.1-01/T1.1R-01
Acceptance Criteria for Moment Frames Based on Structural Testing

ASTM International (American Society for Testing and Materials)
A307-12
Standard Specification for Carbon Steel Bolts and Studs, 60 000 PSI Tensile Strength

A416/A416M-12a
Standard Specification for Steel Strand, Uncoated Seven-Wire for Prestressed Concrete

A421/A421M-10
Standard Specification for Uncoated Stress-Relieved Steel Wire for Prestressed Concrete

A496-07/A496M-07
Standard Specification for Steel Wire, Deformed, for Concrete Reinforcement

A497/A497M-07
Standard Specification for Steel Welded Wire Reinforcement, Deformed, for Concrete

A722/A722M-12
Standard Specification for Uncoated High-Strength Steel Bar for Prestressing Concrete

A1064/A1064M-13
Standard Specification for Carbon-Steel Wire and Welded Wire Reinforcement, Plain and Deformed, for Concrete

C330/C330M-09
Standard Specification for Lightweight Aggregates for Structural Concrete

AWS (American Welding Society)
D1.1/D1.1M:2004
Structural Welding Code — Steel

LATBSDC (Los Angeles Tall Buildings Structural Design Council)
Alternate Procedure for Seismic Analysis and Design of Tall Buildings Located in the Los Angeles Area (2011)

NRCC (National Research Council Canada)
National Building Code of Canada, 2015

User's Guide — NBC 2015: Structural Commentaries (Part 4)

Other publications
ACI-ASCE Committee 550. 1993. "Design recommendations for precast concrete structures". *ACI structural journal.* 90:115–121.

Canadian Precast/Prestressed Concrete Institute. 2005. Design manual: Precast and prestressed concrete. 4th ed. Ottawa: Canadian Precast/Prestressed Concrete Institute.

Cement Association of Canada. 2016. Concrete design handbook. 4th ed. Ottawa: Cement Association of Canada.

Precast/Prestressed Concrete Institute. 2010. PCI design handbook: Precast and prestressed concrete. 7th ed. Chicago: Precast/Prestressed Concrete Institute.

3 Definitions and symbols

3.1 Definitions
The following definitions apply in this Standard:

Auxiliary member — a rib or edge beam that serves to strengthen, stiffen, or support the shell. Auxiliary members usually act jointly with the shell.

Beam — an element subjected primarily to loads and forces producing flexure.

Bell — an enlargement at the bottom of a pre-drilled cast-in-place concrete pile.

Bonded tendon — a prestressing tendon that is bonded to concrete either directly or through grouting.

Boundary elements — portions of a wall, typically at the ends, that are reinforced by vertical reinforcement and can contain transverse reinforcement. Boundary elements do not necessarily require an increase in wall thickness.

Buckling prevention ties — ties that meet the requirements of Clause 21.2.8.1 and are intended to prevent buckling of the longitudinal reinforcement under reverse cyclic loading.

Collector — an element that serves to transfer forces within a structural diaphragm to members of the seismic force resisting system.

Column — a member that has a ratio of height to least lateral dimension of 3 or greater and is used primarily to support axial compressive load.

Column capital — an enlargement of the column adjacent to the underside of a slab to improve the shear strength of the slab.

Note: *The dimensions c_1 and c_2 and the clear span ℓ_n are based on an effective support area defined by the intersection of the bottom surface of the slab, or of the drop panel if there is one, with the largest right circular cone, right pyramid, or tapered wedge whose surfaces are located within the column and capital or bracket and are oriented not more than 45° to the axis of the column.*

Column strip — that portion of the design strip with a width on each side of a column centreline equal to $0.25\ell_2$ or $0.25\ell_1$, whichever is less. The column strip includes beams, if any.

Composite concrete flexural members — concrete flexural members of precast or cast-in-place concrete elements, or both, constructed in separate placements but interconnected so that all elements respond to loads as a unit.

Concrete —

Plain concrete — concrete that contains no reinforcing or prestressing steel or less reinforcing or prestressing steel than the specified minimum for reinforced concrete.

Reinforced concrete — concrete that is reinforced with not less than the minimum amount of reinforcement required by Clauses 7 to 21 and 23 and is designed on the assumption that the two materials act together in resisting forces.

Structural low-density concrete — concrete having a 28 day compressive strength not less than 20 MPa and an air-dry density not exceeding 1850 kg/m³.

Structural semi-low-density concrete — concrete having a 28 day compressive strength not less than 20 MPa and an air-dry density between 1850 and 2150 kg/m³.

Concrete cover — the distance from the concrete surface to the nearest surface of reinforcement or prestressing tendon.

Confinement reinforcement — reinforcement that meets the requirements of Clause 21.2.8.2 and are intended to provide confinement to the enclosed concrete.

Connection — a region that joins two or more members, of which one or more is precast.

Ductile connection — a connection that experiences yielding as a result of the design displacement.

Strong connection — a connection that remains elastic while adjoining members experience yielding as a result of the design displacement.

Conventional construction — a seismic-force-resisting system with low ductility capacity designed in accordance with Clauses 1 to 18 or Clause 23 with the additional requirements of Clause 21.6.

Conventional tilt-up construction — a seismic-force-resisting system with tilt-up wall panels having low ductility capacity designed in accordance with Clause 23. This seismic-force-resisting system qualifies for a force modification factor, R_d, of 1.3 in the *National Building Code of Canada*.

Core — that part of the member cross-section confined by the perimeter of the transverse reinforcement measured from out-to-out of the transverse reinforcement.

Cover — see **Concrete cover**.

Critical section — a section where a plastic hinge can start to form under earthquake loading.

Crosstie — a reinforcing bar that passes through the core and is anchored around reinforcing bars on opposite sides of a member.

Deep foundation — a structural element that transfers loads from the superstructure to the deeper bearing soil or rock strata by end bearing, friction, or both.
Note: *Examples of deep foundations include driven piles, drilled cast-in-place piles, and slurry walls.*

Deformed reinforcement — deformed reinforcing bars, deformed wire, welded smooth wire fabric, and welded deformed wire fabric complying with Clause 4.1.3.

Design cross-section — the representative panel cross-section at the maximum moment and deflection locations of the panel for which the design forces and deflections are determined and from which the resistance and stiffness are calculated.

Design displacement — the total lateral displacement expected for the design basis earthquake calculated in accordance with Clause 4.1.8 of the *National Building Code of Canada.*

Designer — the person responsible for the design.

Design strip — the portion of a slab system that includes beams and supports along a column line and is bound by the centreline of the panels on each side.

Design width — the width of a tilt-up panel to be reinforced to withstand the factored loads tributary to it.

Development length — the length of embedded reinforcement required to develop the design strength of reinforcement.

Development length for a bar with a standard hook in tension — the length measured from the critical section to the outside end of the hook (the straight embedment length between the critical section and the start of the hook [point of tangency] plus the radius of the bend and one bar diameter).

Drilled pile — a pile cast-in-place in a pre-drilled hole.

Driven pile — a reinforced concrete, prestressed concrete, structural steel, timber, or composite pile driven into the ground.

Drift ratio — the ratio of lateral displacement to height over which the displacement occurs.

Drop panel — thickening of the slab in the area adjacent to a column for deflection control, extra shear strength, or extra flexural depth.

Ductile coupled shear wall — a shear wall system that complies with Clauses 21.2 and 21.5 and has ductile shear walls connected by ductile coupling beams where at least 66% of the base overturning moment resisted by the wall system is carried by axial tension and compression forces resulting from shear in the coupling beam(s). This seismic-force-resisting system qualifies for a force modification factor, R_d, of 4.0 in accordance with the *National Building Code of Canada.*

Ductile coupling beam — a coupling beam designed to dissipate energy that complies with Clauses 21.2 and 21.5.

Ductile moment-resisting frame — a moment-resisting frame that dissipates energy primarily through beam flexural yielding and complies with Clauses 21.2 and 21.3. This seismic-force-resisting system qualifies for a force modification factor, R_d, of 4.0 in accordance with the *National Building Code of Canada.*

Ductile partially coupled shear wall — a coupled wall system that has ductile wall piers connected by ductile coupling beams where less than 66% of the base overturning moment resisted by the wall system is carried by axial tension and compression forces in the wall piers resulting from shears in the coupling beams and complies with Clauses 21.2 and 21.5. This seismic-force-resisting system qualifies for a force modification factor, R_d, of 3.5 in accordance with the *National Building Code of Canada.*

Ductile shear wall — a cantilever wall that dissipates energy through flexural yielding in a plastic hinge near the base and complies with Clauses 21.2 and 21.5. This seismic-force-resisting system qualifies for a force modification factor, R_d, of 3.5 in accordance with the *National Building Code of Canada.*

Effective prestress — the stress remaining in prestressing tendons after all losses have occurred.

Elastic analysis — an analysis of deformations and internal forces based on equilibrium, compatibility of strains, and assumed elastic behaviour.

Embedment length — the length of embedded reinforcement provided beyond a critical section.

Factored load effect — the effect of factored load combinations specified in Clause 8.3 (including earthquake load effects determined in accordance with Clause 4.1.8 of the *National Building Code of Canada*).

Flat plate — a flat slab without drop panels.

Folded plate — a special class of shell structures formed by joining flat, thin slabs along their edges to create a three-dimensional spatial structure.

Footing — a shallow structural element that transfers loads from the superstructure to the bearing strata (soil or rock).

Gravity-load resisting frame — a frame consisting of slabs and/or beams supported by columns and/or walls all of which are not considered to be part of the seismic-force-resisting-system.
Note: *See Clause 21.11 for the design of gravity-load resisting frame members for seismic displacement.*

Headed bar — a bar with a welded or forged head at one or both ends, with the head dimensioned to be capable of developing the nominal tensile strength of the reinforcing bar at the head-bar interface without failure of the head or crushing failure of the concrete under the head.

Helical tie — a continuously-wound reinforcement in the form of a cylindrical helix enclosing longitudinal reinforcement.

Hoop — a closed tie or continuously-wound tie. A closed tie can be made up of several reinforcing elements with seismic hooks at each end. A continuously wound tie should also have seismic hooks at each end. Seismic crossties within a hoop may be considered to provide effective hoop reinforcement.

Jacking force — a temporary force exerted by the device that introduces tension into prestressing tendons.

Lifting stresses — stresses in a tilt-up panel during lifting.

Δ **Limited ductility tilt-up construction** — a seismic force resisting system with tilt-up wall panels designed using a force-based approach in accordance with Clauses 21.2 and 21.7. This seismic-force-resisting system qualifies for a force modification factor, R_d, of 1.5 in accordance with the *National Building Code of Canada*.

Limit states — those conditions of a structure at which it ceases to fulfill the function for which it was designed.

Load —

   Dead load — a specified dead load as defined in the *National Building Code of Canada*.

   Factored load — the product of a specified load and its load factor.

   Live load — a specified live load as defined in the *National Building Code of Canada*.

   Specified load — a load specified by the *National Building Code of Canada* without load factors.

   Sustained load — the specified dead load plus that portion of the specified live load expected to act over a period of time sufficient to cause significant long-term deflection.

Load factor — a factor applied to a specified load that, for the limit state under consideration, takes into account the variability of the loads and load patterns and analysis of their effects.

Low-density aggregate — aggregate that complies with ASTM C330.

Middle strip — that portion of the design strip bounded by two column strips.

Moderately ductile coupled shear wall — a coupled wall system that has moderately ductile wall piers connected by moderately ductile coupling beams where at least 66% of the base overturning moment resisted by the wall system is carried by axial tension and compression forces in the wall piers resulting from shear in the coupling beams and complies with Clauses 21.2 and 21.5. This seismic-force-resisting system qualifies for a force modification factor, R_d, of 2.5 in the *National Building Code of Canada*.

Moderately ductile coupling beam — a coupling beam that dissipates energy by yielding of longitudinal or diagonal reinforcement and complies with Clauses 21.2 and .

Moderately ductile moment-resisting frame — a moment-resisting frame that complies with Clauses 21.2 and 21.4, that resists seismic forces, and that dissipates energy through beam flexural yielding. This seismic-force-resisting system qualifies for a force modification factor, R_d, of 2.5 in the *National Building Code of Canada*.

Moderately ductile partially coupled shear wall — a coupled wall system that has moderately ductile wall piers connected by moderately ductile coupling beams where less than 66% of the base overturning moment resisted by the wall system is carried by axial tension and compression forces in the wall piers resulting from shear in the coupling beams and complies with Clauses 21.2 and 21.5. This seismic-force-resisting system qualifies for a force modification factor, R_d, of 2.0 in the *National Building Code of Canada*.

Moderately ductile shear wall — a cantilever wall that dissipates energy through flexural yielding in a plastic hinge near the base and complies with Clauses 21.2 and 21.5. This seismic-force-resisting system qualifies for a force modification factor, R_d, of 2.0 in accordance with the *National Building Code of Canada*.

Δ **Moderately ductile tilt-up construction** — a seismic-force-resisting system with tilt-up wall panels having moderate ductility capacity that complies with Clauses 21.2 and 21.7. The design of the system includes the explicit consideration of the inelastic displacement demands on the tilt-up wall panels. This seismic-force-resisting system qualifies for a force modification factor, R_d, of 2.0 in accordance with the *National Building Code of Canada*.

Modulus of rupture of concrete — the flexural strength of concrete determined using the third-point loading test method specified in CSA A23.2.

Moment-resisting frame — a frame in which columns, beams, and joints resist forces through flexure, shear, and compression.

Panel — a slab area bounded by column, beam, or wall centrelines on all sides.

Pedestal — an upright compression member with a ratio of unsupported height to least lateral dimension of less than 3.

Pile — an elongated structural element drilled or driven into the ground for supporting loads by end bearing, friction, or both.

Pile cap — a reinforced concrete element connected to the top of a pile or pile group that transfers loads from the superstructure to the pile or pile group.

Pile shaft — that portion of the pile from the pile toe to the pile top, excluding any bell or cap.

Pile toe — the bottom of the pile.

Plastic hinge — a region of a member where inelastic flexural curvatures occur.

Post-tensioning — a method of prestressing in which the tendons are tensioned after the concrete has hardened.

Precast concrete — concrete elements cast in a location other than their final position in service.

Prestressed concrete — concrete in which internal stresses have been initially introduced so that the subsequent stresses resulting from dead load and superimposed loads are counteracted to a desired degree.
Note: *This can be accomplished by post-tensioning or pretensioning.*

Pretensioning — a method of prestressing in which the tendons are tensioned before the concrete is placed.

Probable moment resistance — the moment resistance of a section calculated using axial loads P_s and P_p, where applicable; $1.25f_y$ as the stress in the tension reinforcement; and the specified values of f_c', with ϕ_c and ϕ_s taken as 1.0.

Regular two-way slab system — a slab system consisting of approximately rectangular panels and supporting primarily uniform gravity loading. Such systems meet the following geometric limitations:
a) within a panel, the ratio of longer to shorter span, centre-to-centre of supports, is not greater than 2.0;
b) for slab systems with beams between supports, the relative effective stiffness of beams in the two directions $(\alpha_1\ell_2^2)/(\alpha_2\ell_1^2)$ is not less than 0.2 or greater than 5.0;
c) column offsets are not greater than 20% of the span (in the direction of offset) from either axis between centrelines of successive columns; and

d)   the reinforcement is placed in an orthogonal grid.

Reinforcement — non-prestressed steel that complies with Clauses 4.1.2 and 4.1.3.

Resistance —

   Factored resistance — the resistance of a member, connection, or cross-section calculated in accordance with this Standard, including the application of appropriate resistance factors.

   Nominal resistance — resistance calculated using axial loads P_s and P_n where applicable and the specified values of f_c and f_y, with ϕ_c and ϕ_s taken as 1.0.

Resistance factor — the factor, specified in Clause 8.4 and applied to a specified material property or to the resistance of a member for the limit state under consideration, which takes into account the variability of dimensions, material properties, quality of work, type of failure, and uncertainty in the prediction of resistance.

Sandwich panel — a panel consisting of two concrete layers or wythes separated by a layer of insulation.

Seismic crosstie — a single bar having a seismic hook at one end and a hook not less than 90° with at least a six-bar-diameter extension at the other end. The hooks engage peripheral longitudinal bars. The 90° hooks of successive crossties engaging the same longitudinal bar are alternated end for end.

Seismic-force-resisting system (SFRS) — that part of the structural system that has been considered in the design to provide the required resistance to the earthquake forces and effects in accordance with Clause 4.1.8 of the *National Building Code of Canada*.

Seismic hook — a hook with at least a 135° bend with a six-bar-diameter extension (but not less than 100 mm) that engages the longitudinal reinforcement and is anchored in the confined core.

Slab band — a continuous extension of a drop panel between supports or between a support and another slab band.

Specified strength of concrete — the compressive strength of concrete used in the design and evaluated in accordance with Clause 4.

Spiral — a helical tie complying with Clauses 7.6.4 and 10.9.4.

Stirrup — reinforcement used to resist shear and torsion stresses in a structural member.
Note: *The term "stirrups" is usually applied to lateral reinforcement in flexural members and the term "ties" to lateral reinforcement in compression members.*

Structural diaphragm — a structural member, such as a floor or roof slab, that transmits forces to or between lateral-force-resisting members.

Tendon — a steel element such as a wire, bar, or strand, or a bundle of such elements, that is used to impart prestress to concrete and complies with Clause 4.1.4.

Thin shell — a three-dimensional spatial structure made up of one or more curved slabs or folded plates whose thicknesses are small compared to their other dimensions.
Note: *Thin shells are characterized by their three-dimensional load-carrying behaviour, which is determined by the geometry of their form, the manner in which they are supported, and the nature of the applied load.*

Tie — a loop of reinforcing bar or wire enclosing longitudinal reinforcement. See also **Stirrup**.

Tilt-up wall panel — a reinforced concrete panel that is site-cast on a horizontal surface and subsequently tilted to a vertical orientation to form a vertical- and lateral-load-resisting building element.

Transfer — the act of transferring force in prestressing tendons from jacks or the pretensioning anchorage to the concrete member.

Tributary width — the width of a panel attracting vertical and horizontal loads that the design width must support.

Wall — a vertical element in which the horizontal length, ℓ_w, is at least six times the thickness, t, and at least one-third the clear height of the element.

> **Bearing wall** — a wall that supports
> a) factored in-plane vertical loads exceeding $0.04 f_c A_g$;
> b) weak axis moments about a horizontal axis in the plane of the wall; and
> c) the shear forces necessary to equilibrate the moments specified in Item b).
>
> **Flexural shear wall** — a shear wall that resists in-plane lateral loads by flexural action. Flexural shear walls have a height, h_w, above the section of maximum moment in the walls that is greater than $2\ell_w$.
>
> **Non-bearing wall** — a wall that supports factored in-plane vertical loads less than or equal to $0.04 f_c A_g$ and, in some cases, moments about a horizontal axis in the plane of the wall and the shear forces necessary to equilibrate those moments.
>
> **Shear wall** — a wall or an assembly of interconnected walls considered to be part of the lateral-load-resisting system of a building or structure. Shear walls support
> a) vertical loads;
> b) moments about horizontal axes perpendicular to the plane of the wall (strong axis bending); and
> c) shear forces acting parallel to the plane of the wall.
>
> Weak axis bending can also be present.
>
> **Squat shear wall** — a shear wall with a height, h_w, above the section of maximum moment in the wall that does not exceed $2\ell_w$.

Wall pier — a vertical wall adjacent to an opening between coupling beams in a coupled or partially coupled wall.

Yield strength — the specified minimum yield strength or yield point of reinforcement.

3.2 Symbols

The following symbols apply in this Standard:

a = depth of equivalent rectangular stress block

a_g = specified nominal maximum size of coarse aggregate

a_s = length of uniform bearing stress in soil or rock required to resist the applied loads (see Clause 21)

A	= area of that part of cross-section between flexural tension face and centroid of gross section (see Clause 18)
	= effective tension area of concrete surrounding the flexural tension reinforcement and extending from the extreme tension fibre to the centroid of the flexural tension reinforcement and an equal distance past that centroid, divided by the number of bars or wires. When the flexural reinforcement consists of different bar or wire sizes, the number of bars or wires used to compute A is to be taken as the total area of reinforcement divided by the area of the largest bar or wire used (see Clause 10)
A_b	= area of an individual bar
A_c	= area enclosed by outside perimeter of concrete cross-section, including area of holes (if any) (see Clause 11)
	= area of core of spirally reinforced compression member measured to outside diameter of spiral (see Clause 10)
A_{ch}	= cross-sectional area of core of a structural member
A_{cs}	= area of concrete in strips along exposed side faces of beams (see Clause 10)
	= effective cross-sectional area of concrete compressive strut (see Clause 11)
A_{ct}	= area of concrete on flexural tension side of member (see Figure 11.1)
A_{cv}	= area of concrete section resisting shear transfer (see Clause 11)
	= net area of concrete section bounded by web thickness and length of section in the direction of lateral forces considered (see Clause 21)
A_f	= area of flange
A_g	= gross area of section
A_j	= minimum cross-sectional area within a joint in a plane parallel to the axis of the reinforcement generating the shear in the joint, equal to the lesser of A_g of the column or $2b_w h_{col}$
A_o	= area enclosed by shear flow path, including area of holes (if any)
A_{oh}	= area enclosed by centreline of exterior closed transverse torsion reinforcement, including area of holes (if any)
A_p	= area of prestressing tendons (see Clause 10)
	= area of prestressing tendons in tension zone (see Clause 18)
	= area of tendons on the flexural tension side of the member (see Clause 11)
A_s	= area of longitudinal reinforcement on the flexural tension side of the member (see Clause 11)
	= area of non-prestressed tension reinforcement (see Clauses 12, 13, 18, and 23)
A_s'	= area of compression reinforcement
A_{sb}	= minimum area of bottom reinforcement crossing one face of the periphery of a column and connecting the slab to the column or support to provide structural integrity
$A_{s,eff}$	= effective area of tension reinforcement
A_{sh}	= total cross-sectional area of transverse reinforcement (including crossties) within spacing s and perpendicular to dimension h_c
$A_{s,min}$	= minimum area of tension reinforcement
A_{ss}	= area of reinforcement in compression strut
A_{st}	= area of reinforcement in tension tie (see Clause 11)

	=	total area of longitudinal reinforcement (see Clause 10)
A_t	=	area of one leg of closed transverse torsion reinforcement (see Clause 11)
	=	area of structural steel shape, pipe, or tubing in a composite section (see Clause 10)
A_{tr}	=	total cross-sectional area of reinforcement that is within spacing s and crosses the potential plane of bond splitting through the reinforcement being developed
A_v	=	area of shear reinforcement within a distance s
A_{ve}	=	effective shear cross-section area of coupling beam to be used for analysis
A_{vf}	=	area of shear-friction reinforcement
A_{vs}	=	cross-sectional area of headed shear reinforcement on a line parallel to the perimeter of the column
A_w	=	area of an individual wire to be developed or spliced
A_{xe}	=	effective axial cross-section area to be used for analysis
A_1	=	loaded area
A_2	=	area of the lower base of the largest frustum of a pyramid, cone, or tapered wedge contained wholly within the support, having for its upper base the loaded area and having side slopes of 1 vertical to 2 horizontal
b	=	width of compression face of member (see Clauses 9, 10, and 21)
	=	width of compression face of panel within design width (see Clause 23)
	=	width of member (see Clause 22)
b_b	=	band width of reinforced concrete slab extending a distance $1.5h_d$ or $1.5h_s$ past the sides of the column or column capital (see Clauses 13 and 21)
	=	bearing width for concentrated load (see Figure 23.2)
b_d	=	design width (see Figure 23.2)
b_f	=	width of flange; width of footing parallel to axis of footing rotation (see Clause 21)
b_o	=	perimeter of critical section for shear in slabs and footings
b_s	=	width of support reaction (see Figure 23.2)
b_t	=	tributary width (see Clause 23)
	=	width of tension zone of section (see Clause 10)
b_v	=	width of cross-section at contact surface being investigated for longitudinal shear
b_w	=	beam web width or diameter of circular section or wall thickness (see Clause 21)
	=	minimum effective web width (see Clause 11)
	=	width of web (see Clause 10)
b_1	=	width of the critical section for shear (see Clause 13) measured in the direction of the span for which moments are determined
b_2	=	width of the critical section for shear (see Clause 13) measured in the direction perpendicular to b_1
c	=	cohesion stress (see Clause 11)
	=	depth of the neutral axis, with the axial loads P_n, P_{ns}, and P_s measured from the compression edge of a wall section (see Clause 21)
	=	distance from extreme compression fibre to neutral axis (see Clauses 9 and 10)

	= distance from extreme compression fibre to neutral axis calculated using factored material strengths and assuming a tendon force of $\phi_p A_p f_{pr}$ (see Clause 18)
	= distance from extreme compression fibre to neutral axis computed for the cracked transformed section (see Clause 23)
c_t	= dimension equal to the distance from the interior face of the edge column to the slab edge measured parallel to c_1, but not exceeding c_1
c_y	= distance from extreme compression fibre to neutral axis calculated using factored material strengths and assuming a tendon force of $\phi_p A_p f_{py}$
c_1	= size of rectangular or equivalent rectangular column, capital, or bracket measured in the direction of the span for which moments are being determined
c_2	= size of rectangular or equivalent rectangular column, capital, or bracket measured in the direction perpendicular to c_1
C	= cross-sectional constant used in the definition of torsional properties
C_m	= factor relating actual moment diagram to an equivalent uniform moment diagram
d	= distance from extreme compression fibre to centroid of longitudinal tension reinforcement, but need not be less than $0.8h$ for prestressed members and circular sections (see Clauses 11 and 18)
	= distance from extreme compression fibre to centroid of tension reinforcement (see Clauses 9,10, 12, 13, 21, and 23)
	= distance from extreme compression fibre to centroid of tension reinforcement for entire composite section (see Clause 17)
d_b	= diameter of bar, wire, or prestressing strand
d_{ba}	= diameter of longitudinal bar anchoring compression strut
d_c	= distance from extreme tension fibre to centre of the longitudinal bar or wire located closest to it
d_{cs}	= the smaller of a) the distance from the closest concrete surface to the centre of the bar being developed; or b) two-thirds of the centre-to-centre spacing of the bars being developed
d_p	= pile shaft diameter (see Clauses 15 and 22)
	= distance from extreme compression fibre to centroid of the prestressing tendons (see Clause 18)
d_v	= effective shear depth, taken as the greater of $0.9d$ or $0.72h$ and for the case of walls need not be taken less than $0.8\ell_w$
e	= distance from centroid of section for critical shear to point where shear stress is being calculated (see Clause 13)
	= eccentricity of P_{tf} parallel to axis measured from the centroid of the section (see Clause 23)
E_c	= modulus of elasticity of concrete
E_p	= modulus of elasticity of prestressing tendons
E_s	= modulus of elasticity of non-prestressed reinforcement
EI	= flexural stiffness of compression member
f'_c	= specified compressive strength of concrete
f'_{cc}	= specified compressive strength of concrete in columns

CSA Group standard A23.3-14

f_{ce}	=	compression stress in the concrete due to effective prestress only (after allowance for all prestress losses) at the extreme fibre of a section where tensile stresses are caused by applied loads
f'_{ce}	=	effective compressive strength of concrete in columns
f'_{ci}	=	compressive strength of concrete at time of prestress transfer
f_{cp}	=	compressive stress in concrete due to prestress (after allowance for all prestress losses) at the centroid of the cross section (see Clause 11.2.9.1)
f'_{cs}	=	specified compressive strength of concrete in slab
f_{cu}	=	limiting compressive stress in concrete strut
f_{cw}	=	specified compressive strength of concrete in the wall
f_{pe}	=	effective stress in prestressing tendons after allowance for all prestress losses
f_{po}	=	stress in prestressing tendons when strain in the surrounding concrete is zero (may be taken as $0.7f_{pu}$ for bonded tendons outside the transfer length and f_{pe} for unbonded tendons)
f_{pr}	=	stress in prestressing tendons at factored resistance
f_{pu}	=	specified tensile strength of prestressing tendons
f_{py}	=	yield strength of prestressing tendons
f_r	=	modulus of rupture of concrete
f_s	=	calculated stress in reinforcement at specified loads
f_y	=	specified yield strength of non-prestressed reinforcement or anchor steel
f'_y	=	specified yield strength of compression non-prestressed reinforcement
f_{yh}	=	specified yield strength of hoop reinforcement
f_{yt}	=	specified yield strength of transverse reinforcement
f_{yv}	=	specified yield strength of headed shear reinforcement
F_a	=	site coefficient, as specified in the *National Building Code of Canada*
F_{lc}	=	required tension force in longitudinal reinforcement on flexural compression side of member (see Clause 11.3.9.3)
F_{lt}	=	required tension force in longitudinal reinforcement on flexural tension side of member (see Clause 11.3.9.2)
F_y	=	specified yield strength of structural steel section
G_0	=	initial shear modulus of soil or rock immediately below the foundation (see Clause 21)
h	=	overall thickness or height of member
h_a	=	height of effective embedment of tension tie (see Figure 11.5)
h_b	=	distance from soffit of supporting beam to soffit of supported beam (see Figure 11.1)
h_c	=	clear vertical distance between successive floor slabs attached to the shear wall assembly (see Clause 14)
	=	dimension of concrete core of rectangular section measured perpendicular to the direction of the hoop bars to outside of peripheral hoop (see Clause 21)
h_{col}	=	column dimension parallel to shear force in the joint
h_d	=	overall thickness at a drop panel

h_s = overall thickness of slab; for slabs with drop panels, the overall thickness of the slab away from the drop panel

h_u = unsupported vertical height of wall between horizontal supports

h_w = vertical height of wall (see Clause 21)

      = vertical height of wall above the section of maximum moment in the wall (see Clause 14)

h_x = maximum horizontal centre-to-centre spacing between longitudinal bars on all faces of the column that are laterally supported by seismic hoops or crosstie legs

h_1 = overall height of supporting beam (see Figure 11.1)

h_2 = overall height of supported beam (see Figure 11.1)

I = moment of inertia of section about centroidal axis

I_b = moment of inertia about centroidal axis of gross section of beam

I_{cr} = moment of inertia of cracked section transformed to concrete

I_e = effective moment of inertia

I_{ec} = value of I_e at continuous end

I_{em} = value of I_e at midspan

I_{e1} = value of I_e at end 1 of a continuous beam span

I_{e2} = value of I_e at end 2 of a continuous beam span

I_g = moment of inertia of gross concrete section about centroidal axis, neglecting reinforcement

I_s = moment of inertia about centroidal axis of gross section of slab, equal to $\ell_{2a}h_s^3/12$

I_{st} = moment of inertia of reinforcement about centroidal axis of member cross-section

I_t = moment of inertia of structural steel shape, pipe, or tubing about centroidal axis of composite member cross-section

I_E = earthquake importance factor of the structure, as specified in the *National Building Code of Canada*

J = property of the critical shear section analogous to the polar moment of inertia

k = effective length factor

k_n = factor accounting for effectiveness of transverse reinforcement, equal to $n_\ell/(n_\ell-2)$

k_p = axial load ratio, equal to $P_f/A_g\alpha_1 f_c'$

      = factor for type of prestressing in Equation 18.1

k_1 = bar location factor

k_2 = coating factor

k_3 = concrete density factor

k_4 = bar size factor

k_5 = welded deformed wire fabric factor

K_{bf} = panel bending stiffness at factored loads

K_{bs} = panel bending stiffness at service loads

K_c = flexural stiffness of column; moment per unit rotation

K_{ec} = flexural stiffness of equivalent column; moment per unit rotation

K_t = torsional stiffness of member; moment per unit rotation

K_{tr}	= transverse reinforcement index
ℓ	= effective panel height
ℓ_a	= additional embedment length at support or at point of inflection (see Clause 12)
	= length of effective bearing area for strut anchored by reinforcement (see Figure 11.5)
ℓ_b	= length of bearing (see Figure 11.5)
ℓ_c	= length of a compression member in a frame, measured from centre-to-centre of the joints in the frame (see Clause 10)
	= length of the outermost compression segment of a coupled wall (see Clause 21)
	= the lesser of h_c and w_c (see Clause 14)
	= vertical clear distance between supports or unsupported length of the drilled pile (see Clause 22)
ℓ_{cg}	= horizontal distance between centroids of walls on either side of coupling beam
ℓ_d	= development length of reinforcement
ℓ_{db}	= basic development length
ℓ_{dh}	= development length of standard hook in tension, measured from critical section to outside end of hook (straight embedment length between critical section and start of hook [point of tangency] plus radius of bend and one bar diameter) (see Clauses 12 and 21)
ℓ_f	= length of footing perpendicular to axis of footing rotation (see Clause 21)
ℓ_{hb}	= basic development length of standard hook in tension
ℓ_j	= dimension of joint in the direction of reinforcement passing through the joint
ℓ_n	= clear span (see Clauses 9 and 16)
	= length of clear span in the direction that moments are being determined, measured face-to-face of supports (see Clause 13)
ℓ_o	= minimum length measured from the face of the joint along the axis of the structural member, over which transverse reinforcement needs to be provided (see Clause 21)
	= overall length of tendon between anchors (see Clause 18)
ℓ_t	= length of attached torsional member, equal to the smaller of ℓ_{1a} or ℓ_{2a} of spans adjacent to the joint
ℓ_u	= clear span or unsupported length between floors or other effective horizontal lines of lateral support (see Clause 21)
	= unsupported length of compression member (see Clause 10)
ℓ_w	= horizontal length of wall
ℓ_1	= length of span in the direction that moments are being determined, measured centre-to-centre of supports
ℓ_{1a}	= average ℓ_1 for spans adjacent to a column
ℓ_2	= length of span transverse to ℓ_1, measured centre-to-centre of supports
ℓ_{2a}	= average ℓ_2 for the adjacent spans transverse to ℓ_1
	= distance from edge to panel centreline for spans along an edge
L	= variable load due to intended use and occupancy, including loads due to cranes, pressure of liquids in containers, or related moments or forces

m	=	confinement factor (see Clause 11.4.4.1)
m_x	=	bending moment per unit length on section perpendicular to the x-axis
	=	total design moment per unit length on section perpendicular to the x-axis
m_{xy}	=	torsional moment per unit length on section
m_y	=	bending moment per unit length on section perpendicular to the y-axis
	=	total design moment per unit length on section perpendicular to the y-axis
M_a	=	maximum moment in member at load stage at which deflection is computed or at any previous load stage
M_b	=	maximum factored moment in panel at load stage at which deflection is computed, not including P-Δ effects
M_{bs}	=	maximum moment in panel due to service loads at load stage at which deflection is computed, not including P-Δ effects
M_c	=	magnified factored moment to be used for design of compression member
M_{cr}	=	cracking moment
M_{dc}	=	decompression moment, equal to the moment when the compressive stress on the tensile face of a prestressed member is zero
M_f	=	factored moment at interior support resisted by elements above and below the slab (see Equation 13.24)
	=	factored moment, including P-Δ effects (see Clause 23)
	=	moment due to factored loads (see Clauses 10, 11, 18, 20, and 21)
	=	unbalanced moment about the centroid of the critical shear section (see Equation 13.9)
M_{fs}	=	factored strong axis moment acting on a shear wall
M_{fw}	=	factored weak axis moment acting on a shear wall
M_{nc}	=	nominal flexural resistance of a column
M_o	=	total factored static moment
M_{pb}	=	probable flexural resistance of a beam
M_r	=	factored moment resistance
M_s	=	factored end moment on a compression member due to loads that result in appreciable sway, calculated using a first-order elastic frame analysis (see Clause 10)
	=	maximum moment due to service loads, including P-Δ effects (see Clause 23)
	=	moment due to specified loads (see Clause 18)
	=	portion of slab moment balanced by support moment (see Clauses 7.4.3.1 and 21)
M_1	=	smaller factored end moment on a compression member associated with the same loading case as M_2 (positive if member is bent in single curvature, negative if bent in double curvature)
M_{1ns}	=	factored end moment on a compression member at the end at which M_1 acts, due to loads that cause no appreciable sway, calculated using a first-order elastic frame analysis
M_{1s}	=	factored end moment on a compression member at the end at which M_1 acts, due to loads that cause appreciable sway, calculated using a first-order elastic frame analysis
M_2	=	larger factored end moment on a compression member (always positive)
M_{2ns}	=	factored end moment on a compression member at the end at which M_2 acts, due to loads that cause no appreciable sway, calculated using a first-order elastic frame analysis

CSA Group standard A23.3-14

M_{2s} = factored end moment on a compression member at the end at which M_2 acts, due to loads that cause appreciable sway, calculated using a first-order elastic frame analysis

n = number of bars or wires being spliced or developed along the potential plane of bond splitting

n_ℓ = total number of longitudinal bars in the column cross-section that are laterally supported by the corner of hoops or by hooks of seismic crossties

N = unfactored permanent compressive load perpendicular to the shear plane (see Clause 11)

N_c = tensile force in concrete

N_f = factored axial load normal to the cross-section occurring simultaneously with V_f, including effects of tension due to creep and shrinkage (taken as positive for tension and negative for compression)

N_r = factored resistance in tension

p_c = outside perimeter of the concrete cross-section

p_h = perimeter of the centreline of the closed transverse torsion reinforcement

P_c = critical axial load

P_f = factored axial load (see Clauses 10 and 20)

P_f = factored load at mid-height of panel (see Clause 23)

= maximum factored axial load for earthquake loading cases (see Clause 21)

P_n = earthquake-induced transfer force resulting from interaction between elements of a linked or coupled wall system, taken as the sum of the end shears corresponding to the nominal flexural resistance in the coupling beams above the section

P_{ns} = nominal net force on a cross-section for the direction being considered due to yielding in tension or compression of concentrated and distributed reinforcement during plastic hinge formation (positive for tension)

P_o = nominal axial resistance at zero eccentricity

P_p = earthquake-induced transfer force resulting from interaction between elements of a linked or coupled wall system, taken as the sum of the end shears corresponding to the probable flexural resistance in the coupling beams above the section

P_r = factored axial load resistance of wall

$P_{r,max}$ = maximum axial load resistance calculated in accordance with Equation 10.10

P_{ro} = factored axial load resistance at zero eccentricity

P_s = axial force at section resulting from factored dead load plus factored live load using earthquake load factors (see Clause 21)

= service load at mid-height of panel (see Clause 23)

P_{tf} = factored load from tributary roof or floor area

P_{ts} = service load from tributary roof or floor area

P_{wf} = factored weight of panel tributary to and above design section

P_{ws} = unfactored weight of panel tributary to and above design section

q_s = uniform bearing stress in soil or rock resisting a vertical load and overturning moment on a footing (see Clause 21)

Q = stability index for a storey

r = radius of gyration of cross-section of a compression member

R_d = ductility-related force modification factor, as specified in the _National Building Code of Canada_

R_o = overstrength-related force modification factor, as specified in the _National Building Code of Canada_

R_E = reduction factor on two-way shear stress as a function of interstorey deflection

s = factor for creep deflections under sustained loads (see Clause 9)

   = maximum centre-to-centre spacing of transverse reinforcement within ℓ_d (see Clause 12)

   = spacing of headed shear reinforcement or stirrups measured perpendicular to b_o (see Clause 13)

   = spacing of shear or torsion reinforcement measured parallel to the longitudinal axis of the member (see Clause 11)

   = spacing of transverse reinforcement measured along the longitudinal axis of the structural member (see Clause 21)

s_w = spacing of wire to be developed or spliced

s_x = longitudinal spacing of transverse reinforcement

s_z = crack spacing parameter dependent on crack control characteristics of longitudinal reinforcement (see Figure 11.2)

s_{ze} = equivalent value of s_z that allows for influence of aggregate size

S = variable loads due to ice, rain, and snow (including associated rain)

$S(T)$ = design spectral response acceleration for a period of T, as specified in the _National Building Code of Canada_

$S_a(0.2)$ = damped spectral response acceleration for a period of 0.2 s, as specified in the _National Building Code of Canada_

S_p = moment, shear, or axial force at connection corresponding to development of probable strength at intended yield locations, based on the governing mechanism of inelastic lateral deformation, considering both gravity and earthquake load effects

S_r = factored flexural, shear, or axial resistance of a connection

t = wall thickness (see Clauses 14 and 22)

   = wall thickness of box section (see Clause 11)

T = effects of imposed deformations due to moisture changes, shrinkage, creep, temperature, and ground settlement or combinations thereof (see Clause 9); period in seconds (see Clause 21)

T_a = fundamental lateral period of vibration of the building in the direction under consideration, determined in accordance with the _National Building Code of Canada_

T_{cr} = pure torsional cracking resistance

T_f = factored torsional moment

T_r = factored torsional resistance provided by circulatory shear flow

v_c = factored shear stress resistance provided by the concrete

v_f = factored shear stress

v_r = factored shear stress resistance (see Clauses 13 and 18)

   = factored shear stress resistance of shear plane (see Clause 11)

v_s = factored shear stress resistance provided by shear reinforcement

V_c	=	shear resistance attributed to the concrete factored by ϕ_c
V_f	=	factored horizontal shear in a storey (see Clause 10)
	=	factored shear force (see Clauses 11, 12, 13, 17, 20, and 22)
V_{fb}	=	factored shear force through a beam-column joint acting parallel to beam bars
V_p	=	component in the direction of the applied shear of the effective prestressing force factored by ϕ_p; for variable depth members, the sum of the component of the effective prestressing force and the components of flexural compression and tension in the direction of the applied shear, positive if resisting applied shear, factored by ϕ_p
V_r	=	factored shear resistance
$V_{r\ell}$	=	factored longitudinal shear resistance
$V_{r,max}$	=	maximum possible factored shear resistance
V_s	=	shear resistance provided by shear reinforcement factored by ϕ_s
V_{se}	=	shear transmitted to column or column capital due to specified loads
w_b	=	width of a bearing for a concentrated vertical load acting on a wall
w_c	=	clear horizontal distance between adjacent shear wall webs, if webs are present
w_{df}	=	factored dead load per unit area
w_f	=	factored load per unit area (see Clause 13)
	=	factored load per unit length of beam or per unit area of slab (see Clause 9)
	=	factored uniformly distributed lateral load (see Clause 23)
w_{lf}	=	factored live load per unit area
w_s	=	service uniformly distributed lateral load
x	=	anchorage length of tension tie (see Clause 11)
	=	centroidal x-axis of a critical section (see Clause 13)
	=	direction of coordinates in elastic plate theory (see Clause 13.6.4)
	=	shorter overall dimension of rectangular part of cross-section (see Clause 13)
x_d	=	dimension from face of column to edge of drop panel (see Figure 13.1)
y	=	centroidal y-axis of a critical section (see Clause 13.3.5.5)
	=	direction perpendicular to coordinate x in elastic plate theory (see Clause 13.6.4)
	=	longer overall dimension of rectangular part of cross-section (see Clause 13.8.2.9)
y_t	=	distance from centroidal axis of gross section, neglecting reinforcement, to extreme fibre in tension (see Clause 9)
	=	distance from centroidal axis of section to extreme fibre in tension (see Clause 18)
z	=	quantity limiting distribution of flexural reinforcement
α	=	angle between inclined stirrups or bent-up bars and the longitudinal axis of the member (see Clause 11)
	=	ratio of moment of inertia of beam section to moment of inertia of a width of slab bounded laterally by centrelines of adjacent panels (if any) on each side of the beam, equal to I_b / I_s (see Clause 13)
α_c	=	section property reduction factor used for column effective stiffness properties
α_f	=	angle between shear friction reinforcement and shear plane

α_m = average value of α for beams on the four sides of a panel

α_s = factor that adjusts v_c for support dimensions

α_w = section property reduction factor used for wall effective stiffness properties

α_1 = ratio of average stress in rectangular compression block to the specified concrete strength (see Clause 10)

    = α in direction of ℓ_1 (see Clause 13)

α_2 = α in direction of ℓ_2

β = factor accounting for shear resistance of cracked concrete (see Clauses 11 and 21)

    = ratio of clear spans in long to short directions (see Clause 13)

    = ratio of long side to the short side of footing (see Clause 15)

β_b = ratio of area of cut-off reinforcement to total area of tension reinforcement at section

β_c = ratio of long side to short side of concentrated load or reaction area

β_d = for non-sway frames and for strength and stability checks of sway frames carried out in accordance with Clauses 10.16.4 and 10.16.5, the ratio of the maximum factored sustained axial load to the maximum factored axial load associated with the same load combination

    = for sway frames, except as required by Clauses 10.16.4 and 10.16.5, the ratio of the maximum factored sustained shear within a storey to the maximum factored shear in that storey

β_p = shear stress factor (see Clause 18)

β_1 = ratio of depth of rectangular compression block to depth to the neutral axis

γ_c = density of concrete

γ_f = fraction of unbalanced moment transferred by flexure at slab-column connections

γ_v = fraction of unbalanced moment transferred by eccentricity of shear at slab-column connections

γ_w = wall overstrength factor equal to the ratio of the load corresponding to nominal moment resistance of the wall system to the factored load on the wall system, but need not be taken as less than 1.3

Δ_f = lateral deflection at top of wall calculated using the modified section properties in Clause 21.2 and the factored seismic loads calculated in accordance with the *National Building Code of Canada*

Δ_h = additional thickness of the drop panel below the soffit of the slab

Δ_o = initial panel out-of-straightness (see Clause 23)

    = relative deflection of the top and bottom of a storey, computed in accordance with Clause 10

Δ_s = panel mid-height deflection under service lateral and vertical loads

δ_b = moment magnification factor to reflect the $P\text{-}\Delta$ effect at factored loads

δ_{bs} = moment magnification factor to reflect the $P\text{-}\Delta$ effect at service loads

δ_i = interstorey drift ratio equal to interstorey deflection divided by the interstorey height calculated in accordance with the *National Building Code of Canada*

δ_s = moment magnification factor accounting for second-order effects of vertical load acting on a structure in a laterally displaced configuration

ε_{cu} = maximum strain at the extreme concrete compression fibre at ultimate

ε_s	= strain in reinforcement (see Clause 8)
	= tensile strain in tensile tie reinforcement due to factored loads (see Clause 11)
ε_x	= longitudinal strain at mid-depth of the member due to factored loads (positive when tensile) (see Clause 11)
ε_1	= principal tensile strain in cracked concrete due to factored loads (see Clause 11)
ζ_s	= deflection multiplier for sustained loads
θ	= angle of inclination of diagonal compressive stresses to the longitudinal axis of the member
θ_{ic}	= wall or coupling beam inelastic rotational capacity
θ_{id}	= wall or coupling beam inelastic rotational demand
θ_s	= smallest angle between compressive strut and adjoining tensile ties
λ	= factor to account for low-density concrete
μ	= coefficient of friction
ρ	= ratio of non-prestressed tension reinforcement, equal to A_s/bd
ρ'	= reinforcement ratio for compression reinforcement, equal to A_s'/bd
ρ_h	= ratio of area of horizontal distributed reinforcement to gross concrete area perpendicular to this reinforcement
ρ_n	= ratio of area of distributed reinforcement parallel to the plane to A_{cv} to gross concrete area perpendicular to that reinforcement
ρ_s	= ratio of volume of spiral reinforcement to total volume of core (out-to-out of spirals) of a spirally reinforced compression member
ρ_{sk}	= ratio of area of skin reinforcement to A_{cs}
ρ_t	= ratio of total area of longitudinal reinforcing steel to gross concrete section
ρ_v	= ratio of shear friction reinforcement
σ	= effective normal stress
ϕ	= resistance factor applied to a specified material property or to the resistance of a member, connection, or structure, which for the limit state under consideration takes into account the variability of dimensions and material properties, quality of work, type of failure, and uncertainty in the prediction of resistance
ϕ_a	= resistance factor for structural steel
ϕ_c	= resistance factor for concrete
ϕ_m	= member resistance factor
ϕ_p	= resistance factor for prestressing tendons
ϕ_s	= resistance factor for non-prestressed reinforcing bars
ψ	= adjustment factor for moment of inertia for prismatic modelling of columns
$\psi_{h,V}$	= factor used to modify shear strength of anchors located in concrete members with $h < 1.5_{c1}$, as specified in Clause D.7.2.8
ω	= flange buckling factor

3.3 Standard notation and calculations

3.3.1 Standard notation for loads and resistances

In this Standard, the subscript f denotes a load effect based on factored loads and the subscript r denotes a resistance calculated using factored material strengths.

3.3.2 Standard notation for reinforcing bars

In this Standard, the standard notation for metric reinforcing bars is the bar designation number followed by the letter M.

3.3.3 Bar diameter for calculations

Except for calculations involving bar areas, the diameter, d_b, of metric reinforcing bars may be taken as the bar designation number.

4 General requirements

4.1 Materials — Reinforcement

4.1.1

Reinforcement and prestressing tendons shall comply with Clause 6 of CSA A23.1.

Notes:
1) *See also Clause 8.5.*
2) *Pretensioned epoxy-coated strands should not be used in building structures because, in the event of a fire, heat will soften the coating and reduce bond.*

4.1.2

All reinforcement shall be deformed bars, except that plain bars may be used for spirals and plain bars smaller than 10 mm in diameter may be used for stirrups or ties.

4.1.3

Deformed reinforcement shall include
a) reinforcing bars having deformations and complying with CSA G30.18;
b) welded wire fabric complying with ASTM A1064/A1064M, with welded intersections not farther apart than 200 mm in the direction of the principal reinforcement, and with crosswires having a cross-sectional area of not less than 35% of that of the principal reinforcement [see also Clause 11.2.4 b)];
c) welded wire fabric complying with ASTM A497/A497M, with welded intersections not farther apart than 400 mm in the direction of the principal reinforcement, and with crosswires having a cross-sectional area of not less than 35% of that of the principal reinforcement [see also Clause 11.2.4 b)]; and
d) deformed wire for concrete reinforcement complying with ASTM A496 and not smaller than size MD25.

4.1.4

Prestressing tendons shall comply with the applicable requirements of ASTM A416/A416M, ASTM A421/A421M, and ASTM A722/A722M.

4.2 Concrete and other materials

4.2.1
Cast-in-place concrete and constituent materials shall comply with CSA A23.1.

4.2.2
Precast concrete and constituent materials shall comply with CSA A23.4, except as specified in Clause 16.2.2.

4.3 Concrete quality, mixing, and placement

4.3.1 Quality

4.3.1.1
Concrete shall be proportioned and produced in accordance with CSA A23.1 or CSA A23.4, as applicable.

4.3.1.2
The compressive strength of concrete, f'_c, shall be determined by testing as specified in CSA A23.1/A23.2 or CSA A23.4, as applicable.

4.3.1.3
Unless otherwise specified, f'_c shall be based on 28 day tests.

4.3.2 Mixing and placement
Concrete shall be mixed, placed, and cured in accordance with CSA A23.1 or CSA A23.4, as applicable.

5 Drawings and related documents
In addition to the information required by the applicable building codes, the drawings and related documents for structures designed in accordance with this Standard shall include
a)   the size and location of all structural elements, reinforcement, and prestressing tendons;
b)   provision for dimensional changes resulting from prestress, creep, shrinkage, and temperature;
c)   the locations and details of expansion or contraction joints and permissible locations and details for construction joints;
d)   the magnitude and location of prestressing forces;
e)   the specified strength of concrete in various parts of the structure at stated ages or stages of construction and the nominal maximum size and type of aggregate;
f)   the required cover;
g)   identification of the applicable reinforcing steel Standard and the specified type and grade of reinforcement;
h)   the anchorage length and the location and length of lap splices;
i)   the type and location of welded splices and mechanical connections of reinforcement;
j)   the type and grade of prestressing steel; and
k)   identification of the protective coatings for reinforcement, prestressing tendons, and hardware.

6 Formwork, falsework, embedded pipes, and construction joints

6.1 General

Formwork, falsework, construction joints, and the placement of embedded pipes and hardware shall be as specified in CSA A23.1 or CSA A23.4, as applicable.

6.2 Embedded pipes and openings

Embedded pipes and openings for mechanical and other services shall be located so as to have a negligible impact on the strength of the construction or their effects on member strength shall be considered in the design.

6.3 Construction joints

Provision shall be made for the transfer of shear and other forces through construction joints.

Note: *Construction joints in floors should generally be located near the midspan of slabs, beams, or girders unless a beam intersects a girder in that location. In such cases, the joint in the girder should be offset a distance at least equal to the depth of the beam.*

7 Details of reinforcement

Note: *The clauses of CSA A23.1 referred to in this Clause are reproduced in Annex A.*

7.1 Hooks, bends, and headed bars

7.1.1 General

Standard hooks and bends shall comply with Clause 6.6.2 of CSA A23.1. Non-standard hooks or bends shall be detailed on the drawings.

7.1.2 Stirrups and ties

Stirrups and ties shall be anchored by standard stirrup and tie hooks or by heads of headed bars. The standard stirrup and tie hooks shall have a bend of at least 135° unless the concrete cover surrounding the hook is restrained against spalling, in which case there may be a bend of at least 90°. Standard tie hooks with a bend of at least 90° may be used for ties in columns having a specified concrete compressive strength equal to or less than 50 MPa. Stirrups and ties of size 20M and 25M shall have inside bend diameters in accordance with Table 16 of CSA A23.1.

7.1.3 Crossties

Crossties shall be anchored by standard tie hooks or by heads of headed bars. The standard tie hooks shall have a bend of at least 135° at one end and a standard tie hook with a bend of at least 90° at the other end. The hooks shall engage peripheral longitudinal bars. The 90° hooks of successive crossties engaging the same longitudinal bar shall be alternated end for end.

7.1.4 Headed bars and studs

Headed bars and studs with a head of an area equal to ten times the bar area shall be deemed capable of developing the tensile strength of the bar without crushing of the concrete under the head provided that the specified concrete compressive strength is equal to or greater than 25 MPa and the yield strength of the bar used in the design does not exceed 500 MPa.

7.2 Placing of reinforcement

7.2.1 General

Placing of reinforcement shall be shown on the drawings and shall be as specified in CSA A23.1 or CSA A23.4, as applicable.

7.2.2 Draped fabric

When welded wire fabric with wire of 6 mm diameter or less is used for slab reinforcement in slabs not exceeding 3 m in span, the reinforcement may be curved from a point near the top of the slab over the support to a point near the bottom of the slab at midspan, provided that such reinforcement is either continuous over or securely anchored at the support.

7.3 Tolerances

7.3.1

The tolerances for placing of reinforcement shall comply with CSA A23.1 or CSA A23.4, as applicable.

7.3.2

When design requirements necessitate closer tolerances than those specified in Clause 7.3.1, such tolerances shall be clearly indicated on the construction drawings.

7.4 Spacing of reinforcement and tendons

7.4.1 Bars

7.4.1.1

The minimum clear distance between parallel bars shall comply with CSA A23.1.

7.4.1.2

In walls and one-way slabs other than concrete joist construction, the principal reinforcement shall be spaced not farther apart than the smaller of three times the wall or slab thickness or 500 mm.

7.4.1.3

The clear distance between adjacent longitudinal reinforcing bars in compression members shall not be greater than 500 mm.

7.4.2 Bundled bars

7.4.2.1

Groups of parallel reinforcing bars bundled in contact to act as a unit shall be limited to four bars in any one bundle. Bundled bars shall be tied, wired, or otherwise fastened together to ensure that they remain in position.

7.4.2.2

Bars larger than 35M shall not be bundled in beams or girders.

7.4.2.3

Individual bars in a bundle cut off within the span of flexural members shall terminate at different points at least 40 bar diameters apart.

7.4.2.4

Where spacing limitations and clear concrete cover are based on bar size, a unit of bundled bars shall be treated as a single bar of a diameter derived from the equivalent total area.

7.4.3 Pretensioning tendons

7.4.3.1

The clear distance between pretensioning wires or strands at each end of the member shall be not less than $4d_b$ for wire and not less than $3d_b$ for strands, except that if specified compressive strength of concrete at time of prestress transfer, f_{ci} is 27.5 MPa or greater, minimum centre-to-centre spacing of strands shall be 45 mm for 12.7 mm nominal diameter or smaller and 50 mm for strands of 15.2 mm nominal diameter. Closer vertical spacing and bundling of strands may be used in the middle portion of the span.

7.4.3.2

The minimum clear space between groups of bundled strands shall be not less than 1.3 times the nominal maximum size of the coarse aggregate.

7.4.4 Post-tensioning tendons

The minimum clear distance between post-tensioning tendons and the requirements for bundling of post-tensioning tendons shall comply with CSA A23.1.

7.5 Special details for columns and walls

7.5.1 Offset bars

7.5.1.1

Where offset bent bars are used, the slope of the inclined portion of the bar with respect to the axis of the column shall not exceed 1:6 and the portions of the bar above and below the offset shall be parallel to the axis of the column. These details shall be shown on the drawings.

7.5.1.2

Adequate horizontal support at the offset bends shall be treated as a design matter and shall be provided by ties, spirals, or parts of the floor construction. Horizontal thrust to be resisted shall be taken as 1.5 times the horizontal component of the factored resistance in the inclined portion of the bar. Ties or spirals, if used, shall be placed not more than 150 mm from the point of the bend.

7.5.1.3

Where a column or wall face is offset by more than 75 mm, longitudinal bars shall not be offset bent.

7.5.2 Splices and load transfer in metal cores

In composite columns,
a)   splices of structural steel cores shall be made as specified in CSA S16; and

b)   provision shall be made at column bases to transfer the loads to the footings as specified in Clause 15.9.

7.6 Transverse reinforcement

7.6.1 General

Transverse reinforcement shall comply with Clauses 7.6.2 to 7.6.6 and, where shear or torsion reinforcement is required, with Clause 11.

7.6.2 Composite columns

Transverse reinforcement in composite columns shall comply with Clauses 10.18 and 10.19.

7.6.3 Prestressing tendons

Transverse reinforcement for prestressing tendons shall comply with Clause 18.13.

7.6.4 Spirals for compression members

7.6.4.1

Spiral reinforcement for compression members shall comply with Clause 10.9.4 and, with respect to construction and spacers, with CSA A23.1.

7.6.4.2

Spiral reinforcement shall have a minimum diameter of 10 mm.

7.6.4.3

The clear spacing between successive turns of a spiral shall not be less than 25 mm or greater than 75 mm.

7.6.5 Ties for compression members

7.6.5.1

In compression members, all non-prestressed longitudinal bars of sizes 30M or smaller, except as noted in Clause 14.1.8.7, shall be enclosed by ties having a diameter of at least 30% of that of the largest longitudinal bar. All non-prestressed longitudinal bars of sizes 35M, 45M, and 55M and all bundled bars shall be enclosed by ties of at least size 10M. Deformed wire or welded wire fabric of equivalent area may be used.

7.6.5.2

Tie spacing shall not exceed the smallest of
a)   16 times the diameter of the smallest longitudinal bars or the smallest bar in a bundle;
b)   48 tie diameters;
c)   the least dimension of the compression member; and
d)   300 mm in compression members containing bundled bars.

For specified concrete compressive strengths exceeding 50 MPa, the tie spacing determined in accordance with Items a) to d) shall be multiplied by 0.75.

7.6.5.3

Ties shall be located not more than one-half of a tie spacing above the slab or footing and shall be spaced as specified in Clause 7.6.5.2 to not more than one-half of a tie spacing below the lowest reinforcement in the slab or drop panel above. Where a slab is not continuous beyond one or more faces of the column, the ties that engage the vertical steel on any face not confined by a slab shall continue within the depth of the slab.

7.6.5.4

Where beams or brackets frame into a column from four directions, the ties may be terminated not more than 75 mm below the lowest reinforcement in the shallowest of such beams or brackets. Where a beam or bracket is not continuous beyond one or more faces of the column, the ties which engage the vertical steel on any face not confined by a beam or bracket shall continue within the depth of the beam or bracket. See also Clause 7.7.

7.6.5.5

Ties shall be arranged so that every corner and alternate longitudinal bar shall have lateral support provided by the corner of a tie having an included angle of not more than 135° and no bar shall be farther than 150 mm clear on either side from such a laterally supported bar.

7.6.5.6

Where the bars are located around the periphery of a circle, a complete circular tie may be used, provided that the ends of the ties are lap welded or bent at least 135° around a longitudinal bar or otherwise anchored within the core of the column.

7.6.5.7

Welded wire fabric of equivalent area may be used if spliced in accordance with Clauses 12.18 and 12.19. The required splice lengths shall be shown on the drawings.

7.6.5.8

Where anchor bolts are placed in the tops of columns or pedestals, they shall be enclosed by lateral reinforcement that also surrounds at least four vertical bars of the column or pedestal. The lateral reinforcement shall be distributed within 125 mm of the top of the column or pedestal and shall consist of at least two 10M bars.

7.6.6 Beams and girders — Transverse reinforcement

7.6.6.1

Compression reinforcement in beams and girders shall be enclosed by ties or stirrups satisfying the size and spacing requirements of Clauses 7.6.5.1 and 7.6.5.2 or by welded wire fabric of an equivalent area. Such ties or stirrups shall be provided along the length where compression reinforcement is required.

7.6.6.2

Transverse reinforcement for flexural framing members subject to stress reversals or to torsion at supports shall consist of closed stirrups or spirals extending completely around all main reinforcement.

7.6.6.3

Closed ties or stirrups shall be
a)   formed in one piece by overlapping standard stirrup or tie end hooks around a longitudinal bar;

b) formed in one or two pieces spliced in accordance with the requirements for a Class B splice having a lap of $1.3\ell_d$; or

c) anchored as specified in Clause 12.13.

7.7 Special details for beam-column connections

7.7.1

At connections of principal framing elements, such as beams and columns, an enclosure shall be provided for end anchorage of reinforcement terminating in such connections.

7.7.2

The enclosure specified in Clause 7.7.1 may consist of transverse framing members, internal closed ties, spirals, or stirrups.

7.7.3

When gravity load, wind, or other lateral forces cause the transfer of moments from beams to columns, column ties in accordance with Clause 7.6.5, having a maximum spacing of 150 mm but not less than two column ties, shall be provided within beam column connections. Except for connections that are part of a primary seismic force resisting system, this requirement may be waived if the connection is restrained on four sides by beams or slabs of approximately equal depth. See also Clause 12.11.2.

7.8 Minimum reinforcement in slabs

7.8.1

A minimum area of reinforcement of $0.002A_g$ shall be provided in each direction.

7.8.2

For exposure conditions where crack control is essential, reinforcement exceeding that required by Clause 7.8.1 shall be provided.

7.8.3

Minimum reinforcement shall not be spaced farther apart than the smaller of five times the slab thickness or 500 mm.

7.8.4

At all sections where it is required, minimum reinforcement shall be developed in tension for its specified yield strength in compliance with Clause 12.

7.8.5

Prestressing tendons used as minimum reinforcement shall comply with Clause 18.12.6.

7.9 Concrete protection for reinforcement

Concrete cover for reinforcement shall comply with the cover requirements of CSA A23.1, CSA A23.4, or CSA S413, as applicable, unless special conditions dictate otherwise. In all cases, concrete cover shall be indicated on the drawings.

8 Design — Limit states, load combinations, and material properties

8.1 Limit states

8.1.1 Durability
Concrete structures shall satisfy the durability requirements of CSA A23.1, CSA A23.4, or CSA S413, as applicable, for the intended use and exposure conditions.

8.1.2 Fire resistance
Concrete structures shall satisfy the fire resistance requirements of the applicable building code.

8.1.3 Ultimate limit states
Structures, structural members, and connections shall be designed such that factored resistance is greater than or equal to the effect of factored loads, with the effect of factored loads being determined as specified in Clauses 8.2 and 8.3 and the factored resistance being determined as specified in Clause 8.4.

8.1.4 Serviceability limit states

8.1.4.1 Deflections
Structures and structural members shall be designed to satisfy the deflection control requirements of Clauses 9.8 and 13.2.7, with loadings as specified in Clause 8.3.3.

8.1.4.2 Local damage and cracking
Structural members and connections shall be designed to meet the minimum reinforcement area and maximum reinforcement spacing requirements of this Standard as well as the requirements of Clauses 10.6 and 18.1 to 18.4, with loadings as specified in Clause 8.3.3.
Note: *This Standard does not specifically limit crack widths.*

8.1.4.3 Vibrations
In the design of structures and structural members, consideration shall be given to controlling vibrations within acceptable limits for the intended use.

8.1.5 Structural integrity
Consideration shall be given to the robustness of the overall structural system to minimize the likelihood of a progressive type of collapse.
Notes:
1) *Provisions for structural integrity are required for two-way slabs (Clause 13.10.6), precast concrete structures (Clause 16.5), and tilt-up structures (Clause 23.2.9).*
2) *The requirements in this Standard generally provide a satisfactory level of structural integrity for most concrete structures for buildings. It is possible that supplementary provisions for structural integrity will be needed for mixed or unusual structural systems or for structures exposed to severe loads such as vehicle impacts or explosions. For further guidance, refer to Commentary B in the NRCC's User's Guide to Part 4 of the* National Building Code of Canada.

8.2 Loading

8.2.1 General

Loads shall be determined in accordance with the requirements of the applicable building code.

8.2.2 Imposed deformations

8.2.2.1 General

The short-term and long-term forces and effects resulting from the interaction of the stiffness of the structure and imposed deformations such as differential settlement, non-uniform or restrained temperature changes, and restraint of shrinkage and creep shall be considered.

Notes:
1) *Imposed deformations produce self-equilibrating moments, reactions, and stresses.*
2) *Imposed deformations can require considerable redistribution of internal forces, which can lead to excessive cracking at service load or to brittle failure.*
3) *Estimates of differential settlement, creep, shrinkage, or temperature change should be based on realistic assessments of such effects occurring in service. The magnitude of the internal forces and the effects of imposed deformations depend on the magnitude of the deformation, the stiffness of the structure (cracked or uncracked) resisting the deformations, and the time necessary for the deformations to occur.*

8.2.2.2 Load factor for T-loads

When deemed necessary by the designer, imposed deformations, T, shall be included in the appropriate load combinations, with the load factor specified in the applicable building code.

8.2.3 Prestress

In statically indeterminate structures, prestress normally causes secondary moments and reactions. These shall be included in ultimate limit state design calculations, with the load factor specified in the applicable building code.

8.3 Load combinations and load factors

Note: *See Annex C.*

8.3.1 General

Structures, structural members, and connections shall be designed to resist the bending moments, axial loads, shear forces, and torsions computed from the factored loads and load combinations specified in Clauses 8.3.2 and 8.3.3 and the applicable building code.

8.3.2 Load combinations for ultimate limit states

The effect of factored loads acting on structures, structural members, and connections shall be determined in accordance with the factored load combinations specified in the applicable building code.

Note: *See Table C.1a.*

8.3.3 Load combinations for serviceability limit states

A building and its structural components shall be checked for the applicable serviceability limit states specified in Clause 8.1.4 under the effects of the service loads. The applicable load combination shall be taken as the one that results in the most unfavourable effect for the limit state under consideration.

8.4 Factored resistance

Note: *See Note 3) of the preliminary Notes to Annex C.*

8.4.1 General

The factored resistance of a member, its cross-sections, and its connections shall be taken as the resistance calculated as specified in this Standard, using the material resistance factors specified in Clauses 8.4.2 and 8.4.3.

Notes:
1) *Member resistance factors are used in Clauses 10.15.3, 10.16.3.2, and 23.3.1.3.*
2) *In a few cases the member rigidity, EI, is multiplied by a member resistance factor, ϕ_m, specified in the applicable clauses.*

8.4.2 Factored concrete strength

The factored concrete compressive strengths used in checking ultimate limit states shall be taken as $\phi_c f_c'$. The factored concrete tensile strengths used in checking ultimate limit states are given in terms of $\phi_c \sqrt{f_c'}$, where $\phi_c = 0.65$, except as specified in Clause 16.1.3.

8.4.3 Factored reinforcement and tendon force

The factored force in reinforcing bars, tendons, and structural shapes shall be taken as the product of the appropriate resistance factor, ϕ, and the respective steel force as specified in the applicable clause of this Standard, where
a) $\phi_s = 0.85$ for reinforcing bars and embedded steel anchors;
b) $\phi_p = 0.90$ for prestressing tendons; and
c) $\phi_a = 0.90$ for structural steel.

8.5 Reinforcement and tendon properties for design

8.5.1 Design strength for reinforcement

Design calculations shall be based on the specified yield strength of reinforcement, f_y, which shall not exceed 500 MPa except for prestressing tendons.

8.5.2 Compression reinforcement

For compression reinforcement having a specified yield strength exceeding 400 MPa, the value of f_y assumed in design calculations shall not exceed the stress corresponding to a strain of 0.35%.

Note: *CSA G30.18 defines the yield strength of Grade 500 reinforcement at a strain of 0.35%.*

8.5.3 Stress-strain curve for reinforcement

8.5.3.1 Reinforcement and tendon stress-strain curve

The force in the reinforcement shall be calculated as ϕ_s for reinforcing bars and ϕ_p for prestressing tendons, multiplied by the force determined from strain compatibility based on a stress-strain curve representative of the steel.

8.5.3.2 Simplified reinforcement stress-strain curve

For reinforcement with a specified yield strength of 500 MPa or less, the following assumptions may be used:
a)   for strains, ε_s, less than the yield strain, f_y / E_s, the force in the reinforcement shall be taken as $\phi_s A_s E_s \varepsilon_s$; and

b)   for strains, ε_s, greater than the yield strain, the force in the reinforcement shall be taken as $\phi_s A_s f_y$.

8.5.4 Modulus of elasticity of reinforcement

8.5.4.1

The modulus of elasticity of reinforcing bars, E_s, shall be taken as 200 000 MPa.

8.5.4.2

The modulus of elasticity for tendons, E_p, shall be determined by tests or supplied by the manufacturer.
Note: *Typical values of E_p range from 190 000 to 200 000 MPa.*

8.5.5 Coefficient of thermal expansion of reinforcement

The coefficient of thermal expansion may be taken as 10×10^{-6} / °C.

8.6 Concrete properties for design

8.6.1 Design strength of concrete

8.6.1.1

Specified concrete compressive strengths used in design shall not be less than 20 MPa or more than 80 MPa, except as allowed by Clauses 8.6.1.2, 8.6.1.3, and 22.1.1 or restricted by Clauses 11.3.6.3, 12.1.2, 18.12.3.3, and 21.2.6.
Note: *Designers planning to use specified concrete strengths exceeding 50 MPa should determine whether the appropriate concretes are available. Higher strengths can require prequalification of concrete suppliers and contractors and special construction techniques.*

8.6.1.2

The upper limit on the specified concrete compressive strength specified in Clause 8.6.1.1 may be waived if the structural properties and detailing requirements of reinforced concretes having a strength exceeding 80 MPa are established for concretes similar to those to be used.
Note: *High-strength concretes vary in their brittleness and need for confinement.*

8.6.1.3

Strengths lower than those specified in Clause 8.6.1.1 may be used for mass concrete, plain concrete, or strength evaluation of existing structures.

8.6.2 Modulus of elasticity

8.6.2.1

The modulus of elasticity of concrete in compression, E_c, used in design shall be taken as the average secant modulus for a stress of $0.40 f_c'$ determined for similar concrete in accordance with ASTM C469. If the modulus of elasticity is critical to the design, a minimum value of E_c shall be specified and shown on the drawings.
Note: *If the modulus of elasticity is critical to the design, the designer should establish whether such concrete can be produced.*

8.6.2.2

In lieu of results from tests of similar concrete, the modulus of elasticity, E_c, for concrete with γ_c between 1500 and 2500 kg/m³ may be taken as

$$E_c = (3300\sqrt{f_c'} + 6900)\left(\frac{\gamma_c}{2300}\right)^{1.5}$$

Equation 8.1

8.6.2.3

In lieu of Clauses 8.6.2.1 and 8.6.2.2, the modulus of elasticity, E_c, of normal density concrete with compressive strength between 20 and 40 MPa may be taken as

$$E_c = 4500\sqrt{f_c'}$$

Equation 8.2

Note: *The value of E_c is affected by the aggregate fraction in the mix, the modulus of elasticity of the aggregates, and the loading rate. The modulus of elasticity of Canadian concretes will generally be between 80 and 120% of the values specified in Clauses 8.6.2.2 and 8.6.2.3.*

8.6.3 Concrete stress-strain relationship

The concrete compressive stress-strain relationship used in design shall conform to Clause 10.1.6.

8.6.4 Modulus of rupture of concrete

The modulus of rupture, f_r, shall be taken as

$$f_r = 0.6\lambda\sqrt{f_c'}$$

Equation 8.3

8.6.5 Modification factors for concrete density

The effect of low-density aggregates on tensile strength and other related properties shall be accounted for by the factor λ, where
a) $\lambda = 1.00$ for normal density concrete;
b) $\lambda = 0.85$ for structural semi-low-density concrete in which all the fine aggregate is natural sand; and
c) $\lambda = 0.75$ for structural low-density concrete in which none of the fine aggregate is natural sand.

Linear interpolation may be applied based on the fraction of natural sand in the mix.

8.6.6 Coefficient of thermal expansion of concrete

For the purpose of structural analysis, the coefficient of thermal expansion of concrete may be taken as $10 \times 10^{-6}/°C$.

Note: *The value of the coefficient of thermal expansion depends on the type of aggregates, the moisture state of the concrete, and the temperature of the concrete. It can vary between approximately $6 \times 10^{-6}/°C$ to $13 \times 10^{-6}/°C$ for concrete at temperatures between 0 and 80 °C.*

9 Structural analysis and computation of deflections

9.1 Methods of analysis

9.1.1

All members of frames or continuous construction shall be designed for the maximum effects of the factored loads as determined by an analysis carried out in accordance with one of the methods of analysis specified in Clauses 9.2 to 9.7.

9.1.2

All structural analyses shall satisfy equilibrium conditions.

9.2 Elastic frame analysis

Load effects may be determined by elastic analysis based on the assumptions specified in Clauses 9.2.1 to 9.2.4.

9.2.1 Stiffness

9.2.1.1

Assumptions for computing the relative flexural and torsional stiffnesses of columns, walls, floors, and roof systems shall be consistent throughout the analysis.

9.2.1.2

Member stiffnesses used in analyses for lateral deflection or in second-order frame analyses shall be representative of the degree of member cracking and inelastic action at the limit state for which the analysis is being carried out.

Note: *For wind effects, to obtain reasonable predictions of the deformations and the period of vibration, approximate member stiffnesses are provided in the explanatory notes. For second-order frame analyses at Ultimate Limit States, Clause 10.14.1.2 provides suitable member stiffness properties. For seismic design, Clause 21.2.5 specifies member stiffnesses for members of the seismic force resisting system.*

9.2.1.3

The effect of variable cross-sections shall be considered both in determining bending moments and in the design of the members.

9.2.2 Span length

9.2.2.1

For determining moments in continuous frames, the span length shall be taken as the distance from centre-to-centre of supports.

9.2.2.2

For beams or one-way slabs built integrally with their supports, or for columns in continuous frames, moments at the faces of the joints may be used for design.

9.2.2.3

The span length of a member that is not built integrally with its supports shall be taken as the clear span plus, at each end, half of its depth, but need not exceed the distance between centres of supports.

9.2.2.4

In the analysis of frames containing shear walls, the effect of the width of the wall on the stiffness of the beams framing into the wall shall be considered.

9.2.3 Arrangement of loads

9.2.3.1 Continuous beams and one-way slabs

For continuous beams and one-way slabs, the arrangements of live and dead loads may be limited to combinations of

a) factored dead load of the structure and factored permanent superimposed dead load on all spans, with factored partition load and factored live load on two adjacent spans;

b) factored dead load of the structure and factored permanent superimposed dead load on all spans, with factored partition load and factored live load on alternate spans; and

c) factored dead and factored live load on all spans.

Note: *The superimposed dead load can (but need not) be patterned, depending on the circumstances.*

9.2.3.2 Two-way slabs

Two-way slabs analyzed using the elastic frame method shall be analyzed for the loading patterns specified in Clause 13.8.4.

9.2.4 Redistribution of moments in continuous flexural members

Except when approximate values for bending moments are used, the negative moments at the supports of continuous flexural members calculated by elastic analysis for any assumed loading arrangement may each be increased or decreased by not more than $(30 - 50c/d)\%$, but not more than 20%, and the modified negative moments shall be used for calculating the moments at sections within the spans.

9.3 Approximate frame analysis

9.3.1 General

Except for prestressed concrete, approximate methods of frame analysis may be used for buildings having typical spans, storey heights, and types of construction.

9.3.2 Floor and roof loads

The moments due to floor and roof loads may be computed using an elastic analysis of a portion of the frame consisting of the floor or roof in question, with the columns above and below the floor assumed fixed at their far ends.

9.3.3 Moment and shear coefficients

In lieu of a more accurate method of frame analysis, the approximate moments and shears specified in Table 9.1 may be used in the design of continuous beams and one-way slabs, provided that

a) there are two or more spans;

b) the spans are approximately equal, with the longer of two adjacent spans not greater than the shorter by more than 20%;

c)   the loads are uniformly distributed;

d)   the factored live load does not exceed twice the factored dead load; and

e)   the members are prismatic.

For calculating negative moments at interior supports, ℓ_n shall be taken as the average of the adjacent clear span lengths.

Table 9.1
Approximate moments and shears
(See Clause 9.3.3.)

Moment or shear	Value
Positive moments	
End spans	
Discontinuous end unrestrained	$w_f \ell_n^2 / 11$
Discontinuous end integral with support	$w_f \ell_n^2 / 14$
Interior spans	$w_f \ell_n^2 / 16$
Negative moments	
Negative moment at exterior face of first interior support	
Two spans	$w_f \ell_n^2 / 9$
More than two spans	$w_f \ell_n^2 / 10$
Negative moment at other faces of interior supports	$w_f \ell_n^2 / 11$
Negative moment at interior face of exterior support for members built integrally with supports	
Where the support is a spandrel beam or girder	$w_f \ell_n^2 / 24$
Where the support is a column	$w_f \ell_n^2 / 16$
Shear	
Shear in end members at face of first interior support	$1.15 w_f \ell_n / 2$
Shear at faces of all other supports	$w_f \ell_n / 2$

9.4 Analysis by strut-and-tie models
Strut-and-tie models satisfying the requirements of Clause 11.4 may be used to determine the internal force effects, proportion the reinforcement, and confirm the concrete dimensions.

Note: *Such models are particularly appropriate in regions where plane sections do not remain plane.*

9.5 Finite element analysis

9.5.1
Finite element analysis or other numerical techniques may be used to determine load effects, provided

that the differences between the behaviour of the structure and the behaviour assumed in the analysis are accounted for.

Note: *The analysis should account for the effects of cracking. If the effects of cracking are not included, the redistribution of stresses due to the anticipated cracking and the effects of this redistribution on the reinforcement layout should be explicitly considered in the design of the reinforcement.*

9.5.2

Mesh patterns and boundary conditions shall be consistent with geometry, loading, and restraint conditions. Alternative loading cases shall be considered where applicable. Care shall be taken to ensure realistic modelling of the size and stiffness of supporting elements.

9.5.3

Principal reinforcement may be concentrated in bands or tension ties. Anchorage of the reinforcement shall be explicitly considered.

9.5.4

The analysis shall be checked using independent techniques satisfying equilibrium.

9.5.5

Crack control and deflections shall be considered.

9.6 Elastic plate analysis

Analysis of planar structural elements may be based on elastic plate theory (see Clause 13.6).

9.7 Plastic analysis

9.7.1

A plastic analysis shall satisfy either the upper bound theorem or the lower bound theorem of plasticity.

9.7.2

A plastic analysis may assume either a rigid-plastic or an elastic-plastic behaviour.

9.7.3

Hinging sections shall be detailed to provide the rotational capacity assumed in the analysis.

9.7.4

Plastic analyses shall not be used for sway frames.

9.8 Control of deflections

9.8.1 General

Reinforced concrete members subject to flexure shall be designed to have adequate stiffness to limit deflections or any deformations that could adversely affect the strength or serviceability of the structure.

9.8.2 One-way construction (non-prestressed)

9.8.2.1 Minimum thickness

The minimum thickness specified in Table 9.2 shall apply to one-way construction not supporting or attached to partitions or other construction likely to be damaged by large deflections, unless computation of deflection indicates a lesser thickness can be used without adverse effects.

Note: *It is possible that Table 9.2 will not apply to members that have high ratios of superimposed dead or live loads to the self weight.*

Table 9.2
Thicknesses below which deflections are to be computed for non-prestressed beams or one-way slabs not supporting or attached to partitions or other construction likely to be damaged by large deflections
(See Clauses 9.8.2.1, 9.8.5.1, 9.8.5.2, and 13.2.6.)

	Minimum thickness, h			
	Simply supported	One end continuous	Both ends continuous	Cantilever
Solid one-way slabs	$\ell_n/20$	$\ell_n/24$	$\ell_n/28$	$\ell_n/10$
Beams or ribbed one-way slabs	$\ell_n/16$	$\ell_n/18$	$\ell_n/21$	$\ell_n/8$

Notes:
1) *This Table gives traditional values that provide guidance for preliminary proportioning but are insufficient for beams or one-way slabs supporting partitions or other construction likely to be damaged by large deflections.*
2) *The values specified in this Table shall be used directly for members with normal-density concrete where $\gamma_c > 2150$ kg/m³ and the reinforcement is Grade 400. For other conditions, the values shall be modified as follows:*
   a) *for structural low-density concrete and structural semi-low-density concrete, the values shall be multiplied by ($1.65 - 0.0003\gamma_c$), but not less than 1.0, where γ_c is the density in kilograms per cubic metre; and*
   b) *for f_y other than 400 MPa, the values shall be multiplied by ($0.4 + f_y/670$).*

9.8.2.2 Immediate deflections

When deflections are to be computed, deflections that occur immediately on application of load shall be computed by methods or formulas for elastic deflections, taking into consideration the effects of cracking and reinforcement on member stiffness.

Note: *Deflections may be calculated using formulas for elastic deflections based on effective moments of inertia as specified in Clauses 9.8.2.3 to 9.8.2.5, or by methods based on the integration of curvatures at sections along the span.*

9.8.2.3 E_c and I_e

Unless deflections are determined by a more comprehensive analysis, immediate deflection shall be computed using elastic deflection equations; a modulus of elasticity, E_c, for concrete as specified in Clause 8.6.2; and the effective moment of inertia, as follows:

Equation 9.1

$$I_e = I_{cr} + \left(I_g - I_{cr}\right)\left[\frac{M_{cr}}{M_a}\right]^3 \leq I_g$$

where

$$M_{cr} = \frac{f_r I_g}{Y_t}$$

Equation 9.2

and f_r shall be taken as half the value given in Equation 8.3.

Note: *Depending on the shoring and reshoring schedule adopted, the maximum M_a may occur during construction. If construction loadings are unknown, M_a may be computed as the maximum moment due to specified dead and live loads for the computation of instantaneous and long-term deflections.*

9.8.2.4 Moment of inertia for continuous spans

For continuous prismatic members, the effective moment of inertia may be taken as the weighted average of the values obtained from Equation 9.1 for the critical positive and negative moment sections, as follows:

a)   two ends continuous:

$$I_{e,avg} = 0.7\, I_{em} + 0.15(I_{e1} + I_{e2})$$

Equation 9.3

b)   one end continuous:

$$I_{e,avg} = 0.85\, I_{em} + 0.15 I_{ec}$$

Equation 9.4

9.8.2.5 Sustained load deflections

Unless values are obtained by a more comprehensive analysis, the total immediate plus long-term deflection for flexural members shall be obtained by multiplying the immediate deflection caused by the sustained load considered by the factor ζ_s, as follows:

$$\zeta_s = \left[1 + \frac{s}{1 + 50\rho'} \right]$$

Equation 9.5

where
ρ' =   the value at midspan for simple and continuous spans and at the support for cantilevers

The time dependent factor, s, for sustained loads, applied when the concrete reaches an age of 28 days or greater, shall be taken to be equal to the following values:

For loads sustained for five years or more	2.0
For loads sustained for 12 months	1.4
For loads sustained for six months	1.2
For loads sustained for three months	1.0

Note: *When a sustained load is applied when the concrete is less than 28 days old, the immediate plus long-term deflection may exceed that computed using Equation 9.5. For concrete loaded at an age between 7 and 28 days, the additional long-term deflection may be estimated by multiplying ζ_s by the factor [1.6 − 0.6 (t − 7)/21] where t is the concrete age, in days, at the time of loading.*

9.8.2.6 Deflection limits

The deflection computed in accordance with Clauses 9.8.2.2 to 9.8.2.5 shall not exceed the limits specified in Table 9.3.

CSA Group standard A23.3-14

9.8.3 Two-way construction (non-prestressed)

Deflection control of two-way slab systems shall be checked using Clause 13.2.

9.8.4 Prestressed concrete construction

9.8.4.1 Immediate deflection

For flexural members designed in accordance with Clause 18, immediate deflection shall be computed by methods or formulas for elastic deflection.

9.8.4.2 Moment of inertia

The moment of inertia of the gross concrete section may be used for sections that are uncracked at service loads.

9.8.4.3 Partially prestressed members

For partially prestressed members [i.e., members not satisfying Clause 18.3.2 c)], the reduction in sectional stiffness caused by cracking shall be taken into account.

9.8.4.4 Sustained load deflections

The additional long-term deflection of prestressed concrete members shall be computed by taking into account stresses in concrete and steel under sustained load, including effects of creep and shrinkage of concrete and relaxation of steel.

9.8.4.5 Deflection limits

The computed deflection shall not exceed the limits specified in Table 9.3.

9.8.5 Composite construction

9.8.5.1 Shored construction

If composite flexural members are supported during construction so that after removal of temporary supports the dead load is resisted by the full composite section, the composite member may be considered equivalent to a monolithically cast member for the computation of deflection. For non-prestressed composite members containing more than one type of concrete, the portion of the member in compression shall determine whether the values specified in Table 9.2 for normal density or low-density concrete shall apply. If deflection is computed, account shall be taken of curvatures resulting from differential shrinkage of precast and cast-in-place components and of axial creep effects in a prestressed concrete member.

9.8.5.2 Unshored construction

If the thickness of a non-prestressed precast flexural member meets the requirements of Table 9.2, deflection need not be computed. If the thickness of a non-prestressed composite member meets the requirements of Table 9.2, deflection occurring after the member becomes composite need not be computed, but the long-term deflection of the precast member should be investigated for magnitude and duration of load before the beginning of effective composite action.

9.8.5.3 Deflection limits

Deflection computed in accordance with Clauses 9.8.5.1 and 9.8.5.2 shall not exceed the limits specified in Table 9.3.

Table 9.3
Maximum permissible computed deflections
(See Clauses 9.8.2.6, 9.8.4.5, 9.8.5.3, 13.2.2, and 13.2.7.)

Type of member	Deflection to be considered	Deflection limitation
Flat roofs not supporting or attached to non-structural elements likely to be damaged by large deflections	Immediate deflection due to specified live load, L, or snow load, S	$\ell_n/180*$
Floors not supporting or attached to non-structural elements likely to be damaged by large deflections	Immediate deflection due to specified live load, L	$\ell_n/360$
Roof or floor construction supporting or attached to non-structural elements likely to be damaged by large deflections	That part of the total deflection occurring after attachment of non-structural elements (sum of the long-term deflection due to all sustained loads and the immediate deflection due to any additional live load)†	$\ell_n/480‡$
Roof or floor construction supporting or attached to non-structural elements not likely to be damaged by large deflections	That part of the total deflection occurring after attachment of non-structural elements (sum of the long-term deflection due to all sustained loads and the immediate deflection due to any additional live load)†	$\ell_n/240§$

* *This limit is not intended to guard against ponding. Ponding should be checked by suitable calculations of deflection, including added deflections due to ponded water, and the long-term effects of all sustained loads, camber, construction tolerances, and reliability of provisions for drainage should be taken into consideration.*
† *Long-term deflections shall be determined in accordance with Clause 9.8.2.5 or 9.8.4.4, but may be reduced by the amount of deflection calculated to occur before the attachment of non-structural elements.*
‡ *This limit may be exceeded if adequate measures are taken to prevent damage to supported or attached elements.*
§ *This limit shall not be greater than the tolerance provided for non-structural elements. It may be exceeded if camber is provided so that total deflection minus camber does not exceed the limit.*

Notes:
1) *For two-way slab construction, ℓ_n shall be taken as the clear span in the long direction, measured face-to-face of supports in slabs without beams and face-to-face of beams or other supports in other cases.*
2) *In some instances, the total deflection may be critical, not the incremental deflection. For example, the installation of long solid millwork units and the performance of some flooring depend on total deflection.*

10 Flexure and axial loads

10.1 General principles

10.1.1 General

The factored moment and axial load resistance of members shall be based on strain compatibility and equilibrium using material resistance factors and material properties specified in Clause 8 and the additional assumptions specified in Clauses 10.1.2 to 10.1.7.

10.1.2 Plane sections assumption

The strain in reinforcement and concrete shall be assumed to be directly proportional to the distance from the neutral axis, except for unbonded tendons, deep flexural members (see Clause 10.7), and regions of discontinuities.

10.1.3 Maximum concrete strain

The maximum strain at the extreme concrete compression fibre shall be assumed to be 0.0035.

10.1.4 Balanced strain conditions

Balanced strain conditions shall exist at a cross-section when the tension reinforcement reaches its yield strain just as the concrete in compression reaches its maximum strain of 0.0035.

10.1.5 Tensile strength of concrete

The tensile strength of concrete shall be neglected in the calculation of the factored flexural resistance of reinforced and prestressed concrete members.

10.1.6 Concrete stress-strain relationship

The relationship between the compressive stress and concrete strain may be based on stress-strain curves or assumed to be any shape that results in a prediction of strength in substantial agreement with the results of comprehensive tests.

Note: *To account for differences between the in-place strength and the strength of standard cylinders, stress blocks should be based on stress-strain curves with a peak stress not greater than $0.9\,f_c'$. The equations in Clause 10.1.7 include this factor.*

10.1.7 Equivalent rectangular concrete stress distribution

The requirements of Clause 10.1.6 may be satisfied by an equivalent rectangular concrete stress distribution defined by the following:

a) a concrete stress of $\alpha_1 \phi_c f_c$ shall be assumed to be uniformly distributed over an equivalent compression zone bounded by edges of the cross-section and a straight line located parallel to the neutral axis at a distance $a = \beta_1 c$ from the fibre of maximum compressive strain;

b) the distance c shall be measured in a direction perpendicular to that axis; and

c) the factors α_1 and β_1 shall be taken as follows:

$\alpha_1 = 0.85 - 0.0015 f_c'$ (but not less than 0.67)   **Equation 10.1**

$\beta_1 = 0.97 - 0.0025 f_c'$ (but not less than 0.67)   **Equation 10.2**

10.2 Flexural members — Distance between lateral supports

10.2.1

Unless a stability analysis, including the effects of torsional loading, is carried out, beams shall comply with the limits specified in Clauses 10.2.2 and 10.2.3.

10.2.2

For a simply supported or continuous beam, the distance between points at which lateral support is provided shall not exceed the smaller of $50b$ or $200b^2/d$.

10.2.3

For a cantilever beam having lateral restraint at the support, the distance between the face of the support and the end of the cantilever shall not exceed the smaller of 25b or 100b^2/d.

10.3 Flexural members — T-beams

10.3.1

In T-beams, the flange and web shall be built integrally or otherwise effectively bonded together.

10.3.2

A floor topping shall not be included as part of a structural member unless it is placed monolithically with the floor slab or designed in accordance with Clause 17.

10.3.3

The effective flange width of T-beams shall be based on overhanging flange widths on each side of the web, which shall not exceed the smallest of
a)   one-fifth of the span length for a simply supported beam;
b)   one-tenth of the span length for a continuous beam;
c)   12 times the flange thickness; or
d)   one-half of the clear distance to the next web.

10.3.4

For beams with a slab on one side only, the effective overhanging flange width shall not exceed the smallest of
a)   1/12 of the span length of the beam;
b)   six times the flange thickness; or
c)   one-half of the clear distance to the next web.

10.4 Flexural members — Joist construction

10.4.1

Joist construction shall consist of a monolithic combination of regularly spaced ribs and a top slab arranged to span in one direction or two orthogonal directions. Joist construction shall meet the following limits:

Minimum rib width	100 mm
Maximum rib depth	3.5 times the minimum width of rib
Maximum clear distance between ribs	800 mm
Minimum slab thickness	1/12 of the clear distance between ribs, but not less than 50 mm

10.4.2

Construction not meeting the limitations of Clause 10.4.1 shall be designed as slabs and beams.

10.5 Flexural members — Reinforcement

10.5.1 Minimum reinforcement

10.5.1.1

At every section of a flexural member where tensile reinforcement is required by analysis, minimum reinforcement shall be proportioned so that

$$M_r \geq 1.2M_{cr} \qquad \qquad \text{Equation 10.3}$$

where the cracking moment, M_{cr}, is calculated using the modulus of rupture, f_r, specified in Clause 8.6.4.

10.5.1.2

In lieu of Clause 10.5.1.1, minimum reinforcement may be determined as follows:
a)   for slabs and footings, as specified in Clause 7.8; and
b)   for other flexural members, as follows:

$$A_{s,min} = \frac{0.2\sqrt{f'_c}}{f_y} b_t h \qquad \qquad \text{Equation 10.4}$$

where
b_t =   the width of the tension zone of the section considered

For T-beams with the flange in tension, b_t need not exceed $1.5b_w$ for beams with a flange on one side of the web or $2.5b_w$ for beams with a flange on both sides of the web.

10.5.1.3

The requirements of Clauses 10.5.1.1 and 10.5.1.2 may be waived if the factored moment resistance, M_r, is at least one-third greater than the factored moment, M_f.

10.5.2 Limit of c/d for yielding of tension reinforcement

The tension reinforcement in flexural members shall not be assumed to reach yield unless

$$\frac{c}{d} \leq \frac{700}{700 + f_y} \qquad \qquad \text{Equation 10.5}$$

For flexural members without axial loads, the area of tension reinforcement shall be limited such that Equation 10.5 is satisfied. In columns or walls, when c/d exceeds this limit, the stress in the tension reinforcement shall be computed based on strain compatibility.

10.5.3 Reinforcement in T-beam flanges

10.5.3.1 Flexural tension reinforcement

Where flanges are in tension, part of the flexural tension reinforcement shall be distributed over an overhanging flange width equal to 1/20 of the beam span, or the width specified in Clause 10.3, whichever is smaller. The area of this reinforcement shall be not less than 0.004 times the gross area of the overhanging flange.

10.5.3.2 Transverse reinforcement

Where the principal reinforcement in the slab forming a T-beam flange is parallel to the beam, transverse reinforcement meeting the requirement of Equation 10.4 shall extend past the face of the web a distance of 0.3 times the clear distance between the webs of the T-beams and shall extend at least to the outer bars of the flexural tension reinforcement required by Clause 10.5.3.1.

10.6 Beams and one-way slabs — Crack control

10.6.1 Crack control parameter

Bars in flexural tension zones shall be spaced so that the quantity z given by

$$z = f_s (d_c A)^{1/3}$$

Equation 10.6

does not exceed 30 000 N/mm for interior exposure and 25 000 N/mm for exterior exposure. The calculated stress in reinforcement at specified load, f_s, shall be computed as the moment divided by the product of the steel area and the internal moment arm. In lieu of such computations, f_s may be taken as 60% of the specified yield strength f_y. In calculating d_c and A, the effective clear concrete cover need not be taken to be greater than 50 mm. If epoxy-coated reinforcement is used, the value of z given by Equation 10.6 shall be multiplied by a factor of 1.2.

Note: *It is possible that the requirements of this Clause will not be sufficient for structures subject to very aggressive exposure or designed to be watertight.*

10.6.2 Skin reinforcement

For reinforced members with an overall depth, h, exceeding 750 mm, longitudinal skin reinforcement shall be uniformly distributed along the exposed side faces of the member for a distance $0.5h − 2(h − d)$ nearest the principal reinforcement. The total area of such reinforcement shall be $\rho_{sk} A_{cs}$, where A_{cs} is the sum of the area of concrete in strips along each exposed side face, each strip having a height of $0.5h − 2(h − d)$ and a width of twice the distance from the side face to the centre of the skin reinforcement (but not more than half the web width), and where $\rho_{sk} = 0.008$ for interior exposure and 0.010 for exterior exposure.

The maximum spacing of the skin reinforcement shall be 200 mm. Such skin reinforcement may be included in strength calculations if a strain compatibility analysis is conducted to determine the stresses in individual bars.

10.7 Deep flexural members

10.7.1

Flexural members with clear span to overall depth ratios less than 2 shall be designed as deep flexural members, taking into account non-linear distribution of strain, lateral buckling, and the increased anchorage requirements in such members. In lieu of more accurate procedures, the strut-and-tie model of Clause 11.4 may be used. See also Clause 12.10.5.

10.7.2

Minimum horizontal and vertical reinforcement in the side faces of deep flexural members shall satisfy the requirements of Clauses 10.6.2 and 11.4.5.

10.8 Design of bearing zones

10.8.1

The factored bearing resistance of concrete, other than at post-tensioning anchorages, shall not exceed $0.85\phi_c f_c A_1$, except that when the supporting surface is wider on all sides than the loaded area, the bearing resistance on the loaded area may be multiplied by $\sqrt{A_2/A_1}$, but not more than 2.

10.8.2

Reinforcement shall be provided where required in bearing zones to resist bursting, splitting, and spalling forces.

Note: *Guidance can be found in Chapter 3 of the* Design manual: Precast and prestressed concrete *published by the Canadian Precast/Prestressed Concrete Institute.*

10.9 Compression members — Reinforcement limits

10.9.1

The area of longitudinal bars for columns shall be not less than 0.01 times the gross area, A_g, of the section, except as permitted by Clause 10.10.5.

10.9.2

The area of longitudinal bars for compression members, including regions containing lap splices, shall not exceed 0.08 times A_g of the section (see Clause 12.17.2).

Note: *The use of more than 4% of reinforcement in a column outside of the region of lap splices can involve serious practical difficulties in placing and compacting the concrete, and in placing reinforcement in beam column joints.*

10.9.3

The minimum number of longitudinal reinforcing bars in compression members shall be four for bars within rectangular or circular ties, three for bars within triangular ties, and six for bars enclosed by spirals complying with Clause 10.9.4.

10.9.4

The ratio of spiral reinforcement shall be not less than the value given by

$$\rho_s = 0.5\left(\frac{A_g}{A_c} - 1\right)^{1.4} \frac{f_c'}{f_y}$$

Equation 10.7

where
f_y = the specified yield strength of spiral reinforcement (not to be taken more than 500 MPa)

10.10 Compression members — Resistance

10.10.1

Compression members shall be designed to have adequate factored resistance under the combinations of factored axial load and moment giving the maximum and minimum ratios of moment to axial load.

10.10.2

Compression members supporting two-way slabs shall be designed to meet the additional requirements of Clause 13.

10.10.3

Slender compression members shall be designed for moments magnified in accordance with Clauses 10.13 to 10.16.

10.10.4

The maximum factored axial load resistance, $P_{r,max}$, of compression members shall be

a) for spirally reinforced columns:

$$P_{r,max} = 0.90P_{ro}$$ **Equation 10.8**

b) for tied columns and walls tied along the full length in accordance with Clause 7.6.5:

$$P_{r,max} = (0.2 + 0.002h)P_{ro} \le 0.80P_{ro}$$ **Equation 10.9**

c) for other walls:

$$P_{r,max} = (0.15 + 0.002h)P_{ro} \le 0.75P_{ro}$$ **Equation 10.10**

where

h is the wall thickness or the minimum column dimension, and

$$P_{ro} = \alpha_1 \phi_c f'_c \left(A_g - A_{st} - A_t - A_p \right) + \phi_s f_y A_{st} + \phi_a F_y A_t - f_{pr} A_p$$ **Equation 10.11**

10.10.5

Columns with ρ_t, smaller than 0.01 but larger than 0.005 may be used, provided that the factored axial and flexural resistances, including $P_{r,max}$, are multiplied by the ratio 0.5 $(1 + \rho_t/0.01)$.

10.11 Columns — Design dimensions

10.11.1 Equivalent circular column

In lieu of using the full gross area in resistance calculations, a compression member with a square, octagonal, or other regular polygonal cross-section may be considered a circular section with a diameter equal to the least lateral dimension of the actual shape. The gross area considered, the required percentage of reinforcement, and the resistance shall be based on that circular section.

10.11.2 Column built monolithically with wall

The outer limits of the effective cross-section of a spirally-reinforced or tied-reinforced compression member, built monolithically with a concrete wall or pier, shall not extend a distance greater than the specified concrete cover outside of the spiral or tie reinforcement.

10.11.3 Isolated column with interlocking spirals

The outer limits of the effective cross-section of a compression member with two or more interlocking spirals shall not extend a distance greater than the specified concrete cover outside of the extreme limits of the spirals.

10.12 Columns — Transmission of loads through floor system

10.12.1

When the specified compressive strength of concrete in a column is greater than that specified for a floor system, transmission of load through the floor system shall be as specified in Clause 10.12.2 or 10.12.3.

10.12.2

Concrete of the strength specified for the column, f'_{cc}, shall be placed in the floor at the column location. The top surface of the column concrete placed in the floor shall extend at least 500 mm into the floor from the face of the column. The column concrete shall be well integrated with the floor concrete.

10.12.3

The resistance of the column in the joint region shall be based on an effective concrete compressive strength, f'_{ce}, equal to

a) for interior columns:

$$f'_{ce} = 1.05f'_{cs} + 0.25f'_{cc} \le f'_{cc}$$ **Equation 10.12**

b) for edge columns:

$$f'_{ce} = 1.4f'_{cs} \le f'_{cc}$$ **Equation 10.13**

c) for corner columns:

$$f'_{ce} = f'_{cs}$$ **Equation 10.14**

Vertical dowels, spirals, or hoops may be added to increase the effective strength of the joint region.

10.13 Slenderness effects — General

10.13.1

Except as allowed by Clause 10.13.2, the design of compression members, restraining beams, and other supporting members shall be based on the factored forces and moments from a second-order analysis that considers material non-linearity and cracking as well as the effects of member curvature and lateral drift, the duration of the loads, shrinkage and creep, and interaction with the supporting foundation.

10.13.2

In lieu of the procedure specified in Clause 10.13.1, the design of compression members, restraining beams, and other supporting members may be based on axial forces and moments from the analyses specified in Clauses 10.14 to 10.16, provided that $k\ell_u/r$ for all compression members is not greater than 100.

10.14 Member properties for computation of slenderness effects

10.14.1 General

10.14.1.1

The factored axial forces, P_f; the factored moments, M_1 and M_2, at the ends of the column; and, where required, the first-order lateral storey deflection, Δ_o, shall be computed using an elastic first-order frame analysis with the section properties calculated by taking into account the influence of axial loads, the presence of cracked regions along the length of the member, and the effects of duration of the loads.

10.14.1.2

The following properties may be used to determine the section properties specified in Clause 10.14.1.1:

Modulus of elasticity	E_c from Clause 8.6.2
Moment of inertia:	
Beams	$0.35I_g$
Columns	$0.70I_g$
Walls — uncracked	$0.70I_g$
Walls — cracked	$0.35I_g$
Flat plates and flat slabs	$0.25I_g$
Area	A_g

10.14.1.3

For computation of Δ_o and $\delta_s M_s$, flexural stiffness determined from Clause 10.14.1.2 shall be divided by $(1 + \beta_d)$ to account for creep due to sustained loads.

β_d shall be based on
a)   sustained axial loads (for Clauses 10.16.4 and 10.16.5); and
b)   sustained shear (for Clauses 10.14.4 and 10.16.3).

10.14.2 Radius of gyration

The radius of gyration, r, may be taken equal to $0.30h$ for rectangular compression members and 0.25 times the diameter for circular compression members. For other shapes, the radius of gyration may be computed using the gross concrete section.

10.14.3 Unsupported length of compression members

10.14.3.1

The unsupported length, ℓ_u, of a compression member shall be taken as the clear distance between floor slabs, beams, or other members capable of providing lateral support in the direction being considered. For walls, the unsupported vertical height, h_u, shall be used in place of ℓ_u wherever it appears.

10.14.3.2

Where column capitals or haunches are present, the unsupported length shall be measured to the lower extremity of the capital or haunch in the plane considered.

10.14.4 Designation as non-sway

Storeys in structures shall be designated non-sway if $Q \leq 0.05$ where

$$Q = \frac{\Sigma P_f \Delta_o}{V_f \ell_c}$$

Equation 10.15

where

$\sum P_f$ = the total factored vertical load in the storey in question

Δ_o = the first-order relative deflection of the top and bottom of that storey due to V_f

V_f = the factored storey shear in the storey in question

The deflection, Δ_o, shall be determined using the flexural stiffness determined from Clause 10.14.1.2, except as required by Clause 10.16.4.

10.14.5 Columns in non-sway frames or storeys

The design of columns in non-sway frames or storeys shall be based on the analysis specified in Clause 10.15.

10.14.6 Columns in sway frames or storeys

The design of columns in sway frames or storeys shall be based on the analysis specified in Clause 10.16.

Note: *If the value of Q exceeds 0.2, a more rigid structure can be required to provide stability.*

10.15 Slenderness effects — Non-sway frames

10.15.1 Effective length factor

For compression members in non-sway frames, the effective length factor, k, shall be taken as 1.0 unless analysis shows that a lower value is justified. The calculation of k shall be based on the properties specified in Clause 10.14.1.2.

10.15.2 Non-sway frames

In non-sway frames, slenderness effects may be ignored for compression members that satisfy the following equation:

$$\frac{k\ell_u}{r} \le \frac{25 - 10(M_1/M_2)}{\sqrt{P_f/\left(f_c'A_g\right)}}$$

Equation 10.16

where M_1/M_2 is not taken less than –0.5. M_1/M_2 shall be taken as positive if the member is bent in single curvature.

10.15.3 Member stability effect

10.15.3.1

Compression members shall be designed for the factored axial load, P_f, and the moment amplified for the effects of member curvature, M_c, as follows:

$$M_c = \frac{C_m M_2}{1 - \dfrac{P_f}{\phi_m P_c}} \ge M_2$$

Equation 10.17

where

$\phi_m = 0.75$

$$P_c = \frac{\pi^2 EI}{(k\,\ell_u)^2}$$

Equation 10.18

where

$$EI = \frac{0.2E_c\,I_g + E_s\,I_{st}}{1 + \beta_d}$$

Equation 10.19

or

$$EI = \frac{0.4E_c\,I_g}{1 + \beta_d}$$

Equation 10.20

M_2 in Equation 10.17 shall not be taken as less than $P_f\,(15 + 0.03h)$ about each axis separately with the member bent in single curvature with C_m taken as 1.0. β_d in Equations 10.19 and 10.20 shall be based on the sustained axial load, except when used as specified in Clause 10.16.3.

10.15.3.2

For members without transverse loads between supports, C_m shall be taken as

$$C_m = 0.6 + 0.4\frac{M_1}{M_2} \geq 0.4$$

Equation 10.21

10.15.3.3

For members with transverse loads between supports, C_m shall be taken as 1.0.

10.15.3.4

For compression members subject to bending about both principal axes, the moment about each axis shall be magnified separately based on the conditions of restraint corresponding to that axis.

10.16 Slenderness effects — Sway frames

10.16.1 Effective length factor

For compression members not braced against sway, the effective length factor, k, shall be determined based on the properties specified in Clause 10.14.1.2 and shall be greater than 1.0.

10.16.2 End moments

The moments, M_1 and M_2, at the ends of an individual compression member shall be taken as

$$M_1 = M_{1ns} + \delta_s M_{1s}$$

Equation 10.22

$$M_2 = M_{2ns} + \delta_s M_{2s}$$

Equation 10.23

where $\delta_s M_{1s}$ and $\delta_s M_{2s}$ shall be computed as specified in Clause 10.16.3.

10.16.3 Calculation of $\delta_s M_s$

10.16.3.1

The magnified sway moments, $\delta_s M_s$, shall be taken as the column end moments calculated using a second-order analysis based on the member stiffnesses specified in Clause 10.14.1.3.

10.16.3.2

δ_s may be calculated as follows:

$$\delta_s = \frac{1}{1 - \dfrac{\sum P_f}{\phi_m \sum P_c}}$$

Equation 10.24

where

$\sum P_f$ = the summation for all vertical loads in a storey

$\sum P_c$ = the summation for all sway-resisting columns in a storey

P_c shall be computed from Equation 10.18 using k from Clause 10.16.1 and EI from Equation 10.19 or 10.20, with β_d based on the sustained shear.

10.16.3.3

If $Q \le 1/3$, δ_s may be computed as

$$\delta_s = \frac{1}{1 - 1.2Q}$$

Equation 10.25

10.16.4 Slenderness limit

If an individual compression member has

$$\frac{\ell_u}{r} > \frac{35}{\sqrt{P_f / \left(f'_c A_g\right)}}$$

Equation 10.26

it shall also be designed for the factored axial load, P_f, and the moment, M_c, computed using Clause 10.15.3, in which M_1 and M_2 are computed as specified in Clause 10.16.2. β_d shall be based on the sustained axial load evaluated for the factored load combination used to compute P_f, with k in Equation 10.18 as specified in Clause 10.15.1.

10.16.5 Strength and stability checks

In addition to load cases involving lateral loads, the strength and stability of the structure as a whole under factored gravity loads shall be considered using the following criteria, with β_d based on the sustained axial load:

a) When $\delta_s M_s$ is computed as specified in Clause 10.16.3.1, the ratio of second-order lateral deflections to first-order lateral deflections under factored gravity loads plus a lateral load applied to each storey equal to 0.005 multiplied by the factored gravity load on that storey shall not exceed 2.5.

b) When δ_s is computed as specified in Clause 10.16.3.2, δ_s computed using $\sum P_f$ and $\sum P_c$ under factored gravity load shall be positive and shall not exceed 2.5.

10.16.6 Moment magnification for flexural members

Flexural members in sway frames shall be designed for the total magnified end moments of the compression members at the joint.

10.17 Composite columns — General

10.17.1
Composite compression members shall include all such members reinforced longitudinally with bars and structural steel shapes, pipes, or hollow structural sections (HSS).

10.17.2
The resistance of a composite member shall be computed for the same limiting conditions applicable to ordinary reinforced concrete members.

10.17.3
In the calculation of factored capacity, the ends of a composite column shall be assumed to be hinged unless definite provisions are made to resist moment at the ends.

10.17.4
Longitudinal reinforcement shall comply with Clauses 10.9.1 and 10.9.2.

10.17.5
The total cross-section area of the metal core and reinforcement shall not exceed 20% of the gross area of the column.

10.17.6
The yield strength of the structural steel core used in the design shall be the specified minimum yield strength for the grade of structural steel used but shall not exceed 350 MPa.

10.17.7
The surface of the structural steel member in contact with concrete shall be unpainted.

10.17.8
The axial load resistance assigned to the concrete of a composite member shall be transferred to the concrete by direct bearing or shear.

10.17.9
The axial load resistance not assigned to the concrete of a composite member shall be developed by direct connection to the structural steel.

10.17.10
The structural steel elements shall be designed in accordance with CSA S16 for any construction or other load applied before attainment of composite action.

10.17.11
The design of composite columns with a concrete core encased by structural steel shall be as specified in CSA S16.

CSA Group standard A23.3-14

10.18 Composite column with spiral reinforcement

10.18.1

Spiral reinforcement shall be as specified in Clause 10.9.4.

10.18.2

For evaluation of slenderness effects, the radius of gyration of a composite section with spiral reinforcement shall be not greater than the value given by

$$r = \sqrt{\frac{(E_c\,I_g\,/\,5) + E_s\,I_t + E_s\,I_{st}}{(E_c\,A_g\,/\,5) + E_s\,A_t + E_s\,A_{st}}}$$

Equation 10.27

For computing P_c in Equation 10.18, EI of the composite section shall be not greater than

$$EI = \frac{0.2\,E_c\,I_g}{1 + \beta_d} + E_s\,I_t + E_s\,I_{st}$$

Equation 10.28

10.19 Composite column with tie reinforcement

10.19.1

Lateral ties shall extend completely around the structural steel core.

10.19.2

At least 10M ties shall be used when the greatest side dimension of a composite column is 500 mm or less.

10.19.3

At least 15M ties shall be used when the greatest side dimension of a composite column is greater than 500 mm.

10.19.4

Vertical spacing of lateral ties shall not exceed the smallest of 16 longitudinal bar diameters, one-half of the least side dimension of the composite member, or 500 mm.

10.19.5

Welded wire fabric with an area of horizontal wires per unit length of the column not less than that determined as specified in Clauses 10.19.2 to 10.19.4 may be used.

10.19.6

A longitudinal bar shall be located at every corner of a rectangular cross-section, with other longitudinal bars spaced not farther apart than one-half of the least side dimension of the composite member.

10.19.7

For evaluation of slenderness effects, the radius of gyration of a composite section with tie reinforcement shall be not greater than the value given by

$$r = \sqrt{\frac{(E_c I_g / 5) + E_s I_t}{(E_c A_g / 5) + E_s A_t}}$$

Equation 10.29

For computing P_c in Equation 10.18, *EI* of the composite section shall be not greater than

$$EI = \frac{0.2 E_c I_g}{1 + \beta_d} + E_s I_t$$

Equation 10.30

11 Shear and torsion

11.1 General

11.1.1 Flexural regions
Regions of members in which it is reasonable to assume that plane sections remain plane shall be proportioned for shear and torsion using either the method specified in Clause 11.3 or the strut-and-tie model specified in Clause 11.4. In addition, the applicable requirements of Clause 11.2 shall be satisfied.

11.1.2 Regions near discontinuities
Regions of members in which the plane sections assumption of flexural theory is not applicable shall be proportioned for shear and torsion using the strut-and-tie model specified in Clause 11.4. In addition, the applicable requirements of Clause 11.2 shall be satisfied.

11.1.3 Interface regions
Interfaces between elements such as webs and flanges, between dissimilar materials, and between concretes cast at different times, or at existing or potential major cracks along which slip can occur, shall be proportioned for shear transfer as specified in Clause 11.5.

11.1.4 Slabs and footings
Slab-type regions shall be proportioned for punching shear as specified in Clause 13.

11.1.5 Alternative methods
In lieu of the methods specified in Clauses 11.1.1 to 11.1.4, the resistance of members in shear or in shear combined with torsion may be determined by satisfying the applicable conditions of equilibrium and compatibility of strains and by using appropriate stress-strain relationships for reinforcement and for diagonally cracked concrete.

11.2 Design requirements

11.2.1 Tension due to restraint
In the design for shear, the effects of axial tension due to creep, shrinkage, and thermal effects in restrained members shall be considered wherever applicable.

11.2.2 Variable depth members
For variable depth members, the components of flexural compression and tension in the direction of the applied shear shall be taken into account if their effect is unfavourable, and may be taken into account if their effect is favourable.

11.2.3 Openings

In determining shear resistance, the effect of any openings in members shall be considered.

Note: *Regions of members near openings may be designed using the strut-and-tie model (see Clause 11.4).*

11.2.4 Types of shear reinforcement

Transverse reinforcement provided for shear shall consist of the following:

a)   stirrups or ties perpendicular to the axis of the member;

b)   welded wire fabric with wires perpendicular to the axis of the member, provided that these wires can undergo a minimum elongation of 4% measured over a gauge length of at least 100 mm that includes at least one crosswire;

c)   stirrups making an angle of 45° or more with the longitudinal tension reinforcement, inclined to intercept potential diagonal cracks;

d)   for non-prestressed members, shear reinforcement consisting of 35M or smaller longitudinal bars bent to provide an inclined portion having an angle of 30° or more with the longitudinal bars and crossing potential diagonal cracks. Only the centre three-quarters of the inclined portion of these bars shall be considered effective;

e)   headed shear reinforcement that meets the requirements of Clause 7.1.4 or 13.3.8.1; or

f)   spirals.

11.2.5 Anchorage of shear reinforcement

Stirrups and other bars or wires used as shear reinforcement shall be anchored at both ends as specified in Clause 12.13 to develop the design yield strength of the reinforcement.

11.2.6 Types of torsion reinforcement

Torsion reinforcement shall consist of longitudinal reinforcement and one or more of the following types of transverse reinforcement:

a)   closed stirrups perpendicular to the axis of the member;

b)   a closed cage of welded wire fabric, with wires meeting the minimum elongation requirements of Clause 11.2.4 b) located perpendicular to the axis of the member; and

c)   spirals.

11.2.7 Anchorage of torsion reinforcement

Transverse torsion reinforcement shall be anchored

a)   by 135° standard stirrup hooks; or

b)   as specified in Item a) or b) of Clause 12.13.2 in regions where the concrete surrounding the anchorage is restrained against spalling.

A longitudinal reinforcing bar or bonded prestressing tendon shall be placed in each corner of closed transverse reinforcement required for torsion. The nominal diameter of the bar or tendon shall be not less than $s/16$.

Longitudinal torsion reinforcement shall be anchored as specified in Clause 12.1.

11.2.8 Minimum shear reinforcement

11.2.8.1

A minimum area of shear reinforcement shall be provided in the following regions:

a)   in regions of flexural members where the factored shear force, V_f, exceeds $V_c + V_p$;

b)   in regions of beams with an overall thickness greater than 750 mm; and

c)   in regions of flexural members where the factored torsion, T_f, exceeds $0.25T_{cr}$.

Note: *Footings and pile caps designed using strut-and-tie models in accordance with Clause 11.4 need not satisfy the minimum shear reinforcement requirements of Clause 11.2.8.*

11.2.8.2

Where shear reinforcement is required by Clause 11.2.8.1 or by calculation, the minimum area of shear reinforcement shall be such that

$$A_v \geq 0.06\sqrt{f_c'}\,\frac{b_w s}{f_y}$$

Equation 11.1

11.2.8.3

In calculating the term A_v in Equation 11.1, inclined reinforcement and transverse reinforcement used to resist torsion may be included.

11.2.8.4

The requirement for minimum shear reinforcement specified in Clause 11.2.8.1 may be waived if it can be shown by tests that the required flexural and shear resistances can be developed when shear reinforcement is omitted. Such tests shall simulate the effects of differential settlement, creep, shrinkage, and temperature change based on a realistic assessment of such effects occurring in service.

11.2.9 Consideration of torsion

11.2.9.1

If the magnitude of the torsion, T_f, determined from analysis using stiffnesses based on uncracked sections exceeds $0.25T_{cr}$, torsional effects shall be considered and torsional reinforcement designed as specified in Clause 11.3 shall be provided. Otherwise, torsional effects may be neglected.

In lieu of more detailed calculations, T_{cr} may be taken as

$$T_{cr} = (A_c^2 / p_c)0.38\lambda\phi_c\sqrt{f_c'}\sqrt{1 + \frac{\phi_p f_{cp}}{0.38\lambda\phi_c\sqrt{f_c'}}}$$

Equation 11.2

For a hollow section, A_c in Equation 11.2 shall be replaced by $1.5A_g$ if the wall thickness is less than $0.75A_c / p_c$.

11.2.9.2

In a statically indeterminate structure where reduction of torsional moment in a member can occur because of redistribution of internal forces, the maximum factored torsion, T_f, at the face of the support may be reduced to $0.67T_{cr}$ provided that the corresponding adjustments to torsions, moments, and shears are made in the member and in adjoining members to account for the redistribution. For a spandrel beam where the torsion is caused by a slab, the factored torsion in the spandrel can be assumed to vary linearly from zero at midspan to $0.67T_{cr}$ at the face of the support.

11.2.10 Effective web width

11.2.10.1

Unless otherwise permitted by Clause 11.2.10.3 or 11.2.10.4, the effective web width shall be taken as the minimum concrete web width within depth d.

11.2.10.2

In determining the concrete web width at a particular level, one-half the diameters of ungrouted post-tensioning ducts or one-quarter the diameters of grouted ducts at that level shall be subtracted from the total web width.

11.2.10.3

For circular members, b_w may be taken as the diameter.

11.2.10.4

For members with tapering webs, b_w may be taken as the average web width calculated over a contiguous height that includes the minimum web width location but does not include any regions of the section where the side faces of the section slope outward at more than 20° from the direction of the applied shear.

11.2.10.5

The minimum area of shear reinforcement specified by Equation 11.1 is calculated using the unspalled web width. When the area of shear reinforcement exceeds eleven times this calculated minimum, spalling of the concrete cover shall be accounted for in determining b_w; otherwise spalling may be neglected. If spalling is to be accounted for, the concrete cover down to the centerline of the outermost reinforcement shall be assumed to have spalled off unless the ends of the compression diagonals are restrained against spalling.

11.2.11 Reduced prestress in transfer length

In pretensioned members, the reduction in prestress in the transfer length of prestressing tendons shall be considered when computing V_P, f_{po}, and the tensile force that can be resisted by the longitudinal reinforcement. The prestress force may be assumed to vary linearly from zero at the point at which bonding commences to a maximum at a distance from the end of the tendon equal to the transfer length, assumed to be 50 diameters for strand and 100 diameters for single wire.

11.2.12 Hanger reinforcement for beams supporting other beams

11.2.12.1

When a load is applied to a side face of a beam, additional transverse reinforcement shall be provided. In lieu of a strut-and-tie model design in accordance with Clause 11.4, the requirements of Clause 11.2.12.2 may be used, provided that the soffit of the supported beam is not lower than the soffit of the supporting beam.

11.2.12.2

Additional transverse reinforcement capable of transmitting a tensile force of $(1 - h_b/h_1)$ times the factored shear being transferred shall be provided, with h_b being the distance from the soffit of the supporting beam to the soffit of the supported beam and h_1 being the overall depth of the supporting beam. This additional full-depth transverse reinforcement shall be placed in the supporting beam to intercept 45° planes starting on the shear interface at one-quarter of the depth of the supported beam above its bottom face and spreading down into the supporting beam (see Figure 11.1). The bottom longitudinal reinforcing bars in the supported beam shall be placed above the bottom bars in the supporting beam.

Figure 11.1
Location of additional transverse reinforcement
(See Clauses 3.2 and 11.2.12.2.)

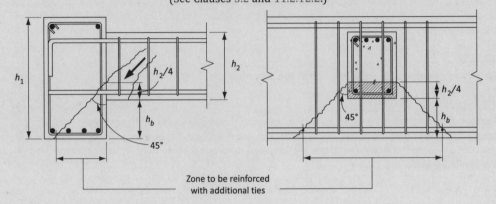

11.2.12.3

The requirements of Clauses 11.2.12.1 and 11.2.12.2 may be waived if

a)   the interface transmitting the load extends to the top of the supporting member; and

b)   the average shear stress on this interface is not greater than $0.23\lambda\phi_c\sqrt{f'_c}$.

11.2.13 Termination of longitudinal reinforcement in flexural tension zones

11.2.13.1

The reductions of shear resistance caused by terminating longitudinal reinforcement in flexural tension zones shall be taken into account. It can be assumed that the reductions in shear capacity occur over a length d_v centred upon the termination point.

11.2.13.2

If the factored shear resistance has been calculated using the simplified method of either Clause 11.3.6.2 or Clause 11.3.6.3 then the calculated shear resistance within the length specified in Clause 11.2.13.1 shall be reduced by 15%.

11.2.13.3

If transverse shear reinforcement is required near the termination point, the spacing, *s*, of this reinforcement shall not exceed $0.35d_v$.

11.3 Design for shear and torsion in flexural regions

11.3.1 Required shear resistance

Members subjected to shear shall be proportioned so that

$V_r \geq V_f$ **Equation 11.3**

11.3.2 Sections near supports

11.3.2.1

Sections located less than a distance d_v from the face of the support may be designed for the same shear, V_f, as that computed at a distance d_v, provided that

a) the reaction force in the direction of applied shear introduces compression into the member;

b) no concentrated load that causes a shear force greater than $0.3\lambda\phi_c\sqrt{f_c'}\,b_w d_v$ is applied within the distance d_v from the face of the support; and

c) loads applied within distance d_v from the face of the support do not increase the absolute magnitude of the shear at the face by more than 20%.

11.3.2.2

For support regions satisfying Clause 11.3.2.1 a) and b) but not satisfying c), sections located less than $0.5d_v$ from the face of the support may be designed for the same shear, V_f, as that computed at a distance of $0.5d_v$ from the support face.

11.3.3 Factored shear resistance

The factored shear resistance shall be determined by

$V_r = V_c + V_s + V_p$ **Equation 11.4**

However, V_r shall not exceed

$V_{r,max} = 0.25\phi_c f_c'\, b_w\, d_v + V_p$ **Equation 11.5**

11.3.4 Determination of V_c

The value of V_c shall be computed from

$V_c = \phi_c\, \lambda\, \beta\, \sqrt{f_c'}\, b_w\, d_v$ **Equation 11.6**

where β is determined as specified in Clause 11.3.6, however β need not be taken less than 0.05.

In the determination of V_c, the term $\sqrt{f_c'}$ shall not be taken greater than 8 MPa.

11.3.5 Determination of V_s

11.3.5.1

For members with transverse reinforcement perpendicular to the longitudinal axis, V_s shall be computed from

$V_s = \dfrac{\phi_s\, A_v\, f_y\, d_v \cot\theta}{s}$ **Equation 11.7**

where θ is determined as specified in Clause 11.3.6.

11.3.5.2

For members with transverse reinforcement inclined at an angle α to the longitudinal axis, V_s shall be computed from

$$V_s = \frac{\phi_s\, A_v\, f_y\, d_v (\cot\theta + \cot\alpha)\, \sin\alpha}{s}$$

Equation 11.8

where θ is determined as specified in Clause 11.3.6.

11.3.6 Determination of β and θ

11.3.6.1 Members subjected to significant axial tension

For members subjected to significant axial tension, the values of β and θ shall be determined as specified in Clause 11.3.6.4.

11.3.6.2 Values for special member types

Unless otherwise permitted by Clause 11.3.6.3 or Clause 11.3.6.4, the value of β shall be taken as 0.21 and θ shall be taken as 42° for any of the following member types:

a) slabs or footings with an overall thickness not greater than 350 mm;
b) footings in which the distance from the point of zero shear to the face of the column, pedestal, or wall is less than two times the effective shear depth, d_v, of the footing;
c) beams with an overall thickness not greater than 250 mm;
d) concrete joist construction defined by Clause 10.4; and
e) beams cast integrally with slabs where the overall depth is not greater than one-half the width of web or 550 mm.

11.3.6.3 Simplified method

In lieu of more accurate calculations in accordance with Clause 11.3.6.4, and provided that the specified yield strength of the longitudinal steel reinforcement does not exceed 400 MPa and the specified concrete strength does not exceed 60 MPa, θ shall be taken as 35° and β shall be determined as follows:

a) If the section contains at least the minimum transverse reinforcement as specified by Equation 11.1, β shall be taken as 0.18.
b) If the section contains no transverse reinforcement and the specified nominal maximum size of coarse aggregate is not less than 20 mm, β shall be taken as

$$\beta = \frac{230}{(1000 + d_v)}$$

Equation 11.9

c) Alternatively, the value of β for sections containing no transverse reinforcement may be determined for all aggregate sizes by replacing the parameter d_v in Equation 11.9 by the equivalent crack spacing parameter, s_{ze}, where

$$s_{ze} = \frac{35 s_z}{15 + a_g}$$

Equation 11.10

However, s_{ze} shall not be taken as less than $0.85 s_z$. The crack spacing parameter, s_z, shall be taken as d_v or as the maximum distance between layers of distributed longitudinal reinforcement, whichever is less. Each layer of such reinforcement shall have an area at least equal to $0.003 b_w s_z$ (see Figure 11.2).

When the simplified method specified in this Clause is used, all other clauses of Clause 11 shall apply, except Clause 11.3.6.4. Accordingly, this simplified method shall not be used for members subjected to significant tension, and the longitudinal reinforcement for all members shall be proportioned as specified in Clause 11.3.9.

CSA Group standard A23.3-14

Figure 11.2
Terms in shear design equations
(See Clauses 3.2 and 11.3.6.3.)

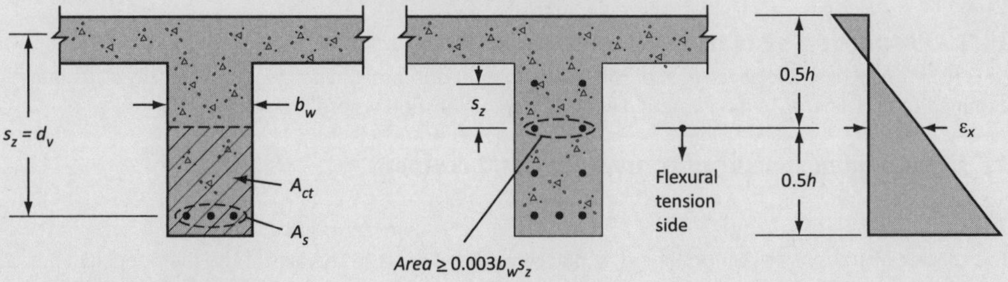

Area $\geq 0.003b_w s_z$

11.3.6.4 General method

The value of β shall be determined from the following equation:

$$\beta = \frac{0.40}{(1 + 1500\varepsilon_x)} \cdot \frac{1300}{(1000 + s_{ze})} \qquad \text{Equation 11.11}$$

For sections containing at least the minimum transverse reinforcement required by Equation 11.1, the equivalent crack spacing parameter, s_{ze}, in Equation 11.11 shall be taken as equal to 300 mm. Otherwise, s_{ze} shall be computed using Equation 11.10. If f_c' exceeds 70 MPa, the term a_g shall be taken as zero in Equation 11.10. As f_c' goes from 60 to 70 MPa, a_g shall be linearly reduced to zero.

The angle of inclination, θ, of the diagonal compressive stresses shall be calculated as

$$\theta = 29 + 7000\varepsilon_x \qquad \text{Equation 11.12}$$

In lieu of more accurate calculations, the longitudinal strain, ε_x, at mid-depth of the cross-section shall be computed from

$$\varepsilon_x = \frac{M_f / d_v + V_f - V_p + 0.5N_f - A_p f_{po}}{2\left(E_s A_s + E_p A_p\right)} \qquad \text{Equation 11.13}$$

In evaluating Equation 11.13, the following conditions shall apply:
a) V_f and M_f shall be taken as positive quantities and M_f shall not be taken as less than $(V_f - V_p)d_v$.
b) In calculating A_s, the area of bars that are terminated less than their development length from the section under consideration shall be reduced in proportion to their lack of full development. If longitudinal bars are terminated in a flexural tension zone, the value of ε_x as given by Equation 11.13 at the cutoff location shall be increased by 50%.
c) If the value of ε_x calculated from Equation 11.13 is negative, it shall be taken as zero or the value shall be recalculated with the denominator of Equation 11.13 replaced by $2(E_s A_s + E_p A_p + E_c A_{ct})$. However, ε_x shall not be taken as less than -0.20×10^{-3}.
d) For sections closer than d_v to the face of the support, the value of ε_x calculated at d_v from the face of the support may be used in evaluating β and θ.
e) If the axial tension is large enough to crack the flexural compression face of the section, the resulting increase in ε_x shall be taken into account. In lieu of more accurate calculations, the value calculated from Equation 11.13 shall be doubled.

f) β and θ may be determined from Equations 11.11 and 11.12, respectively, using a value of ε_x that is greater than that calculated from Equation 11.13. However, ε_x shall not be taken greater than 3.0 × 10^{-3}.

11.3.7 Proportioning of transverse reinforcement

Near locations where the spacing, s, of the transverse reinforcement changes, the quantity A_v/s may be assumed to vary linearly over a length h centred on the location where the spacing changes.

11.3.8 Maximum spacing of transverse reinforcement

11.3.8.1

The spacing of transverse reinforcement, s, placed perpendicular to the axis of the member shall not exceed $0.7d_v$ or 600 mm.

11.3.8.2

Inclined stirrups and bent longitudinal reinforcement shall be spaced so that every line inclined at 35° to the axis of the member and extending toward the reaction from mid-depth of the member to the longitudinal flexural tension reinforcement shall be crossed by at least one line of effective shear reinforcement. See Clause 11.2.4 d).

11.3.8.3

If V_f exceeds $0.125\lambda\phi_c f_c' b_w d_v + V_p$ or if T_f exceeds $0.25T_{cr}$, the maximum spacings specified in Clauses 11.3.8.1 and 11.3.8.2 shall be reduced by one-half.

11.3.8.4

The maximum spacing of 600 mm specified in Clause 11.3.8.1 can be waived if β is determined from Equation 11.11 and in this equation, s_{ze} is taken as $(s-300)$.

11.3.9 Proportioning of longitudinal reinforcement

11.3.9.1 Extension of longitudinal reinforcement

At every section, the longitudinal reinforcement shall be designed to resist the additional tension forces caused by shear as specified in Clauses 11.3.9.2 and 11.3.9.3. Alternatively, for members not subjected to significant tension or significant torsion, these requirements may be satisfied by extending the flexural tension reinforcement a distance of $d_v \cot\theta$ beyond the location needed by flexure alone.

11.3.9.2 Flexural tension side

Longitudinal reinforcement on the flexural tension side shall be proportioned so that the factored resistance of the reinforcement at all sections, taking account of the stress that can be developed in this reinforcement, shall be greater than or equal to the force F_{lt}, as follows:

$$F_{lt} = \frac{M_f}{d_v} + 0.5N_f + (V_f - 0.5V_s - V_p)\cot\theta$$

Equation 11.14

where M_f and V_f are taken as positive quantities and N_f is positive for axial tension and negative for axial compression. In Equation 11.14, V_s shall not be taken greater than V_f and d_v may be taken as the flexural lever arm corresponding to the factored moment resistance.

11.3.9.3 Flexural compression side

At sections where the moment term, M_f/d_v, in Equation 11.14 is less than the sum of the terms accounting for axial load and shear, longitudinal reinforcement on the flexural compression side of the section shall be proportioned so that the factored tensile resistance of this reinforcement, taking account of the stress that can be developed in this reinforcement, shall be greater than or equal to the force F_{lc}, as follows:

$$F_{lc} = 0.5N_f + (V_f - 0.5V_s - V_p)\cot\theta - \frac{M_f}{d_v}$$

Equation 11.15

where M_f and V_f are taken as positive quantities and N_f is positive for axial tension and negative for axial compression. In Equation 11.15, V_s shall not be taken greater than V_f.

11.3.9.4 Compression fan regions

In regions adjacent to maximum moment locations, the area of longitudinal reinforcement on the flexural tension side of the member need not exceed the area required to resist the maximum moment acting alone. This provision shall apply only if the support or the load at the maximum moment location introduces direct compression into the flexural compression face of the member and the member is not subject to significant torsion.

11.3.9.5 Anchorage of longitudinal reinforcement at end supports

At exterior direct bearing supports, the longitudinal reinforcement on the flexural tension side of the member shall be capable of resisting a tensile force of $(V_f - 0.5V_s - V_p) \cot\theta + 0.5N_f$, where θ is as specified in Clause 11.3.6 and V_s is based on the transverse reinforcement provided within a length of $d_v \cot\theta$ from the face of the support. However, V_s shall not be taken as greater than V_f. The tension force in the reinforcement shall be developed at the point where a line inclined at angle θ to the longitudinal axis and extending from the inside edge of the bearing area intersects the centroid of the reinforcement. See Figure 11.5 b).

11.3.10 Sections subjected to combined shear and torsion

11.3.10.1 Transverse reinforcement for combined shear and torsion

The transverse reinforcement for combined shear and torsion shall be at least equal to the sum of that required for shear and that required for the coexisting torsion.

11.3.10.2 Transverse reinforcement for torsion

The amount of transverse reinforcement required for torsion shall be such that

$$T_r \geq T_f$$

Equation 11.16

11.3.10.3 Factored torsional resistance

The value of T_r shall be computed from

$$T_r = 2A_o\frac{\phi_s A_t f_y}{s}\cot\theta$$

Equation 11.17

where
A_o = $0.85A_{oh}$
θ = as specified in Clause 11.3.6.

11.3.10.4 Cross-sectional dimensions to avoid crushing

The cross-sectional dimensions to avoid crushing shall be as follows:

a)   for box sections:

$$\frac{V_f - V_p}{b_w d_v} + \frac{T_f p_h}{1.7 A_{oh}^2} \leq 0.25 \phi_c f_c'$$

Equation 11.18

If the wall thickness of the box section is less than A_{oh}/p_h, the second term in Equation 11.18 shall be replaced by $T_f/(1.7 A_{oh}t)$ where t is the wall thickness at the location where the stresses are being checked.

b)   for other sections:

$$\sqrt{\left(\frac{V_f - V_p}{b_w d_v}\right)^2 + \left(\frac{T_f p_h}{1.7 A_{oh}^2}\right)^2} \leq 0.25 \phi_c f_c'$$

Equation 11.19

11.3.10.5 Determination of ε_x for general method

If β and θ are being determined using Clause 11.3.6.4, the value of ε_x for a section subjected to torsion shall be determined by replacing the term $(V_f - V_p)$ in Equation 11.13 and in Clause 11.3.6.4 a) with the expression

$$\sqrt{(V_f - V_p)^2 + \left(\frac{0.9 p_h T_f}{2 A_o}\right)^2}$$

Equation 11.20

11.3.10.6 Proportioning longitudinal reinforcement

The longitudinal reinforcement shall be proportioned to satisfy the requirements of Clause 11.3.9, except that the term $(V_f - 0.5 V_s - V_p)$ shall be replaced by the expression

$$\sqrt{(V_f - 0.5 V_s - V_p)^2 + \left(\frac{0.45 p_h T_f}{2 A_o}\right)^2}$$

Equation 11.21

11.4 Strut-and-tie model

11.4.1 Structural idealization

11.4.1.1 General

The strength of reinforced concrete structures, members, or regions may be investigated by idealizing the reinforced concrete as a series of reinforcing steel tensile ties and concrete compressive struts interconnected at nodes to form a truss capable of carrying all of the factored loads to the supports. In determining the geometry of the truss, account shall be taken of the required dimensions of the struts and ties.

11.4.1.2 Simplified and refined strut-and-tie models

The crack control reinforcement may also be used as tension ties in the strut-and-tie model provided this reinforcement is well anchored in accordance with Clause 11.4.3.3 (see Figure 11.3).

Figure 11.3
Simplified and refined strut-and-tie models for deep beam
(See Clause 11.4.1.2.)

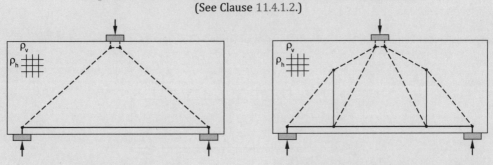

a) Simplified strut-and-tie model

b) Refined strut-and-tie model using crack control
reinforcement as additional tension ties

11.4.1.3 Modelling members subjected to uniform loads

In modelling members subjected to uniform loads, a series of struts shall be used to represent the areas where the compressive stresses fan out from the bearing areas. [see Figure 11.4 a) and b)]. However, where the uniform load is applied to the flexural compression face and the member contains crack control reinforcement the fanning area can be modelled by a single strut located at the resultant of the load [see Figure 11.4 c)].

Figure 11.4
Modelling fanning regions in slabs and footings subjected to uniform loads
(See Clause 11.4.1.3.)

a) Modelling of fanning compression with a series of struts — Tension tie at narrow part of fan.

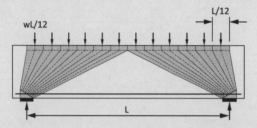

b) Modelling of fanning compression with a series of struts — Tension tie at wide part of fan.

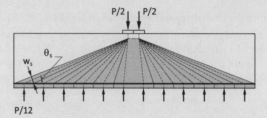

c) Modelling each fanning area with a single strut for members containing crack control reinforcement.

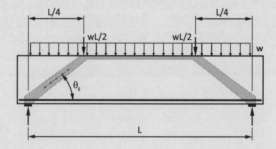

11.4.2 Proportioning of strut

11.4.2.1 Strength of strut

The dimensions of a strut shall be large enough to ensure that the calculated compressive force in the strut does not exceed $\phi_c f_{cu} A_{cs}$ where f_{cu} and A_{cs} are determined as specified in Clauses 11.4.2.2 and 11.4.2.3.

11.4.2.2 Effective cross-sectional area of strut

The value of A_{cs} shall be calculated by considering both the available concrete area and the anchorage conditions at the ends of the strut, as shown in Figure 11.5. When a strut is anchored only by reinforcement, the effective concrete area may be considered to extend a distance of up to eight bar diameters from the bar anchoring the closed stirrups and the concrete cover should be neglected as shown in Figure 11.5 a).

Figure 11.5
Influence of anchorage conditions on effective cross-sectional area of strut
(See Clauses 3.2, 11.3.9.5, and 11.4.2.2.)

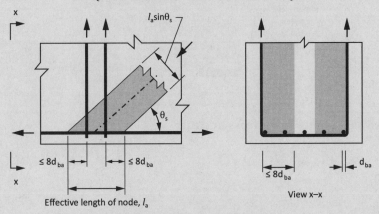

a) Strut anchored by reinforcement

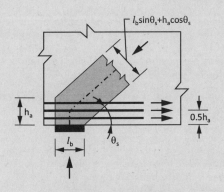

b) Strut anchored by bearing plate and reinforcement

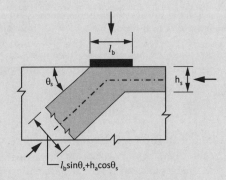

c) Strut anchored by bearing plate and strut

When a fanning region, with the tension tie at the narrow part of fan, is modeled by a series of struts the area A_{cs} shall be taken as being equal for each strut and shall be determined at the location where the strut connects to the nodal region as shown in Figure 11.6.

Figure 11.6
Determining area A_{cs} for critical strut in fan region — Tension tie at narrow part of fan
(See Clause 11.4.2.2.)

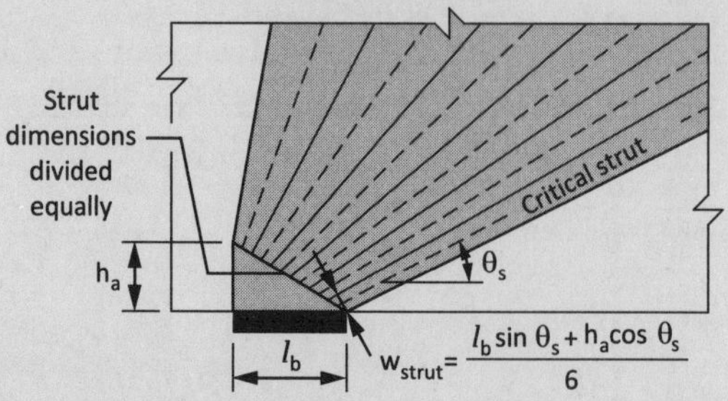

11.4.2.3 Limiting compressive stress in struts

The value of f_{cu} shall be computed from

$$f_{cu} = \frac{f'_c}{0.8 + 170\varepsilon_1} \leq 0.85f'_c \qquad \text{Equation 11.22}$$

where

$$\varepsilon_1 = \varepsilon_s + (\varepsilon_s + 0.002)\cot^2\theta_s \qquad \text{Equation 11.23}$$

and θ_s is the smallest angle between the strut and the adjoining ties and ε_s is the tensile strain in the tie inclined at θ_s to the strut.

In lieu of using Equation 11.22, the limiting compressive stress, f_{cu}, may be calculated using Equation 11.24 provided that the specified yield strength of the reinforcing steel does not exceed 400 MPa,

$$f_{cu} = \frac{f'_c}{1.14 + 0.68\cot^2\theta_s} \leq 0.85f'_c \qquad \text{Equation 11.24}$$

11.4.2.4 Reinforced struts

If a strut contains reinforcing bars that are parallel to the strut, have been detailed to develop their yield strength in compression, and are enclosed by transverse reinforcement complying with Clause 7.6.5, the calculated force in the strut shall not exceed $\phi_c f_{cu} A_{cs} + \phi_s f_y A_{ss}$.

11.4.3 Proportioning of ties

11.4.3.1 Strength of ties

The area of reinforcement in the tie shall be large enough to ensure that the calculated tensile force in the tie does not exceed $\phi_s f_y A_{st} + \phi_p (f_{po} + 400) A_p$.

11.4.3.2 Anchorage of ties in node regions

The tie reinforcement shall be anchored to the nodal zones by straight bar embedment or standard hooks in accordance with Clause 12, or by headed bars or by prestressing anchorages so that it is capable of resisting the calculated tension in the reinforcement at the location where the centroid of this reinforcement crosses the edge of the adjoining strut. For straight bars extending a distance x beyond the critical location where $x < \ell_d$, the calculated stress shall not exceed $\phi_s f_y (x/\ell_d)$, where ℓ_d is computed as specified in Clause 12.

11.4.3.3 Anchorage of ties anchoring compressive struts

Tension ties anchoring compressive struts in regions away from bearing regions shall be detailed as closed stirrups with each bend enclosing a longitudinal bar. Crack control reinforcement used as tension ties shall consist of closed stirrups with each bend enclosing a longitudinal bar.

11.4.4 Proportioning of node regions

11.4.4.1 Stress limits in node regions

Unless special confinement is provided, the calculated concrete compressive stress in the node regions shall not exceed the following:

a) $0.85 \phi_c m f_c'$ in node regions bounded by struts and bearing areas;

b) $0.75 \phi_c m f_c'$ in node regions anchoring a tie in only one direction; and

c) $0.65 \phi_c m f_c'$ in node regions anchoring ties in more than one direction.

where m is the confinement modification factor taken as $\sqrt{A_2 / A_1}$ but not more than 2.0 as defined in Clause 10.8.1. The factor m shall be taken as 1.0 unless reinforcement capable of controlling cracking is provided.

Note: *Other beneficial effects of confinement can be accounted for if substantiated by test results.*

11.4.4.2 Satisfying stress limits in node regions

The stress limits in node regions may be considered satisfied if

a) the bearing stress on the node regions produced by concentrated loads or reactions does not exceed the stress limits specified in Clause 11.4.4.1; and

b) the tie reinforcement is uniformly distributed over an effective area of concrete at least equal to the tie force divided by the stress limits specified in Clause 11.4.4.1.

11.4.5 Crack control reinforcement

Structures, members, or regions (other than slabs or footings) that have been designed in accordance with Clause 11.4 shall contain an orthogonal grid of reinforcing bars near each face. The ratio of reinforcement area to gross concrete area shall be not less than 0.002 in each direction. The spacing of this reinforcement shall not exceed 300 mm. If located within the tie, the crack control reinforcement may also be considered as tie reinforcement.

11.5 Interface shear transfer

11.5.1 General

A crack shall be assumed to occur along the shear plane and relative displacement shall be considered to be resisted by cohesion and friction maintained by the shear friction reinforcement crossing the crack. The factored shear stress resistance of the plane shall be computed from

$$v_r = \lambda \phi_c (c + \mu\sigma) + \phi_s \rho_v f_y \cos\alpha_f \qquad \text{Equation 11.25}$$

where the expression $\lambda \phi_c (c + \mu\sigma)$ shall not exceed $0.25\phi_c f_c'$ and α_f is the angle between the shear friction reinforcement and the shear plane.

11.5.2 Values of c and μ

The following values shall be taken for c and μ:

a) For concrete placed against hardened concrete with the surface clean but not intentionally roughened:

c = 0.25 MPa

μ = 0.60

b) For concrete placed against hardened concrete with the surface clean and intentionally roughened to a full amplitude of at least 5 mm:

c = 0.50 MPa

μ = 1.00

c) For concrete placed monolithically:

c = 1.00 MPa

μ = 1.40

d) For concrete anchored to as-rolled structural steel by headed studs or by reinforcing bars:

c = 0.00 MPa

μ = 0.60

11.5.3 Alternative equation for shear stress resistance

For concrete placed monolithically or placed against hardened concrete with the surface clean and intentionally roughened to a full amplitude of at least 5 mm, the factored shear stress resistance may be computed using the following equation in lieu of Equation 11.25:

$$v_r = \lambda \phi_c k \sqrt{\sigma f_c'} + \phi_s \rho_v f_y \cos \alpha_f \qquad \text{Equation 11.26}$$

where

k = 0.5 for concrete placed against hardened concrete

    = 0.6 for concrete placed monolithically

and the expression $\lambda \phi_c k \sqrt{\sigma f_c'}$ shall not exceed $0.25 \phi_c f_c$ and α_f is the angle between the shear friction reinforcement and the shear plane.

11.5.4 Values of σ and ρ_v

The value of σ shall be computed as

$$\sigma = \rho_v f_y \sin \alpha_f + \frac{N}{A_g} \qquad \text{Equation 11.27}$$

where

$$\rho_v = \frac{A_{vf}}{A_{cv}} \qquad \text{Equation 11.28}$$

and N is the unfactored permanent load perpendicular to the shear plane, positive for compression and negative for tension.

11.5.5 Inclined shear friction reinforcement

In determining the area of inclined shear friction reinforcement to be used in Equation 11.28, only that reinforcement inclined to the shear plane at an angle, α_f, such that the shear force produces tension in the inclined reinforcement, shall be included.

11.5.6 Anchorage of shear friction reinforcement

The shear friction reinforcement shall be anchored on each side of the shear plane so that the specified yield strength can be developed.

11.6 Special provisions for brackets and corbels

11.6.1

Brackets and corbels shall be designed in accordance with Clause 11.4 and Clauses 11.6.2 to 11.6.8.

11.6.2

The depth, d, at the face of a support shall be not less than the distance between the load and the face of the support.

11.6.3

The depth at the outside edge of the bearing area shall be not less than one-half of the depth at the face of the support.

11.6.4

The external tensile force, N_f, acting on the bearing area shall not be taken as less than $0.2V_f$ unless special provisions are made to avoid tensile forces.

11.6.5

In lieu of the crack control reinforcement specified in Clause 11.4.5, closed stirrups or ties parallel to the primary tensile tie reinforcement, A_{st}, and having a total area of not less than 50% of A_{st}, shall be distributed within two-thirds of the effective depth adjacent to A_{st}.

11.6.6

The ratio A_{st}/bd calculated at the face of the support shall be not less than $0.04\,(f'_c/f_y)$.

11.6.7

At the front face of the bracket or corbel, the primary tensile tie reinforcement, A_{st}, shall be anchored to develop the required force in the tension tie.

11.6.8

The bearing area of the load on the bracket or corbel shall not project beyond the straight portion of the tension tie bars or beyond the interior face of the transverse anchor bar, if one is provided.

11.7 Shear in joints

When gravity load, wind, earthquake, or other lateral forces cause transfer of moment at connections of framing elements to columns, joint shear reinforcement satisfying the requirements of Clause 7.7 shall be provided.

12 Development and splices of reinforcement

12.1 Development of reinforcement — General

12.1.1
The calculated tension or compression in reinforcement at each section of reinforced concrete members shall be developed on each side of that section by embedment length, hook, or mechanical device, or by a combination thereof. Hooks may be used in developing bars in tension only.

12.1.2
The maximum permissible value of $\sqrt{f'_c}$ in Clause 12 shall be 8 MPa.

12.2 Development of deformed bars and deformed wire in tension

12.2.1 Minimum development length
The development length, ℓ_d, of deformed bars and deformed wire in tension shall be determined from either Clause 12.2.2 or Clause 12.2.3, but ℓ_d shall be not less than 300 mm.

12.2.2 General development length equation
The development length, ℓ_d, of deformed bars and deformed wire in tension shall be

$$\ell_d = 1.15 \frac{k_1\, k_2\, k_3\, k_4}{(d_{cs} + K_{tr})} \frac{f_y}{\sqrt{f'_c}} A_b$$

Equation 12.1

but the term $(d_{cs} + K_{tr})$ shall not be taken greater than $2.5d_b$ where

$$K_{tr} = \frac{A_{tr} f_{yt}}{10.5sn}$$

12.2.3 Simplified development length equations
The development length, ℓ_d, of deformed bars and deformed wire in tension may be taken from Table 12.1, provided that the clear cover and clear spacing of the bars or wire being developed are at least d_b and $1.4d_b$, respectively.

Table 12.1
Development length, ℓ_d, of deformed bars and deformed wire in tension
(See Clause 12.2.3.)

Cases	Minimum development length, ℓ_d
Member containing minimum ties (Clause 7.6.5) or minimum stirrups (Clause 11.2.8.2) within ℓ_d Slabs, walls, shells, or folded plates having clear spacing of not less than $2d_b$ between bars being developed	$0.45 k_1\, k_2\, k_3\, k_4 \dfrac{f_y}{\sqrt{f_c'}} d_b$
Other cases	$0.6 k_1\, k_2\, k_3\, k_4 \dfrac{f_y}{\sqrt{f_c'}} d_b$

Note: *The clear cover and clear spacing requirements specified in Clause 12.2.3 meet the requirements of CSA A23.1 (see Annex A).*

12.2.4 Modification factors
The following modification factors shall be used to calculate the development length in Clauses 12.2.2 and 12.2.3:

a)   bar location factor, k_1:

   k_1 = 1.3 for horizontal reinforcement placed in such a way that more than 300 mm of fresh concrete is cast in the member below the development length or splice

   = 1.0 for other cases

b)   coating factor, k_2:

   k_2 = 1.5 for epoxy-coated reinforcement with clear cover less than $3d_b$ or with clear spacing between bars being developed less than $6d_b$

   = 1.2 for all other epoxy-coated reinforcement

   = 1.0 for uncoated reinforcement

c)   concrete density factor, k_3:

   k_3 = 1.3 for structural low-density concrete

   = 1.2 for structural semi-low-density concrete

   = 1.0 for normal-density concrete

d)   bar size factor, k_4:

   k_4 = 0.8 for 20M and smaller bars and deformed wires

   = 1.0 for 25M and larger bars

The product $k_1 k_2$ need not be taken greater than 1.7.

12.2.5 Excess reinforcement
The development length, ℓ_d, may be multiplied by the factor (A_s required) / (A_s provided) where reinforcement in a flexural member exceeds that required by analysis, except where anchorage or development for f_y is specifically required or the reinforcement is designed as specified in Clause 21.

12.3 Development of deformed bars in compression

Δ ### 12.3.1 Development length

The development length, ℓ_d, for deformed bars in compression shall be computed as the product of the basic development length, ℓ_{db}, specified in Clause 12.3.2 and the applicable modification factors specified in Clause 12.3.3, but ℓ_d shall be not less than 200 mm.

12.3.2 Basic development length

The basic compression development length, ℓ_{db}, shall be $0.24 d_b f_y / \sqrt{f_c'}$, but not less than $0.044 d_b f_y$.

12.3.3 Modification factors

The basic development length, ℓ_{db}, may be multiplied by the following factors, as applicable:
a)   for reinforcement exceeding that required by analysis: (A_s required) / (A_s provided); and
b)   for reinforcement enclosed within spiral reinforcement of not less than 6 mm diameter and not more than 100 mm pitch or within 10M ties in compliance with Clause 7.6.5 and spaced at not more than 100 mm on centre: 0.75.

12.4 Development of bundled bars

The development length of individual bars within a bundle in tension or compression shall be that for the individual bar increased by 10% for a two-bar bundle, 20% for a three-bar bundle, and 33% for a four-bar bundle.

12.5 Development of standard hooks in tension

12.5.1 Tension development length

Except as specified in Clause 12.13, the development length, ℓ_{dh}, for deformed bars in tension terminating in a standard hook as defined in Clause 6.6.2.2 of CSA A23.1 (reprinted in Annex A) shall be computed as the product of the basic development length, ℓ_{hb}, specified in Clause 12.5.2 and the applicable modification factor or factors specified in Clause 12.5.3, but shall be not less than $8 d_b$ or 150 mm, whichever is greater.

12.5.2 Basic development length

The basic development length, ℓ_{hb}, for a hooked bar with f_y equal to 400 MPa shall be $100 d_b / \sqrt{f_c'}$.

12.5.3 Factors modifying hook development length

The basic development length, ℓ_{hb}, shall be multiplied by the following factor(s), as applicable:

a) For bars with f_y other than 400 MPa	$f_y / 400$
b) For 35M or smaller bars where the side cover (normal to plane of hook) is not less than 60 mm and for 90° hooks where the cover on the bar extension beyond the hook is not less than 50 mm	0.7
c) For 35M or smaller bars where the hook is enclosed vertically or horizontally within at least three ties or stirrup ties spaced along a length at least equal to the inside diameter of the hook at a spacing not greater than $3 d_b$, where d_b is the nominal diameter of the hooked bar	0.8
d) Where anchorage or development for f_y is not specifically required for reinforcement exceeding that required by analysis	(A_s required) / (A_s provided)

| e) For structural low-density concrete | 1.3 |
| f) For epoxy-coated reinforcement | 1.2 |

12.5.4 Confinement of hooks

For bars being developed by a standard hook at the ends of members where both the side cover and the top (or bottom) cover over the hook is less than 60 mm, the hook shall be enclosed within at least three ties or stirrup ties spaced along a length at least equal to the inside diameter of the hook at a spacing not greater than $3d_b$, where d_b is the nominal diameter of the hooked bar. For this case, the factor specified in Clause 12.5.3 c) shall not apply.

12.5.5 Development of bars in compression

Hooks shall not be considered effective in developing bars in compression.

12.6 Mechanical anchorage

12.6.1

Any mechanical anchorage, including heads of headed bars or headed studs, demonstrated by test to be capable of developing the strength of reinforcement without damage to the concrete, may be used.

12.6.2

The development of reinforcement may consist of a combination of mechanical anchorage and additional embedment length of reinforcement between the point of maximum bar stress and the mechanical anchorage.

12.7 Development of welded deformed wire fabric in tension

12.7.1

The development length, ℓ_d, of welded deformed wire fabric shall be computed as the product of the development length, ℓ_d, specified in Clause 12.2.2 or 12.2.3 and the applicable wire fabric factor, k_5, or factors specified in Clause 12.7.2 or 12.7.3, but shall be not less than 200 mm, except in the computation of lap splices by the method specified in Clause 12.18 and in the development of web reinforcement by the method specified in Clause 12.13.

12.7.2

For welded deformed wire fabric with at least one crosswire within the development length and not less than 50 mm from the point of the critical section, the wire fabric factor, k_5, shall be the greater of

$$k_5 = \frac{f_y - 240}{f_y}$$ **Equation 12.2**

or

$$k_5 = \frac{5d_b}{s_w}$$ **Equation 12.3**

but need not be taken greater than 1.0.

12.7.3

For welded deformed wire fabric with no crosswires within the development length or with a single crosswire less than 50 mm from the point of the critical section, the wire fabric factor, k_5, shall be taken as 1.0.

12.8 Development of welded smooth wire fabric in tension

The yield strength of welded smooth wire fabric shall be considered to be developed by the embedment of two crosswires, with the closer crosswire not less than 50 mm from the critical section. However, the development length, ℓ_d, measured from the critical section to the outermost crosswire shall be not less than

$$\ell_d = 3.3k_3\frac{A_w}{S_w}\frac{f_y}{\sqrt{f'_c}}$$

Equation 12.4

If excess reinforcement is present, this length may be reduced in accordance with Clause 12.2.5. ℓ_d shall be not less than 150 mm except in the computation of lap splices by the method specified in Clause 12.19.

12.9 Development of pretensioned strand

12.9.1

Three- or seven-wire pretensioning strand shall be bonded beyond the critical section for a development length, ℓ_d, not less than

$$\ell_d = 0.145\left(f_{pr} - 0.67f_{pe}\right)d_b$$

Equation 12.5

12.9.2

Where bonding of a strand does not extend to the end of a member and the design includes tension at specified loads in the precompressed tensile zone as permitted by Clause 18.3.2 or 18.3.3, the development length specified in Clause 12.9.1 shall be doubled.

12.10 Development of flexural reinforcement — General

12.10.1

Tension reinforcement may be anchored into the compression zone by bending it across the web to be anchored or made continuous with the reinforcement on the opposite face of the member.

12.10.2

Critical sections for development of reinforcement in flexural members are located at points of maximum stress and at points within the span where adjacent reinforcement terminates or is bent. The location of the points of maximum stress and the points at which reinforcement is no longer required to resist flexure shall be derived from the factored bending moment diagram.

12.10.3

Reinforcement shall extend beyond the point at which it is no longer required to resist flexure as specified in Clause 11.3.9.

12.10.4

Continuing reinforcement shall have an embedment length of not less than the development length, ℓ_d, plus the longer of the effective depth of the member or $12d_b$ beyond the point where bent or terminated tension reinforcement is no longer required to resist flexure.

12.10.5

Special attention shall be given to providing adequate anchorage for tension reinforcement in flexural members such as sloped, stepped, or tapered footings; brackets; deep flexural members; or members in which the tension reinforcement is not parallel to the compression face.

12.11 Development of positive moment reinforcement

12.11.1

At least one-third of the positive moment reinforcement in simply supported members and one-quarter of the positive moment reinforcement in continuous members shall extend along the same face of the member into the support. In beams constructed monolithically with the support, such reinforcement shall extend into the support at least 150 mm, but not less than required by Clause 11.3.9.

12.11.2

When a flexural member is part of a primary lateral load resisting system, the positive moment reinforcement required by Clause 12.11.1 to be extended into the support shall be anchored to develop the specified yield strength, f_y, in tension at the face of the support.

12.11.3

At simple supports and at points of inflection, the positive moment tension reinforcement shall be limited to a diameter such that ℓ_d computed for f_y by the method specified in Clause 12.2 shall satisfy the following equation:

$$\ell_d \leq \frac{M_r}{V_f} + \ell_a$$

Equation 12.6

where, at a support, ℓ_a shall be the embedment length beyond the centre of the support, and at a point of inflection, ℓ_a shall be limited to the effective depth of the member or $12d_b$, whichever is greater.

However, Equation 12.6 need not be satisfied for reinforcement terminating beyond the centreline of simple supports by a standard hook or a mechanical anchorage at least equivalent to a standard hook.

The value of M_r/V_f may be increased by 30% when the ends of the reinforcement are confined by a compressive reaction.

12.12 Development of negative moment reinforcement

12.12.1

Negative moment reinforcement in a continuous, restrained, or cantilever member, or in any member of a rigid frame, shall be anchored in or through the supporting member by embedment length, hooks, or mechanical anchorage.

12.12.2

At least one-third of the total tension reinforcement provided for negative moment at a support shall have an embedment length beyond the point of inflection of not less than the effective depth of the member, $12d_b$, or 1/16 of the clear span, whichever is greater.

12.13 Anchorage of shear reinforcement

12.13.1

Web reinforcement shall be carried as close to the compression and tension surfaces of a member as cover requirements and proximity of other reinforcement will permit.

12.13.2

Transverse reinforcement provided for shear shall be anchored by one of the following means:
a) for 15M and smaller bars, and for MD200 and smaller wire, by a standard stirrup hook (see Clause 7.1.2) around longitudinal reinforcement;
b) for 20M and 25M stirrups, by a standard hook (see Clause 7.1.2) around longitudinal reinforcement, plus an embedment between mid-depth of the member and the outside end of the hook equal to or greater than $0.33\ell_d$;
c) for each leg of welded smooth wire fabric forming simple U-stirrups, either
    i) two longitudinal wires located at a 50 mm spacing along the member at the top of the U; or
    ii) one longitudinal wire located not more than $d/4$ from the compression face and a second wire closer to the compression face and spaced not less than 50 mm from the first wire. The second wire may be located on the stirrup leg beyond a bend or on a bend with an inside diameter of not less than $8d_b$;
d) for each end of a single-leg stirrup of welded smooth or deformed wire fabric, two longitudinal wires at a minimum spacing of 50 mm, with the inner wire at least $d/4$ from the mid-depth of the member. The outer longitudinal wire at the tension face shall not be farther from that face than the portion of primary flexural reinforcement closest to the face; or
e) mechanical anchorage capable of developing the yield strength of the bar.

12.13.3

Between anchored ends, each bend in the continuous portion of a stirrup shall enclose a longitudinal bar.

12.13.4

Longitudinal bars bent to act as shear reinforcement, if extended into a region of tension, shall be continuous with the longitudinal reinforcement and, if extended into a region of compression, shall be anchored beyond the mid-depth, $d/2$, as specified for development length in Clause 12.2 for that part of f_y required to satisfy Clause 11.3.9.

12.13.5

Pairs of U-stirrups or ties placed so as to form a closed unit shall be considered properly spliced when the length of the laps is $1.3\ell_d$. Alternatively, in members at least 450 mm deep, where $A_b f_y$ is not more than 40 kN per leg, the splice shall be considered adequate if the stirrup legs extend the full available depth of the member.

12.14 Splices of reinforcement — General

12.14.1 Limitations on use
Splices of reinforcement shall be made only as required or permitted by design drawings or specifications, or as authorized by the designer.

12.14.2 Lap splices

12.14.2.1
Lap splices shall not be used for bars larger than 35M, except as specified in Clauses 12.16.2 and 15.9.2.4.

12.14.2.2
Lap splices of bundled bars shall be based on the lap splice length required for individual bars within a bundle, increased by 10% for a two-bar bundle, 20% for a three-bar bundle, and 33% for a four-bar bundle. Individual bar splices within a bundle shall not overlap.

12.14.2.3
Bars spliced by lap splices in flexural members shall have a transverse spacing not exceeding the lesser of one-fifth of the required lap splice length or 150 mm.

12.14.3 Welded splices and mechanical connections

12.14.3.1
Welded splices and other mechanical connections may be used.

12.14.3.2
All welding shall comply with to CSA W186.

12.14.3.3
A full welded splice shall have bars welded to develop, in tension, at least 120% of the specified yield strength, f_y, of the bar, but not less than 110% of the actual yield strength of the bar used in the test of the welded splice.

12.14.3.4
A full mechanical connection shall develop, in tension or compression as required, at least 120% of the specified yield strength, f_y, of the bar, but not less than 110% of the actual yield strength of the bar used in the test of the mechanical connection.

12.14.3.5
Welded splices and mechanical connections not meeting the requirements of Clause 12.14.3.3 or 12.14.3.4 may be used as specified in Clause 12.15.4.

12.15 Splices of deformed bars and deformed wire in tension

12.15.1

The minimum length of lap for tension lap splices shall be as required for a Class A or B splice, but not less than 300 mm, where
a)   the Class A splice length is $1.0\ell_d$; and
b)   the Class B splice length is $1.3\ell_d$.

In Items a) and b), ℓ_d is the tensile development length for the specified yield strength, f_y, as specified in Clause 12.2, but without the modification factor specified in Clause 12.2.5.

12.15.2

Lap splices of deformed bars and deformed wire in tension shall be Class B splices, except that Class A splices shall be permitted when
a)   the area of reinforcement provided is at least twice that required by analysis at the splice location; and
b)   less than one-half of the total reinforcement is spliced within the required lap length.

12.15.3

Welded splices or mechanical connections used where the area of reinforcement provided is less than twice that required by analysis shall meet the requirements of Clause 12.14.3.3 or 12.14.3.4.

12.15.4

Welded splices or mechanical connections used where the area of reinforcement provided is at least twice that required by analysis shall meet the following requirements:
a)   splices shall be staggered by at least 600 mm and in such a manner as to develop, at every section, at least twice the factored tensile force at that section, but not less than 140 MPa for the total area of reinforcement provided; and
b)   in computing the tensile resistance developed at each section, spliced reinforcement shall be rated at the specified splice strength. Unspliced reinforcement shall be rated at that fraction of f_y defined by the ratio of the shorter actual development length to the development length, ℓ_d, required to develop the specified yield strength, f_y.

12.15.5

Splices in tension tie members shall be made with a full welded splice or a full mechanical connection as specified in Clause 12.14.3.3 or 12.14.3.4. Splices in adjacent bars shall be staggered by at least 800 mm.

12.16 Splices of deformed bars in compression

12.16.1 Minimum lap length
The minimum lap length for compression lap splices shall be $0.073f_y d_b$ for f_y less than or equal to 400 MPa or $(0.133f_y - 24)d_b$ for f_y greater than 400 MPa, but shall not be taken less than 300 mm.

12.16.2 Lap length for bars of different sizes
When bars of different sizes are lap spliced in compression, the splice length shall be the larger of the development length of the larger bar or the splice length of the smaller bar. Bar sizes 45M and 55M may be lap spliced to 35M and smaller bars.

12.16.3 Welded splices or mechanical connections

Welded splices or mechanical connections used in compression shall meet the requirements of Clause 12.14.3.3 or 12.14.3.4.

12.16.4 End-bearing splices

12.16.4.1

In bars required for compression only, the compressive stress may be transmitted by the bearing of square cut ends held in concentric contact by a suitable device.

12.16.4.2

Bar ends shall terminate in flat surfaces within 1-1/2° of a right angle to the axis of the bars and shall be fitted to within 3° of full bearing after assembly.

12.16.4.3

End-bearing splices shall be used only in members containing closed ties, closed stirrups, or spirals.

12.17 Special splice requirements for columns

12.17.1 General

Lap splices, butt-welded splices, mechanical connections, or end-bearing splices shall satisfy the applicable requirements of Clauses 12.17.2 to 12.17.5 for all load combinations for the column.

12.17.2 Reinforcement

Where welded splices, mechanical connections, or end-bearing splices are used, the amount of reinforcement spliced at any location shall not exceed 0.04 times the gross area of the section. Where the gross area of reinforcement exceeds 0.04 times the gross area of the section, connection or splice locations shall be spaced not less than 750 mm apart (see Clause 10.9.2).

12.17.3 Lap splices in columns

12.17.3.1

Where the bar stress due to factored loads is compressive, lap splices shall comply with Clauses 12.16.1 and 12.16.2, and, where applicable, with Clause 12.17.3.4 or 12.17.3.5.

12.17.3.2

Where the bar stress due to factored loads is tensile and does not exceed $0.5f_y$, lap splices shall be Class B if more than one-half of the bars are spliced at any section or Class A if one-half or fewer of the bars are spliced at any section and alternate lap splices are staggered by ℓ_d.

12.17.3.3

Where the bar stress due to factored loads is greater than $0.5f_y$ in tension, lap splices shall be Class B.

12.17.3.4

In tied reinforced compression members where ties throughout the lap splice length have an effective area of not less than $0.0015hs$, the lap splice length, computed as specified in Clauses 12.16.1 and

12.16.2, may be multiplied by 0.83, but the lap splice length shall be not less than 300 mm. Tie legs perpendicular to dimension *h* shall be used in determining the effective area.

12.17.3.5

In spirally reinforced compression members, the lap splice length of bars within a spiral, computed as specified in Clauses 12.16.1 and 12.16.2, may be multiplied by 0.75, but the lap splice length shall be not less than 300 mm.

12.17.4 Welded splices or mechanical connections in columns

Welded splices or mechanical connections in columns shall meet the requirements of Clause 12.14.3.3 or 12.14.3.4.

12.17.5 End-bearing splices in columns

End-bearing splices meeting the requirements of Clause 12.16.4 may be used for column bars stressed in compression, provided that the splices are staggered or additional bars are provided at splice locations. The continuing vertical bars in each face of the column shall have an area of at least 0.25 of the area of the vertical reinforcement in that face.

12.18 Splices of welded deformed wire fabric in tension

12.18.1

The minimum length of lap for lap splices of welded deformed wire fabric measured between the ends of each fabric sheet shall be not less than the greater of $1.3\ell_d$ and 200 mm and the overlap measured between the outermost crosswires of each fabric sheet shall be not less than 50 mm, where ℓ_d shall be the development length, as specified in Clause 12.7, for the specified yield strength, f_y.

12.18.2

The lap splices of welded deformed wire fabric with no crosswires within the lap splice length shall be determined as for deformed wire.

12.19 Splices of welded smooth wire fabric in tension

12.19.1

The minimum length of lap for lap splices of welded smooth wire fabric shall be as specified in Clauses 12.19.2 and 12.19.3.

12.19.2

When the area of reinforcement provided is less than twice that required at the splice location, the length of overlap measured between the outermost crosswires of each fabric sheet shall be not less than the greater of
a)   one spacing of crosswires plus 50 mm;
b) $1.5\ell_d$; and
c)   150 mm,

where ℓ_d shall be the development length, as specified in Clause 12.8, for the specified yield strength, f_y.

12.19.3

When the area of reinforcement provided is at least twice that required at the splice location, the length of overlap measured between the outermost crosswires of each fabric sheet shall be not less than the greater of $1.5\ell_d$ and 50 mm, where ℓ_d shall be the development length, as specified in Clause 12.8, for the specified yield strength, f_y.

13 Two-way slab systems

13.1 General

13.1.1

Clause 13 shall apply to the design of slab systems reinforced for flexure in more than one direction, with or without beams between supports.

13.1.2

A slab system may be supported on columns or walls.

13.2 Minimum slab thickness

13.2.1 General

The minimum slab thickness, h_s, shall be based on serviceability requirements but shall be not less than 120 mm.

13.2.2 Two-way slab systems

For regular two-way slab systems (see Clause 3.1), the requirement specified in Clause 9.8.2.6 to show by computation that deflections will not exceed the limits stipulated in Table 9.3 may be waived when the slab thicknesses provided are not less than the minimum thicknesses specified in Clauses 13.2.3 to 13.2.6.

Note: *It is possible that the minimum thickness specified in Clauses 13.2.3 to 13.2.6 will not be adequate for certain sequences of shoring during construction or for large live to dead load ratios.*

13.2.3 Slabs without drop panels

The thickness, h_s, shall satisfy

$$h_s \geq \frac{\ell_n\left(0.6 + f_y / 1000\right)}{30} \qquad \text{Equation 13.1}$$

where
ℓ_n = the longer clear span

At discontinuous edges, an edge beam shall be provided with a stiffness ratio, α, of not less than 0.80 or the thickness required by Equation 13.1 shall be multiplied by 1.1 in the panel with the discontinuous edge or edges.

13.2.4 Slabs with drop panels

The thickness, h_s, shall satisfy

$$h_s \geq \frac{\ell_n\left(0.6 + f_y / 1000\right)}{30} - \frac{2x_d}{\ell_n}\Delta_h \qquad \text{Equation 13.2}$$

where ℓ_n is the longer clear span and Δ_h is the additional thickness of the drop panel below the soffit of the slab and shall not be taken larger than h_s.

In Equation 13.2 $(2x_d/\ell_n)$ is the smaller of the values determined in the two directions and x_d shall not be taken greater than $(\ell_n/4)$.

At discontinuous edges, an edge beam shall be provided with a stiffness ratio, α, of not less than 0.80 or the thickness required by Equation 13.2 shall be multiplied by 1.1 in the panel with the discontinuous edge or edges.

13.2.5 Slabs with beams between all supports

The minimum thickness, h_s, shall be

$$h_s \geq \frac{\ell_n\left(0.6 + f_y / 1000\right)}{30 + 4\beta\alpha_m} \qquad \text{Equation 13.3}$$

where ℓ_n is the longer clear span, α_m shall not be taken greater than 2.0 and the value α may be determined by taking I_b equal to

$$I_b = \frac{b_w h^3}{12}\left(2.5\left(1 - \frac{h_s}{h}\right)\right) \qquad \text{Equation 13.4}$$

13.2.6 Slab bands

The minimum thickness of slab bands shall be that required for beams in Table 9.2.

13.2.7 Computation of slab deflections

A slab thickness less than the minimum thickness required by Clauses 13.2.2 to 13.2.5 may be used if computations show that deflection will not exceed the limits specified in Table 9.3. Deflections shall be computed by taking into account the size and shape of the panel, the conditions of support, and the nature of restraints at the panel edges. For deflection computations, the modulus of elasticity, E_c, for concrete shall be as specified in Clause 8.6.2. The effective moment of inertia shall be that specified by Equation 9.1. The moment, M_a, shall take into consideration construction loads, where known and the loading conditions assumed in Clause 9.8.2.3. Other values of I_e may be used if the computed deflection is in reasonable agreement with the results of comprehensive tests. The effective modulus of rupture of the concrete shall be taken as one-half of the value specified by Equation 8.3. Additional long-term deflection shall be computed as specified in Clause 9.8.2.5.

13.3 Design procedures for shear for slabs without beams

13.3.1 General

In the vicinity of concentrated loads or reactions, the factored shear stress resistance, v_r, shall be equal to or greater than the maximum factored shear stress, v_f, due to the factored shear force and unbalanced moments. The stress, v_f, shall be determined for full load on all spans as well as any other patterns of loading that might result in larger stresses.

13.3.2 One-way and two-way shear

Slabs in the vicinity of columns shall be designed for two-way shear as specified in Clauses 13.3.3 to 13.3.5. Slabs shall also be designed for one-way shear as specified in Clause 13.3.6.

13.3.3 Critical shear section for two-way action

13.3.3.1

The critical section for two-way action shall be a section perpendicular to the plane of the slab and located so that its perimeter, b_0, is a minimum, but the section need not approach closer than $d/2$ to the perimeter of the concentrated load or reaction area.

13.3.3.2

At changes in slab thickness, a critical section located in the thinner portion at a distance not greater than $d/2$ from the face of the thicker portion and located such that the perimeter, b_0, is a minimum, shall also be investigated.

13.3.3.3

For square or rectangular load or reaction areas, the critical section may be assumed to have four straight sides. For edge supports, the critical section may be assumed to have three straight sides. For corner supports, the critical section may be assumed to have two straight sides. At edge and corner supports where the slab cantilevers beyond the exterior face of the support, the critical section may be assumed to extend into the cantilevered portion of the slab for a distance not exceeding d.

13.3.3.4

When openings in slabs are located at a distance of less than ten times the slab thickness from a concentrated load or reaction area or when openings in slabs without beams are located within a column strip, that part of the perimeter of the critical section which is enclosed by straight lines projecting from the centre of the load or reaction area and tangent to the boundaries of the openings shall be considered ineffective.

13.3.4 Maximum shear stress resistance without shear reinforcement

13.3.4.1

The factored shear stress resistance, v_r, shall be the smallest of
a)

$$v_r = v_c = \left(1 + \frac{2}{\beta_c}\right)0.19\lambda\phi_c\sqrt{f'_c}$$

Equation 13.5

where
β_c = the ratio of long side to short side of the column, concentrated load, or reaction area

b)

$$v_r = v_c = \left(\frac{\alpha_s d}{b_o} + 0.19\right)\lambda\phi_c\sqrt{f'_c}$$

Equation 13.6

where

α_s = 4 for interior columns, 3 for edge columns, and 2 for corner columns

c)

$$v_r = v_c = 0.38\lambda\phi_c\sqrt{f'_c}$$

Equation 13.7

13.3.4.2

The value of $\sqrt{f'_c}$ used to calculate v_c in Equations 13.5 to 13.7 and 13.10 shall not exceed 8 MPa.

13.3.4.3

If the effective depth, d, used in two-way shear calculations exceeds 300 mm, the value of v_c obtained from Equations 13.5 to 13.7 shall be multiplied by 1300/(1000+d).

13.3.4.4

The requirements of Clause 13.3.4.3 need not be applied to the design of footings or mat foundations where the distance from the point of zero shear to the face of the column, pedestal, or wall is less than $2d$.

13.3.5 Factored shear stress

13.3.5.1

For corner supports not meeting the requirements of Clause 13.3.6.2, and interior and edge supports, the shear forces and unbalanced moments to be transferred to the support shall be resolved into a single shear force acting at the centroid of the critical section and moments about the centroidal axes (x and y directions) of the critical section.

13.3.5.2

The shear stress due to the factored shear force acting at the centroid of the section shall be assumed to be uniformly distributed over the critical shear section.

13.3.5.3

The fraction of the unbalanced moment transferred by eccentricity of shear at interior, edge, and corner columns, γ_v, shall be

$$\gamma_v = 1 - \frac{1}{1 + \dfrac{2}{3}\sqrt{\dfrac{b_1}{b_2}}}$$

Equation 13.8

13.3.5.4

The shear stress due to moment transfer by eccentricity of shear shall be assumed to vary linearly about the centroid of the critical shear section.

13.3.5.5

The factored shear stress, v_f, shall be computed from the following equation, with the factored shear force and unbalanced moments about the x and y directions obtained from a consistent loading:

$$v_f = \frac{V_f}{b_o d} + \left(\frac{\gamma_v M_f e}{J} \right)_x + \left(\frac{\gamma_v M_f e}{J} \right)_y \qquad \text{Equation 13.9}$$

13.3.5.6

The fraction of the unbalanced moment not transferred by eccentricity of shear stress shall be transferred by flexure as specified in Clause 13.10.2.

13.3.6 One-way shear

13.3.6.1 General

One-way shear for a slab with a critical section extending in a plane across the entire width and located at a distance, d_v, from the face of the concentrated load or reaction area shall be as specified in Clauses 11.1 to 11.3. The one-way shear shall be distributed between the column strip and the middle strip in proportion to the design negative moments in each strip.

13.3.6.2 Corner columns

The factored shear resistance, V_c, of slabs in the vicinity of corner columns shall be taken as

$$V_c = \phi_c \lambda \beta \sqrt{f_c'} b_o d_v \qquad \text{Equation 13.10}$$

where β is as specified in Clauses 11.3.6.2 and 11.3.6.3 and b_o is determined for a critical shear section located not farther than $d/2$ from the edge of the column or column capital. The value of $\sqrt{f_c'}$ used to calculate V_c in Equation 13.10 shall not exceed 8 MPa.

Where the slab cantilevers beyond the face of the corner column or the corner column capital, the length of the critical section may be taken as extended into the cantilevered portion for a length not exceeding d.

Corner columns meeting the requirements of this Clause shall be deemed to have satisfied the requirements of Clauses 13.3.4 and 13.3.5.

Δ **Note:** *For slabs greater than 350 mm deep, or slabs with beams exceeding the limitations specified in Clause 11.3.6.2, application of the one-way shear provisions specified in Clauses 11.3.6.3 and 11.3.6.4 should take into account the reduction of allowable concrete shear stress resulting from the effect of depth in such members.*

13.3.7 Shear reinforcement for slabs without beams

13.3.7.1

Shear reinforcement consisting of headed shear reinforcement, stirrups, or shearheads may be used to increase the shear capacity of slabs and footings. The design of shearheads shall be based on the concepts in ACI 318M/318RM.

13.3.7.2

The shear resistance shall be investigated at the section specified in Clause 13.3.3.1 and at successive sections more distant from the support.

13.3.7.3

Within the shear reinforced zone, the factored shear stress resistance, v_r, shall be computed as $(v_c + v_s)$, where v_c and v_s shall be computed as specified in Clauses 13.3.8.3 and 13.3.8.5 for headed shear reinforcement and as specified in Clauses 13.3.9.3 and 13.3.9.4 for stirrups.

13.3.7.4

Shear reinforcement shall be extended to the section where v_f is not greater than $0.19\lambda\phi_c\sqrt{f'_c}$, but at least a distance $2d$ from the face of the column.

13.3.8 Headed shear reinforcement

13.3.8.1

Headed shear reinforcement shall be mechanically anchored at each end by a plate or head bearing against the concrete in such a manner that it is capable of developing the yield strength of the bar. The area of the plate or head shall be at least ten times the cross-sectional area of the bar unless a smaller area can be justified experimentally (see Clause 7.1.4).

13.3.8.2

When headed shear reinforcement is provided, the factored shear stress, v_f, shall be not greater than $0.75\lambda\phi_c\sqrt{f'_c}$.

13.3.8.3

In the zone reinforced by headed shear reinforcement, the factored shear stress resistance of the concrete, v_c, shall be $0.28\lambda\phi_c\sqrt{f'_c}$.

13.3.8.4

Headed shear reinforcement shall be located along concentric lines that parallel the perimeter of the column cross-section.

13.3.8.5

The factored shear stress resistance of headed shear reinforcement, v_s, shall be computed as

$$v_s = \frac{\phi_s A_{vs} f_{yv}}{b_o s}$$

Equation 13.11

where
A_{vs} = the cross-sectional area of the headed shear reinforcement on a concentric line parallel to the perimeter of the column

13.3.8.6

The distance between the column face and the first line of headed shear reinforcement shall be $0.35d$ to $0.4d$. The upper limits for the spacing, s, between lines of headed shear reinforcement shall be based on the value of v_f at a critical section $d/2$ from the column face, as follows:
a) $s \leq 0.75d$ when

$$v_f \leq 0.56\lambda\phi_c\sqrt{f'_c}$$

Equation 13.12

b) $s \leq 0.5d$ when

$$v_f > 0.56\lambda\phi_c\sqrt{f'_c}$$

Equation 13.13

13.3.8.7

Unless the headed shear reinforcement is otherwise protected, the minimum concrete cover over the heads shall be the same as the minimum cover for the flexural reinforcement as specified in Clause 7.9. The concrete cover shall not exceed the minimum cover plus one-half the bar diameter of the flexural reinforcement.

13.3.9 Stirrup reinforcement

13.3.9.1

Stirrups anchored as specified in Clauses 7.1.2 and 12.13 may be used as shear reinforcement provided that the overall thickness of the slab is not less than 300 mm.

13.3.9.2

When stirrups are provided, the factored shear stress, v_f, shall not be greater than $0.55\lambda\phi_c\sqrt{f'_c}$.

13.3.9.3

In the zone reinforced by stirrups, the factored shear stress resistance of the concrete, v_c, shall be $0.19\lambda\phi_c\sqrt{f'_c}$.

13.3.9.4

The factored shear stress resistance, v_s, shall be computed from Equation 13.11, with A_{vs}, the cross-sectional area of the stirrups, on a line parallel to the perimeter of the column.

13.3.9.5

The stirrup spacing, s, shall not exceed $d/2$, with the first stirrup placed at $d/4$ from the column face.

13.4 Shear in slab systems with beams

13.4.1

Beams with $(\alpha_1\ell_{2a}/\ell_1)$ equal to or greater than 1.0 shall be designed to resist shear caused by factored loads on tributary areas bounded by 45° lines drawn from the corners of the panels and the centrelines of the adjacent panels parallel to the long sides.

13.4.2

Beams with $(\alpha_1\ell_{2a}/\ell_1)$ less than 1.0 may be designed to resist shear obtained by linear interpolation, assuming beams carry no load at $\alpha_1 = 0$.

13.4.3

In addition to resisting shears calculated as specified in Clauses 13.4.1 and 13.4.2, beams shall be designed to resist shears caused by factored loads applied directly on the beams.

13.4.4

Slab shears may be computed on the assumption that load is distributed to supporting beams as specified in Clause 13.4.1 or 13.4.2. Resistance to total shear occurring on a panel shall be provided.

13.4.5

The shear resistance of beams shall satisfy the requirements of Clause 11.

13.5 Design procedures for flexure

Note: _See also Clauses 13.6 to 13.12 and Annex B._

13.5.1

A slab system may be designed using any procedure satisfying conditions of equilibrium and compatibility with the supports, provided that it is shown that the factored resistance at every section is at least equal to the effects of the factored loads and that all serviceability conditions, including specified limits on deflections, are met.

13.5.2

For lateral loads, analysis of unbraced frames shall take into account the effects of cracking and reinforcement on stiffness of frame members.

13.5.3

The results of the gravity load analysis shall be combined with the results of the lateral load analysis.

13.5.4

Openings of any size may be provided in slab systems if it is shown by analysis that the factored resistance is at least equal to the effects of factored loads in accordance with Clauses 8.3, 8.4, and 13.3.3.4, and that all serviceability conditions, including the specified limits on deflections, are met.

Note: _Clause 13.10.10 provides simple rules for regular slabs without beams._

13.6 Elastic plate theory

13.6.1

Analysis of slab systems may be based on elastic plate theory that uses either classical or numerical techniques.

Note: _The successful application of the results of analysis using elastic plate theory requires proper consideration of factors such as selection of thickness, moment redistribution due to the effects of cracking, creep, shrinkage effects, and construction loading._

13.6.2

Care shall be taken to ensure realistic modelling of the size and effective stiffness of the supporting elements, including beams, if any.

13.6.3

Appropriate loading patterns shall be considered to ensure determination of maximum values for all stress resultants at each section.

13.6.4

When reinforcement is placed as an orthogonal mat in the x and y directions, the factored design moments shall be adjusted to account for the effects of torsion. In lieu of more detailed calculations, the design moment intensities, $m_{x,des}$ or $m_{y,des}$, in the x and y directions at any point shall be computed as follows:

a) positive design moments:

$$m_{x,des} = m_x + \left| m_{xy} \right|$$

Equation 13.14

$$m_{y,des} = m_y + |m_{xy}|$$ **Equation 13.15**

If either $m_{x,des}$ or $m_{y,des}$ is negative, it shall be taken as zero.

b)   negative design moments:

$$m_{x,des} = m_x - |m_{xy}|$$ **Equation 13.16**

$$m_{y,des} = m_y - |m_{xy}|$$ **Equation 13.17**

If either $m_{x,des}$ or $m_{y,des}$ is positive, it shall be taken as zero.

13.6.5

Uniformly spaced reinforcement shall be placed in bands such that

a)   the total reinforcement provided within a band shall be sufficient to resist the total factored moment computed for that band; and

b)   the moment resistance per unit width within the band shall be at least two-thirds of the maximum factored moment intensity within the band.

Note: *Additional information on the application of finite element analysis design techniques is provided by the Cement Association of Canada's Concrete design handbook.*

13.7 Theorems of plasticity

13.7.1

Analysis of slab systems for factored loads may be based on either the lower bound or upper bound theorems of plasticity.

Note: *The successful application of the results of plastic analysis requires proper assumptions that will ensure that serviceability requirements, including creep and shrinkage effects, are satisfied.*

13.7.2

The size and effective stiffness of the supporting elements shall be considered in the analysis.

13.7.3

When strength design is based on the upper bound theorem (e.g., yield line method), the factored moments shall be obtained from calculations based on a need for a mechanism to form over the whole or part of the slab at collapse. The mechanism that is the most critical shall be used for the design of the slab.

13.7.4

Factored moments obtained using lower bound theory (e.g., strip method) shall satisfy the requirements of equilibrium and the boundary conditions applicable to the slab.

13.7.5

Reinforcement may be uniformly spaced in bands, with band widths selected to ensure that serviceability requirements are satisfied.

13.8 Slab systems as elastic frames

13.8.1 Definition of frame geometry

13.8.1.1

A regular two-way slab system (see Clause 3.1) may, for purposes of analysis, be considered a series of plane frames acting longitudinally and transversely through the building. Each frame shall be composed of equivalent line members intersecting at member centrelines, shall follow a column line, and shall include the portion of slab bounded laterally by the centreline of the panel on each side.

Note: *A floor system with beams between supports that does not satisfy the limits specified in the definition of a regular two-way slab system in Clause 3.1 may be analyzed as specified in this Clause, but the reinforcing distribution specified in Clause 13.12 will normally not be applicable.*

13.8.1.2

Each floor and roof slab with attached columns may be analyzed separately, with the far ends of the columns considered fixed.

13.8.1.3

Where slab-beams are analyzed separately, it may be assumed in determining moment at a given support that the slab-beam is fixed at any support two panels distant from the slab-beam, provided that the slab continues beyond that point.

13.8.1.4

The change in length of columns and slabs due to direct stress, and deflections due to shear, may be neglected.

13.8.1.5

Member stiffness used in the analysis of the elastic frame shall be selected to simulate the behaviour of the slab system.

13.8.2 Non-prismatic modelling of member stiffness

13.8.2.1

When members are modelled as non-prismatic elements, the member stiffness may be as specified in Clauses 13.8.2.2 to 13.8.2.10.

13.8.2.2

The moment of inertia of column and slab-beam elements at any cross-section outside of joints or column capitals shall be based on the gross area of concrete at that section.

13.8.2.3

The moment of inertia of slab-beams from the centre of the column to the face of the column, bracket, or capital shall be assumed to be equal to the moment of inertia of the slab-beam at the face of the column, bracket, or capital divided by the quantity $(1 - c_2/\ell_{2a})^2$, where c_2 and ℓ_{2a} are measured transverse to the direction of the span for which moments are being determined.

13.8.2.4

The moment of inertia of column elements from top to bottom of the slab-beam at a joint shall be assumed to be infinite.

13.8.2.5

An equivalent column shall be assumed to consist of the actual columns above and below the slab-beam plus an attached torsional member transverse to the direction of the span for which moments are being determined.

13.8.2.6

The flexibility of an equivalent column shall be taken as the sum of the flexibilities of the actual columns above and below the slab-beam and the flexibility of the attached torsional member, as follows:

$$\frac{1}{K_{ec}} = \frac{1}{\Sigma K_c} + \frac{1}{K_t}$$

Equation 13.18

13.8.2.7

Attached torsional members shall be assumed to have a constant cross-section throughout their length consisting of the largest of the following:

a) a portion of slab having a width equal to that of the column, bracket, or capital in the direction of the span for which moments are being determined;

b) for monolithic or fully composite construction, the portion of slab specified in Item a) plus that part of the transverse beam above and below the slab; or

c) a transverse beam which includes that portion of slab on each side of the beam extending a distance equal to the projection of the beam above or below the slab, whichever is greater, but not greater than four times the slab thickness.

13.8.2.8

The stiffness, K_t, of attached torsional members shall be calculated as follows:

$$K_t = \Sigma \frac{9E_cC}{\ell_t\left(1 - \frac{c_2}{\ell_t}\right)^3}$$

Equation 13.19

13.8.2.9

The section parameter, C, in Equation 13.19 may be evaluated for the cross-section by dividing it into separate rectangular parts and carrying out the following summation:

$$C = \Sigma\left(1 - 0.63\frac{x}{y}\right)\frac{x^3y}{3}$$

Equation 13.20

13.8.2.10

Where beams frame into columns in the direction of the span for which moments are being determined, the value of K_t shall be multiplied by the ratio of the moment of inertia of the slab with such beam to the moment of inertia of the slab without such beam.

13.8.3 Prismatic modelling of member stiffness

13.8.3.1
When members are modelled as prismatic elements, the member stiffness may be assigned as specified in Clauses 13.8.3.2 and 13.8.3.3.

13.8.3.2
For prismatic modelling of slab-beam elements, the moment of inertia shall be based on the gross area of the concrete outside the joints or column capitals. When the moment of inertia varies outside the joint, e.g., in drop panels, the slab-beam elements may be modelled as a series of prismatic elements with moments of inertia based on the gross concrete dimensions.

13.8.3.3
For prismatic modelling of column elements, the effective moment of inertia shall be taken as equal to ψ times the moment of inertia based on the gross area outside the joints, where ψ is given as follows:

a) for $\quad \ell_2/\ell_1 \leq 1.0$: $\quad \psi = 0.3 + 0.7\dfrac{\alpha_1 \ell_2}{\ell_1}$ **Equation 13.21**

b) for $\quad \ell_2/\ell_1 > 1.0$: $\quad \psi = 0.6\left(\dfrac{\ell_2}{\ell_1} - 0.5\right) + \left(1.3 - 0.6\dfrac{\ell_2}{\ell_1}\right)\dfrac{\alpha_1 \ell_2}{\ell_1}$ **Equation 13.22**

In Equations 13.21 and 13.22, ψ shall not be taken less than 0.3 or greater than 1.0, and $\alpha_1 \ell_2/\ell_1$ shall not be taken greater than 1.0.

13.8.4 Arrangement of live load

13.8.4.1
When the loading pattern is known, the frame shall be analyzed for that load.

13.8.4.2
When the live load is uniformly distributed and does not exceed three-quarters of the specified dead load or the nature of the live load is such that all panels will be loaded simultaneously, the maximum factored moments may be assumed to occur at all sections with full factored live load on the entire slab system.

13.8.4.3
For loading conditions other than those specified in Clauses 13.8.4.1 and 13.8.4.2, the maximum positive factored moment near midspan of a panel may be assumed to occur with three-quarters of the full factored uniformly distributed live load on the panel and on alternate panels, and the maximum negative factored moment in the slab at a support may be assumed to occur with three-quarters of the full factored uniformly distributed live load on adjacent panels only.

13.8.4.4
Factored moments shall not be taken as less than those occurring with full factored live loads on all panels.

13.8.5 Critical sections

13.8.5.1

Except as required by Clause 13.8.5.2, at interior and exterior supports the critical section for the negative factored moment shall be taken at the face of rectilinear supports, but not at a distance greater than $0.175\ell_1$ from the centre of the column.

13.8.5.2

In addition to the requirements specified in Clause 13.8.5.1, at exterior supports that include brackets or capitals, the critical section for the negative factored moment in the span perpendicular to an edge shall be taken at a distance from the face of the supporting element not greater than one-half of the projection of the bracket or capital beyond the face of the supporting element.

13.8.5.3

When the critical section for the negative design moment is being located, circular or regular polygonal supports shall be treated as square supports with the same area.

13.8.5.4

Reinforcement to resist the moments at the critical sections shall be selected in accordance with Clauses 13.10 to 13.12.

13.8.5.5

The flexural capacity shall be checked at any change in the slab depth, e.g., at the edges of drop panels and slab bands.

13.9 Direct design method

13.9.1 Limitations

13.9.1.1

Regular two-way slab systems (see Clause 3.1) that comply with the limitations specified in Clauses 13.9.1.2 to 13.9.1.5 may be designed using the direct design method.

Note: *It is possible that in some circumstances the requirements specified in Clauses 13.9.1.2 to 13.9.1.5 will not address concerns related to slab systems with drop panels and/or beams as rigorously as the requirements specified in Clause 13.8.*

13.9.1.2

There shall be a minimum of three continuous spans in each direction.

13.9.1.3

Successive span lengths centre-to-centre of supports in each direction shall not differ by more than one-third of the longer span.

13.9.1.4

All loads shall be due to gravity only and uniformly distributed over an entire panel. The factored live load shall not exceed twice the factored dead load.

13.9.1.5

Variations from the limitations of Clauses 13.9.1.2 to 13.9.1.4 shall be acceptable if it is demonstrated by analysis that the requirements specified in Clause 13.5.1 are satisfied.

13.9.2 Total factored static moment for a span

13.9.2.1

The total factored static moment for a span shall be determined in a strip bound laterally by the centrelines of the panels on each side of the centreline of supports.

13.9.2.2

For each span of each strip, the sum of the absolute values of the positive and the average negative factored moments, in each direction, shall be not less than

$$M_o = \frac{w_f \ell_{2o} \ell_n^2}{8}$$

Equation 13.23

13.9.2.3

The clear span, ℓ_n, shall extend from face-to-face of columns, capitals, brackets, or walls. The value of ℓ_n used in Equation 13.23 shall be not less than $0.65\ell_1$.

13.9.3 Negative and positive factored moments

13.9.3.1

In an interior span, the total static moment, M_o, shall be distributed as follows:

Negative factored moment at the face of support:	0.65
Positive factored moment at midspan:	0.35

13.9.3.2

In an end span, the total factored static moment, M_o, shall be distributed as specified in Table 13.1.

Table 13.1
Distribution factors for total factored static moment
(See Clause 13.9.3.2.)

Moment	Exterior edge unre-strained	Slab with beams between all supports	Slab without beams between interior supports	Exterior edge fully restrained
Interior negative factored moment	0.75	0.70	0.70	0.65
Positive factored moment	0.66	0.59	0.52	0.35
Exterior negative factored moment	0	0.16	0.26	0.65

13.9.3.3

Negative and positive factored moments may be modified by 15% provided that the total static moment for a span in the direction considered is not less than that required by Equation 13.23.

13.9.3.4

Negative moment sections shall be designed to resist the larger of the two interior negative factored moments determined for spans framing into a common support; however, the moments may first be modified in accordance with Clause 13.9.3.3.

13.9.4 Unbalanced factored moments in columns and walls

At an interior support, the joint and supporting elements above and below the slab shall resist the factored moment specified in the following equation in direct proportion to their stiffness:

$$M_f = 0.07\left(\left(w_{df} + 0.5w_{lf}\right)\ell_{2a}\ell_n^2 - w'_{df}\ell'_{2a}(\ell'_n)^2\right)$$

Equation 13.24

where w'_{df}, ℓ_{2a}, and ℓ'_n refer to the shorter span.

13.9.5 Selection of reinforcement

Reinforcement to resist the moments at the critical sections shall be selected in accordance with Clauses 13.10 to 13.12.

13.10 Slab reinforcement

13.10.1 General

Reinforcement in each direction for two-way slab systems shall be determined from moments at critical sections but shall be not less than that required by Clause 7.8.1.

Note: *Where strict crack control is a concern, slabs with drop panels, particularly in a corrosive environment, can require additional reinforcement in the negative middle strip region to limit cracking. This additional reinforcement is not included in the calculation of moment resistance. The reinforcement required to limit cracking is generally more than that required by Clause 7.8.1.*

13.10.2 Shear and moment transfer

When gravity load, wind, earthquake, or other lateral forces cause transfer of moment between slab and column, a fraction of unbalanced moment given by

$$\gamma_f = 1 - \gamma_v$$

Equation 13.25

shall be transferred by flexural reinforcement placed within a width b_b.

Note: *For exterior supports, including corner columns, Clause 13.10.3 satisfies this requirement.*

13.10.3 Exterior columns

Reinforcement for the total factored negative moment transferred to the exterior columns shall be placed within a band width b_b. Temperature and shrinkage reinforcement determined as specified in Clause 7.8.1 shall be provided in that section of the slab outside of the band region defined by b_b, or as required by Clause 13.10.9.

13.10.4 Spacing

Except for portions of slab area that are of cellular or ribbed construction, spacing of reinforcement at critical sections shall not exceed the following limits:

Negative reinforcement in the band defined by b_b:	$1.5h_s$, but $s \le 250$ mm
Remaining negative moment reinforcement:	$3h_s$, but $s \le 500$ mm
Positive moment reinforcement:	$3h_s$, but $s \le 500$ mm

In the slab over cellular spaces, reinforcement shall be provided as required by Clause 7.8.

13.10.5 Anchorage

13.10.5.1

Positive moment reinforcement perpendicular to a discontinuous edge shall have embedment, straight or hooked, at least 150 mm into the spandrel beams, columns, or walls.

13.10.5.2

Negative moment reinforcement perpendicular to a discontinuous edge shall be bent, hooked, or otherwise anchored in spandrel beams, columns, or walls, and shall be developed at the face of the support as specified in Clause 12.

13.10.5.3

Where a slab is not supported by a spandrel beam or wall at a discontinuous edge or where a slab cantilevers beyond the support, both the top and bottom reinforcement shall extend to the edge of the slab.

13.10.6 Structural integrity reinforcement

13.10.6.1

The summation of the area of bottom reinforcement connecting the slab, drop panel, or slab band to the column or column capital on all faces of the periphery of the column or column capital shall be

$$\sum A_{sb} = \frac{2V_{se}}{f_y} \qquad \text{Equation 13.26}$$

Integrity reinforcement shall not be required if there are beams containing shear reinforcement in all spans framing into the column.

13.10.6.2

The reinforcement specified in Clause 13.10.6.1 shall consist of at least two bars or two tendons that extend through the column core or column capital region in each span direction.

13.10.6.3

The bottom reinforcement required by Clause 13.10.6.1 shall be provided by one or more of the following:
a) bottom reinforcement extended such that it is lap spliced over a column or column capital, with the bottom reinforcement in adjacent spans using a Class A tension lap splice;

b) additional bottom reinforcement passing over a column or column capital such that an overlap of $2\ell_d$ is provided, with the bottom reinforcement in adjacent spans;

c) at discontinuous edges, bottom reinforcement extended and bent, hooked, or otherwise anchored over the supports such that the yield stress can be developed at the face of the column or column capital as specified in Clause 12; or

d) continuous tendons draped over column capitals, with a minimum total area of prestressing steel calculated using Equation 13.26, but with f_y replaced by f_{py}.

13.10.7 Effective depth at drop panels

Where a drop panel is used to reduce the amount of negative moment reinforcement over the column, the thickness of the drop panel below the slab shall not be assumed greater than one-quarter of the distance from the edge of the drop panel to the edge of the column or column capital.

13.10.8 Curtailment of reinforcement

13.10.8.1

For regular two-way slabs (see Clause 3.1) that comply with the requirements specified in Clauses 13.9.1.2 to 13.9.1.5, minimum extensions shall be as shown in Figure 13.1.

13.10.8.2

The required extensions for slabs not complying with the requirements specified in Clauses 13.9.1.2 to 13.9.1.5 shall meet the requirements specified in Clauses 12.11 and 12.12, but shall be not less than those shown in Figure 13.1.

13.10.8.3

Where adjacent spans are unequal, the extension of negative reinforcement beyond the face of the support, as shown in Figure 13.1, shall be based on the longer span.

Figure 13.1
Minimum length of reinforcement for slabs without interior beams
(See Clauses 3.2 and 13.10.8.1–13.10.8.3.)

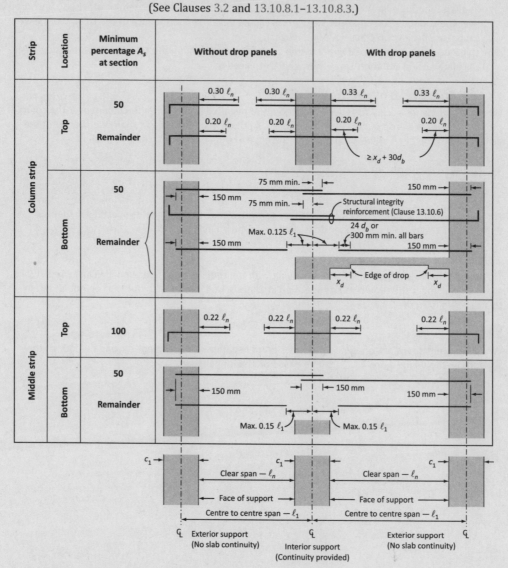

13.10.9 Top reinforcement at slab edges

Slab edges shall be reinforced with top reinforcement perpendicular to the edge to resist the factored moments caused by edge loads, but not less than that required by Clause 7.8.1.

13.10.10 Openings

13.10.10.1

Openings may be placed in regular two-way slabs without beams (see Clause 3.1) without the special analysis required by Clause 13.5.4, provided that the requirements specified in Clauses 13.10.10.2 to 13.10.10.5 are met.

13.10.10.2

Openings of any size may be located in the area common to intersecting middle strips, provided that the total amount of reinforcement required for the panel without the opening is maintained.

13.10.10.3

In the area common to intersecting column strips, not more than one-eighth of the width of the column strip in either span shall be interrupted by openings. An amount of reinforcement equivalent to that interrupted by an opening shall be added adjacent to the sides of the opening.

13.10.10.4

In the area common to one column strip and one middle strip, not more than one-quarter of the reinforcement in either strip shall be interrupted by openings. An amount of reinforcement equivalent to that interrupted by an opening shall be added adjacent to the sides of the opening.

13.10.10.5

The shear requirements specified in Clause 13.3.3.4 shall be satisfied.

13.11 Lateral distribution of moments for slabs without interior beams

13.11.1 General

In addition to the requirements specified in Clause 13.10, slabs without beams designed as specified in Clauses 13.8 and 13.9 shall be reinforced for flexure as specified in Clauses 13.11.2 and 13.11.3.

13.11.2 Factored moments in column strip

13.11.2.1

The column strip shall be designed to resist the total negative or positive factored moments at the critical sections multiplied by an appropriate factor as specified in Clauses 13.11.2.2 to 13.11.2.5.

13.11.2.2

The following multiplication factors shall apply to slabs without drop panels (with or without spandrel beams):

a) Negative moment at an interior column	0.70 to 0.90
b) Negative moment at an exterior column	1.00
c) Positive moment at all spans	0.55 to 0.65

13.11.2.3

The following multiplication factors shall apply to slabs with drop panels (with or without spandrel beams):

a) Negative moment at an interior column	0.75 to 0.90
b) Negative moment at an exterior column	1.00
c) Positive moment at all spans	0.55 to 0.65

13.11.2.4

The following multiplication factors shall apply to slabs with slab bands, in the direction of the slab band:

Negative moment at an interior column	0.80 to 1.00
Negative moment at an exterior column	1.00
Positive moment at all spans	0.80 to 1.00

13.11.2.5

The following multiplication factors shall apply to slabs with slab bands, in the direction perpendicular to the slab band:

Negative moment at an interior column in width b_b	Not less than 0.05 to 0.15, with the remaining negative moment assumed evenly distributed over the entire frame width
Negative moment at an exterior column	1.00
Positive moment at all spans where $(\ell_1/\ell_2) \geq 1.0$	0.50 to 0.60
Positive moment at all spans where $(\ell_1/\ell_2) < 1.0$	$0.5\,(\ell_1/\ell_2)$ to $0.6\,(\ell_1/\ell_2)$

13.11.2.6

For negative moment at an exterior column in slabs with spandrel beams, the requirements specified in Clause 13.11.2.2 b) or 13.11.2.3 b) shall apply.

13.11.2.7

Except as permitted in Clause 13.11.2.5, at interior columns, the band width, b_b, shall be designed to resist at least one-third of the total factored negative moment in the entire design strip.

13.11.3 Factored moments in middle strips

13.11.3.1

That portion of negative and positive factored moments not resisted by column strips shall be proportionately assigned to corresponding half middle strips.

13.11.3.2

Each middle strip shall be proportioned to resist the sum of the factored moments assigned to its two half middle strips.

13.11.3.3

A middle strip adjacent to and parallel with an edge supported by a wall shall be proportioned to resist twice the factored moment assigned to the half middle strip corresponding to the first row of interior supports.

13.11.3.4

At slab edges, the requirements specified in Clause 13.10.9 shall be satisfied.

13.12 Reinforcement for slabs with beams between all supports

13.12.1 General

In addition to the requirements specified in Clause 13.10, slabs with beams designed as specified in Clauses 13.8 and 13.9 shall be reinforced for flexure as specified in Clauses 13.12.2 to 13.12.5.

13.12.2 Factored moments in beams

13.12.2.1

Beams shall be reinforced to resist the following fraction of the positive or interior negative factored moments determined by analysis or determined as specified in Clause 13.9.3:

$$\frac{\alpha_1}{0.3 + \alpha_1}\left(1 - \frac{\ell_2}{3\ell_1}\right)$$

13.12.2.2

Beams shall be proportioned for 100% of the exterior negative moment.

13.12.2.3

In addition to moments calculated for uniform loads applied to the slab as specified in Clauses 13.12.2.1 and 13.12.2.2, beams shall be proportioned to resist moments caused by concentrated or linear loads applied directly to the beams, including the weight of the beam stem.

13.12.3 Slab reinforcement for positive moment

The slab shall be reinforced to resist the factored positive moments not supported by the beams. This reinforcement may be distributed uniformly over the width of the slab.

13.12.4 Slab reinforcement for negative moment

13.12.4.1 Interior supports

The slab shall be reinforced to resist the interior negative moments not resisted by the beams. This reinforcement shall be uniformly distributed over the width of the slab.

13.12.4.2 Exterior supports

The reinforcement for the exterior factored negative moment in the beam shall be placed within a band with a width b_b unless calculations show that reinforcement placed outside this limit can develop its full capacity.

13.12.5 Corner reinforcement

13.12.5.1

In slabs with beams between supports with a value of α greater than 1.0, top and bottom slab reinforcement shall be provided at exterior corners for a distance, in each direction, equal to one-fifth of the shorter span.

13.12.5.2

The reinforcement shall be sufficient to resist a moment per unit width equal to the maximum positive moment per unit width in the slab.

13.12.5.3

The reinforcement at the top of the slab shall be provided to resist moments about axes perpendicular to the diagonal from the corner. The bottom reinforcement shall be provided to resist moments about axes parallel to the diagonal. The reinforcement may be placed in bands parallel to the sides of the slab.

14 Walls

Note: *See Clause 3.1 under "Wall" for wall type definitions.*

14.1 General requirements for all walls

14.1.1 Application

Clauses 14.1.2 to 14.4.6 shall apply to the design of walls, except where the additional requirements specified in Clauses 16 and 21 to 23 apply.

14.1.2 Lateral support of walls

Walls shall be considered laterally supported if
a) walls or other vertical bracing elements are arranged in two directions so as to provide lateral stability to the structure as a whole; and
b) connections between the wall and its lateral supports are designed to resist a horizontal force not less than 2% of the total factored vertical load that the wall is designed to carry at the level of the lateral support, but not less than 5 kN per metre length of the wall.

14.1.3 Design length of wall for the distribution of concentrated vertical loads

14.1.3.1

In lieu of a detailed analysis, each concentrated compressive vertical load acting on a wall shall be assumed to be uniformly distributed over a horizontal length ℓ_b of wall. At any position below the level of the concentrated load, the portion of ℓ_b on each side of the centre of the concentrated load shall be one-half of the width of the bearing plus the width enclosed by a line sloping downward at two vertical to one horizontal on each side, limited by intersection with the end of the wall. This stressed width shall not be assumed to exceed nine times the wall thickness on each side of the bearing area. For a wall subjected to more than one concentrated load, the design shall take into account the overlapping of uniformly distributed loads from each of the concentrated loads.

14.1.3.2

Cracking resulting from transverse tensile stresses caused by the spread of the concentrated loads acting on the wall shall be taken into account in the design.

Note: *Strut-and-tie models can be used to compute the amount of reinforcement required to resist the transverse force under bearing loads and to control cracking.*

14.1.4 Columns built integrally with walls

Columns built integrally with walls shall be designed as specified in Clause 10, with outside dimensions that comply with Clause 10.11.2.

14.1.5 Transfer of vertical wall loads through floor

When the specified compressive strength of the concrete in the walls, f'_{cw}, exceeds that specified for the floor, f'_{cs}, the strength of a wall-to-floor joint shall be determined using the lower of the concrete strengths in the wall and the floor. The strength of this joint can be increased by adding dowels or by increasing the strength of the concrete in the floor under and adjacent to the wall. Such concrete shall extend at least 500 mm into the floor from each face of the wall.

14.1.6 Transfer of horizontal wall forces across construction joints

Transfer of horizontal wall forces across construction joints shall be as specified in Clause 11.5. The area of the reinforcement crossing the shear plane shall be the larger of
a)   the reinforcement area provided for flexure and axial loads; and
b)   the reinforcement area required for shear friction.

In flanged walls, only the vertical reinforcement in those portions of the section assumed to resist horizontal shear shall be included in this calculation.

14.1.7 Minimum thickness of walls

14.1.7.1 Bearing walls and shear walls

The thickness of bearing walls and the webs and flanges of shear walls shall be not less than the smaller of $\ell_w/25$ or $h_u/25$, but not less than 150 mm.

14.1.7.2 Non-bearing walls

The thickness of non-bearing walls shall be not less than 1/30 of the unsupported height or length, whichever is shorter, or less than 100 mm.

14.1.8 Details of wall reinforcement

14.1.8.1 Distributed and concentrated reinforcement

Walls shall have distributed vertical and horizontal reinforcement in layers in accordance with Clauses 14.1.8.2 to 14.1.8.7. Walls shall also have concentrated vertical reinforcement in accordance with Clause 14.1.8.8.

14.1.8.2 Maximum diameter of distributed reinforcement

The diameter of bars used for distributed reinforcement shall not exceed one-tenth of the wall thickness.

14.1.8.3 Number of layers of wall reinforcement

Except for exterior basement walls or retaining walls, bearing or shear walls more than 210 mm thick shall have the reinforcement for each direction placed in two layers. Each layer shall be placed not more than $t/3$ from the surface of the wall.

14.1.8.4 Spacing of reinforcement

The vertical and horizontal reinforcement in each layer shall not be spaced farther apart than three times the wall thickness or 500 mm, whichever is less.

14.1.8.5 Distributed vertical reinforcement

The minimum area of distributed vertical reinforcement between boundary elements shall be $0.0015A_g$.

14.1.8.6 Distributed horizontal reinforcement

The minimum area of distributed horizontal reinforcement shall be $0.002A_g$. However, where crack control is critical or wall geometry or the length of the wall between joints causes significant restraint of shrinkage or thermal strains, reinforcement additional to that specified in this Clause, or other crack control measures, shall be considered.

14.1.8.7 Ties for distributed vertical compression reinforcement

Distributed vertical reinforcement required as compression reinforcement shall be tied and detailed in accordance with the requirements for column reinforcement specified in Clause 7, except that ties may be omitted if
a)   the area of vertical steel is less than $0.005A_g$; and
b)   the bar size is 20M or smaller.

14.1.8.8 Concentrated vertical reinforcement

14.1.8.8.1 Nominal concentrated vertical reinforcement

Concentrated vertical reinforcement consisting of not fewer than two 15M vertical bars shall be provided at each end of all walls.

14.1.8.8.2 Reinforcement for flexure

Concentrated vertical reinforcement shall be provided in boundary elements of shear walls to provide that part of the resistance to strong-axis bending not provided by the reinforcement specified in Clause 14.1.8.5.

14.1.8.8.3 Concentrated vertical reinforcement limits

The reinforcement ratio within any region of concentrated reinforcement, including regions containing lap splices, shall be not more than 0.08.

14.1.8.8.4 Ties for concentrated vertical reinforcement

Concentrated vertical reinforcement in excess of two 20M bars shall be tied and detailed as specified in Clause 7.

14.1.8.9 Reinforcement at openings

In addition to the reinforcement required by Clauses 14.1.8.5, 14.1.8.6, and 14.1.8.8.1, not less than one 15M bar per layer, or reinforcement having the same area, shall be provided around all window and door or similar openings. Such bars shall extend to develop the bar, but not less than 600 mm beyond each corner of the opening.

14.2 Structural design of bearing walls

14.2.1

Except as permitted by Clause 14.2.2, bearing walls shall be designed as specified in Clauses 7, 10, and 11.

14.2.2

14.2.2.1

Subject to the requirements specified in Clause 14.2.2.2, bearing walls may be designed using the following equation:

$$P_r = \frac{2}{3} \alpha_1 \phi_c f_c' A_g \left(1 - \left(\frac{kh_u}{32t} \right)^2 \right)$$

Equation 14.1

14.2.2.2

Clause 14.2.2.1 shall apply only if the following requirements are met:
a)   the wall has a solid rectangular cross-section that is constant over the height of the wall;
b)   the principal moments act about a horizontal axis parallel to the plane of the wall;
c)   the resultant of all factored axial loads, including the effects of the principal moment, is located within the middle third of the overall wall thickness; and
d)   the wall is supported against lateral displacement along at least the top and bottom edges.

14.2.2.3

The effective length factor, *k*, in Equation 14.1 shall have the following values:

For walls restrained against rotation at one or both ends (top, bottom, or both)	0.8
For walls unrestrained against rotation at both ends	1.0

14.2.3

If present, the calculation of the factored resistance of bearing walls shall account for significant strong axis bending moments in accordance with Clause 10.

Note: *Strong axis bending moments may be applied to bearing walls due to the resultant of the axial load not being at the centroid of the section due to in-plane offset of the wall or may be induced by deformation of the lateral force resisting system subjected to the factored lateral loads such as wind and seismic loads.*

14.3 Structural design of non-bearing walls

Non-bearing walls, including retaining walls and transversely loaded walls, shall be designed in accordance with the provisions of Clauses 10 and 11.

14.4 Structural design of shear walls

14.4.1 General
In addition to the requirements specified elsewhere in Clause 14, the following shall apply to shear walls:
a)   flexural shear walls shall be designed for factored axial load, factored moment about one or both axes, and factored shear as specified in Clauses 10 and 11; and
b)   squat shear walls may be designed using strut-and-tie models in accordance with Clause 11.4 and the applicable provisions of Clause 14.1.

14.4.2 Design of flexural shear walls
14.4.2.1 General
The design of flexural shear walls shall satisfy either Clause 14.4.2.2 or Clause 14.4.2.3.

14.4.2.2 Low axial compression
When the factored axial compression applied to a wall is such that the tension reinforcement will reach yield in accordance with Clause 10.5.2, the compression end of the wall shall have a wall thickness of at least $h_u/20$ unless
a)   the compression strain depth, c, is smaller than the lesser of $4b_w$ or $0.3\ell_w$ or;
b)   a continuous line of lateral support is provided to the compression end of the wall by a cross wall or wall flange having a width not less than $h_u/5$.

14.4.2.3 High axial compression
When the factored axial compression applied to a wall is such that the tension reinforcement will not reach yield in accordance with Clause 10.5.2, the design of the wall shall consider slenderness effects. However, the influence of wall slenderness need not apply to any part of a wall that lies within a distance of $3b_w$ from a continuous line of lateral support provided by a cross wall or a flange having a width not less than $h_u/5$.

The required thickness of a wall subjected to the factored axial compression and moment about the strong axis may be determined using a reduced length of wall. The reduced length of wall shall be such that the resultant axial force representing axial load and moment acts at the centre of the reduced length. The thickness of the wall shall satisfy the slenderness requirements of Clause 10.15 for the factored axial load applied to the reduced length of wall.

14.4.3 Assemblies of interconnected shear walls

14.4.3.1 Shear connection
In assemblies of interconnected shear walls designed to act as a unit, reinforcement shall be provided to transmit the shear stresses necessary for the assembly of interconnected walls to act as a unit.

14.4.3.2 Compression flanges of assemblies of interconnected shear walls
If a compression flange of an assembly of interconnected shear walls has a thickness less than $h_c/15$, or less than $w_c/15$ if adjacent shear wall webs are present, the factored axial and moment resistances of the wall assembly shall both be multiplied by

$$\omega = 1.0 - 0.025(\ell_c/t - 15)$$ **Equation 14.2**

where ℓ_c is the lesser of w_c and h_c and ω shall not be less than 0.75 or greater than 1.0.

14.4.3.3 Maximum widths of overhanging flanges

The effective widths of overhanging flanges of walls shall not be assumed to extend farther from the face of the web than the smaller of
a) half the clear distance to an adjacent shear wall web; or
b) 25% of the total wall height above the section under consideration.

14.4.4 Horizontal reinforcement in shear walls

Horizontal reinforcement shall extend to the ends of the wall with horizontal reinforcement required for shear to be anchored in accordance with Clause 12.13.2 or anchored within regions of concentrated reinforcement at the ends of the wall.

14.4.5 Weak axis bending

Weak axis bending of shear walls shall be considered in conjunction with strong axis bending.

14.4.6 Diaphragms

Floor and roof diaphragms shall be designed to transfer lateral forces between walls or other lateral-load-resisting elements and floor and roof diaphragms. Connections between the diaphragms and the frames or other lateral-load-resisting elements shall be designed to resist the forces that are transferred.

14.4.7 Coupling beams

The diameter of flexural reinforcing bars in coupling beams shall be selected to provide a development length not more than one-half of the clear beam span. Alternatively, diagonal reinforcement shall be provided as specified in Clause 21.5.8.2. However, ties satisfying the requirements specified in Clause 7.6 may be provided in lieu of hoops or spirals.

15 Foundations

15.1 General

Clauses 15.2 to 15.12 shall apply to the design of isolated footings and, where applicable, to combined footings, mats, and deep foundations.

15.2 Loads and reactions

15.2.1

Footings, piles, and pile caps shall be proportioned to resist the factored loads and induced reactions.

15.2.2

The base area of the footing or the number and arrangement of piles shall be selected based on the principles of soil mechanics. Where the analysis of footings is based on other than linear distributions of soil pressure, the assumed distributions shall be based on an analysis of the interaction of the soil and the footing in accordance with the stiffness of both elements.

15.2.3

Piles and pile caps in deep foundations shall be designed on the assumption that each axial pile reaction acts at an eccentricity, in any direction, equal to the specified pile location tolerance, but not less than 50 mm.

15.3 Footings and pile caps supporting circular or regular polygonal columns or pedestals

In lieu of detailed analysis, circular or regular polygonal concrete columns or pedestals may be treated as square members, with the same area, for the location of critical sections for moment, shear, and development of reinforcement in the footings or pile caps.

15.4 Flexural design of footings

15.4.1

Design for flexure shall meet the requirements of Clause 10.

Note: *For many types of footings, the strut-and-tie method specified in Clause 11.4 can be used for design.*

15.4.2

The external moment on any section of a footing shall be determined by passing a vertical plane through the footing and computing the moment of the forces acting over the entire area of the footing on one side of that vertical plane.

15.4.3

The maximum factored moment for an isolated footing shall be computed at the critical sections located as follows:

a) for footings supporting a concrete column, pedestal, or wall: at the face of the column, pedestal, or wall;

b) for footings supporting a masonry wall: halfway between the middle and the edge of the wall; and

c) for footings supporting a column with steel base plates: as determined by considering the dimensions and the stiffness of the base plate.

Note: *In many cases, the critical section can be taken halfway between the face of the column and the edge of the base plate.*

15.4.4

15.4.4.1

In two-way rectangular footings, reinforcement shall be distributed as follows:

a) reinforcement in the long direction shall be distributed uniformly across the entire width of the footing; and

b) for reinforcement in the short direction, a portion of the total reinforcement specified in Clause 15.4.4.2 shall be distributed uniformly over a band width (centred on the centreline of the column or pedestal) equal to the length of the short side of the footing or equal to the length of the supported wall or column, whichever is greater. The remainder of the reinforcement required in the short direction shall be distributed uniformly outside the centre band width.

15.4.4.2

The portion of the total reinforcement in the short direction distributed over the band width [see Clause 15.4.4.1 b)] is as follows:

$$\frac{\text{Reinforcement in band width}}{\text{Total reinforcement in short direction}} = \frac{2}{(\beta + 1)}$$

Equation 15.1

15.5 Shear design of footings and pile caps

15.5.1

Design for shear shall meet the requirements of Clauses 11 and 13.

Note: *For many types of footings, the strut-and-tie method specified in Clause 11.4 can be used for design.*

15.5.2

The location of the critical section for shear, as specified in Clause 13.3, shall be measured from the face of the column, pedestal, or wall for footings supporting a column, pedestal, or wall. For footings supporting a column or pedestal with steel base plates, the critical section shall be measured from the location specified in Clause 15.4.3 c).

15.5.3

Shear on any section through a pile cap shall be computed in accordance with the following:

a) the entire reaction from any pile whose centre is located $d_p/2$ or more outside the section shall be considered as producing shear on that section;

b) the reaction from any pile whose centre is located $d_p/2$ or more inside the section shall be considered as producing no shear on that section; and

c) for intermediate positions of the pile centre, the portion of the pile reaction to be considered as producing shear on the section shall be based on a straight-line interpolation between the full value at $d_p/2$ outside the section and zero value at $d_p/2$ inside the section.

15.6 Development of reinforcement in footings and pile caps

15.6.1

The development of reinforcement in footings and pile caps shall be computed in accordance with Clause 12.

15.6.2

When the strut-and-tie method is used, the development of tension reinforcement shall be as specified in Clause 11.4.3.2.

15.6.3

The critical sections for development of reinforcement shall be assumed to be at the locations specified in Clause 15.4.3 for the maximum factored moment and at all other vertical planes where changes of section or reinforcement occur. See also Clause 12.10.5.

15.7 Minimum depth of footings

The depth of footings above the bottom reinforcement shall be not less than 150 mm.

15.8 Piles

15.8.1 Design of piles

The moments and shears in the piles caused by lateral loads shall be calculated using procedures that account for the pile-soil interaction and non-linear soil behaviour.

15.8.2 Special requirements for piles

15.8.2.1

The stability of portions of piles without lateral restraint from soil shall be assessed as specified in Clause 10.

15.8.2.2

The outer 25 mm concrete layer of uncased drilled piles shall be neglected when the factored resistance of the pile shaft and the end-bearing resistance is determined.

15.8.2.3

For uncased drilled piles, a reduction factor of 0.90 shall be applied to the factored resistance specified in Clauses 10 and 11.

15.8.2.4

Selection of the pile bell diameter and bell side slope shall be based on the concrete shear resistance and the type of the soil (see ACI 336.3R).

15.8.2.5

For the seismic design of piles, the additional requirements specified in Clause 21.11.4 shall be met.

15.8.2.6

Where required by applicable codes, piles shall be interconnected.

15.8.3 Minimum depth of pile caps

The depth of pile caps above the bottom reinforcement and above the top of the pile shall be not less than 300 mm.

15.9 Transfer of force at base of column, pile cap, wall, or pedestal

15.9.1 General

15.9.1.1

The forces and moments at the base of a column, pile cap, wall, or pedestal shall be transferred to the supporting footing or pile.

15.9.1.2

Bearing on concrete at the contact surface between the supported and supporting members shall not exceed the factored bearing resistance of either member specified in Clause 10.8.

15.9.1.3

Reinforcement, dowels, or mechanical connectors between supported and supporting members shall be adequate to transfer

a)   all compressive force that exceeds the concrete bearing strength of either member; and

b)   any computed tensile force across the interface.

In addition, reinforcement, dowels, or mechanical connectors shall meet the requirements of Clause 12 and of Clause 15.9.2.2 or 15.9.2.3.

15.9.1.4

Lateral forces shall be transferred to the supporting pedestals, caps, piles, and footings in accordance with the interface shear transfer requirements of Clause 11.5 or by other appropriate means.

15.9.2 Cast-in-place construction

15.9.2.1

For columns, pile caps, piles, and pedestals, the area of reinforcement across the interface shall be not less than 0.005 times the gross area of the supported member.

15.9.2.2

For cast-in-place walls, the area of reinforcement across the interface shall be not less than the minimum vertical reinforcement required by Clause 14.1.8.

15.9.2.3

The size of dowels shall not exceed the size of the vertical bars by more than one bar size.

15.9.2.4

At footings, 45M and 55M longitudinal bars (in compression only) may be lap spliced with dowels to provide the reinforcement required to satisfy Clause 15.9.1. Dowels shall not be larger than 35M and shall extend into the supported member for a distance of not less than the development length of 45M or 55M bars or the splice length of the dowels, whichever is greater, and into the footing for a distance of not less than the development length of the dowels.

15.9.2.5

If a pinned or rocker connection is provided in cast-in-place construction, the connection shall also comply with Clause 15.9.3.

15.9.3 Precast concrete construction

15.9.3.1

In precast concrete construction, the reinforcement required to satisfy Clause 15.9.1 may be provided by anchor bolts or suitable mechanical connectors.

15.9.3.2

Anchor bolts and mechanical connectors shall be designed to reach their factored resistance prior to anchorage failure of the surrounding concrete.

Note: *See Annex D for more information.*

15.10 Sloped or stepped footings

15.10.1

In sloped or stepped footings, the angle of the slope or the depth and location of the steps shall be such that design requirements are satisfied at every section.

15.10.2

Sloped or stepped footings designed as a unit shall be constructed to ensure action as a unit.

15.11 Combined footings and mats

15.11.1

Footings supporting more than one column, pedestal, or wall (combined footings or mats) shall be proportioned, in accordance with the applicable design requirements of this Standard, to resist the factored loads and induced reactions.

15.11.2

The distribution of soil pressure under combined footings and mats shall be consistent with the properties of the soil and the structure and with the established principles of soil mechanics.

15.12 Plain concrete footings and deep foundations

Plain concrete footings and deep foundations shall comply with Clause 22.

16 Precast concrete

16.1 General

16.1.1

All requirements of this Standard not specifically excluded and not in conflict with the requirements of Clauses 16.1.2 to 16.5.3.7 shall apply to structures incorporating precast concrete elements.
Note: *See CSA A23.4 for the suggested division of design responsibilities between the designer and the precast concrete manufacturer.*

16.1.2

Clauses 7.7, 7.8, 10.4, and 13 shall not apply to precast concrete.

16.1.3

For elements produced in manufacturing plants prequalified in accordance with CSA A23.4, the concrete material resistance factor, ϕ_c, specified in Clause 8.4.2 of this Standard may be taken as 0.70.

16.2 Prequalification of manufacturer

16.2.1

All precast concrete elements covered by this Standard shall be manufactured and erected in accordance with CSA A23.4.

16.2.2

Exemptions to the requirements specified in Clause 16.2.1 may be made by the designer of the building for the following reinforced concrete elements:

a)   minor structural elements such as stair flights, stair landings, lintels, and sills; and

b)   precast slabs for lift slab construction.

The designer shall clearly indicate whether such reinforced precast elements are to be manufactured in accordance with CSA A23.4, in which case certification shall be required, or in accordance with CSA A23.1, in which case the certification requirement may be waived by the designer.

16.3 Drawings

In addition to the requirements specified in Clause 5, drawings and related documents shall include the following:

a)   sufficient dimensions to permit preparation of the shop drawings;

b)   sufficient indication of the work supporting, supported by, or attached to the precast concrete to permit preparation of the shop drawings;

c)   the class of surface finish required for structural purposes;

d)   any non-standard tolerances required for the precast concrete elements or the building structure;

e)   any superimposed loads on the precast concrete elements, the location of connections, and the factored forces to be developed at the connections to the elements;

f)   when precast elements are to act as diaphragms, the factored external forces and shears acting on the diaphragms; and

g)   the expected deformations of the structure under specified loads, insofar as they affect the design of the precast concrete elements or associated connections. Deformations due to specified earthquake loads shall be shown separately.

16.4 Design

16.4.1 General

16.4.1.1

The design shall take into account loading and restraint conditions from the initial fabrication to the intended use of the structure, including forces from stripping, storage, transportation, and erection.

16.4.1.2

The effects of initial and long-term deformations shall be considered, including the effects on interconnected elements.

16.4.2 Distribution of forces among elements

16.4.2.1

The distribution of forces that are perpendicular to the plane of the elements shall be established by analysis or test.

16.4.2.2

In-plane forces shall be transferred between the elements of a precast floor or wall system in accordance with the following:

a)   load paths for in-plane forces shall be transferred through both connections and elements;

b)   where tension forces occur, a load path of reinforcement or tendons shall be provided; and
c)   the design of joints, connections, and bearings shall include the effects of all forces to be transmitted, including the effects of specified loads, tolerances, elastic deformation, temperature, creep, and shrinkage.

16.4.3 Reinforcement of precast concrete elements

16.4.3.1
The minimum reinforcement ratio in each direction shall be not less than 0.0016 for reinforcement or 0.0004 for prestressing tendons, except as permitted by Clauses 16.4.3.2 and 16.4.3.3. Additional reinforcement shall be provided at openings and other discontinuities.

16.4.3.2
For one-way floor and roof slabs and for one-way precast, prestressed wall panels, all not exceeding 3660 mm in width, and where elements are not connected to cause restraint in the transverse direction, the minimum transverse reinforcement requirements of Clause 16.4.3.1 may be waived.

16.4.3.3
For non-prestressed walls, the minimum reinforcement ratio shall be not less than 0.001 in each direction. Spacing of reinforcement shall not exceed the smaller of five times the wall thickness or 500 mm.

16.4.4 Joints and connections

16.4.4.1
Forces shall be transferred between elements by grouted joints, shear keys, mechanical connectors, reinforcement, topping, or a combination of these means.

16.4.4.2
Precast segments, when joined and post-tensioned in accordance with CSA A23.1, may be considered homogeneous structural members.

16.4.4.3
The design of each component of a connection shall be based on the most severe combination of load eccentricities, as limited by fabrication and erection tolerances.

16.4.4.4
Special attention shall be given to the design of connections when there is a possibility of corrosion, and in particular to connections in inaccessible locations in the finished structure.

16.4.4.5
Provision for movement of elements due to earthquake shall accommodate $R_d R_o / I_E$ times the elastic deflection of the lateral force resisting system.

Note: *See the* National Building Code of Canada *for more information.*

16.4.4.6

In the design of connections that accommodate movement by deformation of the connection material, consideration shall be given to the magnitude and frequency of the movement and to the fatigue properties and ductility of the connection.

16.4.4.7

In the design of connections that accommodate movement by sliding, the increase of friction due to the tightness of the fastening, the effects of corrosion, and construction tolerances shall be taken into account.

Note: *For connections whose capacity is sensitive to erection tolerances and for connections in inaccessible locations that can be subject to corrosive conditions, connection resistance should be increased.*

16.4.5 Bearing

16.4.5.1

The allowable bearing stress at the contact surface between supported and supporting elements and between any intermediate bearing elements shall not exceed the bearing resistance for either surface as specified in Clause 10.8 or 11.4.4.

16.4.5.2

Unless tests or analysis show that performance will not be impaired, the following minimum requirements shall be met:
a) Each member and its supporting system shall have design dimensions selected so that, after consideration of tolerances, the distance from the edge of the support to the end of the precast member in the direction of the span is at least 1/180 of the clear span, ℓ_n, but not less than the following:

For solid or hollow-core slabs	50 mm
For beams or stemmed members	75 mm

b) Bearing pads at unarmoured edges shall be set back a minimum of 12 mm from the face of the support or the chamfer dimension at chamfered edges, whichever is larger.

16.5 Structural integrity

16.5.1

In buildings where precast concrete elements constitute a portion of the structural system, all structural elements shall be effectively tied together.

16.5.2

16.5.2.1

Except as specified in Clause 16.5.3, precast concrete structures shall meet the structural integrity requirements specified in Clauses 16.5.2.2 to 16.5.2.6.

Note: *Guidance on designing for structural integrity of structural systems incorporating precast elements can be obtained from the following publications:*
a) *ACI-ASCE Joint Committee 550, "Design recommendations for precast concrete structures";*
b) *Canadian Precast/Prestressed Concrete Institute, Design manual;*

c)   *Cement Association of Canada,* Concrete design handbook*; and*
d)   *Precast/Prestressed Concrete Institute,* PCI design handbook*.*

16.5.2.2

Longitudinal and transverse tensile tie reinforcement shall be incorporated so as to provide a load path to the lateral load resisting system, as specified in Clause 16.4.2.2 b).

16.5.2.3

Where precast elements form floor or roof diaphragms, the connections between the diaphragm and those elements being laterally supported shall be designed for all factored loads but shall have a factored tensile resistance of not less than 5 kN/m.

16.5.2.4

Vertical tension tie requirements shall apply to the horizontal joints in all vertical structural elements, except cladding, and shall meet the following requirements:
a)   precast columns shall have a factored tensile resistance of not less than $1.4A_g$ N;
b)   for columns with a larger cross-section than required by analysis, a reduced effective area may be substituted for A_g, but it shall be not less than $A_g/2$; and
c)   precast wall panels shall have a minimum of two ties per panel, with a factored resistance of not less than 30 kN per tie.

16.5.2.5

When factored forces and moments result in compression at the base, the ties required by Clause 16.5.2.4 c) may be anchored to the floor slab on grade.

16.5.2.6

Ties and connections shall be designed in such a manner that the resistance is governed by yielding of the steel component.

16.5.3

16.5.3.1

Structures that are three or more storeys high and are constructed with precast concrete bearing walls shall be tied together as specified in Clauses 16.5.3.2 to 16.5.3.5.

16.5.3.2

Tension ties shall be incorporated in floor and roof systems to provide a factored resistance of not less than 14 kN per metre of horizontal wall length for longitudinal ties and 14 kN per metre of floor or roof span for transverse ties. Tie paths shall be provided over interior wall supports and to exterior walls. Ties shall be located in the floor or roof system or within 600 mm of the plane of the floor or roof system.

16.5.3.3

Longitudinal tension ties parallel to the floor or roof spans shall be spaced not more than 3000 mm on centres. Provisions shall be made to transfer forces around openings.

CSA Group standard A23.3-14

16.5.3.4

Transverse tension ties perpendicular to the span of the floor or roof shall be spaced at a distance not greater than the distance between the bearing walls.

16.5.3.5

Tension ties around the perimeter of each floor and roof, within 1500 mm of the edge, shall provide a factored tensile resistance of not less than 60 kN.

16.5.3.6

Vertical tension ties shall be provided in all walls and shall be continuous over the full height of the building. They shall provide a factored tensile resistance of not less than 40 kN per metre of horizontal wall length. Not fewer than two tension ties shall be provided for each precast wall panel.

16.5.3.7

During checking for structural integrity, any beneficial effects of friction caused by gravity loads shall not be considered for the transfer of horizontal loads.

17 Composite concrete flexural members

Note: *This Clause uses the terms "transverse shear" and "longitudinal shear". For a composite beam with a horizontal axis, "transverse shear" refers to vertical shear forces and "longitudinal shear" refers to shear on a horizontal plane.*

17.1 General

17.1.1

Clauses 17.1.2 to 17.5.4 shall apply to the design of composite concrete flexural members consisting of concrete elements constructed in separate placements, but interconnected in such a manner that all elements act as a unit.

17.1.2

All of the requirements of this Standard shall apply to composite flexural members, except where modified by Clauses 17.1.3 to 17.5.4.

17.1.3

An entire composite member or portions thereof may be assumed to resist shear and moment.

17.1.4

Individual elements shall be investigated for all critical stages of loading.

17.1.5

If the specified strength, density, or other properties of the elements differ, the properties of the individual elements shall be used for the analysis.

Note: *Differential creep and shrinkage can affect the distributions of strains and deformations in the individual elements.*

17.1.6

In strength computations for composite members, no distinction shall be made between shored and unshored members.

17.1.7

All elements shall be designed to support all loads introduced prior to full development of the design strength of composite members.

17.1.8

Reinforcement shall be provided, as necessary, to control cracking and prevent separation of individual elements of composite members.

17.1.9

Composite members shall meet the requirements for control of deflections specified in Clause 9.8.

17.2 Shoring

When used, shoring shall not be removed until the supported elements have developed the design properties required to support all loads and to limit deflections and cracking at the time of shoring removal.

17.3 Transverse shear resistance

17.3.1

When an entire composite member is assumed to resist transverse shear, the design shall meet the requirements specified in Clause 11 for a monolithically cast member of the same cross-sectional shape.

17.3.2

Shear reinforcement shall be fully anchored into interconnected elements as specified in Clause 12.13.

17.4 Longitudinal shear resistance

17.4.1

For a composite member, steps shall be taken to ensure full transfer of the longitudinal shear forces at the contact surfaces of the interconnected elements.

17.4.2

Longitudinal shear shall be investigated in accordance with Clause 17.4.3 or 17.4.4.

17.4.3

17.4.3.1

Unless calculated as specified in Clause 17.4.4, the design of cross-sections subject to longitudinal shear shall be based on

$$V_{r\ell} \geq V_f \hspace{4cm} \text{Equation 17.1}$$

17.4.3.2

When contact surfaces are clean, free of laitance, and intentionally roughened, the factored longitudinal shear resistance, $V_{r\ell}$, shall not be taken as greater than $0.7\phi_c\, b_v\, d$ unless ties are provided to transfer longitudinal shear.

17.4.3.3

When minimum ties are provided as specified in Clause 17.5 and contact surfaces are clean and free of laitance but not intentionally roughened, the factored longitudinal shear resistance, $V_{r\ell}$, shall not be taken as greater than $0.7\phi_c\, b_v\, d$.

17.4.3.4

When the factored shear force, V_f, at the section being considered exceeds $0.7\phi_c\, b_v\, d$, the design for longitudinal shear shall be as specified in Clause 11.5.

17.4.4

Longitudinal shear may be investigated by computing the actual compressive or tensile force in any segment and provisions shall be made to transfer that force as longitudinal shear to the supporting element. The factored longitudinal shear force shall not exceed the factored longitudinal shear resistance, $V_{r\ell}$, as specified in Clauses 17.4.3.2 to 17.4.3.4, with the area of contact surface, A_{cv}, substituted for $b_v\, d$.

17.4.5

When tension exists across any contact surface between interconnected elements, shear transfer by contact may be assumed only when minimum ties are provided as specified in Clause 17.5.

17.5 Ties for longitudinal shear

17.5.1

When ties are provided to transfer longitudinal shear, the tie area shall be not less than that required by Clause 11.2.8, and the tie spacing shall not exceed four times the least dimension of the supported element or 600 mm, whichever is less.

17.5.2

Ties for longitudinal shear shall consist of a single bar or wire, multiple leg stirrups, vertical legs, or welded wire fabric (smooth or deformed).

17.5.3

Ties shall be anchored into the interconnected elements as specified in Clause 12.13.

17.5.4

Reinforcement for transverse shear that is anchored into the interconnected elements as specified in Clause 12.13 may be included as ties for longitudinal shear.

18 Prestressed concrete

18.1 General

18.1.1

Clauses 18.1.2 to 18.13.4 shall apply to members prestressed with wires, strands, or bars that comply with the requirements for prestressing steels specified in Clause 4.1.4 and in CSA A23.1.

Note: *Unbonded tendons are more susceptible to corrosion than bonded tendons. The durability of structures with unbonded prestressing tendons is a function of the environment, occupancy type, and quality of work during construction. Ingress of moisture or chlorides, sulphides, nitrates, carbonates, or other industrial, food processing, or agricultural chemicals can cause corrosion or even failure of the tendons. Water, including rainwater, can enter the sheath during tendon shipping, storage, or construction, and in some cases after occupancy of the structure, if adequate protection is not provided. Materials and quality of work should meet the requirements specified in CSA A23.1.*

18.1.2

All of the requirements of this Standard not specifically excluded and not in conflict with the requirements specified in Clauses 18.1.1 and 18.1.3 to 18.13.4 shall apply to prestressed concrete.

18.1.3

The requirements specified in Clauses 10.3.3, 10.3.4, 10.4, 10.5.1, 10.5.2, 10.6.2, 10.9, 13, 14.1.7.2, and 14.2 shall not apply to prestressed concrete unless otherwise specified.

18.1.4

Prestressed members shall meet the strength requirements specified in this Standard.

18.1.5

The effects of the loads at all loading stages that could be critical during the life of the member from the time the prestress is first applied shall be considered.

18.1.6

The stresses in prestressed members at transfer and under specified loads shall satisfy the requirements of Clause 18.3.

18.1.7

Stress concentrations due to prestressing shall be considered. Adequately anchored transverse reinforcement shall be provided to control splitting.

18.1.8

The deflection of prestressed concrete members shall be determined as specified in Clause 9.8.4.

18.1.9

When adjoining parts of the structure can restrain the elastic and long-term deformations (deflections, changes in length, and rotation) of a member caused by prestressing, applied loading, foundation settlement, temperature, and shrinkage, the restraint shall be estimated and its effects on the member and on the restraining structure shall be considered.

18.1.10

The possibility of buckling in a member between points where concrete and prestressing tendons are in contact and of buckling in thin webs and flanges shall be considered.

18.1.11

In computing section properties, the loss of area due to open ducts or conduits shall be considered.

18.2 Design assumptions for flexure and axial load

18.2.1

The design of prestressed members for flexure and axial loads shall be based on the assumptions specified in Clause 10.1.

18.2.2

For investigation of the stress limits specified in Clauses 18.3 and 18.4, linear elastic material behaviour may be assumed. Concrete may be assumed to resist tension at sections that are uncracked.

18.3 Permissible stresses in concrete flexural members

18.3.1

18.3.1.1

Stresses in concrete immediately after prestress transfer due to prestress, and the specified loads present at transfer, shall not exceed the following:

a) Extreme fibre stress in compression except as permitted by Item b)	$0.6f'_{ci}$
b) Extreme fibre stress in compression at ends of simply supported members	$0.67f'_{ci}$
c) Extreme fibre stress in tension, except as permitted by Item d)	$0.25\lambda\sqrt{f'_{ci}}$
d) Extreme fibre stress in tension at ends of simply supported members	$0.5\lambda\sqrt{f'_{ci}}$

18.3.1.2

The stress specified in Clause 18.3.1.1 a) may be exceeded if tests or analyses demonstrate that performance will not be impaired.

18.3.1.3

Where computed tensile stresses exceed the values specified in Items b) and c) of Clause 18.3.1.1, bonded reinforcement with a minimum area of $A_s = N_c / (0.5f_y)$ shall be provided in the tensile zone to resist the total tensile force, N_c, in the concrete computed on the basis of an uncracked section.

18.3.2

Stresses in concrete under specified loads and prestress (after allowance for all prestress losses) shall not exceed the following:

a) Extreme fibre stress in compression due to sustained loads	$0.45f_c'$
b) Extreme fibre stress in compression due to total load	$0.60f_c'$
c) Extreme fibre stress in tension in precompressed tensile zone, except as specified in Clause 18.3.3	$0.50\lambda\sqrt{f_c'}$
d) Extreme fibre stress in tension in precompressed tensile zone exposed to a corrosive environment	$0.25\lambda\sqrt{f_c'}$

18.3.3

18.3.3.1
Partially prestressed members may exceed the requirements specified in Clause 18.3.2 c) provided that tests or analyses demonstrate adequate fatigue resistance as well as adequate deflection and crack control under specified loads.

18.3.3.2
Partially prestressed members not subjected to fatigue conditions and not exposed to a corrosive environment may be deemed to have adequate deflection and crack control if the requirements of Clauses 9.8.4 and 18.8 are met.

18.4 Permissible stresses in tendons
Tensile stress in tendons shall not exceed the following:

Stress due to tendon jacking force for post-tensioning tendons	$0.85f_{pu}$, but not greater than $0.94f_{py}$
Stress due to tendon jacking force for pretensioning tendons	$0.80f_{pu}$
Stress immediately after prestress transfer	$0.82f_{py}$, but not greater than $0.74f_{pu}$
Stress in post-tensioning tendons at anchorages and couplers immediately after tendon anchorage	$0.70f_{pu}$

However, the stress due to tendon jacking force for post-tensioning and pretensioning tendons shall not exceed the maximum value recommended by the manufacturer of the prestressing tendons or anchorages. If pretensioned tendons are subjected to a temperature drop prior to concreting, the stress at the reduced temperatures shall not exceed $0.80\,f_{pu}$.

Note: *The specified yield strength of prestressing tendons is based on the requirements specified in ASTM A 416/A 416M, ASTM A 421/A 421M, and ASTM A 722/A 722M, which specify the following minimum values for f_{py}:*
a) *low relaxation strand or wire: $0.90f_{pu}$;*
b) *stress-relieved strand or wire: $0.85f_{pu}$;*
c) *plain prestressing bars: $0.85f_{pu}$; and*
d) *deformed prestressing bars: $0.80f_{pu}$.*

18.5 Loss of prestress
To determine the effective prestress, f_{pe}, allowance for the following sources of loss of prestress shall be considered:
a)   anchorage seating loss;
b)   elastic shortening of concrete;

c)   friction loss due to intended and unintended curvature in post-tensioning tendons;
d)   creep of concrete;
e)   shrinkage of concrete; and
f)   relaxation of tendon stress.

18.6 Flexural resistance

18.6.1
Strain compatibility analyses shall be based on the stress-strain curves of the steels to be used.

18.6.2
In lieu of a more accurate determination of f_{pr} based on strain compatibility, the following approximate values of f_{pr} may be used:

a)   for members with bonded tendons, provided that c/d_p is not greater than 0.5 and f_{pe} is not less than $0.6f_{py}$:

$$f_{pr} = f_{pu}\left(1 - k_p \frac{c}{d_p}\right)$$

Equation 18.1

where
$$k_p = 2(1.04 - f_{py}/f_{pu})$$

and c shall be determined assuming a stress of f_{pr} in the tendons;

Note: *Further information can be found in the Cement Association of Canada's* Concrete design handbook.

b)   for members with unbonded tendons:

$$f_{pr} = f_{pe} + \frac{8000}{\ell_o} \sum_n \left(d_p - c_y\right) \le f_{py}$$

Equation 18.2

where
$$\sum_n \left(d_p - c_y\right) = \text{sum of the distance } d_p - c_y \text{ for each of the plastic hinges in the span under consideration and } c_y \text{ shall be determined by assuming a stress of } f_{py} \text{ in the tendons.}$$

18.6.3
Tension and compression reinforcement may be considered to contribute to the flexural resistance with forces of $\phi_s A_s f_y$ and $\phi_s A_s' f_y'$, provided that they are located at least $0.75c$ from the neutral axis. Other reinforcement may be included in resistance computations if a strain compatibility analysis is conducted to determine the stress in such reinforcement.

18.7 Minimum factored flexural resistance
At every section of a flexural member, except two-way slabs, the following shall apply:

$$M_r \ge 1.2M_{cr}$$

Equation 18.3

where
$$M_{cr} = \frac{I}{y_t}(f_{ce} + f_r)$$

where
$$f_r = 0.6\lambda\sqrt{f_c'}$$

unless the factored flexural resistance at the section is at least one-third greater than M_f.

18.8 Minimum bonded reinforcement

18.8.1

The minimum requirements for bonded reinforcement in beams and slabs shall be as specified in Table 18.1.

18.8.2

The bonded reinforcement required by Table 18.1 shall be uniformly distributed within the precompressed tensile zone as close to the extreme tensile fibre as the cover will permit.

Table 18.1
Minimum area of bonded reinforcement
(See Clauses 18.8.1, 18.8.2, and 18.9.2.)

	Concrete stress [see Clause 18.3.2 c)]			
	Tensile stress $\leq 0.5\lambda\sqrt{f_c'}$		Tensile stress $> 0.5\lambda\sqrt{f_c'}$	
	Type of tendon		Type of tendon	
Type of member	**Bonded**	**Unbonded**	**Bonded**	**Unbonded**
Beams	0	0.004A	0.003A	0.005A
One-way slabs	0	0.003A	0.002A	0.004A
Two-way slabs				
Negative moment regions	0	$0.0006h\ell_n$	$0.00045h\ell_n$	$0.00075h\ell_n$
Positive moment regions, concrete stress $> 0.2\lambda\sqrt{f_c'}$	0	0.004A	0.003A	0.005A
Positive moment regions, concrete tensile stress $\leq 0.2\lambda\sqrt{f_c'}$	0	0	—	—

18.8.3

For partially prestressed beams and one-way slabs, the distribution of the bonded tendons and reinforcement shall be such that the quantity z in Equation 10.6 does not exceed 20 kN/mm for interior exposure and 15 kN/mm for exterior exposure. In lieu of more detailed analysis, the steel stress, f_s, in Equation 10.6 may be calculated as the difference between the stress in the non-prestressed reinforcement due to the specified load moment, M_s, and the stress due to the decompression moment, M_{dc}, specified in the following equation:

$$M_{dc} = f_{ce}\frac{I}{y_t}$$

Equation 18.4

Only the bonded steel shall be considered for the calculation of A. A bonded post-tensioned cable or a bundle of pretensioned tendons may be considered as one bar of equal area or disregarded in the calculation of z.

18.9 Minimum length of bonded reinforcement

18.9.1
Where bonded reinforcement is provided for flexural resistance, the minimum length shall comply with Clause 12.

18.9.2
The minimum length of bonded reinforcement required by Table 18.1 shall be as specified in Clauses 18.9.3 and 18.9.4.

18.9.3
In positive moment areas, the minimum length of bonded reinforcement shall be one-half of the clear span length and shall be centred in the positive moment area.

18.9.4
In negative moment areas, bonded reinforcement shall extend, on each side of the support, one-sixth of the longer clear span beyond the face of the support.

18.10 Frames and continuous construction
Moments for computing the required strength shall be the sum of the moments due to reactions induced by prestressing (with a load factor of 1.0) and the moments due to factored loads specified in Clause 8.3. Where a minimum area of bonded reinforcement is provided as specified in Clause 18.8, negative moments may be redistributed as specified in Clause 9.2.4.

18.11 Compression members — Combined flexure and axial loads

18.11.1 General
The design of prestressed concrete members subject to combined flexure and axial loads shall be based on Clauses 10.9 to 10.16. The effects of prestress, creep, shrinkage, and temperature change shall be included.

18.11.2 Limits for reinforcement of prestressed compression members

18.11.2.1
Members with average prestress, f_{cp}, less than 1.5 MPa shall have the minimum reinforcement specified in Clauses 7.6 and 10.9 for columns or Clause 14.1.8 for walls.

18.11.2.2
Except for walls, members with average prestress, f_{cp}, equal to or greater than 1.5 MPa shall have all of their prestressing tendons enclosed by spirals or lateral ties as follows:
a)   spirals shall comply with Clause 7.6.4; and
b)   ties shall comply with Clause 7.6.5, excluding Clauses 7.6.5.2 a) and 7.6.5.5.

18.12 Two-way slab systems

18.12.1 General

Factored moments and shears in prestressed slab systems reinforced for flexure in two directions shall be determined as specified in Clause 13.8 or by more detailed design procedures.

18.12.2 Stresses under specified loads

18.12.2.1

When Clause 13.8 is used, flexural stresses due to unfactored gravity loads in column strips shall be determined by taking 75% of interior negative moments, 100% of exterior negative moments, and 60% of positive moments unless a more detailed analysis is performed.

18.12.2.2

Concrete stresses due to prestressing may be assumed to be uniformly distributed across the slab unless a more detailed analysis is performed.

18.12.2.3

The minimum average compressive stress, f_{cp}, shall be 0.8 MPa.

18.12.3 Shear resistance

18.12.3.1

In the vicinity of concentrated loads or reactions, the maximum factored shear stress, v_f, calculated as specified in Clauses 13.3.5 and 13.3.6, shall not exceed v_r.

18.12.3.2

The factored shear stress resistance, v_r, in two-way slabs shall be not greater than the factored shear stress resistance provided by the concrete, v_c, computed as specified in Clause 13.3.4 or 18.12.3.3, unless shear reinforcement is provided as specified in Clause 13.3.7, 13.3.8, or 13.3.9.

18.12.3.3

At columns supporting two-way slabs of uniform thickness, the factored shear stress resistance provided by the concrete shall be determined by

$$v_c = \beta_p \lambda \phi_c \sqrt{f'_c} \sqrt{1 + \frac{\phi_p f_{cp}}{0.33 \lambda \phi_c \sqrt{f'_c}}} + \frac{V_p}{b_o d}$$

Equation 18.5

where

β_p = the smaller of 0.33 or $(\alpha_s d / b_o + 0.15)$

α_s = 4 for interior columns, 3 for edge columns, and 2 for corner columns

b_o = the perimeter of the critical section specified in Clause 13.3.3

f_{cp} = the average value of f_{cp} for the two directions and shall not be taken greater than 3.5 MPa

V_p = the factored vertical component of all prestress forces crossing the critical section

f_c' shall not be taken greater than 35 MPa and the slab shall extend at least $4h_s$ from all faces of the column. Equation 13.5, 13.6, or 13.7 shall apply to edge and corner columns when the slab extends less than $4h_s$ from a column face.

18.12.4 Shear and moment transfer

The fraction of the unbalanced moment transferred by eccentricity of shear shall comply with Clause 13.3.5.3.

18.12.5 Minimum bonded non-prestressed reinforcement

18.12.5.1

The minimum requirements for bonded reinforcement in two-way slabs shall be as specified in Clauses 18.8, 18.9, and 18.12.5.2.

18.12.5.2

In negative moment areas at column supports, the bonded reinforcement, A_s, shall be distributed within a zone equal to the column width plus 1.5 times the slab thickness beyond each side of the column. At least four bars or wires shall be provided in each direction. The spacing of the bonded reinforcement shall not exceed 300 mm.

18.12.6 Spacing of tendons

18.12.6.1

The spacing of tendons or groups of tendons in one direction shall not exceed eight times the slab thickness or 1500 mm unless adequate additional bonded reinforcement is provided so that the slab has the strength to span between tendons.

18.12.6.2

Tendon spacing shall be given special consideration in slabs supporting concentrated loads.

18.12.6.3

In slabs without beams, a minimum of two tendons or bars shall be provided in each direction over each column. These tendons or bars shall satisfy the requirements specified in Clause 13.10.6.

18.13 Tendon anchorage zones

18.13.1

Post-tensioning anchorage zones shall be designed to resist the specified tensile strength of the tendons.

18.13.2

One of the following methods shall be used for the design of anchorage zones:
a) equilibrium based on strut-and-tie models (see Clause 11.4);
b) elastic stress analysis (finite element methods or equivalent);
c) methods based on tests; or
d) simplified equations where applicable.

18.13.3

End blocks shall be provided where necessary for support bearing or distribution of concentrated prestressing forces.

18.13.4

Regions of stress concentrations due to abrupt changes in section or other causes shall be adequately reinforced.

18.13.5

Three dimensional effects shall be considered in design and analyzed using three-dimensional procedures or approximated by considering the summation of effects for two orthogonal planes.

19 Shells and folded plates

19.1 General

19.1.1

Clauses 19.1.2 to 19.5.2 shall apply to thin shell and folded plate concrete structures, including ribs and edge members.

19.1.2

All of the requirements of this Standard not specifically excluded and not in conflict with the requirements of Clauses 19.1 and 19.2 to 19.5.2 shall apply to thin shell structures.

19.2 Analysis and design

19.2.1

Elastic behaviour shall be an acceptable basis for determining internal forces and displacements of thin shells. This behaviour may be established by computations based on an analysis of the uncracked concrete structure in which the material is assumed to be linearly elastic, homogeneous, and isotropic. Poisson's ratio of concrete may be assumed to be equal to zero.

Note: *See Clause 13.7 for further guidance on analysis and design.*

19.2.2

Equilibrium checks of internal resistances and external loads shall be conducted to ensure consistency of results.

19.2.3

Experimental or numerical analysis procedures shall be used only when it can be shown that they provide a safe basis for design.

19.2.4

Approximate methods of analysis not satisfying compatibility of strains either within the shell or between the shell and auxiliary members shall be used only when it can be shown that they provide a safe basis for design.

19.2.5

For prestressed shells, the analysis shall also consider behaviour under loads induced during prestressing, at cracking load, and at factored load. Where prestressing tendons are draped within a shell, the design shall take into account the force components on the shell resulting from the tendon profiles not lying in one plane.

19.2.6

The thickness, *h*, of a thin shell and its reinforcement shall be proportioned for the required strength and serviceability.

19.2.7

The shell designer shall investigate and preclude the possibility of general or local instability.

19.2.8

Auxiliary members shall be designed in accordance with the applicable requirements of this Standard. A portion of the shell equal to the flange width specified in Clause 10.3 may be assumed to act with the auxiliary member. In such portions of the shell, the reinforcement perpendicular to the auxiliary member shall be at least equal to that required for the flange of a T-beam by Clause 10.5.3.2.

19.3 Specified yield strength of reinforcement

For non-prestressed reinforcement, the yield strength used in calculations shall not exceed 400 MPa.

19.4 Shell reinforcement

19.4.1

Shell reinforcement shall be provided to resist tensile stresses from the internal membrane forces, to resist bending and twisting moments, to control shrinkage and temperature cracking, and as special reinforcement at shell boundaries, load attachments, and shell openings.

19.4.2

Membrane reinforcement shall be provided in two or more directions in all parts of the shell.

19.4.3

The area of shell reinforcement in two orthogonal directions at any section shall be not less than the minimum slab reinforcement required by Clause 7.8, except as specified in Clause 19.4.7.

19.4.4

The reinforcement necessary for resisting shell membrane forces shall be provided so that the factored resistance in any direction shall be at least equal to the component of the principal membrane forces in the same direction due to the factored loads.

19.4.5

The area of shell tension reinforcement shall be limited so that the reinforcement will yield before crushing of concrete in compression can take place.

19.4.6

In regions of high tension, membrane reinforcement shall, if practical, be placed in the general directions of the principal tensile membrane forces. Where this is not practical, membrane reinforcement may be placed in two or more directions.

Note: *If the direction of reinforcement varies more than 15° from the direction of principal tensile membrane force, it is possible that the amount of reinforcement will have to be increased to limit the width of possible cracks under specified loads.*

19.4.7

When the magnitude of the principal tensile membrane stress within the shell varies greatly over the area of the shell surface, reinforcement resisting the total tension may be concentrated in the regions of largest tensile stress if it can be shown that this provides a safe basis for design. However, the ratio of shell reinforcement in any portion of the tensile zone shall be not less than 0.0035 based on the overall thickness of the shell.

19.4.8

Reinforcement required to resist shell bending moments shall be proportioned with due regard for the simultaneous action of membrane axial forces at the same location. When shell reinforcement is required in only one face to resist bending moments, equal amounts shall be placed near both surfaces of the shell, even if calculations do not indicate reversal of bending moments.

19.4.9

When splitting of the shell near its mid-thickness can occur because of transverse tensile stresses, transverse reinforcement shall be provided to prevent the cracks from propagating.

19.4.10

Shell reinforcement in any direction shall not be spaced farther apart than 500 mm or five times the shell thickness. Where the principal membrane tensile stress on the gross concrete area due to factored loads exceeds $0.4\lambda\phi_c\sqrt{f_c'}$, reinforcement shall not be spaced farther apart than three times the shell thickness.

19.4.11

Shell reinforcement at the junction of the shell and supporting members or edge members shall be anchored in or extended through such members in accordance with Clause 12, except that the minimum development length shall be $1.2\ell_d$ but not less than 500 mm.

19.4.12

Splice development lengths of shell reinforcement shall meet the requirements of Clause 12, except that the minimum splice length of tension bars shall be 1.2 times the value specified in Clause 12 but not less than 500 mm. The number of splices in principal tensile reinforcement shall be kept to a practical minimum. Where splices are necessary, they shall be staggered at least ℓ_d, with not more than one-third of the reinforcement spliced at any section.

19.5 Construction

19.5.1

When removal of formwork is based on a specific modulus of elasticity of concrete because of stability or deflection considerations, the value of the modulus of elasticity, E_c, shall be determined from flexural tests of field-cured beam specimens. The number and dimensions of the test beam specimens, and the test procedures, shall be specified by the designer.

Note: *For guidance see CSA A23.2-3C.*

19.5.2

If a thin shell is constructed with deviations from the shape greater than the tolerances specified by the designer, an analysis of the effect of such deviations shall be conducted and all necessary remedial actions shall be taken to ensure the shell's safe behaviour.

20 Strength evaluation procedures

Notes:
1) *This Clause specifies requirements and procedures for evaluating the strength or safe load rating of structures or structural elements where*
   a) *doubt exists about their adequacy because of apparent or suspected deficiencies or defects;*
   b) *the strength or load-bearing capacity is unknown;*
   c) *a change of function creates loading characteristics different from those provided for in the design of the structure; or*
   d) *damage that has possibility reduced the strength or load-bearing capacity has occurred.*
2) *If the structure under investigation does not meet the requirements specified in Clause 20.2.3, 20.3.1.10, or 20.3.2.1, a lower load rating for the structure based on the results of the load test or analysis may be assigned.*

20.1 General

When the safety of a structure or structural member is in doubt and a structural strength investigation is necessary, it shall be carried out by analysis, by means of load tests, or by a combination of these methods.

20.2 Analytical investigation

20.2.1

If the strength evaluation is performed by analytical means, a thorough field investigation of the dimensions and details of the members as actually built, of the properties of the materials, and of other pertinent conditions of the existing structure shall be conducted.

20.2.2

If drawings or other documents are used in the evaluation specified in Clause 20.2.1, their completeness and any modifications of the structure not reflected on the drawings shall be considered in the evaluation.

20.2.3

The analysis based on the investigation specified in Clause 20.2.1 shall satisfy the requirements of this Standard.

20.3 Load tests

Notes:
1) *Although load tests should be conducted in a manner that will provide for safety of life and structure, safety measures should not interfere with the load test procedures or affect results.*

2)   *Load testing prestressed systems with unbonded tendons where corrosion is suspected is generally not an*
      acceptable method for evaluating such tendons.

20.3.1 General

20.3.1.1

Before conducting a load test in accordance with this Clause, calculations shall be made to ensure that the expected failure mode is ductile. If the expected failure mode is brittle, load testing using the provisions of this Clause shall not be carried out.

Note: *The provisions of Clause 20 are based on deflection recovery of systems or members with capacities that are governed by ductile flexural failure. A load test in accordance with Clause 20 is inappropriate for assessing the reliability of a member with a brittle failure mode.*

20.3.1.2

If the strength evaluation is based on load tests, an engineer experienced in such evaluations shall control the tests.

20.3.1.3

A load test shall generally not be conducted until the portion of the structure subjected to load is at least 28 days old.

Note: *When the owner of the structure, the contractor, and all other involved parties mutually agree, the test may be conducted when the structure is less than 28 days old.*

20.3.1.4

The structure or portion of the structure to be load tested shall be loaded in such a manner as to test adequately the suspected weakness and to allow for the characteristics and pattern of the expected loads.

20.3.1.5

A load to simulate the effect of the portion of the dead loads not already present shall be applied 24 h before application of the test load and shall remain in place until all testing has been completed.

20.3.1.6

The superimposed test load shall be applied in not fewer than four approximately equal increments without shock to the structure and in a manner that avoids arching of the load materials.

20.3.1.7

When an entire structural system in doubt is load tested or an entire questionable portion of a system is load tested, the test load shall be 90% of the factored loads M_f, V_f, and P_f.

20.3.1.8

When only a portion of a structural system in doubt is tested and the results of the tests are taken as representative of the structural adequacy of untested portions of the system, the test load shall be equal to the factored loads M_f, V_f, and P_f.

20.3.1.9

The test load shall be left on the structure for 24 h.

20.3.1.10

If the portion of the structure tested fails or shows visible indications of impending failure, it shall be considered to have failed the test.

20.3.2 Load tests of flexural systems or members for moment resistance

20.3.2.1

Note: *The requirements of this Clause are in addition to the requirements specified in Clause 20.3.1.10.*

When flexural systems or members, including beams and slabs, are load tested for moment resistance, they shall have a deflection recovery, within 24 h of removal of the test load, as follows:

Non-prestressed members	
First test	60%
Retest	75%
Prestressed members	80%

20.3.2.2

Deflections of beams, cantilevers, and one-way slabs shall be measured relative to the ends of the span.

20.3.2.3

In the case of two-way slabs, the central slab deflection shall be measured relative to the deflection at the supporting columns or walls.

20.3.2.4

Immediately before application of the test load, the necessary initial readings shall be made as a datum for the measurements of deflections caused by the application of the test load.

20.3.2.5

After the test load has been in position for 24 h, deflection readings shall be taken.

20.3.2.6

Following the action specified in Clause 20.3.2.5, the test load shall be removed. Deflection readings shall be taken 24 h after removal of the test load.

20.3.2.7

Retests of non-prestressed construction shall not be conducted until 72 h after removal of the first test load.

21 Special provisions for seismic design

21.1 Scope

Clauses 21.2 to 21.11 specify requirements for the design and construction of reinforced concrete members of structures for which the design earthquake forces have been determined on the basis of energy dissipation from the non-linear response of the seismic-force-resisting system (SFRS).

21.2 General

21.2.1 Capacity design

The structures identified in Clause 21.1 shall be the subject of capacity design. In the capacity design of structures, kinematically consistent mechanisms are chosen, and the energy-dissipating elements are designed and detailed as specified in Clauses 21.2 to 21.8. All other structural elements in the SFRS are then provided with sufficient reserve capacity to ensure that the chosen energy-dissipating mechanisms are maintained in the selected locations throughout the deformations that can occur.

21.2.2 Seismic-force-resisting systems

Clauses 21.2 to 21.8 specify requirements covering the design and detailing of the standard seismic-force-resisting systems (SFRSs) identified in the *National Building Code of Canada (NBCC)*.

Clauses 21.2 to 21.8 were developed for the design of individual SFRSs that are continuous over the full building height and do not have significant discontinuity in strength or stiffness.

When an SFRS has a strength, stiffness, or geometrical irregularity as defined by the *NBCC*, or when combinations of SFRSs acting in the same direction are not continuous over the building height, or when elements from two or more SFRS types are combined to create a hybrid system, the design of the SFRS and gravity-load resisting frame shall account for the actual inelastic behaviour of the SFRS. An evaluation shall be carried out to
a)   verify the compatibility of the system(s);
b)   confirm the assumed inelastic (energy-dissipating) mechanism(s);
c)   confirm that the inelastic demands are less than the inelastic capacities; and
d)   account for redistribution of forces.

The requirement for such an evaluation may be waived if the performance has been previously verified by experimental evidence and analysis.

A reinforced concrete seismic-force-resisting system other than those specified in Clauses 21.2 to 21.8 may be used as an alternative solution if it can be demonstrated through testing, research, and analysis that the seismic performance of the structural system is at least equivalent to that of a standard SFRS that meets the requirements of Clauses 21.2 to 21.8.

Note: *The requirements for determining R_d and R_o of the system are given in the* National Building Code of Canada *and Commentary J, and the Compliance requirements for alternative solutions are given in Division A of NBCC.*

21.2.3 Design based on nonlinear dynamic analysis

Nonlinear dynamic analysis used for the basis of design shall include a sufficient number of appropriate ground motion time histories and shall include appropriate nonlinear material models for the structural elements that consider the reversed cyclic loading characteristics such as strength and stiffness degradation, ductility capacity and general hysteretic response. The nonlinear analysis and resulting design shall be reviewed by a qualified independent review panel.

Note: *The* National Building Code of Canada *and Commentary J provide the requirements for a special study using nonlinear dynamic analysis. The 2011 LATBSDC (Los Angeles Tall Buildings Structural Design Council) Alternate Procedure for Seismic Analysis and Design of Tall Buildings Located in the Los Angeles Area provides the requirements for a qualified independent review panel.*

21.2.4 Applicable clauses

21.2.4.1

The requirements of Clauses 1 to 18 and 23 shall apply to the design and detailing of structural members unless modified by the requirements of Clause 21.

21.2.4.2

Structural members below the base of the structure that are intended to transmit earthquake-induced forces to the foundation shall meet the requirements of Clause 21.

21.2.4.3

Regardless of the type of seismic-force-resisting system (SFRS), all members of the structure assumed not to be part of the SFRS might be required to satisfy Clause 21.11 depending on the value of $I_E F_a S_a(0.2)$ and the calculated maximum interstorey drift as given in Clause 21.11.1.1.

21.2.5 Analysis and proportioning of structural members

21.2.5.1

The interaction of all structural and non-structural elements that materially affect the linear and non-linear response of the structure to earthquake motions shall be considered in the analysis.

21.2.5.2

For the purpose of determining forces in and deflections of the structure, reduced section properties shall be used. The effective section property to be used as a fraction of the gross section property shall be as specified in Table 21.1.

Table 21.1
Section properties for analysis
(See Clause 21.2.5.2.)

Element type	Effective property
Beam	$I_e = 0.4\,I_g$
Column	$I_e = \alpha_c\,I_g$
Coupling beam (Clause 21.5.8.1)	$A_{ve} = 0.15\,A_g$; $I_e = 0.4\,I_g$
Coupling beam (Clause 21.5.8.2)	$A_{ve} = 0.45\,A_g$; $I_e = 0.25\,I_g$
Slab frame element	$I_e = 0.2\,I_g$
Wall	$A_{xe} = \alpha_w\,A_g$; $I_e = \alpha_w\,I_g$

Where the values of α_c and α_w specified in Table 21.1 shall be determined as follows:
a)

$$\alpha_c = 0.5 + 0.6\frac{P_s}{f_c' A_g} \leq 1.0$$

Equation 21.1

b)

$$\alpha_w = 1.0 - 0.35\left(\frac{R_d R_o}{\gamma_w} - 1.0\right) \geq 0.5 \text{ and } \leq 1.0 \qquad \textbf{Equation 21.2}$$

Where γ_w in Equation 21.2 shall be determined at the base of the wall, and in lieu of more detailed analysis, γ_w may be taken equal to R_o.

21.2.5.3

In the calculation of the slenderness effects for sway frames in accordance with Clause 10.16, Q shall be calculated with Δ_0 multiplied by $R_d R_o/I_E$. The value of Q shall not exceed 1/3.

21.2.6 Concrete in members resisting earthquake-induced forces

21.2.6.1

Specified concrete compressive strengths used in the SFRS shall not exceed 80 MPa.

Note: *See Clauses 10.12 and 14.1.5 for transmission of column and wall loads through floor systems.*

21.2.6.2

The specified compressive strength of structural low-density concrete used in the SFRS shall not exceed 30 MPa unless experimental evidence demonstrates that structural members made with such concrete provide strength and toughness equal to or exceeding the strength and toughness of comparable members made with normal-density concrete of the same strength.

21.2.6.3

Where the term $\sqrt{f_c'}$ is used in calculations of capacity in Clause 21, its value shall be limited to 8 MPa.

21.2.7 Reinforcement in members resisting earthquake-induced forces

21.2.7.1 Reinforcement grade

21.2.7.1.1

Reinforcement for SFRS designed with a force modification factor, R_d, greater than 2.5 shall be weldable grade in compliance with CSA G30.18. Reinforcement for SFRS designed with a force modification factor, R_d, of 2.5 or less shall comply with CSA G30.18; but need not be weldable grade.

21.2.7.1.2

The design, detailing, and ductility requirements for structures designed using a reinforcement grade greater than 400 shall account for the increased strain demands.

Note: *The procedures specified in Clause 21, with the exception of Clause 21.2.8.2 were developed for Grade 400 reinforcement. The additional strains required for higher yield-strength steel will generally reduce ductility.*

21.2.7.2 Lap splices

21.2.7.2.1

Clause 12.2.5, which permits a reduction of lap splice length when the area of reinforcing steel provided exceeds the area required, shall not apply to reinforcement resisting earthquake-induced forces.

21.2.7.2.2

Restrictions or special requirements for lap splices are given in Clauses 21.3.1.3.3 and 21.3.2.5.2 for ductile moment-resisting frame members; Clause 21.5.4.1 for moderately ductile and ductile shear walls; Clause 21.5.6.5 for ductile walls; Clause 21.6.3.7.2 for conventional walls; Clause 21.8.2.1 for precast concrete frames; and Clauses 21.9.4.3 and 21.9.4.4 for structural diaphragms.

21.2.7.3 Mechanical splices

21.2.7.3.1

Mechanical splices shall be classified as either Type 1 or Type 2, as follows:
a) Type 1 mechanical splices shall comply with Clause 12.14.3.4.
b) Type 2 mechanical splices shall comply with Clause 12.14.3.4 and shall develop the minimum tensile strength of the spliced bar.

Note: *See CSA G30.18 for determining the minimum tensile strength.*

21.2.7.3.2

Type 1 mechanical splices shall not be used within a distance equal to twice the member depth from the column or beam face or from sections where yielding of the reinforcement is likely to occur as a result of inelastic lateral displacements. Type 2 mechanical splices may be used in any location.

21.2.7.3.3

Restrictions or special requirements for mechanical splices are given in Clause 21.5.4.2 for moderately ductile and ductile walls; Clause 21.8.2.1 for ductile moment-resisting frames constructed using precast concrete; and Clause 21.9.4.4 for structural diaphragms.

21.2.7.4 Welded splices

21.2.7.4.1

Welded splices in reinforcement resisting earthquake-induced forces shall comply with Clause 12.14.3.3 and shall not be used within a distance equal to twice the member depth from the column or beam face or from sections where yielding of the reinforcement is likely to occur as a result of inelastic lateral displacements.

21.2.7.4.2

Welding of stirrups, ties, inserts, or similar elements to longitudinal reinforcement that is required by design shall not be permitted.

21.2.8 Special ties for compression members

21.2.8.1 Buckling prevention ties

Buckling prevention ties shall comply with Clause 7.6.5.5 or 7.6.5.6 and shall be detailed as hoops, seismic crossties or spirals. The tie spacing shall not exceed the smallest of
a) six longitudinal bar diameters;
b) 24 tie diameters;
c) one-half of the least dimension of the member.

21.2.8.2 Confinement reinforcement

Confinement reinforcement shall satisfy the following conditions:

a) the volumetric ratio of circular hoop reinforcement, ρ_s, shall be not less than

$$P_s = C_c\, k_p \frac{f'_c}{f_{yh}}$$ **Equation 21.3**

where

C_c = 0.3 for systems with R_d = 2.0 or 2.5

= 0.4 for systems with R_d > 2.5

f_{yh} = shall not be taken as greater than 500 MPa

ρ_s = shall not be less than that required by Equation 10.7

b) the total effective area in each of the principal directions of the cross-section within spacing s of rectangular hoop reinforcement, A_{sh}, shall be not less than the larger of the following:

$$A_{sh} = C_h\, k_n\, k_p \frac{A_g f'_c}{A_{ch} f_{yh}} sh_c$$ **Equation 21.4**

$$A_{sh} = 0.09 \frac{f'_c}{f_{yh}} sh_c$$ **Equation 21.5**

where

C_h = 0.15 for systems with R_d = 2.0 or 2.5

= 0.2 for systems with R_d > 2.5

f_{yh} = shall not be taken as greater than 500 MPa

c) transverse reinforcement may be provided by single or overlapping hoops. Seismic crossties of the same bar size and spacing as the hoops may be used. Each end of the crosstie shall engage a peripheral longitudinal reinforcing bar; and

d) if the thickness of the concrete outside the confining transverse reinforcement exceeds 100 mm, additional transverse reinforcement shall be provided within the cover at a spacing not exceeding 300 mm.

21.3 Ductile moment-resisting frames (R_d = 4.0)

21.3.1 Ductile moment-resisting frame members subjected to predominant flexure

21.3.1.1 General

The requirements of Clause 21.3.1 shall apply to ductile moment-resisting frame members that are subjected to an axial compressive force due to factored load effects not exceeding $A_g f'_c / 10$. Where the compressive force exceeds $A_g f'_c / 10$, these members shall be designed in accordance with Clause 21.3.2

21.3.1.2 Dimensional limitations

Ductile moment-resisting frame members subjected to primarily flexure shall satisfy the following:

a) the clear span of the member shall be not less than four times its effective depth;

b) the width of the member, b_w, shall not be less than the smaller of 0.3h and 250 mm; and

c) the width of the member shall not exceed the width of the supporting member, c_2, plus a distance on each side of the supporting member equal to the smaller of the width of the supporting member, c_2, and 0.75 times the depth of the supporting member, c_1.

Ductile frame members not meeting these dimensional limitations shall be designed as specified in Clause 21.11 and shall not be considered part of the SFRS.

21.3.1.3 Longitudinal reinforcement

21.3.1.3.1

At any section of a flexural member, the areas of top reinforcement and bottom reinforcement shall each be not less than $1.4 b_w d / f_y$, and the reinforcement ratio, ρ, shall not exceed 0.025. At least two effectively continuous bars shall be provided at both top and bottom.

21.3.1.3.2

The positive moment resistance at the face of a joint shall be not less than one-half of the negative moment resistance provided at that face of the joint. Neither the negative nor the positive moment resistance at any section along the member length shall be less than one-quarter of the maximum moment resistance provided at the face of either end joint.

21.3.1.3.3

Lap splices of flexural reinforcement may be used only if hoop reinforcement is provided over the lap length. The maximum spacing of the transverse reinforcement enclosing the lapped bars shall not exceed $d/4$ or 100 mm. Lap splices shall not be used
a)   within the joints;
b)   within a distance of $2d$ from the face of the joint; and
c)   within a distance d from any plastic hinge caused by inelastic lateral displacements.

21.3.1.4 Transverse reinforcement

21.3.1.4.1

Hoops shall be provided in the following regions of frame members:
a)   over a length equal to $2d$, measured from the face of the joint; and
b)   over regions where plastic hinges can occur and for a distance d on either side of these hinge regions.

21.3.1.4.2

The first hoop shall be located not more than 50 mm from the face of a supporting member. The maximum spacing of the hoops shall not exceed
a) $d/4$;
b)   eight times the diameter of the smallest longitudinal bars;
c)   24 times the diameter of the hoop bars; or
d)   300 mm.

21.3.1.4.3

In regions where hoops are required, longitudinal bars on the perimeter shall have lateral support complying with Clauses 7.6.5.5 and 7.6.5.6.

21.3.1.4.4

Hoops in flexural members may be replaced by the following two pieces of reinforcement:
a)   a U-stirrup enclosing the longitudinal reinforcement with seismic hooks at the ends; and
b)   a seismic crosstie to make a closed hoop.

If the longitudinal reinforcing bars secured by the crossties are confined by a slab only on one side of the flexural frame member, the 90° hooks of the crossties shall all be placed on that side.

21.3.1.4.5

Where hoops are not required, stirrups with seismic hooks at each end shall be spaced not more than $d/2$ throughout the length of the member.

21.3.1.5 Shear resistance requirements

21.3.1.5.1 Design forces

The factored shear resistance of frame members shall be at least equal to the shear determined by assuming that moments equal to the probable moment resistance act at the faces of the joint so as to produce maximum shear in the member, and that the member is then loaded with the tributary transverse load along the span. The moments corresponding to probable resistance shall be calculated using the properties of the member at the faces of the joint. The factored shear need not exceed that determined from factored load combinations, with load effects calculated using $R_d R_o$ equal to 1.3.

21.3.1.5.2 Shear reinforcement

Shear reinforcement shall be designed to the requirements of Clause 11, with the following exceptions:
a) the values of $\theta = 45°$ and $\beta = 0$ shall be used in the regions specified in Clause 21.3.1.4.1; and
b) transverse reinforcement required to resist shear shall be hoops over the lengths of members, as specified in Clause 21.3.1.4.1.

21.3.2 Ductile moment-resisting frame members subjected to flexure and significant axial load

21.3.2.1 General

The requirements of Clause 21.3.2 shall apply to ductile moment-resisting frame members that are subjected to an axial compressive force due to factored load effects that exceeds $A_g f'_c /10$

21.3.2.2 Dimensional limitations

Ductile moment-resisting frame members subjected to flexure and significant axial load shall satisfy the following:
a) the shortest cross-sectional dimension, measured on a straight line passing through the geometric centroid, shall be not less than 300 mm; and
b) the ratio of the shortest cross-sectional dimension to the perpendicular dimension shall be not less than 0.4.

21.3.2.3 Design of nonconforming members

Ductile frame members not meeting the requirements of Clause 21.3.2.2 shall be designed as specified in Clause 21.11 and shall not be considered part of the SFRS.

21.3.2.4 Minimum flexural resistance of columns

21.3.2.4.1

The flexural resistance of any column proportioned to resist a factored axial compressive force exceeding $A_g f'_c /10$ shall meet the requirements of Clause 21.3.2.4.2. Columns not meeting the requirements of Clause 21.3.2.4.2 shall not be considered as contributing to the resistance of the SFRS and shall meet the requirements of Clause 21.11.

21.3.2.4.2

The flexural resistances of the columns and the beams shall satisfy

$$\Sigma M_{nc} \geq \Sigma M_{pb}$$

Equation 21.6

where

ΣM_{nc} = the sum of moments, at the centre of the joint, corresponding to the nominal resistance of the columns framing into the joint. The nominal resistance of the columns shall be calculated for the factored axial force, consistent with the direction of the lateral forces considered, that results in the lowest flexural resistance

ΣM_{pb} = the sum of moments, at the centre of the joint, corresponding to the probable resistance of the beams and girders framing into that joint. In T-beam construction where the slab is in tension under moments at the face of the joint, slab reinforcement within an effective slab width specified in Clause 10.3 shall be assumed to contribute to flexural resistance if the slab reinforcement is developed at the critical section for flexure

Flexural resistances shall be summed such that the column moments oppose the beam moments. Equation 21.6 shall be satisfied for beam moments acting in either direction.

21.3.2.4.3

Axial design loads in frame columns shall account for beams yielding at levels above the level being considered. The shears from the beams shall be those given by the method specified in Clause 21.3.1.5.1 and using nominal rather than probable resistance. Allowance may be made for the reduction in accumulated beam shears with increasing numbers of storeys.

Note: *Cut off at $R_d R_o$ equal to 1.3 is included in Clause 21.3.1.5.1.*

21.3.2.5 Longitudinal reinforcement

21.3.2.5.1

The area of longitudinal reinforcement shall be not less than 0.01 or more than 0.06 times the gross area, A_g, of the section.

21.3.2.5.2

Lap splices may be used only within the centre half of the member length, shall be designed as tension lap splices, and shall be enclosed within transverse reinforcement complying with Clauses 21.3.2.6.2 and 21.3.2.6.3.

21.3.2.6 Transverse reinforcement

21.3.2.6.1

Shear reinforcement shall meet the requirements of Clause 21.3.2.7.

21.3.2.6.2

Confinement reinforcement in accordance with Clause 21.2.8.2 shall be provided unless a larger amount is required by Clause 21.3.2.6.3 or 21.3.2.7.

21.3.2.6.3

Confinement reinforcement shall be spaced at distances not exceeding the smallest of the following:
a)   one-quarter of the minimum member dimension;
b)   six times the diameter of the smallest longitudinal bar; or
c) s_x, as follows:

$$s_x = 100 + \left(\frac{350 - h_x}{3}\right)$$ **Equation 21.7**

21.3.2.6.4

On each face of a column, the distance h_x shall not exceed the greater of 200 mm or one-third of the core dimension in that direction, and shall not be more than 350 mm.

21.3.2.6.5

Confinement reinforcement shall be provided over a length, ℓ_o, from the face of each joint and on both sides of any section where flexural yielding can occur as a result of inelastic lateral displacement of the frame. The length, ℓ_o, shall be determined as follows:
a)   where $P_f \le 0.5\phi_c f_c' A_g$, ℓ_o shall be not less than 1.5 times the largest member cross-section dimension or one-sixth of the clear span of the member; and
b)   where $P_f > 0.5\phi_c f_c' A_g$, ℓ_o shall be not less than twice the largest member cross-section dimension or one-sixth of the clear span of the member.

21.3.2.6.6

Columns that can develop plastic hinges because of their connection to rigid members such as transfer girders, foundations or discontinued walls, or because of their position at the base of the structure shall be provided with confinement reinforcement over their clear height. This transverse reinforcement shall continue into the rigid member for at least the development length of the largest longitudinal reinforcement in the column. If the column terminates on a footing or mat, this transverse reinforcement shall extend into the footing or mat as required by Clause 21.10.4.

21.3.2.6.7

Where confinement reinforcement is not provided throughout the length of the column, the remainder of the column length shall contain hoop reinforcement with centre-to-centre spacing not exceeding the smaller of six times the diameter of the longitudinal column bars or 150 mm.

21.3.2.7 Shear resistance

21.3.2.7.1

A column shall have a factored shear resistance that exceeds the greater of
a)   shear forces due to the factored load effects; or
b)   the design shear force determined from consideration of the maximum forces that can be generated at the joints at each end of the member. These joint forces shall be determined using the maximum probable moment resistance of the member associated with the range of factored axial loads on the member. The member shears need not exceed those determined from strengths based on the probable moment resistance of the transverse members framing into the joint.

The factored shear resistance of the column need not be greater than the factored load effect calculated using $R_d R_o$ equal to 1.3.

21.3.2.7.2

Shear reinforcement shall be designed to the requirements of Clause 11, with the following exceptions:

a) values of $\beta \leq 0.10$ and $\theta \geq 45°$ shall be used in the region specified in Clause 21.3.2.6.5; and

b) the transverse reinforcement required to resist shear shall be hoops or spirals.

21.3.3 Joints of ductile moment-resisting frames

21.3.3.1 General

21.3.3.1.1

The requirements of Clauses 21.3.3.1.2 to 21.3.3.5.7 shall apply to joints of ductile frames serving as parts of the SFRS.

21.3.3.1.2

Factored forces in joints shall be determined by assuming that the tensile stress in the longitudinal beam reinforcement at the joint is $1.25f_y$, except that they need not exceed the forces determined from the factored load combinations with factored load effects calculated using $R_d R_o$ equal to 1.3.

21.3.3.1.3

Longitudinal beam reinforcement terminated in a column shall be extended to the far face of the confined column core and anchored in tension as specified in Clause 21.3.3.5 and in compression as specified in Clauses 12.3 and 12.5.5.

21.3.3.2 Transverse reinforcement in joints

21.3.3.2.1

Confinement reinforcement, as specified in Clauses 21.2.8.2 and 21.3.2.6 and calculated using the larger of f_c for the column or the joint, shall be provided within the joint unless the joint is confined by structural members as specified in Clause 21.3.3.2.2.

21.3.3.2.2

Within the depth of the shallowest framing member, transverse reinforcement equal to at least one-half of the amount required by Clause 21.2.8.2 but not less than the amount required by Clause 21.3.2.6.3 shall be provided where members frame into all four sides of the joint and each member width is at least three-quarters of the column width. At these locations, the spacing, s_x, specified in Clause 21.3.2.6.3 may be taken as 150 mm.

21.3.3.2.3

Longitudinal beam reinforcement outside the column core shall be confined by transverse reinforcement passing through the column that satisfies spacing requirements of Clause 21.3.1.4.2, and the requirements of Clauses 21.3.1.4.3 and 21.3.1.4.4, if such confinement is not provided by a beam framing into the joint.

21.3.3.3 Longitudinal column reinforcement

21.3.3.3.1
Longitudinal column reinforcement in round column cores shall be uniformly distributed around the column core with a centre-to-centre spacing not exceeding the larger of
a)   200 mm; or
b)   one-third of the column core diameter.

21.3.3.3.2
Longitudinal column reinforcement in rectangular column cores shall have the reinforcement in each face uniformly distributed along that face, with a centre-to-centre spacing corresponding to the tie spacing specified in Clause 21.3.2.6.4.

21.3.3.4 Shear resistance of joints

21.3.3.4.1
The factored shear resistance of the joint shall not exceed the following, where f_c' is the strength of the concrete in the joint:
a)   for confined joints: $2.2\lambda\phi_c\sqrt{f_c'}A_j$;
b)   for joints confined on three faces or on two opposite faces: $1.6\lambda\phi_c\sqrt{f_c'}A_j$; and
c)   for other joints: $1.3\lambda\phi_c\sqrt{f_c'}A_j$.

A member that frames into a face shall be considered to provide confinement to the joint if at least three-quarters of the face of the joint is covered by the framing member. A joint shall be considered confined if such confining members frame into all faces of the joint.

21.3.3.4.2
The shear force, V_{fb}, in the joint determined using the forces specified in Clause 21.3.3.1.2, and accounting for other forces on the joint, shall not exceed the factored resistance specified in Clause 21.3.3.4.1.

21.3.3.5 Development length for tension reinforcement in joints

21.3.3.5.1
Beam longitudinal reinforcement terminated in a column shall be extended to the far face of the column core and anchored in tension using standard 90° hooks.

21.3.3.5.2
For normal-density concrete, the development length, ℓ_{dh}, for a bar with a standard 90° hook shall not be less than the greatest of
a) $8d_b$;
b)   150 mm; or
c)   for bar sizes of 35M and smaller, the length given by

$$\ell_{dh} = 0.2\frac{f_y}{\sqrt{f_c'}}d_b$$

Equation 21.8

21.3.3.5.3
For structural low-density concrete, the development length for a bar with a standard hook shall be not less than 1.25 times that required by Clause 21.3.3.5.2.

21.3.3.5.4
For bar sizes of 35M and smaller, the development length, ℓ_d, for a straight bar in a joint shall be not less than:
a) 2.5 times the length required by Clause 21.3.3.5.2 or 21.3.3.5.3, if the depth of the concrete cast in one lift beneath the bar does not exceed 300 mm; and
b) 3.5 times the length required by Clause 21.3.3.5.2 or 21.3.3.5.3, if the depth of the concrete cast in one lift beneath the bar exceeds 300 mm.

21.3.3.5.5
Straight bars terminated at a joint shall pass through the confined core of a column. Any portion of the straight embedment length not within the confined core shall be considered 60% effective.

21.3.3.5.6
The diameter of straight beam and column bars passing through the joint shall satisfy the following equation:

$$d_b \leq \lambda \frac{\ell_j}{24k_2}$$

Equation 21.9

21.3.3.5.7
If epoxy-coated reinforcement is used, the development lengths specified in Clauses 21.3.3.5.2 to 21.3.3.5.5 shall be multiplied by the applicable factor specified in Clause 12.2.4 or 12.5.3.

21.4 Moderately ductile moment-resisting frames (R_d = 2.5)

21.4.1 General
The requirements specified in Clause 21.4 shall apply to moment-resisting frames SFRS designed using a force modification factor, R_d, of 2.5.

21.4.2 Dimensional limitations

21.4.2.1 Beams
Beams shall satisfy the following dimensional limitations:
a) the clear span of the member shall be not less than three times its effective depth;
b) the width-to-depth ratio of the cross-section shall be not less than 0.3; and
c) the width shall be not less than 250 mm and not more than the width of the supporting member (measured on a plane perpendicular to the longitudinal axis of the flexural member) plus distances on each side of the supporting member not exceeding the smaller of the width of the supporting member or three-quarters of the depth of the supporting member.

21.4.2.2 Columns
Columns shall satisfy the following dimensional limitations:
a) the shortest cross-sectional dimension, measured on a straight line passing through the geometric centroid, shall be not less than 250 mm; and

b) the ratio of the shortest cross-sectional dimension to the perpendicular dimension shall be not less than 0.4.

21.4.3 Detailing of beams

21.4.3.1
The positive moment resistance at the face of the joint shall be not less than one-third of the negative moment resistance provided at that face of the joint. Neither the negative nor the positive moment resistance at any section along the length of the member shall be less than one-fifth of the maximum moment resistance provided at the face of either joint.

21.4.3.2
At both ends of the member, 10M or larger stirrups detailed as hoops shall be provided over lengths equal to twice the member depth measured from the face of the supporting member toward mid-span. The first stirrup shall be located not more than 50 mm from the face of the supporting member and the spacing shall not exceed the smallest of
a) $d/4$;
b) eight times the diameter of the smallest longitudinal bar enclosed;
c) 24 times the diameter of the stirrup bar; or
d) 300 mm.

21.4.3.3
Stirrups shall be spaced not more than $d/2$ throughout the length of the member.

21.4.4 Detailing of columns

21.4.4.1
Transverse reinforcement shall be detailed as hoops and seismic crossties or spirals.

21.4.4.2
The sum of the factored flexural resistances of the column sections framing into a joint, accounting for axial loads, shall exceed the sum of the nominal flexural resistances of the beams framing into the same joint. In T-beam construction where the slab is in tension under moments at the face of the joint, slab reinforcement within an effective slab width as specified in Clause 10.3 shall be assumed to contribute to flexural resistance if the slab reinforcement is developed at the critical section for flexure.

Flexural resistances shall be summed in such a manner that the column moments oppose the beam moments. This requirement shall be satisfied for beam moments acting in either direction. The design column forces need not exceed those determined from the factored load combinations, with factored load effects calculated using $R_d R_o$ equal to 1.3.

21.4.4.3
Confinement reinforcement in accordance with Clause 21.2.8.2 shall be provided at both ends of the columns over a length equal to the largest of one-sixth of the clear height, the maximum cross-sectional dimension, or 450 mm, with a spacing not exceeding the smallest of
a) eight longitudinal bar diameters;
b) 24 tie diameters; or
c) one-half of the minimum column dimension.

21.4.4.4

In the direction perpendicular to the longitudinal axis of the column, crossties or legs of overlapping hoops shall have centre-to-centre spacings not exceeding 350 mm.

21.4.4.5

Columns that can develop plastic hinges because of their connection to rigid members such as transfer girders, foundations or discontinued walls, or because of their position at the base of the structure, shall be provided with transverse confinement reinforcement over their clear height in accordance with the requirements of Clause 21.2.8.2.

21.4.5 Shear in frames

The factored shear resistance of beams and columns resisting earthquake effects shall be not less than the lesser of
a)   the sum of the maximum shear associated with development of nominal moment resistances of the member at each restrained end of the clear span and the shear calculated using earthquake load combinations for gravity loads; or
b)   the maximum shear obtained from factored load combinations, with factored load effects calculated using $R_d R_o$ equal to 1.3.

21.4.6 Joints in frames

21.4.6.1

The design shear forces acting in a beam column joint shall be those induced by the nominal resistance of the beams or the columns framing into the joint, whichever is less, except that they need not exceed those determined from the factored load combinations, with factored load effects calculated using $R_d R_o$ equal to 1.3. Where beams frame into the joint from two directions, each direction may be considered independently.

21.4.6.2

The factored shear resistance of the joint shall not exceed the following, where f_c' is the strength of the concrete in the joint:
a)   for confined joints: $1.7\lambda\phi_c\sqrt{f_c'}A_j$;
b)   for joints confined on three faces or on two opposite faces: $1.2\lambda\phi_c\sqrt{f_c'}A_j$; and
c)   for other joints: $1.0\lambda\phi_c\sqrt{f_c'}A_j$.

A member that frames into a face shall be considered to provide confinement to the joint if at least three-quarters of the face of the joint is covered by the framing member. A joint shall be considered to be confined if such confining members frame into all faces of the joint.

21.4.6.3

The amount of transverse reinforcement in each joint shall not be less than
a)   the larger of the amount of transverse reinforcement provided in the column above the joint and the column below the joint; or
b)   one half of the amount required in Item a) for confined joints as defined in Clause 21.4.6.2.

21.4.6.4

Transverse hoop reinforcement shall be provided over the depth of the joint and spaced a maximum distance of 150 mm. Longitudinal column reinforcement shall have a centre-to-centre spacing not exceeding 300 mm and shall not be cranked within the joint.

21.4.6.5

The diameter of straight beam and column bars passing through the joint, d_b, shall satisfy the following equation:

$$d_b \leq \lambda \frac{\ell_j}{20k_2}$$

Equation 21.10

21.5 Ductile and moderately ductile walls (R_d = 2.0, 2.5, 3.5, or 4.0)

21.5.1 General

21.5.1.1 Minimum requirements

All shear walls shall satisfy the requirements of Clause 14 except as modified by the requirements of Clause 21.5.

21.5.1.2 Shear walls designed for flexural ductility

All shear walls and coupled or partially coupled shear walls with $h_w/\ell_w > 2.0$ and designed for forces calculated using $R_d \geq 2.0$ shall meet the additional requirements specified in Clauses 21.5.2 to 21.5.9.

21.5.1.3 Walls with multi-level openings

A wall with large openings at multiple levels shall be designed in accordance with the additional requirements of Clause unless the openings are limited to a small portion of the wall height and the solid wall segment(s) above and below the openings, that connect the vertical wall piers, have sufficient strength and stiffness for the wall assembly to act as a single cantilever wall.

Note: *The intent of this Clause is to ensure that any wall that may act as a coupled or partially coupled wall satisfies all the requirements for one of the four systems in Clause .*

21.5.1.4 Squat walls

All shear walls with $h_w/\ell_w \leq 2.0$ shall meet the additional requirements specified in Clause 21.5.10.

21.5.1.5 Tilt-up and precast walls

Tilt-up concrete walls shall be designed in accordance with Clause 21.7. Precast walls shall be designed in accordance with Clause 21.8, except that solid precast wall panels may be designed in accordance with Clauses 21.7 if the wall panels also meet the requirements of Clause 23.

21.5.2 Requirements for strength and ductility over height

21.5.2.1 Plastic hinge regions in walls

21.5.2.1.1 General

Shear walls and coupled or partially coupled shear walls with $h_w/\ell_w > 2.0$ and $R_d \geq 2.0$ shall be designed for flexural ductility resulting from yielding of the vertical reinforcement in plastic hinge regions.

21.5.2.1.2 Minimum height of plastic hinge regions

A plastic hinge region shall extend a minimum distance of $0.5\ell_w + 0.1h_w$ above the critical section where the vertical reinforcement will first yield; where ℓ_w is the length of the longest shear wall or overall length of the coupled shear walls in the direction under consideration. The plastic hinge region shall extend below the critical section where the vertical reinforcement will first yield in accordance with Clauses 21.5.2.1.3 and 21.5.2.1.4.

21.5.2.1.3 Plastic hinge region at base

When first yielding of the vertical reinforcement in a wall is expected to occur at a well-defined critical section near the base of the wall and the SFRS does not contain structural irregularity types 1, 3, 4, 5, or 6 defined in the *NBCC* anywhere over the building height, the walls may be designed for a single plastic hinge region at the well-defined critical section at the base.

The plastic hinge region at the base shall extend below the critical section all the way to the footing unless all walls have adequate flexural over-strength in accordance with Clause 21.5.2.2.4 to ensure that yielding will not occur below the critical section; in which case the plastic hinge region shall extend down the distance specified in Clause 21.5.2.1.2 or to the footing, whichever is less.

21.5.2.1.4 Plastic hinge regions at irregularities

For buildings containing a Type 1 (vertical stiffness) irregularity or Type 3 (vertical geometrical) irregularity defined in the *NBCC* anywhere over the building height, the walls shall be detailed for plastic hinge regions at the base and at the location of each irregularity. The plastic hinge region shall extend from the minimum distance specified in Clause 21.5.2.1.2 above the irregularity to the minimum distance specified in Clause 21.5.2.1.2 below the irregularity.

In addition, each individual wall that contains a significant structural irregularity, such as a large opening, anywhere over the height, shall be designed such that there is no discontinuity in flexural capacity and shear capacity or shall be detailed for plastic hinging at the location of the irregularity.

21.5.2.2 Design for shear force and bending moment

21.5.2.2.1 Shear force and bending moment envelopes

The factored shear force envelope and factored bending moment envelope shall be calculated for each wall in accordance with the *NBCC* and increased as required by Clauses 21.5.2.2.2 to 21.5.2.2.9.

Note: *The* National Building Code of Canada *(NBCC) specifies when a dynamic analysis must be used to determine the shear force and bending moment envelopes and when the equivalent static force procedure may be used.*

21.5.2.2.2 Design for bending moment at base

Each wall shall be proportioned such that the factored bending resistance calculated in accordance with Clause 10 is greater than the factored bending moment at the critical section defined in Clause 21.5.2.1.2.

The properties of the wall cross section that affect the bending resistance of the wall shall be maintained over the height of the plastic hinge specified in Clause 21.5.2.1.2.

Note: *The cross sectional properties that affect bending resistance include concrete geometry, concrete strength and the reinforcing steel. The bending resistance of the wall will reduce over the height of the plastic hinge due to the reduction in axial compression force from gravity loads, which is not a property of the cross section.*

21.5.2.2.3 Design for bending moment above plastic hinge at base

The factored bending moment envelopes determined in accordance with Clause 21.5.2.2.1 shall be increased to ensure that flexural yielding of the wall will not first occur above the plastic hinge region as follows:

a)   When dynamic analysis is used to determine the bending moment envelope, the factored bending moments at all elevations above the plastic hinge region shall be increased by the ratio of factored bending moment resistance to factored bending moment, calculated at top of plastic hinge region.

b)   When the equivalent static force procedure is used, the factored bending moment in the wall shall be assumed to vary linearly from the factored bending moment resistance at the top of the plastic hinge region to zero at a point located the height given in Clause 21.5.2.1.2 above the top of the wall.

21.5.2.2.4 Design for bending moment below plastic hinge at base

To ensure adequate flexural over-strength below the plastic hinge region at the base, each wall shall satisfy all of the following:

a)   the factored flexural resistance at any point below the critical section shall be greater than the factored bending moment determined by analysis in accordance with Clause 21.5.2.2.1 increased by the ratio of nominal bending moment resistance to factored bending moment, both calculated at the bottom of the plastic hinge region;

b)   the factored flexural resistance at any point below the critical section shall be greater than the factored bending moment determined by analysis in accordance with Clause 21.5.2.2.9; and

c)   the portion of wall immediately below the critical section at the base shall contain a minimum of 20% additional flexural tension reinforcement than the wall immediately above the critical section.

21.5.2.2.5 Design for shear force at base

Each wall shall be proportioned such that the factored shear resistance calculated in accordance with Clause 21.5.9 is greater than the factored shear force at the base. The factored shear force at the base shall be determined in accordance with Clause 21.5.2.2.1, increased to account for flexural overstrength in accordance with Clause 21.5.2.2.6, and further increased for inelastic effects of higher modes in accordance with Clause 21.5.2.2.7. The factored shear force need not be taken larger than the shear force resulting from design load combinations that include earthquake, with load effects calculated using $R_d R_o$ equal to 1.3.

The properties of the wall cross section that affect the shear resistance of the wall shall be maintained over the height of the plastic hinge region specified in Clause 21.5.2.1.2.

Note: *The cross sectional properties that affect shear resistance include concrete geometry, concrete strength, and reinforcing steel.*

21.5.2.2.6 Accounting for flexural overstrength

The factored shear force at the base determined in accordance with Clause 21.5.2.2.1 shall be increased by the ratio of the bending moment capacity given below to the factored bending moment, both calculated at the base.

	$R_d \leq 2.5$	$R_d \geq 3.5$
Bending moment capacity:	nominal	probable

21.5.2.2.7 Accounting for inelastic effects of higher modes

Except for coupled and partially coupled shear walls, the increased factored shear force determined in accordance with Clause 21.5.2.2.6 shall be further increased depending on the fundamental lateral period of vibration of the building T_a in the direction under consideration as follows:

$T_a \leq T_L$	$T_a \geq T_U$
1.0	$1.0 + 0.25\left({R_d R_o}/_{\gamma_w} - 1 \right) \leq 1.5 \text{ and } \geq 1.0$

For T_a between T_L and T_U, linear interpolation shall be used, where T_L and T_U shall be determined as follows:

	T_L	T_U
$S(0.2)/S(2.0) < 10.0$	0.5 s	1.0 s
$S(0.2)/S(2.0) \geq 10.0$	0.2 s	0.5 s

21.5.2.2.8 Design for shear force above plastic hinge at base

The factored shear force envelope for each wall over the height of the structure determined in accordance with Clause 21.5.2.2.1 shall be increased by a constant factor over the height including the base equal to the amount that the factored shear force at the base must be increased in accordance with Clause 21.5.2.2.5.

21.5.2.2.9 Design for shear force below plastic hinge at base

When a shear wall is connected to a stiff supporting structure, such as large foundation walls, by multiple floor diaphragms below the plastic hinge, the factored shear force and corresponding factored bending moment applied to the shear wall below the plastic hinge shall be determined using an analysis that considers the lower-bound or upper-bound value of effective stiffnesses of the members as appropriate to determine a safe estimate of the factored shear force.

Note: *A description of the type of simplified analyses that can be done considering only the structure below the plastic hinge and the appropriate effective stiffnesses, accounting for the level of cracking and quantity of reinforcement, are given in the explanatory notes of the Cement Association of Canada's Concrete Design Handbook.*

21.5.3 Minimum wall thickness

21.5.3.1 Plastic hinge region

The wall thickness within a plastic hinge shall be not less than limit A except as permitted by Clause 21.5.3.3, but in no case shall be less than limit B:

	$R_d \leq 2.5$	$R_d \geq 3.5$
Limit A	$\ell_u / 14$	$\ell_u / 10$
Limit B	$\ell_u / 20$	$\ell_u / 14$

21.5.3.2 Outside plastic hinge region

The wall thickness outside a plastic hinge shall be not less than limit B given in Clauses 21.5.3.1 except as permitted by Clause 21.5.3.3, but in no case shall be less than $\ell_u/20$.

21.5.3.3 Conditions for reduced wall thickness

Limit A in Clause 21.5.3.1 and Limit B in Clause 21.5.3.2 shall not be required to apply to

a) any part of a wall that under factored vertical and lateral loads are not more than halfway from the neutral axis to the compression face of the wall section;

b) any part of a wall that lies within a distance of $3b_w$ from a continuous line of lateral support provided by a flange or cross wall; the width of flange providing effective lateral support shall be not less than $\ell_u/5$; and

c) simple rectangular walls where the distance from the neutral axis to the compression face, calculated for factored load effects, is located within a distance of the lesser of $4b_w$ or $0.3\ell_w$ from the compression face of the wall section.

21.5.4 Reinforcement

21.5.4.1 General

All concentrated reinforcement and all distributed reinforcement over the full height of all walls shall meet the following requirements:

a) Reinforcing bars shall not be offset bent.

b) Lap splices shall have a minimum length of $1.5\ell_d$.

c) Reinforcing bars shall be anchored, spliced, or embedded in accordance with the requirements for reinforcement in tension specified in Clause 12 except as modified by Clause 21.5.4.2.

21.5.4.2 Mechanical splices

Where Type 2 mechanical splices are used, not more than alternate bars in each layer of distributed reinforcement and concentrated reinforcement shall be spliced at any section, and the centre-to-centre distance between splices of adjacent bars shall be not less than $40d_b$, measured along the longitudinal axis of the wall.

21.5.4.3 Maximum percentage

The reinforcement ratio within any region of concentrated reinforcement, including regions containing lap splices, shall be not more than 0.06 in walls designed with $R_d \geq 3.5$.

21.5.5 Distributed reinforcement

21.5.5.1 Minimum amount

Both vertical and horizontal distributed reinforcement shall be provided in such a manner that the reinforcement ratio for this distributed reinforcement is not less than 0.0025 in each direction.

21.5.5.2 Maximum spacing

In plastic hinge regions, the spacing of horizontal reinforcement shall not exceed the following values:

$R_d \leq 2.5$	$R_d \geq 3.5$
400 mm	300 mm

Note: *The maximum spacing of vertical and horizontal wall reinforcement is 500 mm according to Clause 14.1.8.4.*

21.5.5.3 Anchorage of horizontal reinforcement

Horizontal reinforcement shall extend to the ends of walls and shall be anchored at each end as follows:

For wall systems designed using:	Permitted Anchorage
R_d = 1.5	Type 1, 2, or 3
R_d = 2.0 or 2.5	Type 2 or 3
R_d = 3.5 or 4.0	Type 3

In plastic hinge regions of walls designed with R_d = 3.5 or 4.0, the horizontal reinforcement required for shear resistance shall be anchored with straight bar embedment, hook, or mechanical anchorage to develop $1.25f_y$ within the region of tied concentrated vertical reinforcement.

Anchorage types shall be as follows:

Type	Brief description	Figure
1	Standard 90° hook around vertical end bar	
2	U-bar around vertical end bars; staggered lap splices minimum five times wall thick from end of wall	
3	Anchored within tied vertical reinforcement	

21.5.5.4 Ties for vertical distributed reinforcement

In plastic hinge regions, if the area of vertical distributed reinforcement is greater than $0.005A_g$ or the maximum bar size is greater than 20M; the vertical distributed reinforcement shall be tied with buckling prevention ties.

Note: *Clause 14.1.8.7 requires that such reinforcement be tied as a compression member in accordance with Clause 7.6.5 outside the plastic hinge region.*

21.5.6 Concentrated vertical reinforcement

21.5.6.1 Minimum amount

Over the full height of all walls, concentrated vertical reinforcement consisting of a minimum of four bars placed in at least two layers shall be provided at the ends of all walls. The minimum area of concentrated reinforcement at each end of the wall shall be as follows:

$R_d \leq 2.5$	$R_d \geq 3.5$
$0.0005\,b_w\ell_w$	$0.001\,b_w\ell_w$

21.5.6.2 Plastic hinge regions

In regions of plastic hinging, the minimum area of concentrated reinforcement at each end of the wall shall be as follows:

$R_d \leq 2.5$	$R_d \geq 3.5$
$0.00075\,b_w\ell_w$	$0.0015\,b_w\ell_w$

21.5.6.3 Flanged walls

In the case of flanged walls, concentrated reinforcement at the end(s) of the effective flanges may supply up to one-half of the required minimum area of the concentrated reinforcement specified in Clauses 21.5.6.1 and 21.5.6.2, with the remainder placed at the end of the wall web.

21.5.6.4 Ties for concentrated reinforcement

All concentrated reinforcement shall, as a minimum, be tied as a compression member in accordance with Clause 7.6.5 and all ties shall be detailed as hoops or seismic crossties. In regions of plastic hinging, all concentrated reinforcement shall have buckling prevention ties.

21.5.6.5 Limited splicing in ductile walls

When $R_d \geq 3.5$, not more than 50% of the reinforcement at each end of the walls in plastic hinge regions shall be spliced at the same location and a total of at least one-half of the height of each storey shall be completely clear of lap splices in the concentrated reinforcement.

21.5.7 Ductility of walls

21.5.7.1 Requirements above and within plastic hinge region

21.5.7.1.1 Above plastic hinge region

To ensure a wall has adequate ductility to tolerate limited yielding of vertical reinforcement due to higher mode bending moments, at any point over the height of the wall, the distance, c, determined in accordance with Clause 21.5.7.4 shall not be greater than
a) $0.5\ell_w$ for walls designed with $R_d \leq 2.5$; or
b) $0.4\ell_w$ for walls designed with $R_d \geq 3.5$.

CSA Group standard A23.3-14

21.5.7.1.2 Within plastic hinge region

To ensure a wall has adequate ductility within the plastic hinge region, the inelastic rotational capacity of the wall, θ_{ic}, determined in accordance with Clause 21.5.7.3, shall be greater than the inelastic rotational demand, θ_{id}, determined in accordance with Clause 21.5.7.2.

21.5.7.2 Inelastic rotational demand at base

The inelastic rotational demand at the base of a wall, θ_{id}, shall be taken as

$$\theta_{id} = \frac{\left(\Delta_f R_o R_d - \Delta_f \gamma_w\right)}{\left(h_w - \ell_w / 2\right)}$$

Equation 21.11

but shall not be taken less than 0.003 for R_d = 2.0 and 0.004 for R_d = 3.5,

where
$\Delta_f R_o R_d$ = the design displacement,
$\Delta_f \gamma_w$ = the elastic portion of the displacement,
ℓ_w = the length of the longest wall (in the hinge region) in the direction considered

21.5.7.3 Inelastic rotational capacity

The inelastic rotational capacity of a wall, θ_{ic}, shall be taken as

$$\theta_{ic} = \left(\frac{\varepsilon_{cu}\ell_w}{2c} - 0.002\right)$$

Equation 21.12

but shall not be taken greater than 0.025,

where
ℓ_w = the length of the individual wall under consideration

c = the neutral axis distance determined in accordance with Clause 21.5.7.4 and ε_{cu} shall be taken as 0.0035 unless the compression region of the wall contains confinement reinforcement in accordance with Clause 21.5.7.5

Note: *The value of 0.025 is the upper limit on inelastic rotation capacity governed by tension steel strain.*

21.5.7.4 Compression strain depth in wall

The distance from the extreme compression fibre to the neutral axis, c, when concrete reaches the maximum compression strain ε_{cu} at the extreme compression fibre shall be determined by plane sections analysis for the factored axial load acting on the wall and a bending moment causing the maximum compression strain at the extreme compression fibre, or as follows:

$$c = \frac{P_s + P_n + P_{ns} - \alpha_1 \phi_c f_c' A_f}{\alpha_1 \beta_1 \phi_c f_c' b_w}$$

Equation 21.13

21.5.7.5 Confinement of concrete

When ε_{cu} in Clause 21.5.7.3 is taken greater than 0.0035, the compression region of the wall shall contain confinement reinforcement. The amount of confinement reinforcement shall be determined with k_p taken as $(0.1 + 30\varepsilon_{cu})$. This reinforcement shall be provided over a distance of not less than $c(\varepsilon_{cu} - 0.0035)/\varepsilon_{cu}$ from the compression face of the wall. The minimum vertical reinforcement ratio in any part of this confined region shall be 0.005. ε_{cu} shall not be taken greater than 0.014.

21.5.7.6 Simplified procedure for moderately ductile walls

For shear walls designed with $R_d \leq 2.0$, the requirements of Clause 21.5.7.1.2 shall be considered satisfied if the distance , c, determined in accordance with Clause 21.5.7.4 satisfies either one of the following two conditions:

a) $c \leq 0.33\ell_w$ when deflection of top of wall due to effects of factored loads, Δ_f, does not exceed $h_w/350$; or

b) $c \leq 0.15\ell_w$ when Δ_f does not meet the condition given in Item a), or Δ_f is not calculated.

21.5.8 Additional requirements for coupled shear walls (R_d = 2.5 or 4.0) and partially coupled shear walls (R_d = 2.0 or 3.5)

Note: *There are four types of coupled or partially coupled wall systems as follows:*

	Moderately Ductile	Ductile
Coupled (DOC ≥ 66%)	R_d = 2.5	R_d = 4.0
Partially Coupled (DOC < 66%)	R_d = 2.0	R_d = 3.5

Degree of coupling (DOC) is the portion of base overturning moment resistance provided by axial forces in wall piers resulting from shear in coupling beams.

21.5.8.1 Design of coupling beams without diagonal reinforcement

21.5.8.1.1 Dimensional limitations

Coupling beams without diagonal reinforcement shall satisfy the following requirements:

a) The dimensional limitations of Clause 21.3.1.2 shall be satisfied for R_d = 4.0 or 3.5 and the dimensional limitations of Clause 21.4.2.1 shall be satisfied for R_d = 2.5 or 2.0.

b) The clear span, ℓ_u, shall be not less than $2\ell_d$.

c) The maximum shear force shall be limited to $0.1(\ell_u/d)\sqrt{f'_c}\,b_w d$.

21.5.8.1.2 Design as frame members

Coupling beams with longitudinal and transverse reinforcement shall meet the requirements of Clause 21.3.1 for R_d = 4.0 or 3.5 and Clause 21.4.3 for R_d = 2.5 or 2.0.

21.5.8.1.3 Anchorage of longitudinal reinforcement

Anchorage of the longitudinal reinforcement into the wall shall meet the requirements of Clause 21.3.3.1.3. Alternatively, the anchorage of the longitudinal reinforcement shall meet the requirements of Clause 21.5.8.2.5.

21.5.8.1.4 Wide beams

If a coupling beam is wider than the thickness of the wall pier, the following additional requirements shall be met:

a) the front interface between the coupling beam and the wall pier shall be designed for the beam forces within the wall width; and

b) the side interface(s) between the coupling beam and the wall pier shall be designed to transfer all of the forces in the beam overhang(s) to the wall.

21.5.8.1.5 Non-centred beams

If a coupling beam is not centred on the wall pier, the following additional requirements shall be met:

a)   the coupling beam and adjoining wall piers shall be designed for the eccentricity; and

b)   the coupling beam stiffness shall be reduced to account for the out-of-plane deformations.

21.5.8.2 Design of coupling beams with diagonal reinforcement

21.5.8.2.1 Dimensional limitations

Coupling beams with diagonal reinforcement shall satisfy the following requirements:

a)   the beam depth shall be not greater than $2.0\ell_u$;

b)   the beam width shall be less than or equal to the wall thickness;

c)   the beam shall be centred on the wall pier; and

d)   the wall piers at each end of coupling beam shall have sufficient length to contain the diagonal reinforcement embedment specified in Clause 21.5.8.2.5.

21.5.8.2.2 Quantity of diagonal reinforcement

Coupling beams with diagonal reinforcement shall be designed such that the entire factored in-plane shear force and factored bending moment is resisted by diagonal reinforcement in two directions.

Note: *When dimensions of a coupling beam are such that the factored shear force exceeds $1.0\sqrt{f'_c}\,bh$, it can be difficult to construct the beam due to reinforcement congestion, particularly at the intersection with the concentrated wall reinforcement.*

21.5.8.2.3 Concentric reinforcement

The centroid of each group of diagonal reinforcing bars shall be centred in the beam.

21.5.8.2.4 Buckling prevention ties on diagonal reinforcement

The diagonal reinforcement in each direction shall be enclosed by hoops or spirals that extend up to the concentrated reinforcement specified in Clause 21.5.8.3.1. The maximum spacing of the hoops or pitch of the spiral shall not exceed the smallest of

a)   six diagonal bar diameters;

b)   24 tie diameters; or

c)   100 mm.

21.5.8.2.5 Anchorage of diagonal reinforcement

The diagonal reinforcing bars shall be anchored into the wall at each end by one of the following:

a)   a minimum straight embedment of $1.5\ell_d$, where 1.5 includes the top bar factor; but not the bundled bar factor;

b)   a minimum straight embedment of $1.0\ell_d$ plus a standard hook contained within confinement reinforcement; or

c)   for headed and mechanically-anchored bars, the minimum straight embedment shall satisfy the minimum tension embedment for seismic applications; but shall not be less than the basic compression development length unless it can be shown that the concrete breakout resistance of the head or mechanical anchorage is able to transfer the compression force into the wall with the contribution of the straight embedment ignored.

21.5.8.3 Design of wall piers

21.5.8.3.1 Concentrated wall reinforcement at coupling beams

Concentrated vertical reinforcement, as specified in Clause 21.5.6.1, shall be provided in the wall piers at both ends of all coupling beams. The concentrated reinforcement shall be tied as specified in Clause 21.5.6.4, except that for wall systems designed with R_d = 4.0 or 3.5, the concentrated reinforcement shall have buckling prevention ties over the full height.

21.5.8.3.2 Bending resistance of wall piers

Except as permitted by Clause 21.5.8.3.3, the wall pier at each end of a coupling beam shall be designed such that the factored bending moment resistance of the wall pier about its centroid, calculated using axial loads P_s and $\pm P_n$, exceeds the bending moment at its centroid resulting from the nominal resistance of the coupling beams framing into the wall pier and the factored bending moment applied to the wall pier.

21.5.8.3.3 Plastic hinges in wall pier

If the wall pier at one end of a coupling beam has a factored bending resistance that does not meet the condition specified in Clause 21.5.8.3.2, the following additional requirements shall be satisfied:
a) the coupling beam shall meet the requirements of Clause 21.5.8.1;
b) the wall pier shall be designed to the requirements specified in Clauses 21.3.2.6.2, 21.3.2.6.3, 21.3.2.6.6, and 21.3.2.7 for R_d = 4.0 or 3.5,
    and shall be designed to the requirements specified in Clauses 21.4.4 and 21.4.5 for R_d = 2.5 or 2.0; and
c) the joint between the wall and coupling beam shall meet the requirements specified in Clause 21.3.3 for R_d = 4.0 or 3.5; and shall meet the requirements specified in Clause 21.4.6 for R_d = 2.5 or 2.0.

21.5.8.3.4 Axial forces in wall piers

All coupled and partially coupled shear walls shall be designed with the portion of factored overturning moment resisted by axial forces in the wall piers increased at each level by the ratio of sum of coupling beam nominal or factored capacity as given in the table below, to the sum of factored forces in coupling beams above the level under consideration. For assemblies of coupled and partially coupled shear walls connected together by coupling beams that function as a closed tube(s) the factored forces in the coupling beams used to calculate the ratio shall be determined without accidental torsion.

	R_d = 4.0 or 3.5	R_d = 2.5 or 2.0
Coupling beam capacity:	nominal	factored

21.5.8.4 Ductility

21.5.8.4.1 General

To ensure ductility of coupled wall systems,
a) the inelastic rotational demand on wall piers determined in accordance with Clause 21.5.8.4.2 shall not be greater than the inelastic rotational capacity of wall piers determined in accordance with Clause 21.5.8.4.3; and

b) the inelastic rotational demand on coupling beams determined in accordance with Clause 21.5.8.4.4 shall not be greater than the inelastic rotational capacity of coupling beams determined in accordance with Clause 21.5.8.4.5.

21.5.8.4.2 Inelastic rotational demand at base of wall piers

The inelastic rotational demand on coupled and partially coupled wall piers shall be taken as

$$\theta_{id} = \frac{\Delta_f R_o R_d}{h_w}$$

Equation 21.14

but shall not be taken less than 0.003 for R_d = 2.5 or 2.0 and 0.004 for R_d = 4.0 or 3.5, where

$\Delta_f R_o R_d$ = the design displacement

21.5.8.4.3 Inelastic rotational capacity of wall piers

The inelastic rotational capacity of wall piers shall be calculated using the methods given in Clause 21.5.7.3, except that ℓ_w shall be taken as the length of the longest individual wall pier in the direction considered for partially coupled walls and as the overall length of the interconnected wall piers for coupled walls.

21.5.8.4.4 Inelastic rotational demand on coupling beams

The inelastic rotational demand on coupling beams shall be taken as

$$\theta_{id} = \left(\frac{\Delta_f R_o R_d}{h_w} \right) \frac{\ell_{cg}}{\ell_u}$$

Equation 21.15

21.5.8.4.5 Inelastic rotational capacity of coupling beams

The inelastic rotational capacity of coupling beams, θ_{ic}, shall be taken as
a) 0.02 for coupling beams without diagonal reinforcement; and
b) 0.04 for coupling beams with diagonal reinforcement designed in accordance with Clause 21.5.8.2.

21.5.9 Shear resistance of flexural shear walls

21.5.9.1 General

The shear design of flexural shear walls shall meet the requirements specified in Clauses 11, 14, and 21.5.9.2 to 21.5.9.5.

21.5.9.2 Shear depth

The effective shear depth, d_v, of a wall need not be taken as less than $0.8\ell_w$.

21.5.9.3 Opening in walls

The effect of openings in walls shall be accounted for.

Note: *Strut-and-tie models in accordance with Clause 11.4 can be used to confirm that the diagonal compression due to shear force in a wall can be transmitted around an opening and can be used to determine the additional reinforcement required around an opening.*

21.5.9.4 Outside plastic hinge regions

Outside regions of plastic hinging, the shear resistance of a flexural wall can be determined using the procedures of Clause 11.3 except that the maximum possible shear resistance $V_{r,max} = 0.2\phi_c f_c' b_w d_v$.

The following simplified procedure may be used:
a)   the value of β in Clause 11.3.4 shall be taken as 0.18; and
b)   the value of θ in Clause 11.3.5 shall be taken as 35°.

21.5.9.5 Plastic hinge regions

21.5.9.5.1 General
In regions of plastic hinging, the shear resistance of a flexural wall shall be determined using the procedures of Clause 11.3 except that the shear resistance shall be reduced to account for the inelastic rotational demand in accordance with Clauses 21.5.9.5.2 to 21.5.9.5.3.

21.5.9.5.2 General method for ductile and moderately ductile walls
The shear resistance shall be calculated as follows:
a)   The maximum possible shear resistance $V_{r,max} = 0.1\phi_c f_c' b_w d_v$ unless it is shown that the inelastic rotational demand on the wall, θ_{id} given by Equation 21.11 or 21.14 is less than 0.015. When $\theta_{id} \leq$ 0.005, the maximum possible shear resistance $V_{r,max} = 0.15\phi_c f_c' b_w d_v$. For inelastic rotational demands between these limits, linear interpolation may be used.
b)   The value of β specified in Clause 11.3.4 shall be taken as zero unless it is shown that the inelastic rotational demand on the wall, θ_{id}, given by Equation 21.11 or 21.14 is less than 0.015. When $\theta_{id} \leq$ 0.005, the value of β shall not be taken greater than 0.18. For inelastic rotational demands between these limits, linear interpolation may be used.
c)   The value of θ in Clause 11.3.5 shall be taken as 45° unless the axial compression $(P_s + P_p)$ acting on the wall is greater than $0.1f_c' A_g$. When $(P_s + P_p) \geq 0.2f_c' A_g$, the value of θ shall not be taken less than 35°. For axial compressions between these limits, linear interpolation may be used.

21.5.9.5.3 Simplified method for moderately ductile walls
In lieu of the requirements of Clause 21.5.9.5.2, the following simplified procedure may be used for shear walls designed with $R_d \leq 2.5$:
a)   the maximum possible shear resistance $V_{r,max} = 0.125\phi_c f_c' b_w d_v$;
b)   the value of β in Clause 11.3.4 shall be taken as 0.1, and;
c)   the value of θ in Clause 11.3.5 shall be taken as 45°.

21.5.9.6 Strut-and-tie models
When strut-and-tie models in accordance with Clause 11.4 are used for shear design, the following exceptions shall apply in regions of plastic hinging:
a)   The limiting compressive stress in the strut shall be taken as 0.8 times the value determined from Equation 11.22.
b)   A compression strut that, during the reverse direction of seismic loading, is a tension tie designed to yield, shall contain a minimum of four bars placed in at least two layers. This reinforcement shall be tied as a compression member in accordance with Clause 7.6.5, and the ties shall be detailed as hoops. In addition, the spacing of the ties shall not exceed the smallest of six longitudinal bar diameters, 24 tie diameters, or 100 mm.

21.5.10 Moderately ductile squat shear walls (R_d = 2.0)

21.5.10.1 General
The requirements specified in Clauses 21.5.10.2 to 21.5.10.8.7 shall apply to walls with h_w / ℓ_w of 2.0 or less designed using an R_d = 2.0.

21.5.10.2 Capacity design

The foundation and diaphragm components of the SFRS shall have factored resistances that are greater than the nominal wall capacity; but need not be taken larger than the forces calculated with design load combinations that include earthquake effects calculated using $R_d R_o$ equal to 1.3. The nominal wall capacity shall be taken as the smaller of

a) the shear corresponding to the development of the nominal moment capacity of the wall; or

b) the nominal shear resistance of the wall, which shall be taken as not less than $0.25\sqrt{f'_c}\,b_w l_w$

Note: *Squat walls can develop either a flexural or a shear mechanism that will limit the seismic forces resisted by the wall. The procedures used to calculate nominal shear resistance assumes that the concrete is fully cracked; however, the seismic forces may be as large as the diagonal cracking shear.*

21.5.10.3 Wall thickness

The wall thickness shall be not less than $\ell_u / 20$.

21.5.10.4 Reinforcement

The requirements specified in Clause 21.5.4 shall apply.

21.5.10.5 Distributed reinforcement

Both vertical and horizontal distributed reinforcement shall be provided in such a manner that the reinforcement ratio for this distributed reinforcement is not less than 0.002 in each direction.

When the shear force assigned to the wall exceeds $0.18\phi_c\sqrt{f'_c}\,b_w \ell_w$,

a) the reinforcement ratio for both the vertical and horizontal distributed reinforcement shall be not less than 0.003 in each direction;

b) at least two curtains of reinforcement shall be provided;

c) the reinforcement spacing in each direction shall not exceed 400 mm; and

d) the horizontal reinforcement shall be anchored in accordance with Clause 21.5.5.3 for R_d = 2.0.

21.5.10.6 Concentrated reinforcement

When the shear force assigned to the wall exceeds $0.18\phi_c\sqrt{f'_c}\,b_w \ell_w$, concentrated vertical reinforcement consisting of a minimum of four 15M reinforcing bars placed in at least two layers shall be provided at the end of the wall and at junctions of intersecting walls. The concentrated vertical reinforcement shall be at least tied as a compression member in accordance with Clause 7.6.5 and the ties shall be detailed as hoops.

21.5.10.7 Overturning resistance

The vertical tension force required to resist overturning may be provided by a combination of concentrated reinforcement and distributed vertical reinforcement. Plane-sections analysis may be used for these calculations. When the height-to-length ratio of the wall is less than 1.0, the distributed vertical reinforcement required for shear in accordance with Clause 21.5.10.8.7 shall not be considered to contribute to the overturning moment resistance of the wall.

Note: *While plane sections will often not remain plane in squat walls, the method correctly accounts for compatibility of concrete and reinforcement strains at any point along the wall and satisfies equilibrium.*

21.5.10.8 Shear design of squat walls

21.5.10.8.1 General
The shear design of squat walls can be done in accordance with the strut-and-tie method in Clause 11.4 and with Clauses 21.5.10.8.2 or may be done in accordance with Clauses 21.5.10.8.3 to 21.5.10.8.7.

21.5.10.8.2 Strut-and-tie models
When the strut-and-tie models in accordance with Clause 11.4 are used for squat walls, the additional requirements of Clause 21.5.9.6 shall apply.

21.5.10.8.3 Opening in walls
The effect of openings in walls shall be accounted for.

Note: *Strut-and-tie models in accordance with Clause 11.4 may be used to confirm that the diagonal compression due to shear force in a wall can be transmitted around an opening and may be used to determine the additional reinforcement required around an opening.*

21.5.10.8.4 Shear stress
The factored shear stress, v_f, shall be computed from the following equation, from the factored shear force and dimensions of the wall:

$$v_f = V_f/(b_w \cdot 0.8\,\ell_w)$$

Equation 21.16

21.5.10.8.5 Maximum shear stress
The factored shear stress applied to a wall shall not exceed $0.15\phi_c f_c'$.

21.5.10.8.6 Distributed horizontal reinforcement
The required amount of distributed horizontal reinforcement for shear, ρ_h, shall be determined from Equation 21.17 using a value of θ chosen between a maximum value of 45° and a minimum value of 30°; however the same value of θ shall be used to determine the required amount of distributed vertical reinforcement for shear in accordance with Clause 21.5.10.8.7.

$$\rho_h = v \cdot \tan\theta/\phi_s f_y$$

Equation 21.17

21.5.10.8.7 Distributed vertical reinforcement
The required amount of distributed vertical reinforcement required to resist shear shall be determined from Equation 21.18 as a function of the required amount of distributed horizontal reinforcement, ρ_h, determined in accordance with Clause 21.5.10.8.6, and the same value of θ used to determine the required amount of distributed horizontal reinforcement.

$$\rho_v = \rho_h \cot^2\theta - \frac{P_s}{\phi_s f_y A_g}$$

Equation 21.18

When the height-to-length ratio of the wall is less than 1.0, the distributed vertical reinforcement required for shear given by Equation 21.18 shall be in addition to the distributed vertical reinforcement that contributes to the overturning moment resistance of the wall determined in accordance with Clause 21.5.10.7.

Note: *When h_w/ℓ_w is less than 1.0, the shear force is resisted by diagonal compression stresses that are relatively uniform across the base of the wall. The required vertical reinforcement given by Equation 21.18 is needed to balance the vertical component of this compression.*

21.6 Conventional construction (R_d = 1.3 or 1.5)

21.6.1 General

21.6.1.1

All members of the structure assumed not to be part of the SFRS might be required to satisfy Clause 21.11 depending on the value of $I_E F_a S_a (0.2)$ and the calculated maximum interstorey drift as given in Clause 21.11.1.1.

21.6.1.2

The foundation supporting the SFRS shall satisfy the requirements of Clause 21.10.

21.6.1.3

The elements of the SFRS shall satisfy the requirements of Clauses 4 to 18 and 23, and the additional requirements of Clauses 21.6.2 to 21.6.4.

21.6.2 Moment-resisting frames (R_d = 1.5)

21.6.2.1 Required resistance

All members of a moment-resisting frame, including beams, columns and beam-column joints, shall have factored shear and bending moment resistances greater than the factored forces due to lateral loads calculated in accordance with *NBCC*.

21.6.2.2 Column ties

Except when $I_E F_a S_a (0.2)$ is less than 0.2 or the factored resistances of the columns are greater than the effects of factored loads calculated using $R_d R_o$ equal to 1.3, columns shall contain buckling prevention ties satisfying Clause 21.2.8.1 over the storey height when

a) the sum of the factored resistances of columns framing into a joint is not greater than the factored resistance of the beams framing into the joint; or

b) columns can develop plastic hinges because of their connection to rigid members such as transfer girders, foundations or discontinued walls, or because of their position at the base of the structure.

21.6.2.3 Shear resistance of frame members

Except when $I_E F_a S_a (0.2)$ is less than 0.2 or the factored resistance of the frame is greater than the effects of factored loads calculated using $R_d R_o$ equal to 1.3, frame members shall have a factored shear resistance not less than the lesser of

a) the sum of the maximum shear associated with development of factored moment strengths of the member at each restrained end of the clear span and the shear calculated using earthquake load combinations for gravity loads; or

b) the shear force resulting from design load combinations that include earthquake calculated using $R_d R_o$ equal to 1.3.

21.6.2.4 Shear resistance of joints in frames

21.6.2.4.1 Design shear forces

The design shear forces acting in a beam column joint shall be those induced by the factored moments acting on the beam or beams framing into the joint. Where beams frame into the joint from two directions, each direction may be considered independently.

21.6.2.4.2 Factored shear resistance of joints

The factored shear resistance of the joint shall satisfy the requirements of Clause 21.4.6.2.

Note: *Additional requirements for beam-column joints are given in Clauses 7.7, 11.7, and 12.11.2.*

21.6.3 Shear walls (R_d = 1.5)

21.6.3.1 Minimum requirements

All shear walls shall meet the requirements of Clause 14.

21.6.3.2 Anchorage of horizontal reinforcement

Anchorage of horizontal reinforcement shall be in accordance with requirements of Clause 21.5.5.3.

21.6.3.3 Design of squat shear walls

The design of squat walls with h_w / ℓ_w of 2.0 or less shall be done in accordance with the strut-and-tie method in Clause 11.4 or shall be done in accordance with the appropriate parts of Clause 21.5.10 as follows:

a) The shear design shall be in accordance with Clauses 21.5.10.8.3 to 21.5.10.8.7, except that the maximum factored shear stress given in Clause 21.5.10.8.5 shall be increased to $0.20\phi_c f_c'$.

b) The design for overturning resistance of squat walls shall be in accordance with Clause 21.5.10.7.

The additional requirements in Clauses 21.6.3.4 to 21.6.3.7 shall not apply.

21.6.3.4 Design shear force

The factored shear force envelope determined in accordance with *NBCC* shall be increased by the ratio of the factored bending resistance to factored bending moment both calculated at the base of the wall; however, the factored shear force need not be taken larger than that resulting from design load combinations including earthquake, with load effects calculated using $R_d R_o$ equal to 1.3.

21.6.3.5 Shear resistance

The shear resistance of a flexural wall with h_w / ℓ_w greater than 2.0 shall be determined using the procedures of Clause 11.3 except that the maximum shear resistance of the wall shall not exceed $V_{r,max} = 0.2\phi_c f_c' b_w d_v$, where the effective shear depth, d_v, of a wall need not be taken less than $0.8\ell_w$.

21.6.3.6 Ductility requirements above potential hinge region

At every section above the potential plastic hinge region, the distance from the extreme compression fibre to the neutral axis, c, determined by plane sections analysis for the factored axial load acting on the wall and a bending moment causing the maximum compression strain ε_{cu} at the extreme compression fibre, shall not exceed $0.6\ell_w$. If the distance from the extreme compression fibre to the neutral axis, c, exceeds $0.3\ell_w$, concentrated vertical reinforcement consisting of a minimum of four bars placed in at least two layers shall be provided at the ends of all walls. This reinforcement shall be at least tied as a compression member in accordance with Clause 7.6.5 and the ties shall be detailed as hoops.

Note: *The intent is to ensure that if the shear wall was subjected to a sufficiently large bending moment, vertical reinforcement at the tension end of the wall will yield before concrete will crush at the compression end of the wall. The compression strain depth c depends primarily on the geometry of the cross section, the concrete strength and the axial compression force applied to the wall.*

21.6.3.7 Additional requirements at base of wall

21.6.3.7.1 Height of potential plastic hinge region

Shear walls designed with $R_d = 1.5$ are expected to experience yielding of vertical reinforcement when subjected to the design earthquake forces. The region of possible yielding shall be assumed to extend a minimum distance of $1.0\ell_w$ above the critical section where the vertical reinforcement will first yield.

21.6.3.7.2 Splices

Over the height defined in Clause 21.6.3.7.1, splices of the vertical reinforcement shall satisfy Clause 21.2.7.2.1.

21.6.3.7.3 Wall thickness

Over the height defined in Clause 21.6.3.7.1, the wall thickness shall be not less than $\ell_u / 20$ except as permitted by Clauses 21.5.3.3, but no case shall be less than $\ell_u / 25$.

Note: *The minimum wall thickness according to Clause 14.1.7 is $\ell_u / 25$.*

21.6.3.7.4 Concentrated reinforcement

Over the height defined in Clause 21.6.3.7.1, concentrated vertical reinforcement consisting of a minimum of four bars placed in at least two layers shall be provided at the ends of all walls. This reinforcement shall be at least tied as a compression member in accordance with Clause 7.6.5 and the ties shall be detailed as hoops.

21.6.3.7.5 Ductility

Over the height defined in Clause 21.6.3.7.1, the distance from the extreme compression fibre to the neutral axis, c, determined by plane sections analysis for the factored axial load acting on the wall and a bending moment causing the maximum compression strain ε_{cu} at the extreme compression fibre, shall not exceed $0.5\ell_w$.

Note: *The intent is to ensure that the vertical reinforcement at the tension end of the wall will yield before concrete will crush at the compression end of the wall. The compression strain depth c depends primarily on the geometry of the cross section, the concrete strength, and the axial compression force applied to the wall.*

21.6.4 Two-way slabs without beams ($R_d = 1.3$)

21.6.4.1

The factored slab moment at support including earthquake effect shall be determined for factored load combinations including earthquake effects. All reinforcement provided to resist M_s, the portion of slab moment balanced by support moment, shall be placed within the column strip (see Clause 4.1).

21.6.4.2

The fraction of the moment, M_s, determined using Equation 13.5 shall be resisted by reinforcement placed within the effective width b_b. The effective slab width for exterior and corner connections shall not extend beyond the column face a distance greater than c_t, measured perpendicular to the slab span.

21.6.4.3

Not less than one-half of the reinforcement in the column strip at a support shall be placed within the effective slab width b_b.

21.6.4.4

Not less than one-quarter of the top reinforcement at the support in the column strip shall be continuous throughout the span.

21.6.4.5

Continuous bottom reinforcement in the column strip shall be not less than one-third of the top reinforcement at the support in the column strip.

21.6.4.6

Not less than one-half of all bottom middle strip reinforcement and all bottom column strip reinforcement shall be continuous and shall develop its yield strength at the face of support as specified in Clause 13.8.5.1.

21.6.4.7

At discontinuous edges of the slab, all top and bottom reinforcement at a support shall be developed at the face of support as specified in Clause 13.8.5.1.

21.6.4.8

At the critical section for columns specified in Clause 13.3.3.1, two-way shear caused by factored gravity loads shall not exceed $0.4V_c$, where V_c shall be calculated as specified in Clause 13.3.4 for non-prestressed slabs and in Clause 18.12.3.3 for prestressed slabs. This requirement may be waived if the slab design satisfies the requirements of Clause 21.11.4.2.

21.7 Tilt-up construction (R_d = 1.5 or 2.0)

21.7.1 General

21.7.1.1 Application

Clause 21.7 provides seismic design requirements for reinforced concrete wall panels ranging from solid wall panels to wall panels with large openings (frames). All tilt-up wall panels shall meet the requirements of Clause 23.

21.7.1.2 Types of seismic-force-resisting systems

The *NBCC* specifies three types of seismic-force-resisting systems for concrete tilt-up construction. Clauses 21.7.1 to 21.7.4 provide design requirements for concrete tilt-up walls and frames designed with $R_d \geq 1.5$. Clause 21.7.5 provides additional requirements for concrete tilt-up walls and frames designed with R_d = 2.0.

Note: *Limited Ductility (R_d = 1.5) walls and frames may be designed using a force-based approach, while moderately ductile (R_d = 2.0) walls and frames are designed using a displacement-based approach that explicitly accounts for the inelastic displacement demands on wall panels.*

21.7.1.3 Governing ultimate limit state

21.7.1.3.1 Ductile limit states

All tilt-up construction with $R_d \geq 1.5$ shall be designed such that the governing ultimate limit state of the tilt-up walls is ductile. Acceptable limit states include
a)　rocking of individual wall panels or wall panel groups;
b)　sliding along the base of the tilt-up wall; or

c)   for panels with large openings (frames), yielding of the beams and columns.

Note: *Rocking of individual wall panels or wall panel groups might require yielding of panel-to-panel shear connectors and/or tie-down connectors. Sliding along the base of walls can be difficult to achieve unless walls have a simple configuration, and post-earthquake damage due to sliding can be difficult to repair.*

21.7.1.3.2 Non-ductile limit states

The following non-ductile ultimate limit states shall be prevented:

a)   failure of any connection between the wall panels and roof diaphragm; and

b)   shear failure of a wall panel or portion of a wall panel.

21.7.1.4 Building lateral period

When established methods of mechanics considering roof diaphragm flexibility are used to determine the fundamental lateral period of a tilt-up building in accordance with the *NBCC*, the wall panels in the building shall meet the requirements for moderately ductile (R_d = 2.0) walls and frames.

Note: *When the influence of the flexible diaphragm is accounted for in the calculation of the building period, a displacement-based approach is used to account for the increased inelastic displacement demands on wall panels due to the flexible roof diaphragm.*

21.7.2 Seismic force demands

21.7.2.1 In-plane shear

21.7.2.1.1 Factored in-plane shear force

Wall panels shall be designed for the factored in-plane shear forces transferred to the panel by the diaphragm and the additional in-plane shear force due to the panel self-weight. A rational analysis shall be used to distribute the in-plane shear force to individual panels in one wall.

Note: *A rational analysis needs to account for the deformation compatibility of the panels and structural members used to transfer the in-plane shear such as drag struts and collector elements, as well as the deformation capacity of all connectors.*

21.7.2.1.2 Minimum shear resistance

Wall panels shall have a factored shear resistance greater than the shear force due to the effects of factored loads determined in accordance with Clause 21.7.2.1.1, but not less than the smaller of

a)   the shear force corresponding to the development of the factored overturning moment capacity for R_d = 1.5, or nominal overturning moment capacity for R_d = 2.0, of the individual wall panel or wall panel group; or

b)   the shear force resulting from design load combinations that include earthquake effect, with loads calculated using $R_d R_o$ equal to 1.3.

21.7.2.2 Out-of-plane shear and bending moment

Wall panels shall be designed for the out-of-plane bending moments and shear forces resulting from the wall panel acting as a flexural member spanning between lateral supports. Out-of-plane forces shall be calculated in accordance with the *NBCC*.

21.7.2.3 Transfer of forces to foundation

A reliable load path shall be provided to transfer all in-plane and out-of-plane forces to the supporting soil.

Note: *A direct or indirect connection to the wall footing may be used to provide a reliable load path. Slab-sliding resistance is difficult to predict and unreinforced or jointed floor slabs might not be reliable.*

21.7.2.4 Connection forces

21.7.2.4.1 Out-of-plane forces

The connections to wall panels shall be designed for the factored out-of-plane forces calculated in accordance with the requirements for the connection of elements to the structure in the *NBCC* assuming a flexible element (wall panel) and non-ductile connections; but not less than the forces specified in Clause 23.2.9.2.

Note: *The Cement Association of Canada's* Concrete Design Handbook *summarizes the appropriate values of C_p, A_p, and R_p to be used.*

21.7.2.4.2 In-plane forces

Wall panel connections that transfer in-plane shear forces shall be designed for the factored forces resulting from design load combinations that include earthquake effect, with loads calculated using $R_d R_o$ that depends on the type of connector as follows:

a) Ductile wall connections shall be designed using the same $R_d R_o$ as the seismic-force-resisting-system.

b) Non-ductile wall connections shall be designed using $R_d R_o$ equal to 1.3.

c) When a ductile structural member is used to transmit the in-plane shear force to a non-ductile connection, the non-ductile connection need not be designed for a force greater than the probable capacity of the ductile member.

21.7.3 Design requirements

21.7.3.1 Strength and ductility of connectors

All wall panel connectors shall be designed based on experimentally-established strengths and ductility or shall be designed in accordance with established design procedures such as given in Annex D.

Note: *The Cement Association of Canada's* Concrete Design Handbook *has information about standard tilt-up connectors that have experimentally established strengths and ductility.*

21.7.3.2 Overturning capacity

The required factored overturning moment capacity of wall panels shall be provided using any combination of the panel self weight, vertical load acting directly on the panel, panel-to-panel shear connectors and tie-down anchors. Panel-to-panel shear connectors shall be ductile. For other connections, if non-ductile connectors or anchors are used, the displacement compatibility of the connectors shall be accounted for. The effective length of the wall panel shall account for concrete spalling at the edge of the panel.

Note: *When a panel rocks up on a corner, the concrete outside of tied vertical reinforcement will likely spall off thereby reducing the effective length of the panel.*

21.7.3.3 Sliding shear resistance at base of wall

The required factored sliding shear resistance shall be provided by a combination of shear friction and shear connectors. All wall panels shall have shear connectors at the base and cannot rely only on shear friction. The sliding shear friction resistance between the base of wall panels and foundation shall be determined in accordance with Clause 11.5.1 with $c = 0$, $\mu = 0.75$, and $\phi_c = 0.65$

21.7.3.4 Shear design of solid panels

If the applied in-plane shear stress exceeds $0.1\phi_c\sqrt{f_c'}$, both vertical and horizontal distributed reinforcement shall be provided in such a manner that the reinforcement ratio for this distributed reinforcement is not less than 0.002 in each direction, and the shear design of the wall panel shall be in accordance with Clause 21.6.3.3.

21.7.3.5 Design of compression members

Portions of a wall panel, such as a column or edge of a solid panel, subjected to axial compression stresses greater than $0.09\phi_c f_c$ due to load combinations including earthquake effects shall be designed for slenderness effects in accordance with Clause 10.15 and shall contain tied vertical reinforcement in accordance with Clause 21.7.3.6.

Note: *The compression edge of unconnected panels are particularly prone to slenderness effects.*

21.7.3.6 Ties for tilt-up compression members

Where required according to Clause 21.7.3.5, tilt-up compression members shall contain vertical reinforcement with ties that satisfy the following:
a) The ties shall be arranged such that every corner and alternate longitudinal bar shall have lateral support.
b) Crossties or legs of overlapping hoops shall have centre-to-centre spacings not exceeding 350 mm.
c) The tie shall consist of a 10M bar or larger.
d) The maximum spacing of the ties shall not exceed the smallest of 16 times the diameter of the smallest enclosed longitudinal bar, 300 mm or the thickness of the panel.
e) In panels designed using $R_d = 2.0$, all ties shall be detailed as hoops or seismic crossties and the spacing of the ties shall not exceed 12 times the diameter of the smallest enclosed longitudinal bar.

21.7.4 Design of tilt-up frames

21.7.4.1 General

Wall panels with openings shall either be designed as solid panels with the forces transmitted around the openings or shall be designed as a frame in accordance with Clauses 21.7.4.2 to 21.7.4.5.

Note: *Strut-and-tie models in accordance with Clause 11.4 may be used to confirm that the forces applied to a solid wall panel can be transmitted around an opening by concrete compression stresses and additional reinforcement provided around the opening.*

21.7.4.2 Influence of panel connectors on ductility

When determining that the governing ultimate limit state of a tilt-up frame is ductile as required by Clause 21.7.1.3, the influence of forces due to panel connections shall be accounted for.

Note: *Panel-to-panel shear connections between panel legs (lower columns) can influence the load distribution or failure mode of the panel legs.*

21.7.4.3 Design for plastic hinging

21.7.4.3.1 Columns

When a plastic hinge is expected to form in a column, the following requirements shall be satisfied:
a) The column dimension perpendicular to the axis of bending shall not be less than 600 mm.

b)   The plastic hinge region shall not be taken less than 1.5 times the largest column dimension from the face of the joint.

c)   Over the plastic hinge region defined in Item b) and over the beam-column joint for a height not less than the largest column dimension, the column shall contain ties in accordance with Clause 21.7.3.6, except that

   i)   all ties shall be detailed as hoops or seismic crossties for panels designed using R_d = 2.0; and

   ii)   the spacing of the ties shall not exceed 12 times the diameter of the smallest enclosed longitudinal bar for panels designed using R_d = 1.5 and 8 times the diameter of the smallest enclosed longitudinal for panels designed using R_d = 2.0.

21.7.4.3.2 Beams

When a plastic hinge is expected to form in a beam, the plastic hinge region shall not be taken less than twice the beam depth from the face of the joint. Over the plastic hinge region, the beam shall contain 10M or larger stirrups spaced at the smallest of

a) $d/4$;

b)   12 times the diameter of the smallest longitudinal bar in the top or bottom layer of reinforcement; and

c)   300 mm.

In panels designed using R_d = 2.0, the stirrups shall be detailed as hoops.

21.7.4.3.3 Cover spalling

When calculating the factored moment resistance of a column or beam, the influence of cover spalling on the compression face of the member shall be accounted for.

21.7.4.4 Minimum shear resistance of frame members

The factored shear resistance of beams and columns resisting earthquake effects shall be not less than the lesser of

a)   the sum of the maximum shear force associated with development of the factored moment resistances for R_d = 1.5, or nominal moment resistances for R_d = 2.0, of the member at each restrained end of the clear span and the shear calculated using earthquake load combinations for gravity loads; or

b)   the shear force resulting from design load combinations that include earthquake effect, with loads calculated using $R_d R_o$ equal to 1.3.

The moment resistances in Item a) shall not be reduced due to cover spalling.

21.7.4.5 Design of joints

The joints of tilt-up frames shall satisfy the requirements of Clauses 21.4.6.1 to 21.4.6.3. The diameter of straight beam and column reinforcing bars passing through the joint shall not be larger than one-eighth of the panel thickness for R_d = 1.5, or one-tenth of the panel thickness for R_d = 2.0.

Note: *The maximum bar diameter does not apply to a bar that is anchored beyond the joint by a standard hook.*

21.7.5 Additional requirements for Moderately Ductile wall panels (R_d = 2.0)

21.7.5.1 Ductile roof diaphragm

The flexible roof diaphragm of low-rise tilt-up buildings designed for earthquake loads calculated using R_d = 2.0 shall be designed to exhibit ductile behaviour in accordance with the applicable CSA standard.

21.7.5.2 Inelastic displacement demand

The inelastic displacement demand at the top of the wall shall be calculated as $(\Delta_f R_d R_o - \Delta_f Y_w)$.

Note: *The inelastic displacement demand is assumed to equal the design displacement at the top of the wall panel minus an estimated elastic portion of the displacement.*

21.7.5.3 Displacement design of solid wall panels

The inelastic displacement capacity of the wall and connections shall be greater than the inelastic displacement demand.

Note: *The inelastic displacement demands in solid wall panels is usually concentrated in the panel-to-panel shear connections and/or the panel-to-base connections. The Cement Association of Canada's Concrete Design Handbook contains information about the displacement capacity of standard tilt-up connections.*

21.7.5.4 Displacement design of tilt-up frames

Panels with openings designed as frames shall not have rotational demands greater than 0.04 on any of the members. When the rotational demand on any member exceeds 0.02 radians, the entire frame shall satisfy all the requirements of Clause 21.4.

21.8 Precast concrete

21.8.1 General

The seismic design of ductile moment-resisting frames, ductile flexural walls, and moderately ductile flexural walls constructed using precast concrete shall comply with Clause 21.8. Solid precast wall panels may be designed in accordance with Clause 21.7 if the wall panels also meet the requirements of Clause 23.

21.8.2 Ductile moment-resisting frames constructed using precast concrete (R_d = 4.0)

21.8.2.1

Ductile moment-resisting frames with ductile connections constructed using precast concrete shall satisfy the following requirements, as well as all requirements for ductile moment-resisting frames constructed with cast-in-place concrete:

a) the factored shear resistance for connections computed as specified in Clause 11.5.1 shall be greater than or equal to 150% of the shear calculated as specified in Clause 21.3.1.5.1 or 21.3.2.7.1; and

b) mechanical splices of beam reinforcement shall be located not closer than $h/2$ from the joint face and shall meet the requirements of Clause 21.2.7.3.

21.8.2.2

Ductile moment-resisting frames with strong connections constructed using precast concrete shall satisfy the following requirements as well as all requirements for ductile moment-resisting frames constructed with cast-in-place concrete:

a) the requirements of Clause 21.3.1.1 b) shall apply to segments between locations where flexural yielding is intended to occur as a result of design displacements;

b) the factored resistance of the strong connection, S_r, shall be not less than S_p;

c) primary longitudinal reinforcement shall be made continuous across connections and shall be developed outside both the strong connection and the plastic hinge region; and

d) column-to-column connections shall have a factored resistance not less than $1.4S_p$. At column-to-column connections, the factored resistance shall be not less than 0.4 times the maximum probable bending resistance for the column within the storey height and the factored shear resistance of the connection shall be not less than that determined in accordance with Clause 21.3.2.7.1.

21.8.2.3

Ductile moment-resisting frames constructed using precast concrete and not meeting the requirements of Clause 21.8.2.1 or 21.8.2.2 shall comply with the acceptance criteria for moment frames based on structural testing (ACI 374.1) and the following requirements:

a) the details and materials used for the test specimens shall be representative of those used in the structure; and

b) the design procedure used to proportion the test specimens shall define the mechanism by which the frame resists gravity and earthquake effects and shall establish acceptance values for sustaining that mechanism. Portions of the mechanism that deviate from code requirements shall be contained in the test specimens and shall be tested to determine upper bounds for acceptance values.

21.8.3 Ductile shear walls constructed using precast concrete (R_d = 3.5 or 4.0)

Ductile shear walls constructed using precast concrete shall meet all of the requirements of Clause 21.5 for cast-in-place ductile shear walls and shall contain strong connections. The factored resistance of the strong connection, S_r, shall be not less than S_p.

21.8.4 Moderately ductile shear walls constructed using precast concrete (R_d = 2.0)

21.8.4.1

Moderately ductile shear walls constructed using precast concrete shall meet all of the requirements of Clause 21.5 for cast-in-place moderately ductile walls unless they are designed in accordance with Clause 23, in which case the requirements of Clause 21.7 shall apply.

21.8.4.2

In connections between wall panels, yielding shall be restricted to steel elements or reinforcement. If connections between the wall panels and the foundations are relied on for energy dissipation, the reinforcement shall be adequately anchored to both the wall panel and the foundation to develop the probable strength of reinforcement, in accordance with Clause 12.

21.8.4.3

Elements of the connection that are not designed to yield shall develop at least 150% of the specified yield strength of the yielding element.

21.9 Structural diaphragms (R_d = 2.0, 2.5, 3.5, or 4.0)

21.9.1 General

Floor and roof systems acting as structural diaphragms to transmit and transfer forces induced by earthquake ground motions shall be designed in accordance with Clauses 21.9.2 to 21.9.8.

21.9.2 Design forces

Design forces for diaphragms and their connections shall comply with the requirements of the *NBCC*.

CSA Group standard A23.3-14

21.9.3 Diaphragm systems

21.9.3.1

A diaphragm shall be idealized as a system consisting of the following components arranged to provide a complete load path for the forces:
a) chords proportioned to resist diaphragm moments as tensions and compression forces;
b) collectors arranged to transfer the forces to, from, and between the vertical SFRSs; and
c) either
  i) shear panels to transfer forces to, from, and between the chords and collectors; or
  ii) continuous strut-and-tie in-plane shear trusses.

21.9.3.2

Diaphragm elements shall be made effectively continuous by the provisions for force transfer at all edges and ends. Embedment, tying, and anchorage shall be provided at all edges of shear panels to transfer shears to adjacent chords, collectors, and shear panels. Collectors shall be anchored to the vertical SFRSs.

21.9.4 Reinforcement

21.9.4.1

The minimum reinforcement ratio for structural diaphragms shall comply with Clause 7.8. Reinforcement spacing in each direction in non-post-tensioned floor and roof systems shall not exceed 500 mm.

Reinforcement provided for shear strength shall be continuous and shall be distributed uniformly across the shear plane.

21.9.4.2

The diameter of the bars used in diaphragm struts, ties, chords, and collector elements shall not exceed one-sixth of the minimum element dimension at the bar location.

21.9.4.3

All continuous reinforcement in struts, ties, chords, and collector elements shall be anchored or spliced as specified in Clauses 12 and 21.2.7.3. Anchorage and splice lengths for reinforcement not contained within confinement reinforcement or buckling prevention ties shall be increased by 50% or, for splices, laps shall be staggered with at least one lap length from the end of one lap to the start of the next.

21.9.4.4

Splices of tensile reinforcement in the chords and collector elements of diaphragms shall develop the yield strength of the reinforcement. Mechanical and welded splices shall comply with Clauses 21.2.7.3 and 21.2.7.4, respectively. Type 2 splices shall be required where mechanical splices are used to transfer forces between collectors and the vertical components of the SFRS.

21.9.4.5

Bonded prestressing tendons used as primary reinforcement in diaphragm chords or collectors shall be proportioned in such a manner that the stress due to design seismic forces does not exceed 400 MPa. Precompression from unbonded tendons may be used to resist diaphragm design forces if a complete load path is provided.

21.9.5 Monolithic concrete systems

21.9.5.1
Slabs serving as shear panels shall be not less than 50 mm thick for joist and waffle systems and 100 mm for all other systems.

21.9.5.2
The factored shear resistance of a shear panel shall be taken as

$$V_r = A_{cv}(0.2\,\phi_c\sqrt{f_c'} + \phi_s\,\rho_n\,f_y) \le 0.8\,\phi_c\,A_{cv}\sqrt{f_c'}$$

Equation 21.19

21.9.5.3
Chords, collectors, struts, and ties shall be proportioned to have compressive stresses less than $0.2f_c$ or shall be provided with buckling prevention ties. The dimensions of the section shall provide for a minimum cover of 2-1/2 bar diameters, but not less than 50 mm for all longitudinal reinforcement, and a minimum clear spacing of three diameters, but not less than 40 mm at splices and anchorage zones.

21.9.6 Precast systems

21.9.6.1
Cast-in-place composite and non-composite toppings may be used to serve as shear panels. Composite toppings shall be not less than 50 mm thick and non-composite toppings not less than 65 mm thick. The surface of the previously hardened concrete on which composite topping slabs are placed shall be clean, free of laitance, and intentionally roughened.

21.9.6.2
The factored shear resistance of a shear panel shall be taken as

$$V_r = \phi_s\,A_{cv}\,\rho_n\,f_y \le 0.6\,\phi_c\,A_{cv}\sqrt{f_c'}$$

Equation 21.20

where A_{cv} is calculated based on the thickness of the topping slab. The required web reinforcement shall be distributed uniformly in both directions. Where welded wire fabric is used as the distributed reinforcement, the wires parallel to the span of the precast elements shall be spaced not less than 250 mm on centre.

21.9.6.3
Chords, collectors, struts, and ties shall comply with Clause 21.9.5.3.

21.9.7 Composite systems

21.9.7.1
Composite concrete toppings on steel decks may be used as shear panels. The composite toppings shall be not less than 60 mm thick above the top of the flutes.

21.9.7.2
The factored shear resistance of composite toppings on steel decks may be taken from manufacturer's data, with appropriate modifications of the published data to account for the effects of reverse cyclic loading.

21.9.7.3

For decks bounded by steel beams and girders designed as full composite members with headed stud shear connectors, the shear resistance of a reinforced topping slab shall be taken as

$$V_r = \phi_s A_{cv} \rho_n f_y \leq 0.6 \phi_c A_{cv} \sqrt{f'_c}$$

Equation 21.21

where A_{cv} is calculated based on the topping thickness above the flutes.

21.9.7.4

Chords, collectors, struts, and ties may be structural steel and/or reinforced concrete sections. Structural steel members used for this purpose shall have headed stud shear connectors designed to transfer the shear forces from the topping. Reinforced concrete sections shall comply with Clause 21.9.5.3.

21.9.8 Construction joints

All construction joints in diaphragms shall comply with Clause 6.3. Contact surfaces shall be treated as specified in Clause 11.5.

21.10 Foundations (R_d = 1.3, 1.5, 2.0, 2.5, 3.5, or 4.0)

21.10.1 General

21.10.1.1

Foundations resisting earthquake-induced forces or transferring earthquake-induced forces between a structure and the ground may be designed in accordance with Clause 21.10.2 if the foundation meets the limitations given in Clause 21.10.2.1; otherwise, they shall be designed using the general method specified in Clause 21.10.3.

21.10.1.2

The requirements of Clause 21.10 for piles, drilled piers, caissons, and slabs-on-grade shall be in addition to the requirements specified in Clause 15.

21.10.2 Design of foundations restrained against rotation

21.10.2.1 General

Foundations, including foundation walls and footings, that are restrained from rotating by structural elements may be designed in accordance with Clauses 21.10.2.2 to 21.10.2.3 if the structure restraining foundation movement is shown to have sufficient stiffness and strength to prevent significant increase in displacement of the SFRS; otherwise, the foundation shall be designed in accordance with Clause 21.10.3.

Note: *Examples of foundations that are restrained against rotation include: foundations that are tied down by soil anchors, foundations supported on piles and foundations supporting shear walls that are connected by multiple diaphragms to foundation walls supported on separate foundations. Foundation movements, which may be determined using the procedures in Clause 21.10.3.3.1, can influence the distribution of forces between the foundation and the restraining structure.*

21.10.2.2 Factored resistance

Foundations shall have a factored overturning resistance and a factored shear resistance, including factored shear resistance of walls and factored sliding shear resistance of footings, not less than required to resist the smaller of

a) the factored gravity loads and the nominal overturning capacity of the SFRS and the corresponding shear force; or

b) the forces from design load combinations that include earthquake effects calculated using $R_d R_o$ equal to 1.3.

21.10.2.3 Design of foundation walls restrained by diaphragms

When an SFRS is designed using $R_d \geq 2.0$, all foundation walls that provide the restraint to foundation movement required by Clause 21.10.2.1 due to being interconnected by multiple diaphragms shall be designed for the forces determined in accordance with Clause 21.5.2.2.9. In addition, all foundation walls that are part of the SFRS shall be designed in accordance with Clause 21.5.2.2.4.

Note: *When an SFRS is designed using $R_d < 2.0$, consideration should be given to the large shear forces that can develop due to bending moment reversals in the wall from diaphragm forces.*

21.10.3 Design of foundations — General method

21.10.3.1 General

Foundations, including foundation walls, shall be designed to meet the requirements of Clauses 21.10.3.2 to 21.10.3.4.

21.10.3.2 Factored resistance

21.10.3.2.1 General

All foundations shall satisfy both of the following requirements:

a) The factored overturning resistance of foundations, including foundation walls and footings, shall satisfy one of Clauses 21.10.3.2.2 to 21.10.3.2.4.

b) The factored shear resistance of foundations, including factored shear resistance of walls and factored sliding shear resistance of footings, shall not be less than that required to resist the factored gravity loads and the shear force corresponding to the required factored overturning resistance in Item a); but need not exceed the forces from design load combinations that include earthquake effects calculated using $R_d R_o$ equal to 1.3.

21.10.3.2.2 Maximum required overturning resistance

The overturning capacity of a foundation calculated using a bearing stress in the soil or rock equal to 1.5 times the factored bearing resistance and all other resistances equal to 1.3 times the factored resistance need not exceed the overturning moment resulting from design load combinations that include earthquake effects calculated using $R_d R_o$ equal to 1.0. The factor of 1.3 shall not apply to the portion of resistance to uplift or overturning resulting from gravity loads.

Note: *Overstrength in the bearing resistance of soil or rock can result in a very small increase in overturning capacity of the foundation. Thus, the minimum overstrength is applied to the resistance and the forces are calculated using $R_d R_o$ equal to 1.0 rather than 1.3.*

21.10.3.2.3 Capacity-protected foundations

Except as given in Clauses 21.10.3.2.2 and 21.10.3.2.4, foundations shall have a factored overturning resistance greater than or equal to what is required to resist the factored gravity loads and the overturning capacity of the SFRS given below:

	$R_dR_o/\gamma_w \leq 2.5$	$R_dR_o/\gamma_w > 2.5$
Overturning capacity of SFRS:	Nominal	Probable

When the SFRS is not a concrete wall, the equivalent overstrength factor for the SFRS shall be substituted for γ_w. In lieu of a more detailed analysis, γ_w may be taken equal to R_o.

21.10.3.2.4 Not capacity-protected (NCP) foundations

Foundations that are not restrained against rotation may be designed as NCP foundations if it can be shown that the SFRS and the members not considered part of the SFRS can tolerate the increased displacements. Foundations that are restrained by flexible structures may also be designed as NCP foundations if it can be shown that the restraining structure can also tolerate the increased displacements.

Note: *Examples of foundations that cannot be designed as NCP foundations include foundations tied down by soil anchors, foundations supported on piles, raft foundations, and foundations supporting walls that are restrained by a stiff structure consisting of multiple diaphragms connected to large foundation walls. The procedures in Clause 21.11 can be used to demonstrate that the members not considered part of the SFRS and a flexible restraining structure have adequate displacement capacity.*

NCP foundations shall satisfy the requirements of Clauses 21.10.3.3.3 and 21.10.3.4, and shall have a factored overturning resistance not less than what is required to resist the factored gravity loads and the larger of
a)   75% of the nominal overturning capacity of the SFRS; or
b)   the overturning moment resulting from design load combinations that include earthquake effects calculated using $R_d R_o$ equal to 2.0.

21.10.3.3 Foundation movements

21.10.3.3.1 General

The increased displacements due to movements of foundations shall be accounted for in the design of the SFRS and in the design of the members not considered part of the SFRS.

Note: *A description of how to estimate foundation movements are given in the explanatory notes of the Cement Association of Canada's* Concrete Design Handbook.

21.10.3.3.2 Movements of capacity-protected foundations

When the factored overturning resistance of a foundation satisfies Clause 21.10.3.2.1 or 21.10.3.2.2, the foundation movements may be calculated using a static analysis. The footing rotation is calculated as the difference in vertical displacements at the "toe" and "heel" of the footing, divided by the length of footing, ℓ_f. The analysis shall account for the assumed bearing stress distribution in the soil or rock to resist the applied loads and the corresponding stiffness of the soil or rock.

In lieu of a more detailed analysis, the interstorey drift ratio of the building determined from a fixed-base model shall be increased at every level, including immediately above the footing, by an interstorey drift ratio equal to the footing rotation, in radians.

In lieu of a more detailed analysis, the footing rotation may be estimated from Equation 21.22 when the applied overturning moment is sufficiently large to cause the "heel" of the footing to up-lift, which occurs when $M_f > P_f \ell_f/6$.

$$\theta = 0.3 \left(\frac{q_s}{G_0} \right) \left(\frac{\ell_f}{a_s} \right) \left\{ 1 + 2 \left(\frac{a_s}{b_f} \right)^{1.5} \right\}$$

Equation 21.22

where

θ = footing rotation in radians

a_s = length of uniform bearing stress in soil or rock required to resist the applied loads

b_f = width of footing (parallel to axis of rotation)

q_s = magnitude of uniform bearing stress in soil or rock required to resist the applied loads

Δ G_0 = initial shear modulus of soil or rock, which may be estimated in kPa units from $(\gamma_s V_s^2)/1000$ when γ_s, the density of soil or rock, is in kg/m³, and V_s, the shear wave velocity measured in the soil or rock immediately below the foundation, is in units of m/s

ℓ_f = length of footing (perpendicular to axis of rotation)

When the overturning moment is less than the moment required to cause up-lift, the footing rotation may be assumed to vary linearly from zero at $M_f = 0$ up to the rotation given by Equation 21.22 when $M_f = P_f \ell_f/6$.

21.10.3.3.3 Movements of not capacity-protected (NCP) foundations

Except as given below, the rotations of NCP foundations designed in accordance with Clause 21.10.3.2.4 shall be determined using a dynamic analysis that accounts for the reduced rotational stiffness of the footing due to footing uplift and soil deformation.

In lieu of using dynamic analysis to determine the increased drifts due to rotations of NCP foundations, the interstorey drift ratio of the building determined from a fixed-base model shall be increased at every level, including immediately above the footing, by a value equal to the largest of
a) 50% of the displacement at the top of the SFRS determined from a fixed-base model, divided by the height above the footing;
b) the rotation of the foundation calculated using Equation 21.22 when subjected to an overturning moment equal to the nominal overturning capacity of the SFRS; but need not exceed 3.0 times the rotation of the foundation when subjected to an overturning moment equal to the factored overturning resistance of the foundation; or
c) an interstorey drift ratio equal to 0.005.

Note: *The drift ratio increases are upper-bound values that can be used to avoid calculating the actual increased drift ratios in those cases where the SFRS and the members not considered part of the SFRS can easily tolerate the increases. When an NCP foundation is subjected to an overturning moment greater than its factored overturning resistance for Item b), the magnitude of uniform bearing stress in soil or rock required to resist the applied loads will exceed the factored bearing resistance when calculating rotations using Equation 21.22.*

21.10.3.4 Design of footings in NCP foundations

When NCP foundations are designed in accordance with Clause 21.10.3.2.4, the factored flexural and shear resistances of the footing shall be sufficient to develop the smallest of
a) the forces determined using a bearing stress in the soil or rock equal to 2.5 times the factored bearing resistance;

b) the forces resulting from an applied moment on the foundation equal to the nominal overturning resistance of the SFRS; or

c) the forces from design load combinations that include earthquake effects calculated using $R_d R_o$ equal to 1.3.

Note: *The plan dimensions of the footing, which control the foundation overturning resistance, are determined using the factored bearing resistance of the soil or rock. The required amount of flexural reinforcement in the footing and the shear design of the footing, which may be influenced by the shear span-to-depth ratio, must account for possible overstrength in the bearing resistance of soil or rock. The increase in bearing stress in soil or rock results in the same bearing stress resultant; but the vertical force is located closer to the toe of the foundation.*

21.10.4 Footings, foundation mats, and pile caps

21.10.4.1
Longitudinal reinforcement of columns and structural walls resisting forces induced by earthquake effects shall extend into the footing, mat, or pile cap and shall be fully developed for tension at the interface. In addition, the reinforcement shall satisfy the requirements of Clauses 21.10.4.2 to 21.10.4.4

21.10.4.2
Columns designed assuming fixed-end conditions at the foundation shall comply with Clause 21.10.2.1 and, if hooks are required, longitudinal reinforcement resisting flexure shall have 90° hooks near the bottom of the foundation, with the free end of the bars oriented toward the centre of the column.

21.10.4.3
Concentrated wall reinforcement shall extend to the bottom of the footing, mat, or pile cap and terminate with a 90° hook or mechanical anchorage.

21.10.4.4
Columns or areas of concentrated wall reinforcement that have an edge within one-half of the footing depth from an edge of the footing shall have the same transverse reinforcement provided below the top of the footing as provided above the footing. This transverse reinforcement shall extend into the footing a distance not less than the smaller of the depth of the footing, mat, or pile cap or the development length in tension of the longitudinal reinforcement.

21.10.4.5
Footings or pile caps that are a part of the foundation system resisting tension due to uplift forces shall have top reinforcement in each direction to satisfy the flexural requirements but not less than 0.001 times the gross sectional area in each direction.

21.10.5 Grade beams and slabs on grade

21.10.5.1
Grade beams and slabs designed to act as horizontal ties between pile caps or footings shall have continuous longitudinal reinforcement that shall be developed within or beyond the supporting column or anchored within the pile cap or footing at all discontinuities.

21.10.5.2

Grade beams not connected to a slab designed to act as horizontal ties between pile caps or footings shall be proportioned in such a manner that the smallest cross-sectional dimension shall be equal to or greater than the clear spacing between connected columns divided by 20, but need not be greater than 450 mm. Closed ties shall be provided at a spacing not exceeding one-half of the smallest cross-sectional dimension or 300 mm, whichever is smaller.

21.10.5.3

Grade beams and beams that are part of a mat foundation subject to flexure from columns that are part of the SFRS shall comply with Clause 21.3. Joints between these columns and grade beams shall comply with Clause 21.3.3.

21.10.5.4

Slabs on grade that resist seismic forces from walls or columns that are part of the SFRS shall be designed as structural diaphragms in accordance with Clause 21.9. The design drawings shall clearly state that the slab on grade is a structural diaphragm and part of the SFRS.

21.10.6 Piles

21.10.6.1

The requirements of Clauses 21.10.6.2 to 21.10.6.6 shall apply to concrete piles supporting structures designed for earthquake resistance.

21.10.6.2

Piles resisting tension loads shall have continuous longitudinal reinforcement over the length resisting design tension forces. The longitudinal reinforcement shall be detailed to transfer tension forces within the pile cap to supported structural members.

21.10.6.3

At sites where $I_E F_a S_a(0.2)$ is greater than 0.75 and the factored moment in piles, drilled piers, or caissons is greater than 75% of the factored moment resistance, these members shall have confinement reinforcement at the following locations:
a) at the top of these members for at least five times the largest member's cross-sectional dimension, but not less than 2000 mm below the bottom of the pile cap;
b) along the entire unsupported length plus the length specified in Item a) for members in air, in water, or in soil incapable of providing lateral support; and
c) within five member diameters of the interface between soils of different strength or stiffness.

21.10.6.4

For precast concrete driven piles, the length of transverse reinforcement provided shall be sufficient to account for potential variations in the elevation of pile tips.

21.10.6.5

The slenderness effects of piles shall be considered for the portion of the piles in air, in water, or in soil incapable of providing lateral support.

21.10.6.6

Pile caps incorporating batter piles shall be designed to resist the full compressive strength of the batter piles acting as short columns.

Note: *Batter pile systems should be used with extreme caution because subsoil deformations caused by earthquake effects can cause pile loads far in excess of those due to the seismic forces in the superstructure.*

21.11 Members not considered part of the seismic-force-resisting system (R_d = 1.5, 2.0, 2.5, 3.5, or 4.0)

Note: *One of the most common causes of building collapse during an earthquake is failure of one or more components of the gravity-load resisting frame. The intent of this clause is to ensure an adequate level of strength and/or ductility for all structural members not considered part of the seismic-force-resisting system (SFRS) but subjected to seismically induced deformations. This is accomplished by ensuring elements either remain elastic or yield in bending and contain appropriate detailing to ensure adequate shear resistances and flexural ductility.*

21.11.1 General

21.11.1.1 Application

Independent of the R_d used to design the SFRS, the requirements of Clause 21.11 shall apply to all members of the structure not considered part of the SFRS unless the building is located where $I_E F_a S_a(0.2)$ is less than or equal to 0.35 or the maximum interstorey drift ratio at any level is less than 0.005.

The interstorey drift ratio shall be determined from an analysis in accordance with the National Building Code of Canada, incorporating the effects of torsion, including accidental torsion, and accounting for foundation movements in accordance with Clauses 21.10.3.3.

21.11.1.2

Elements not required to resist either gravity or lateral loading shall be considered non-structural elements. These elements need not be detailed to the requirements of Clauses 21.11.2 to 21.11.4 provided that
a) the effects of non-structural elements are accounted for in the design of structural elements if the non-structural elements increase the seismically induced deformation of or the forces applied to a structural element; and
b) the non-structural elements are attached to the building in accordance with the *NBCC*.

21.11.1.3

Structural members not considered part of the seismic-force-resisting system (SFRS) shall meet the requirements of Clauses 21.11.2 to 21.11.4.

21.11.2 Seismic demands

21.11.2.1 General analysis requirements

An analysis shall be done to determine the forces and deformations induced in structural members not considered to be part of the SFRS due to seismic demands on the SFRS. Such an analysis shall satisfy the following:
a) the complete structure shall be displaced laterally to the design displacements $\Delta_f R_d R_o$, determined from an analysis in accordance with the *NBCC*, incorporating the effects of torsion; including accidental torsion, and accounting for foundation movements in accordance with Clauses 21.10.3.3;

b)   the inelastic displacement profile of the SFRS shall be accounted for;

Note: *Yielding of the SFRS causes concentration of deformations at plastic hinge locations. In lieu of using a nonlinear model of the SFRS, a linear model with appropriately reduced section properties at plastic hinge locations may be used to estimate the inelastic displacement profile.*

c)   cracking of concrete may be accounted for in determining the section properties used for structural members not considered part of the SFRS; however, an upper-bound estimate of effective stiffness shall be used in order to determine a safe estimate of the induced forces.

Note: *Low estimates of average section properties such as those given in Clause 21.2.5.2 are used for the SFRS to make a safe estimate of the design displacements of the overall building. Higher estimates of section properties must be used for each structural member not considered part of the SFRS to make a safe estimate of the forces induced in these members by the design displacements of the SFRS.*

d)   The increased displacements due to foundation movement determined in accordance with Clauses 21.10.3.3 shall be accounted for.

21.11.2.2 Simplified analysis of shear wall buildings

When the SFRS consists of shear walls or coupled walls, the requirements of Clauses 21.11.2.1 a), b), and d) may be satisfied by the following simplified analysis:

a)   The shear force and bending moments induced in members of a gravity-load resisting frame shall be determined at each level by subjecting the frame to the interstorey drift ratio given in Figure 21.1 for that level. The deflection Δ used to calculate the global drift ratio Δ/h_w in Figure 21.1 shall be the design lateral deflection at the top of the gravity-load resisting frame determined from an analysis in accordance with the *NBCC*, incorporating the effects of torsion, including accidental torsional moments, and accounting for foundation movements in accordance with Clause 21.10.3.3. The height of the building h_w shall be measured from the base of the plastic hinge zone in the SFRS. All gravity-load resisting frames shall be investigated in each direction of loading.

Note: *A gravity-load resisting frame may consist of a single column or wall and the attached beams or slabs or may consist of a combination of columns, walls, beams, and slabs.*

Figure 21.1
Envelope of minimum interstorey drift ratios over building height.

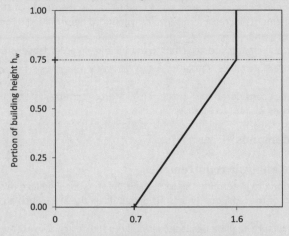

Ratio of interstorey drift ratio δ_i to global drift ratio Δ/h_w

b) The additional vertical load that is induced in vertical-load resisting members due to lateral deformation of the structure shall be determined by summing the shear forces from all horizontal members supported by the vertical-load resisting member using the procedure in Clause 21.11.2.2 a) for each level and summing the contribution for all levels above the level of interest.

c) Over the height of the plastic hinge region of the SFRS, the minimum curvature demand on all columns and walls shall not be taken less than the curvature demand associated with the inelastic rotational demands on the SRFS given in Clauses 21.5.7.2 and 21.5.8.4.2.

21.11.3 Design of members in gravity-load resisting frames

21.11.3.1 Shear resistance
The factored shear resistance of each structural member not considered part of the SFRS shall be sufficient to carry all shear forces due to factored gravity loads in addition to the shear forces induced in the member when the structure is subjected to the seismic demands given in Clause 21.11.2. The factored shear resistance need not exceed the maximum shear force that can develop due to the probable bending moment resistance of the member or adjacent members as given in Clauses 21.3.1.5.1 for beams and 21.3.2.7.1 b) for columns.

21.11.3.2 Resistance of members transferring gravity loads
The factored resistance of all members not considered part of the SFRS that transfer gravity loads from upper floors, including columns, walls, transfer girders and transfer slabs shall have sufficient capacity to resist all vertical forces due to factored gravity loads in addition to the vertical forces induced in the member when the structure is subjected to the seismic deformation demands given in Clause 21.11.2. The additional vertical force due to seismic deformations need not exceed the maximum axial force that can develop due to the nominal flexural resistance of the attached horizontal members.

21.11.3.3 Design of gravity-load resisting columns and bearing walls

21.11.3.3.1 Limitations on thin bearing walls
If the interstorey drift ratio determined from an analysis in accordance with the *NBCC* and incorporating the effects of torsion, including accidental torsional moments, exceeds 0.005 at any point in the structure, all bearing walls in the entire structure that are assumed to support gravity loads shall contain two layers of uniformly distributed reinforcement and the two layers shall have a minimum clear spacing of 50 mm.

Note: *The maximum interstorey drift at any point in the structure is used as an indicator of seismic demands and the flexibility of the structure. Walls with a single layer of reinforcement might not be able to tolerate cycles of combined in-plane and out-of-plane displacement.*

21.11.3.3.2 Plastic hinge regions of shear wall buildings
When the SFRS consists of shear walls or coupled walls, all columns and walls that support gravity loads shall meet the following requirements over the storeys that the SFRS is required to be detailed for plastic hinging to occur as specified in Clause 21.5.2.1:

a) All columns and walls shall have a curvature capacity greater than the curvature demand given in Clause 21.11.2.2 c). This requirement may be met by limiting the distance to the neutral axis, *c*, in these members determined from a plane sections analysis for the factored resistance or from Clause 21.5.7.4 to:

$$c \le \frac{\varepsilon_{cu}}{(2\theta_{id} + 0.004)} \cdot \ell_w \qquad \text{Equation 21.23}$$

where

ℓ_w = the length of the shear walls or coupled walls of the SFRS parallel to the distance c as defined in Clause 21.5.7.2 or 21.5.8.4.3

θ_{id} = the inelastic rotational demand on the SFRS determined from Clause 21.5.7.2 or Clause 21.5.8.4.2

ε_{cu} shall be taken as 0.0035 unless the compression region of the member is confined as a column. When ε_{cu} is taken greater than 0.0035 but less than 0.010, the amount of confinement reinforcement shall be determined with k_p taken as $(0.1 + 30\varepsilon_{cu})$. This reinforcement shall be provided over a distance of not less than c from the compression face of the member.

For shear walls designed with $R_d \le 2.5$, in lieu of determining the limiting distance c in columns and walls from Equation 21.23, the simplified procedure given in Clause 21.5.7.6 may be used.

b) Unless the design displacement $\Delta_f R_o R_d$ is less than $h_w / 200$: all columns shall contain at least buckling prevention ties in accordance with Clause 21.2.8.1 over the full height that the SFRS is required to be detailed for plastic hinging to occur, and; all walls shall have concentrated vertical reinforcement consisting of a minimum of four bars at each end of the wall and at the ends and intersections of all wall flanges. The concentrated reinforcement in walls shall be at least tied as a compression member in accordance with Clause 7.6.5, and the ties shall be detailed as hoops.

21.11.3.3.3 Design of columns and walls for plastic hinging

The seismic design requirements for columns and walls that are part of the gravity-load resisting frame depend on the inelastic flexural deformation demands on the member. When seismic demands on the gravity-load resisting frame are determined using a linear model, the design requirements shall be determined from how much the calculated induced bending moment due to the seismic deformation demands given in Clause 21.11.2 exceeds the factored bending resistance of the member.

Note: *Factored resistances are used to account for the uncertainty in displacement demands – the resistances are reduced rather than the displacement demands increased. Multiples of factored resistance are used as indicators of inelastic displacement demands.*

The calculated induced bending moment determined from a linear analysis shall be limited depending on the type of member, axis of bending in walls, and level of applied axial compression as follows:

Maximum calculated induced bending moment

Type of column or wall [*]	Axial compression [†]	
	$P_s \le 0.2 f_c A_g$	$P_s \ge 0.4 f_c A_g$
Ductile columns satisfying: Clauses 21.3.2.2, 21.3.2.5, 21.3.2.6, 21.3.2.7	$5.0 M_r$	$3.0 M_r$
Moderately ductile columns satisfying: Clauses 21.4.2.2, 21.4.4 except 21.4.4.2, 21.4.5	$3.0 M_r$	$2.0 M_r$
Tied columns satisfying Clause 7.6.5 and the dimensional limitations of Clause 21.4.2.2.	$2.0 M_r$	$1.5 M_r$
Other columns or walls tied as compression members in accordance with Clause 7.6.5 over full length	$1.5 M_r$	$1.0 M_r$

(Continued)

(Concluded)

Type of column or wall *	Axial compression †	
	$P_s \leq 0.2 f_c A_g$	$P_s \geq 0.4 f_c A_g$
Strong-axis bending of walls with two layers of reinf. and concentrated reinf. satisfying Clause 21.6.3.7.4	$1.2M_r^{\ddagger}$	$0.8M_r^{\ddagger}$
Strong-axis and weak-axis bending of walls with two layers of reinforcement.	$1.0M_r^{\ddagger}$	$0.7M_r^{\ddagger}$
Strong-axis and weak-axis bending of walls with single layer of reinforcement.	$0.7M_r^{\ddagger}$	$0.5M_r^{\ddagger}$

* All members shall satisfy the shear design requirements of Clause 21.11.3.1.
† Linear interpolation shall be used for intermediate levels of axial compression.
‡ The induced bending moment in these members shall be determined using $E_c I_e = 1.0 E_c I_g$.

21.11.3.4 Design of gravity-load resisting beams

21.11.3.4.1 General

The design requirements for beams that are part of the gravity-load resisting frame depend on the inelastic flexural deformation demands on the member. When seismic demands on the gravity-load resisting frame are determined using a linear model, the design requirements shall be determined from how much the induced bending moment due to the seismic deformation demands given in Clause 21.11.2 exceeds the factored bending resistance of the flexural member as follows:

Note: *Factored resistances are used to account for the uncertainty in displacement demands – the resistances are reduced rather than the displacement demands increased.*

a)   When the induced bending moment determined from a linear analysis is greater than the given limit, the member shall meet the corresponding detailing requirements as follows:

Induced bending moment	Beam detailing requirements
< $1.0M_r$	No additional requirements
≥ $1.0M_r$; but < $2.0M_r$	Limited ductility — Clause 21.11.3.4.2.
≥ $2.0M_r$; but < $3.0M_r$	Moderately ductile — Clause 21.11.3.4.3.
≥ $3.0M_r$; but < $5.0M_r$	Ductile — Clause 21.11.3.4.4.

b)   When the induced bending moment due to seismic deformation demands determined from a linear analysis is greater than 5.0 times the factored bending resistance, the design of the structure shall be modified to reduce the induced bending moment or increase the bending resistance of the member. The effect of these changes on the seismic demands in the rest of the gravity-load resisting frame shall be accounted for.

21.11.3.4.2 Detailing beams for limited ductility

When a beam in a gravity-load resisting frame requires limited ductility as given in Clause 21.11.3.4.1 a), the member shall meet all of the following requirements:

a) Throughout the length of the beam, at least two effectively continuous longitudinal bars shall be provided at both top and bottom, and stirrups meeting Clauses 21.11.3.1 and 11.2.8.2 shall be spaced at not more than $d/2$.

b) The positive moment reinforcement required by Clause 12.11.1 shall be anchored to develop the specified yield strength, f_y, in tension at the face of the support.

c) At the locations of flexural yielding, the flexural tension reinforcement shall not be less than $1.4 b_w d/f_y$, and the reinforcement ratio, ρ, shall not exceed 0.025.

21.11.3.4.3 Detailing beams for moderately ductile behaviour

When a beam in a gravity-load resisting frame requires moderate ductility as given in Clause 21.11.3.4.1 a), the member shall meet all of the following requirements:

a) All requirements given in Clause 21.11.3.4.2 except as modified below.

b) For a distance d on either side of a section where flexural yielding may occur, stirrups meeting Clause 21.11.3.1 shall be spaced the smaller of $d/4$ and 12 times the diameter of the smallest enclosed longitudinal bar.

c) All top longitudinal reinforcement terminated in a column shall extend to the far face of the column core and be anchored by a standard 90° hook located within the column core so as to develop the yield strength of the reinforcement.

21.11.3.4.4 Detailing beams for ductile behaviour

When a beam in a gravity-load resisting frame requires a high level of ductility as given in Clause 21.11.3.4.1 a), the member shall meet all of the following requirements:

a) All requirements given in Clause 21.11.3.4.3 except as modified below.

b) The clear span of member shall be not less than three times its effective depth.

c) The shear design of the member shall be in accordance with Clause 21.3.1.5.

d) For a distance d on either side of a section where flexural yielding may occur, the stirrups shall be detailed as hoops and seismic crossties and shall be spaced at the smaller of $d/4$ and 8 times the diameter of the smallest enclosed longitudinal bar.

e) Lap splices shall not be located within a distance d on either side of a section where flexural yielding may occur.

f) Transverse hoop reinforcement shall be provided over the depth of the beam-column joints and shall be spaced at a maximum of 8 times the diameter of the smallest enclosed longitudinal column bar.

21.11.4 Design of slab-column connections for seismic drift demands

21.11.4.1 Reduction of punching shear resistance due to drift demands

Where the maximum gravity load two-way shear stresses determined using seismic load combinations and excluding shear stresses from unbalanced bending moment, exceed R_ε times the limiting stresses in Clause 13.3.4 or 18.12.3.3, shear reinforcement shall be provided as specified in Clause 21.11.4.2, with R_ε calculated as follows:

$$R_E = \left(\frac{0.005}{\delta_i} \right)^{0.85} \le 1.0$$

Equation 21.24

where the interstorey drift ratio, δ_i, shall be determined in accordance with Clause 21.11.2. For shear wall or coupled wall buildings, the minimum interstorey drift ratios are given in Clause 21.11.2.2.

21.11.4.2 Design of shear reinforcement in slabs

When shear reinforcement is required by Clause 21.11.4.1, or the slab design is to qualify for the exemption in Clause 21.6.4.8, the following requirements shall be satisfied:

a) Shear reinforcement shall be provided in such a manner that the maximum gravity load two-way shear stresses v_f, excluding shear stresses from unbalanced moment, and determined using seismic load combinations, does not exceed $v_r = R_E(0.5v_c + v_s)$ with v_c calculated in accordance with Clause 13.3.8.3, 13.3.9.3, or 18.12.3.3, and with v_s calculated in accordance with Clause 13.3.8.5 or 13.3.9.4.

b) The factored shear stress resistance of the shear reinforcement, v_s, calculated in accordance with Clause 13.3.8.5, shall be not less than $0.3\sqrt{f'_c}$.

c) The factored shear stress resistance of the shear reinforcement shall be not less than that required by Clause 13.3.

d) Shear reinforcement shall be detailed in accordance with Clause 13.3, except shear reinforcement shall extend a minimum of $4d$ beyond the face of the column and stud spacing shall be $\leq d/2$.

22 Plain concrete

22.1 General

22.1.1

Clause 22 specifies requirements for the design of concrete members containing less reinforcement than the minimum amount specified for reinforced concrete members elsewhere in this Standard. The requirements of Clause 22 shall be limited to pedestals with $\ell_c/h \leq 3$, walls not exceeding 3 m in total height that have continuous vertical support, pad footings, spread footings, drilled piles, and slabs on grade. The requirements of Clause 22 shall be further limited to concretes with compressive strengths not less than 15 MPa.

22.1.2

Plain concrete shall not be used for structural members where ductility is required, such as for earthquake or blast resistance.

22.1.3

Plain concrete shall not be used for pile caps.

22.1.4

Plain concrete shall not be used for members relied on to transmit tension force.

22.2 Control joints

22.2.1

In plain concrete construction, control joints shall be provided to divide a structural member into discontinuous elements. The size of each element shall be limited to control stresses caused by restraint to movements from creep, shrinkage, temperature effects, and differential settlement.

22.2.2

In determining the number and location of control joints, consideration shall be given to

a)   the influence of climatic conditions;

b)   selection and proportioning of materials;

c)   mixing, placing, and curing of concrete;

d)   the degree of restraint to movement; and

e)   stresses due to load.

22.2.3

The locations and details of control joints shall be indicated on the drawings or in the specifications.

22.2.4

Concrete placement shall be interrupted only at control joints.

22.3 Design

22.3.1

The strength design of plain concrete members for factored flexural and axial loads shall be based on a linear stress-strain relationship in both tension and compression.

22.3.2

The flexural tensile strength of concrete may be considered in the design.

22.3.3

No strength shall be assigned to reinforcement that might be present.

22.3.4

The bearing stress on the concrete at the contact surface between supporting and supported members shall not exceed the permissible bearing stress for each surface as specified in Clause 10.8.

22.3.5

The entire cross-section of a member shall be considered in the design, except for footings cast against soil (see Clause 22.6.3).

22.4 Walls

22.4.1

22.4.1.1

The effective length factor, k, for walls braced at the top and bottom against lateral translation shall be as follows:

If restrained against rotation at one or both ends (top, bottom, or both)	0.8
If unrestrained against rotation at both ends	1.0

22.4.1.2

Except as specified in Clause 22.4.1.3, walls subject to combined flexure and axial load shall be proportioned so that the maximum compressive stress under factored loads is limited to

$$0.75\phi_c f_c'\left[1-\left(\frac{k\ell_c}{32t}\right)^2\right]$$

and the maximum tensile stress shall not exceed $0.37\lambda\phi_c\sqrt{f_c'}$. The minimum eccentricity shall be $0.1t$.

22.4.1.3

Plain concrete walls of solid rectangular cross-section may be designed in accordance with the following equation if the resultant of all factored loads, including the effects of lateral loads applied to the wall, is located within the middle third of the overall thickness of the wall:

$$P_f = 0.45\phi_c \alpha_1 f_c' A_g\left[1-\left(\frac{k\ell_c}{32t}\right)^2\right]$$

Equation 22.1

22.4.2

The horizontal length of wall to be considered effective for each concentrated load or reaction shall not exceed the centre-to-centre distance between loads or the width of bearing plus four times the wall thickness.

22.4.3

Plain concrete bearing walls shall have a thickness of not less than 1/20 of the unsupported height or length, whichever is shorter.

22.4.4

Foundation walls and exterior basement walls shall be not less than 190 mm thick.

22.4.5

Walls shall be braced against lateral translation and keyed or dowelled to other intersecting members as required for lateral stability.

22.4.6

Not less than two 15M bars shall be provided around all window and door openings. Such bars shall extend at least 600 mm beyond the corners of the openings.

22.5 Pedestals

Pedestals subject to combined flexural and axial load shall be proportioned so that the maximum compression stress under factored loads does not exceed $0.75\phi_c f_c'$ and the maximum tension stress does not exceed $0.37\lambda\phi_c\sqrt{f_c'}$. The minimum eccentricity shall be $0.1h$.

22.6 Footings

22.6.1 Base area of footing

The base area of the footing shall be determined from forces and moments transmitted by the footing to the soil. The soil pressure shall be selected in accordance with the principles of soil mechanics.

Note: *See the* National Building Code of Canada *for information on limit states design of foundations.*

22.6.2 Minimum thickness

The specified thickness of plain concrete footings shall be not less than 200 mm.

22.6.3 Minimum thickness for calculations

For footings cast against soil, the overall thickness, h, used in calculations shall be taken as 50 mm less than the specified thickness.

22.6.4 Critical sections

22.6.4.1

The critical sections for moment shall be as specified in Clause 15.4.3.

22.6.4.2

For the location of critical sections for moment and shear, circular or regular polygonal concrete columns or pedestals may be treated as square members with the same area.

22.6.5 Strength in bending

The factored resistance in bending shall be based on a maximum stress in tension of $0.37\lambda\phi_c\sqrt{f_c'}$ and a maximum stress in compression of $0.75\phi_c f_c'$.

22.6.6 Shear resistance

22.6.6.1 One-way action

22.6.6.1.1

The maximum factored shear, V_f, shall be computed at a distance h from the face of the support. Sections located closer to the support may be designed for the same shear.

22.6.6.1.2

The factored shear resistance for rectangular sections, V_r, shall be

$$V_r = \frac{2}{3}\left(0.18\lambda\phi_c\sqrt{f_c'}\,bh\right)$$

Equation 22.2

22.6.6.2 Two-way shear

22.6.6.2.1

The maximum factored shear, V_f, shall be computed at a critical section perpendicular to the plane of the footing and located so that its perimeter, b_o, is a minimum, but not closer than $h/2$ to the perimeter of the concentrated load or reaction area.

22.6.6.2.2

The factored shear resistance, V_r, shall be

$$V_r = \frac{2}{3}\left(\left(1+\frac{2}{\beta_c}\right)0.18\,\lambda\,\phi_c\sqrt{f_c'}\,b_o h\right)$$

Equation 22.3

but

$$V_r \leq \frac{2}{3}(0.37\,\lambda\,\phi_c\sqrt{f_c'}\,b_o h)$$

Equation 22.4

22.7 Slabs on grade

Plain concrete slabs shall be designed with due regard to loading and foundation conditions.

Notes:

1) *See CSA A23.1 for additional information on slabs on grade including tolerances for slab thickness, surface flatness, and concrete mix designs.*

2) *See ACI 360R and 302R for information on the design and the construction of slabs on grade and for guidance on curing, curling, and crack control.*

22.8 Drilled piles

22.8.1

In addition to meeting the design eccentricity requirement specified in Clause 15.2, the cross-sections of uncased drilled piles shall be designed for a minimum eccentricity of $0.1d_p$.

22.8.2

The outer 25 mm layer of uncased drilled piles shall be neglected when the pile resistance and the stresses in the pile shaft due to factored loads are determined.

22.8.3

For uncased drilled piles, a reduction factor of 0.8 shall be applied to the maximum factored stresses specified in Clause 22.8.5.

22.8.4

The stability of portions of piles without lateral restraint from soil shall be considered.

Δ **22.8.5**

Drilled piles subjected to combined factored bending moments, shears, and compression loads shall be proportioned so that stresses do not exceed the following limits:

a) flexure and axial loads:

    i)   extreme fibre stress in compression:

$$0.75\phi_c f_c'\left[1-\left(\frac{k\ell_c}{28d_p}\right)^2\right]$$

    ii)   extreme fibre stress in tension:

$$0.37\lambda\,\phi_c\sqrt{f_c'}$$

b) shear:

$$v_r = \frac{3}{4}(0.18\,\lambda\,\phi_c\sqrt{f_c'})$$

Equation 22.5

22.8.6

For proportioning of the pile bell, see Clause 15.8.2.4.

23 Tilt-up wall panels

23.1 General

23.1.1

The requirements of Clauses 23.1.2 to 23.7.2 shall apply to tilt-up wall panels.

23.1.2

The requirements of Clauses 3 to 15 shall apply to tilt-up wall panels, except as modified by the requirements of Clauses 23.1.1 and 23.1.3 to 23.7.2. The seismic design of tilt-up wall panels shall also meet the requirements of Clause 21, where applicable.

23.1.3

Tilt-up panels are slender vertical flexural slabs that resist lateral wind or seismic loads and are subject to very low axial stresses. Because of their high slenderness ratios, they shall be designed for second-order P-Δ effects to ensure structural stability and satisfactory performance under specified loads.

23.2 Design requirements

23.2.1 Effective panel height

The effective panel height, ℓ, shall be the centre-to-centre distance between lateral supports.

23.2.2 Minimum panel thickness

The minimum panel thickness for a prismatic load-bearing panel without stiffening elements shall be 140 mm.

23.2.3 Maximum height-to-thickness ratio

The maximum effective panel height-to-thickness ratio shall be
a)   50 for panels with a single mat of reinforcement at mid-depth; or
b)   65 for panels with a mat of reinforcement near each face.

Δ   ### 23.2.4 Minimum reinforcement

Minimum panel reinforcement shall comply with Clauses 10.5, 14.1.8, and 21.7, as applicable.

23.2.5 Concrete cover and tolerances

23.2.5.1

If quality control procedures are followed so that the designer can be assured that the tilt-up contractor meets the requirements in CSA A23.4 with respect to dimensional control, reinforcement placement, aggregate size, concrete quality, and curing, the cover requirements specified in CSA A23.4 may be used, except as required by Clause 23.2.5.2. Otherwise, the design shall comply with CSA A23.1.

23.2.5.2

The cover and quality of concrete in tilt-up panels that have to withstand the effects of aggressive or corrosive environments shall comply with CSA A23.1.

23.2.5.3

Tilt-up panels requiring a fire resistance rating or forming part of a firewall shall meet the thickness and cover requirements of the applicable building codes.

23.2.6 Thermal effects

The design of tilt-up panels shall take into account the effects of any thermal gradients that could occur through the panel.

23.2.7 Sandwich panels

Sandwich wall panels, in addition to resisting applied loads, shall be designed to resist effects such as composite or non-composite action between wythes, thermal effects between wythes where composite action is assumed, thermal bridging, lifting stresses imposed on one wythe by the other, and vertical and torsional support of one wythe by the other.

23.2.8 Connections

23.2.8.1

The design of connections to tilt-up panels shall take into account in-plane and out-of-plane forces; the additional effects of shrinkage, creep, temperature, movement; and the seismic design requirements where applicable.

23.2.8.2

The resistances of connections between the tilt-up panels and any adjoining elements shall be greater than the effects of factored loads.

23.2.9 Structural integrity

23.2.9.1

Tension ties shall be provided in the transverse and longitudinal directions of the structure and around the perimeter of the structure to effectively tie the elements together and to provide a load path to the lateral load resisting system. Panels supported at the top by steel roof deck, wood decking, or plywood only shall have additional tie struts or continuity ties perpendicular to the wall and connecting the panel back to the primary roof structural members, such as beams or joists. The ties shall be designed for the forces specified in Clause 23.2.9.2. Steel ties shall have a minimum thickness of 3 mm.

23.2.9.2

Connection of tilt-up panels to floor and roof diaphragms, including at the base, shall be designed for the required out-of-plane forces specified in Clause 23.2.8.1. The connection horizontal force shall not be less than 2% of the total factored vertical load that the wall is designed to carry at the level of support or 5 kN per metre length of wall, whichever is greater.

Δ   ### 23.2.10 Effective reinforcement

Where vertical reinforcement is placed in two layers, the effect of compression reinforcement shall be ignored when calculating flexural resistance for out-of-plane forces.

23.3 Analysis and design

23.3.1 Flexure and axial load interaction and slenderness effects

23.3.1.1
All moment and deflection calculations specified in Clauses 23.3.1.2 to 23.3.2 are based on simple support conditions top and bottom. For other support and fixity conditions, moments and deflections shall be calculated using established principles of structural mechanics.

23.3.1.2
In lieu of a more accurate analysis, the procedures specified in Clauses 23.3.1.3 to 23.3.1.5 shall be used when the stress due to factored vertical loads at the cross-section under consideration meets the following requirement:

$$\frac{P_{wf} + P_{tf}}{A_g} < 0.09\phi_c f_c'$$

Equation 23.1

Δ #### 23.3.1.3
The factored moment, M_f, shall be determined at the mid-height of the panel and shall be equal to

$$M_r = M_b \delta_b$$

Equation 23.2

where

$$M_b = \frac{W_f \ell^2}{8} + P_{tf}\frac{e}{2} + \left(P_{wf} + P_{tf}\right)\Delta_o$$

$$\delta_b = \frac{1}{1 - \dfrac{P_f}{\phi_m K_{bf}}} \geq 1.0$$

where

$$P_f = P_{wf} + P_{tf}$$

$$K_{bf} = \frac{48 E_c I_{cr}}{5 \ell^2}$$

where

$$I_{cr} = \frac{bc^3}{3} + \frac{E_s}{E_c}A_{s,\text{eff}}(d - c)^2$$

and the member resistance factor, ϕ_m, is taken as 0.75.

23.3.1.4
The initial out-of-straightness, Δ_o, at mid-height of the panel shall take into account the effects of non-planar and flexible casting beds, deformations caused by the tilting process, thermal gradients through the panel, and creep, and shall not be taken less than $\ell/400$.

23.3.1.5
The factored resisting moment, M_r, provided by the panel cross-section shall be such that

$M_r \geq M_f$ **Equation 23.3**

The resisting moment may be calculated using an effective area of reinforcement, $A_{s,eff}$, as follows:

$$A_{s,eff} = A_s + \frac{P_f}{\phi_s f_y}\left(\frac{h}{2d}\right)$$ **Equation 23.4**

Δ   ## 23.3.2 Deflection limitations

Unless serviceability requirements lead to the conclusion that a larger deflection is acceptable, the horizontal mid-height deflection, Δ_s, under specified lateral and vertical loads shall not exceed $\ell/100$, but it shall not be greater than can be tolerated by attached structural or non-structural elements. The horizontal mid-height deflection may be computed as follows:

$$\Delta_s = \frac{5M_s\ell^2}{48E_cI_e} = \frac{M_s}{K_{bs}}$$ **Equation 23.5**

where
M_s = $M_{bs}\delta_{bs}$

  where

  $$M_{bs} = \frac{W_s\ell^2}{8} + P_{ts}\frac{e}{2} + (P_{ws} + P_{ts})\Delta_o$$

  $$\delta_{bs} = \frac{1}{1 - \dfrac{P_s}{K_{bs}}} \geq 1.0$$

    where
    P_s = $P_{ws} + P_{ts}$

    $$K_{bs} = \frac{48E_cI_e}{5\ell^2}$$

and where I_e is as specified in Clause 9.8.2.3, substituting M_s for M_a.
Note: *Because I_e depends on M_s, iteration is necessary.*

23.4 Effects of openings

23.4.1 Design width

23.4.1.1
A design width on each side of an opening shall support the combined factored axial and lateral loads from its tributary width. This design width shall be used over the full height of the panel.

23.4.1.2
The design width shall be limited to
a)   12 times the thickness of a solid panel; or
b)   12 times the thickness of the structural wythe of a sandwich panel.

23.4.2 Tributary width

The tributary width for design shall be the design width plus one-half the width of adjacent openings (see Figure 23.1).

**Figure 23.1
Effect of openings on design width, b_d**
(See Clause 23.4.2.)

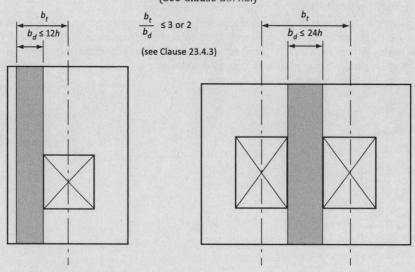

23.4.3 Ratio of tributary width to design width

Unless a more detailed analysis, accounting for the internal force effects, indicates otherwise, the ratio of tributary width to design width shall not exceed 3. For panels with a single layer of reinforcement and $\ell / h > 40$, the ratio shall not exceed 2.

23.5 Concentrated loads or reactions

23.5.1 Design width

The design width, b_d, for a panel subjected to concentrated loads or concentrated reactions shall be determined from Figure 23.2.

CSA Group standard A23.3-14

Δ

Figure 23.2
Effect of concentrated loads or reactions on design width, b_d
(See Clauses 3.2, 23.5.1, and 23.5.4.)

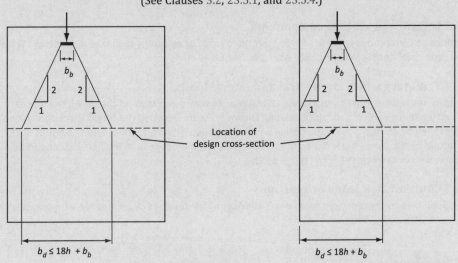

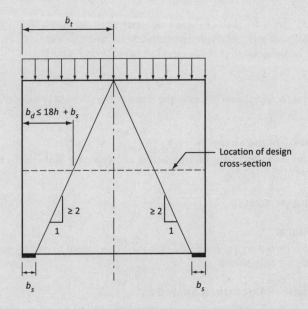

23.5.2 Bearing

The allowable bearing stress at the contact surface between supported and supporting elements and between any intermediate bearing elements shall not exceed the bearing resistance of either element, as specified in Clause 10.8 or 11.4.4.

23.5.3 Lateral and vertical components

The design of connections to panels for concentrated loads or reactions shall take into account lateral and vertical components in accordance with Clause 11.6.4.

23.5.4 Tributary width for vertical and lateral loads

For panels with concentrated vertical and lateral reactions at the bottom of the panel, the tributary width assumed for vertical and lateral loading shown in Figure 23.2 and the total factored axial load and moment shall be carried only by the design width. For panels with continuous lateral support at the top and bottom of the panel, the factored moment at the design cross-section shall be assumed to be uniformly distributed across the full panel width.

23.5.5 Concentrated loads or reactions

Panels subjected to concentrated loads or reactions shall be designed in accordance with Clause 11.4.

23.6 Shear

23.6.1 In-plane shear

23.6.1.1

Where tilt-up panels are used as shear walls, analysis of the panels shall include the effects of in-plane stresses, local buckling, roof diaphragm connections, and panel stability. The connections between panels shall be designed so that the expected failure mode is ductile.

23.6.1.2

The design for factored shear forces in the plane of the panel shall meet the requirements of Clause 11.3.

23.6.2 Out-of-plane shear

The design for shear forces due to loads acting perpendicular to the face of the panel shall meet the requirements of Clause 11.3.

23.7 Lifting stresses

23.7.1 General

The stresses imposed on a panel during lifting shall be limited to ensure that the performance of the erected panel is not impaired.

23.7.2 Elastic — Uncracked analysis

Analysis of tilt-up panels during the lifting operation shall be based on elastic uncracked section properties using specified loads. The effects of suction between the panel and the floor and impact loads from crane equipment shall be considered.

Annex A (informative)
Excerpts from CSA A23.1-14, Concrete materials and methods of concrete construction

Notes:
1) *This Annex is not a mandatory part of this Standard.*
2) *This Annex provides portions from an unpublished draft of CSA A23.1-14.*
3) *A number of clauses from CSA A23.1-14 that are especially important to design engineers are reprinted in this Annex with their original numbering. It is expected that CSA A23.1 will be revised during the life of this Standard, resulting in minor changes to or renumbering of clauses. If this occurs, users should refer to the revised Standard. Users should also check CSA A23.4 and CAN/CSA-S413 to determine whether the requirements of those two Standards affect the applicability of the clauses reprinted in this Annex.*
4) *This Annex reprints only those portions of Clause 2 of CSA A23.1 applicable to the other clauses reprinted in this Annex.*

A.1

2 Reference publications
This Standard and CSA A23.2 refer to the following publications, and where such reference is made, it shall be to the edition listed below, including all amendments published thereto.

CSA Group
A23.3-14
Design of concrete structures

CAN/CSA-G30.18-M92 (R2007)
Billet-steel bars for concrete reinforcement

CAN/CSA-S6-06
Canadian Highway Bridge Design Code

CAN/CSA-S413-07
Parking structures

CAN/CSA-S474-04 (R2009)
Concrete structures

S478-95 (R2007)
Guideline on durability in buildings

CAN/CSA-S806-02 (R2007)
Design and construction of building components with fibre-reinforced polymers

W59-03 (R2008)
Welded steel construction (metal-arc welding)

W186-M1990 (R2007)
Welding of reinforcing bars in reinforced concrete construction

ACI (American Concrete Institute)

201.2R-08
Guide to Durable Concrete

ANSI/AWS (American National Standards Institute/American Welding Society)

D1.1:2008
Structural Welding Code — Steel

PCA (Portland Cement Association)

IS001.08T, 2001
Effects of Substances on Concrete and Guide to Protective Treatments

4 Materials and concrete properties

4.1 Requirements for concrete and alternative methods for specifying concrete

4.1.1 Durability requirements

4.1.1.1 General

4.1.1.1.1

Concrete that will be subjected in service to weathering, sulphate attack, a corrosive environment, or any other process of deterioration covered by this Standard shall meet the requirements of Clauses 4.1.1.1 to 4.1.1.10 and 7.4 and Tables 1 to 4 and 20, as appropriate.

Notes:

1) *Although minimum requirements for concrete durability are specified, it should be stressed that a durable concrete also depends upon the use of high-quality materials, an effective quality control program, and good quality of work in manufacturing, placing, finishing, and curing the concrete.*

2) *For exposure conditions not covered by this Standard and for general information on concrete durability, see ACI MCP, ACI 201.2R, and PCA IS001.08T.*

3) *For parking structures, highway bridges, and offshore structures, see CSA S413, CAN/CSA-S6, and CAN/CSA-S474, respectively.*

6.6 Fabrication and placement of reinforcement

6.6.1 General

The sizes and spacing of the reinforcement and its concrete cover shall be as shown on the construction drawings.

6.6.2 Hooks and bends

6.6.2.1 General

Unless otherwise stated on the construction drawings, fabrication and detailing of hooks shall be as specified in Clauses 6.6.2.2 to 6.6.2.5.

6.6.2.2 Standard hooks

The term "standard hook" as used herein shall mean

a) a semicircular bend plus an extension of at least four bar diameters but not less than 60 mm at the free end of the bar;

b) a 90° bend plus an extension of at least 12 bar diameters at the free end of the bar; or

c) for stirrup and tie anchorage only, either a 90° or 135° bend plus an extension of at least six bar diameters but not less than 60 mm at the free end of the bar. Hooks for stirrups or ties shall have a 135° bend, unless the concrete surrounding the hook is restrained from spalling (see CSA A23.3).

d) Hooks for crossties shall have a bend of a least 135° at one end and a standard tie hook with a bend of at least 90° at the other end. The hooks shall engage peripheral longitudinal bars. The 90° hooks of successive crossties engaging the same longitudinal bar shall be alternated end for end.

6.6.2.3 Minimum bend diameter

The diameter of the bend measured on the inside of the bar for standard hooks, except stirrup and tie hooks, shall be not less than the values in Table 16.

6.6.2.4 Stirrup and tie hooks

6.6.2.4.1

The inside diameter of bends and 90° hooks for stirrups and ties shall be not less than four bar diameters.

6.6.2.4.2

The inside diameter of 135° hooks shall be not less than 20 mm, four bar diameters, or the diameter of the bar enclosed by the hook, whichever is greater.

6.6.2.4.3

The inside diameter of bends in welded wire fabric for stirrups or ties shall be not less than four wire diameters. Bends with an inside diameter less than eight wire diameters shall be not less than four wire diameters from the nearest welded intersection.

6.6.2.5 Bending

6.6.2.5.1

All bars shall be bent at temperatures greater than 16 °C, unless bending tests that are otherwise in accordance with CSA G30.18 confirm that bars bent at temperatures below 16 °C are acceptable.

Note: *See Stecich et al., 1984.*

6.6.2.5.2

No bars partially embedded in concrete shall be field bent except as shown on the drawings or as permitted by the owner.

Notes:

1) *Black (1973) states "Construction conditions might require straightening of bars embedded in concrete. Field bending should not be done without authorization of the engineer. The engineer must determine if the bars should be bent cold or if heating should be employed. Bends should be gradual and must be straightened as required.*

"Tests have shown that Grade 400 reinforcing bars can be cold bent and straightened up to 90° at or near the minimum bend diameter. If cracking or breaking occurs, heating to a maximum temperature of 820 °C should be beneficial for avoiding overstressing and damage for subsequent bars. Bars that fracture during bending or straightening must be spliced outside the bend region.

"Heating must be done in a manner that will avoid damage to the concrete. If the bend area is within approximately 150 mm of the concrete, some protective insulation might be required. Heating of the bar

should be controlled by temperature-indicating crayons or other suitable means. The heated bars should not
be artificially cooled until they have naturally cooled to at least 300 °C".

2)   *See Stecich et al., 1984.*

6.6.2.5.3

The bending tolerances shall be sufficiently accurate to comply with the placing and protection tolerances specified in Clause 6.6.8.

6.6.3 Spirals

6.6.3.1

The size and spacing of spirals shall be as shown on the construction drawings.

6.6.3.5

Anchorage of spiral reinforcement shall be provided by 1-1/2 extra turns of spiral rod or wire at each end of the spiral unit.

6.6.3.6

Splices in spirals shall have a minimum 50 bar diameter lap plus a 90° hook around a longitudinal bar at the free end or shall be welded in accordance with CSA W186.

6.6.3.7

The reinforcing spiral shall extend from the floor level in any storey or from the top of the footing to the level of the lowest horizontal reinforcement in the slab, drop panel, or beam above.

6.6.3.8

Where beams or brackets are not present on all sides of a column, ties shall extend above the termination of the spiral to the bottom of the slab or drop panel.

6.6.3.9

In a column with a capital, the spiral shall extend to a plane at which the diameter or width of the capital is twice that of the column.

6.6.4 Ties

6.6.4.1

The size, spacing, and arrangement of ties shall be as shown on the construction drawings. When welded wire mesh of random length is used as tie reinforcement, the required splice length shall be indicated on the drawings.

6.6.5 Spacing of reinforcement

6.6.5.1

The spacing of bars shall be as shown on the construction drawings.

6.6.5.2

The clear distance between parallel bars or parallel bundles of bars shall be not less than 1.4 times the bar diameter, not less than 1.4 times the nominal maximum size of the coarse aggregate, and not less than 30 mm. This clear distance shall apply to the distance between a contact lap splice and adjacent splices or bars.

6.6.5.3

Where parallel reinforcement is placed in two or more layers, the bars in the upper layer shall be placed directly above those in the bottom layer.

Note: *The intention of this Clause is to provide adequate spacing for concrete to be placed in the presence of closely spaced mats of steel.*

6.6.5.6

Spacing of post-tensioning ducts shall be as specified in Clause 6.8.

6.6.6 Concrete cover

6.6.6.1 General

Concrete cover shall be measured from the concrete surface to the nearest deformation (or surface, for smooth bars or wires) of the reinforcement. Reinforcement includes ties, stirrups, and main reinforcement. For textured architectural surfaces, concrete cover shall be measured from the deepest point of the textured surface.

6.6.6.2 Specified cover for reinforced and prestressed concrete

6.6.6.2.1

The specified cover for reinforcement shall be based on consideration of life expectancy, exposure conditions, protective systems, maintenance, and the consequences of corrosion.

Notes:
1) *The desired service life should be established early in the design process (see CSA S478).*
2) *Requirements for corrosion protection can be influenced by the ease of access for inspection and repair and the feasibility and cost of repair or replacement.*
3) *Service life can be improved by*
   a) *increasing the cover and the duration of moist curing;*
   b) *reducing the water-to-cementing materials ratio;*
   c) *adding supplementary cementing materials, corrosion inhibitors, or membranes; and*
   d) *improving drainage.*
4) *As the positioning of reinforcement is not exact, in some cases it is advisable to increase the specified cover to ensure adequate protection. Service life can be extended by reducing the variability in placement of reinforcement.*

6.6.6.2.2

The specified cover for fibre-reinforced polymer bars, grids, and tendons in prestressed and reinforced concrete shall be in accordance with CAN/CSA-S806.

6.6.6.2.3

The specified cover for steel reinforcement, tendon sheaths, and ducts in prestressed and reinforced concrete shall be not less than the largest of the limits for each relevant exposure condition in Table 17.

Note: *See Clause 6.6.8 for tolerances of concrete cover and Clause 6.8.2.4 for additional cover requirements.*

6.6.6.3 Cover for fire resistance

Where a structural concrete member is required to have a fire-resistant rating, the minimum cover for reinforcement shall be specified by the owner.

Note: *Information can be found in Appendix D of the NBCC.*

6.6.8 Tolerances for location of reinforcement

Unless otherwise specified by the owner, reinforcement, prestressing steel, and post-tensioning ducts shall be placed within the following tolerances:

a) concrete cover: ±12 mm (however, the concrete cover shall in no case be reduced by more than 1/3 of the specified cover);

b) where the depth of a flexural member, the thickness of a wall, or the smallest dimension of a column is

   i) 200 mm or less: ±8 mm;

   ii) larger than 200 mm but less than 600 mm: ±12 mm; and

   iii) 600 mm or larger: ±20 mm;

c) lateral spacing of bars: ±30 mm;

d) longitudinal location of bends and ends of bars: ±50 mm; and

e) longitudinal location of bends and ends of bars at discontinuous ends of members: ±20 mm.

Note: *Where reinforcement is added to provide a more rigid reinforcement mat or cage, i.e. in prefabricated reinforcing cage, such additional reinforcement is not subject to the tolerances of this clause except for the minimum cover requirements.*

6.6.10 Welding of reinforcement

6.6.10.1

Welding of reinforcement shall conform to the requirements of CSA W186. Weldable grade bars shall be used unless a fusion weld is employed.

6.6.10.2

Tack welding of reinforcing bars shall be performed in accordance with CSA W186.

6.7 Fabrication and placement of hardware and other embedded items

6.7.1 General

Clause 6.7 covers the fabrication and placement of hardware for concrete building structures that have been designed in accordance with CSA A23.3. The details and location of this hardware shall be shown on the construction drawings.

Note: *For reinforced concrete structures other than buildings, the owner should show clearly on the drawings and specifications any departures from the requirements of Clauses 6.7.2 to 6.7.5.*

6.7.3 Tolerances for placing anchor bolts and hardware

6.7.3.1

Unless otherwise specified by the owner, the location of anchor bolts and embedded items shall not vary from the dimensions shown on the erection drawings by more than the following (see also Figure 3):

a) 3 mm centre-to-centre of any two bolts within an anchor bolt group, where an anchor bolt group is defined as the set of anchor bolts that receives a single fabricated steel or precast concrete member;

b) 8 mm centre-to-centre of adjacent anchor bolt groups;

c) a maximum accumulation of 8 mm per 30 m along the established column line of multiple anchor bolt groups, but not to exceed a total of 30 mm. The established column line is the actual field line most representative of the centres of the as-built anchor bolt groups along a line of columns; and

d) 8 mm from the centre of any anchor bolt group to the established column line through that group.

The tolerances of Items (b), (c), and (d) apply to offset dimensions, as shown on the construction drawings and measured perpendicular to the nearest column line.

6.7.3.2

Vertical alignment variations for anchor bolts shall not exceed 3 mm or 1 mm in 40 mm, whichever is larger.

6.7.3.3

Slope variations for hardware serving as bearing plates shall not exceed 1 mm in 40 mm, with a maximum of 3 mm for plates having side dimensions less than 300 mm and a maximum of 5 mm for plates having side dimensions of 300 mm or larger.

6.7.4 Welding of hardware

6.7.4.1

Welding of steel hardware shall conform to the requirements of CSA W59 and CSA W47.1.

Note: *Welding procedures should be such that no damage to the concrete will result.*

6.7.4.2

Welding of reinforcing bars to hardware shall conform to the requirements of CSA W186 or to the requirements of CSA W47.1 and CSA W59 at the option of the Contractor.

Note: *Refer to Clause 6.6.10.1 for requirements for welding reinforcing bars.*

6.7.4.3

Material and equipment for stud welding of bars and anchors shall be compatible and shall be used in accordance with the recommendations of the manufacturers of the material and equipment.

Note: *See the Supplement to AWS D1.1/D1.1M.*

6.8 Post-tensioning

6.8.2 Unbonded tendons

6.8.2.4.1

The concrete cover to the anchorage, measured in a direction perpendicular to the tendon, shall be not less than 40 mm.

6.8.2.4.2

The stressing pocket shall be sufficiently deep so that the cover to the end cap, measured parallel to the tendon, will be at least 40 mm and the cover to the anchorage will be at least 60 mm.

Table 1
Definitions of C, F, N, A, and S classes of exposure
(See Clauses 3, 4.1.1.1.1, 4.1.1.5, 4.4.4.1.1.1, 4.4.4.1.1.2, 6.6.7.5.1, and 8.13.3, Tables 2 and 17, and Annex L.)

C-XL	Structurally reinforced concrete exposed to chlorides or other severe environments with or without freezing and thawing conditions, with higher durability performance expectations than the C-1 or A-1 classes.
C-1	Structurally reinforced concrete exposed to chlorides with or without freezing and thawing conditions. Examples: bridge decks, parking decks and ramps, portions of structures exposed to seawater located within the tidal and splash zones, concrete exposed to seawater spray, and salt water pools. For seawater or seawater-spray exposures the requirements for S-3 exposure also have to be met.
C-2	Non-structurally reinforced (i.e., plain) concrete exposed to chlorides and freezing and thawing. Examples: garage floors, porches, steps, pavements, sidewalks, curbs, and gutters.
C-3	Continuously submerged concrete exposed to chlorides, but not to freezing and thawing. Examples: underwater portions of structures exposed to seawater. For seawater or seawaterspray exposures the requirements for S-3 exposure also have to be met.
C-4	Non-structurally reinforced concrete exposed to chlorides, but not to freezing and thawing. Examples: underground parking slabs on grade.
F-1	Concrete exposed to freezing and thawing in a saturated condition, but not to chlorides. Examples: pool decks, patios, tennis courts, freshwater pools, and freshwater control structures.
F-2	Concrete in an unsaturated condition exposed to freezing and thawing, but not to chlorides. Examples: exterior walls and columns.
N	Concrete that when in service is neither exposed to chlorides nor to freezing and thawing nor to sulphates, either in a wet or dry environment. Examples: footings and interior slabs, walls, and columns.
N-CF	Interior concrete floors with a steel-trowel finish that are not exposed to chlorides, nor to sulphates either in a wet or dry environment. Examples: interior floors, surface covered applications (carpet, vinyl tile) and surface exposed applications (with or without floor hardener), ice-hockey rinks, freezer warehouse floors.
A-XL	Structurally reinforced concrete exposed to severe manure and/or silage gases, with or without freeze-thaw exposure. Concrete exposed to the vapour above municipal sewage or industrial effluent, where hydrogen sulphide gas might be generated, with higher durability performance expectations than A-1 class
A-1	Structurally reinforced concrete exposed to severe manure and/or silage gases, with or without freeze-thaw exposure. Concrete exposed to the vapour above municipal sewage or industrial effluent, where hydrogen sulphide gas might be generated. Examples: reinforced beams, slabs, and columns over manure pits and silos, canals, and pig slats; and access holes, enclosed chambers, and pipes that are partially filled with effluents.

(Continued)

Table 1 (Concluded)

A-2	Structurally reinforced concrete exposed to moderate to severe manure and/or silage gases and liquids, with or without freeze-thaw exposure. Examples: reinforced walls in exterior manure tanks, silos and feed bunkers, and exterior slabs.
A-3	Structurally reinforced concrete exposed to moderate to severe manure and/or silage gases and liquids, with or without freeze-thaw exposure in a continuously submerged condition. Concrete continuously submerged in municipal or industrial effluents. Examples: interior gutter walls, beams, slabs, and columns; sewage pipes that are continuously full (e.g., forcemains); and submerged portions of sewage treatment structures.
A-4	Non-structurally reinforced concrete exposed to moderate manure and/or silage gases and liquids, without freeze-thaw exposure. Examples: interior slabs on grade.
S-1	Concrete subjected to very severe sulphate exposures (Tables 2 and 3).
S-2	Concrete subjected to severe sulphate exposure (Tables 2 and 3).
S-3	Concrete subjected to moderate sulphate exposure and to seawater or seawater spray (Tables 2 and 3).
R-1	Residential concrete for footings for walls, columns, fireplaces and chimneys.
R-2	Residential concrete for foundation walls, grade beams, piers, etc.
R-3	Residential concrete for interior slabs on ground not exposed to freezing and thawing or deicing salts.

Notes:
1) *"C" classes pertain to chloride exposure.*
2) *"F" classes pertain to freezing and thawing exposure without chlorides.*
3) *"N" class is exposed to neither chlorides nor freezing and thawing.*
4) *All classes of concrete exposed to sulphates shall comply with the minimum requirements of S class noted in Tables 2 and 3. In particular, Classes A-1 to A-4 in municipal sewage elements could be subjected to sulphate exposure.*
5) *No hydraulic cement concrete will be entirely resistant in severe acid exposures. The resistance of hydraulic cement concrete in such exposures is largely dependent on its resistance to penetration of fluids.*

Table 16
Bend diameter for standard hooks
(See Clause 6.6.2.3.)

Bar size, mm	Minimum bend diameter,* mm		
	Steel grade		
	300R‡	400R or 500R	400W or 500W§
10	60	70	60
15	90	100	90
20	—	120	100
25	—	150	150
30	—	250	200
35	—	300	250
45	—	450†	400
55	—	600†	550
	—		

* *Bend diameters shall not be reduced by more than 10% from those listed unless otherwise permitted by the owner*

† *Special fabrication is required for bends exceeding 90° for bars of these sizes and grades.*

‡ *R refers to "Regular" grade.*

§ *W refers to "Weldable" grade*

Table 17
Concrete cover
(See Clauses 4.3.2.2.1 and 6.6.6.2.3.)

Exposure condition	Exposure class (see Tables 1 and 2)		
	N	F-1, F-2, S-1, S-2, S-3	C-XL, A-XL, C- 1, C-3, A-1, A-2, A-3
Cast against and permanently exposed to earth, including footings and piles	75 mm	75 mm	75 mm
Beams, girders, and columns	30 mm*	40 mm	60 mm
Slabs, walls, joists, shells, and folded plates	20 mm*	40 mm	60 mm
Ratio of cover to nominal bar diameter†	1.0*	1.5	2.0
Ratio of cover to nominal maximum aggregate size	1.0*‡	1.5	2.0

* *This refers only to concrete that will be continually dry within the conditioned space (i.e., members entirely within the vapour barrier of the building envelope).*

† *The cover for a bundle of bars shall be the same as that for a single bar with an equivalent area.*

‡ *The specified cover from screeded surfaces shall be at least 1.5 times the nominal maximum aggregate size to*

(Continued)

Table 17 (Concluded)

reduce interference between aggregate and reinforcement where variations in bar placement result in a cover smaller than specified.

Notes:

1) *Greater cover or protective coatings might be required for exposure to industrial chemicals, food processing, and other corrosive materials. See PCA IS001.08T.*

2) *For information on the additional protective measures and requirements for parking structures, see CSA S413.*

3) *For information on the additional protective measures and requirements for bridges, see CAN/CSAS6.*

Figure 3
Tolerances on anchor bolt placement
(See Clause 6.7.3.1.)

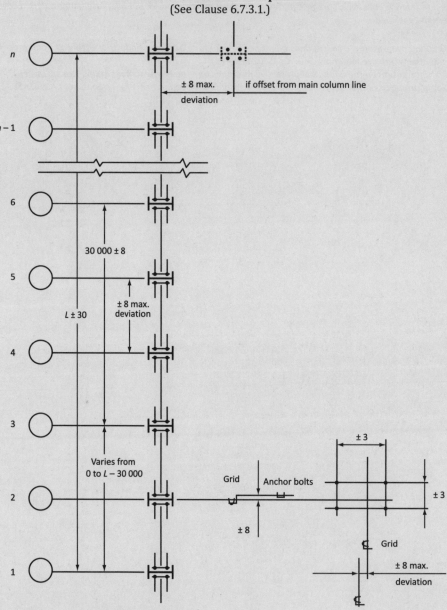

Note: *All measurements are in millimetres*

Annex B (informative)
Rectangular two-way slab systems with stiff supports on four sides

Note: *This Annex is not a mandatory part of this Standard.*

B.1 Introduction

B.1.1

This Annex applies to rectangular two-way systems where the slab is reinforced in two directions and supported on four sides by walls or stiff beams. It may be used to determine slab thicknesses and loads on supporting beams or walls and to determine the moments and shears in slabs.

B.1.2

In this Annex, a stiff supporting beam is one in which $b_w h_b^3 / \ell_n h_n^3$ is not less than 2.0.

B.2 Symbols

The following symbols apply in this Annex:

b_w	=	width of beam web
C_{ad}	=	moment coefficient for positive dead load moment in short span
C_{al}	=	moment coefficient for positive live load moment in short span
$C_a\text{neg}$	=	moment coefficient for negative moment in short span
C_{bd}	=	moment coefficient for positive dead load moment in long span
C_{bl}	=	moment coefficient for positive live load moment in long span
$C_b\text{neg}$	=	moment coefficient for negative moment in long span
h_b	=	overall depth of supporting beam
h_s	=	overall depth of slab
ℓ_a	=	clear span of a two-way slab in the short direction
ℓ_b	=	clear span of a two-way slab in the long direction
ℓ_n	=	clear span of supporting beam
m	=	ratio of short to long span of a two-way slab, equal to ℓ_a/ℓ_b
$M_{ad}\text{ pos}$	=	positive dead load moment in short span
$M_{al}\text{ pos}$	=	positive live load moment in short span
$M_a\text{ neg}$	=	negative moment in short span
$M_{bd}\text{ pos}$	=	positive dead load moment in long span
$M_{bl}\text{ pos}$	=	positive live load moment in long span
$M_b\text{ neg}$	=	negative moment in long span
w_{df}	=	factored dead load per unit area
w_f	=	factored load per unit area
w_{lf}	=	factored live load per unit area

CSA Group standard A23.3-14

B.3 Design method

B.3.1

The minimum slab thickness should be determined in accordance with Clause 13.2, but should not be less than
a)   100 mm;
b)   the perimeter of the slab divided by 140, in the case of slabs discontinuous on one or more edges; or
c)   the perimeter of the slab divided by 160, in the case of fully continuous slabs.

B.3.2

A two-way slab should be considered as consisting of strips in each direction, as follows:
a)   a middle strip, one-half of a panel in width, symmetrical about the panel centreline and extending through the panel in the direction in which moments are considered; and
b)   a column strip, one-half of a panel in width, occupying the two quarter-panel areas outside the middle strip.

B.3.3

Critical sections for moment should be assumed to be as follows:
a)   for negative moment, along the edges of the panel at the faces of the supports; and
b)   for positive moment, along the centrelines of the panels.

B.3.4

Negative bending moments per unit width for the middle strips should be computed in accordance with the following equations and the coefficients specified in Table B.1:
a)

$$M_a neg = C_a neg w_f \ell_a^2$$

Equation B.1

b)

$$M_b neg = C_b neg w_f \ell_b^2$$

Equation B.2

B.3.5

Positive bending moments per unit width should be computed as the sum of Equations B.3 and B.4 for the middle strip in the short direction and Equations B.5 and B.6 for the middle strip in the long direction, using the coefficients specified in Table B.2. These equations are as follows:
a)

$$M_{al} pos = C_{al} w_{lf} \ell_a^2$$

Equation B.3

b)

$$M_{ad} pos = C_{ad} w_{df} \ell_a^2$$

Equation B.4

c)

$$M_{bl} pos = C_{bl} w_{lf} \ell_b^2$$

Equation B.5

d)

$$M_{bd} pos = C_{bd} w_{df} \ell_b^2$$

Equation B.6

B.3.6

The bending moments in the column strips should be two-thirds of the bending moments in the middle strip.

B.3.7

Where the ratio, *m*, of short to long span is less than 0.5, the slab should be considered a one-way slab in the short direction, but reinforcement for negative moments required for *m* equal to 0.5 should be provided in the long direction.

B.3.8

At discontinuous edges of two-way slabs, a negative moment of three-quarters of the positive moment should be assumed.

B.3.9

In all cases, special reinforcement should be provided at exterior corners in accordance with Clause 13.12.5.

B.3.10

Where the negative moment on one side of a support is less than 80% of that on the other side, the difference should be distributed between the two slabs in proportion to their relative stiffnesses.

B.3.11

The shear stresses in the slabs should be computed on the assumption that the load, w_f, is distributed to the supports in accordance with Clause B.4.

B.4 Loads on slab supports

B.4.1

The loads on the supporting beams of a two-way rectangular panel may be assumed to be the load within the tributary areas of the panel bounded by the intersection of 45° lines from the corners and the median line of the panel parallel to the long side.

B.4.2

The bending moments in the supporting beams may be determined for design purposes by using an equivalent uniform load per unit length of beam for each panel supported, as follows:

a)   for the short span:

$$\frac{w_f \ell_a}{3} \qquad\qquad\qquad\qquad\text{Equation B.7}$$

a)   for the long span:

$$\frac{w_f \ell_a}{3} \times \frac{(3 - m^2)}{2} \qquad\qquad\qquad\qquad\text{Equation B.8}$$

Table B.1
Coefficients for negative moments
(See Clause B.3.4.)

$m =$ ℓ_a / ℓ_b	Coefficient	Case 1	Case 2	Case 3	Case 4	Case 5	Case 6	Case 7	Case 8	Case 9
1.00	$C_a neg$	—	0.045	—	0.050	0.075	0.071	—	0.033	0.061
	$C_b neg$	—	0.045	0.076	0.050	—	—	0.071	0.061	0.033
0.95	$C_a neg$	—	0.050	—	0.055	0.079	0.075	—	0.038	0.065
	$C_b neg$	—	0.041	0.072	0.045	—	—	0.067	0.056	0.029
0.90	$C_a neg$	—	0.055	—	0.060	0.080	0.079	—	0.043	0.068
	$C_b neg$	—	0.036	0.070	0.040	—	—	0.062	0.052	0.025
0.85	$C_a neg$	—	0.060	—	0.066	0.082	0.083	—	0.049	0.072
	$C_b neg$	—	0.031	0.065	0.034	—	—	0.057	0.046	0.021
0.80	$C_a neg$	—	0.065	—	0.071	0.084	0.086	—	0.055	0.075
	$C_b neg$	—	0.026	0.061	0.029	—	—	0.051	0.041	0.017
0.75	$C_a neg$	—	0.069	—	0.076	0.085	0.088	—	0.061	0.078
	$C_b neg$	—	0.022	0.056	0.024	—	—	0.044	0.036	0.014
0.70	$C_a neg$	—	0.074	—	0.081	0.086	0.091	—	0.068	0.081
	$C_b neg$	—	0.017	0.050	0.019	—	—	0.038	0.029	0.011
0.65	$C_a neg$	—	0.077	—	0.085	0.087	0.093	—	0.074	0.083
	$C_b neg$	—	0.014	0.043	0.015	—	—	0.031	0.025	0.008
0.60	$C_a neg$	—	0.081	—	0.089	0.088	0.095	—	0.080	0.085
	$C_b neg$	—	0.010	0.035	0.011	—	—	0.024	0.018	0.006
0.55	$C_a neg$	—	0.084	—	0.092	0.089	0.096	—	0.085	0.086
	$C_b neg$	—	0.007	0.028	0.008	—	—	0.019	0.014	0.005
0.50	$C_a neg$	—	0.086	—	0.094	0.090	0.097	—	0.089	0.088
	$C_b neg$	—	0.006	0.022	0.006	—	—	0.014	0.010	0.003

Notes:
1) —— means that supports are free to rotate.
2) ===== means that supports are fixed against rotation.

Table B.2
Coefficients for live and dead load positive moments
(See Clause B.3.5.)

$m =$ ℓ_a / ℓ_b	Coefficient	Case 1	Case 2	Case 3	Case 4	Case 5	Case 6	Case 7	Case 8	Case 9
1.00	C_{al}	0.036	0.027	0.027	0.032	0.032	0.035	0.032	0.028	0.030
	C_{ad}	0.036	0.018	0.018	0.027	0.027	0.033	0.027	0.020	0.023
	C_{bl}	0.036	0.027	0.032	0.032	0.027	0.032	0.035	0.030	0.028
	C_{bd}	0.036	0.018	0.027	0.027	0.018	0.027	0.033	0.023	0.020
0.95	C_{al}	0.040	0.030	0.031	0.035	0.034	0.038	0.036	0.031	0.032

(Continued)

Table B.2 (Concluded)

$m = \ell_a/\ell_b$	Coeffi-cient	Case 1 ℓ_b ℓ_a	Case 2 ℓ_b ℓ_a	Case 3 ℓ_b ℓ_a	Case 4 ℓ_b ℓ_a	Case 5 ℓ_b ℓ_a	Case 6 ℓ_b ℓ_a	Case 7 ℓ_b ℓ_a	Case 8 ℓ_b ℓ_a	Case 9 ℓ_b ℓ_a
	C_{ad}	0.040	0.020	0.021	0.030	0.028	0.036	0.031	0.022	0.024
	C_{bl}	0.033	0.025	0.029	0.029	0.024	0.029	0.032	0.027	0.025
	C_{bd}	0.033	0.016	0.025	0.024	0.015	0.024	0.031	0.021	0.017
0.90	C_{al}	0.045	0.034	0.035	0.039	0.037	0.042	0.040	0.035	0.036
	C_{ad}	0.045	0.022	0.025	0.033	0.029	0.039	0.035	0.025	0.026
	C_{bl}	0.029	0.022	0.027	0.026	0.021	0.025	0.029	0.024	0.022
	C_{bd}	0.029	0.014	0.024	0.022	0.013	0.021	0.028	0.019	0.015
0.85	C_{al}	0.050	0.037	0.040	0.043	0.041	0.046	0.045	0.040	0.039
	C_{ad}	0.050	0.024	0.029	0.036	0.031	0.042	0.040	0.029	0.028
	C_{bl}	0.026	0.019	0.024	0.023	0.019	0.022	0.026	0.022	0.020
	C_{bd}	0.026	0.012	0.023	0.019	0.011	0.017	0.025	0.017	0.013
0.80	C_{al}	0.055	0.041	0.045	0.048	0.044	0.051	0.051	0.044	0.042
	C_{ad}	0.055	0.026	0.034	0.039	0.032	0.045	0.045	0.032	0.029
	C_{bl}	0.023	0.017	0.022	0.020	0.016	0.019	0.023	0.019	0.017
	C_{bd}	0.023	0.011	0.020	0.016	0.009	0.014	0.022	0.015	0.010
0.75	C_{al}	0.061	0.045	0.051	0.052	0.047	0.055	0.056	0.049	0.046
	C_{ad}	0.061	0.028	0.040	0.043	0.033	0.048	0.051	0.036	0.031
	C_{bl}	0.019	0.014	0.019	0.016	0.013	0.016	0.020	0.016	0.014
	C_{bd}	0.019	0.009	0.018	0.013	0.007	0.012	0.020	0.013	0.007
0.70	C_{al}	0.068	0.049	0.057	0.057	0.051	0.060	0.063	0.054	0.050
	C_{ad}	0.068	0.030	0.046	0.046	0.035	0.051	0.058	0.040	0.033
	C_{bl}	0.016	0.012	0.016	0.014	0.011	0.013	0.017	0.014	0.012
	C_{bd}	0.016	0.007	0.016	0.011	0.005	0.009	0.017	0.011	0.006
0.65	C_{al}	0.074	0.053	0.064	0.062	0.055	0.064	0.070	0.059	0.054
	C_{ad}	0.074	0.032	0.054	0.050	0.036	0.053	0.065	0.044	0.034
	C_{bl}	0.013	0.010	0.014	0.011	0.009	0.010	0.014	0.011	0.009
	C_{bd}	0.013	0.006	0.014	0.009	0.004	0.007	0.014	0.009	0.005
0.60	C_{al}	0.081	0.058	0.072	0.067	0.059	0.068	0.077	0.065	0.059
	C_{ad}	0.081	0.034	0.062	0.053	0.037	0.056	0.073	0.048	0.036
	C_{bl}	0.010	0.007	0.011	0.009	0.007	0.008	0.011	0.009	0.007
	C_{bd}	0.010	0.004	0.011	0.007	0.003	0.006	0.012	0.007	0.004
0.55	C_{al}	0.088	0.062	0.080	0.072	0.063	0.073	0.085	0.070	0.063
	C_{ad}	0.088	0.035	0.071	0.056	0.038	0.058	0.081	0.052	0.037
	C_{bl}	0.008	0.006	0.009	0.007	0.005	0.006	0.009	0.007	0.006
	C_{bd}	0.008	0.003	0.009	0.005	0.002	0.004	0.009	0.005	0.003
0.50	C_{al}	0.095	0.066	0.088	0.077	0.067	0.078	0.092	0.076	0.067
	C_{ad}	0.095	0.037	0.080	0.059	0.039	0.061	0.089	0.056	0.038
	C_{bl}	0.006	0.004	0.007	0.005	0.004	0.005	0.007	0.005	0.004
	C_{bd}	0.006	0.002	0.007	0.004	0.001	0.003	0.007	0.004	0.002

Notes:
1)　—— means that supports are free to rotate.
2)　== means that supports are fixed against rotation.

Annex C (informative)
Load combinations and load factors in the National Building Code of Canada, *2015*

Notes:

1) *This Annex is not a mandatory part of this Standard.*

2) *This Annex provides an adapted version of portions of Subsection 4.1.3 from an unpublished draft of the National Building Code of Canada, 2015 (NBCC). Those portions deal with load factors and load combinations. This material has been adapted in accordance with CSA editorial requirements and is included for information only.*

3) *The load factors and load combinations presented in this Annex are discussed in Part 4 of the NBCC User's Guide and should be used in conjunction with the resistance factors specified in Clause 8.4.*

4) *The NBCC defines the following classes of loads:*
   a) *permanent loads such as dead loads, D, and effects of prestress, P;*
   b) *variable loads due to use and occupancy, L, wind loads, W, and snow loads, S;*
   c) *rare loads such as earthquake loads, E; and*
   d) *imposed deformations, T (see Clause 8.2.2).*

5) *The equations used to compute the loads S, W, and E for snow, wind, and earthquake in the NBCC include importance factors I_S, I_w, and I_E, which are a function of the use and occupancy of the building.*

6) *The following symbols are used in this Annex:*

   C = *live load due to cranes including self weight*

   C_7 = *crane bumper impact load*

   C_d = *self weight of all cranes positioned for maximum effects*

   D = *a permanent load due to the weight of building components, as specified in Subsection 4.1.4 of the NBCC*

   E = *earthquake load and effects — a rare load due to an earthquake, as specified in Subsection 4.1.8 of the NBCC*

   H = *load due to lateral earth pressure, including groundwater, and related internal moments and forces*

   L = *variable load due to intended use and occupancy, including loads due to cranes and pressure of liquids in containers, or related moments or forces*

   L_{xc} = *live load exclusive of crane loads*

   P = *effects of prestress, including secondary moments due to prestress*

   R = *nominal resistance of a member, connection, or structure based on the dimensions and on the specified properties of the structural materials*

   S = *variable load due to snow, including ice and associated rain, as specified in Article 4.1.6.2 of the NBCC, or due to rain, as specified in Article 4.1.6.4 of the NBCC*

   T = *effects due to contraction, expansion, or deflection caused by temperature changes, shrinkage, moisture changes, creep, ground settlement, or a combination thereof (see Appendix A of the NBCC)*

   W = *wind load — a variable load due to wind, as specified in Subsection 4.1.7 of the NBCC*

   ϕ = *resistance factor applied to a specified material property or to the resistance of a member, connection, or structure, which for the limit state under consideration takes into account the variability of dimensions and material properties, quality of work, type of failure, and uncertainty in the prediction of resistance*

C.1 Limit states design

Note: *See Appendix A of the NBCC.*

C.1.1 Definitions
The following definitions apply in this Annex:

Companion load — a specified variable load that accompanies the principal load in a given load combination.

Companion-load factor — a factor that, when applied to a companion load in the load combination, gives the probable magnitude of a companion load acting simultaneously with the factored principal load.

Effects — forces, moments, deformations, or vibrations that occur in the structure.

Factored load — the product of a specified load and its principal-load factor or companion-load factor.

Factored resistance — the product of nominal resistance, R, and the applicable resistance factor, ϕ.

Importance factor — a factor applied in Subsections 4.1.6 to 4.1.8 of the *NBCC* to obtain the specified load, to account for the consequences of failure as related to the limit state and the use and occupancy of the building.

Limit states — those conditions of a building structure in which the building ceases to fulfill the function for which it was designed.

Note: *Those states concerning safety are called ultimate limit states (ULS) and include exceeding the load-carrying capacity, overturning, sliding, and fracture. Those states that restrict the intended use and occupancy of the building are called serviceability limit states (SLS) and include deflection, vibration, permanent deformation, and local structural damage such as cracking. Those limit states that represent failure under repeated loading are called fatigue limit states.*

Principal load — the specified variable load or rare load that dominates in a given load combination.

Principal-load factor — a factor applied to the principal load in the load combination to account for the variability of the load and load pattern and analysis of its effects.

Specified loads (*D*, *E*, *H*, *L*, *P*, *S*, *T*, and *W*) — the loads specified in Note (6) of the preliminary Notes to this Annex.

C.1.2 Strength and stability

C.1.2.1
A building and its structural components shall be designed to have sufficient strength and stability so that the factored resistance, ϕR, is greater than or equal to the effect of factored loads, which shall be determined in accordance with Clause C.1.2.2.

C.1.2.2
Except as provided in Clause C.1.2.3, the effect of factored loads for a building or structural component shall be determined in accordance with the requirements of this Clause and the following load combination cases, the applicable combination being that which results in the most critical effect:
a)   for load cases without crane loads, the load combinations listed in Table C.1 a); and
b)   for load cases with crane loads, the load combinations listed in Table C.1 b).

C.1.2.3

Other load combinations that must also be considered are the principal loads acting with the companion loads taken as zero.

C.1.2.4

Where the effects due to lateral earth pressure, *H*, restraint effects from prestress, *P*, and imposed deformation, *T*, affect the structural safety, they shall be taken into account in the calculations, with load factors of 1.5, 1.0, and 1.25 assigned to H, P, and T respectively.

Table C.1 a)
Load combinations without crane loads for ultimate limit states
(See Clauses 8.3.2, C.1.2.2, and C.1.2.4 to C.1.2.8.)

	Load combination *	
Case	**Principal loads**	**Companion loads**
1	$1.4D$†	—
2	$(1.25D$‡ or $0.9D$§$) + 1.5L$**	$1.0S$†† or $0.4W$
3	$(1.25D$‡ or $0.9D$§$) + 1.5S$	$1.0L$††, ‡‡ or $0.4W$
4	$(1.25D$‡ or $0.9D$§$) + 1.4W$	$0.5L$‡‡ or $0.5S$
5	$1.0D$§ $+ 1.0E$§§	$0.5L$††, ‡‡ $+ 0.25S$††

* *See Clauses C.1.2.2, C.1.2.3, and C.1.2.4.*
† *See Clause C.1.2.9.*
‡ *See Clause C.1.2.8.*
§ *See Clause C.1.2.5.*
** *See Clause C.1.2.6.*
†† *See Article 4.1.5.5 of the NBCC.*
‡‡ *See Clause C.1.2.7.*
§§ *See Clause C.1.2.10.*

Notes:
1) *This Table corresponds to Table 4.1.3.2.A of the* NBCC.
2) *The factored load combinations in this Table each include one or more permanent loads, one principal variable load that dominates a given load combination, and one or more companion variable loads that have a magnitude likely to occur in combination with the given principal variable load when that principal variable load acts on the structure.*

Table C.1 b)
Load Combinations With Crane Loads for Ultimate Limit States
(See Clauses 8.3.2, C.1.2.2, and C.1.2.4 to C.1.2.8.)

	Load combination*	
Case	Principal loads	Companion loads
1	$(1.25D^\dagger$ or $0.9D^\ddagger) + (1.5C + 1.0L_{XC})$	$1.0S^\S$ or $0.4W$
2	$(1.25D^\dagger$ or $0.9D^\ddagger) + (1.5L_{XC}^{**} + 1.0C)$	$1.0S^\S$ or $0.4W$
3	$(1.25D^\dagger$ or $0.9D^\ddagger) + 1.5S$	$(1.0C + 1.0L_{XC}^\S, ^{\dagger\dagger})$
4	$(1.25D^\dagger$ or $0.9D^\ddagger) + 1.4W$	$(1.0C^{\ddagger\ddagger} + 0.5L_{XC}^\S, ^{\dagger\dagger})$
5	$(1.25D^\dagger$ or $0.9D^\ddagger) + C_7$	—
6	$1.0D^\ddagger + 1.0E^{\S\S}$	$1.0C_d + 0.5L_{XC}^\S, ^{\dagger\dagger\dagger} + 0.25S^\S$

* *See Clauses C.1.2.2, C.1.2.3, and C.1.2.4.*
† *See Clause C.1.2.8.*
‡ *See Clause C.1.2.5.*
§ *See Article 4.1.5.5 of the* NBCC.
** *See Clause C.1.2.6.*
†† *See Clause C.1.2.7.*
‡‡ *Side thrust due to cranes need not be combined with full wind load.*
§§ *See Clause C.1.2.10.*

C.1.2.5
Except as provided in Sentence 4.1.8.16.(1) of the *NBCC*, the counteracting factored dead load, $0.9D$ in the load combinations specified in Cases 2, 3, and 4 and $1.0D$ in load Case 5 of Table C.1 a) and $0.9D$ in the load combination specified in Cases 1 to 5 and $1.0D$ in load combination Case 6 in Table C.1 b), shall be used when dead load acts to resist overturning, uplift, sliding, and failure due to stress reversal, and to determine anchorage requirements and factored member resistances. See Appendix A of the *NBCC*.

C.1.2.6
The principal-load factor 1.5 for live load, L, in Table C.1 a) and L_{XC} in Table C.1 b) may be reduced to 1.25 for liquids in tanks.

Δ C.1.2.7
The companion-load factor for live load, L, in Table C.1 a) and L_{XC} in C.1 b) shall be increased by 0.5 for storage occupancies and for equipment areas and service rooms in Table 4.1.5.3 of the *NBCC*.

C.1.2.8
Except as provided in Clause C.1.2.9, the load factor 1.25 for dead load, D, for soil, superimposed earth, plants, and trees in Table C.1 a) and C.1 b) shall be increased to 1.5, except that when the soil depth exceeds 1.2 m, the factor may be reduced to $1 + 0.6/h_s$, but not less than 1.25, where h_s is the depth of soil in metres supported by the structure.

C.1.2.9
A principal-load factor of 1.5 shall be applied to the weight of saturated soil used in load combination Case 1 of Table C.1 a).

C.1.2.10

Earthquake load, *E*, in load combination Case 5 of Table C.1 a) and Case 6 of Table C.1 b) includes horizontal earth pressure due to earthquake determined in accordance with Sentence 4.1.8.16.(4) of the *NBCC*.

C.1.2.11

Provision shall be made to ensure adequate stability of a structure as a whole and adequate lateral, torsional, and local stability of all structural parts.

C.1.2.12

Sway effects produced by vertical loads acting on the structure in its displaced configuration shall be taken into account in the design of buildings and their structural members.

C.1.3 Serviceability

A building and its structural components shall be checked for serviceability limit states as defined in Clause 4.1.3.1.(1)(a) of the *NBCC* under the effect of service loads for serviceability criteria specified or recommended in Articles 4.1.3.5 and 4.1.3.6 of the *NBCC* and in the Standards listed in Section 4.3 of the *NBCC* (see Appendix A of the *NBCC*).

CSA Group standard A23.3-14

Annex D (informative)
Anchorage

Note: *This informative (non-mandatory) Annex has been written in normative (mandatory) language to facilitate adoption where users of the Standard or regulatory authorities wish to adopt it formally as additional requirements to this Standard.*

D.1 Introduction

D.1.1
This Annex specifies design requirements for anchors in concrete used to transmit forces to concrete elements by tension, shear, or a combination of tension and shear between
a)   connected structural elements; or
b)   safety-related attachments and structural elements.

The specified safety levels are intended for in-service conditions rather than for short-term handling and construction conditions.

D.1.2
This Annex applies to cast-in anchors and to post-installed expansion (torque-controlled and displacement-controlled), undercut and adhesive anchors (see Figure D.1). Adhesive anchors shall be installed in concrete having a minimum age of 21 days at time of anchor installation. Specialty inserts, through-bolts, multiple anchors connected to a single steel plate at the embedded end of the anchors, grouted anchors, and direct anchors such as powder or pneumatic-actuated nails or bolts are not included in the provisions of Annex D. Reinforcement used as part of the embedment shall be designed in accordance with the applicable clauses of this Standard.

D.1.3
Design provisions are included for the following types of anchors:
a)   Headed studs and headed bolts having a geometry that has been demonstrated to result in a pullout strength in uncracked concrete equal to or exceeding 1.4 N_{pr}, where N_{pr} is given in Equation D.16;
b)   Hooked bolts having a geometry that has been demonstrated to result in a pullout strength without the benefit of friction in uncracked concrete equal to or exceeding 1.4 N_{pr}, where N_{pr} is given in Equation D.17;
c)   Post-installed expansion and undercut anchors that meet the assessment criteria of ACI 355.2/ 355.2R; and
d)   Adhesive anchors that meet the assessment criteria of ACI 355.4M.

D.1.4
Load applications that are predominantly high cycle fatigue or impact are not covered by this Annex.

D.2 Definitions
The following definitions apply in this Annex:

5% fractile — a statistical term meaning 90% confidence that there is a 95% probability of the actual strength exceeding the nominal strength.

Adhesive — chemical components formulated from organic polymers, or a combination of organic polymers and inorganic materials that cure when blended together.

Adhesive anchor — a post-installed anchor, inserted into hardened concrete with an anchor hole diameter not greater than 1.5 times the anchor diameter, that transfers loads to the concrete by bond between the anchor and the adhesive, and bond between the adhesive and the concrete.

Anchor — a steel element either cast into concrete or post-installed into a hardened concrete member and used to transmit applied loads to the concrete. Cast-in anchors include headed bolts, hooked bolts (J- or L-bolts) and headed studs. Post-installed anchors include expansion anchors, undercut anchors, and adhesive anchors. Steel elements for adhesive anchors include threaded rods, deformed reinforcing bars, or internally threaded steel sleeves with external deformations.

Anchor group — a number of similar anchors having approximately equal effective embedment depths with spacing *s* between adjacent anchors such that the projected areas overlap. See Clause D.4.1.2..

Anchor pullout strength — the strength corresponding to the anchoring device or a major component of the device sliding out from the concrete without breaking out a substantial portion of the surrounding concrete (see Figure D.4A).

Anchor reinforcement — reinforcement used to transfer the full design load from the anchors into the structural member. See Clauses D.6.2.9 and D.7.2.9 and Figures D.10, D.17A, and D.17B.

Attachment — the structural assembly, external to the surface of the concrete, that transmits loads to or receives loads from the anchor.

Brittle steel element — an element with a tensile test elongation of less than 14% or reduction in area less than 30%, or both.

Cast-in anchor — a headed bolt, headed stud, or hooked bolt installed before concrete is placed.

Concrete breakout strength — the strength corresponding to a volume of concrete surrounding the anchor or group of anchors separating from the member (see Figures D.4A, D.4B and D.5).

Concrete pryout strength — the strength corresponding to formation of a concrete spall behind a short, stiff anchor, displaced in the direction opposite to the applied shear force (see Figure D.4B).

Distance sleeve — a sleeve that encases the centre part of an undercut anchor, a torque-controlled expansion anchor, or a displacement-controlled expansion anchor but does not expand.

Ductile steel element — an element with a tensile test elongation of at least 14% and a reduction in area of at least 30%. A steel element meeting the requirements of CSA G40.21 or ASTM A307 shall be considered as a ductile steel element. Deformed reinforcing bars meeting the requirements of CSA G30.18, shall be considered as ductile steel elements.

Edge distance — the distance from the edge of the concrete surface to the centre of the nearest anchor.

Effective embedment depth — the overall depth through which the anchor transfers force to or from the surrounding concrete. The effective embedment depth will normally be the depth of the concrete failure surface in tension applications. For cast-in headed anchor bolts and headed studs, the effective embedment depth is measured from the bearing contact surface of the head (see Figure D.1).

Expansion anchor — a post-installed anchor inserted into hardened concrete that transfers loads to and from the concrete by direct bearing, friction, or both. Expansion anchors may be torque controlled (where the expansion is achieved by a torque acting on the screw or bolt) or displacement controlled (where the expansion is achieved by impact forces acting on a sleeve or plug and the expansion is controlled by the length of travel of the sleeve or plug).

Expansion sleeve — the outer part of an expansion anchor that is forced outward by the centre part either by applied torque or impact, to bear against the sides of the predrilled hole.

Headed stud — a headed steel anchor that meets the requirements of CSA W59 or AWS D1.1/AWS D1.1 and is affixed to a plate or similar steel attachment by stud arc welding before casting. The underside of the plate or steel attachment is assumed to be cast flush with the concrete surface.

Hooked bolt — a cast-in anchor anchored mainly by bearing of the 90° bend (L-bolt) or 180° bend (J-bolt) against the concrete at its embedded end and having a minimum e_h of $3d_a$.

Horizontal or upwardly inclined anchor — an anchor installed in a hole drilled horizontally or in a hole drilled at any orientation above horizontal. See Figure D.2.

Manufacturer's Printed Installation Instructions (MPII) — published instructions for the correct installation of the anchor under all covered installation conditions as supplied in the product packaging.

Post-installed anchor — an anchor installed in hardened concrete. Expansion, undercut and adhesive anchors are examples of post-installed anchors.

Projected area — the area on the free surface of the concrete member that is used to represent the larger base of the assumed rectilinear failure surface. See Clauses D.6.2.1 and D.7.2.1.

Projected influence area — the rectilinear area on the free surface of the concrete member that is used to calculate the bond strength of adhesive anchors. See Clause D.6.5.1.

Side-face blowout strength — the strength of anchors with deeper embedment but thinner side cover corresponding to concrete spalling on the side face around the embedded head while no major breakout occurs at the top concrete surface. See Figure D.4A.

Specialty insert — a predesigned and prefabricated cast-in anchor specifically designed for attachment of bolted or slotted connections. Specialty inserts are often used for handling, transportation, and erection, but also for anchoring structural elements. They are not covered by this Annex.

Stretch length — length of anchor, extending beyond concrete in which it is anchored, subject to full tensile load applied to anchor, and for which cross-sectional area is minimum and constant. See Figure D.3.

Supplementary reinforcement — reinforcement that acts to restrain the potential concrete breakout but is not designed to transfer the full design load from the anchors into the structural member.

Undercut anchor — a post-installed anchor that derives its tensile strength from the mechanical interlock provided by undercutting of the concrete at the embedded end of the anchor. The undercutting is achieved with a special drill before installation of the anchor or by the anchor itself during its installation.

D.3 Symbols

The following symbols apply in this Annex:

A_{brg} = bearing area of the head of stud anchor bolt or headed deformed bar, mm^2

A_{Na} = projected influence area of an adhesive anchor or group of adhesive anchors, for calculation of bond strength in tension, mm^2 (see Clause D.6.5.1 and Figure D.11)

A_{Nao} = projected influence area of a single adhesive anchor, for calculation of bond strength in tension if not limited by edge distance or spacing, mm^2. See Clause D.6.5.1 (see Figure D.11)

A_{Nc} = projected concrete failure area of a single anchor, or a group of anchors, for calculation of resistance in tension, mm^2, as specified in Clause D.6.2.1 (see Figure D.7)

A_{Nco} = projected concrete failure area of a single anchor, for calculation of resistance in tension, when not limited by edge distance or spacing, mm^2, as specified in Clause D.6.2.1 (see Figure D.6)

$A_{se,N}$ = effective cross-sectional area of anchor in tension, mm^2

$A_{se,V}$ = effective cross-sectional area of anchor in shear, mm^2

A_{Vc} = projected concrete failure area of a single anchor or group of anchors, for calculation of resistance in shear, mm^2, as defined in Clause D.7.2.1 (see Figure D.13)

A_{Vco} = projected concrete failure area of one anchor, for calculation of resistance in shear, when not limited by corner influences, spacing, or member thickness, mm^2, as specified in Clause D.7.2.1 (see Figure D.12)

c_{ac} = critical edge distance required to develop the basic resistance as controlled by concrete breakout or bond of a post-installed anchor in tension in uncracked concrete without supplementary reinforcement to control splitting, mm, as specified in Clause D.9.7

$c_{a,max}$ = maximum distance from centre of an anchor shaft to the edge of concrete, mm

$c_{a,min}$ = minimum distance from centre of an anchor shaft to the edge of concrete, mm

c_{a1} = distance from the centre of an anchor shaft to the edge of concrete in one direction, mm. If shear is applied to anchor, c_{a1} is taken in the direction of the applied shear. If tension is applied to the anchor, c_{a1} is the minimum edge distance. Where anchors subjected to shear are located in narrow sections of limited thickness, see Clause D.7.2.4 (see Figures D.7 and D.12)

c'_{a1} = limiting value of c_{a1} when anchors are located less than $1.5h_{ef}$ from three or more edges (see Figure D.15)

c_{a2} = distance from centre of an anchor shaft to the edge of concrete in the direction orthogonal to c_{a1} (see Figure D.7)

c_{Na} = projected distance from centre of an anchor shaft on one side of the anchor required to develop the full bond strength of a single adhesive anchor, mm (see Clause D.6.5.1)

d_a = outside diameter of anchor or shaft diameter of headed stud, headed bolt, or hooked bolt, mm (see Clause D.9.4)

d'_a = value substituted for d_a when an oversized anchor is used, mm (see Clause D.9.5)

e_h = distance from the inner surface of the shaft of a J-bolt or L-bolt to the outer tip of the J-bolt or L-bolt

e'_N = eccentricity of normal force on a group of anchors. The distance between the resultant tension load on a group of anchors in tension and the centroid of the group of anchors loaded in tension. e'_N is always positive (see Figure D.9)

e'_v	=	eccentricity of shear force on a group of anchors; the distance between the point of shear force application and the centroid of the group of anchors resisting shear in the direction of the applied shear (see Figure D.16)
f'_c	=	specified compressive strength of concrete
f_r	=	modulus of rupture of concrete
f_t	=	calculated tensile stress in a region of a member
f_{uta}	=	specified tensile strength of anchor steel
f_{ya}	=	specified yield strength of anchor steel
F_a	=	acceleration-based site coefficient, as specified in the *National Building Code of Canada*
h_a	=	thickness of member in which an anchor is anchored, measured parallel to anchor axis
h_{ef}	=	effective anchor embedment depth, mm (see Figure D.1). Where anchors subject to tension are close to three or more edges, see Clause D.6.2.3.
h'_{ef}	=	limiting value of h_{ef} when anchors are located less than 1.5 h_{ef} from three or more edges (see Figure D.8)
I_E	=	earthquake importance factor of the structure, as specified in the *National Building Code of Canada*
k_c	=	coefficient for factored concrete breakout resistance in tension
k_{cp}	=	coefficient for pryout resistance
k_{05}	=	coefficient associated with the 5 percent fractile.
ℓ_e	=	load-bearing length of anchor for shear, not to exceed $8d_a$
n	=	number of anchors in a group
N_{agr}	=	factored bond resistance in tension of a group of adhesive anchors, see Clause D.6.5.1
N_{ar}	=	factored bond resistance in tension of a single adhesive anchor, see Clause D.6.5.1
N_{bar}	=	factored bond resistance of a single adhesive anchor in tension in cracked concrete, see Clause D.6.5.2
N_{br}	=	factored concrete breakout resistance in tension of a single anchor in cracked concrete, as defined in Clause D.6.2.2
N_{cbgr}	=	factored concrete breakout resistance in tension of a group of anchors, as specified in Clause D.6.2.1
N_{cbr}	=	factored concrete breakout resistance in tension of a single anchor, as specified in Clause D.6.2.1
N_{cpr}	=	factored pullout resistance in tension of a single anchor, see Clause D.6.3.1
N_f	=	factored tensile load
N_{fa}	=	factored tensile load on an anchor or individual anchor in a group of anchors
$N_{fa,g}$	=	total factored tensile load applied to an anchor group
$N_{fa,i}$	=	factored tensile load applied to the most highly stressed anchor in the group of anchors
$N_{fa,s}$	=	factored sustained tension load
N_{pr}	=	factored pullout resistance in tension of a single anchor in cracked concrete, as specified in Clause D.6.3.4 or D.6.3.5
N_r	=	factored resistance in tension
N_{sar}	=	factored resistance of a single anchor or individual anchor in a group of anchors in tension as governed by the steel resistance, as specified in Clauses D.6.1.1 and D.6.1.2

N_{sbgr}	=	factored side-face blowout resistance of a group of anchors, as specified in Clause D.6.4.2
N_{sbr}	=	factored side-face blowout resistance of a single anchor, as specified in Clause D.6.4.1
R	=	resistance modification factor, as specified in Clause D.5.3
R_d	=	ductility-related force modification factor, as specified in the *National Building Code of Canada*
R_o	=	overstrength-related force modification factor, as specified in the *National Building Code of Canada*
R_y	=	factor applied to f_{ya} to estimate the probable yield stress, as specified in Clause D.4.3.5.3
s	=	anchor centre-to-centre spacing
s_s	=	sample standard deviation, MPa
$S_a(0.2)$	=	5% damped spectral response acceleration for a period of 0.2 s, as specified in the *National Building Code of Canada*
t	=	thickness of washer or plate
V_{br}	=	factored concrete breakout resistance in shear of a single anchor in cracked concrete, as specified in Clause D.7.2.2 or D.7.2.3
V_{cbgr}	=	factored concrete breakout resistance in shear of a group of anchors, as specified in Clause D.7.2.1
V_{cbr}	=	factored concrete breakout resistance in shear of a single anchor, as specified in Clause D.7.2.1
V_{cpgr}	=	factored concrete pryout resistance of a group of anchors, as specified in Clause D.7.3
V_{cpr}	=	factored concrete pryout resistance of a single anchor, as specified in Clause D.7.3
V_f	=	factored shear force
V_{fa}	=	factored shear force applied to a single anchor or group of anchors
$V_{fa,g}$	=	factored shear force applied to anchor group
$V_{fa,i}$	=	factored shear force applied to the most highly stressed anchor in a group of anchors
V_r	=	factored shear resistance
V_{sar}	=	factored resistance in shear of a single anchor or individual anchor in a group of anchors as governed by the steel resistance, as specified in Clauses D.7.1.1 and D.7.1.2
λ_a	=	factor to account for low-density concrete in certain concrete anchorage applications
ϕ_c	=	material resistance factor for concrete
ϕ_s	=	steel embedment material resistance factor for reinforcement
τ_{cr}	=	characteristic bond stress of adhesive anchor in cracked concrete, MPa (see Clause D.6.5.2)
τ_{uncr}	=	characteristic bond stress of adhesive anchor in uncracked concrete, MPa (see Clause D.6.5.2)
$\psi_{c,N}$	=	modification factor for anchor resistance in tension based on presence or absence of cracks, as specified in Clause D.6.2.6
$\psi_{c,P}$	=	modification factor for pullout resistance of anchors based on presence or absence of cracks as specified in Clause D.6.3.6
$\psi_{c,V}$	=	modification factor for resistance in shear of anchors based on presence or absence of cracks as specified in Clause D.7.2.7

$\psi_{cp,N}$ = factor used to modify the tensile strength of post-installed anchors intended for use in uncracked concrete without supplementary reinforcement to account for splitting tensile stresses due to installation (see Clause D.6.2.7)

$\psi_{cp,Na}$ = factor used to modify tensile strength of adhesive anchors intended for use in uncracked concrete without supplementary reinforcement to account for the splitting tensile stresses due to installation (see Clause D.6.2.7)

$\psi_{ec,N}$ = modification factor for resistance in tension to account for anchor groups loaded eccentrically, as specified in Clause D.6.2.4

$\psi_{ec,Na}$ = factor used to modify tensile strength of adhesive anchors based on eccentricity of applied loads (see Clause D.6.5.5)

$\psi_{ec,V}$ = modification factor for resistance in shear to account for anchor groups loaded eccentrically, as specified in Clause D.7.2.5

$\psi_{ed,N}$ = factor used to modify tensile strength of anchors based on proximity to edges of concrete member (see Clause D.6.2.5)

$\psi_{ed,Na}$ = factor used to modify tensile strength of adhesive anchors based on proximity to edges of concrete members (see Clause D.6.5.4)

$\psi_{ed,V}$ = modification factor for resistance in shear based on proximity to edges of concrete members, as specified in Clause D.7.2.6

$\psi_{h,V}$ = factor used to modify shear strength of anchors located in concrete members with $h_a <$ $1.5c_{a1}$, as specified in Clause D.7.2.8.

D.4 General requirements

D.4.1 Analysis

D.4.1.1
Anchors and anchor groups shall be designed for critical effects of factored loads as determined by elastic analysis. Plastic analysis approaches may be used where factored resistance is controlled by ductile steel elements, provided that deformational compatibility is taken into account.

D.4.1.2
Anchor group effects shall be considered wherever two or more anchors have spacing less than the critical spacing as follows:

Failure mode under investigation	Critical spacing
Concrete breakout strength in tension	$3h_{ef}$
Bond strength in tension	$2c_{Na}$
Concrete breakout in shear	$3c_{a1}$

Only those anchors susceptible to the particular failure mode under investigation shall be included in the group.

D.4.2 Load combinations
Anchors shall be designed for factored load combinations specified in Clause 8.

D.4.3 Seismic considerations

D.4.3.1

Where load combinations include earthquake effects, the applicable additional requirements of Clauses D.4.3.2 to D.4.3.8 shall apply.

D.4.3.2

This Annex shall not apply to the design of anchors in plastic hinge zones of concrete structures under seismic loads.

D.4.3.3

In regions where $I_E F_a S_a(0.2) \geq 0.35$ and the load combinations include earthquake effects, the additional requirements of Clauses D.4.3.4 to D.4.3.8 shall apply.

D.4.3.4

Post-installed anchors shall be qualified for earthquake loading in accordance with ACI 355.2 or ACI 355.4. The factored pullout resistance, N_{pr}, and factored steel resistance of the anchor in shear, V_{sar}, of expansion and undercut anchors shall be based on the results of the ACI 355.2 simulated seismic tests. For adhesive anchors, the steel factored resistance in shear V_{sar} and the characteristic bond stresses τ_{uncr} and τ_{cr} shall be based on results of the ACI 355.4 simulated seismic tests.

D.4.3.5 Requirements for tensile loading

D.4.3.5.1

Where the tension component of the seismic force applied to a single anchor or group of anchors is equal to or less than 20% of the total factored anchor tensile force associated with the same load combination, a single anchor or group of anchors may be designed to satisfy Clauses D.6 and D.5.1.1 and Table D.1.

D.4.3.5.2

Where the tensile component of the seismic force applied to anchors exceeds 20% of the total factored anchor tensile force associated with the same load combination, anchors and their attachments shall be designed in accordance with Clause D.4.3.5.3. The anchor design tensile resistance shall be determined using Clause D.4.3.5.4.

① **D.4.3.5.3**

Anchors and their attachments shall be designed using one of the following options:

a) For single anchors, the nominal concrete-governed resistance shall be greater than the probable steel resistance of the anchor. For anchor groups the ratio of the tensile load on the most highly stressed anchor to the probable steel resistance of the anchor shall be equal to or greater than the ratio of the tensile load on the tension-loaded anchors to the nominal concrete-governed resistance of those anchors:

    i) In each case,

        1) The probable steel resistance shall be the section resistance of the steel anchor determined using a probable stress $R_y f_{uta}$ where R_y is taken as 1.1 and both ϕ_s and R in Equation D.2 are taken as 1.0.

        2) The nominal concrete governed resistance shall be taken as the resistance considering pullout, side-face blowout, concrete breakout, and bond strength as applicable with ϕ_c

taken as 1.0. For consideration of pullout in groups, the ratio shall be calculated for the most highly stressed anchor.

ii) In addition, the following shall be satisfied:

1) Anchors shall transmit tensile loads via a ductile steel element with a stretch length of at least eight anchor diameters unless otherwise determined by analysis.

2) Where anchors are subject to load reversals, the anchor shall be protected against buckling.

3) Where connections are threaded and the ductile steel elements are not threaded over their entire length, the ratio of f_{uta}/f_{ya} shall not be less than 1.3 unless the threaded portions are upset. The upset portions shall not be included in the stretch length. See Figure D.3.

4) Deformed reinforcing bars used as ductile steel elements to resist earthquake effects shall be limited to CSA G30.18 weldable grade, satisfying the requirements of Clause 21.

b) The anchor or group of anchors shall be designed for the maximum probable tension force that can be transmitted to the anchor or group of anchors based on the development of a ductile yield mechanism in the attachment in flexure, shear, or bearing, or a combination of those conditions, and considering both material overstrength and strain hardening effects for the attachment. The anchor design tensile strength resistance shall be calculated from Clause D.4.3.5.4.

c) The anchor or group of anchors shall be designed for the maximum tension force that can be transmitted to the anchors by a non-yielding attachment. The anchor design tensile strength shall be calculated from Clause D.4.3.5.4.

d) The anchor or group of anchors shall be designed for the maximum tension force obtained from design load combinations that include earthquake effects, with loads calculated using $R_d R_o$ equal to 1.3 or as specified in Clause 4.1.8.18 of the *National Building Code of Canada* (*NBCC*). The anchor design tensile strength shall satisfy the tensile strength requirements of Clause D.4.3.5.4.

D.4.3.5.4

The anchor design tensile resistance for resisting earthquake seismic forces shall be determined from consideration of the following for the failure modes given in Table D.1 assuming the concrete is cracked unless it can be demonstrated that the concrete remains uncracked:

a) N_{sra} for a single anchor or for the most highly stressed individual anchor in a group of anchors;

b) $0.75N_{cbr}$ or $0.75N_{cbgr}$, except that N_{cbr} or N_{cbgr} need not be calculated where anchor reinforcement satisfying D.6.2.9 is provided;

c) $0.75N_{cpr}$ for a single anchor or for the most highly stressed individual anchor in a group of anchors;

d) $0.75N_{sbr}$ or $0.75N_{sbgr}$; and

e) $0.75N_{ar}$ or $0.75N_{agr}$.

D.4.3.5.5

Where anchor reinforcement is provided in accordance with Clause D.6.2.9, no reduction in design tension strength beyond that specified in Clause D.6.2.9 shall be required.

D.4.3.6 Requirements for shear loading

D.4.3.6.1

Where the shear component of the strength-level earthquake seismic force (factored earthquake load) applied to the anchor or group of anchors is equal to or less than 20% of the total factored anchor shear force associated with the same load combination, the anchor or group of anchors may be designed to satisfy Clause D.7 and the shear strength requirements of Clause D.5.1.2.

D.4.3.6.2

Where the shear component of the seismic force applied to anchors exceeds 20% of the total factored anchor shear force associated with the same load combination, anchors and their attachments shall be designed in accordance with Clause D.4.3.6.3. The anchor design shear resistance for resisting earthquake forces shall be determined in accordance with Clause D.7.

D.4.3.6.3

Anchors and their attachments shall be designed using one of the following options:
a)   The anchor or group of anchors shall be designed for the maximum probable shear force that can be transmitted to the anchor or group of anchors based on the development of a ductile yield mechanism in the attachment in flexure, shear, or bearing, or a combination of those conditions, and considering both material overstrength and strain hardening effects in the attachment.
b)   The anchor or group of anchors shall be designed for the maximum probable shear force that can be transmitted to the anchors by a non-yielding attachment.
c)   The anchor or group of anchors shall be designed for the maximum shear force obtained from design load combinations that include earthquake effects, with loads calculated using $R_d R_o$ equal to 1.3 or as specified in Clause 4.1.8.18 of the *NBCC*. The anchor design shear resistance shall satisfy the shear resistance requirements of Clause D.5.1.2.

D.4.3.6.4

Where anchor reinforcement is provided in accordance with Clause D.7.2.9, no reduction in design shear strength beyond that specified in Clause D.7.2.9 shall be required.

D.4.3.7

Single anchors or groups of anchors that are subjected to both tension and shear forces shall be designed to satisfy the requirements of Clause D.8, with the anchor design tensile strength calculated from Clause D.4.3.5.4.

D.4.3.8

Anchor reinforcement used in structures where $R_d > 2.5$ shall be deformed reinforcement satisfying the requirements of Clause 21.2.7.1.

D.4.4

Adhesive anchors installed horizontally or upwardly inclined shall be qualified in accordance with ACI 355.4 requirements for sensitivity to installation direction.

D.4.5

For adhesive anchors subjected to sustained tension loading, Clause D.5.1.3 shall be satisfied. For groups of adhesive anchors, Equation D.1 shall be satisfied for the anchor that resists the highest sustained tension load. Installer certification and inspection requirements for horizontal and upwardly-inclined adhesive anchors subjected to sustained tension loading shall be in accordance with Clauses D.10.2.2 through D.10.2.4.

D.4.6

Modification factor λ_a for lightweight concrete in this annex shall be taken as

Cast-in and undercut anchor concrete failure $1.0\,\lambda$

Expansion and adhesive anchor concrete failure $0.8\,\lambda$

Adhesive anchor bond failure per Equation D.24 $0.6\,\lambda$

where λ is determined in accordance with Clause 8.6.5. An alternate value of λ_a may be used where tests have been performed and evaluated in accordance with ACI 355.2 or ACI 355.4.

D.4.7 Concrete strength limit

The values of f_c' used for calculations in this Annex shall not exceed 70 MPa for cast-in anchors and 55 MPa for post-installed anchors. Testing shall be required for post-installed anchors used in concrete with f_c' greater than 55 MPa.

D.5 Resistance of structural anchors

D.5.1

D.5.1.1

The design of structural anchors shall be based on computations that satisfy the requirements of Clause D.5.2 or on test evaluation using the 5% fractile of test results for the following (see Figures D.4A and D.4B):

a) steel strength of anchor in tension (Clause D.6.1);
b) concrete breakout resistance of anchor in tension (Clause D.6.2);
c) pullout resistance of cast-in, post-installed expansion or undercut anchor in tension (Clause D.6.3);
d) concrete side-face blowout strength of headed anchor in tension (Clause D.6.4);
e) bond strength of adhesive anchor in tension (Clause D.6.5);
f) steel strength of anchor in shear (Clause D.7.1);
g) concrete breakout strength of anchor in shear (Clause D.7.2); and
h) concrete pryout resistance of anchor in shear (Clause D.7.3).

In addition, anchors shall satisfy the required edge distances, spacings, and thicknesses to precluding splitting failure as required by Clause D.9.

D.5.1.2

The design of anchors shall be in accordance with Table D.1. In addition, the design of anchors shall satisfy Clause D.4.3 for earthquake loading and Clause D.5.1.3 for adhesive anchors subject to sustained tensile loading.

Table D.1
Required resistance of anchors, except as noted in Clause D.4.3
(See Clause D.5.1.2.)

Failure mode	Single anchor	Anchor group*	
		Individual anchor in a group	Anchors as a group
Steel strength in tension (D.6.1)	$N_{sar} \geq N_{fa}$	$N_{sar} \geq N_{fa,i}$	
Concrete breakout strength in tension (D.6.2)	$N_{cbr} \geq N_{fa}$		$N_{cbgr} \geq N_{fa,g}$
Pullout strength in tension (D.6.3)	$N_{pr} \geq N_{fa}$	$N_{pr} \geq N_{fa,i}$	
Concrete side-face blowout strength in tension (D.6.4)	$N_{sbr} \geq N_{fa}$		$N_{sbgr} \geq N_{fa,g}$
Bond strength of adhesive anchor in tension (D.6.5)	$N_{ar} \geq N_{fa}$		$N_{agr} \geq N_{fa,g}$
Steel strength in shear (D.7.1)	$V_{sar} \geq V_{fa}$	$V_{sar} \geq V_{fa,i}$	
Concrete breakout strength in shear (D.7.2)	$V_{cbr} \geq V_{fa}$		$V_{cbgr} \geq V_{fa,g}$
Concrete pryout strength in shear (D.7.3)	$V_{cpr} \geq V_{fa}$		$V_{cpr} \geq V_{fa,g}$

* Required resistance of anchors in groups shall account for all applicable failure modes for individual anchors and for the group.

D.5.1.3

For the design of adhesive anchors to resist sustained tension loads, in addition to Clause D.5.1.2,

$$0.55\,N_{bar} \geq N_{fa,s} \qquad \text{**Equation D.1**}$$

where N_{bar} is determined in accordance with Clause D.6.5.2.

D.5.1.4

When both N_{fa} and V_{fa} are present, interaction effects shall be considered using an interaction expression that results in computation of strength in substantial agreement with results of comprehensive tests. This requirement shall be considered satisfied by Clause D.8.

D.5.2 Calculating anchor resistance

D.5.2.1

The nominal resistance for any anchor or anchor group shall be based on design models that result in predictions of resistance in substantial agreement with results of comprehensive tests. The materials used in the tests shall be compatible with the materials used in the structure. The nominal resistance shall be based on the 5% fractile of the basic individual anchor resistance. For nominal resistances related to concrete strength, modifications for size effects, the number of anchors, the effects of close spacing of anchors, proximity to edges, depth of the concrete member, eccentric loadings of anchor groups, and presence or absence of cracking shall be accounted for. Limits on edge distances and anchor spacing in the design models shall be consistent with the tests that verified the model. See Figure D.5.

D.5.2.2
The effect of reinforcement provided to restrain the concrete breakout may be included in the design models specified in Clause D.5.2.1. Where anchor reinforcement is provided in accordance with Clauses D.6.2.9 and D.7.2.9, calculation of the concrete breakout strength in accordance with Clauses D.6.2 and D.7.2 is not required.

D.5.2.3
For anchors with diameters not exceeding 100 mm, the concrete breakout resistance shall be considered satisfied by the design procedure specified in Clauses D.6.2 and D.7.2.

D.5.2.4
For adhesive anchors with embedment depths $4d_a \leq h_{ef} \leq 20d_a$, the bond strength requirements shall be considered satisfied by the design procedure of Clause D.6.5.

D.5.3
The resistance modification factor, R, specified in Clauses D.6 and D.7 shall be as follows:
a)   for an anchor governed by strength of a ductile steel element:

Tension loads	0.80
Shear loads	0.75

b)   for an anchor governed by strength of a brittle steel element:

Tension loads	0.70
Shear loads	0.65

c)   for an anchor governed by concrete breakout, side face blowout, pullout, or pryout strength:

	Condition A*	Condition B*
Shear loads	1.15	1.00
Tension loads		
Cast-in headed studs, headed bolts, or hooked bolts	1.15	1.00
Post-installed anchors (category determined in accordance with ACI 355.2 or ACI 355.4		
Category 1 (low sensitivity to installation and high reliability)	1.15	1.00
Category 2 (medium sensitivity to installation and medium reliability)	1.00	0.85
Category 3 (high sensitivity to installation and lower reliability)	0.85	0.75

* Condition A applies where the potential concrete failure surfaces are crossed by supplementary reinforcement proportioned to tie the potential concrete failure prism into the structural member except

where pullout or pryout resistance governs. Condition B applies where such supplementary reinforcement is not provided or where pullout or pryout strength governs.

D.6 Design requirements for tensile loading

D.6.1 Steel resistance of anchor in tension

Δ **D.6.1.1**

The factored resistance of an anchor in tension as governed by the steel, N_{sar}, shall be evaluated by calculations based on the properties of the anchor material and the physical dimensions of the anchor.

D.6.1.2

The factored resistance of an anchor in tension, N_{sar}, shall not exceed

$$N_{sar} = A_{se,N}\phi_s f_{uta}R$$ Equation D.2

where $A_{se,N}$ is the effective cross-sectional area of an anchor in tension, mm², f_{uta} shall not be taken greater than the smaller of $1.9f_{ya}$ or 860 MPa and R is as specified in Clause D.5.3.

D.6.2 Concrete breakout resistance of anchor in tension

D.6.2.1

The factored concrete breakout resistance, N_{cbr} of a single anchor or N_{cbgr} for a group of anchors, shall not exceed
a)   for a single anchor:

$$N_{cbr} = \frac{A_{Nc}}{A_{Nco}}\psi_{ed,N}\psi_{c,N}\psi_{cp,N}N_{br}$$ Equation D.3

b)   for an anchor group:

$$N_{cbgr} = \frac{A_{Nc}}{A_{Nco}}\psi_{ec,N}\psi_{ed,N}\psi_{c,N}\psi_{cp,N}N_{br}$$ Equation D.4

In these equations factors, $\psi_{ec,N}$, $\psi_{ed,N}$, $\psi_{c,N}$, and $\psi_{cp,N}$ are defined in Clauses D.6.2.4, D.6.2.5, D.6.2.6, and D.6.2.7 respectively. N_{br} is the factored concrete breakout resistance value for a single anchor in tension in cracked concrete. A_{Nc} is the projected concrete failure area of a single anchor or anchor group and shall be approximated as the base of the rectilinear geometrical figure that results from projecting the failure surface outward $1.5h_{ef}$ from the centrelines of the anchor, or in the case of an anchor group, from a line through a row of adjacent anchors (see Figure D.7). A_{Nc} shall not exceed nA_{Nco}, where n is the number of tensioned anchors in the group. A_{Nco} is the projected concrete failure area of a single anchor with an edge distance equal to or greater than $1.5h_{ef}$ (see Figure D.6).

$$A_{Nco} = 9h_{ef}^2$$ Equation D.5

D.6.2.2

The factored concrete breakout resistance of a single anchor in tension in cracked concrete, N_{br}, shall not exceed

$$N_{br} = k_c\phi_c\lambda_a\sqrt{f_c'}h_{ef}^{1.5}R$$ Equation D.6

where

k_c = 10 for cast-in headed studs, headed bolts, and hooked bolts

   = 7.0 for post-installed anchors

R = as specified in Clause D.5.3

The k_c factor for post-installed anchors may be increased above 7.0 in accordance with ACI 355.2 or ACI 355.4 product-specific tests, but shall not exceed 10.

Alternatively, for cast-in headed studs and headed bolts with 275 mm ≤ h_{ef} ≤ 625 mm, the factored concrete breakout resistance of a single anchor in tension in cracked concrete, N_{br}, shall not exceed

$$N_{br} = 3.9\phi_c\lambda_a\sqrt{f_c'}\,h_{ef}^{5/3}R \qquad \text{Equation D.7}$$

where R is as specified in Clause D.5.3.

D.6.2.3

Where anchors are located less than 1.5 h_{ef} from three or more edges the value of h_{ef} used for the calculation of A_{Nc} in accordance with Clause D.6.2.1, as well as in Equations D.3 to , D.10, and D.11 shall be the larger of $c_{a,max}/1.5$ and $s/3$ where s is the maximum spacing between anchors within the group (see Figure D.7).

D.6.2.4

The modification factor for anchor groups loaded eccentrically in tension, $\Psi_{ec,N}$, shall be computed as

$$\psi_{ec,N} = \frac{1}{\left(1 + \frac{2e_N'}{3h_{ef}}\right)} \qquad \text{Equation D.8}$$

but $\Psi_{ec,N}$ shall not be taken greater than 1.0 (see Figure D.9).

This equation shall be valid for

$$e_N' \le \frac{s}{2} \qquad \text{Equation D.9}$$

Δ   Where s shall be taken as the distance between the outermost anchors in tension.

If the loading on an anchor group is such that only some anchors are in tension, only those anchors that are in tension shall be considered when determining the eccentricity, e_N', for use in Equation D.8 and for the calculation of N_{cbgr} in accordance with Equation D.4.

In the case where eccentric loading exists about two axes, the modification factor, $\psi_{ec,N}$, shall be computed for each axis individually, and the product of these factors used as $\psi_{ec,N}$ in Equation D.4.

D.6.2.5

The modification factor for edge effects for single anchors or anchor groups loaded in tension, $\Psi_{ed,N}$, shall be computed as

If $c_{a,min}$ ≥ 1.5 h_{ef}, then

$$\psi_{ed,N} = 1.0 \qquad \text{Equation D.10}$$

If $c_{a,min} < 1.5\,h_{ef}$, then

$$\psi_{ed,N} = 0.7 + 0.3\frac{c_{a,min}}{1.5h_{ef}}$$

Equation D.11

D.6.2.6

For anchors located in a region of a concrete member where analysis indicates no cracking ($f_t < f_r$) at service load levels, the following modification factor may be used:

$\psi_{c,N}$ = 1.25 for cast-in anchors; and

$\psi_{c,N}$ = 1.4 for post-installed anchors when the value of k_c = 7.0 is used in Equation D.6.

When the value of k_c used in Equation D.6 is taken from an ACI 355.2 or ACI 355.4 product evaluation report for post-installed anchors qualified for use in both cracked and uncracked concrete, the value of both k_c and $\psi_{c,N}$ shall be based on ACI 355.2 or ACI 355.4 product evaluation report.

Where k_c used in Equation D.6 is taken from an ACI 355.2 or ACI 355.4 product evaluation report for post-installed anchors approved for use in uncracked concrete, $\psi_{c,N}$ shall be taken as 1.0.

Where analysis indicates cracking at service load levels, $\psi_{c,N}$ shall be taken as 1.0 for both cast-in and post-installed anchors. Post-installed anchors shall be qualified for use in cracked concrete in accordance with ACI 355.2 or ACI 355.4. The cracking in the concrete shall be controlled by flexural reinforcement distributed in accordance with Clause 10.6.1, or equivalent crack control shall be provided by confining reinforcement.

D.6.2.7

The modification factor for post-installed anchors designed for uncracked concrete in accordance with Clause D.6.2.6 without supplementary reinforcement to control splitting, $\Psi_{cp,N}$, shall be computed as follows using the critical distance c_{ac} as defined in Clause D.9.7.

If $c_{a,min} \geq c_{ac}$, then

$$\psi_{cp,N} = 1.0$$

Equation D.12

If $c_{a,min} < c_{ac}$, then

$$\psi_{cp,N} = \frac{c_{a,min}}{c_{ac}} \geq \frac{1.5h_{ef}}{c_{ac}}$$

Equation D.13

but $\Psi_{cp,N}$ determined from Equation D.13 shall not be taken less than $1.5h_{ef}/c_{ac}$, where the critical distance, c_{ac}, is as specified in Clause D.9.7.

For all other cases, including cast-in anchors, $\Psi_{cp,N}$, shall be taken as 1.0.

D.6.2.8

When an additional plate or washer is added at the head of the anchor, the projected area of the failure surface may be calculated by projecting the failure surface outward $1.5h_{ef}$ from the effective perimeter of the plate or washer. The effective perimeter shall not exceed the value at a section projected outward a distance t from the outer edge of the head of the anchor, where t is the thickness of the washer or plate.

D.6.2.9

Where anchor reinforcement is developed in accordance with Clause 12 on both sides of the breakout surface, the design strength of the anchor reinforcement may be used instead of the concrete breakout strength in determining N_r. See Figure D.10. The anchor reinforcement capacity shall be taken as:

$$N_r = \phi_s A_s f_y R \hspace{6cm} \text{Equation D.14}$$

where $R = 0.85$.

D.6.3 Pullout resistance of cast-in, post-installed expansion, and undercut anchors in tension

D.6.3.1

The factored pullout resistance of a single cast-in, post-installed expansion, and post-installed undercut anchor in tension, N_{cpr}, shall not exceed

$$N_{cpr} = \psi_{c,P} N_{pr} \hspace{6cm} \text{Equation D.15}$$

where $\Psi_{c,P}$ is defined in Clause D.6.3.6.

D.6.3.2

For post-installed expansion and undercut anchors, the values of N_{pr} shall be based on the 5% fractile of results of tests performed and evaluated in accordance with ACI 355.2. The factored pullout resistance, N_{pr}, for use in Equation D.15 shall be obtained by multiplying the resulting 5% fractile test value by ϕ_c before being applied to Equation D.15. It is not permissible to calculate the pullout strength, N_{pr}, in tension for such anchors.

D.6.3.3

For single cast-in headed studs and headed bolts, the pullout resistance in tension may be calculated using Clause D.6.3.4. For single J-bolts or L-bolts, the pullout resistance in tension may be calculated using Clause D.6.3.5. Alternatively, values of N_{pr} based on the 5% fractile of tensile tests performed in the same manner as the ACI 355.2 procedures but without the benefit of friction may be used. When this procedure is used, the factored pullout resistance, N_{pr}, for use in Equation D.15 shall be obtained by multiplying the resulting 5% fractile test value by ϕ_c before being applied to Equation D.15.

D.6.3.4

The factored pullout resistance in tension of a single headed stud or headed bolt, N_{pr}, for use in Equation D.15 shall not exceed

$$N_{pr} = 8 A_{brg} \phi_c f'_c R \hspace{6cm} \text{Equation D.16}$$

D.6.3.5

The factored pullout resistance in tension of a single J-bolt or L-bolt, N_{pr}, for use in Equation D.15 shall not exceed

$$N_{pr} = 0.9 \phi_c f'_c e_h d_a R \hspace{6cm} \text{Equation D.17}$$

where $3d_a \leq e_h \leq 4.5 d_a$

D.6.3.6

For an anchor located in a region of a concrete member where analysis indicates no cracking ($f_t < f_r$) at service load levels, a modification factor of $\psi_{c,P} = 1.4$ may be used. Otherwise, $\psi_{c,P}$ shall be taken as 1.0.

D.6.4 Concrete side-face blowout resistance of a headed anchor in tension

D.6.4.1

For a single headed anchor with deep embedment close to an edge ($h_{ef} > 2.5c_{a1}$), the factored side-face blowout resistance, N_{sbr}, shall not exceed

$$N_{sbr} = 13.3c_{a1}\sqrt{A_{brg}}\,\phi_c\lambda_a\sqrt{f_c'}\,R \qquad\qquad \text{Equation D.18}$$

If c_{a2} for the single headed anchor is less than $3c_{a1}$, the value of N_{sbr} shall be modified by multiplying it by the factor $(1 + c_{a2}/c_{a1})/4$, where $1.0 \leq c_{a2}/c_{a1} \leq 3.0$.

D.6.4.2

For multiple-headed anchors with deep embedment close to an edge ($h_{ef} > 2.5c_{a1}$) and spacing between anchors less than $6c_{a1}$, the factored resistance of the anchor group for a side-face blowout failure, N_{sbgr}, shall not exceed

$$N_{sbgr} = \left(1 + \frac{s}{6c_{a1}}\right)N_{sbr} \qquad\qquad \text{Equation D.19}$$

where s = distance between the outer anchors along the edge in the group and N_{sbr} is obtained from Equation D.18 without modification for a perpendicular edge distance.

D.6.5 Bond strength of adhesive anchor in tension

D.6.5.1

The factored bond resistance in tension, N_{ar}, of a single adhesive anchor or N_{agr} of a group of adhesive anchors, shall not exceed
a)   For a single adhesive anchor:

$$N_{ar} = \left(\frac{A_{Na}}{A_{Nao}}\right)\psi_{ed,Na}\psi_{cp,Na}N_{bar} \qquad\qquad \text{Equation D.20}$$

b)   For a group of adhesive anchors:

$$N_{agr} = \left(\frac{A_{Na}}{A_{Nao}}\right)\psi_{ec,Na}\psi_{ed,Na}\psi_{cp,Na}N_{bar} \qquad\qquad \text{Equation D.21}$$

Factors $\psi_{ec,Na}$, $\psi_{ed,Na}$, and $\psi_{cp,Na}$ are defined in Clauses D.6.5.3, D.6.5.4, and D.6.5.5, respectively. A_{Na} is the projected influence area of a single adhesive anchor or group of adhesive anchors that shall be approximated as a rectilinear area that projects outward a distance, c_{Na}, from the centerline of the adhesive anchor or, in the case of a group of adhesive anchors, from a line through a row of adjacent adhesive anchors. A_{Na} shall not exceed nA_{Nao}, where n is the number of adhesive anchors in the group that resist tension loads. A_{Nao} is the projected influence area of a single adhesive anchor with an edge distance equal to or greater than c_{Na} (see Figure D.11):

$$A_{Nao} = (2c_{Na})^2 \qquad\qquad \text{Equation D.22}$$

where

$$c_{Na} = 10d_a\sqrt{\frac{\tau_{uncr}}{7.60}}$$

Equation D.23

and constant 7.60 carries the unit of N/mm².

D.6.5.2

The factored bond resistance of a single adhesive anchor in tension in cracked concrete, N_{bar}, shall not exceed

$$N_{bar} = \lambda_a \phi_c \tau_{cr} \pi d_a h_{ef} R$$

Equation D.24

The characteristic bond stress, τ_{cr}, shall be taken as the 5% fractile of results of tests performed and evaluated according to ACI 355.4.

Where analysis indicates cracking at service load levels, adhesive anchors shall be qualified for use in cracked concrete in accordance with ACI 355.4.

For adhesive anchors located in a region of a concrete member where analysis indicates no cracking at service load levels, τ_{uncr} may be used in place of τ_{cr} in Equation D.24 and shall be taken as the 5% fractile of results of tests performed and evaluated in accordance with ACI 355.4.

In lieu of using test results, the minimum characteristic bond stress values in Table D.2 may be used, provided Items a) to e) are satisfied:
a) anchors shall meet the requirements of ACI 355.4;
b) anchors shall be installed in holes drilled with a rotary impact drill or rock drill;
c) concrete at time of anchor installation shall have a minimum compressive strength of 17 MPa;
d) concrete at time of anchor installation shall have a minimum age of 21 days; and
e) concrete temperature at time of anchor installation shall be at least 10 °C.

Table D.2
Minimum characteristic bond stresses*†
(See Clause D.6.5.2.)

Installation and service environment	Moisture content of concrete at time of anchor installation	Peak in-service temperature of concrete, °C	τ_{cr}, MPa	τ_{uncr}, MPa
Outdoor	Dry to fully saturated	80	1.40	4.50
Indoor	Dry	43	2.10	6.90

* Where anchor design includes sustained tension loading, multiply values of τ_{cr} and τ_{uncr} by 0.4.
† Where anchor design includes earthquake loads for structures where, $(I_E F_a S_a(0.2) \geq 0.35)$ multiply values of τ_{cr} by 0.8 and τ_{uncr} by 0.4.

D.6.5.3

The modification factor for adhesive anchor groups loaded eccentrically in tension, $\Psi_{ec,Na}$, shall be computed as

$$\psi_{ec,Na} = \frac{1}{\left(1 + \dfrac{e'_N}{c_{Na}}\right)}$$

Equation D.25

but $\psi_{ec,Na}$ shall not be taken greater than 1.0.

If the loading on an adhesive anchor group is such that only some adhesive anchors are in tension, only those adhesive anchors that are in tension shall be considered when determining the eccentricity e'_N for use in Equation D.25 and for the calculation of N_{agr} in accordance with Equation D.21.

In the case where eccentric loading exists about two orthogonal axes, the modification factor, $\psi_{ec,Na}$, shall be computed for each axis individually and the product of these factors used as $\psi_{ec,Na}$ in Equation D.21.

D.6.5.4

The modification factor for edge effects for single adhesive anchors or adhesive anchor groups loaded in tension, $\psi_{ed,Na}$, shall be computed as

If $c_{a,min} \geq c_{Na}$

then

$$\psi_{ed,Na} = 1.0$$

Equation D.26

If $c_{a,min} < c_{Na}$

then

$$\psi_{ed,Na} = 0.7 + 0.3\left(\frac{c_{a,min}}{c_{Na}}\right)$$

Equation D.27

D.6.5.5

The modification factor for adhesive anchors designed for uncracked concrete in accordance with Clause D.6.5.2 without supplementary reinforcement to control splitting, $\psi_{cp,Na}$, shall be computed as

If $c_{a,min} \geq c_{ac}$

then

$$\psi_{cp,Na} = 1.0$$

Equation D.28

If $c_{a,min} < c_{ac}$

then

$$\psi_{cp,Na} = c_{a,min} / c_{ac}$$

Equation D.29

but $\psi_{cp,Na}$ determined from Equation D.29 shall not be taken less than c_{Na}/c_{ac} where the critical edge distance, c_{ac}, is defined in Clause D.9.7. For all other cases $\psi_{cp,Na}$ shall be taken as 1.0.

D.7 Design requirements for shear loading

D.7.1 Steel resistance of anchor in shear

D.7.1.1
The factored resistance of an anchor in shear as governed by steel, V_{sar}, shall be evaluated by calculations based on the properties of the anchor material and the physical dimensions of the anchor. Where concrete breakout is a potential failure mode, the required steel shear strength shall be consistent with the assumed breakout surface.

D.7.1.2
The factored resistance of an anchor in shear shall not exceed the following Items a) to c):
a) for cast-in headed stud anchors:

$$V_{sar} = A_{se,V} \, \phi_s f_{uta} R \qquad\qquad \text{Equation D.30}$$

where $A_{se,V}$ is the effective cross-sectional area of an anchor in shear, mm^2 and f_{uta} shall not be taken greater than the smaller of $1.9f_{ya}$ or 860 MPa and R is as specified in Clause D.5.3;

b) for cast-in headed bolts, hooked bolt anchors, and post-installed anchors where sleeves do not extend through the shear plane:

$$V_{sar} = A_{se,V} \, \phi_s \, 0.6 f_{uta} R \qquad\qquad \text{Equation D.31}$$

where $A_{se,V}$ is the effective cross-sectional area of a single anchor in shear, mm^2 and f_{uta} shall not be taken greater than the smaller of $1.9f_{ya}$ or 860 MPa; and R is as specified in Clause D.5.3; and

c) for post-installed anchors with sleeves extending through the shear plane, V_{sar} shall be based on the 5% fractile of results of tests performed and evaluated in accordance with ACI 355.2. When this procedure is used, V_{sar} shall be obtained by multiplying the resulting 5% fractile test value by $\phi_s R$. Alternatively, Equation D.31 may be used.

D.7.1.3
Where anchors are used with built-up grout pads, the factored resistances specified in Clause D.7.1.2 shall be multiplied by a 0.80 factor.

D.7.2 Concrete breakout resistance of anchor in shear

Δ D.7.2.1
The factored concrete breakout resistance in shear V_{cbr} of a single anchor or V_{cbrg} of a group of anchors shall not exceed the following (see Figure D.4B):
a) For shear force perpendicular to the edge on a single anchor:

$$V_{cbr} = \frac{A_{Vc}}{A_{Vco}} \, \psi_{ed,V} \psi_{c,V} \psi_{h,V} V_{br} \qquad\qquad \text{Equation D.32}$$

b) For shear force perpendicular to the edge on an anchor group:

$$V_{cbgr} = \frac{A_{Vc}}{A_{Vco}} \, \psi_{ec,V} \psi_{ed,V} \psi_{c,V} \psi_{h,V} V_{br} \qquad\qquad \text{Equation D.33}$$

c) For shear force parallel to an edge, V_{cbr} or V_{cbgr} may be twice the value for shear force determined from Equation D.32 or D.33, respectively, with the shear force assumed to act perpendicular to the free edge and with $\psi_{ed,V}$ taken to be equal to 1.0 (see Figures D.13 and D.14).

d)   For anchors located at a corner, the limiting factored concrete breakout resistance shall be
     determined for each edge and the minimum value shall be used (see Figure D.14).

Factors $\psi_{ec,V}$, $\psi_{ed,V}$, $\psi_{c,V}$, and $\psi_{h,V}$ are defined in Clauses D.7.2.5, D.7.2.6, D.7.2.7, and D.7.2.8,
respectively. V_{br} is the factored concrete breakout resistance value for a single anchor. A_{Vc} is the
projected area of the failure surface on the side of the concrete member at its edge for a single anchor
or anchor group. This area may be evaluated as the base of a truncated half-pyramid projected on the
side face of the member where the top of the half-pyramid is given by the axis of the anchor row
selected as critical. The value of c_{a1} shall be taken as the distance from the edge to this axis. A_{Vc} shall
not exceed nA_{Vco}, where n is the number of anchors in the group. See Figure D.13.

A_{Vco} is the projected area for a single anchor in a deep member and with a distance from edges equal or
greater than $1.5c_{a1}$ in the direction perpendicular to the shear force. This area, A_{Vco}, may be evaluated
as the base of a half-pyramid with a side length parallel to the edge of $3c_{a1}$ and a depth of $1.5c_{a1}$, as
follows (see Figure D.12):

$$A_{Vco} = 4.5(c_{a1})^2 \hspace{4cm} \textbf{Equation D.34}$$

Where anchors are located at varying distances from the edge and are welded to the attachment so as
to distribute the force to all anchors, the strength may be evaluated based on the distance to the
farthest row of anchors from the edge. In this case, the value of c_{a1} may be based on the distance from
the edge to the axis of the farthest anchor row that is selected as critical, and all of the shear shall be
assumed to be carried by this critical anchor row alone. See Figure D.13.

D.7.2.2

The factored concrete breakout resistance in shear of a single anchor in cracked concrete, V_{br}, shall not
exceed the smaller of Item a) or b):

a)

$$V_{br} = 0.58\left(\frac{\ell_e}{d_a}\right)^{0.2} \sqrt{d_a}\,\phi_c\lambda_a\sqrt{f'_c}\,c_{a1}{}^{1.5}R \hspace{3cm} \textbf{Equation D.35}$$

where

ℓ_e =   the load-bearing length of the anchor for shear

ℓ_e = h_{ef} for anchors with a constant stiffness over the full length of embedded section, such as
         headed studs and post-installed anchors with one tubular shell over full length of the
         embedment depth,

ℓ_e = $2d_a$ for torque-controlled expansion anchors with a distance sleeve separated from
         expansion sleeve, and

$\ell_e \leq 8d_a$ in all cases.

b)

$$V_{br} = 3.75\lambda_a\phi_c\sqrt{f'_c}\,(c_{a1})^{1.5}R \hspace{4cm} \textbf{Equation D.36}$$

D.7.2.3

For cast-in headed studs, headed bolts, or hooked bolts that are rigidly welded to steel attachments
having a minimum thickness equal to the greater of 10 mm or half of the anchor diameter, the factored
concrete breakout resistance in shear of a single anchor in cracked concrete, V_{br}, shall be the smaller of
Equations D.36 and D.37:

$$V_{br} = 0.66\left(\frac{\ell_e}{d_a}\right)^{0.2}\sqrt{d_a}\,\phi_c\lambda_a\sqrt{f_c'}\,c_{a1}{}^{1.5}R$$

Equation D.37

where ℓ_e is defined in D.7.2.2 and R is specified in Clause D.5.3,

provided that
a) for an anchor group, the resistance is determined based on the resistance of the row of anchors farthest from the edge;
b) anchor spacing, s, is not less than 65 mm; and
c) supplementary reinforcement is provided at the corners if $c_{a2} \leq 1.5h_{ef}$.

D.7.2.4
Where anchors are located in narrow sections of limited thickness such that both edge distances c_{a2} and thickness h_a are less than $1.5c_{a1}$, the value of c_{a1} used for the calculation of A_{Vc} in accordance with Clause D.7.2.1 as well as in Equation D.34 to D.38 and D.40 to D.42 shall not exceed the largest of
a) $c_{a2}/1.5$, where c_{a2} is the largest edge distance;
b) $h_a/1.5$; and
c) $s/3$, where s is the maximum spacing perpendicular to direction of shear between anchors within a group. See Figure D.15.

Δ ### D.7.2.5
The modification factor for anchor groups loaded eccentrically in shear, $\Psi_{ec,V}$, shall be computed as

$$\Psi_{ec,V} = \frac{1}{1 + \dfrac{2e'_V}{3c_{a1}}}$$

Equation D.38

This equation shall be valid for

$$e'_V \leq \frac{s}{2}$$

Equation D.39

but $\Psi_{ec,V}$, shall not be taken greater than 1.0.

Where s shall be taken as the distance between the outermost anchors in tension.

If the loading on an anchor group is such that only some anchors are loaded in shear in the same direction, only those anchors that are loaded in shear in the same direction shall be considered when determining the eccentricity of e'_V for use in Equation D.38 and for the calculation of V_{cbgr} in accordance with Equation D.33. See Figure D.16.

D.7.2.6
The modification factor for edge effect for a single anchor or group of anchors loaded in shear, $\Psi_{ed,V}$, shall be computed as follows using the smaller value of c_{a2}:

If $c_{a2} \geq 1.5\,c_{a1}$ then $\Psi_{ed,V} = 1.0$

Equation D.40

If $c_{a2} < 1.5\,c_{a1}$ then $\Psi_{ed,V} = 0.7 + 0.3\left(\dfrac{c_{a2}}{1.5c_{a1}}\right)$

Equation D.41

D.7.2.7

For anchors located in a region of a concrete member where an analysis that includes temperature and shrinkage effects indicates no tension ($f_t < f_r$) at service loads, a modification factor of $\psi_{c,V} = 1.4$ may be used.

For anchors located in a region of a concrete member where analysis indicates cracking at service load levels, the following modification factors may be used:

For anchors in cracked concrete without supplementary reinforcement or with edge reinforcement smaller than a 15M bar	$\psi_{c,V} = 1.0$
For anchors in cracked concrete with reinforcement of a 15M bar or greater between the anchor and the edge	$\psi_{c,V} = 1.2$
For anchors in cracked concrete with reinforcement of a 15M bar or greater between the anchor and the edge and with the reinforcement enclosed within stirrups spaced not more than 100 mm apart	$\psi_{c,V} = 1.4$

D.7.2.8

The modification factor for anchors located in a concrete member where $h_a < 1.5c_{a1}$, $\psi_{h,V}$ shall be computed as

$$\psi_{h,V} = \sqrt{\frac{1.5c_{a1}}{h_a}}$$

Equation D.42

but $\psi_{h,V}$ shall not be taken less than 1.0.

D.7.2.9

Where anchor reinforcement is developed in accordance with Clause 12 on both sides of the breakout surface or encloses the anchor and is developed beyond the breakout surface, the design strength of the anchor reinforcement may be used instead of the concrete breakout strength in determining V_r. See Figures D.17A and D.17B. The anchor reinforcement capacity shall be taken as

$$V_r = \phi_s A_s f_y R$$

Equation D.43

where $R = 0.85$.

D.7.3 Concrete pryout resistance of an anchor in shear

The factored pryout resistance, V_{cpr} for a single anchor or V_{cpgr} for a group of anchors, shall not exceed
a)   for a single anchor:

$$V_{cpr} = k_{cp}N_{cpr}$$

Equation D.44

For cast-in, expansion, and undercut anchors, N_{cpr} shall be taken as N_{cbr} determined from Equation D.3, and for adhesive anchors, N_{cpr} shall be the lesser of N_{ar} determined from Equation D.20 and N_{cbr} determined from Equation D.3.
b)   for a group of anchors:

$$V_{cpgr} = k_{cp}N_{cpgr}$$

Equation D.45

For cast-in, expansion, and undercut anchors, N_{cpgr} shall be taken as N_{cbgr} determined from Equation D.4, and for adhesive anchors N_{cpgr} shall be the lesser of N_{agr} determined from Equation D.21 and N_{cbgr} determined from Equation D.4.

In Equations D.44 and D.45,

k_{cp} = 1.0 for $h_{ef} < 65$ mm

= 2.0 for $h_{ef} \geq 65$ mm

D.8 Interaction of tensile and shear forces

D.8.1
Unless determined in accordance with Clause D.5.1.4, anchors or anchor groups that are subjected to both shear and axial loads shall be designed to satisfy the requirements of Clauses D.8.2 to D.8.4. The value of N_r and V_r shall be the required strengths as determined from Clause D.5.1.2 or D.4.3.

D.8.2
If $\frac{V_f}{V_r} \leq 0.2$ for the governing resistance in shear, the full resistance in tension may be used, as follows: $N_r \geq N_f$ (see Figure D.18).

D.8.3
If $\frac{N_f}{N_r} \leq 0.2$, for the governing resistance in tension, the full resistance in shear may be used, as follows (see Figure D.18): $V_r \geq V_f$.

D.8.4
If $\frac{V_f}{V_r} > 0.2$ for the governing resistance in shear, and $\frac{N_f}{N_r} > 0.2$ for the governing resistance in tension, the following shall apply (see Figure D.18):

$$\frac{N_f}{N_r} + \frac{V_f}{V_r} \leq 1.2 \qquad \text{**Equation D.46**}$$

D.9 Required edge distances, spacings, and thicknesses to preclude splitting failure

D.9.1
Minimum spacings and edge distances for anchors and minimum thicknesses of members shall comply with Clauses D.9.2 to D.9.7, unless supplementary reinforcement is provided to control splitting. Lesser values from product-specific tests performed in accordance with ACI 355.2 OR ACI 355.4 may be used.

D.9.2
Unless determined in accordance with Clause D.9.5, the minimum centre-to-centre spacing of anchors shall be $4d_a$ for cast-in anchors that will not be torqued and $6d_a$ for torqued cast-in anchors and post-installed anchors.

D.9.3
Unless determined in accordance with Clause D.9.5, minimum edge distances for cast-in anchors that will not be torqued shall be based on the minimum cover requirements for reinforcement specified in

Clause 7.9. For cast-in anchors that will be torqued, the minimum edge distances shall be $6d_a$.

D.9.4

Unless determined in accordance with Clause D.9.5, minimum edge distances for post-installed anchors shall be based on the greater of the minimum cover requirements for reinforcement specified in Clause 7.9 and the minimum edge distance requirements for the products as determined by tests in accordance with ACI 355.2 OR ACI 355.4, and shall be not less than twice the nominal maximum aggregate size. In the absence of such product-specific ACI 355.2 or ACI 355.4 test information, the minimum edge distance shall not be less than the following:

Adhesive anchors	$6d_a$
Undercut anchors	$6d_a$
Torque-controlled anchors	$8d_a$
Displacement-controlled anchors	$10d_a$

D.9.5

For anchors where installation does not produce a splitting force and that will not be torqued, if the edge distance or spacing is less than that specified in Clauses D.9.2 to D.9.4, calculations shall be performed by substituting for d_a a smaller value d_a' that meets the requirements of Clauses D.9.2 to D.9.4. Calculated forces applied to the anchor shall be limited to the values corresponding to an anchor having a diameter, d_a'.

D.9.6

Unless determined from tests in accordance with ACI 355.2, the value of h_{ef} for an expansion or undercut post-installed anchor shall not exceed the greater of two-thirds of the member thickness, h_a, and the member thickness less 100 mm.

D.9.7

Unless determined from tension tests in accordance with ACI 355.2 OR ACI 355.4, the critical edge distance, c_{ac}, shall not be taken less than the following:

Adhesive anchors	$2h_{ef}$
Undercut anchors	$2.5h_{ef}$
Torque-controlled expansion anchors	$4h_{ef}$
Displacement-controlled expansion anchors	$4h_{ef}$

D.9.8

Contract documents shall specify use of anchors with the minimum edge distance assumed in the design.

D.10 Installation and inspection of anchors

D.10.1

Anchors shall be installed by qualified personnel in accordance with the contract documents. The contract documents shall require installation of post-installed anchors in accordance with the manufacturer's printed installation instructions (MPII). Installation of adhesive anchors shall be performed by personnel trained to install adhesive anchors.

D.10.2

D.10.2.1

The level of inspection required varies by anchor category type for both mechanical and adhesive anchors. Adhesive anchors shall be subject to Clauses D.10.2.2 to D.10.2.4.

D.10.2.2

For adhesive anchors, the contract documents shall specify proof loading where required in accordance with ACI 355.4. For adhesive anchors, the contract documents shall specify either of the following as determined by ACI 355.4:
a)   periodic special inspection; or
b)   continuous special inspection with proof loading where required in accordance with ACI 355.4. The proof loading program shall comply with ACI 355.4.

The contract documents shall also specify all parameters associated with the characteristic bond stress used for the design in accordance with D.6.5 including minimum age of concrete, concrete temperature range, moisture condition of concrete at time of installation, type of lightweight concrete if applicable, and requirements for hole drilling and preparation.

D.10.2.3

Installation of adhesive anchors horizontally or upwardly inclined to support sustained tension loads shall be performed by personnel certified by an applicable certification program.

Certification shall include written and performance tests in accordance with the ACI/CRSI Adhesive Anchor Installer Certification program, or equivalent.

D.10.2.4

Adhesive anchors installed in horizontal and upwardly inclined orientations to resist sustained tension loads shall be continuously inspected during installation by an inspector specially approved for that purpose. The special inspector shall furnish a report to the licensed design professional and building official that the work covered by the report has been performed and that the materials used and the installation procedures used conform with the approved contract documents and the MPII.

Figure D.1
Types of anchors
(See Clauses D.1.2, D.2, and D.3.)

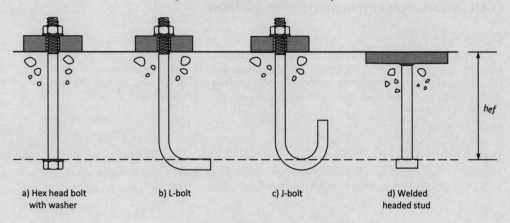

a) Hex head bolt   b) L-bolt   c) J-bolt   d) Welded
with washer   headed stud

a) Cast-in anchors

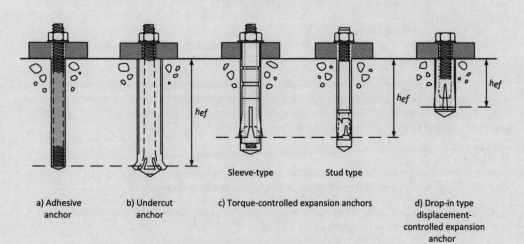

Sleeve-type   Stud type

a) Adhesive   b) Undercut   c) Torque-controlled expansion anchors   d) Drop-in type
anchor   anchor   displacement-
                                                                                      controlled expansion
                                                                                      anchor

b) Post-installed anchors

CSA Group standard A23.3-14

Figure D.2
Possible orientations of horizontal or upwardly inclined anchors
(See Clauses D.2 and D.4.3.5.3.)

Figure D.3
Illustrations of stretch length
(See Clause D.2.)

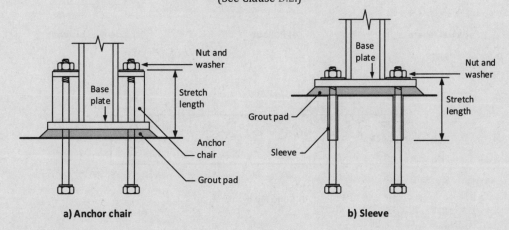

a) Anchor chair   b) Sleeve

Figure D.4A
Failure modes for anchors under tensile loading
(See Clauses D.5.1.1 and D.6.2.1.)

a) Steel failure   b) Pullout   c) Side-face blowout

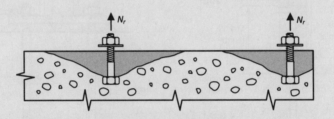

d) Concrete breakout

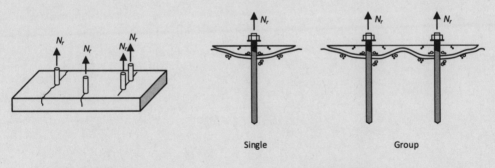

Single   Group

e) Concrete splitting   f) Bond failure

Δ

Figure D.4B
Failure modes for anchors under shear loading
(See Clauses D.5.1.1 and D.7.2.1.)

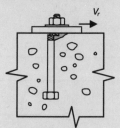

a) Steel failure preceded by concrete spall

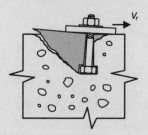

b) Concrete pryout for anchors far from a free edge

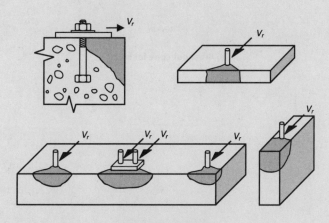

c) Concrete breakout

Figure D.5
Breakout cones
(See Clause D.5.2.1.)

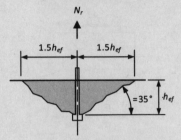

a) Breakout cone for tension

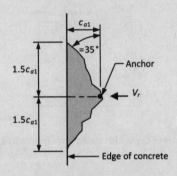

Plan view

b) Breakout cone for shear

Δ

Figure D.6
Calculation of A_{Nco}
(See Clause D.6.2.1.)

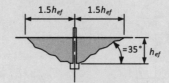

a) Section through failure cone

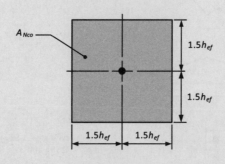

b) Plan view

Notes:
1) *The critical edge distance for headed studs, headed bolts, expansion anchors, and undercut anchors is 1.5 h_{ef}.*
2) $A_{Nco} = (2 \times 1.5 h_{ef}) \times (2 \times 1.5 h_{ef})$
$\qquad = 3 h_{ef} \times 3 h_{ef}$
$\qquad = 9 h_{ef}^2$

Figure D.7
Projected areas for single anchors and groups of anchors
(See Clauses D.6.2.1 and D.6.2.3.)

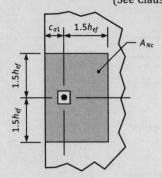

$A_{NC} = (c_{a1} + 1.5h_{ef})(2 \times 1.5h_{ef})$
if $c_{a1} < 1.5h_{ef}$

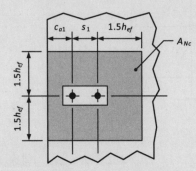

$A_{NC} = (c_{a1} + s_1 + 1.5h_{ef})(2 \times 1.5h_{ef})$
if $c_{a1} < 1.5h_{ef}$ and $s_1 < 3h_{ef}$

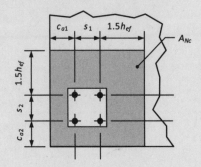

$A_{NC} = (c_{a1} + s_1 + 1.5h_{ef})(c_{a2} + s_2 + 1.5h_{ef})$
if c_{a1} and $c_{a2} < 1.5h_{ef}$
and s_1 and $s_2 < 3h_{ef}$

CSA Group standard A23.3-14

Figure D.8
Example of tension where anchors are located in narrow members
(See Clause 3.)

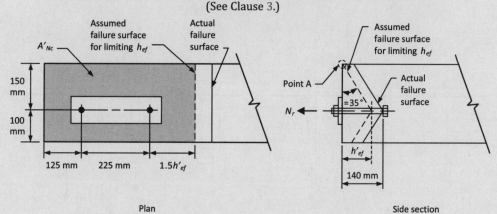

Plan   Side section

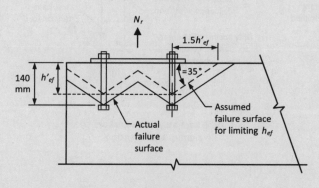

Elevation

Note: *The actual h_{ef} = 140 mm, but three edges are ≤ 1.5 h_{ef} (shown as h'_{ef} in the Figure) is the larger of $c_{a,max}/1.5$ and one-third of the maximum spacing for an anchor group: h'_{ef} = max (150/1.5, 225/3) = 100 mm. Therefore, use h_{ef} = 100 mm for the value of h_{ef} in Equations D.3 to D.10 including the calculation of A_{Nc}. A'_{Nc} = (150 + 100) (125 + 225 + (1.5 x 100)) = 129 032 mm². Point A shows the intersection of the assumed failure surface for limiting h_{ef} with the concrete surface.*

Figure D.9
Definition of dimension e'_N for a group of anchors
(See Clause D.6.2.4.)

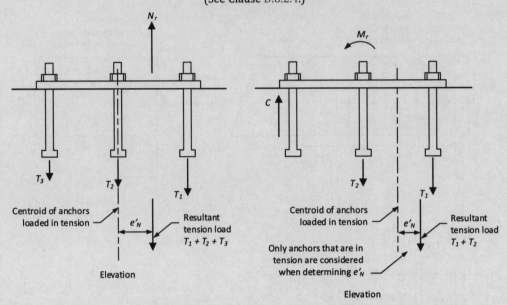

a) **Where all anchors in a**
group are in tension

b) **Where only some anchors**
in a group are in tension

Figure D.10
Anchor reinforcement for tension
(See Clause D.6.2.9.)

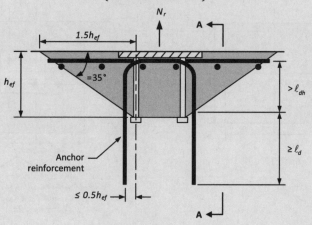

Elevation

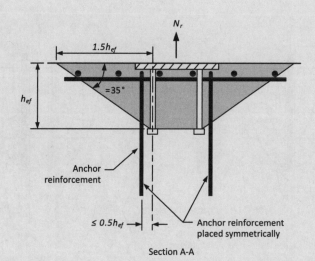

Section A-A

Figure D.11
Calculation of influence areas A_{Nao} and A_{Na}
(See Clause D.6.5.1.)

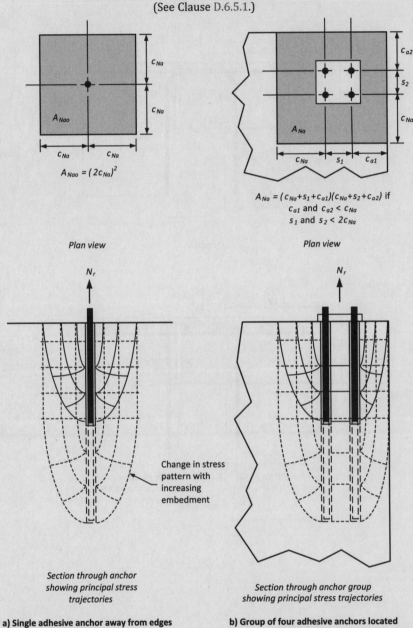

a) Single adhesive anchor away from edges and other anchors

b) Group of four adhesive anchors located near a corner

Figure D.12
Calculation of A_{Vco}
(See Clause D.7.2.1.)

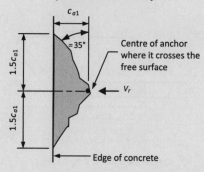

a) Plan view

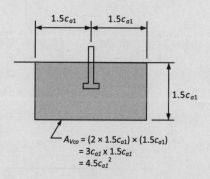

b) Front view

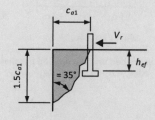

c) Side section

Note: *The critical edge distance for headed studs, headed bolts, expansion anchors, and undercut anchors is $1.5c_{a1}$.*

Figure D.13
Projected areas for single anchors and anchor groups
(See Clause D.7.2.1.)

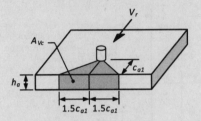

$$A_{Vc} = 2 \times 1.5c_{a1} \times h_a$$

a) A single anchor, if $h_a < 1.5c_{a1}$

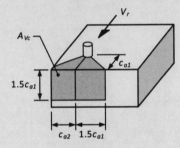

$$A_{Vc} = 1.5c_{a1} \times (1.5c_{a1} + c_{a2})$$

b) A single anchor, if $c_{a2} < 1.5c_{a1}$

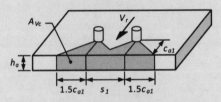

$$A_{Vc} = (2 \times 1.5c_{a1} + s_1) \times h_a$$

c) Two loaded anchors aligned parallel to edge, if $h_a < 1.5c_{a1}$ and $s_1 < 3c_{a1}$

(Continued)

Figure D.13 (Concluded)

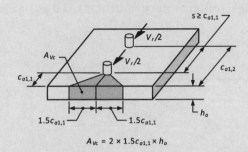

$$A_{Vc} = 2 \times 1.5c_{a1,1} \times h_a$$

Case 1: One assumption of the distribution of forces indicates that half of the shear force would be critical on the front anchor and the projected area. For the calculation of concrete breakout, c_{a1} is taken as $c_{a1,1}$

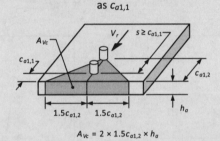

$$A_{Vc} = 2 \times 1.5c_{a1,2} \times h_a$$

Case 2: Another assumption of the distribution of forces indicates that the total shear force would be critical on the rear anchor and its projected area. Only this assumption needs to be considered when anchors are welded to a common plate independent of s. For the calculation of concrete breakout, c_{a1} is taken as $c_{a1,2}$

Note: *For $s \geq c_{a1,1}$, both Case 1 and Case 2 should be evaluated to determine which controls for design except as noted for anchors welded to a common plate.*

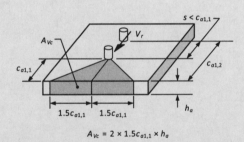

$$A_{Vc} = 2 \times 1.5c_{a1,1} \times h_a$$

Case 3: Where $s < c_{a1,1}$, apply the entire shear load V to the front anchor. This case does not apply for anchors welded to a common plate. For the calculation of concrete breakout, c_{a1} is taken as $c_{a1,1}$.

d) Two loaded anchors aligned perpendicular to edge if $h_a < 1.5 c_{a1}$

Figure D.14
Shear loading parallel or perpendicular to edge, or near a corner
(See Clause D.7.2.1.)

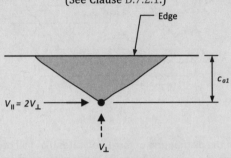

a) Shear force parallel to edge

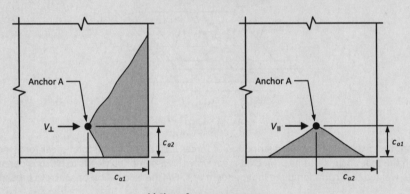

b) Shear force near a corner

Figure D.15
Example of shear where anchors are located in narrow members of limited thickness
(See Clause D.7.2.4.)

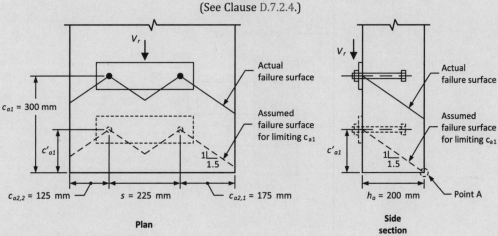

Plan | Side section

a) The actual c_{a1} = 300 mm.
b) The two edge distances c_{a2} as well as h_a are all less than $1.5c_{a1}$.
c) The limiting value of c_{a1} (shown as c'_{a1} in the figure) to be used for the calculation of A_{Vc} and in Equations D.32 to D.38 and D.40 to D.42 is determined as the largest of the following:
$(c_{a2,max})/1.5 = (175)/1.5 = 116.7$ mm.
$(h_a)/1.5 = (200)/1.5 = 133.3$ mm.
$s/3 = 225/3 = 75$ mm.
d) For this case, A_{Vc}, A_{Vco}, $\psi_{ed,V}$, and $\psi_{h,V}$ are determined as follows:
$A_{Vc}= (125 + 225 + 175)(1.5 \times 133.3) = 105\ 000$ mm².
$A_{Vco} = 4.5 \times 133.3^2 = 80\ 000$ mm².
$\psi_{ed,V} = 0.7 + (0.3 \times 125)/133.3 = 0.98$
$\psi_{h,V} = 1.0$ because $c_{a1} = (h_a)/1.5$. Point A shows the intersection of the assumed failure surface with the concrete surface that establishes the limiting value of c_{a1}.

Figure D.16
Definition of dimension e'_v for a group of anchors
(See Clauses D.3 and D.7.2.5.)

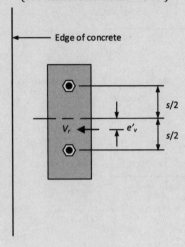

Figure D.17A
Hairpin anchor reinforcement for shear
(See Clause D.7.2.9.)

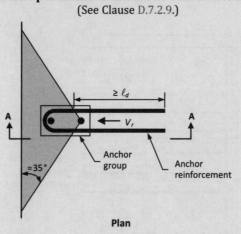

Plan

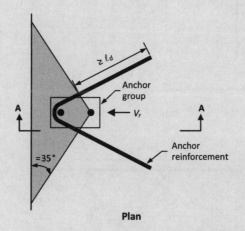

Plan

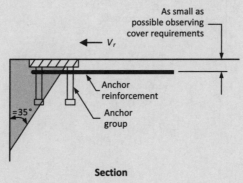

Section

Figure D.17B
Edge reinforcement and anchor reinforcement for shear
(See Clause D.7.2.9.)

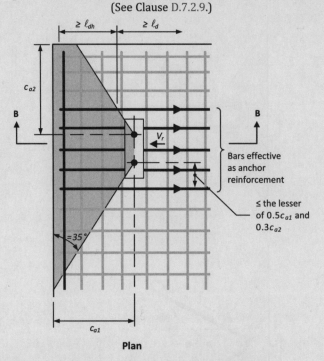

Plan

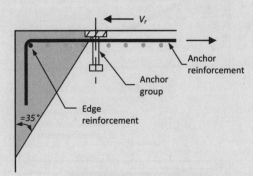

Section B–B

Figure D.18
Shear and tensile load interaction equation
(See Clauses D.8.2 to D.8.4.)

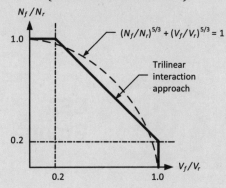

Explanatory Notes on
CSA Group standard A23.3-14 "Design of concrete structures"

These explanatory notes were prepared by:

P. Adebar	W. Kassian
S. Alexander	T. Kokai
C.M. Allen	K. Lemieux
F.M. Bartlett	R. Loov
M.P. Collins	R.J. McGrath
R.H. DeVall	D. Mitchell
H. Dutrisac	J. Mutrie

N1 Scope

N1.5 Units

The equations throughout the standard are consistent with the units listed so that units have been deleted from the remainder of the Standard. A designer may use other units but will then need to revise some of the equations which have units embedded in their constants. An example of this is the equation $\ell_{db} = 0.044 d_b f_y$ in Clause 12.3.2. The constant has units of MPa^{-1} in order to make this equation dimensionally consistent.

N3 Definitions and symbols

N3.3.3 Bar diameter for calculations

In calculations or spacing limits involving the bar diameter, d_b, it is permissible to take d_b equal to the bar designation number.

N4 General requirements

N4.1.1

Geometric properties of standard prestressing tendons are summarized in Table N4.1.1.

Table N4.1.1
Standard prestressing tendons

Tendon type	Grade f_{pu} (MPa)	Size designation	Nominal dimensions		Nominal linear mass (kg/m)
			Diameter (mm)	Area (mm²)	
Seven wire strand	1860	9	9.53	55	0.432
	1860	11	11.13	74	0.582
	1860	13	12.70	99	0.775
	1860	15	15.24	140	1.109
	1760	16	15.47	148	1.173
Prestressing wire	1550	5*	5.00	19.6	0.154
	1720	5	5.00	19.6	0.154
	1620	7	7.00	38.5	0.302
	1760	7	7.00	38.5	0.302
Deformed prestressing bars	1080	15	15.0	177	1.44
	1030	26	26.5	551	4.48
	1100	26**	26.5	551	4.48
	1030	32	32.0	804	6.53
	1100	32**	32.0	804	6.53
	1030	36	36.0	1018	8.27

*   Available with surface indentation.
** Available on special order.

N4.1.3

Reinforcing bars conforming to CSA Standard G30.18 with f_y = 400 MPa (Grade 400) are the most frequently used type of reinforcement. The weldable grade bars conforming to CSA Standard G30.18

have a more closely controlled chemical composition which results in a more predictable and more ductile stress-strain response. Reinforcement for structures subjected to seismic action may need to be weldable grade (see Clause 21.2.7.1.1).

The geometric properties of standard reinforcing bars are summarized in Table N4.1.3

Table N4.1.3
Standard deformed reinforcing bars

Bar number*	Nominal dimension**			Nominal linear mass (kg/m)
	Area (mm²)	Diameter (mm)	Perimeter (mm)	
10M	100	11.3	36	0.785
15M	200	16.0	50	1.570
20M	300	19.5	61	2.355
25M	500	25.2	79	3.925
30M	700	29.9	94	5.495
35M	1000	35.7	112	7.850
45M	1500	43.7	137	11.775
55M	2500	56.4	177	19.625

* Bar numbers are based on the rounded off nominal diameter of the bars.
** Nominal dimensions are equivalent to those of a plain round bar having the same mass per metre as the deformed bar.

N7 Details of reinforcement

N7.1
The CSA Standard A23.1 Clauses concerning hooks and bends are reproduced in Annex A (see Clause 6.6.2).

N7.3.1
See Clause 6.6.8 in Annex A.

N7.4.1.1
See Clause 6.6.5 in Annex A.

N7.4.2.1
Bundled bars are groups of 2, 3, or 4 bars in contact to act as a single unit in which no more than 2 bars of the total bundle are in the same plane. Fig. N.7.4.2.1 illustrates acceptable bar arrangements as intended by Clause 7.4.2.1 for bundled bars.

Fig. N7.4.2.1 Bar arrangements for bundles

N7.4.4
See Clause 6.8.5.3 in CSA A23.1.

N7.5.1

The details and design of ties near bends in offset bars are illustrated in Fig. N7.5.1.

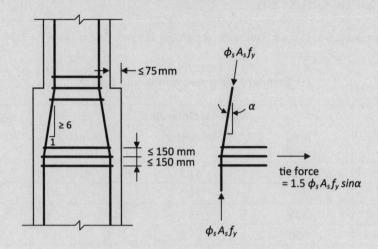

Fig. N7.5.1 Tie reinforcement near offset bars

N7.6.4.1

See Clause 6.6.3 in Annex A.

N7.6.5.2

The purpose of ties is primarily to restrain the longitudinal bars from outward buckling. The diameter and spacing of the ties are therefore related to the diameter of the longitudinal bars with further restrictions relating tie spacing to tie diameter and the least column dimension. For specified concrete strengths greater than 50 MPa, the tie spacings are reduced by 25% to provide more confinement for higher strength concretes.

N7.6.5.5

Fig. N7.6.5.5 illustrates tie arrangements which satisfy the requirements for lateral support of column bars.

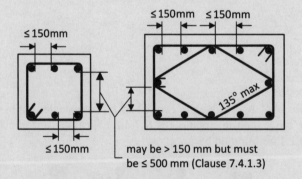

Fig. N7.6.5.5 Requirements for lateral support of column bars

N7.6.5.8

This new clause introduced in the 2004 Standard requires the designer to provide containment ties around anchor bolts placed in the top of a column or pedestal.

N7.6.6.1

Compression reinforcement in beams and girders must be enclosed to prevent buckling.

N7.7.3

This clause prescribes minimum ties in beam-column joints. Edge columns and corner columns and other columns where the connection regions are not restrained by equal depth beams or slabs on all four sides require ties to be placed within the joint region as illustrated in Fig. N7.7.3(a). These ties will help control diagonal cracking in the joint region, and will improve the anchorage of reinforcement terminating in this region. As illustrated in Fig. N7.7.3(b), ties may be omitted where a connection is restrained on 4 sides by beams and does not form part of the primary seismic force resisting system. For additional requirements due to lateral loading, see Clause 12.11.2. For additional requirements due to seismic loading, see Clauses 21.3.3, 21.4.6 and 21.6.2.4.

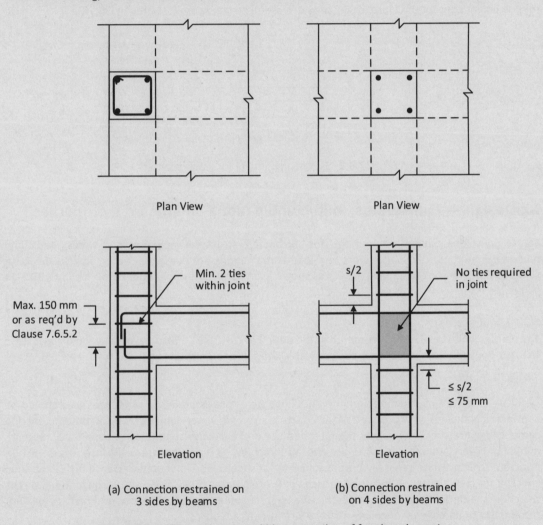

Plan View

Plan View

Min. 2 ties within joint

Max. 150 mm or as req'd by Clause 7.6.5.2

Elevation

s/2

No ties required in joint

≤ s/2
≤ 75 mm

Elevation

(a) Connection restrained on 3 sides by beams

(b) Connection restrained on 4 sides by beams

Fig. N7.7.3 Tie requirement within connection of framing elements

N7.8.1

The purpose of this minimum reinforcement is to provide some control of the cracking caused by shrinkage and temperature effects and to tie the structure together after cracking. It also serves as the means to determine the minimum requirement for flexure when other parts of this standard, such as Clause 10.5.1.2(a) or Clause 13.10.1 refer to Clause 7.8. For minimum reinforcement not subject to flexural requirements, the total minimum reinforcement may be distributed to the top and bottom of the slab or footing, or at a single location, at the discretion of the designer. However, when subjected to flexural requirements, the minimum reinforcement required under Clause 7.8.1, must be satisfied at every location subjected to flexural requirements. It should be noted that most live loads due to use include minimum concentrated loads by code which will likely result in flexure perpendicular to the line of action of a one way slab and this could impact the minimum reinforcement requirement for both directions.

N7.8.2

The amounts of shrinkage and temperature reinforcement given in the previous standards have been found to be inadequate in preventing wide shrinkage and temperature cracks in slabs. In deciding upon appropriate distribution and amounts of reinforcement needed for better crack control the skin reinforcement concept of Clause 10.6.2 provides useful guidance as illustrated in Fig. N7.8.2.

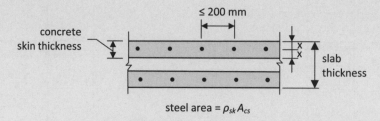

Fig. N7.8.2 Skin reinforcement for crack control

N8 Design — Limit states, load combinations and material properties.

Clause 8 includes general requirements for all concrete structures including limit states, loads, and material properties. The load factors and load combinations are consistent with those in the 2015 National Building Code of Canada (NBCC) as shown in an abridged form in Annex C of the CSA A23.3-14 standard.

N8.1 Limit states

The various limit states to be considered in the design of concrete structures are listed in Clauses 8.1.1 to 8.1.5. For specialized structures, such as water tanks, other limit states such as resistance to leakage may also apply.

With the exception of structural integrity, the limit states are listed in the order that they should be considered in the design process. First, the concrete strength, water-cement ratio, air entrainment and cement type are chosen to satisfy the intended use and exposure conditions (Clause 8.1.1). Second, minimum covers and member sizes are chosen to achieve the desired fire resistance (Clause 8.1.2). Concrete structures are generally proportioned to satisfy ultimate limit states (Clause 8.1.3) and then checked for compliance with various serviceability limit states (Clauses 8.1.4.1 through 8.1.4.3). The selection and detailing of the overall structural system should ensure that localized damage will not result in major damage to, or collapse of, the structure as a whole (Clause 8.1.5).

N8.2 Loading

The loads, load factors and load combinations used to design concrete structures in this standard should be obtained from the applicable building code, typically a provincial building code based on the 2015 National Building Code of Canada. If other types of structures are designed, such as tunnel liners, it may be necessary to use load factors derived specifically for these structures.

Some designers have expressed concern that tributary-area-based live-load reduction factors should not be used for the design of two-way slabs.

N8.2.2 Imposed deformations

Loads caused by the restraint of imposed deformations, including secondary reactions and internal force effects in indeterminate prestressed structures, are not included in the general load combinations for ultimate limit states specified in the 2015 National Building Code of Canada. While these loads are self-equilibrated and so do not alter the load that causes a full plastic collapse mechanism to form in a ductile structure, they should generally be considered for concrete structures having limited ductility. Load factors for T and P loads specified in the 2015 NBCC are presented in Annex C, Section C.1.2.4 of the CSA A23.3-14 standard.

N8.3 Load combinations

The "companion action" format has been retained in the 2015 NBCC for all load combinations. This format is recognized internationally for its simplicity and appropriateness for combining transient loads. Each load combination specifies the magnitude of a principal transient load plus magnitudes of companion transient loads that are consistent with the time period while the principle load acts at its maximum value.

Load factors are intended to account for variability and uncertainty of the magnitude, position and combination of the loads, inaccuracies introduced by the simplified modelling of the loads (e.g., the use of uniform floor loads) and inaccuracies introduced by assumptions made in the structural analysis.

Ultimate limit states load combinations are presented in Annex C, Tables C.1.a) and C.1.b), of the CSA A23.3-14 standard without and with crane loads, respectively. It is noted that the load factor for companion loads S or L in cases 2 and 3 in Table C.1.a) and case 2 in Table C.1.b) has increased from 0.5 to 1.0.

Additional information on serviceability limit states load combinations can be found in the Commentary entitled Limit Sates Design in the User's Guide – NBC 2015, Structural Commentaries (Part 4 of Division B).

N8.4 Factored resistance

To account for variability of dimensions and material properties, workmanship, type of failure and uncertainty in the prediction of resistance, a resistance factor is applied to a specified material property or to the resistance of a member, connection or structure. The material resistance factor for non-prestressed reinforcing bars, ϕ_s, is intended to account for variations in resistance that result from the variability of the mechanical properties of the reinforcement, the normal tolerances of bar placement, and inaccuracies resulting from the steel terms in the design equations. The material resistance factor for concrete, ϕ_c, accounts for a similar set of variations resulting from the variability of the concrete strength, cross section geometry, and model error in the design equations. When computing the factored moment resistance of a beam, M_r, the designer would compute:

$$M_r = \phi_s A_s f_y \left[d - \frac{\phi_s A_s f_y}{2\phi_c \alpha_1 f'_c b} \right]$$

If the factored resistance of a beam or beam column is being computed using a plane sections analysis, the material resistance factor is applied to the stress at any strain to give factored stress-strain relationships as shown in Fig. N8.4.

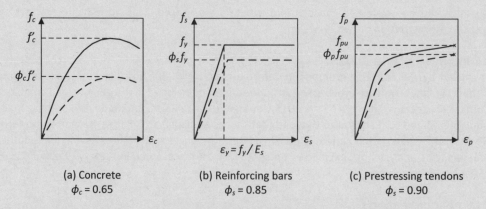

Fig. N8.4 Factored material stress-strain relationships

Equations defining empirical limits, such as Eq. (10-4) in Clause 10.5.1.2 or the equations in Clause 12, do not include ϕ factors because they are recognized to already include a safety margin.

N8.4.3 Factored reinforcement and tendon force

Clauses 8.4.3 and 8.4.5 require that, when determining the factored resistance of bars and tendons, the resistance factor is applied regardless of whether the steel has yielded or not. For example, as shown in Fig. N8.4, the resistance factor ϕ_s is applied to the bar force $\phi_s A_s f_y$ or $\phi_s A_s E_s \varepsilon_s$ to account for deviations of the location of the reinforcement and uncertainty in the prediction of the resistance as well as variability of the yield strength.

N8.5.1 Design strength for reinforcement

CSA Standard G30.18 specifies requirements for steels with yield strengths of 400 and 500 MPa. Crack widths and deflections may be excessive in beams with f_y in excess of 500 MPa.

N8.5.2 Compression reinforcement

Section 10.1.3 defines the maximum strain at the extreme concrete compression fibre to be 0.0035. Thus the maximum compressive strain that can be developed in the reinforcement before the concrete crushes is 0.0035, and steels supplied in accordance with a specification that defines the yield strength at greater than a strain of 0.0035 may not yield before the concrete crushes. For this reason, Clause 8.5.2 limits the value of f_y that can be used in design calculations to 400 MPa, which can be achieved by a strain of 0.0035, or to the stress corresponding to a strain of 0.0035.

N8.6.1 Design strength of concrete

The strength equations and detailing rules of this standard are applicable for concretes with compressive strengths from 20 to 80 MPa. Clause 12.1.2 limits the value of $\sqrt{f_c'}$ for use in bond and anchorage calculations to 8 MPa. This is not intended to imply an upper limit on f_c' of 64 MPa, but merely reflects the upper limit of extensive bond test data. Similarly, the limitations given in Clauses 11.3.6.3 and 18.12.3.3 reflect the upper limit of compressive strengths investigated in tests used to establish design equation constants empirically. Clause 21.2.6 permits specified compressive strengths of up to 80 MPa for some forms of construction involving normal density concrete, but limits the maximum compressive strength of structural low-density concretes to 30 MPa and limits the maximum value of $\sqrt{f_c'}$ used in calculations to 8 MPa. Some structural low density concretes have displayed brittle compression failures.

Concrete strengths greater than 80 MPa may be used if the designer can establish the structural properties and detailing requirements for the concrete to be used. Major areas requiring documentation are requirements for column ties and confining reinforcement in columns, beams and beam-column joints.

CSA Standard A23.1-14 defines concretes having compressive strengths of 70 MPa or higher as high-strength concretes and gives special requirements for producing and testing such concretes.

N8.6.2 Modulus of elasticity

The modulus of elasticity computed using either Eq. (8.1) in Clause 8.6.2.2 or Eq. (8.2) in Clause 8.6.2.3 represents a secant modulus as shown in Fig N8.6.2. The modulus of elasticity of Canadian concretes varies markedly depending on the concrete strength, the concrete density and, especially for higher strength concretes, on the type of coarse aggregate.

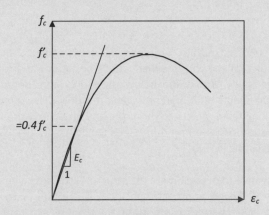

Fig. N8.6.2 Modulus of elasticity of concrete, E_c

N8.6.5 Modification factors for concrete density

The tensile strength of some low-density concretes is lower than that for normal density concrete. This is accounted for by the factor λ that appears in equations for the tensile strength of concrete and shear carried by concrete in Clauses 11, 13, 18, 21, 22 and Annex D.

N9 Structural analysis and computation of deflections

N9.1 Methods of analysis

The methods of analysis considered in Clause 9 are elastic frame analysis, approximate frame analysis, analysis by strut-and-tie methods, finite element analysis, elastic plate analysis and plastic analysis.

N9.2.1 Stiffness

As stated in Clause 9.2.1.2, the member stiffnesses used in elastic analyses to determine lateral deflections of frames, or in second-order frame analyses should be representative of the degree of cracking and inelastic action at the loading stage that the calculations apply to. Thus, when computing second-order effects in unbraced or lightly braced structures to enable the beams and columns to be designed for strength, the EI assumptions should be representative of the stage just prior to ultimate. In this case, the values specified in Clause 10.14.1 should be used.

At service loads, the member stiffnesses are greater than at ultimate because the extent of cracking and inelastic action is less. For analysis of lateral frame deflections at service loads the EI of the columns should be taken as 1.0 EI_g, where I_g is the gross moment of inertia, or (1.0/0.7 =) 1.4 times the value given in Clause 10.14.1. Similarly, the EI of beams, walls and slabs used in a service-load analysis may be taken as 1.4 times the values given in Clause 10.14.1.

If needed, the torsional stiffness may be taken as 0.15 GJ for an analysis at ultimate loads or 0.20 GJ at service loads.

For the analysis of moments in braced frames, where second-order effects are not significant, it is only necessary that the relative magnitudes of the beam and column stiffnesses be modelled accurately. Again in this case the EI values in Clause 10.14.1 can be used.

Values of E and I to be used for the computation of the deflection of beams subjected to gravity loads are given in Clauses 9.8.2.3 and 9.8.2.4.

Additional information concerning member EI values to be used to determine the structural response due to wind loads is presented in N9.2.1.2.

N9.2.1.2

Inter-storey drift limits are specified in NBCC Sentences 4.1.3.5(3) and 4.1.3.5(4). Inter-storey drift limits should be checked accounting for the combined effect of translations and rotations for corresponding points on the floors immediately above and below the storey considered. Usually the floor plate corners are governed by the effects of in-plane torsional response. The combined effects of wind and gravity loads, considering long-term effects of shrinkage and creep and the P-Delta effects, should be investigated. More information may be found in User's Guide - NBC 2015 Structured Commentaries (Part 4), Commentary I and Griffis (1993)[9.2].

While it is generally conservative to overestimate the structural stiffness when determining earthquake loads using the force-based design approach specified in the NBCC, the opposite is true when determining wind loading. It is therefore important to quantify accurately any potential stiffness reduction over the entire design life of the structure and the associated effects on the building periods and lateral deflections. Hence when conducting linear-elastic analysis of the lateral system, a bounded approach should be adopted that assigns distinct cracked stiffness parameters for wind and earthquake load cases.

The equivalent static wind loads specified in the NBCC are independent of the building periods or damping, unless the detailed approach given in Commentary I is used to quantify the gust effect factor. To compute the lateral deflections of the building, appropriate member stiffness parameters must be used. Table N.9.2.1.2 summarizes typical effective stiffness parameters for different structural members that have been used for linear elastic analysis[9.4]. Higher values may be used if justified by non-linear analysis that accounts for post-elastic material behaviour. Consideration should be given to critical elements with local stiffnesses that markedly affect the overall building stiffness, such as: transfer beams, transfer slabs, outrigger walls, belt beams, etc. Sensitivity studies or detailed non-linear analysis should be used to bound the stiffness of these elements.

It is expected that the values shown may evolve in future editions based on research findings and experience.

Wind loads determined by wind tunnel testing are a function of the building period and inherent damping. Both depend on the member stiffnesses, which depend on the expected cracking at a given load level, so the procedure for quantifying the wind loads and lateral deflections is iterative. Building periods for the first iteration can be computed using the effective member stiffnesses shown in Table N.9.2.1.2. For some building and structural system geometries, subsequent iterations may converge on effective stiffness values that differ markedly from the initial values.

Explanatory Notes on CSA A23.3-14

Table N9.2.1.2:
Typical Effective Member Stiffnesses for Wind Load Quantification

Member Type	Ranges for Linear-Elastic Analyses	
	Serviceability/SLS	Strength/ULS
Non-diagonally Reinforced Coupling Beams	$0.50\,I_g$ $0.40\,A_g$	$0.40\,I_g$ $0.25\,A_g$
Diagonally Reinforced Coupling Beams	$0.45\,I_g$ $0.45\,A_g$	$0.35\,I_g$ $0.40\,A_g$
Shear Walls	$0.95\,I_g$ $0.95\,A_g$	$0.75\,I_g$ $0.75\,A_g$
Shear Walls in net tension	Refined Calculation Required	
Slabs with mild reinforcement	$0.35\,I_g$	$0.20\,I_g$
PT slabs	$0.60\,I_g$	$0.45\,I_g$
Beams (excluding coupling beams)	$0.50\,I_g$ $0.75\,A_g$	$0.40\,I_g$ $0.50\,A_g$
Columns	$1.0\,I_g$ $1.0\,A_g$	$0.70\,I_g$ $0.70\,A_g$
Columns in net tension	Refined Calculation Required	

Commentary I of the NBCC allows the damping assumed for reinforced concrete structures to be 1 to 2% of the critical damping. Reported in-situ damping measurements of structures subjected to wind loads indicate that damping decreases significantly with the building height and that the NBCC values may be unconservative when the height exceeds 100 metres[9.1, 9.5, 9.6 & 9.8]. The majority of buildings over 200 meters tall are reported to have less than 1% inherent damping, whether the construction is reinforced concrete, steel, or composite[9.1].

N9.2.2 Span length
The span lengths used in the analysis of continuous frames should be taken centre-to-centre of joints. Clause 9.2.2.2 allows the moments at the faces of the joints to be used for the design of members. The computation of the moments at the face of the joints should account for the increase in negative moments due to the higher stiffness within the joint. Thus for uniformly loaded prismatic beams it is customary to compute the reduced negative moment at the face of the joint, M_F, as:

$$M_F = M_{CL} + Vc/3$$

where M_{CL} is the negative moment in the beam at the centre of the joint, V, taken postive, is the shear in the beam at the centre of the joint, and c is the width of the column in the direction parallel to the beam. The factor of 1/3 in this equation empirically accounts for the increase of the fixed end moments at the center of the joint and the resulting reduction of the moments at the face of the columns.

N9.2.2.4
When a structure containing shear walls deflects laterally, the deflections of the walls impose a relative displacement on the ends of the beams as shown in Fig. N9.2.2.4. The effect of the width of the shear wall can be idealized by assigning very high moments of inertia to the extensions of the beams within the shear walls. The localized reduction of the stiffness of the coupling beams due to cracking within the column-wall joints is sometimes modelled by terminating the region of very high beam stiffness about half the beam depth inside the wall from the face of the wall.

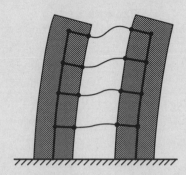

Fig. N9.2.2.4 Idealization of beams in shear-wall frame structure

N9.2.3.1 Continuous beams and one-way slabs

Dead loads due to the self weight of materials depend on density and construction tolerances and so are usually highly correlated from span to span. Thus they are not patterned, but according to Clause 9.2.3.1 (a), (b) and (c) are applied uniformly with a dead load factor of 1.25 in all spans or with a dead load factor of 0.90 in all spans. Superimposed dead loads, such as permanent machinery, partitions, or earth fill, may in some cases be placed on the structure in a patterned manner and in such circumstances can be patterned with zero superimposed dead load in some spans and with a dead load factor of 1.25 times the superimposed dead load in other spans.

N9.2.4 Redistribution of moments in continuous flexural members

Redistribution of elastic bending moments can occur prior to failure due to inelastic rotations in regions with high moments. Beam sections having low percentages of tension reinforcement or containing compression reinforcement have low c/d values and so can tolerate larger redistributions. Due to redistribution, the computed bending moments at a support may be reduced provided that the bending moments in each adjacent span are increased to satisfy equilibrium for the loading case under consideration. Since the loading that causes the maximum moment at a support is different from the loading case causing maximum moments in the adjacent spans, accounting for moment redistribution can result in a reduction of the required flexural reinforcement at both the support and span regions, as shown in Fig. N9.2.4.

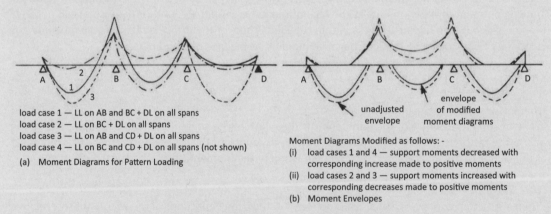

load case 1 — LL on AB and BC + DL on all spans
load case 2 — LL on BC + DL on all spans
load case 3 — LL on AB and CD + DL on all spans
load case 4 — LL on BC and CD + DL on all spans (not shown)

(a)   Moment Diagrams for Pattern Loading

Moment Diagrams Modified as follows: -
(i)   load cases 1 and 4 — support moments decreased with corresponding increase made to positive moments
(ii) load cases 2 and 3 — support moments increased with corresponding decreases made to positive moments
(b)   Moment Envelopes

Fig. N9.2.4 Illustration of moment redistribution

Clause 9.2.4 refers to the redistribution of negative moment since this is the normal case in design. Occasionally, as for example, in the case of a continuous inverted T-beam, the amount of redistribution may be limited by the c/d ratio at the point of maximum positive moment.

N9.3 Approximate frame analysis

Figure N9.3.3 summarizes the approximate moments and shears that may be used in lieu of performing a series of frame analyses that consider the various live load patterns specified in Clause 9.2.3.1. Redistribution of these moments is not permitted.

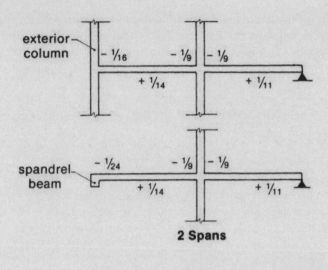

2 Spans

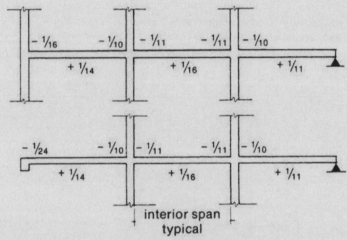

More than 2 Spans

Note: shear force = 1.15 $w_f \ell_n / 2$ in end members at face of first interior support and $w_f \ell_n / 2$ at face of all other supports

$$\text{moment} = \text{coefficient} \times w_f \ell_n^2$$

Fig. N9.3.3 Approximate moments and shears for the design of flexural members satisfying the conditions of Clause 9.3.3

N9.4 Analysis by strut-and-tie models

Although strut-and-tie models can be used to proportion all types of concrete structures, they are generally used in regions where the plane sections theory of flexure is not applicable such as deep beams, members with discontinuities such as holes, dapped ends and corbels, beam-column joints and prestress anchorage zones.

Clause 9.4 permits the use of strut-and-tie models. Clause 11.4 and the Notes on that clause present design guidance. The most important single requirement of a strut-and-tie model is that it be a complete force field in equilibrium with the applied loads and reactions.

N9.5 Finite element analysis

Clause 9.5 sets out requirements for the use of finite element analyses in design. A major requirement of Clauses 9.5.1 is that differences between the idealized finite element model and the reinforced concrete structure must be implicitly considered. This is particularly true if an elastic finite element analysis that ignores cracking is conducted. Clause 9.5.4 requires an independent check of the analysis.

N9.7 Plastic analysis

Braced frames or slabs may be designed using plastic analysis. The use of plastic analysis in two-way slab design is discussed in Clause 13.7.

N9.8 Control of deflections

This clause addresses deflections of beams due to gravity loads. The selection of two-way slab thicknesses to control deflection and the computation of two-way slab deflections are considered in Clause 13.2. The control of lateral deflections of frames subjected to service loads is not specifically addressed in this standard. Note N9.2.1 suggests EI values to be used for such an analysis.

N9.8.2.3 E_c and I_e

As shown in Fig. N9.8.2.3, the flexural stiffness of a beam decreases after cracking and approaches the fully cracked flexural stiffness, $E_c I_{cr}$. Equation 9.1 gives an expression for the effective secant stiffness for this case. The cracking moment, M_{cr}, in Equation 9.1 is computed using a modulus of rupture equal to half the value computed using Clause 8.6.4 as described in detail in Chapter 6 of the Concrete Design Handbook.

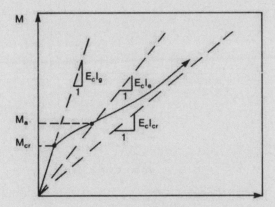

Fig. N9.8.2.3 Effective flexural stiffness

N9.8.2.5 Sustained load deflections

The term $S / (1 + 50\rho')$ accounts for the long-term deflections caused by shrinkage and by creep due to sustained loads. The total deflection is computed using:

$$\Delta_t = (\Delta_{sw} + \Delta_{sd\ell} + \Delta_{\ell s})\left(1 + \frac{S}{1 + 50\rho'}\right) + (\Delta_\ell - \Delta_{\ell s})$$

where:

Δ_t = total immediate and long-term deflection

Δ_{sw} = immediate deflection due to member self-weight loads

$\Delta_{sd\ell}$ = immediate deflection due to superimposed dead loads

Δ_ℓ = immediate deflection due to live loads

$\Delta_{\ell s}$ = immediate deflection due to sustained portion of live loads

S = creep and shrinkage deflection factor, which depends on the load duration as shown in Figure N.9.8.2.5

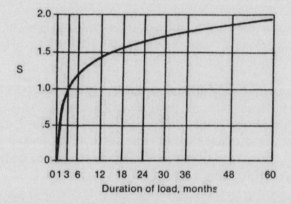

Fig. N9.8.2.5 Variation of shrinkage and creep deflection factor, S, with load duration

The incremental deflection, Δ_i, that occurs after partitions are installed (considering the partitions to be superimposed dead loads), is computed using:

$$\Delta_i = \Delta_d \left(\frac{S_\infty - S_{t1}}{1 + 50\,\rho'} \right) + (\Delta_{sd\ell} + \Delta_{\ell s}) \left(\frac{S_\infty}{1 + 50\,\rho'} \right) + \Delta_\ell$$

where S_∞ is the creep and shrinkage deflection factor for an infinite load duration (from Fig. N9.8.2.5, $S_\infty = 2$) and S_{t1} is the creep and shrinkage deflection factor corresponding to the time, t_1, when the partitions are installed. The application of this equation is illustrated in Chapter 6 of the CAC Concrete Design Handbook.

N9.8.2.6 Deflection limits
In checking the limits stipulated in Table 9.3, it is usually necessary to compute the long-term deflection that will occur after attachment of non-structural elements. It may be necessary to check the total deflection in the context of an aesthetic of functional requirements, such as objectionable visual sagging, ponding of water, improper operation of sliding doors or unsatisfactory performance of floorings.

N9.8.3 Two-way construction (non-prestressed)
Calculated deflections, particularly for two-way non-prestressed concrete construction are by nature approximate. Nevertheless, deflection analyses should account for the effects of construction sequencing and stripping procedures, early-age concrete properties, cracking initiators, cracked

stiffnesses, redistribution of moments, cracking after initial cracking, and other project-specific factors. For multi-story construction, maximum moments due to construction loads should be used to compute the effective moment of inertia, I_e[9.7].

Designers and contractors should appreciate the influence of various shoring and re-shoring procedures on the magnitude of construction loadings. Continuous shoring while stripping can cause loads that exceed twice the slab self-weight[9.3]. These may exceed the specified dead and live loadings while the concrete is still young, resulting in damage to the slab and excessive deflection. Construction documents should specify that loads imposed by construction procedures should not exceed the specified dead and live in-service loadings. The design engineer should require documentation from the contractor confirming maximum construction loading and the stripping and re-shoring procedure. As described in Section 6.3.2.1 of the Concrete Design Handbook, completely stripping the slab and then re-shoring does subject slabs to early age loading but results in lower maximum construction load. Alternatively, the shores of systems with "permanent" reshores may be temporarily released during the stripping procedure to achieve the same effect.

Where floor finishes require "flat" structural floor surfaces, consideration should be given to require an allowance for floor filling material in the construction documents. Even following this approach, the floor slab may not remain flat due to ongoing long-term deflections.

NTable 9-3 Maximum permissible computed deflections
Ponding may be a problem for medium- to long-span roofs in regions where snow loads are light. See Commentary H of the "User's Guide - NBC 2015 Structural Commentaries (Part 4 of Division B)" for further guidance. Minor cracking of partitions may occur even if the ℓ / 480 deflection limit is satisfied.

N10 Flexure and axial loads

Clause 10.1 presents the basic assumptions for both flexural and axial load resistance. Clauses 10.2 through 10.7 deal with concerns related to flexural members. Items such as T-beam flanges and joist geometry are located here. Clause 10.8 deals with bearing and Clauses 10.9 through 10.19 deal with columns and other compression members.

N10.1 General principles
Fig. N10.1 illustrates the plane section method that uses equilibrium conditions, compatibility conditions and stress-strain relationships for concrete and reinforcement.

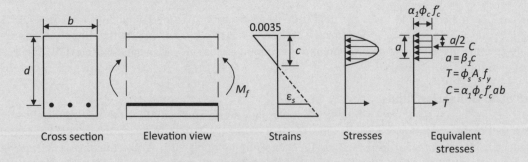

Fig. N10.1 Plane sections method

N10.1.3 Maximum concrete strain
A strain of 0.0035 is representative of the strain at peak load for higher strength concretes.

N10.1.4 Balanced strain conditions

The balanced strain condition is illustrated in Fig. N10.1.4.

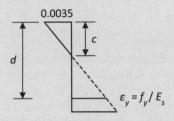

Strain Distribution

$$\frac{c}{d} = \frac{0.0035}{0.0035 + \varepsilon_y} = \frac{700}{700 + f_y}$$

Fig. N10.1.4 Balanced strain conditions

N10.1.6 Concrete stress-strain relationship

The concrete in a structure is not expected to be as strong as the control cylinders that are cast from the same batch. This occurs from a variety of causes including bleeding, differences in compaction and differences in loading and restraint.

N10.1.7 Equivalent rectangular concrete stress distribution

The value of β_1 is larger than that traditionally used and a variable α_1 replaces the traditional constant of 0.85. These coefficients take into account the more nearly triangular stress block of higher strengths of concrete and result in more conservative M_r values for columns. To keep these factors simple, straight-line variations have been assumed that are applicable throughout the range of the current standard (20 MPa to 80 MPa). The minimum values of 0.67 do not apply until $f'_c > 120$ MPa.

N10.2 Flexural members — Distance between lateral supports

Lateral instability is more critical for narrow deep beams and for beams subjected to eccentric or inclined loads.

N10.5.1 Minimum reinforcement

The provision of a minimum amount of flexural reinforcement is intended to prevent a brittle failure at first cracking by providing adequate post-cracking strength.

N10.5.1.2

Footings of uniform thickness can be designed according to Clause 7.8. Specific guidance is provided for determining b_t, the width of the tension zone for the negative moment region of T-beams with a flange on one or both sides of the web.

N10.5.2 Limit of c/d for yielding of tension reinforcement

The strain distribution corresponding to Eq. (10.5) is illustrated in Fig. N10.1.4. The factored concrete strength $\phi_c \alpha_1 f'_c$ and the factored bar force $\phi_s A_s f_s$ are used when calculating the neutral axis depth $c = a/\beta_1$.

Over-reinforced beams that do not meet the c/d limit of Eq. (10.5) are not permitted. Compression members, on the other hand, generally have c/d ratios larger than this value. This is permitted, but the strains in the different layers of reinforcement have to be calculated. The stress of 700 MPa is a consequence of assuming a limiting concrete strain of 0.0035 at failure with an E_s of 200, 000 MPa.

N10.5.3 Reinforcement in T-beam flanges

To help the designer, the required reinforcing is explicitly defined. The intent is to ensure sufficient reinforcement in the tension zone of the slab adjacent to the web so that cracks in this region will be adequately controlled.

N10.5.3.2 Transverse reinforcement

This situation normally occurs when a number of smaller beams supporting a one-way slab are supported by a girder, which therefore is parallel to the one-way slab. The transverse reinforcement in the girder is required to extend beyond the web of the girder, a distance equal to 0.3 of the clear spacing between the smaller beams. The purpose of this Clause is to control the cracks that will tend to occur in the flange above the edge of the web, and to avoid the necessity of complex computations to determine a suitable amount of reinforcement.

N10.6.1 Crack control parameter

Equation (10.6) is intended to provide a distribution of flexural reinforcement that will provide reasonable control of flexural cracking at specified loads. It is based on Gergely and Lutz's empirical equation[10-1].

$$w \approx 11\, f_s \sqrt[3]{d_c A}\, \frac{h_2}{h_1} \times 10^{-6}\, \text{mm}$$

where,

w = crack width at tensile face
h_1 = distance from centroid of tension steel to neutral axis
h_2 = distance from extreme tension fibre to neutral axis.

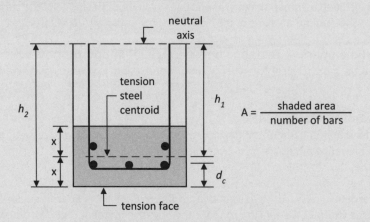

Fig. N10.6.1 Crack width parameters

Limiting z to 30 kN/mm and 25 kN/mm corresponds to limiting crack widths to about 0.4 mm and 0.33 mm respectively.

It may be difficult to satisfy Eq. (10.6) if covers greater than 50 mm are required for durability, fire resistance or in such members as footings. For this reason, it is not necessary to take the cover greater than 50 mm when computing A and d_c.

N10.6.2 Skin reinforcement

While the main tension reinforcement satisfying Eq. (10.6) should provide adequate crack control in the shaded area shown in Fig. N10.6.1, it is possible that wider cracks may form on the side faces of the beam in the zone between the neutral axis and the main tension reinforcement. For this reason skin reinforcement is needed in the area A_{cs} shown shaded in Fig. N10.6.2.

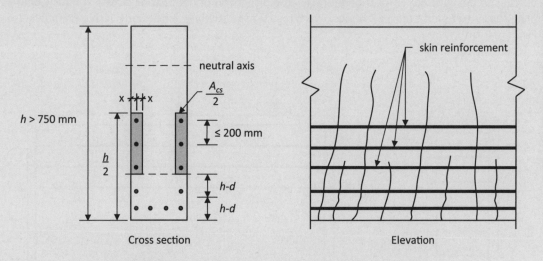

Fig. N10.6.2 Side-face cracks controlled by skin reinforcement

Clause 10.6.2 is based on tests reported in Franz and Breen[10.2]. The value of ρ_{sk} required by Clause 10.6.2 is somewhat lower than that proposed by Franz and Breen.

N10.7 Deep flexural members

The flow of forces in deep flexural members can be investigated with the aid of the strut-and-tie model described in Clause 11.4.

N10.8 Design of bearing zones

When the loaded area is surrounded on all sides by unloaded concrete, this unloaded concrete confines and hence increases the bearing capacity of the loaded area. Fig. N10.8 illustrates the determination of A_2 for two different situations of bearing and confinement.

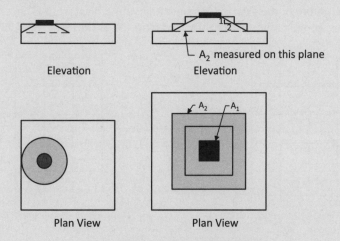

Fig. N10.8 Determination of A_2

See Clause 18.13 for information on bearing stresses associated with tendon anchorage zones.

N10.8.2

In bearing zones the possibility of bursting, splitting or spalling should be considered. If the unconfined concrete cover is directly loaded in bearing it may spall off as shown in Fig. N10.8.2(a). Hence, direct bearing on the concrete cover is undesirable. The dispersion of the bearing stresses under a bearing plate causes transverse tensile stresses, which may lead to splitting, particularly in thin members. (see Fig. N10.8.2(b)).

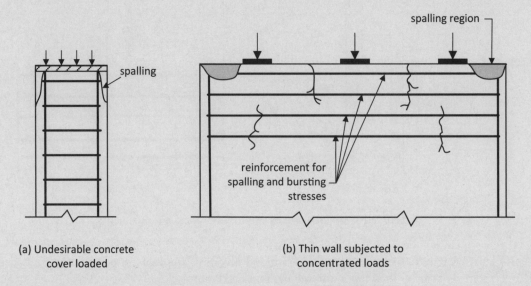

(a) Undesirable concrete cover loaded

(b) Thin wall subjected to concentrated loads

Fig. N10.8.2 Examples of spalling and splitting

N10.9.4

The amount of spiral reinforcement provided by Eq. (10.7) is intended to provide sufficient confinement to the core concrete so that the capacity lost when the concrete cover spalls off, can be regained due to the increased capacity of the confined core. In general, the revised equation specifies a lower ratio of spiral reinforcement than in previous Standards.[10.3]

N10.10.1

Due to the non-linear nature of the axial load-moment curvature diagram, it is necessary to check the column for at least two combinations of axial load and moment as shown in Fig. N.10.10.1.

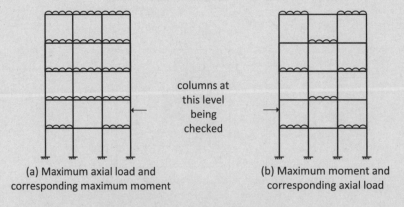

columns at this level being checked

(a) Maximum axial load and corresponding maximum moment

(b) Maximum moment and corresponding axial load

Fig. N10.10.1 Live load patterns to be considered for column design

Explanatory Notes on CSA A23.3-14

N10.10.4 Maximum axial load resistance

Limiting the factored axial load resistance to $P_{r,max}$ is intended to account for eccentricities not considered in the analysis, (see Fig. N10.10.4) and for the possibility that the concrete strength may be reduced by sustained high axial loads.

$P_{r,max}$ for spiral columns given by Eq. (10.8) has been increased because test results show the superior capacity of spiral columns. $P_{r,max}$ for tied columns remains the same. However, walls with fully tied vertical reinforcement are now specifically included in Eq. (10.9). $P_{r,max}$ for walls without fully tied vertical reinforcement is limited to a lower value by Eq. (10.10). Eqs. (10.9) and (10.10) include a lower limit for thin walls and columns with small h.[10.4]

Equation 10.11 is a general equation applicable to all types of concrete compression members. In the normal case of a reinforced column, A_t and A_p are equal to zero. There is no ϕ factor in the final term with A_p in Eq. (10.11) because this term reduces the capacity. The computed axial load resistance is reduced from that traditionally used by using the variable factor α_1 instead of 0.85. The strength of compression members does not increase in direct proportion to increased concrete strength.

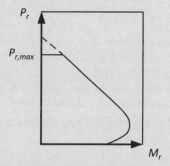

Axial Load – Moment Interaction Diagram

Fig. N10.10.4 Limiting factored axial load resistance

N10.10.5

This clause has been revised so that the load reduction for columns with $0.005 \leq \rho_t < 0.01$ is also applied to $P_{r,max}$ as well as the factored axial and flexural resistances.

N10.12 Columns — Transmission of loads through floor system

Application of the concrete placement procedure described in Clause 10.12.2 requires the placing of two different concrete mixes in the floor system. The lower strength mix must be placed while the higher strength concrete is still plastic and must be adequately vibrated to ensure the concretes are well integrated. This requires careful co-ordination of the concrete deliveries and possible use of a retarder. It is important that the high strength concrete in the floor in the region of the column be placed before the lower strength concrete in the remainder of the floor to prevent accidental placing of the low strength concrete in the column area. It is the designer's responsibility to indicate on the drawings where the high and low strength concretes are to be placed.

N10.12.3

Test results indicate that under some circumstances the code provisions in the 1984 standard were unsafe. For interior columns the current provisions result in an effective strength of column concrete equal to the specified column concrete for $1.4\ f'_{cc} \leq 1.4\ f'_{cs}$. For higher ratios of f'_{cc} / f'_{cs}, the effective strength of the column concrete increases more slowly than predicted by the equation in the 1984 Standard.

The effective strength of the concrete in edge columns also remains equal to that of the specified strength of the column concrete for $f'_{cc} \leq 1.4 f'_{cs}$. However, further increases in the specified strength of the column concrete do not further increase the effective strength.

Because of the lack of lateral restraint, the effective strength of the concrete in corner columns may not be taken higher than the specified strength of the slab concrete.[10.5, and 10.6]

N10.13 Slenderness effects — General

A conventional frame analysis (first-order analysis) neglects the influence of the changing geometry caused by deflections. A second-order analysis includes these effects when calculating moments and forces.

The stiffness, EI, used in an elastic analysis for strength design should represent the stiffness of the members immediately prior to failure. This is particularly true for second-order analyses that should predict the lateral deflections at loads approaching ultimate. The EI values should not be based totally on the moment-curvature relationship for the most highly loaded section along the length of the member. Instead, they should correspond to the moment-end rotation relationship for a complete member.

In a second-order analysis the axial loads in all compression members that are not part of the lateral load resisting system but depend on these elements for stability must be included.

The term "effect of member curvature" refers to amplification of the compression member moments to account for moments induced by deflection of the member relative to the chord line joining the ends of the member. This is illustrated in Fig. N10.13(a) for a column in a non-sway frame. To account for the deflection between the ends of the member, the maximum moment is taken as the magnified moment M_c.

The term "effect of lateral drift" refers to the additional moments caused by vertical loads acting on a structure that has been displaced laterally. The first order compression member moments, M_s due to factored lateral loads acting on a frame are shown in Fig. N10.13(b). These cause lateral deflections as shown, and the interaction of these deflections and the gravity loads, P, causes an increase in the member moment for M_s to $\delta_s M_s$ as shown. Lateral drift effects usually result from loadings involving combinations of vertical and lateral loads but can occur due to vertical loads acting on an unsymmetric structure.

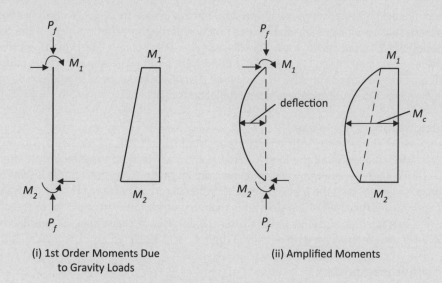

(i) 1st Order Moments Due
to Gravity Loads

(ii) Amplified Moments

(a) Members Stability Effect - Amplification of Gravity Load Moments Due to
Deflections Between Member Ends

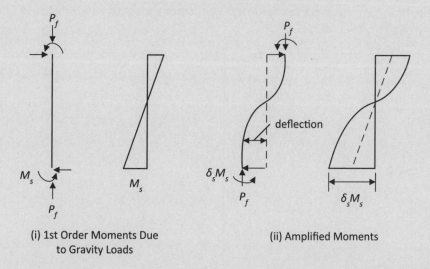

(i) 1st Order Moments Due
to Gravity Loads

(ii) Amplified Moments

(b) Lateral Drift Effect - Amplification of lateral Load Moments Due to Relative End Deflections

Fig. N10.13 Slenderness effects

In lieu of a second order analysis the standard permits an approximate evaluation of the influence of deflection on moments and forces provided the $k\ell_u/r$ ratios for all compression members is not greater than 100.

N10.14.1 General

It is generally sufficiently accurate to take I_g of a T-beam as two times the I_g for the web.

If the factored moments from an analysis of a wall based on the moment of inertia taken equal to $0.70I_g$ indicate that the wall will crack in flexure, based on the modulus of rupture, the analysis should be repeated with $I_g = 0.35I_g$ in those storeys where cracking is predicted at factored loads.

The term β_d is defined differently for non-sway and sway frames. See Cl. 10.14.1.3. Sway deflections due to short-time loads such as wind or earthquake are a function of the short-time stiffness of the columns following a period of sustained gravity load. For this case $\beta_d = 0$. Sustained lateral loads, which result in non-zero values of β_d, might exist, for example, if there were permanent lateral loads resulting from unequal earth pressures on opposite sides of a building. Sustained lateral loads should not be resisted by a column-beam frame because excessive lateral deflections may occur.

N10.14.4 Designation as non-sway

A frame is "non-sway" if the lateral drift effects are resisted by stiff bracing elements such as shear walls, elevator shafts, stairwells and the like. A frame is a "sway frame" if the lateral drift effects are resisted by the frame itself. Generally it will be obvious from inspection whether a frame is sway or non-sway since the lateral stiffness of the bracing elements generally greatly exceeds that of the frame. Eq. (10.15) provides a means for categorizing structures that are not obviously in one class or the other. In the unlikely event that the frame is subjected to sustained lateral loads, the stiffness EI must be reduced by dividing by $1 + \beta_d$ where β_d is based on definition (b) in Cl. 10.14.1.3.

N10.15.1 Effective length factor

The effective length factor, k, is frequently estimated using the Jackson and Moreland alignment charts reproduced in Fig. N10.15.1. Because of the assumptions made in deriving these charts, they tend to underestimate the value of k. This is unconservative. For this reason it is desirable to err on the high side when computing ψ for use in these charts. It is considered satisfactory to compute ψ using the member stiffnesses given in Clause 10.14.1.2.

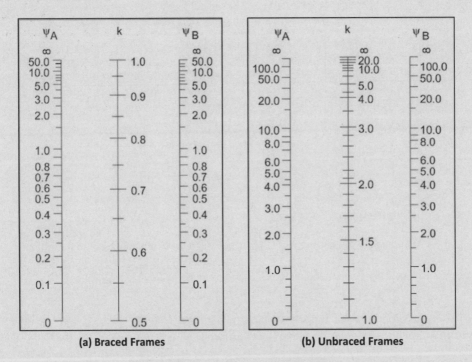

(a) Braced Frames   (b) Unbraced Frames

Fig. N10.15.1 Effective length factors

N10.15.2 Non-sway frames

In evaluating the slenderness limits in Clause 10.15.2, k can be taken as 1.0 or based on Fig. N10.15.2.

Studies of actual structures indicate that slenderness effects can be neglected for about 90 per cent of the columns in non-sway frames[10-7]

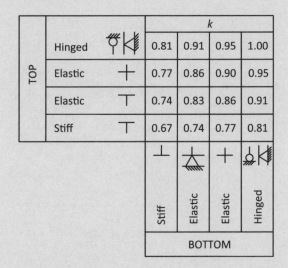

Fig. N10.15.2 Effective length factors for non-sway frames

N10.15.3 Member stability effect

The design of compression members in a non-sway frame involves the calculation of magnified moments using Eq. (10.17) with M_2 taken as the moments from a conventional frame analysis. A minimum value of M_2 is specified in cases where the calculated moments are close to zero. Equation 10.17 gives the magnified M_c for the design of the member. If M_c is less than the maximum end moment, M_2, the maximum moment is at the end of the member and the member should be designed for P_f and M_2.

Eqns. (10.19) and (10.20) give approximate lower bound expressions for the flexural stiffness of individual compression members. The effect of sustained loads must now be considered for Eq. (10.20) as well as for Eq. (10.19). Since both equations are lower bounds, it follows logically that it is appropriate to select the larger value. More accurate values of EI may be used provided they can be shown to give good agreement with tests. For short-time loads the EI calculated from the moment and curvature corresponding to balanced failure has been shown to give such agreement except for low axial loads.[10.8]

N10.15.3.2

For compression members bent in single curvature, the ratio of M_1/M_2 is between 0 and +1.0. For double curvature it is between 0 and -1.0.

N10.16 Slenderness effects — Sway frames

Sway-frames are more sensitive to stability problems than braced frames and as a result the design process is considerably more complex.

The effect of lateral drift must be considered for compression members in a sway frame as illustrated in Fig. N10.16 for a symmetrical frame subjected to gravity load moments and lateral load moments. The first-order end moments M_{ns} due to gravity loads are shown in Fig. 10.16(a). The moments M_s and $\delta_s M_s$ due to lateral loads are shown in Fig. N10.16(b). The total moments at each end of the compression members are obtained by adding the moments M_{ns} and $\delta_s M_s$ at each end, see Fig N10.16(c).

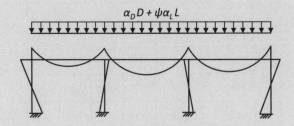

(a) Moments due to vertical loads, M_{ns}

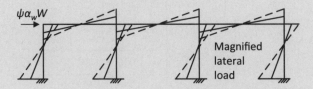

(b) Moments due to lateral loads, M_s and
magnified lateral load moments, $\delta_s M_s$

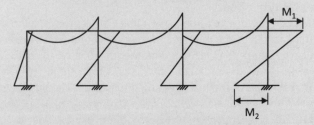

(c) Vertical load moments plus magnified lateral
load moments, $M_{ns} + \delta_s M_s$

Fig. N10.16 End moments M_1 and M_2 for column in sway frame

NBCC 2015 requires a check under three load combinations that don't include lateral loads:

(i)   1.4D;
(ii) (1.25 or 0.9)D + 1.5L + 1.0S;
(iii) (1.25 or 0.9)D + 1.0L + 1.5S

Three combinations that do include lateral loads must then be considered:

Compute factored gravity load moments, M_{ns}, resulting from the following factored loads:

(i)   (1.25 or 0.9)D + 1.5(L or S);
(ii) (1.25 or 0.9)D + 0.5(L or S);
(iii) 1.0D + 0.5L + 0.25S.

Combine these three load cases with lateral load moments, M_s, from the corresponding three factored lateral loads:

(i)   0.4W;
(ii) 1.4W;
(iii) 1.0E.

Explanatory Notes on CSA A23.3-14

Magnify the lateral load moments according to Clause 10.16.3 to account for the lateral drift effect. This gives $\delta_s M_s$.

Add the gravity load moments, M_{ns}, to the magnified lateral load moments, $\delta_s M_s$, at both ends of each column to get M_1 and M_2 as shown in Fig. N10.16.

If ℓ_u/r for any column exceeds the limit given in Eq. (10.26) check whether the moment between the ends of that column exceeds the end moment M_2. This is done using Clause 10.15.3. If M_c is less than M_2, the maximum moment M_2 occurs at the end of the column. If M_c exceeds M_2 the maximum moment M_c will occur between the ends of the column.

If a frame undergoes appreciable lateral deflections under gravity loads, serious consideration should be given to rearranging the frame to make it more symmetrical because with time, creep will amplify these deflections leading to both serviceability and strength problems.

N10.16.3 Calculation of $\delta_s M_s$

Lateral drift effects are considered for frames that undergo appreciable lateral drift due to lateral loads or combined lateral and gravity loads. The standard allows the designer to compute $\delta_s M_s$ using either a second order analysis (Clause 10.16.3.1) or Eq. (10.24) or Eq. (10.25). (Eq. (10.25) predicts a larger δ_s than the 2004 Standard.) The second-order analysis in Clause 10.16.3.1, is not the same second-order analysis referred to in Clause 10.13.1. Rather, it is an elastic second-order analysis based on the member stiffnesses prescribed in Clause 10.14.1. The iterative $P\Delta$ analysis for second-order moments can be represented by an infinite series. The summation of this series is given by Eq. (10.25).

In checking the stability of a storey using Eq. (10.24), δ_s is computed as an average value based on he use of ΣP_f and ΣP_c because the top of the storey moves as a unit relative to the bottom of the storey. This procedure is appropriate when the lateral drifts of all columns in a storey are equal. If significant torsional displacements exist, Eqs. (10.24) and (10.25) may underestimate the magnified moments for columns farthest from the centre of twist. In such cases a second-order analysis is recommended.

N10.16.4 Slenderness limit

Normally the maximum moment in a column in a sway frame is at one end of the column. However, for very slender columns in sway frames, the moment at a point between the ends of the column may exceed the maximum end moment. If ℓ_u/r exceeds the value given by Eq. (10.26), this may occur. Clause 10.16.4 specifies how this moment should be determined:

(a) M_1 and M_2 are computed using Clause 10.16.2.
(b) The maximum moment along the length of the column is computed using these values of M_1 and M_2 in Eqs. (10.21) and (10.17).

The EI values used to compute P_c are those given by Eqs. (10.19) or (10.20). β_d corresponds to definition (a) in Clause 10.14.1.3.

N10.16.5 Strength and stability checks

Because the factored gravity loads may be greater in cases not involving lateral loads than they are in cases involving lateral loads, and because the EI for gravity loads is reduced by dividing by $1 + \beta_d$ there is a possibility that a sway frame may buckle under gravity loads alone. Clauses 10.16.5(a) and (b) describe two additional loading cases, one of which may have to be checked, depending on how $\delta_s M_s$ or δ_s was calculated.

Clause 10.16.5(a) deals with cases designed using second-order analysis where appreciable lateral deflections occur due to gravity loads acting on a symmetrical or unsymmetrical frame, and the factored lateral load. The frame should be analyzed twice, once using a first-order analysis and once using a second order analysis. If one storey is much more flexible than the others, the deflection ratio should be based on that storey. In unsymmetric frames, which deflect laterally under gravity loads alone, the lateral load should act in the direction for which it will increase the lateral deflections. Since it is the ratio of the lateral deflections that is determined, the precise value of this load is not important. The factored value has been chosen for convenience.

The limit on δ_s in Clause 10.16.5(b) is intended to prevent instability under gravity loads alone. For values of δ_s above the limit, the frame would be very susceptible to variations in EI, foundation rotations and the like. If δ_s exceeds 2.5 the frame must be stiffened to reduce δ_s.

N10.16.6 Moment magnification for flexural members
The lateral drift of a sway frame will cause the moments in both the columns and the beams to be magnified (see Fig. N.10.14.6(b)). The beams must be designed to resist these magnified moments.

N11 Shear and torsion

N11.1.1 Flexural regions
Typical beams, columns and walls are designed using engineering beam theory, which assumes that plane sections remain plane and that the shear stresses are distributed in a reasonably uniform manner over the depth of the member. Such members can be designed by the sectional method of Clause 11.3, or the strut-and-tie method of Clause 11.4.

N11.1.2 Regions near discontinuities
Engineering beam theory studies the response of a member section-by-section and is not concerned with the details of how the forces are introduced into the member. Because of this, the theory is not appropriate for regions of members near static or geometric discontinuities, such as abrupt changes in cross-sectional dimensions or cross-sectional forces. See examples in Fig. N11.1.2(a). Such regions should be designed by the strut-and-tie method of Clause 11.4, which is capable of more accurately modelling the actual flow of forces in these regions.

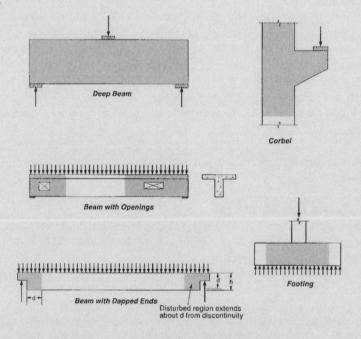

Fig. N11.1.2(a) Examples of disturbed regions

Explanatory Notes on CSA A23.3-14

An example of applying both the strut-and-tie model of Clause 11.4 and the sectional model of Clause 11.3 is illustrated in Fig. N11.1.2(b), which shows how the shear strength of a simply supported reinforced concrete beam loaded with two point loads changes as the "shear span", a, changes. It can be seen that when the load is closer than about 2d to the support, the sectional model is inappropriate. For such "deep beams" the strut-and-tie model provides more accurate results.

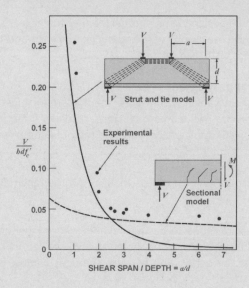

Fig. N11.1.2(b) Use of strut-and-tie model and sectional model to predict the strengths of a series of large beams (d = 540 mm) tested by Kani[11.1]

N11.1.3 Interface regions

The possibility of a shear failure involving sliding along a defined plane of weakness should be checked by the shear friction procedures of Clause 11.5.

N11.1.4 Slabs and footings

Two-way shear provisions applicable to slabs and footings are given in Clauses 13.3 and 13.4.

N11.1.5 Alternative methods

The resistance of components in shear can be determined by performing a detailed analysis that considers equilibrium, compatibility, and appropriate stress-strain relationships. Such an analysis could be a non-linear finite element analysis, which could be used for regions near discontinuities, or a detailed sectional analysis, which could be used for flexural regions.

An example of appropriate stress-strain relationships for cracked concrete are those given by the "modified compression field theory" of Vecchio and Collins[11.2].

N11.2.1 Tension due to restraint

Axial tension reduces the shear capacity of beams, with the reduction being particularly severe for members containing only small amounts of longitudinal reinforcement and not containing stirrups. In continuous frame structures, which have widely spaced expansion joints and stiff vertical elements, the restraint of shrinkage strains and other volume change effects may result in significant axial tension building up in the beams over time. The detrimental effect of such axial tensions on the shear strength should be taken into account.

N11.2.2 Variable depth members

If the member depth increases as the moment increases, the vertical components of the flexural compression and tension forces help to resist the applied shear. These forces can be treated in a similar manner to the vertical component of the prestressing force, V_p.

N11.2.3 Openings

Webs with openings need to be designed in a rational manner to ensure that the forces and moments can be adequately transferred in the vicinity of the openings. The strut-and-tie model of Clause 11.4 can be used for the design of these disturbed regions.

N11.2.4 Types of shear reinforcement

(b) To effectively increase shear capacity, transverse reinforcement must be capable of undergoing substantial strains prior to failure. Welded wire fabric, particularly if fabricated from small wires and not stress-relieved after fabrication, may fail before the required strain is reached. Such failures may occur at or between the cross-wire intersections.

(c) There is concern that stirrups inclined at less than 45° to the longitudinal reinforcement will slip along the longitudinal bars.

(d) In tests, major inclined cracks tend to occur at points where longitudinal reinforcement is bent up. The effective portion of bent-up bars is restricted to 75% of their inclined length due to concern with anchorage conditions at the bends, and because the effectiveness of these bars is sensitive to misplacement.

N11.2.5 Anchorage of shear reinforcement

To be effective, transverse shear reinforcement must tie together the longitudinal tension reinforcement and the flexural compression zone of the member. Further, the reinforcement must be anchored so that it can develop its yield strength without suffering any significant slip. To this end, stirrups require 135° hooks for most situations. See Clause 7.1.2.

N11.2.7 Anchorage of torsion reinforcement

Diagonal compressive stresses in the concrete due to torsion push outwards at the corners of the beam tending to spall the cover concrete. This spalling renders 90° hooks ineffective. The longitudinal corner bars help to support the outward thrusts in the zones between the hoops. Torsion causes tension in the longitudinal reinforcement. Longitudinal torsional reinforcement should be anchored so that it can develop its yield stress in tension at the face of the support.

N11.2.8.1

Minimum shear reinforcement controls the propagation of diagonal cracks and changes the pattern of cracking prior to shear failure. Regions with such reinforcement, if overloaded in shear, will display a number of wide diagonal cracks, prior to failure. On the other hand, regions without such reinforcement can fail in shear upon the formation of the first diagonal crack. The benefits of minimum shear reinforcement are particularly significant for large beams ($h > 750$ mm) and so it is required in all regions of such members irrespective of the calculated value of V_f.

N11.2.8.2

The amount of shear reinforcement required to control the propagation of diagonal cracks increases as the strength of concrete increases.

N11.2.8.4

The requirements for large beams ($h > 750$) to contain minimum shear reinforcement can be waived if appropriate tests show that the beams behave in a satisfactory manner even when the shear

Explanatory Notes on CSA A23.3-14

reinforcement is omitted. In determining "the required flexural and shear resistances" to compare with test results, careful attention must be given to the appropriate treatment of the resistance factors ϕ_c, ϕ_p and ϕ_s. The test results can be taken as corresponding to the case where these factors are all one. Before a comparison with the factored moments and shear forces is made, the test values should be reduced by the appropriate resistance factors.

N11.2.9.1

Torques that do not exceed one-quarter of the pure torsional cracking torque will not cause significant reduction in either flexural or shear strength and hence, can be neglected.

Equation (11.2) is an approximate expression for the torsion causing cracking. The expression has been derived by replacing the actual section with an equivalent thin walled tube with a wall thickness $0.75 A_c / p_c$ and an area enclosed by the tube centreline of two-thirds of A_c. The cracking stress is assumed to be $0.38\,\lambda\phi_c\,\sqrt{f_c'}$.

For a hollow section replacing A_c in Equation (11.2) by $1.5 A_g$ will lead to a rather conservative estimate of the pure torsional cracking load. This is appropriate as hollow sections display a stronger interaction between cracking shear and cracking torsion than do solid sections.

N11.2.9.2

After cracking, there is a substantial reduction in the torsional stiffness relative to the flexural stiffness. If the torsion in a member is a function of torsional stiffness, the resulting redistribution of internal forces will maintain the maximum torsion in the member at about the cracking torque, even as the loads are increased. This cracking torque will be about two-thirds of the pure torsional cracking load.

N11.2.10.2

Post-tensioning ducts act as stress-raisers and hence can reduce the crushing strength of the concrete web. To account for this, the effective web width is reduced at locations containing ducts.

N11.2.10.3

For circular sections, the highest shear stresses typically occur near mid-depth where the width of the section is equal to the diameter.

N11.2.10.4

The use of this clause is illustrated in Fig. N11.2.10.4

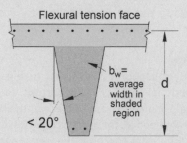

Fig. N11.2.10.4 Determination of b_w for section of continuous joist with tapered web

N11.2.10.5

For members with large amounts of shear reinforcement there is a significant risk that under high loads the side cover concrete may spall reducing the effective web width of the member. The high diagonal compressive stresses in the cover concrete must change direction as the flexural tension and compression faces of the member are approached causing tensile stresses perpendicular to the plane of the shear reinforcement. The concrete cover may then split off over the whole depth of the member on the plane of weakness caused by the shear reinforcement. See Fig. N11.2.10.5. If there are flanges on both the flexural tension and compression faces they will resist the diagonal compression stresses in the cover concrete of the web and so this type of spalling will not occur.

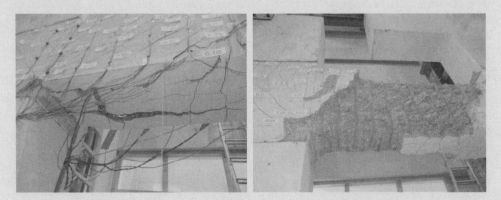

Fig. N11.2.10.5 Spalling of coupling beam recorded by Fisher[11.3]

N11.2.11 Reduced prestress in transfer length

The reduced prestress in the transfer length reduces V_p and f_{p0} and also reduces the tensile force that can be resisted by the tendons near the ends of members. For a strand, the increase of stress from zero to say 1300 MPa in a length of 50 strand diameters corresponds to an average bond stress of about 5 MPa.

N11.2.12 Hanger reinforcement

The intersection of two beams is a disturbed region and, as such, the flow of forces in this region can be represented by a strut-and-tie model in accordance with Clause 11.4. However, if the sectional model of Clause 11.3 is used, additional transverse reinforcement will be needed to ensure that a push-out failure of the supporting beam does not occur. For this additional reinforcement to be effective, it should be placed in a zone close to the loaded interface. This zone is defined in Figure 11.1. If the shear stress is low enough that diagonal cracks are unlikely to form under factored loads, no additional reinforcement is needed.

N11.3.1 Required shear reinforcement

Members need to be proportioned so that at every section, the factored shear resistance is at least equal to the factored shear load.

N11.3.2 Sections near supports

Loads applied in regions near direct supports are carried to the support by strut action, see Fig. N11.1.2(b), and do not cause additional stresses in the stirrups. Hence, the stirrups in these regions may be designed for the shear at a distance d_v from the face of the support. However, if the support is such that direct strut action will be ineffective, the stirrups must be designed for the shear at the face of the support. See Fig. N11.3.2. If a significant concentrated load is applied within a distance d_v from the face of the support, the full shear at the face of the support must be used in the shear design. If loads applied within distance d_v from the face of the support increase the absolute magnitude of the shear at the support by more than 20% then sections near the support should be designed for the shear at $0.5d_v$ from the face of the support.

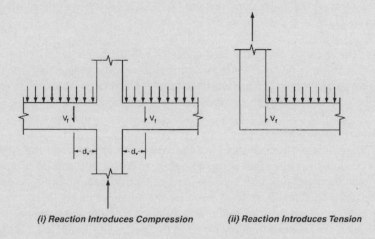

(i) Reaction Introduces Compression   *(ii) Reaction Introduces Tension*

Fig. N11.3.2 Influence of support conditions on location of critical section for shear

N11.3.3 Factored shear resistance

Shear resistance may be separated into a component, V_c, which relies on stresses transmitted across cracks via aggregate interlock action, a component, V_s, which relies on tensile stresses in the transverse reinforcement, and V_p, which relies on the vertical component of the factored effective prestressing force.

The intent of Eq. (11.5) is to ensure that the transverse reinforcement will yield prior to the diagonal crushing of the web concrete.

N11.3.4 Determination of V_c

In Eq. (11.6), the factor β accounts for the ability of concrete to transmit shear stresses across cracks by aggregate interlock action. While β depends on the width of the cracks, the size of the aggregate and the concrete strength, a reasonable lower bound on its value is 0.05. The upper limit of 8 MPa for the value of $\sqrt{f_c'}$ has been set because aggregate interlock is less effective for higher strength concretes which typically have smoother cracks.

N11.3.5 Determination of V_s

The expressions for V_s are the traditional equations for the shear carried by the tensile stresses in the transverse reinforcement for the case where the diagonal compressive stresses in the cracked concrete are inclined at an angle of θ to the longitudinal axis of the member. See Fig. N11.3.5.

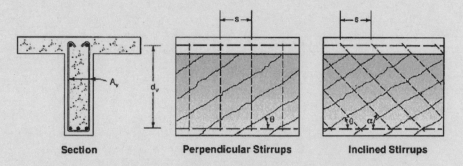

Section   Perpendicular Stirrups   Inclined Stirrups

Fig. N11.3.5 Parameters involved in determination of V_s

Stirrups inclined to intersect the diagonal cracks, see Fig. N11.3.5, are more effective in resisting shear. This is reflected in Eq. (11.8).

The expression for the shear at which the web concrete will crush, Eq. (11.5), does not distinguish between members with perpendicular stirrups and members with inclined stirrups. For the same shear force, members with inclined stirrups will have smaller diagonal compressive stresses in the web concrete and hence, can tolerate higher shears prior to web crushing.

N11.3.6 Determination of β and θ

This clause gives three different procedures for determining the factor β and the angle θ. The most direct of these procedures specifies that β can be taken as 0.21 and θ can be taken as 42° for the types of members specified in Clause 11.3.6.2. The most general procedure, which is specified in Clause 11.3.6.4, gives equations for β and θ which account for the influence of axial load, prestressing, crack spacing, amount of longitudinal reinforcement, and moment-to-shear ratio on shear resistance. The third procedure, which can be used in many practical designs, is the simplified method described in Clause 11.3.6.3.

N11.3.6.1 Members subjected to significant axial tension

If the axial tension is large enough to crack the flexural compression face of the member, or large enough to cause a significant stress increase (say, 50 MPa), in the longitudinal reinforcement near the flexural tension face, then its detrimental effect on shear strength needs to be accounted for using the general method.

N11.3.6.2 Values for special member types

If β is taken as 0.21, and θ is taken as 42°, the expressions for V_c and V_s result in designs that are comparable to those given by the traditional ACI expressions for shear strength. The use of 42° rather than the traditional 45° compensates for the use of d_v as the shear depth rather than d. Research has shown that these traditional procedures can be very unconservative for large members not containing transverse shear reinforcement and because of this, these procedures are restricted to members with relatively small depths. An exception to this is the case of footings such as that shown in Fig. N11.3.6.2(a) where the loads and reactions cause significant vertical compressive stresses. These beneficial clamping stresses counteract the detrimental effects of large size. Experiments on large lightly-reinforced footings by Perkins[11.4] have shown that the ratio of L_o/d_v needs to be about 2 or less before it can be safely assumed that β equals 0.21. See Fig. N11.3.6.2(b) for the case with 0.75% of flexural reinforcement.

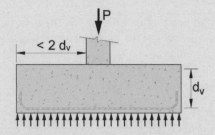

Fig. N11.3.6.2(a) Footing for which β = 0.21

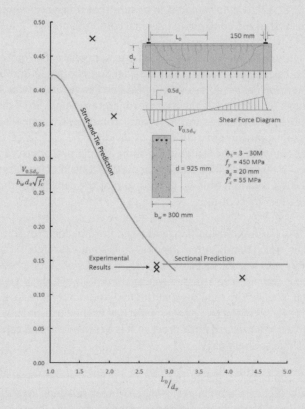

Fig. N11.3.6.2(b) Influence of ratio of effective shear span, L_o, to effective shear depth, d_v, on failure shear stress of deep footings

N11.3.6.3 Simplified method

The β and θ values given by the simplified method are derived from the general method by assuming that $\varepsilon_x = 0.85 \times 10^{-3}$. This corresponds to a strain in the flexural tension reinforcement somewhat less than the yield strain of 400 MPa reinforcement. For members without transverse reinforcement, aggregate interlock stresses transmit a large portion of the shear across the flexural cracks. Hence the shear resistance of such members depends on the maximum aggregate size. If the concrete strength exceeds about 60 MPa, the cracks cleave through the aggregate particles and, hence, the size of the aggregate no longer influences the shear strength. For these higher strength concretes, the smoother crack surfaces reduce aggregate interlock capacity. Equation 11.10 allows the effect of different aggregate sizes to be accounted for by calculating an effective crack spacing parameter, s_{ze}.

N11.3.6.4 General method

The derivation of the simple expressions for β and θ is explained by Bentz and Collins[11.5].

The values of β are based on calculating the stresses that can be transmitted across diagonally cracked concrete. As the cracks get wider, the stress that can be transmitted decreases. Crack widths can be taken as the average tensile strain multiplied by the crack spacing. That is, a strain factor times a spacing factor. The factor β accounts for the ability of concrete to transmit shear stresses across cracks by aggregate interlock action. The equation for β, Eq. (11.11), consists of a strain factor multiplied by a spacing factor. As the strains in the member become larger, β becomes smaller which can be called the strain effect in shear. As the crack spacing becomes larger, β again becomes smaller, which is called the size effect in shear.

The equation for θ, Eq. (11.12), was formulated to ensure that transverse reinforcement, when used, would yield prior to crushing of the concrete in diagonal compression.

To understand the background to Eq. (11.13), it is helpful to appreciate the "more accurate calculations" which could be used to calculate ε_x. The actual cross section is represented by an idealized section consisting of a flexural tension flange, a flexural compression flange, and a web. The area of concrete in the flexural tension flange, A_{ct}, is taken as the area of concrete within 0.5h of the flexural tension face, see Fig.11.2. Similarly, the concrete area in the flexural compression flange is taken as the concrete area within 0.5h of the flexural compression face. In dividing the total area of reinforcing bars and prestressing tendons between the two flanges, the same simple procedure can be followed. Thus A_p can be taken as the area of tendons within 0.5h of the flexural tension face. Alternatively the total area of tendons could be divided between the two flanges so that the centroid of the tendon area matches the actual location of the tendon centroid.

The forces resisted by the flexural tension flange and the flexural compression flange of the idealized section are shown in Fig. N11.3.6.4(a). After diagonal cracks have formed in the web, the shear force applied to the web concrete V_f-V_p, will be primarily carried by diagonal compressive stresses in the web concrete. These diagonal compressive stresses will result in a longitudinal compressive force in web concrete of $(V_f$-$V_p)$ cot θ. Equilibrium requires that this longitudinal compressive force in the web needs to be balanced by tensile forces in the two flanges, with half of the force, that is, 0.5$(V_f$-$V_p)$ cot θ, being taken by each flange. To avoid a trial and error process, it is a convenient and conservative simplification to take this flange force due to shear as $(V_f$-$V_p)$.

The axial strains in the compression flange (ε_c) and the axial strain in the tension flange (ε_t) can be calculated from the axial forces in the flanges using a bilinear relationship such as that shown in Fig. N11.3.6.4(b). The longitudinal strain, ε_x, at mid-depth of the section can then be calculated as $(\varepsilon_t + \varepsilon_c)/2$. Note that ε_c will usually be a small negative quantity. For this case, it is a convenient and conservative assumption to take ε_x as $\varepsilon_t /2$. This is the basis of Eq. 11.13.

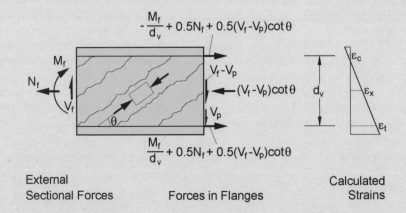

External Sectional Forces   Forces in Flanges   Calculated Strains

Fig. N11.3.6.4(a) More accurate procedure for determining ε_x.

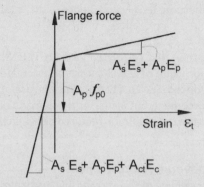

Fig. N11.3.6.4(b) Determination of ε_t from flexural tension flange force

The following explanations apply to the conditions a) to f) that apply to Eq. 11.13.

a) If M_f is less than $(V_f - V_p)d_v$, then ε_c may become tensile, which would render unconservative the assumption that ε_x is $\varepsilon_t/2$.

b) Termination of longitudinal bars in a flexural tension zone results in a concentration of cracking and higher straining at the cut-off location. See Fig. N11.3.6.4(c). This strain concentration is accounted for by the 1.5 factor.

JB1 Ten 25M bottom bars 6 m long. Span 5.4 m. Failure Point Load = 913 kN

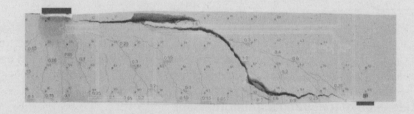

JB2 Five of ten bars cut off 1 m from centre of support. Failure Load = 726 kN

Fig. N11.3.6.4(c) Influence of longitudinal bar cut-offs on shear behaviour as recorded by Junji Masukawa[11.6]

c) Eq. (11.13) assumes that ε_t is tensile and hence the axial stiffness of the concrete in the tension flange can be neglected. If the tension flange is prestressed or if the section has axial compression applied, ε_t may be compressive and then it is necessary to account for the stiffness of the concrete in compression, see Fig. N11.3.6.4(b).

e) Under high axial tension ε_c will become tensile and, hence, either ε_x should be calculated as $(\varepsilon_t + \varepsilon_c)/2$ or, for simplicity, as ε_t.

f) The use of a higher value of ε_x than that calculated with Eq. (11.13) will result in a higher value of θ and a lower value of β. A higher value of θ will cause the calculated force which the longitudinal reinforcement must resist to be reduced, See Eq. (11.14). Thus the use of a higher value of ε_x reduces the demand on the longitudinal reinforcement, but increases the demand on the transverse reinforcement. The upper limit of $\varepsilon_x = 0.003$ limits the redistribution required between the demands on the longitudinal and transverse reinforcements.

N11.3.7 Proportioning of transverse reinforcement

Because a shear failure caused by yielding of the stirrups involves yielding of this reinforcement over a certain length of a member, there will not be an abrupt change in shear strength at the location where the stirrup spacing changes. As shown in Fig. N11.3.7, the stirrup spacing is chosen so that the provided quantity of stirrups, A_v / s, is large enough to ensure that V_r equals or exceeds V_f.

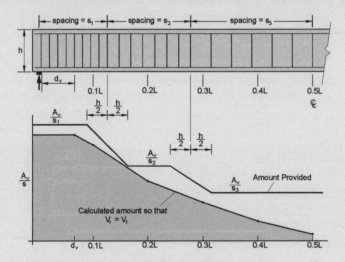

Fig. N11.3.7 Proportioning of transverse reinforcement

N11.3.8.4

For members such as slabs or footings with large depths, stirrup spacing may be controlled by the maximum spacing limit of 600 mm. This limit is intended to ensure that the size effect for members with stirrups can be safely ignored (i.e. $s_{ze} = 300$ mm). More widely spaced stirrups can be used if the resulting increase in crack spacing is accounted for.

N11.3.9.1 Extension of longitudinal reinforcement

In a cracked beam shear causes additional tension in the longitudinal reinforcement. A conservative approach to account for this additional tension is to extend the longitudinal reinforcement a distance of $d_v \cot \theta$ beyond the location dictated by flexure alone. For a member subjected to point loads this is equivalent to assuming that the additional tension in the longitudinal reinforcement on the flexural tension side of the member is equal to $V_f \cot \theta$.

N11.3.9.2 Flexural tension side

The influence of moment, axial load and shear on the tensile force F_{lt} in the longitudinal reinforcement can be seen from the free body diagram in Fig. N11.3.9.2. The figure illustrates a region of the beam with constant shear force, V_f, where F_{lt} is being calculated a distance x from the centre of the support. The diagonal crack at inclination θ to the longitudinal axis of the member intersects a number of

Explanatory Notes on CSA A23.3-14

stirrups and the resultant force from these stirrups equals V_s. The shear stresses on the crack face v_c contribute to resisting the applied shear V_f but also require additional tensile stresses in the longitudinal reinforcement. The vertical component of the prestress, V_p, if present, also contributes to resisting V_f. Taking moments about point O gives:

$$V_f (x + d_v \cot \theta) + N_f\, 0.5d_v = F_{lt}d_v + V_s\, 0.5d_v \cot \theta + V_p d_v \cot \theta$$

With the moment at location x called M_f, this can be rearranged to produce Eq. (11.14).

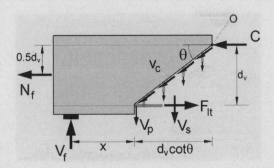

Fig. N11.3.9.2 Free body diagram showing member forces at a crack.

In determining the stress that can be developed in the longitudinal reinforcement at sections near bar cut-off locations, it can be assumed that the tensile capacity of a bar varies linearly from zero at the free end, to a value of $\phi_s A_b f_y$ at a distance of ℓ_d from the free end, where A_b is the bar area and ℓ_d is the development length.

N11.3.9.4 Compression fan regions

At maximum moment locations, the shear force changes sign and hence, the inclination of the diagonal compressive stresses changes. At direct supports and point loads, this change of inclination is associated with a fan-shaped pattern of compressive stresses radiating from the point load or the direct support, as shown in Fig. N11.3.9.4(a). This fanning of the diagonal stresses reduces the tension in the longitudinal reinforcement caused by shear (i.e., angle θ becomes steeper). Due to this effect, the tension in the reinforcement does not exceed that due to the maximum moment alone.

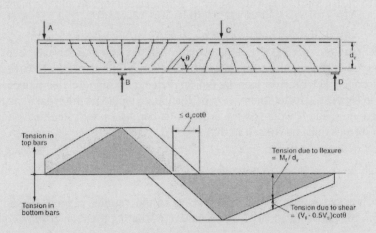

Fig. N11.3.9.4(a) Influence of shear on required tensile forces in longitudinal reinforcement of beam on direct supports subjected to point loads

If a member is indirectly loaded or supported, then a pattern of parallel diagonal cracks is likely to occur near the maximum moment locations. See Fig. N.11.3.9.4(b). In this case, the maximum tension required in the longitudinal reinforcement will be greater than that required for flexure alone.

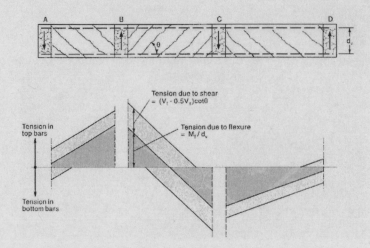

Fig. N11.3.9.4(b) Influence of shear on required tensile forces in longitudinal reinforcement of beam indirectly loaded and indirectly supported by crossbeams

N11.3.9.5 Anchorage of longitudinal reinforcement at end supports

The expression for the tensile force in the longitudinal reinforcement given in this clause is the same as Eq. (11.14) except that the influence of the small moment at the support is neglected. In evaluating the tensile capacity of the longitudinal reinforcement at end supports, it can be assumed that the linear variation of capacity described in N11.3.9.2 is applicable.

N11.3.10.1 Transverse reinforcement for combined shear and torsion

The shear stresses due to torsion and shear will add on one side of the section and counteract on the other side. The transverse reinforcement must be designed for the side where the effects are additive. Usually the loading that causes the highest torsion differs from the loading that causes the highest shear. While it is conservative to design for the highest torsion combined with the highest shear, it is only necessary to design for the highest shear and its associated torsion and the highest torsion and its associated shear.

In calculating the required spacing of transverse reinforcement care must be exercised in combining the A_v / s term required to provide the needed V_s from Eq. (11.7) with the A_t / s term required to provide the needed T_r from Eq. (11.17). Consider the typical rectangular spandrel beam reinforced with closed stirrups shown in Fig. N11.3.10.1. If there were no torsion, A_v would be the area of the two vertical bars, $2A_b$. If there were no shear, A_t would be the area of one bar, A_b. Under combined loading, the spacing, s, of the closed stirrups must be chosen so that:

$$\frac{A_b}{s} \geq 0.5 \frac{A_v}{s} + \frac{A_t}{s}$$

For the hollow box in Fig. N11.3.10.1, the spacing of the "double legged" closed stirrups can be determined from the above inequality with A_b now representing the area of the two legs within each wall.

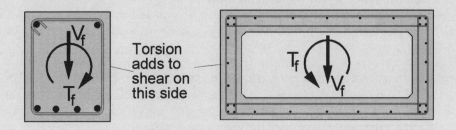

Fig. N11.3.10.1 Sections subjected to combined shear and torsion

N11.3.10.3 Factored torsional resistance

Equation (11.17) is based on a space truss analogy, see Fig. N11.3.10.3, which assumes that the cracked concrete carries no tension and that the diagonal stresses spiral around the member at an inclination of θ to the longitudinal axis. Transverse reinforcement for torsion is required on all sides of the member and should be in the form of closed stirrups.

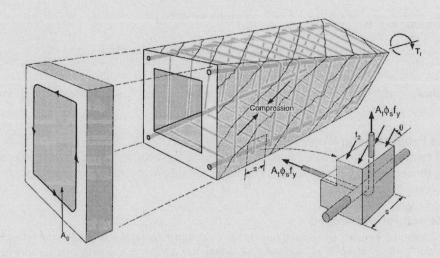

Fig. N11.3.10.3 Design of transverse reinforcement for torsion

N11.3.10.4 Cross-sectional dimensions to avoid crushing

For a box girder, the shear stress due to shear and the shear stress due to torsion will add together on one side of the box girder. Further, the magnitude of these stresses is largely determined by statics. For other cross-sectional shapes such as a solid rectangle, there is the possibility of considerable redistribution of shear stresses. To make some allowance for this favourable redistribution, a "root-mean-square" approach is used in calculating the nominal shear stress under combined torsion and shear for these cross-sections.

The 1.7 factor in the torsional shear stress expression of Eqns. (11.18) and (11.19) was introduced to better predict the crushing load of heavily reinforced sections loaded in combined torsion and shear. If the actual wall thickness of a box section is less than A_{oh}/p_h the torsional shear stress is calculated from the traditional thin-walled box expression. That is, the torsional shear stress is equal to $T_f/(2A_o t)$. If A_o is taken as $0.85A_{oh}$ as specified in Clause 11.3.10.3, the torsional shear stress becomes $T_f/(1.7A_{oh}t)$.

N11.3.10.5 Determination ε_x for general method

For members subjected to combined flexure, axial load, torsion and shear, the longitudinal strain at mid-depth of the member, ε_x, can be calculated from a space truss model such as that shown in Fig. 11.3.10.5.

The axial load and moments would be resisted by longitudinal forces in the four chords while the torsion and shears would be resisted by shear flows in the four walls. For cracked concrete these shear flows would cause tensions in the adjacent chords as well. The strains in each of the four chords could then be calculated and ε_x taken as the average of the four chord strains.

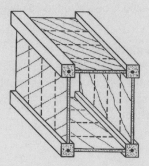

Fig. N11.3.10.5 Space truss model for combined loading

As a simplification of this procedure, Eq. (11.13) can be used except that the shear term is replaced by the root mean squared term given in Eq. (11.20).

N11.3.10.6 Proportioning longitudinal reinforcement

To account for the fact that on one side of the section the torsional and shear stresses will counteract each other, the required equivalent tension is taken as the square root of the sum of the squares of the individually calculated tensions.

N11.4.1 Structural idealization

Cracked reinforced concrete carries load principally by compressive stresses in the concrete and tensile stresses in the reinforcement. After significant cracking has occurred, the principal compressive stress trajectories in the concrete tend towards straight lines and hence, can be approximated by straight struts. Ties are used to model the principal reinforcement. The regions of the concrete subjected to multi-directional stresses, where the struts and ties meet (the nodes of the truss) are represented by node regions.

A number of typical strut-and-tie models are shown in Fig. N11.4.1. In sketching such models it should be kept in mind that space must be left to accommodate the required dimensions of the struts and the ties. A second important consideration is to ensure that the angles between the struts and the adjoining ties, θ_s, are not too small.

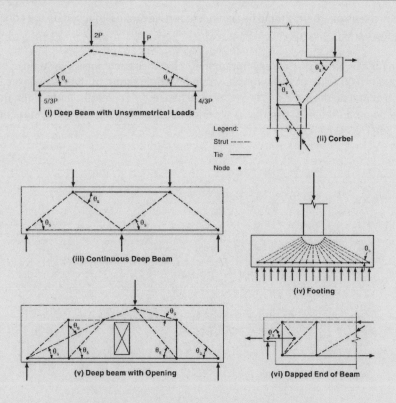

Fig. N11.4.1 Examples of strut-and-tie models

While, for each situation, a number of different strut-and-tie models are feasible, those which involve the most direct path for the loads to travel to the supports will be the most efficient.

In some cases it may be appropriate to choose a strut-and-tie model with multiple load paths, e.g., Fig. N11.4.1(v). For these internally statically indeterminate trusses, the load may be assigned between the alternative load paths based on the yield capacity of the ties.

N11.4.1.3 Modelling members subjected to uniform loads

The previously discussed results of Perkins, see Fig. N11.3.6.2(b), have shown that the shear capacity of large footing-type specimens not containing crack control reinforcement can be overestimated if the simplified strut-and-tie model shown in Fig. 11.4(c) is used. The appropriate models for such members are shown in Fig. 11.4(a) and (b).

N11.4.2.2 Effective cross-sectional area of strut

The effective cross-sectional area of a strut is typically controlled by the anchorage conditions at the end of the strut. Figure 11.5 suggests that, for a strut anchored by reinforcement, the effective concrete area will extend to a distance of up to eight bar diameters from the anchored bar.

N11.4.2.3 Limiting compressive stress in struts

This clause requires that, in determining the limiting compressive stress in the concrete, some consideration be given to the strains imposed on the cracked concrete.

If the concrete is not subjected to principal tensile strains greater than about 0.002, it can resist a compressive stress of $0.85f'_c$. This will be the limit for regions of the struts that are not crossed by or joined to ties. The reinforcing bars of a tie are bonded to the surrounding concrete. If the reinforcing bars are to yield in tension, there should be significant tensile strains imposed on the concrete. As these tensile strains increase, f_{cu} decreases.

The expression for ε_1 is based on the assumption that the principal compressive strain ε_2 in the direction of the strut equals 0.002 and that the tensile strain in the direction of the tie equals ε_s. As the angle between the strut and tie decreases, ε_1 increases and hence, f_{cu} decreases. In the limit, no compressive stresses would be permitted in a strut that is superimposed on a tie, i.e., $\theta_s = 0$, a situation that violates compatibility. See Fig. N11.4.2.3.

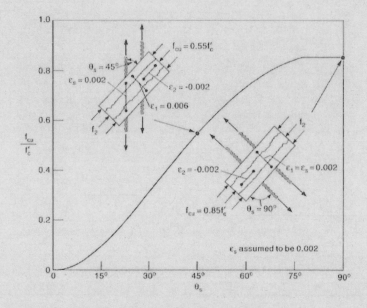

Fig. N11.4.2.3 Crushing strength of strut as a function of angle between strut and adjoining tie

For a tie consisting of reinforcing bars, ε_s can be taken as the tensile strain due to factored loads in the reinforcing bars. For a tie consisting of prestressing tendons, ε_s can be taken as zero until the tensile stress in the tendon exceeds the decompression stress f_{po}. For higher stresses, ε_s would equal $(f_{pr} - f_{po})/E_p$. Equation 11.24 is based on the assumption that the tensile strain in the tie is 0.002.

Some strut-and-tie models may involve two struts, say "a" and "b", that "share" the same concrete. See example at left support of deep beam in Fig. N11.4.1(v). One conservative approach to check the crushing of the concrete in this situation is to assume that the compressive stresses in the two struts, f_{2a} and f_{2b}, and the limiting compressive stresses for these two struts, f_{cua} and f_{cub}, should satisfy the following limit:

$$\frac{f_{2a}}{f_{cua}} + \frac{f_{2b}}{f_{cub}} \leq 1.0$$

N11.4.2.4 Reinforced struts
To be effective as compression reinforcement, the bars would have to be enclosed in column ties.

N11.4.3.2 Anchorage of ties in node regions
Figure N11.4.3.2 illustrates some aspects of this clause.

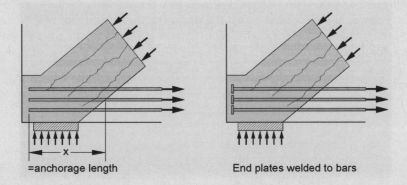

Fig. N11.4.3.2 Anchorage of tie by straight embedment or mechanical anchorage

N11.4.4.1 Stress limits in node regions

The allowable concrete compressive stresses in nodal regions, which are illustrated in Fig. N11.4.4.1, are related to the degree of confinement in these regions. The reduced stress limits for nodal regions anchoring ties are based on the detrimental effect of the tensile straining caused by these ties. If the ties consist of post-tensioned tendons and the stress in these tendons does not need to exceed f_{po}, no tensile straining of the nodal regions will be required. For this case, the $0.85f'_c$ limit is appropriate.

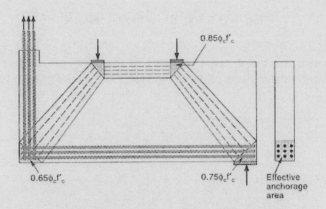

Fig. N11.4.4.1 Stress limits in node regions

N11.4.4.2 Satisfying stress limits in node regions

The stresses in the nodal regions are reduced by increasing the size of the bearing plates, by increasing the dimensions of the struts, and by increasing the effective anchorage area of the ties.

N11.4.5 Crack control reinforcement

This reinforcement is intended to control the width of the cracks and to ensure a minimum ductility for the member so that, if required, significant redistribution of internal stresses is possible. The 0.002 limit was chosen to be similar to the traditional minimum reinforcement limits used for walls and deep beams.

N11.5.1 General

Figure N11.5.1(a) illustrates the shear friction concept for the case where the reinforcement is perpendicular to the potential failure plane. Because the interface is rough, shear displacement will cause a widening of the crack. This crack opening will cause tension in the reinforcement balanced by compressive stresses, σ, in the concrete across the crack. The shear resistance of the face is assumed to be equal to the cohesion, c, plus the coefficient of friction, μ, times the compressive stress, σ, across the face. Hence, for this case,

$$v_r = \lambda \phi_c (c + \mu \sigma)$$

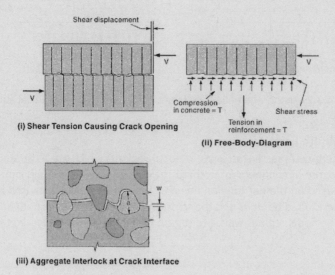

(i) Shear Tension Causing Crack Opening

(ii) Free-Body-Diagram

(iii) Aggregate Interlock at Crack Interface

Fig. N11.5.1(a) Shear friction concept

If inclined reinforcement is crossing the crack, part of the shear can be directly resisted by the component, parallel to the shear plane, of the tension force in the reinforcement. See Fig. N11.5.1(b)

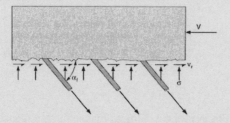

Fig. N11.5.1(b) Shear-friction reinforcement inclined to crack

The upper limit on the term $\lambda \phi_c (c + \mu \sigma)$ is to avoid concrete crushing failures.

N11.5.3 Alternative Equation for shear stress resistance

The alternative method given in this clause is based on the work of Loov and Patnaik[11.7]. In this method, the shear resistance is a function of both the concrete strength and the amount of reinforcement crossing the failure crack. For small amounts of reinforcement, this method can give values of factored shear resistance that are higher than those from Eq. (11.24).

N11.6 Special provisions for brackets and corbels

Parameters used in this clause are illustrated in Fig. N11.6.

Explanatory Notes on CSA A23.3-14

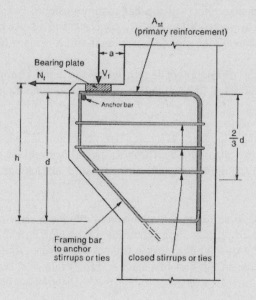

Fig. N11.6 Parameters in design of corbel

N11.6.3

A minimum depth at the outside edge of the bearing area is specified because of concern with failures involving an inclined crack propagating from below the bearing area to the outer sloping face.

N11.6.4

This provision allows for the tension on the corbel caused by the restraint of shrinkage, creep and temperature movements. Connection details shall be such that the tension can be transmitted into the corbel by shear friction or by mechanical anchorage.

N11.6.7

This anchorage may be achieved by welding the tension tie reinforcement to a structural steel plate, bar, or angle, or by bending the tie bars into a horizontal loop. Anchorage by means of a vertical hook should be avoided because the concrete outside the hook will tend to split off. If vertical hooks must be used, the outside edge of the bearing plate under the load should not be closer to the edge of the corbel than the point of tangency at the start of the hook, after allowing for tolerances in bar placement.

N11.7 Shear in joints

This clause references Clause 7.7 for minimum shear reinforcement (ties) in joints. For additional requirements and limits due to seismic loading, see Clauses 21.3.3, 21.4.6 and 21.6.2.4.

N12 Development and splices of reinforcement

N12.2.2

Equation (12.1) is a modified form of the general equation for the development length of deformed bars or wires in tension proposed by ACI Committee 408[12.1] which is based on the research carried out by Orangun et al.[12.2] In the Standard, the term, d_{cs}, is taken as the smaller of the minimum cover measured to the centre of the bar or two-thirds of the centre-to-centre spacing of the bars. The factor, K_{tr}, represents the contribution of transverse reinforcement across potential planes of splitting.

The factor k_1 reflects the adverse effects of top-bar casting position, k_2 is the epoxy-coating factor, k_3 reflects the lower tensile strength of low-density concrete and k_4 is a factor reflecting the more favourable performance of smaller diameter deformed bars and wires (see N12.2.4 for more details).

Equation (12.1) expresses the development length when the bond strength is limited by splitting failures. The term $(d_{cs} + K_{tr})$ is limited to $2.5d_b$ to safeguard against pullout type failures.

N12.2.3

Table 12.1 gives the development length of deformed bars and deformed wires in tension in a simplified format, as a function of the bar diameter, d_b. These simplified expressions have been determined by substituting into Equation (12.1) minimum values of cover and spacing and/or minimum amounts of transverse reinforcement.

For example, consider a case where bars in a slab have a minimum clear cover of $1.0d_b$ and a clear spacing between the bars of $2d_b$. It is assumed that the slab reinforcement perpendicular to the bars being developed serve to control splitting cracks in the cover concrete. Thus the bond strength would be controlled by splitting between the bars in a layer and the value of d_{cs} would be controlled by the bar spacing, giving d_{cs} equal to 2/3 x $3.0d_b$ = $2.0d_b$. For this case where K_{tr} equals zero, Equation (12.1) becomes:

$$\ell_d = 1.15 \frac{k_1 k_2 k_3 k_4}{(2d_b + 0)} \frac{f_y}{\sqrt{f_c'}} \frac{\pi d_b^2}{4} = 0.45 k_1 k_2 k_3 k_4 \frac{f_y}{\sqrt{f_c'}} d_b$$

This simplified equation is also used for the case where the minimum clear cover is $1.0d_b$, the minimum clear spacing is $1.4d_b$ and confinement in the form of minimum ties or stirrups is provided.

For the situation where a minimum clear cover of $1.0d_b$ and a minimum clear spacing between bars of $1.4d_b$ are provided, without any transverse reinforcement, then d_{cs} becomes the smaller of $1.5 d_b$ or 2/3 x $2.4d_b = 1.6d_b$. Hence the simplified equation for the case labelled "other cases" in Table 121 becomes:

$$\ell_d = 1.15 \frac{k_1 k_2 k_3 k_4}{(1.5 d_b + 0)} \frac{f_y}{\sqrt{f_c'}} \frac{\pi d_b^2}{4} = 0.6 k_1 k_2 k_3 k_4 \frac{f_y}{\sqrt{f_c'}} d_b$$

The equations in Table 12.1 may be readily evaluated for commonly occurring situations as simple multiples of d_b. For example, for normal density concrete (k_3 = 1.0) with f_c' = 35 MPa and using uncoated 20M or larger bottom bars ($k_2 = k_4 = k_1$ = 1.0) with f_y = 400 MPa these expressions, with rounding, reduce to:

$$\ell_d = 30d_b$$
and $\quad \ell_d = 40d_b$

N12.2.4

The bar location factor, k_1, accounts for the position of the bar in freshly placed concrete. The factor was reduced from 1.4 in the 1984 Standard to 1.3 in 1994 in light of research[12.3,12.4]. This factor remains unchanged at 1.3 in the 2014 edition.

Studies[12.5,12.6,12.7] of the mechanical anchorage of epoxy-coated bars show that bond strength is reduced because the coating significantly reduces both adhesion and friction between the bar and the concrete. The factor, k_2, reflects the type of anchorage failure likely to occur. When the cover or spacing is small, a splitting failure can occur and the anchorage or bond strength is substantially reduced. If the cover and spacing between bars is large, a splitting failure is precluded and the effect of the epoxy coating on anchorage strength is not as large. Studies[12.2] have shown that although the cover or spacing may be small, the anchorage strength may be increased by adding transverse steel crossing the plane of splitting, and restraining the splitting crack.

Although no studies on the effect of coated transverse steel have been reported to date, the addition of coated transverse steel should improve the anchorage strength of epoxy-coated bars. Since the bond of epoxy-coated bars is already reduced due to loss of adhesion between the bar and the concrete, an upper limit of 1.7 is established for the product of the top reinforcement and epoxy-coated reinforcement factors.

The low-density concrete factor, k_3, has been rounded to reflect the degree of accuracy associated with this factor.

N12.2.5
The reduction factor based on area is not used in those cases where anchorage development for full f_y is required. For example, the excess reinforcement factor does not apply for development of positive moment reinforcement at supports according to Clause 12.11.2, for development of shrinkage and temperature reinforcement according to Clause 7.8.4, or for development of reinforcement provided according to Clause 13.10.6.3.

N12.3.2
Bars in compression have shorter development lengths because the development length is not crossed by cracks due to tension in the concrete and because the end bearing of the bars on the concrete is usually beneficial.

N12.4
An increased development length is required when three or four bars are bundled together. The extra extension is needed because the grouping makes it more difficult to mobilize bond resistance from the "core" between the bars.

The designer should also note Clause 7.4.2.3 relating to the cutoff points of individual bars within a bundle and Clause 12.14.2.2 relating to splices of bundled bars.

N12.5.1
The definition of hook development length is shown in Fig. N12.5.1. This development length is typically controlled by splitting of the concrete in the plane of the hook caused by high local stresses shown.

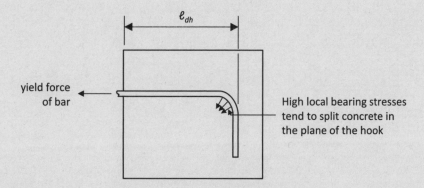

Fig. N12.5.1 Hook development length

N12.5.2

Fig. N12.5.2 and Table N12.5.2 gives geometric details for standard hooks and basic hook development length ℓ_{hb} for the case of f_y = 400 MPa.

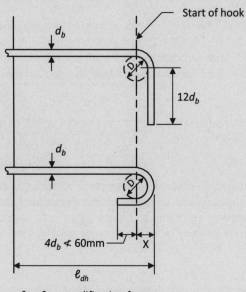

$\ell_{dh} = \ell_{hb}$ x modification factor

Fig. N12.5.2 Hook geometry details

N12.5.3

Fig. N12.5.3 illustrates some situations in which the basic hook development length is modified.

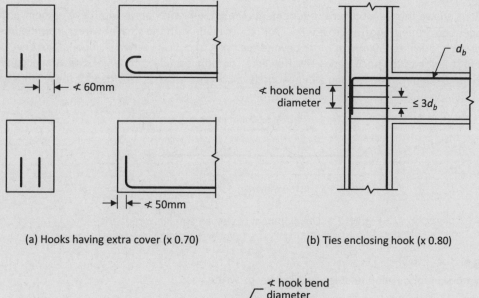

(a) Hooks having extra cover (x 0.70)

(b) Ties enclosing hook (x 0.80)

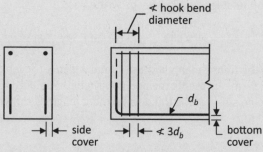

(c) Stirrups required if both side and bottom cover
are less than 60 mm (0.80 factor not applicable)
If side or bottom cover exceeds 60 mm (x 0.80)

Fig. N12.5.3 Factors modifying hook development length for 35M or smaller bars

N12.6.2

Total development of a bar simply consists of the sum of all the parts that contribute to the anchorage. When a mechanical anchorage is not capable of developing the required strength of the reinforcement, additional embedment length of reinforcement must be provided.

N12.7

Fig. N12.7 shows the development requirements for deformed wire fabric with one cross wire within the development length. Some of the development is assigned to the welds and some assigned to the length of deformed wire.

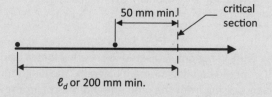

Fig. N12.7 Development of deformed wire fabric

N12.8

Fig. N12.8 shows the development requirements for smooth wire fabric with development primarily dependent on properly located cross wires. For fabrics made with the smaller wires, an embedment of at least two cross wires 50 mm or more beyond the point of critical section is adequate to develop the full yield strength of the anchored wires. However, for fabrics made with larger closely spaced wires a longer embedment is required and a minimum development length is provided for these fabrics.

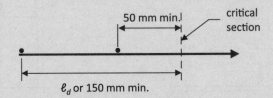

Fig. N12.8 Development of welded smooth wire fabric

N12.9.1

The expression for development length, ℓ_d, may be written as:

$$\ell_d = 0.048\, f_{pe}\, d_b + 0.145\, (f_{pr} - f_{pe})\, d_b$$

The first term represents the transfer length of the strand which is the length over which the prestress, f_{pe}, develops. The second term represents the additional length required to increase the stress from f_{pe} to f_{pr}. The variation of strand stress along the development length is shown in Fig. N12.9.1.

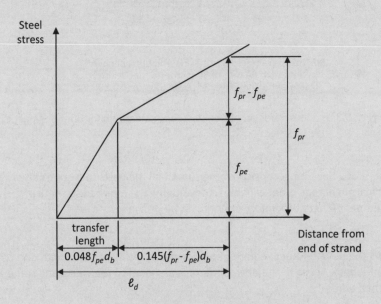

Fig. N12.9.1 Development of prestressing strand

N12.10.3

The inclined cracking which occurs in regions subjected to shearing forces leads to bar forces which are larger than those calculated from the bending moment diagram. The longitudinal reinforcement needs to be designed for the tensions arising from the moment and the shear at every section. In the 2004 edition of A23.3 both the Simplified and General Methods of shear design require that longitudinal reinforcement be proportioned in accordance with Clause 11.3.9 to account for the above effects.

The 1994 requirements of extending reinforcement a distance "d" past the point where it is no longer needed for flexure, no longer applies to Simplified Shear design. Clause 11.3.9.1 provides an alternative solution for members not subjected to significant tension or torsion. In these members it calls for all reinforcement to be extended a distance $d_v \cot \theta$ past the point where it is needed for flexure alone. Clause 12.10.3 has been modified to reflect these changes. Bar cut-offs are determined to ensure that the M_r provided exceeds the equivalent moments at all sections, see Fig N12.10.3.

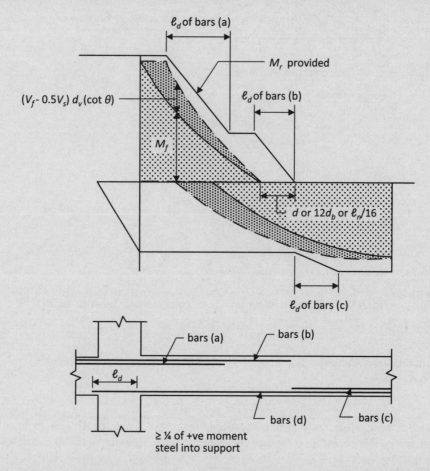

Fig. N12.10.3 Development of longitudinal reinforcement in continuous beam with shear reinforcement as required by Clause 11.3.9

N12.10.5

In these types of members the required tension in the reinforcement is not directly proportional to the moment. This is illustrated in Fig. N12.10.5 for a tapered footing. In evaluating the variation of this force, the strut and tie model of Clause 11.4 will often be useful.

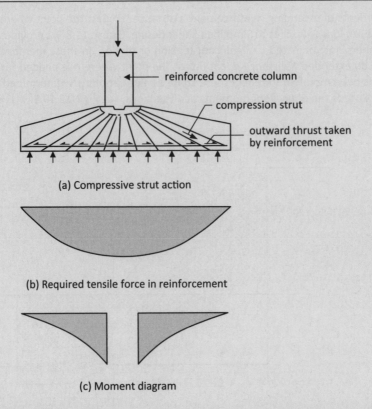

(a) Compressive strut action

(b) Required tensile force in reinforcement

(c) Moment diagram

Fig. N12.10.5 Required tension in reinforcement for tapered footing

N12.11.1

These traditional requirements are intended to give the structure an ability to tolerate some unanticipated actions.

N12.11.2

Loadings such as wind or earthquakes may cause load reversals. To provide a minimum level of ductility for these situations it is necessary to anchor the required reinforcement so that it can develop its yield stress.

N12.11.3

In regions of low moment and high shear the tension force in the reinforcing bars will increase rapidly in the direction of increasing moment. This clause is intended to assure that the bond characteristics of such bars will enable this rapid build up of force to occur. As illustrated in Fig. N12.11.3, the "bond" characteristics are considered adequate if the development length of the bars, ℓ_d, is less than $\ell_a + M_r$ $/V_f$. When this requirement is not satisfied, reduce the bar diameter (ℓ_d reduced). The 1.3 factor is usable only if the reaction confines the ends of the reinforcement.

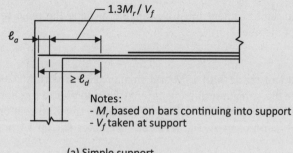

Notes:
- M_r based on bars continuing into support
- V_f taken at support

(a) Simple support

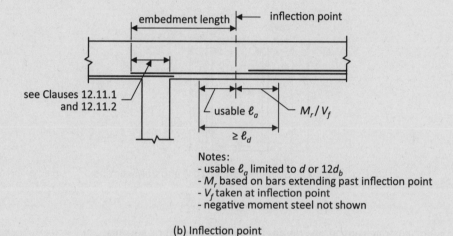

Notes:
- usable ℓ_a limited to d or $12d_b$
- M_r based on bars extending past inflection point
- V_f taken at inflection point
- negative moment steel not shown

(b) Inflection point

Fig. N12.11.3 Development of positive moment reinforcement at simple support and inflection point

N12.12

Fig. N12.12 illustrates the development requirements for negative moment reinforcement.

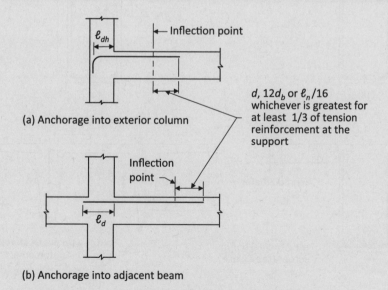

(a) Anchorage into exterior column

d, $12d_b$ or $\ell_n/16$ whichever is greatest for at least 1/3 of tension reinforcement at the support

(b) Anchorage into adjacent beam

Fig. N12.12 Development of negative moment reinforcement

N12.13.1

To be effective, web reinforcement must be capable of tying the main tension reinforcement to the compression zone of the beam.

N12.13.2

For shear reinforcement made with 15M and smaller bars or with MD200 and smaller wire there is no need to calculate the straight embedment length in addition to the hook. However, Clause 12.13.1 requires "full-depth" web reinforcement and in addition the web reinforcement must be anchored around longitudinal reinforcement. Fig. N12.13.2 illustrates stirrup anchorage requirements for 20M and 25M stirrups.

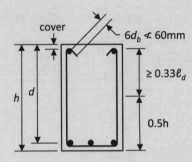

Fig. N12.13.2 Development of 20M and 25M stirrups

N12.13.2.(c)

Fig. N12.13.2(c) illustrates anchorage details for welded wire fabric stirrups.

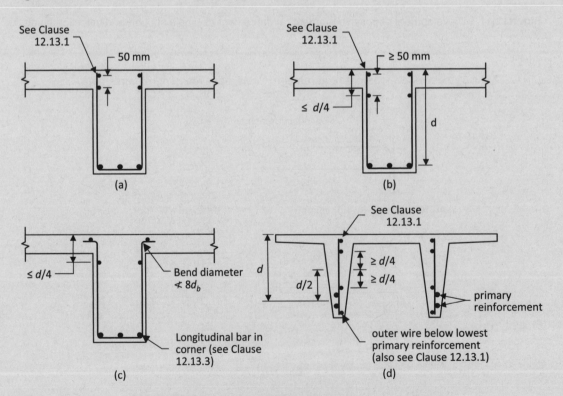

Fig. N12.13.2(c) Anchorage of welded wire fabric stirrups

N12.13.4
See Fig. N12.13.4.

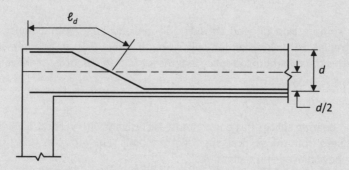

Fig. N12.13.4 Anchorage of inclined longitudinal bars used as shear reinforcement

N12.13.5
See Fig. N12.13.5.

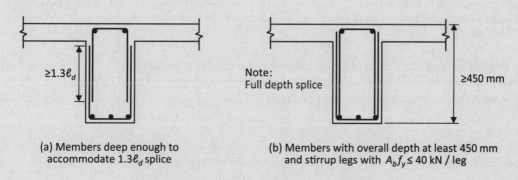

(a) Members deep enough to accommodate $1.3\ell_d$ splice

(b) Members with overall depth at least 450 mm and stirrup legs with $A_b f_y \leq 40$ kN / leg

Fig. N12.13.5 Overlapping U-stirrups

N12.14.2.2
In calculating the lap splice length required for individual bars within a bundle the increases in development length of Clause 12.4 should not be included as these would duplicate the increases required by Clause 12.14.2.2 for the effect of bundling.

N12.15.1
In calculating ℓ_d, the modification factor of (A_s required / A_s provided) of Clause 12.2.5 is not to be applied as this factor is already taken into account in the classifications of Clause 12.15.2. Where feasible, splices should be located in regions of low stress in the reinforcement and the splices should be staggered. Clause 12.15.2 requires longer splice lengths when these conditions cannot be met.

N12.15.4
This clause describes situations where welded splices or mechanical connections of less strength than 1.20 times the specified yield strength of the reinforcement may be used.

N12.15.5
Lap splices are not permitted in tension tie members. Examples of tension tie members are arch ties, hangers and tension elements in a truss. In determining if a member should be classified as a tension tie, considerations must be given to the importance, function, proportions and stress conditions of the

member. For example, a circular tank with many bars and with well-staggered, widely spaced splices should not be classified as a tension tie member.

N12.16

Splice strengths in compression depend considerably on end bearing and hence do not increase proportionally in strength for increasing lap splice length. Table 3.10 in Chapter 3 of the Concrete Design Handbook gives the minimum lap splice lengths for bars in compression having a yield strength of 400 MPa.

N12.16.4.1

Experience with end-bearing splices has been almost exclusively with vertical bars in columns. If bars are significantly inclined from the vertical, special attention is required to ensure that adequate end-bearing contact can be achieved and maintained.

N12.17

In columns subject to flexure and axial loads, tension stresses may occur on one face of the column if moderate or large moments must be transmitted. When such tensions occur, Clause 12.17 requires tension splices to be used or an adequate tensile resistance provided. Furthermore, a minimum tension capacity is required in each face of all columns even where analysis indicates compression only. This is achieved by requiring at least compression splices, which give tension capacities of at least one-quarter f_y.

Note that the column splice must satisfy requirements for all load combinations for the column. A load combination, including wind or seismic loads, may induce tensions greater than $0.5f_y$ in some column bars, in which case the column splice must be Class B.

N12.17.2

The intent of this clause is to avoid excessive congestion at splice locations and to give guidance concerning the staggering of splice locations in very heavily reinforced columns.

N12.17.3.4

To qualify for the 0.83 reduction factor a rectangular column must satisfy the $0.0015hs$ tie area requirement for both directions. As an example, for the column shown in Fig. N12.17.3.4 we would have:

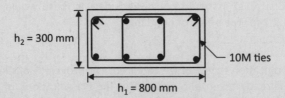

$h_2 = 300$ mm

10M ties

$h_1 = 800$ mm

Fig. N12.17.3.4 Rectangular tied column for example calculation

In the direction perpendicular to h_1 there are 4 legs, hence the required spacing is $(4 \times 100)/(0.0015 \times 800) = 333$ mm. In the direction perpendicular to h_2 there are 2 legs, hence the required spacing is $(2 \times 100)/(0.0015 \times 300) = 444$ mm. Hence ties must be spaced at no greater than 333 mm and must be placed throughout the lap splice length to qualify.

N12.17.3.5

Spirals meeting the requirements of Clauses 7.6.4 and 10.9.4 increase splitting resistance and hence enable compression lap splice lengths to be reduced.

N12.18

Fig. N12.18 illustrates the tension lap splice requirements for welded deformed wire fabric. In computing the ℓ_d from Clause 12.7, the 200 mm minimum length of that clause is neglected. As shown in Fig. N12.18, a 200 mm minimum is applied to the overall splice length.

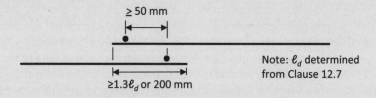

(a) Cross wires within lap length (Clause 12.18.1)

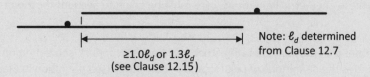

(b) No cross wires within lap length (Clause 12.18.2)

Fig. N12.18 Lap splices of deformed fabric

N12.19

The strength of lap splices of welded smooth fabric is dependent primarily on the anchorage obtained from the cross wires, rather than on the length of wire in the splice. Hence the lap is specified in terms of overlap of cross wires (see Fig. N12.19).

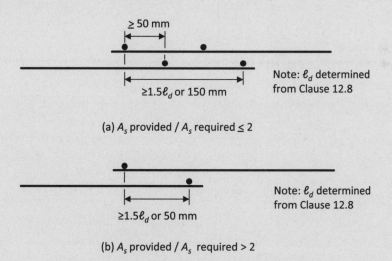

Fig. N12.19 Lap splices of smooth fabric

N13 Two-way slab systems

The 2014 edition has not changed substantially from the 2004 edition. Minor changes were made to make one-way shear provisions in Clause 13 consistent with those in Clause 11.

N13.1 General

Regular two-way slab systems (see definition in Clause 3.1) are slab systems that can deform and carry load in two orthogonal directions. Many of the provisions for their design are based on studies in which the curvatures in the two directions are equal or nearly equal. As the ratio of long to short clear spans increases, there is a tendency for the curvatures in the central portion of the panel to be more uniform in one direction than the other. For slabs without beams this tendency will be in the long span direction whereas for slabs with stiff beams on all sides this tendency will be in the short span direction. The geometric limitations listed are to ensure that the curvatures in the two directions will be approximately equal resulting in two-way behaviour. When provisions for regular two-way slab systems are used for slabs not meeting these geometric limitations, care must be taken to account for the manner in which the load is carried.

Fig. N13.1(a) illustrates that portion of a capital that qualifies as a support (see definition in Clause 3.1). Fig. N13.1(b) illustrates the definitions of column and middle strips (see definition in Clause 3.1).

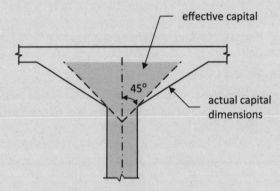

Fig. N13.1(a) Effective column capital

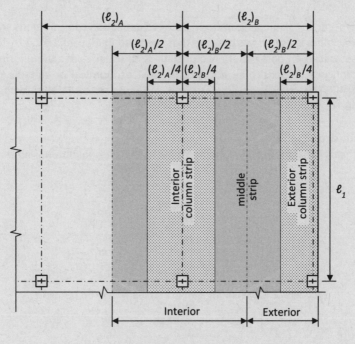

(a) Column strip for $\ell_2 \leq \ell_1$

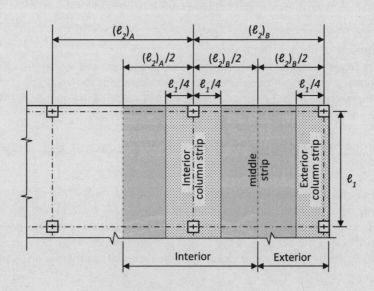

(b) Column strip for $\ell_2 > \ell_1$

Fig. N13.1(b) Definition of design strip

N13.2.1

This clause requires that all slabs designed using the provisions of Clause 13 shall have a thickness sufficient to ensure that slab deflections and crack widths will be satisfactory for the intended use.

N13.2.2

For many commonly occurring slab configurations, detailed deflection computations are not required if the minimum slab thickness is as least as great as that specified in Clauses 13.2.2 to 13.2.6. These are minimum thicknesses based on past experience of slabs with usual values of uniform gravity loading and good construction practice and may not be the most economical or suitable thickness for all applications. For f_y = 400 MPa, these expressions result in clear span to overall thickness ratios, ℓ_n/h, in the range of 30 to 46.

N13.2.4 Slabs with drop panels

Fig. 13.2.4 depicts the dimensions used in Equation 13.2 to calculate minimum slab thickness.

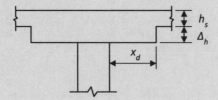

Fig. N13.2.4 Minimum slab thickness with drop panels

N13.2.6 Slab bands

Slab bands are defined in Clause 3.1 as a continuous extension of a drop panel between supports or between a support and another slab band. Clause 13.2.6 provides minimum depth requirements for slab bands.

N13.2.7 Computation of slab deflections.

Clause 13.2.7 gives requirements for the selection of factors to be used in computing deflections of two-way slab systems. It should be noted that in these calculations the modulus of rupture of the concrete, f_r, shall be taken as $0.3\,\lambda\,\sqrt{f_c'}$ or one-half the value specified in Equation 8.3. The computed deflections must be not greater than those permitted by Clause 9.8.5.3.

N13.3 Design procedures for shear for slabs without beams

This Clause consolidates the shear provisions for slabs.

N13.3.3 Critical section for two-way action

Critical sections that must be investigated for shear are illustrated in Fig. N13.3.3. Expressions for the maximum shear stress resistance to be used when evaluating the punching shear capacity are given in Clause 13.3.4.1. In checking the capacity of the critical section around a large drop panel such as that shown in Fig. N13.3.3, the maximum shear stress resistance approaches that for one-way shear.

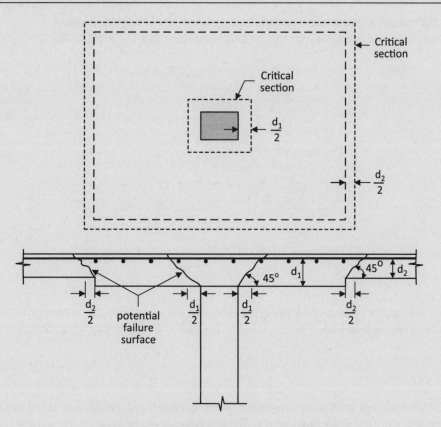

Fig. N13.3.3 Critical section for punching shear

N13.3.3.4 Openings in slabs

The reduction in critical shear perimeter to account for the effect of openings located at a distance less than 10 times the slab thickness is shown in Fig N13.3.3.4(a). When the concentrated load or reaction area (column) is located near a free edge, the free edge may be considered as a large opening. Although the Standard is not specific as to the appropriate reduction in the critical section for this case, a procedure suggested by the CEB (Comité Euro - International du Béton) Code is illustrated in Fig N13.3.3.4(b) and is recommended.

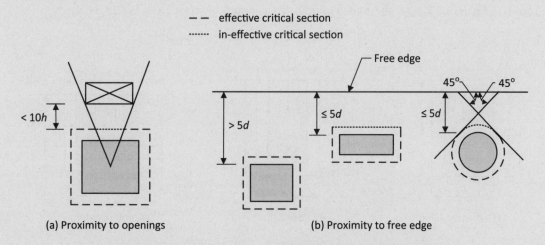

(a) Proximity to openings   (b) Proximity to free edge

Fig. N13.3.3.4 Effect of openings and free edges on critical sections

N13.3.4 Maximum shear stress resistance without shear reinforcement

The determination of β_c for a non-rectangular column is illustrated in Fig. N13.3.4.

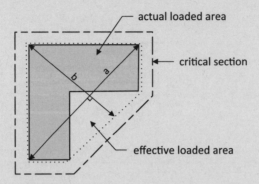

Fig. N13.3.4 β_c for a non-rectangular column

N13.3.4.1

The nominal resistances provided by the expressions for shear in Clause 13 are consistent with those provided by the ACI 318-05 Code. For example, the nominal punching shear stress corresponding to Eq. (13-7) is:

$$v_n = 0.33\lambda \sqrt{f'_c} \text{ MPa}$$

To ensure this consistent level of nominal shear resistance, the coefficients in Eqs. (13-5) to (13-7) have been increased over those contained in ACI 318. This was necessary to offset the greater reduction in capacity provided by the lower value of ϕ_c in comparison to the ACI 318 ϕ factor for shear. With the increase in ϕ_c from 0.60 to 0.65 in A23.3-04, the shear coefficients were adjusted to ensure that the nominal shear capacity remains unchanged.

N13.3.4.4

The length of shear span for which scale effects need not be considered is reduced from the previous edition to 2d. This reflects recent results from large-scale testing.

N13.3.5.1

The critical sections and orientation of the centroidal axes (x and y) for typical column locations are shown in Fig. N13.3.5.1. An alternative solution for a corner column is given in N13.3.6.2.

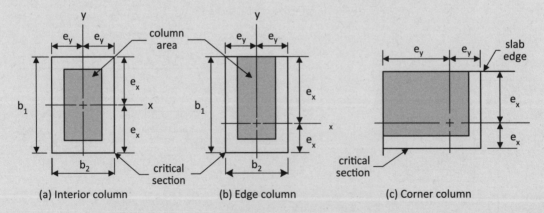

Fig. N13.3.5.1 Critical sections and centroidal axis at columns

N13.3.5.4

The vertical shear distributions caused by the shear force and the fraction of the unbalanced moment transferred by shear for an interior column are shown in Fig. N13.3.5.4.

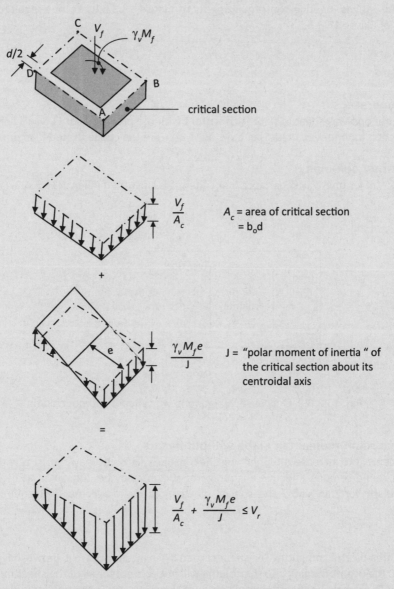

$$\frac{V_f}{A_c}$$

A_c = area of critical section
    = $b_o d$

$$\frac{\gamma_v M_f e}{J}$$

J = "polar moment of inertia" of the critical section about its centroidal axis

$$\frac{V_f}{A_c} + \frac{\gamma_v M_f e}{J} \leq V_r$$

Fig. N13.3.5.4 Vertical shear stress distribution due to V_f and $\gamma_f M_f$

N13.3.5.5

In Equation.13.9, values of M_{fx} and M_{fy} are the factored moments about the x and y axes, respectively. In assigning values of V_f, M_{fx} and M_{fy} some judgement is required as the maximum values for these quantities may not occur simultaneously. For an interior column, the value of V_f occurs with all adjacent panels loaded whereas the maximum values of M_f usually occur with selected pattern loading. It is suggested that a satisfactory value of v_f can be obtained by adding the maximum V_f term to the larger unbalanced moment term using maximum values of M_f. For an edge column, the sum of all three terms is required but the term considering the unbalanced moment about an axis perpendicular to the edge, M_{fy}, must be obtained from an analysis that considers both adjacent panels loaded. This term can be neglected when the spans along the edge are equal. For a corner column, the maximum value for all three terms occurs when the corner panel is loaded.

Corner column designs meeting the requirements of Clause 13.3.6.2 are not required to meet the requirements of Clause 13.3.5.5.

N13.3.5.6
See Fig. N13.10.2.

N13.3.6.1 General
The treatment of one-way shear in slabs is consistent with the provisions of Clause 11. The location of the critical section for one-way shear is at a distance, d_v, from the concentrated load or reaction.

N13.3.6.2 Corner columns
The critical section for one-way shear at corner columns is illustrated in Fig. N13.3.6.2.

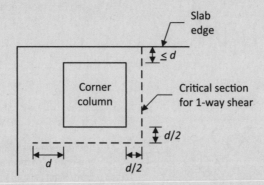

Fig. 13.3.6.2 Critical section for one-way shear at corner column

N13.3.7 Shear reinforcement in slabs without beams
Shear reinforcement to increase the punching shear capacity of slabs may consist of either stirrups or headed shear reinforcement. Effective anchorage of stirrups may be difficult to achieve by standard hooks, particularly for thin slabs, and special mechanical anchorage may be required (see Clause 13.3.8.1).

N13.4.1
The tributary area used in computing the shear carried by an interior beam is shown in Fig. N13.4.1. For $\alpha_1 \ell_1 / \ell_2 < 1.0$ the beams framing into the column will not account for all of the shear force transferred to the column. The remaining shear force will produce shear stresses in the slab around the column. For these cases the total shear strength of the slab-beam-column connection must be checked.

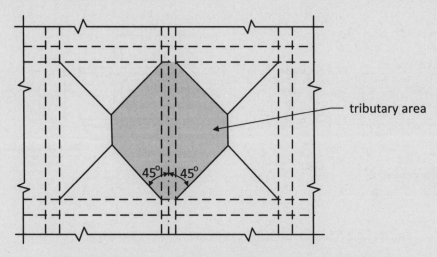

tributary area

Fig. N13.4.1 Tributary area for calculating shear on interior beam

N13.5.1
This section permits a designer to base a design directly on the fundamental principles of structural mechanics provided it is demonstrated that all safety and serviceability criteria are satisfied. Guidance for applying many of the more commonly used procedures are given in Clauses 13.6 to 13.12.

N13.6.2
When slab systems are analyzed using classical or numerical techniques based on elastic theory, it is necessary that stiffness assigned to the various slab components reflect the effects of cracking, creep and shrinkage of the concrete. Stiffness based on gross concrete dimensions is not satisfactory.

N13.7 Theorems of plasticity
The analysis of many slabs with irregular geometry is simplified using techniques based on plasticity. The designer must ensure that when selecting reinforcement the ductility demand requirements are met. For slabs, this can generally be considered satisfied by selecting reinforcement with a failure strain greater than or equal to 0.03. Since the theorems of plasticity only ensure strength requirements, serviceability requirements at service load must be evaluated independently.

N13.8 Slab systems as elastic frames
Probably the most frequently used method to determine design moments in regular two-way slab systems is to consider the slab as a series of two-dimensional frames that are analyzed elastically. When using this analogy, it is essential that stiffness properties of the elements of the frame be selected to properly represent the behaviour of the three-dimensional slab system.

In a typical frame analysis it is assumed that at a beam-column connection all members meeting at the joint undergo the same rotation. For slabs supported only by columns the slab will be restrained only locally by the column. For uniform gravity loading this reduced restraint is accounted for by reducing the effective stiffness of the column by either Clause 13.8.2 or Clause 13.8.3.

N13.8.2 Non-prismatic modelling of member stiffness
Examples of the variation in moment of inertia along typical slab-beams and columns are given in Fig. N13.8.2.

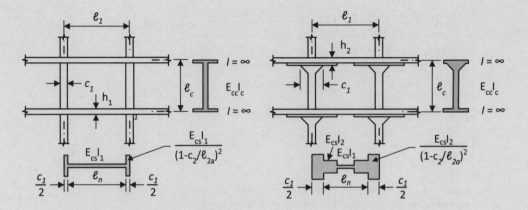

Fig. N13.8.2 Variation of moment of inertia for slab beams and columns

N13.8.2.5 and N13.8.2.6

In the non-prismatic modelling procedure, the effective column stiffness is reduced using the attached torsional member concept. The effective column stiffness is a function of the stiffness of the column and the torsional stiffness of the attached members framing into the sides of the column.

N13.8.2.7

Fig. N13.8.2.7 illustrates that portion of the slab that is to be included in computing the stiffness of the attached torsional member.

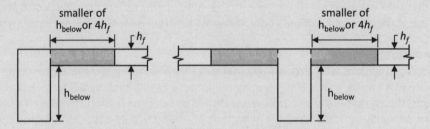

Fig N13.8.2.7 Portions of slab to be included with torsional members

N13.8.2.8

The stiffness, K_t, is the sum of the stiffnesses of the attached torsional members perpendicular to the direction in which moments are being computed. Thus for an interior column K_t accounts for the stiffness of two torsional members while for an edge column K_t will account for only one torsional member when moments are being calculated in a direction parallel to the face edge.

N13.8.2.9

The term C is a property of the cross section having the same relationship to the torsional rigidity of a non-circular cross section as does the polar moment of inertia for a circular cross section. The value of C is computed by dividing the cross section of the torsional member into separate rectangles and summing the C-values for each of the component rectangles. Since the value of C obtained by summing the values for each of the component rectangles making up a section will always be less than the theoretically correct value, it is appropriate to subdivide the cross section in such a way as to result in the highest possible value of C.

Explanatory Notes on CSA A23.3-14

N13.8.2.10

The stiffening effect on the slab due to the presence of beams between the columns causes the rotation of the slab-beam at a joint to be closer to the rotation of the column at that joint as assumed in a planar frame analysis. This reduces the need to reduce the effective stiffness of the column. Increasing the value of K_t reduces the effect of the attached torsional members.

N13.8.3

When analysis of the elastic frame is performed using a standard frame analysis program based on direct stiffness formulation, the reduced rotational restraint at the joint when the slab is supported on columns can be accounted for by reducing the effective moment of inertia of the column by the factor ψ.

N13.8.5

Generally, the output from an elastic frame analysis will give the moments at the ends of the members. From these the moments at the critical sections are calculated. The location of the critical sections for large rectilinear interior supports and for exterior supports with brackets are shown in Fig. N13.8.5.

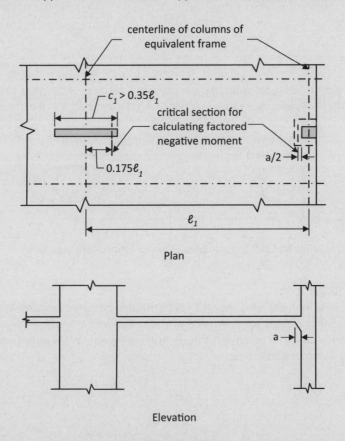

Fig. N13.8.5 Critical sections for negative factored moment for cases with large rectilinear interior supports and exterior supports with brackets

N13.9 Direct design method

Although the name has been retained, the Direct Design Method in CSA Standard A23.3-14 has been reduced from a complete design method to a procedure for determining moments at the critical sections and so is essentially a simplified elastic frame analysis. That portion of the design related to the lateral distribution of moments across the critical sections is applicable to all elastic frame solutions and has been incorporated in Clauses 13.11 and 13.12.

N13.9.1.2
When the design strip consists of only two spans the magnitude of the negative moment at the interior support is significantly greater than when there are three or more spans. Distribution coefficients in Table 13.1 are based on three or more spans.

N13.9.1.3
The limitation of this clause is to prevent the possibility of developing negative moments beyond the point where the negative moment reinforcement is terminated according to Fig. 13.1.

N13.9.1.4
The distribution coefficients in Table 13.1 are essentially those from an elastic analysis for a uniformly distributed loading on all spans. In the absence of provisions to adequately handle pattern loadings the factored live load is limited to two times the factored dead load.

N13.9.2.1
See Fig. N13.1(b).

N13.9.2.3
When circular or regular polygonal supports are used, it is recommended that the clear span, ℓ_n, be calculated by treating the supports as square sections with the same area as illustrated in Fig. N13.9.2.3.

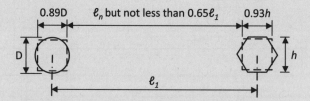

Fig. N13.9.2.3 Examples of equivalent square supports

N13.9.3.1 and N13.9.3.2
The total factored static moment for a span, M_o, is distributed between negative and positive moment regions in a manner that reflects the influence of the stiffness of the supporting members. See Fig. N13.9.3 for some examples. The positive factored moments given in this clause are maximum values and do not necessarily occur at mid span.

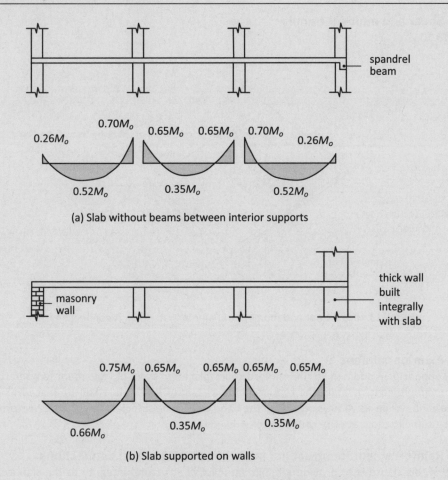

(a) Slab without beams between interior supports

(b) Slab supported on walls

Fig. N13.9.3 Examples of design moments in slabs

N13.9.3.3

This clause reflects the amount of moment redistribution that can occur in regular slab systems. For slabs without beams between interior supports, unless an edge beam is provided, it is recommended that the exterior negative moment not be reduced when calculating maximum factored shear stress due to the moment transfer by eccentricity of shear.

N13.10.1 General

Experience has shown that when stiff drop panels are used there is a greater tendency for the slab to crack in the negative middle strip region. In those applications where crack control is important (i.e. where a brittle topping is used or the slab is located in a corrosive environment) additional reinforcement is required.

N13.10.2 Shear and moment transfer
See Fig. N13.10.2.

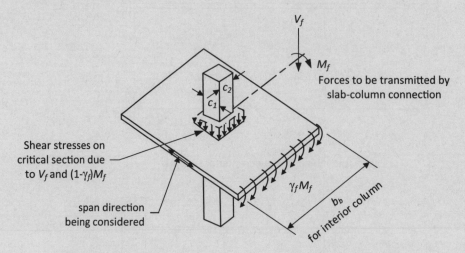

Fig. N13.10.2 Shear and moment transfer at slab-column connections

N13.10.3 Exterior columns
At exterior supports, in addition to the reinforcement placed in band b_b, minimum temperature and shrinkage reinforcement meeting the requirements of Clause 7.8.1 must still be placed in regions outside the band. While curvatures outside of the band will not be sufficient to yield the reinforcement, they may be sufficient to crack the concrete.

N13.10.6 Reinforcement for structural integrity at slab-column connections
The intent of this clause is to provide a minimum level of structural integrity to the slab system to limit the spread from a local failure that would result in progressive collapse. The provision of properly anchored bottom reinforcing bars or tendons enables the slab to hang from the supports after the initial local failure occurs (see Fig. N13.10.6).

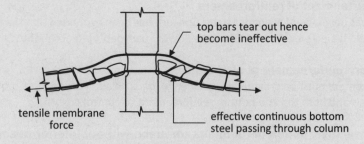

top bars tear out hence become ineffective

tensile membrane force

effective continuous bottom steel passing through column

(a) Effective continuous bottom reinforcement providing post punching failure resistance

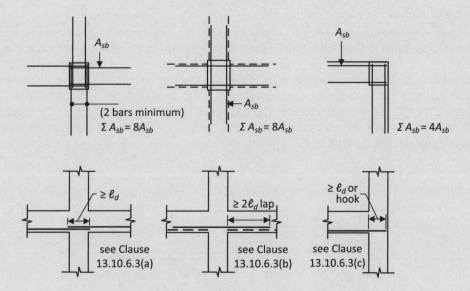

A_{sb}

(2 bars minimum)
$\Sigma A_{sb} = 8A_{sb}$

A_{sb}

$\Sigma A_{sb} = 8A_{sb}$

A_{sb}

$\Sigma A_{sb} = 4A_{sb}$

$\geq \ell_d$

see Clause 13.10.6.3(a)

$\geq 2\ell_d$ lap

see Clause 13.10.6.3(b)

$\geq \ell_d$ or hook

see Clause 13.10.6.3(c)

(b) Ways of providing effectively continuous bottom reinforcement

Fig. N13.10.6 Structural integrity requirements for slabs

N13.10.7 Effective depth at drop panels

See Fig. N13.10.7.

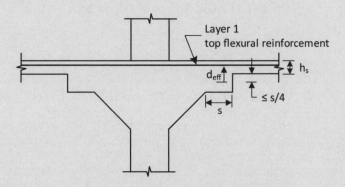

Layer 1
top flexural reinforcement

h_s

d_{eff}

$\leq s/4$

s

Fig. N13.10.7 Effective depth at drop panel

N13.10.8 Curtailment of reinforcement

Figure 13.1 was developed for slender slabs. Concern has been expressed that the minimum lengths for top bars should be increased for thicker slabs (lower span/depth) to account for shear lag.

N13.10.9 Top reinforcement at slab edge

Edge reinforcement must be provided to resist edge loads. In addition, twisting moments at the edge of a slab may demand both top and bottom reinforcement to control cracking.

N13.11 Lateral distribution of moments for slabs without interior beams

When laterally distributing design moment, the objective is to assign moment to those sections that will experience the greatest curvature or have the greatest stiffness. These distribution factors were developed from FEA studies and proven historical practice.

N13.11.2.6

This clause draws the designers attention to the fact that the requirements of Clause 13.11.2.2 and 13.11.2.3 are applicable to slabs with spandrel beams for negative moments at exterior supports.

If the maximum calculated torque is less than 25% of the cracking torque, T_{cr}, of the spandrel beam, then, from Clause 11.2.9.1, the torsion can be neglected. If the calculated torque exceeds $0.67T_{cr}$, then, from Clause 11.2.9.2, this maximum torque may be reduced to $0.67T_{cr}$ to account for the reduction in torsional stiffness that will occur after cracking. If the torsion is reduced, the slab moments must be adjusted accordingly (see Fig. N13.11.2.6 (b)).

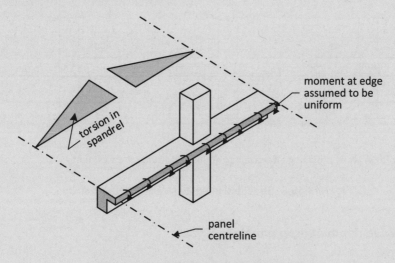

Fig. N13.11.2.6(a) Torsion at exterior edge

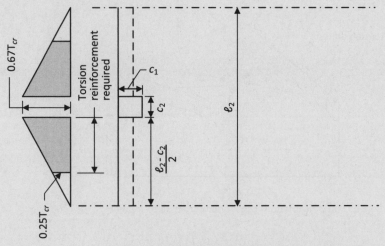

(i) Torsion diagram if calculated torsion exceeds $0.67T_{cr}$
(see Clause 11.2.9.2)

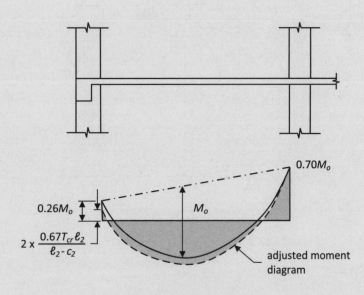

(ii) Adjusted moment diagram

Fig. N13.11.2.6(b) Redistribution of moments caused by reduced torsional stiffness of spandrel beam after cracking

N13.12.5 Corner of reinforcement

Fig. N13.12.5(a) illustrates the deformation of the slab in the vicinity of an exterior corner due to the high twisting moments present. These result in tension in both the top and bottom of the slab as shown. Fig N13.12.5(b) shows two ways of providing reinforcement to control cracking in these regions. Generally the orthogonal arrangement of bars is used.

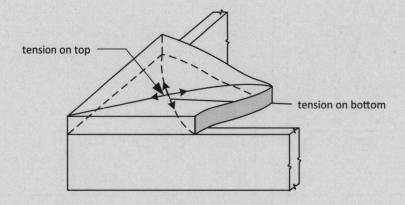

(a) Deformations of exterior corner slab element

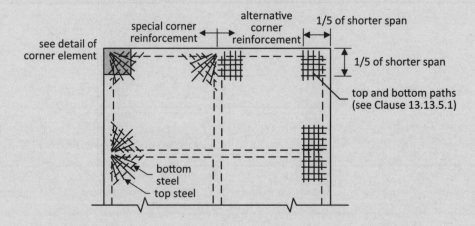

(b) Plan view of slab supported on walls or stiff beams showing reinforcement

Fig. N13.12.5 Special slab reinforcement at exterior corners

N14 – Walls

Clause 3 provides a definition of a "wall" to distinguish between this structural element and a column. Five different types of walls are defined. Clause 14 has general requirements which apply to all walls but also specific requirements that apply to each of the different wall types. The designer will have to be familiar with these different wall types to be able to correctly interpret the provisions of Clause 14.

N14.1.3.1
See Fig. N14.1.3.1.

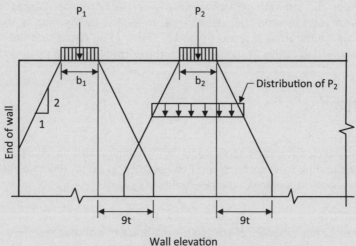

Wall elevation

b_1 and b_2 are bearing widths of concentrated loads P_1 and P_2

Fig. N14.1.3.1 Distribution of concentrated loads on wall of thickness "t"

N14.2.2
The provisions for the design of bearing walls using the simplified expression of equation 14.1 clarify the conditions when this equation can be used. The wall must be a bearing wall with principal moments acting about a horizontal axis parallel to the plane of the wall. This equation does not apply to shear walls in which moments act about a horizontal axis perpendicular to the wall.

N14.2.2.1
Eccentric loads and lateral forces are used to determine the total eccentricity of the factored axial load, P_f. Only loads which produce moments about a horizontal axis parallel to the plane of wall may be considered for the use of equation 14.1. When the resultant load for all applicable load combinations falls within the middle third of the wall thickness (eccentricity not greater than $t/6$ at all sections along the length of the wall), the design method of Clause 14.2.2.1 may be used. The design is then carried out considering P_f as a concentric load which must be less than P_r computed by Eq. (14.1). The factored resistance is computed based on an equivalent rectangular stress block equal to 2/3 of the wall thickness. This places the resisting force in line with the assumed load.

In investigating a wall subjected to vertical concentrated loads, A_g in Eq. (14.1) should account for the effective horizontal length for the uniform distribution of the concentrated loads as defined in Clause 14.1.3.1.

The effective length factors given in Clause 14.2.2.3 are intended to reflect the general range of end conditions encountered in wall designs. The end condition "restrained against rotation", required for a *k* factor of 0.8, implies attachment to a member having a flexural stiffness, EI/ℓ, at least as large as that of the wall. Pinned conditions at both ends can occur in some precast and tilt-up applications.

The term in Eq. (14.1) accounting for wall slenderness effects is intended to result in relatively comparable strengths by Clause 14.2 or Clause 10 for walls loaded with an eccentricity of $t/6$.

N14.4
This expanded Clause provides additional guidance for designers of shear walls.

N14.4.3.2
This clause provides for strength reduction factors for compression flanges of assemblies of interconnected shear walls in which the slenderness, measured by the ratio of the length between supports and the flange thickness is greater than 15. It should be noted that further restrictions on slenderness are provided in Clause 21, depending on the ductility demand required for the shear wall system.

N15 Foundations

N15.2.2
The footing area is selected to satisfy service and ultimate limit states based on service and factored soil resistances. The footing cross sections are then designed to satisfy ultimate limit states based on factored soils stresses corresponding to the selected footing area.

N15.2.3
This criterion affects the pile cap shear check and the pile design. Piles shall therefore always be checked for an eccentric pile reaction.

N15.4.3
Fig. N15.4.3 illustrates the critical sections where flexural resistance and development of reinforcement must be checked.

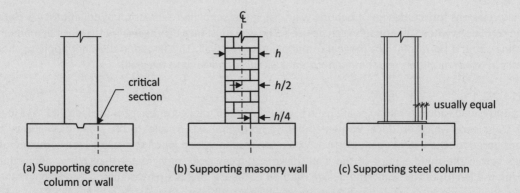

(a) Supporting concrete column or wall   (b) Supporting masonry wall   (c) Supporting steel column

Fig. N15.4.3 Critical sections for moment in footings

N15.4.4
The amount of flexural reinforcement in the short direction is determined by considering the moment acting on the critical section (see Fig. N15.4.4). In recognition of the fact that the moment per unit length will be higher in the vicinity of the column, the flexural reinforcement is concentrated in this region (see Fig. N15.4.4).

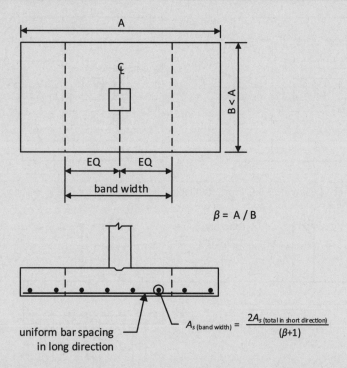

Fig. N15.4.4 Distribution of flexural reinforcement in a rectangular footing

N15.5.2

Fig. N15.5.2(a) illustrates the critical sections (Cl. 13.3.3.1. and Cl. 11.3.2.) for which shear resistance must be investigated in accordance with Clauses 11 & 13.

When investigating punching shear for closely spaced piles where the individual critical perimeters overlap, a critical section around the pile group may govern (see Fig. N15.5.2(b)).

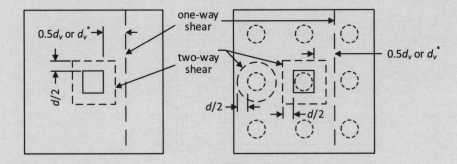

*See Clauses 11.3.2 and 13.3.6.1 for establishing critical section for one-way shear.

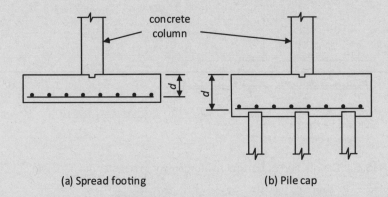

(a) Spread footing   (b) Pile cap

Fig. N15.5.2 (a) Critical sections for shear

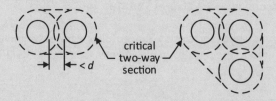

Fig. N15.5.2 (b) Critical sections for groups of closely spaced piles

N15.8.1
Cross-sectional forces in piles shall be determined by considering the soil-pile interaction and non-linear soil behaviour. Usually finite element analysis using linear or non-linear springs are used to capture pile-soil interaction. Stiffness reduction (EI) of the pile shall be considered.

N15.9
Joints between cast-in-place columns or walls and footings should be designed in accordance with Clauses 15.9.1 and 15.9.2. Joints between precast columns or walls and footings shall satisfy Clauses 15.9.1 and 15.9.3.

N15.9.1.1
Factored soil stresses and pile reactions shall be determined by accounting for column or wall base moments. Additional shear due to unbalanced moments in spread footings supporting columns shall be calculated as defined in Cl. 13.3.5.

N15.9.1.2

Bearing of the contact surfaces shall consider the beneficial effect of the reinforcement. Minimum reinforcement (dowel area) is defined in Cl. 15.9.2.1.

Column bearing: $B_r = 0.85\phi_c f'_c A_{col} + \phi_s f_y A_{dowel}$

Footing bearing: $B_{r,footing} = 0.80\phi_c f'_c A_{col}\sqrt{\dfrac{A_2}{A_{col}}} + \phi_s f_y A_{dowel}$ where A_2 is per Cl.10.8.1.

N15.9.1.3

When net uplift or moments (resulting in tensile stresses in the reinforcement) are transferred to footings or pile caps the reinforcement shall be anchored accordingly.

N16 Precast concrete

N16.1.3

The ϕ_c factor for precast concrete has been increased to 0.70 to reflect the better quality control in certified plants.

N16.4.1

While the design of precast concrete follows the same rules presented for cast-in-place concrete, special considerations are necessary for precast concrete. The use of the strength design method based on 28-day strengths may not be appropriate for the design of elements subjected to the effects of stripping and handling at earlier ages. Cracking of the concrete, although acceptable from structural considerations, may result in unacceptable appearance. Some architectural finishes may tend to exaggerate the effects of early cracking. Further guidance on the design of precast concrete elements and connections can be obtained from the CPCI *Design Manual*.

N16.4.1.1

The loads imposed on precast elements during the period from casting to placement may be greater than the actual service loads.

The behaviour of precast concrete structures may differ substantially from that of monolithic cast-in-place structures. Design of joints to transmit forces due to shrinkage, creep, temperature, elastic deformation, wind forces and earthquake forces requires particular care in precast construction. Details of such joints are especially important for adequate performance of precast construction.

N16.4.3.1

The minimum reinforcement ratios of Clause 16.4.3.1 are not sufficient to control the width of full depth cracks caused by the restraint of shrinkage, creep and thermal movements. If it is necessary to limit the width of such cracks, additional reinforcement will be required unless special provisions are made to relieve restraint forces.

N16.4.4

Guidelines summarizing current practice for the design of connections can be found in the CPCI *Design Manual*.

N16.4.5.2

To prevent spalling under heavily loaded bearing areas, bearing pads should not extend to the edge of the support unless the edge is armoured. Edges can be armoured with anchored steel plates or angles. Clause 11.6.8 provides additional requirements for bearing areas on brackets or corbels.

N17 Composite concrete flexural members

N17.1.6
The stresses in, and the deflections of, a composite member at specified loads will be influenced by whether or not the first element cast was shored during casting and curing of the subsequent element(s). However, tests and analysis show that the strength of such a member is not measurably affected by shoring due to the inelastic stress redistributions that occur prior to failure.

N17.1.8
The extent of cracking permitted is dependent on such factors as environment, aesthetics and type of loading. Irrespective of these considerations, cracks wide enough to impair shear transfer cannot be tolerated.

N17.1.9
Premature loading of precast elements can cause excessive deflections as a result of the high creep of young concrete.

N17.4.3.1
This simplified procedure is based on the assumption that the horizontal shear stress on the interface equals the factored shear force divided by the area, $b_v d$.

N17.4.3.2
Surfaces are intentionally roughened to provide satisfactory interlock. It is noted that in Clauses 11.5 and 17.4 "intentionally roughened" implies an interface roughened to a full amplitude of at least 5 mm.

N17.4.4
Fig N17.4.4 illustrates the application of this clause. It is conventional to calculate the average longitudinal shear stress between the maximum moment section and the adjacent zero-moment section.

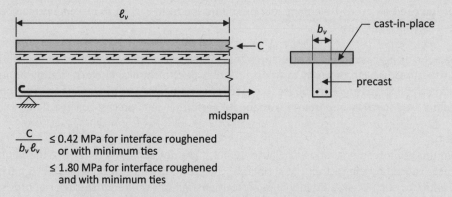

$$\frac{C}{b_v \ell_v} \leq 0.42 \text{ MPa for interface roughened or with minimum ties}$$

$$\leq 1.80 \text{ MPa for interface roughened and with minimum ties}$$

Fig. N17.4.4 Example of investigating longitudinal shear

N18 Prestressed concrete

N18.1.3
The empirical provisions of Clauses 10.3.3 and 10.3.4 limiting the geometry of T-beams were developed for conventionally reinforced concrete and if applied to prestressed concrete would exclude many standard prestressed products in satisfactory use today (e.g. see standard T-beams in CPCI Design Manual). Note that when applying Clause 10.5.3 to prestressed T-beams with tapered flanges the spacing limit may be based on the average flange thickness.

The empirical limits for concrete joist construction apply for conventionally reinforced concrete but not for prestressed concrete. Hence Clause 10.4 is excluded. Experience and judgement must be used for prestressed concrete joists.

The limitations on reinforcement amounts given in Clauses 10.5.1, 10.9.1 and 10.9.2 are replaced by those in Clauses 18.8, 18.11.2 and 18.12.5.

The skin reinforcement requirements of Clause 10.6.2 were derived for conventionally reinforced concrete members and were not intended to apply to prestressed concrete members.

Many of the design procedures of Clause 13 are not appropriate for prestressed concrete two-way slabs. The prestressed concrete provisions are given in Clause 18.12.

The empirical design method of Clause 14.2 is not applicable to prestressed concrete walls. These elements should be designed by the more general procedures specified in Clauses 10 and 11.

N18.1.5
Loading stages that are typically considered include:

(1) jacking stage, or transfer of prestress stage - when the prestressing force is high, and the concrete strength is normally low

(2) specified load stage - after all prestress losses have occurred and the member is subjected to specified loads,

(3) factored load stage - when the resistance of the member is checked.

Other load stages that may need to be investigated include: handling, transportation, erection and other construction stages.

N18.2.2
In these stress calculations transformed section properties accounting for the beneficial effects of bonded reinforcement may be used.

N18.3.1.1
These stresses are intended to prevent crushing or cracking of the young concrete due to the high prestress force.

Simply supported beams pretensioned with straight strands will initially have high tensile stresses in the top concrete fibres near the ends of the beams. Experience has shown that a small amount of cracking in these zones can be tolerated and hence higher tensile stresses are permitted. The compressive transfer limit at the ends of simply supported members has been raised from $0.60\, f'_{ci}$ to $0.67\, f'_{ci}$ in the 2014 edition of the Standard to reflect the findings of research.

N18.3.1.3
The tensile stress limits can be exceeded if appropriate reinforcement is provided to control the resulting cracking. This crack control reinforcement should consist of a well distributed array of smaller bars. See Fig. N18.3.1.3.

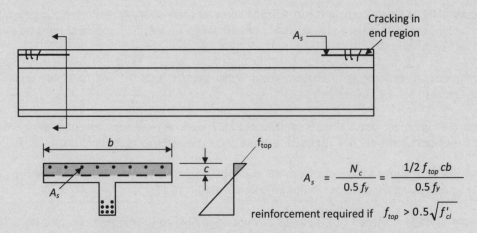

Fig. N18.3.1.3 Control of cracking occurring at transfer

N18.3.2

The tensile stress limits in this clause are intended to control or avoid cracking after all prestress losses have occurred and the full specified loads have been applied. The tensile zones being investigated are those regions of the member where the prestress causes compressive stresses (precompressed) but are in tension under specified loads.

The consequences of cracking for a structure in a corrosive environment (e.g. a parking garage) are much more severe and hence lower tensile stress limits and larger concrete covers should be used.

When low density concrete is used the tensile stress limits should be modified to account for the lower cracking stress of such concretes (e.g. multiply limits by the λ factor of Clause 8.6.5).

N18.3.3. Partial prestressing

A member is considered to be partially prestressed if the tensile stresses under specified loads exceed the allowable limits of Clause 18.3.2(c). Partially prestressed members are not permitted in corrosive environments.

In checking the deflection of partially prestressed members the reduction in stiffness caused by cracking must be accounted for (see Clause 9.8.4.3). Fig. N18.3.3 illustrates the bi-linear approximation of the load-deflection curve for a simply-supported, partially prestressed, uniformly loaded member. In such calculations the cracking stress may be taken as $0.6\lambda\sqrt{f_c'}$.

The control of crack widths can be investigated by the procedures of Clause 18.8.3. Crack control in situations involving frequently repeated loads requires further investigation.

To investigate fatigue resistance the maximum stress range caused by the repeating loads is calculated and compared to acceptable limits. The allowable stress range is a function of, amongst other things, tendon type and tendon curvature. For strands a limit of 100 MPa will typically be conservative. Anchorages and couplings typically have poor fatigue resistance and hence should not be located in zones subjected to large stress ranges.

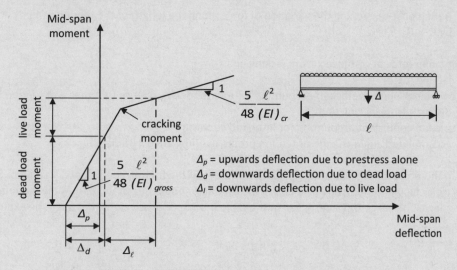

Fig. N18.3.3 Calculating deflection of a partially prestressed member

N18.4 Permissible stresses in tendons

The maximum tensile stress in tendons at jacking and after transfer is limited in order to provide a margin of safety against tendon fracture, to avoid inelastic tendon deformation, and to limit relaxation losses. These stress limits are tabulated below for different types of tendons in terms of the tensile strength f_{pu}.

Table N18.4
Stress-limits in terms of f_{pu}

Tendon Type	f_{py}	At jacking		After Transfer
		Post-tensioned	Pretensioned	
Low relaxation strand or wire	0.90	0.85	0.80	0.74*
Normal stress relieved strand or wire	0.85	0.80	0.80	0.70
Plain prestressing bars	0.85	0.80	0.80	0.70
Deformed prestressing bars	0.80	0.75	0.80	0.66

* Post-tensioned tendons limited to 0.70 f_{pu} at anchorages and couplers.

N18.5 Prestress losses

Prestress losses may be expected to vary considerably in different situations. Actual losses will have little effect on member strength but will affect serviceability (deflections, stresses and cracking). Either over-estimating or under-estimating prestress losses may cause serviceability problems (e.g. excessive camber or excessive cracking and deflection). Information on calculating prestress losses is given in the CAC Concrete Design Handbook and the CPCI Design Manual. Comments on the different losses to be considered are given below:

(a) The anchorage seating loss can be determined from the anchorage set characteristic of the post-tensioning system being used (see Fig. N18.5).

(b) The concrete around the tendons shortens as the prestressing force is applied to it. Those tendons which are already bonded to the concrete shorten with it.

(c) During post-tensioning the variation of force along the length of the tendon can be computed by $P_x = P_s e^{-(Kx+\mu\alpha)}$

where:

P_x = tendon force at distance x from jacking end

P_s = jacking force

K = wobble friction coefficient accounting for unintended curvature (per metre of tendon length)

x = distance from jacking end

μ = friction coefficient accounting for intended curvature

α = accumulated angle change of tendon profile over distance x (radians)

The use of this equation is illustrated in Fig. N18.5 Values of the friction coefficients, K and μ to be used for a particular type of tendon and particular types of ducts should be obtained from the manufacturers of the tendons. The range of values given in the table below serve as values that might be expected.

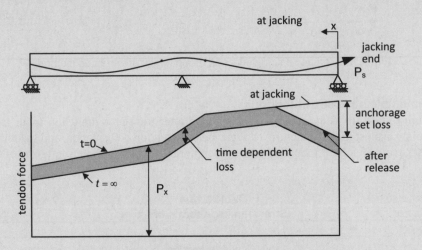

Fig. N18.5 Variation in tendon force due to losses

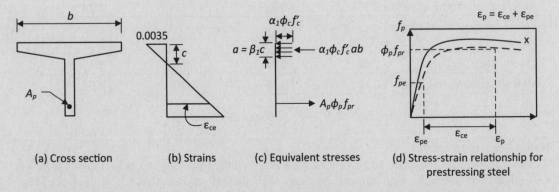

(a) Cross section   (b) Strains   (c) Equivalent stresses   (d) Stress-strain relationship for prestressing steel

Fig. N18.6.1 Strain compatibility analysis for prestressed concrete members with bonded tendons

N18.6.2(a)

It can be seen from Fig. N18.6.1 that as the depth of compression increases, the stress in the tendon decreases. For bonded members with $c \leq 0.5\,d_p$ and $f_{pe} \leq 0.6\,f_{py}$ Eq. (18-1) gives a conservative estimate of f_{pr}. The term k_p accounts for the shape of tendon stress-strain curve. Values of k_p are given in Table N18.6.2.

Explanatory Notes on CSA A23.3-14

Table N18.6.2
Values of k_p

Tendon Type	k_p
Low relaxation strand or wire	0.28
Normal stress relieved strand or wire	0.38
Plain prestressing bars	0.38
Deformed prestressing bars	0.48

The value of the neutral axis depth c in Eq. 18-1 can be established by trial and error, or from the equilibrium of internal forces. With $\Sigma T = \Sigma C$ we get for the T-beam of Fig. N18.6.2(a):

$$\phi_p f_{pr} A_p + \phi_s f_y A_s = \alpha_1 \phi_c f_c' b_w \beta_1 c + \alpha_1 \phi_c f_c'(b - b_w)h_f + \phi_s A_s' f_y$$

Substituting $f_{pr} = f_{pu}(1 - k_p c/d_p)$ - Eq.(18-1) - and solving for c/d_p we find

$$\frac{c}{d_p} = \frac{\phi_p f_{pu} A_p + \phi_s f_y A_s - \phi_s f_y' A_s' - \alpha_1 \phi_c f_c'(b - b_w)h_f}{\alpha_1 \phi_c f_c' \beta_1 b_w d_p + k_p \phi_p f_{pu} A_p}$$

This equation is general and applies for $A_s = 0$ and/or $A_s' = 0$ and/or $b = b_w$. If $h_f > \beta_1 c$ the beam should be considered to be a rectangular beam of width b.

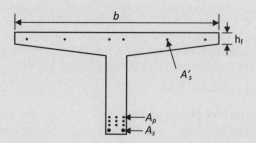

Fig. N18.6.2(a) Cross-section of prestressed concrete beam

After determining f_{pr} from Eq. (18-1) the rectangular stress block depth, a, at factored resistance can be found. Thus, for the beam in Fig. N18.6.2(a)

$$a = \frac{\phi_p A_p f_{pr} + \phi_s A_s f_s - \phi_s A_s' f_s'}{\alpha_1 \phi_c f_c' b}$$

where f_s and f_s' are the reinforcing bar stresses determined from strain compatibility for a neutral axis depth of $c = a/\beta_1$.

N18.6.2(b)

While bonded tendons exhibit large stress increases in regions of high moment (particularly at crack locations) unbonded tendons must average out their stress increase over the total length between the anchorages (see Fig. N18.6.2(b)).

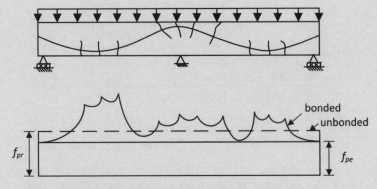

Fig. N18.6.2(b) Tendon stress variation

Eq. (18-2) gives a conservative estimate of the stress in unbonded tendons at the factored resistance. The length ℓ_o is the overall length of the tendon between anchors. The summation sign has been introduced in order to get the sum of the values $(d_p\text{-}c_y)$ for each of the plastic hinges in the span under consideration, which is illustrated in Fig. N18.6.2(b).

N18.8.1
Table 18-1 summarizes the requirements for minimum amounts of bonded non-prestressed reinforcement. The two columns for tensile stress $> 0.5\lambda\sqrt{f'_c}$ apply to partially prestressed members.

N18.8.3
For partially prestressed beams and one way slabs, the bonded flexural reinforcement must be distributed to provide adequate crack control. Because of the additional uncertainties in computing crack widths for partially prestressed members and because prestressing steel is more susceptible to corrosion, the z limits for these members are smaller than for reinforced concrete members (see Clause 10.6.1).

N18.10 Frames and continuous construction
When a statically indeterminate structure is post-tensioned, the deformation of the structure caused by the prestressing is restrained by the supports. The moments produced in the structure by these restraint reactions are usually referred to as "secondary moments". In design, an elastic analysis is first performed to determine the moments due to factored loads and the secondary moments. The standard then permits a certain amount of redistribution of these elastic moments, provided that minimum bonded reinforcement is present at the supports. See comments for Clause 9.2.4.

N18.12 Two-way slab systems
This clause permits the use of the methods of analysis defined in Clause 13.8 to determine the moments and shears in prestressed concrete two-way slab systems. More detailed procedures such as a finite element analysis are also permitted. Note that the elastic moments must include the restraint effects explained in N18.10 (i.e. secondary moments).

N18.12.5 Minimum bonded nonprestressed reinforcement
This clause summarizes the minimum amounts of bonded reinforcement required and its distribution in the negative moment areas.

N18.12.6.1
This Clause provides specific guidance concerning tendon distribution that will permit the use of banded tendon distributions in one direction.

N18.13.5

In addition to designing the localized region immediately surrounding the anchorage device and any confining reinforcement, the three dimensional effects of transferring the concentrated tendon force to the concrete and distributing this force more uniformly across the member's cross section must be considered. See Fig. N18.13.5.

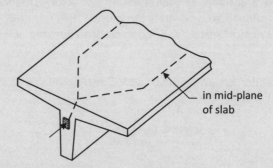

in mid-plane of slab

Fig. N18.13.5 Three dimensional effects in T-beam anchorage zone

N19 Shells and folded plates

N19.2.1

Linear elastic theory will usually provide an acceptable analytical model for determining internal forces. Cracking, local yielding of reinforcement under factored loads, and time-dependent effects (e.g., creep. shrinkage, thermal loading and load history) may lead to significant redistribution of the internal forces. This redistribution may be accounted for in the analysis. For shells and folded plates of unusual size, shape or complexity, the analysis should consider the full response of the structure from the elastic, uncracked state up to failure.

N19.2.3

The Finite Element Method is the most widely used numerical analysis procedure. Experience is required in selecting appropriate element types and sizes so that internal forces can be determined to the required degree of accuracy. Note that Clause 19.3.2 requires that the results of the analysis must be checked to ensure that the calculated internal forces are in equilibrium with the external loads.

N19.2.4

Analysis methods satisfying equilibrium and compatibility that include both membrane and bending effects are preferred. Approximate methods which satisfy statics but neglect strain compatibility should be used only when documented evidence exists of the reliability of the given method of analysis for the design of the specific type of shell or folded plate under consideration. Such methods include beam type analyses for barrel shells and folded plates having large ratios of span to either width or radius of curvature and membrane analyses for simple shells of revolution.

N19.2.5

Prestressed shell and folded plate structures must be designed to satisfy the requirements of Clause 18.

N19.2.6

The shell's thickness and reinforcement must be proportioned to resist the internal forces obtained from analysis (i.e. factored resistance ≥ factored load). In choosing shells thickness, attention should also be given to limiting deflections at specified loads, to providing the required concrete cover over reinforcement and to the practicalities of construction.

N19.2.7

The stability of thin shells is influenced by: (1) overall geometry, (2) geometric imperfections, (3) non-linear material properties, (4) creep and shrinkage of concrete, (5) cracking, (6) location, amount and orientation of reinforcement, and (7) deformation of supporting elements. Practical procedures for investigating the stability of shells is given in "Recommendations for Reinforced Concrete Shells and Folded Plates" (International Association of Shell and Spatial Structures, Madrid, 1979, 66 pp.), "Design and Construction of Circular Prestressed Concrete Structures (1970 report of ACI Committee 344, also in ACI Manual of Concrete Practice, Part 4), and "Concrete Shell Buckling", (SP67, ACI, 1981, 234 pp.).

N19.2.8

As shown in Fig. N19.2.8, reinforcement should be added near both faces to account for the possibility of moment reversals (see Clause 19.4.8).

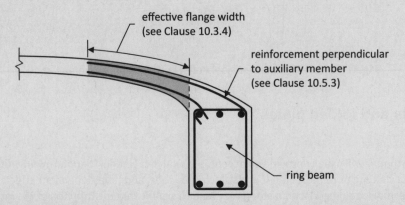

Fig. N19.2.8 Auxiliary member consisting of ring beam plus effective flange width

N19.4.1

At any point in a shell two different kinds of internal forces may occur simultaneously: those associated with membrane action, and those associated with bending of the shell (see Fig. N19.4.1). The membrane forces are assumed to act in the tangential plane mid-way between the surfaces of the shell, and are the two axial forces N_x and N_y, and the membrane shears, V_{xy}. Flexural effects include bending moments, M_x and M_y, twisting moment, T_{xy}, and the associated transverse shears, V_{xy} and V_{yz}, as shown in Fig. N19.4.1.

N19.4.2

Membrane reinforcement must be provided in at least two approximately orthogonal directions. In some highly stressed regions, it may be appropriate to utilize reinforcement in three directions.

N19.4.3

Minimum reinforcement corresponding to slab shrinkage and temperature reinforcement must be provided even if the calculated membrane forces are compressive. In regions subjected to significant tensile membrane forces the minimum reinforcement ratio of 0.002 traditionally used for slabs in flexure will be insufficient. Clause 19.4.8 suggests a minimum ratio of 0.0035 for these cases.

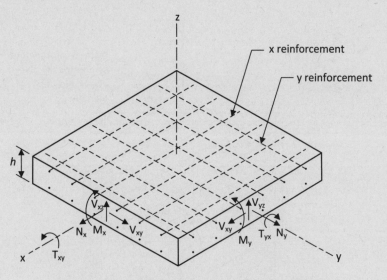

Fig. N19.4.1 Membrane actions and bending actions

N19.4.4

The reinforcement for an element subjected to membrane forces only can be designed using the principles of the Compression Field Theory described in Clause 11.4. The two sets of reinforcing bars are designed to carry the forces F_x and F_y, where:

$$F_x = N_x + \frac{|V_{xy}|}{tan\,\theta}$$

$$F_y = N_y + |V_{xy}|\,tan\,\theta$$

where all of the above actions are expressed in terms of force per unit length.

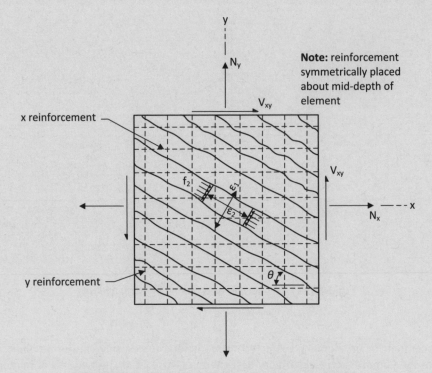

Fig. N19.4.4 Element subjected to membrane forces

N19.4.5
The principal compressive stress in the concrete, f_2, see Fig. N19.4.4, can be computed as:

$$f_2 = (tan\,\theta + \frac{1}{tan\,\theta})\frac{|V_{xy}|}{h}$$

To avoid crushing $f_2 \leq f_{2max}$ given in Clause 11.4.2.3 where f_{2max} is a function of the principal tensile strain ε_1.

N19.4.7
The practice of concentrating tensile reinforcement in the regions of maximum tensile stress has led to a number of successful designs primarily for long folded plates, long barrel vaulted shells and for domes. The requirement of providing the minimum reinforcement in the remaining tensile zone is intended to control cracking.

N19.4.8
One way of accounting for the interaction between bending effects and membrane effects is to model the shell element as a sandwich consisting of 2 outer reinforced concrete layers joined by an unreinforced middle layer acting as a shear connector. The applied forces and moments may be transformed into statistically equivalent membrane forces on the outer layers as shown in Fig. N19.4.8. Each layer is then designed for its resulting membrane forces by the procedures described under N19.4.4.

Bending moment diagrams for shells characteristically display a wavelike shape as the moments oscillate between positive and negative values over relatively short lengths of the shell. For this reason, equal amounts of bending reinforcement are to be placed near both outer surfaces of the shell.

Explanatory Notes on CSA A23.3-14

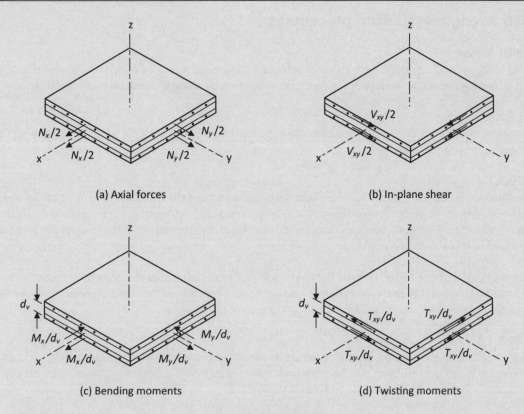

(a) Axial forces

(b) In-plane shear

(c) Bending moments

(d) Twisting moments

Fig. N19.4.8 Transforming sectional forces into statically equivalent membrane forces on outer reinforced concrete layers

N19.4.9

Transverse ties may be required to control splitting of the shell near its centre surface due to high transverse shears and/or transverse tensile stresses (see Fig. N19.4.9). Transverse tensile stresses may be increased by the presence of curved prestressing tendons.

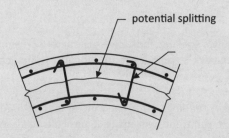

Fig. N19.4.9 Transverse ties to control shell splitting

N19.4.11 and N19.4.12

On curved shell surfaces it is more difficult to control the alignment of precut reinforcement. These clauses specify extra reinforcement lengths to maintain sufficient splice and development lengths.

N20 Strength evaluation procedures

N20.1 General
Load testing is not intended as a method of accepting designs known to be deficient. See also N20.2.3. It is generally preferable to carry out a structural evaluation by analysis rather than load testing.

N20.2.1
Guidance on determining in-situ concrete strength can be found in Annex A of CSA Standard A23.2 "Methods of Test for Concrete".

N20.2.3
The analysis must demonstrate that the intent of this Standard and the National Building Code has been satisfied. The intent of this Standard and NBC is to ensure public safety. In general it should be shown that the building will have a strength close to, or in excess of, that envisaged in the original design or as required by this Standard and NBC.

Commentary L of the 2015 National Building Code of Canada discusses the structural evaluation of existing buildings and allows a relaxation in load factors as a function of the completeness of the review process and the risk to human safety if the structure were to fail.

N20.3.1.1
The selection of the portion of the structure to be tested, pre-test preparation, testing, and the interpretation of the results should be done under the direction of a qualified engineer experienced in structural investigations, field tests, and measurements.

N20.3.1.3
Tests to investigate the shear resistance of precast members should simulate the effects of differential settlement, creep, shrinkage and temperature change based on a realistic assessment of such effects occurring in service.

When only a portion of the structural system is tested there is a high likelihood that some of the loads will be resisted by structural elements outside the loaded area. This should be considered in the selection of the area to be tested.

N20.3.1.9
Visible evidence of failure includes spalling, indicative of concrete crushing failure, cracks wide enough to indicate yielding of reinforcement or significant non-linearity in the load-deflection response.

N20.3.2.1
It is desirable to take deflection readings after each increment of load is added. These will help in assessing the resolution of the data and will make it possible to detect non-linear load-deflection response due to cracking or other causes.

N21 Special Provisions for Seismic Design

N21.1 Scope
Ground shaking due to a seismic event (earthquake) will cause a structure to deform. The magnitude of the resulting loads imparted on the structure will depend on the stiffness and the strength of the structure. Stiffer structures generally attract larger loads, while more flexible structures will be subjected to smaller loads. Structures with lower strengths will need to dissipate more seismic energy through "plastic" (non-linear) deformation, which requires the structure to be more ductile, i.e., to be able to maintain force resistance while deforming in the inelastic range. Observations of concrete building

performance during earthquakes and nonlinear analysis of concrete buildings has shown that buildings must possess an adequate combination of strength and ductility in order to withstand the effects of earthquake motions without collapsing. Buildings with more ductility can have a lower strength, while buildings with less ductility must have a higher strength.

The *National Building Code of Canada (NBCC)* Subsection 4.1.8 specifies the seismic demands on a linear structure. The factored design loads for earthquake are determined by dividing the loads on a linear structure by the ductility force reduction factor R_d and the overstrength force reduction factor R_o. NBCC defines a variety of concrete building types with different seismic-force-resisting systems that have a range of force reduction factors R_d and R_o. Clause 21 provides the design and detailing rules to achieve the corresponding levels of ductility. Many of the requirements in Clause 21 are written so as to explicitly account for the actual strength in determining the ductility requirements.

The product of R_d and R_o is as high as 6.8 for certain concrete structures. For the loading case including earthquake loads, all load factors are generally 1.0 except for some live loads (LL) where it is reduced to 0.5. The net result is that, unlike the design for all other types of loads where the design strength must be larger than the maximum expected load, the design strength for earthquake will be much less than the predicted maximum earthquake loads based on the analysis of a linear structure.

N21.2.1 Capacity design
Capacity design is an approach where the designer controls the inelastic mechanism of the structure by providing overstrength in certain parts of the structure. For example, additional strength can be provided in non-ductile elements to limit yielding to the ductile elements only; e.g., providing overstrength in columns to ensure yielding occurs primarily in the beams of a seismic-force-resisting frame. Another example of capacity design is to provide overstrength in order to avoid an undesirable failure mode such as shear failure of a wall. A simple analogy of this approach is a chain that is provided with ductile weak links to prevent failure of the stronger brittle links. As long as the weak links have sufficient ductility, the complete chain will have sufficient ductility. Thomas Paulay was a strong proponent of using capacity design for the seismic design of concrete structures, and further reading on this subject can be found in his book.[21.1]

N21.2.2 Seismic-force-resisting systems
The design and detailing rules in Clause 21 cover the standard seismic-force-resisting systems (SFRS) given in Table 4.1.8.9 of 2015 NBCC. The 15 different concrete SFRS given NBCC are summarized in Table N21.2.2. The 14 standard systems (not including 'Other') come in three levels of ductility. For cast-in-place reinforced concrete frames and walls, the three levels of ductility are: ductile, moderately ductile and conventional construction. There are three types of concrete wall systems: coupled, partially coupled and shear walls (cantilever walls); however the distinction between the three wall systems is not made for conventional construction. Note that conventional construction is not an accurate name as Clause 21.6 contains significant seismic design requirements for these systems. Tilt-up concrete construction also comes in three levels of ductility; but in this case moderately ductile, limited ductility and conventional, where the latter refers to a system with no special seismic design requirements.

The design and detailing requirements given in Clause 21 were developed for standard SFRS that are substantially uniform in strength and stiffness over the building height so that the uniform inelastic mechanisms shown in Fig. N.21.2.2 will develop. The black dots in the figure identify the locations of hinges (inelastic rotation). When systems are not substantially uniform over the building height or where combinations of systems are employed or unclassified systems are used, nonlinear analysis is needed, for example, to determine if the inelastic rotational demand at any point exceeds the inelastic rotational capacity provided. This does not necessarily mean complex nonlinear analysis by computer, but it does mean consideration of issues beyond what can be determined from a linear analysis. Linear analysis can be used to determine the total displacement demand of the SFRS if the appropriate effective section properties are used (see Clause 21.2.5.2). Linear analysis can also be used to determine a set of design forces that satisfy equilibrium; but consideration needs to be given to how the force distribution will change when the structure is in the inelastic range. Linear analysis cannot be used to determine the concentration of inelastic action in certain portions of the structure, and this is the most important reason for requiring a nonlinear analysis.

Table N21.2.2
Concrete seismic-force-resisting systems (SFRS) designed and detailed according to CSA A23.3 Clause 21 (adapted from 2015 National Building Code of Canada Table 4.1.8.9).

Type of SFRS	$R_d{}^{(1)}$	$R_o{}^{(2)}$	Restrictions[3] – Cases Where:				
			$I_E F_a S_a\,(0.2)$				$I_E F_v S_a\,(1.0)$
			< 0.2	≥ 0.2; < 0.35	≥ 0.35; ≤ 0.75	> 0.75	> 0.3
Ductile:							
Moment-resisting frames	4.0	1.7	NL	NL	NL	NL	NL
Coupled walls	4.0	1.7	NL	NL	NL	NL	NL
Partially coupled walls	3.5	1.7	NL	NL	NL	NL	NL
Shear walls	3.5	1.6	NL	NL	NL	NL	NL
Moderately ductile:							
Moment-resisting frames	2.5	1.4	NL	NL	60	40	40
Coupled walls	2.5	1.4	NL	NL	NL	60	60
Partially coupled walls	2.0	1.4	NL	NL	NL	60	60
Shear walls	2.0	1.4	NL	NL	NL	60	60
Conventional construction:							
Moment-resisting frames	1.5	1.3	NL	NL	20	15	10[4]
Shear walls	1.5	1.3	NL	NL	40	30	30
Two-way slabs without beams	1.3	1.3	20	15	NP	NP	NP
Tilt-up Construction:							
Moderately ductile walls & frames	2.0	1.3	30	25	25	25	25
Limited ductility walls & frames	1.5	1.3	30	25	20	20	20[5]
Conventional walls & frames	1.3	1.3	25	20	NP	NP	NP
Other concrete SFRS(s) not above	1.0	1.0	15	15	NP	NP	NP

[1] R_d = Ductility-related force modification factor.
[2] R_o = Overstrength-related force modification factor.
[3] Numbers are maximum height limits above grade in metres; NL = No height limit; NP = Not permitted.
[4] Frames limited to a maximum of 2 storeys.
[5] Frames limited to a maximum of 3 storeys.
Note: The most stringent requirement governs.

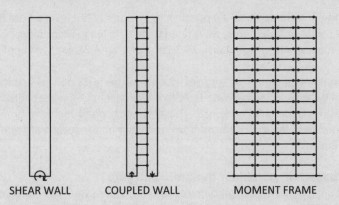

SHEAR WALL   COUPLED WALL   MOMENT FRAME

Fig. N21.2.2 Inelastic mechanisms in the three main types of seismic-force-resisting systems.

For many situations, the inelastic analysis that is needed can be done using relatively simple calculations. Clause 21.5.7 and 21.5.8 provide rational procedures that can be extrapolated to ensure the inelastic rotational demands in concrete walls will not exceed inelastic rotation capacities. The inelastic analysis that is needed to develop the expression for inelastic rotation demand in a uniform shear wall is given in N21.5.7.2. These procedures can be modified to account for different situations. For example, if a concrete wall system is not uniform over the full height of a structure (perhaps larger in section at the bottom), the designer could decide to use a capacity design approach to force yielding to occur at a higher elevation in the building. Equation (21-11) would then need to be modified to account for the actual height of the wall above the centre of the plastic hinge. Note that as the height of hinge formation increases, the inelastic rotation demand increases. The procedures given in Clause 21.5.7.3 for determining the inelastic rotational capacities of walls are general enough to be applied to such situations as well.

Where two recognized systems are employed in parallel, the need for special studies depends on whether they have similar inelastic mechanisms. Frames typically deform beyond the linear range in a beam-hinging shear-sway mechanism with hinges developing at multiple levels. Cantilever shear walls, on the other hand, deform with a single flexural wall hinge usually near the base. Two or more wall systems, even if they include coupled walls, have similar final mechanisms – flexural hinge at the plastic hinge level. An example of two recognized systems with very different inelastic mechanisms is a shear wall and a frame employed in parallel. The typical elastic analysis that is used to determine how the two systems share the lateral load at each floor level is not valid once the building enters the inelastic range. Concrete floor slabs usually enforce compatible deformations between the two systems so the frame must follow the plastic deformations of the wall over the wall's plastic hinge length. This means either the frame must be strong enough to prevent plastic rotations in the wall (not likely), or the frame columns must be able to undergo the same curvature as the wall's inelastic curvature over the height of the wall plastic hinge. When shear walls and frames are used as a combined system, the frame columns need to have a deformation capacity that is greater than the deformation demand. Clause 21.11 provides simple procedures for estimating the deformation demands on gravity-load frames that are interconnected with concrete shear walls.

Discontinuous systems should be avoided if possible as extremely high inelastic demands can occur near the discontinuities. This can lead to collapse of the structure under the design earthquake or can cause large damage due to the motions from a frequent (smaller) earthquake. Wall systems that are not continuous from their top to the foundation are only allowed by NBCC in restricted circumstances and should be avoided. Frames are not subject to the same restrictions in NBCC; but such systems must meet the additional requirements of Clause 21.2.2. Where walls or frames are not continuous from the foundation to the top of the main roof of a building, an alternative to an inelastic analysis would be to treat the continuing elements as if a plastic hinge occurs at the level where the other element(s) terminate. For the continuing elements, walls need to be detailed in accordance with Clause 21.5.2.1.4 and frames in accordance with either Clause 21.3.2.6.6 or Clause 21.4.4.5, as applicable.

Buildings that have induced lateral or torsional forces in the SFRS due to gravity loading cannot be considered uniform systems. Buildings with lateral or torsional forces in the SFRS due to gravity loading will have magnified inelastic deformations. These systems need inelastic time history analysis to determine if the combined inelastic deformations under simultaneous gravity and seismic loading are within acceptable limits.

N21.2.3 Design based on nonlinear dynamic analysis

Nonlinear dynamic analysis is increasingly being used in the United States for the so-called 'performance-based' seismic design of concrete buildings. A very important part of that process is the role played by the qualified independent peer review panel. If nonlinear dynamic analysis is used for the basis of a design according to CSA A23.3, the analysis and resulting design must also be reviewed by a qualified independent peer review panel. The following are the requirements for such a review panel (adapted from the 2011 LATBSDC Alternative Analysis and Design Procedure).

A qualified independent peer review panel (PRP) shall be convened to provide an independent, objective, technical review of those aspects of the structural design of the building that relate to seismic performance. The PRP participation is not intended to replace quality assurance measures ordinarily exercised by the Engineer of Record (EOR) in the structural design of a building. The PRP should include a minimum of three members with recognized expertise in relevant fields, such as structural engineering, earthquake engineering research, performance-based earthquake engineering, nonlinear dynamic response analysis, concrete building design, earthquake ground motion, geotechnical engineering, and other such areas of knowledge and experience relevant to the issues in the project. PRP members shall bear no conflict of interest with respect to the project and shall not be part of the design team for the project.

The general scope of services for the PRP shall include review of the following: earthquake hazard determination, ground motion characterizations, seismic design methodology, seismic performance goals, acceptance criteria, mathematical modeling and simulation, seismic design and results, drawings and specifications. The PRP should be convened as early in the structural design phase as practicable to afford the PRP opportunity to evaluate fundamental design decisions that could disrupt design development if addressed later in the design phase. Early in the design phase, the EOR and the PRP should jointly establish the frequency and timing of PRP review milestones, and the degree to which the EOR anticipates the design will be developed for each milestone. The PRP shall provide written comments to the EOR, and the EOR shall prepare written responses thereto. The PRP shall maintain a log that summarizes PRP comments, EOR responses to comments, and resolution of comments.

N21.2.5.2

A number of the seismic design requirements depend on the predicted displacements of the structure. Thus the section properties that are to be used to predict displacements are specified. Due to the variation of concrete cracking from one section to another and the variation of cracking as the lateral load is increased, the response of concrete structures is generally nonlinear. The reduction factors provided in this clause are the single average value to be used for the entire structure in a linear analysis used to estimate the displacement demand.

For columns, the effective moment of inertia I_e depends on the level of axial compression due to gravity load P_s applied to the member as given by Equation 21.1. For walls, the effective stiffness depends only on the ratio of the elastic bending moment demand M_e to the nominal moment resistance M_n (both calculated at the section with the maximum elastic bending moment demand).[21.2] In Equation 21.2, the flexural strength ratio is expressed as $R_d R_o / \gamma_w$. Note that the factored bending moment $M_f = M_e R_d R_o$, while the wall overstrength factor $\gamma_w = M_n / M_f$. Thus $R_d R_o / \gamma_w = M_e / M_n$.

The effective stiffness of concrete shear walls was previously thought to be primarily related to the level of axial compression similar to columns. Recent research[21.2] has demonstrated that while axial compression reduces the amount of flexural cracking and hence results in a more linear loading curve, it also closes the flexural cracks when the lateral load levels are reduced during lateral load reversals. This reduces the amount of hysteretic energy dissipation that occurs, which results in larger displacements. The flexural strength ratio given in Equation 21.2 reflects the level of damage and hence softening of the wall that will occur during an earthquake.[21.2]

For multiple wall segments, a single reduction factor based on an average value of elastic bending moment demand to nominal moment resistance may be used to estimate the overall effective stiffness of the structure. However, if separate cantilever walls have significantly different stiffnesses and significantly different flexural strength ratios, separate reduction factors should be used.

The flexural stiffness of a coupled wall system depends on the axial stiffness of the walls, and thus the axial stiffnesses of walls need to be reduced to account for cracking using the same reduction factor as the flexural stiffness of cantilever walls.

Shear deformations of coupling beams must be included in the analysis of coupled wall systems, and effective shear areas A_{ve} are given for coupling beams in order to account for the influence of diagonal cracking. Coupling beams with diagonal reinforcement (Clause 21.5.8.2) have better diagonal crack control; but less effective flexural crack control compared to coupling beams with conventional reinforcement (21.5.8.1). The combined effect of the shear and flexural reduction factors given in Table 21.1 are similar to the effect of single reduction factors on flexural rigidities that have been suggested.[21.1] To account for strain penetration into the ends of adjoining walls, the length of coupling beams should be taken as 20% longer than the clear span of the beams.

N21.2.5.3
The R_d portion of inelastic deformations must be included in the stability design of sway frames. See also NBCC Commentary.

N21.2.6.1
Research[21.3] has shown that with the appropriate detailing specified in Clause 21, ductile behaviour can be achieved with concrete having a compressive strength up to 80 MPa.

N21.2.7.1.1
Reinforcement complying with the weldable grade requirements of CSA G30.18 has a more closely controlled chemical composition which results in a more predictable and more ductile stress-strain response. Use of reinforcement with yield strength higher than that assumed in design will lead to higher shear and bond stress at the development of yield moments. This may lead to unexpected brittle failures and hence should be avoided. These more stringent requirements on the properties of the reinforcing steel are not necessary for lateral load resisting systems designed with a modification factor, R_d of 2.5 or less.

N21.2.7.2 Lap splices
Lateral force resisting elements are expected to develop their yield capacity and deform inelastically under the action of seismic forces. Under these circumstances all reinforcement provided is expected to yield and must therefore be spliced for full tension capacity.

N21.2.7.3.1

Type 2 mechanical splices are required to develop the minimum tensile strength of the reinforcement to ensure the bar will yield prior to failure of the splice. CSA G30.18 defines the minimum tensile strength of Grade 400 reinforcement (minimum yield strength = 400 MPa) as 540 MPa; but not less than 1.15 times the actual yield strength.

N21.2.7.4.2

Welding or tack welding of crossing reinforcing bars can lead to local embrittlement of the steel. If such welding is needed to facilitate fabrication it must be done only on additional bars added expressly for this purpose. Welding performed to splice bars using a controlled procedure with adequate inspection is permitted.

N21.2.8.2

The traditional ratio of spiral reinforcement for columns is given by Eq. 10-7. Round columns that are large or have high axial loading will require the larger ρ_s given by Eq. 21-3. Note that ρ_s was mistakenly written as P_s in equation 21.3. This will be corrected in a future update to the Standard. A new relation described by Eq. 21-4 has been introduced for rectangular columns, adding consideration of the effect of axial loading and reinforcement arrangement. Removing the "k"s from Eq. 21-4 gives the following equation where you can see the terms that affect the steel quantity.

$$A_{sh} = \left(0.15 \, or \, 0.2\right) \frac{n_\ell}{\left(n_\ell - 2\right)} \frac{P_f}{P_0} \frac{A_g}{A_{ch}} \frac{f'_c}{f_{yh}} sh_c$$

The term 0.15 or 0.2 is a coefficient, $\dfrac{n_\ell}{\left(n_\ell - 2\right)}$ is the bar arrangement, $\dfrac{P_f}{P_0}$ is the axial load level, $\dfrac{A_g}{A_{ch}}$ is the ratio of the gross concrete area to the concrete area within the ties, $\dfrac{f'_c}{f_{yh}}$ is the ratio of the concrete strength to tie strength, s is the tie spacing and h_c is the hoop dimension.

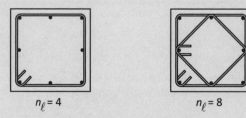

$n_\ell = 4$ $n_\ell = 8$

Fig. N21.2.8.2 Definition of n_l

N21.3 Ductile moment-resisting frames (R_d = 4.0)

In the previous edition of this Standard, the requirements for ductile moment-resisting frames were separated into three clauses that deal with beams (21.3), columns (21.4) and joints (21.5). All requirements for ductile moment-resisting frames have been amalgimated into this one clause.

N21.3.1.1

Frame members subjected to significant axial compression have different behaviour and must be designed and detailed according to the requirements for columns in Clause 21.3.2.

N21.3.1.3.1 and N21.3.1.3.2

These Clauses ensure continuity of reinforcement and some positive and negative moment capacity throughout the beam to allow for unexpected deformations and moment redistributions from severe earthquake loading. The reinforcement limits are intended to ensure that the section displays adequate ductility. The upper limit of 0.025 is to avoid excessive steel congestion and excessive joint shear stresses.

N21.3.1.3.3
Lap splices are unreliable for inelastic cyclic loading and hence are not permitted within the plastic hinge regions of beams.

N21.3.1.4.1
These hoops are intended to prevent buckling of the longitudinal bars in the compression zone in plastic hinge regions where both the top and bottom reinforcement can be subjected to yielding in tension and compression due to reversed cyclic flexure. Bars that buckle in compression and are subsequently stressed to yield in tension usually rupture.

N21.3.1.4.1
(b) When a plastic hinge region is deliberately relocated away from the column then hoop reinforcement must be provided within and adjacent to the plastic hinge region.

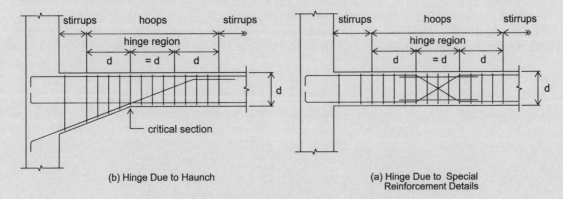

(b) Hinge Due to Haunch

(a) Hinge Due to Special Reinforcement Details

Fig. N21.3.1.4.1 Plastic hinges located away from column faces

N21.3.1.4.5
The need for hoops in other regions of the beam where only positive moment hinging can occur is a matter of judgement. In these regions the danger of buckling of the top compression bars is far less since these bars will never have yielded in tension in a previous load cycle. Bottom longitudinal bars that are not subjected to compression need not be laterally supported to prevent buckling.

N21.3.2.4 Minimum flexural resistance of columns
The energy dissipation necessary for a multi-storey frame to survive a severe earthquake should in general occur by the formation of ductile plastic hinges in beams (see Fig. N21.3.2.4(b)). Plastic hinges in beams are capable of tolerating larger rotations than hinges in columns. Further, as can be seen from Fig. N21.3.2.4(b), mechanisms involving beam hinges cause energy to be dissipated at many locations throughout the frame. An additional consideration is that extensive hinging in columns (see Fig. N21.3.2.4(a)) may critically reduce the gravity load carrying capacity of the structure.

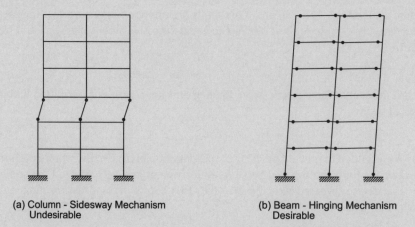

(a) Column - Sidesway Mechanism
   Undesirable

(b) Beam - Hinging Mechanism
   Desirable

Fig. N21.3.2.4 Inelastic mechanisms in moment-resisting frames

N21.3.2.4.2

To achieve the desired beam hinging mechanism, the Standard specifies a "strong column-weak beam" design approach. Eq. (21-6) requires that the total nominal resistance of the columns must be greater than the total probable resistance, based on $\phi_s = 1.25$, of the beams framing into the joint.

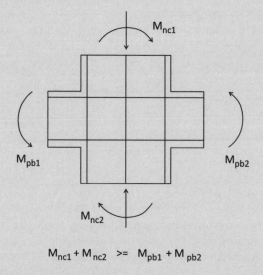

$$M_{nc1} + M_{nc2} \geq M_{pb1} + M_{pb2}$$

Fig. N21.4.2.2 Strong column – weak beam requirement

N21.3.2.5.1

The lower limit addresses the concern for the effects of time-dependent deformation of columns and the desire to have post-cracking capacity. The upper limit reflects concern for steel congestion.

N21.3.2.5.2

Because spalling of the shell concrete in the high moment regions near the ends of columns will reduce the capacity of lap splices, such splices must be located near the mid-height of columns and be contained within confinement reinforcing.

N21.3.2.6.3
The spacing limits are intended to provide a minimum degree of confinement of the core and also to provide lateral support for the longitudinal reinforcing bars.

N21.3.2.6.4
Fig. N21.3.2.6.4 illustrates the requirements of this clause.

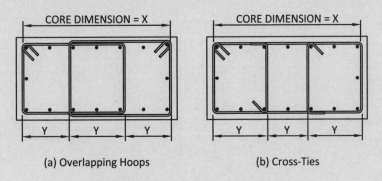

(a) Overlapping Hoops   (b) Cross-Ties

If X ≤ 600 mm then Y ≤ 200 mm
If X > 600 mm then Y ≤ X/3 but ≤ 350 mm

Fig. N21.3.2.6.4

N21.3.2.6.5
The figure illustrates the requirements of this clause.

ℓ_o not less than $\dfrac{L_{clear}}{6}$

and $\ell_o = 1.5\ Col_{max}$ when $P_f \le 0.5\phi_c f_c' A_g$

and $\ell_o = 2.0\ Col_{max}$ when $P_f > 0.5\phi_c f_c' A_g$

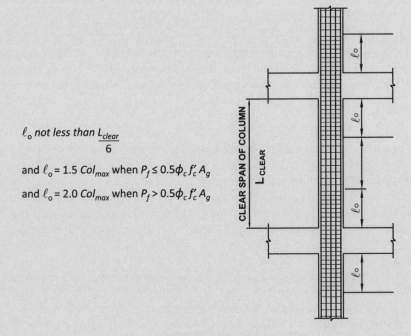

Fig. N21.3.2.6.5

N21.3.2.6.6
It is important to appreciate that during a severe earthquake some column hinging (e.g. at the base of the column in Fig 21.4.2(b)) and some yielding of columns will occur even if the "strong column-weak

beam" philosophy has been followed. For this reason columns, need to be detailed for ductility in accordance with the requirement of Clause 21.3.2.6.6.

N21.3.3.1.2
Fig. N21.3.3.1.2 illustrates the procedure for determining the factored shear in joints of ductile frames. The 1.25 factor is intended to account for the expected (higher than specified) yield stress in the bars when plastic hinges form in the beams.

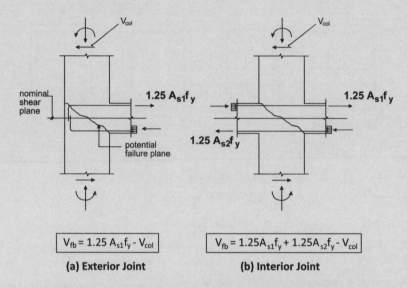

$$V_{fb} = 1.25\ A_{s1}f_y - V_{col}$$

(a) Exterior Joint

$$V_{fb} = 1.25A_{s1}f_y + 1.25A_{s2}f_y - V_{col}$$

(b) Interior Joint

Fig. N21.3.3.1.2 Determining factored shear force in joints

N21.3.3.2.1 and N21.3.3.2.2
Regardless of the magnitude of the calculated shear force in a joint, confining reinforcement must be provided through the joint around the column reinforcement. This confining reinforcement may be reduced if horizontal members framing into all four sides of the joint provide sufficient external confinement.

N21.3.3.2.3
This Clause may apply in situations where beams are wider than columns.

N21.3.3.3 Longitudinal column reinforcement
Confinement of the joint core is provided by the cage formed from the longitudinal steel and the corresponding hoops and ties. Depending on the size of the column the maximum spacing between adjacent longitudinal bars is between 200 mm (Clause 21.3.3.3) and 350 mm (Clause 21.3.2.6.4).

N21.3.3.4 Shear resistance of joints
The shear force is transferred through a joint by diagonal compressive struts in the concrete acting together with tensile forces in the vertical reinforcing bars. Rather than calculating the required amount of joint shear reinforcement, the approach taken is that a joint containing transverse and longitudinal reinforcement satisfying Clauses 21.3.3.2 and 21.3.3.3 will have the factored shear resistance given in this clause.

N21.3.3.5.2
35M bars and smaller can be anchored with standard 90 deg. hooks. The development lengths for bars with $f_y = 400$ MPa are:

Bar Size	X (mm)	ℓ_{dh} (mm)				
		f'_c MPa				
		20	25	30	35	40
10M	44	179	160	150	150	150
15M	64	268	240	219	203	190
20M	80	358	320	292	270	253
25M	100	447	400	365	338	316
30M	150	537	480	438	406	379
35M	216	626	560	511	473	443

These lengths were determined by considering the beneficial effects of confinement which must be present. See Fig. N21.3.3.5.2 for illustration of the case.

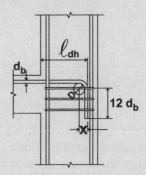

Fig. N21.3.3.5.2 Values of development lengths for hooked bars with f_y = 400 MPa anchored in confined column cores

N21.3.3.5.6
A straight bar passing through a beam-column joint may be subjected to tension on one side of the joint and compression on the other side of the joint (see Fig. N21.5.1.2). Limiting the bar diameter to $\ell/24$ of the joint length provides some control of the bond stresses.

N21.4.3.1
Continuity of reinforcement and some positive and negative moment capacity throughout the beam is required to allow for unexpected deformations and moment distributions from severe earthquake loading.

N21.4.3.2
Closely spaced stirrups in regions of potential inelastic action are required to prevent buckling of reinforcement under compression.

N21.4.4.2
The requirement for columns to be stronger than beams similar to 21.3.2.4.2 for R_d = 4.0 frames is new in this edition of the Standard.

N21.4.4.5
Closely spaced column ties are required in regions of potential inelastic action. Plastic hinges can be expected to develop in ground floor columns or in columns of storeys adjacent to a substantial change in structural stiffness.

N21.4.5 Shear in frames

The factored shear resistance for beams and columns shall be based on member capacities not factored load effects so that flexural yielding will occur prior to shear failure. An upper limit is introduced corresponding to an elastic response level.

N21.4.6 Joints in frames

The design of Moderately Ductile Frame Joints is similar, in general, to the approach for joints in Ductile Frames as discussed in N21.3.3 but with the following modifications.

N21.4.6.1 Design shear force

Clause 21.4.6.1 is similar to 21.3.3.12 except nominal reinforcement strengths are used to determine forces in the joint instead of probable strengths.

N21.4.6.2 Factored shear resistance

Clause 21.4.6 is similar to Clause 21.3.3.4 except the joint factored shear resistance is reduced because the amount of transverse reinforcement required by Clause 21.4.6.3 is less than that required by Clause 21.3.3.2. See N21.4.6.3

N21.4.6.3 Transverse reinforcement

Transverse reinforcement in the columns is run through the joint and is determined by the confinement reinforcement formulae for Moderately Ductile Columns and this provides less reinforcement than that for Ductile Columns.

N21.4.6.5 Maximum bar size for bars going through the joint

Clause 21.4.6.5 allows a larger bar through the joint than that for a ductile column joint as the non-linear demand is less. Development lengths for hooked or straight bars developed within the joint are as per Chapter 12.

N21.5.1.1 Minimum requirements

All requirements in Clause 21 for walls that were redundant with the requirements of Clause 14 have been removed from Clause 21 for the 2014 edition. Thus it is important that all shear walls meet the minimum requirements given in Clause 14. In particular, see Clause 14.1.6 Transfer of horizontal wall forces across construction joints, Clause 14.1.7 Minimum thickness of walls, Clause 14.1.8 Details of wall reinforcement, and Clause 14.4.3.3 for effective flange widths of walls.

N21.5.1.3 Walls with multi-level openings

Clause 21.5.8 specifies additional requirements for coupled wall systems, and it is important that these requirements are satisfied if a wall system may act as a coupled wall. The question sometimes arises whether a wall system with multiple openings can be designed as a cantilever wall. The analysis to determine whether the wall segments above and below the openings have adequate stiffness and strength to ensure the wall will act similar to a cantilever wall is complex. The horizontal wall segments (coupling beams) experience extremely high demands during an earthquake and significant damage is expected in these members even at small global displacement demands. Thus the definition of when a wall with openings at multiple levels may be designed as a single cantilever wall has been made simpler and more restrictive in the current edition of CSA A23.3. It is important to note however the additional requirements for coupled walls in Clause 21.5.8 have been relaxed in the current edition of CSA A23.3, and a new system, moderately ductile coupled walls, with less onerous design requirements has been added.

N21.5.1.4 Squat walls

Walls with a height-to-length ratio as low as 1.0 may develop a flexural failure mechanism; however such a wall will likely not develop a ductile flexural hinge. Thus all walls with a height-to-length ratio equal to or less than 2.0 must meet the special design requirements for squat walls given in Clause 21.5.10.

N21.5.1.5 Tilt-up and precast walls
New requirements for tilt-up walls have been introduced in Clause 21.7 and these can also be used design precast walls with some limitations.

N21.5.2 Requirements for strength and ductility over height
This new clause spells out in detail the requirements for plastic hinging (ductility) and the design forces (shear and bending moment) over the height of the shear wall.

N21.5.2.1 Plastic hinge regions in walls
It is very important that the special detailing required for the plastic hinge regions of walls be provided wherever yielding may occur in walls. When a building is substantially uniform, it is possible to design a wall so that there is one well-defined plastic hinge region near the base of the building.

In the plastic hinge region of a wall, the inelastic curvatures and inelastic tension strains in the vertical reinforcement typically vary linearly from a maximum value at the critical section (normally where the vertical reinforcement first yields) to zero.[21.4] For simplicity, the inelastic curvatures and inelastic tension strains are usually assumed to be uniform and equal to the actual maximum value when relating wall displacements to wall strains such as in the analysis done in Clause 21.5.7. The idealized plastic hinge with assumed uniform inelastic curvatures and uniform inelastic tension strains has an idealized length – the so-called plastic hinge length – that is about half the actual vertical length (height) that the inelastic curvatures and inelastic strains vary linearly. That is, the idealized plastic hinge length used in the analysis in Clause 21.5.7 is about half the actual length over which special detailing is required because of inelastic curvatures.

Bohl and Adebar[21.4] developed the following expression for the idealized plastic hinge length (length of assumed uniform inelastic curvatures) in a shear wall:

$$\ell_p = 0.2\ell_w + 0.05 \, (M/V) \, (1 - 1.5P/f'_c A_g) \le 0.8\ell_w$$

where ℓ_w is the length of the wall, M/V is the bending moment to shear ratio at the critical section (typically base of wall), and P is the axial compression force applied to the wall. A safe (larger than actual) estimate of plastic hinge length results from assuming no axial compression applied to the wall and M/V is equal to the height of the wall h_w. Thus a safe estimate of the plastic hinge length is given by:

$$\ell_p = 0.2\ell_w + 0.05h_w$$

The expression given in Clause 21.5.2.1.2 for the minimum height of the plastic hinge region, where special detailing is required, is essentially twice this value. In the previous edition of CSA A23.3, the minimum height of the plastic hinge region was $1.5\ell_w$. Thus the new expression in Clause 21.5.2.1.2 provides a relaxation of the requirements when the height-to-length ratio h_w/ℓ_w is less than 10.

When walls of different length are tied together by multiple floor slabs, the plastic hinge length will be essentially equal in all the walls, i.e., the inelastic curvatures will be concentrated over a similar height in all walls.[21.4] While a weighted average wall length provides the best estimate of plastic hinge length,[21.4] the longest wall or wall segment in the direction under consideration is used to ensure the length of special detailing is safe.

N21.5.2.2.2 Design for bending moment at base

The properties of the wall cross section, such as geometry, concrete strength and reinforcing steel, need to be relatively uniform over the plastic hinge region in order for the inelastic curvatures to spread thereby reducing the strain demands at any one section. Large wall openings in the plastic hinge region of a wall may cause a concentration of the inelastic curvatures over a much smaller height of the wall and consequently cause very large strain demands in the concrete and vertical reinforcement. Small openings that do not significantly influence the calculated flexural capacity will have much less influence.

A design approach that has been used to deal with difficult architecture is to provide flexural overstrength in the walls over a portion of a building that has aspects making it undesirable as the region of plastic hinging. For example, increased flexural strength has been provided near the base of the wall in order to force yielding higher up in the structure. This is an application of the capacity design approach discussed in N21.2.1. In calculating the required overstrength, it is important to note that vertical reinforcement in the plastic hinge region may develop very large tension stresses due to strain hardening of the steel. As described in N21.2.7.3.1, Grade 400 reinforcement meeting CSA G30.18 has a minimum tensile strength of 540 MPa, and tension stresses over 600 MPa ($1.5f_y$) may develop in Grade 400 reinforcement at large tension strains in the plastic hinge region.

As discussed in N21.5.2.1, as walls in buildings are normally tied together by multiple (rigid) floor slabs, the inelastic curvature profiles in the walls must be very similar.[21.4] Thus all walls in one direction must have the plastic hinge region located at the same elevation.

N21.5.2.2.3 Design for bending moment above plastic hinge at base

The bending moment envelope used to design the vertical reinforcement above the plastic hinge region must be adjusted to account for the actual flexural overstrength at the top of the plastic hinge region. Once the geometry of the wall and all the vertical reinforcement in the plastic hinge region (both concentrated and distributed reinforcement) has been established, the factored bending moment resistance of the wall can be determined. The overstrength is the ratio of factored bending moment resistance to the factored bending moment demand. Fig. N21.5.2.2.3 illustrates the initial bending moment envelope determined from a dynamic analysis, the factored bending moment resistance over the plastic hinge region of the wall, and the adjusted bending moment envelope accounting for overstrength. Fig. N21.5.2.2.3 also illustrates the bending moment envelope to be used when the equivalent static procedure is used to determine the design forces. Note that it is not necessary to increase the bending moment envelope so as to eliminate all possibility of some yielding in the wall above the plastic hinge because the curvature demands will generally be small in the upper portions of the wall[21.5] and new requirements have been added to ensure a minimum level of curvature capacity above the plastic hinge region in Clause 21.5.7.1.1.

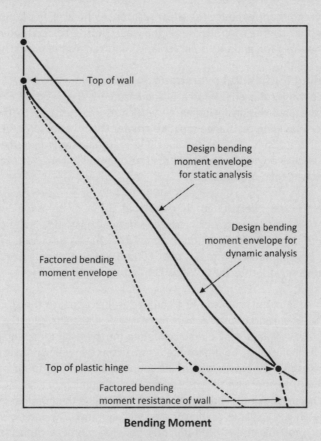

Fig. N21.5.2.2.3: Factored bending moment envelopes.

N21.5.2.2.4 Design for bending moment below plastic hinge at base

Concrete walls are often supported below the plastic hinge region by stiff floor diaphragms connected to other walls such as perimeter foundation walls. The overturning moment in the full-height (tower) walls can be transferred down to the foundation below the wall; or can be transferred to the other walls by force couples in two or more floor diaphragms. When a large portion of the overturning moment in the tower walls is transferred by force couples in two or more diaphragms, the shear force (bending moment gradient) in the tower walls reverses below the flexural hinge. If damage due to flexural yielding occurs in the tower walls below the diaphragms, the mechanism transferring the overturning moment to the foundation will become more flexible and thus the overturning moment will be resisted mostly by the force couples in the diaphragms. This will result in larger reverse shear forces in the walls that could result in a shear failure of the wall.[21.6] Thus it is important that flexural yielding not occur in the walls between the stiff diaphragms. Additional discussion of this topic is given in N21.5.2.2.9.

N21.5.2.2.5 Design for shear force at base

In order for a concrete wall to dissipate energy in a flexural mode, shear failure must be prevented. If a wall has excess flexural strength, i.e., overstrength, the shear strength must be correspondingly increased. The increase for inelastic effects of higher modes is a separate increase; but is dependent on much the design shear force is less than the elastic demand. That is, as the shear force is increased because of flexural overstrength, the additional amplification required to account for inelastic effects of higher modes is reduced.[21.7]

Openings in a wall may significantly reduce the shear resistance of a wall. In particular, an opening will restrict the flow of diagonal compression stresses in the wall. Clause 21.5.9.3 requires that the effect of openings in wall be accounted for, and this is particularly important in the plastic hinge region.

N21.5.2.2.6 Accounting for flexural overstrength

For moderately ductile walls, the shear force is increased by the ratio of the nominal bending resistance (based on the final design including all vertical reinforcement) to the factored bending moment. As the factored bending resistance must be greater than the factored bending moment, the nominal overstrength is the result of using the specified material strengths rather than the factored material strengths, as well as any excess bending resistance coming from, for example, extra vertical reinforcement or larger wall than required.

For ductile walls, the flexural overstrength is calculated using a stress of $1.25f_y$ in the vertical reinforcement in order to provide a greater factor of safety against shear failure in these members which are designed with larger force reduction factors. Note that as discussed in N21.5.2.2.2, Grade 400 reinforcement my develop tension stresses over 600 MPa ($1.5f_y$) when subjected to large tension strains in the plastic hinge region, thus the $1.25f_y$ is not an upper-bound value.

The overturning (bending moment) capacity of a coupled wall is equal to the sum of the overturning moment resisted by the (equal and opposite) axial forces in the wall piers, plus the sum of the bending moment capacities of the individual wall piers accounting for the axial force applied to the wall pier. The axial forces in the wall piers may be determined from linear dynamic analysis (in order to account for higher modes) increased by the ratio of sum of coupling beam nominal or probable capacity, as given in Clause 21.5.2.2.6, to the sum of factored forces in coupling beams over the height of the structure. The flexural capacities of the individual wall piers shall be the nominal or probable values as appropriate depending on the R_d value of the coupled wall systems. The ratio of nominal-to-factored (moderately ductile) or probable-to-factored (ductile) bending moment capacities of coupled walls, calculated by summing all contributions, shall be used to calculate a single factor used to increase the total shear applied to the coupled wall system. Note that as no additional shear magnification factor is applied to coupled walls to account for inelastic effects of higher modes, it is important to accurately determine the magnification of the shear due to flexural overstrength. In a highly-coupled wall, most of the overturning resistance comes from the equal and opposite axial forces in the outer two wall piers. Thus the flexural overstrength of such a wall system depends mainly on the increase in the axial forces in the outer wall piers. The axial forces resisting overturning may be limited either by the capacity of the coupling beams or the quantity of vertical reinforcement that resists the uplift force in excess of the gravity load acting on the tension wall pier. As the wall piers are all tied together by the closely spaced floor slabs, the bending resistance of the individual wall piers must be calculated at similar curvature levels. The increase in bending resistance of the individual wall piers usually makes a small contribution to the increase in bending resistance of the wall system.

N21.5.2.2.7 Accounting for inelastic effects of higher modes

A linear dynamic analysis is normally used to determine the factored forces on concrete walls. Such an analysis can be used to estimate the ratio of maximum bending moment to maximum shear force prior to flexural yielding of the wall. As the level of ground shaking increases, the maximum bending moment is limited once a flexural hinge forms in a concrete wall; but the shear force will continue to increase significantly. A flexural hinge will limit the maximum shear force in a single degree-of-freedom system where the bending moment is due to a single lateral (shear) force ($M = V \times h$); but will not limit the shear force in a multi-degree of freedom system such as a cantilever shear wall. This concept is illustrated in Fig. N21.5.2.2.7 where the mode shapes and shear force envelopes are compared for a fixed-base cantilever wall and an idealized pinned-base cantilever wall. Mode 1 of the pinned-base cantilever is a rigid body rotation that has no associated bending moment or shear force, while the second modes and third modes of the pinned-base and fixed-base cantilever are very similar. The idealized frictionless pin at the base of a cantilever does not eliminate the higher mode shear demands. The amplification factor to account for the inelastic effects of higher modes is really a correction factor – the shear force on cantilever walls is reduced by the same force reduction factors as the bending moment when in reality it should not be because the flexural hinge limits only the first mode shear force.

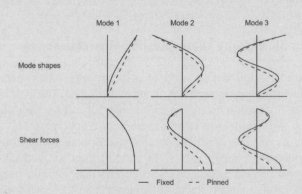

Fig. N21.5.2.2.7: Comparison of mode shapes and shear force envelopes in a fixed-base cantilever (solid lines) and an idealized pinned-base cantilever (dashed lines).[21.7]

Considerable research has been done on this topic and many different recommendations exist for how much the shear correction (amplification) factor should be. The shear correction factor that has been adopted[21.7] in the current edition of CSA A23.3 is a lower-bound value when compared to other recommendations.[21.8] This correction factor was adjusted for the spectral shapes in eastern Canada (using different T_L and T_U values) based on the work of Paultre.[21.8] A full description of why a lower-bound value is appropriate is presented in Ref. 21.7. A brief summary of some of the important issues are: (i) the maximum shear force occurs only once during an earthquake and lasts for a very short time; (ii) well detailed concrete walls have shear ductility, and; (iii) the maximum shear force generally does not occur when the base rotation is maximum, while the current CSA A23.3 shear design procedures for concrete walls assumes that it does.

As explained in N21.2.5, $R_d R_o / \gamma_w$ is equal to the ratio of elastic bending moment demand to nominal bending moment resistance M_e / M_n (both calculated at the section with the maximum elastic bending moment demand). When calculating the shear correction factor, the factored load used to calculate the wall overstrength factor γ_w (or the elastic bending moment demand M_e) can be taken directly from a linear dynamic analysis without scaling the bending moment to 80% or 100% of the lateral earthquake design force determined from the equivalent static force procedure with $T_a = 4.0$ s. The minimum force level in NBCC calculated using $T_a = 4.0$ s is meant to limit the ductility demands on tall buildings. The suggested refinement results in a larger γ_w (smaller M_e) which may result in a somewhat smaller shear correction factor.

When the fundamental lateral period of vibration of the building T_a is greater than T_U (1.0 s in "western Canada" and 0.5 s in "eastern Canada") and $R_d R_o / \gamma_w$ exceeds 3.0, the shear correction factor is limited to the maximum value of 1.5. Otherwise the shear correction factor will be in the range of 1.0 to 1.5 depending on $R_d R_o / \gamma_w$ and on T_a.

Coupled walls generally require a lower shear correction factor than cantilever walls.[21.9] This can be explained in part by the fact that, unlike cantilever walls which deform entirely in a flexural mode, the deformation of coupled walls includes a significant shear (sway) mode due to the deformation of the coupling beams. In the current edition of CSA A23.3, coupled walls and partially coupled walls need to be designed for increased shear forces due to the flexural overstrength of the system, which can result in a significant increase; but the shear forces do not need to be further increased to account for the inelastic effects of higher modes.

N21.5.2.2.8 Design for shear force above plastic hinge at base

The shear correction factor determined at the base of the wall must be applied to the entire shear force envelope.

N21.5.2.2.9 Design for shear force below plastic hinge at base

Below the plastic hinge region, concrete walls are often connected by multiple floor diaphragms to other walls, such as perimeter foundation walls or podium walls. This results in an indeterminate system for resisting the overturning moment below the plastic hinge. The overturning moment can be transferred directly to the foundation below the tower walls, or can be transferred to the foundation walls or podium walls by force couples in two or more floor diaphragms. This alternate load path is sometimes referred to as the backstay effect.[21.10] When a significant portion of the overturning moment is transferred by force couples in the diaphragms, the bending moment gradient (which is equal to the shear force) in the tower walls will reverse below the flexural hinge. This may create large reverse shear forces in the tower walls that are significantly larger than the base shear force.[21.6] Note that the stiffness of the diaphragms and foundation or podium walls below the plastic hinge must be stiff enough to cause the bending moment gradient (shear force) in the tower walls to reverse in order for these elements to be 'below the plastic hinge.'

In order to design a safe structure, an assessment must be made to determine what portion of the overturning moment in the tower walls may be resisted by each load path. As the stiffness properties of the elements in each load path may significantly influence the forces, and these properties are difficult to determine accurately, the analysis must consider a range of possible stiffness properties. In order to ensure that the design provides adequate strength in the structural elements of each load path, multiple analyses with upper-bound or lower-bound stiffness properties of the elements as appropriate must be done to determine the maximum forces in each load path.

The recommendations below are from Rad and Adebar[21.6] and ATC 72-1.[21.10] The latter recommends nonlinear response history analysis (NLRHA) of the complete building to determine the design forces in the structure below the plastic hinge, while Rad and Adebar[21.6] used the results of NLRHA to develop a simple linear static analysis procedure of the structure below the plastic hinge to estimate the design forces. Information is provided below about the stiffness to be used in either type of analysis and the forces to be used in a linear static analysis. The forces to be applied to the structure below the plastic hinge in a static analysis include an upper-bound overturning moment and either an upper-bound or lower-bound horizontal force. The upper-bound overturning moment is equal to either the nominal or probable bending moment capacity of the tower walls accounting for the level of axial compression applied to the walls. This bending moment is applied at the base of the plastic hinge. The upper-bound horizontal force is equal to the factored shear force at the base of the tower walls as defined in Clause 21.5.2.2.6, while the lower-bound horizontal force is equal to zero. The lower-bound horizontal force results in less deformation of the diaphragms and thus results in the maximum reverse shear force in the tower walls.[21.6]

The analysis can be grouped into the follow cases:

Case	Design forces (or deformation) to be determined:
1	Maximum bending moments in *tower walls*; design forces for foundation below *tower walls*
2A	Forces in diaphragms, podium structure, *other walls* and associated connections
2B	Maximum (reverse) shear force in *tower walls*
3	Inter-story drift ratio of *tower walls* at top of structure restraining foundation movements

Applied forces and stiffness assumptions:	Case			
	1	**2A**	**2B**	**3**
Applied overturning moment	M_n	M_p	M_p	M_n
Applied horizontal force	$V@M_n$	$V@M_p$	0	$V@M_n$
Flexural stiffness of *tower walls*	**UB**	LB	LB	BE
Stiffness of footings and supporting soil/rock below *tower walls*	**UB**	LB	LB	BE
Shear stiffness of *tower walls*	LB	**UB**	**UB**	BE
Stiffness of diaphragms	LB	**UB**	**UB**	BE
Stiffnesses of *other walls*, supporting footings and soil/rock	LB	**UB**	**UB**	BE
Lateral passive soil pressures on perpendicular foundation walls	LB	LB	**UB**	BE

M_n, M_p = nominal, probable bending moment capacity of the tower walls accounting for level of axial compression; LB = lower-bound stiffness; UB = upper-bound stiffness; BE = best estimate

Tower walls must be designed for the shear force from Case 2B, or if larger, the shear forces associated with factored bending moments described in Clause 21.5.2.2.4 (a) and (b); *tower walls* and supporting foundations must also be designed to meet all requirements of Clause 21.5.2.2.4. *Other walls* include perimeter foundation walls and/or podium walls.

Note that if the shear force does not reverse in Case 1 (the bending moment in the tower walls does not reduce below the plastic hinge), the tower walls must be designed for plastic hinging down to a level where the lower-bound stiffness of the supporting structure is sufficient to cause the reverse shear force or must be designed for plastic hinging down to the foundation.

Flexural stiffness of tower walls
The effective flexural rigidity that is used for the wall immediately below the plastic hinge is a sectional property unlike the property given in Clause 21.2.5.2, which is an average property reflecting the global response of the structure. Clause 21.5.2.2.4 requires that the portion of wall immediately below the critical section (base of plastic hinge) shall contain a minimum of 20% additional flexural tension reinforcement compared to the plastic hinge region of the wall. This additional vertical reinforcement will reduce strain penetration into the segment of wall below the plastic hinge, which if it occurred, would cause a significant reduction in flexural stiffness and hence an increase in the reverse shear force.

The upper limit on effective flexural rigidity $E_c I_e$ of the tower walls is the uncracked flexural rigidity $E_c I_g$ and this can be used as a safe upper-bound (UB) value for Case 1. The lower limit is the effective flexural rigidity when the bending moment demand reaches the nominal bending capacity given by $E_c I_e = M_n \ell_w / 0.0025$ (where M_n = the nominal flexural capacity of the tower wall at the particular level and $0.0025 / \ell_w$ = the curvature of the wall at initial yielding of vertical reinforcement). This can be used as a safe lower-bound (LB) value for Cases 2A and 2B.

If the calculated bending moments in Case 1 exceeds the cracking bending moment accounting for the axial compression on the wall, the upper-bound flexural rigidity $E_c I_e$ can be reduced from $1.0 E_c I_g$. Similarly, if the calculated bending moment in Case 2A or 2B is significantly less than the nominal bending moment M_n, the lower-bound flexural rigidity $E_c I_e$ can be increased. Chapter 11 (Section 11.5) of the CAC Handbook presents an example calculation, and Ref. 21.11 gives further details on how to determine a refined stiffness. Because of the important role that the flexural stiffness of the tower wall plays, it may be appropriate to use a different flexural rigidity at every level below grade depending on the calculated bending moment.

Soil supporting footings below tower walls

The procedures in Clause 21.10.3.3.2 can be used to determine the rotation of a wall footing for a given applied bending moment. The response is approximated as linear up until the applied overturning moment exceeds the overturning moment to cause uplift of the footing "heel" $M_{UL} = P_f \ell_f / 6$. The upper-bound rotational stiffness of the soil below the footing is given by M_{UL} / θ where the footing rotation θ is determined from Equation 21.22, Eq. N21.10.1, or a refined method given in Ref. 21.11. Once the overturning moment causes the footing to uplift, the response is generally nonlinear. Thus iteration may be required to determine the correct effective (linear) stiffness; however the need to iterate can be reduced by the fact that a smaller than actual (LB) rotational stiffness of soil is safe for Case 2A and 2B and a larger than actual rotational stiffness is safe for Case 1. Calculation of the footing rotation requires the initial shear modulus of the soil or rock G_0. Because of the uncertainty in determining soil properties, a number of reference documents recommend that when modelling soil, use a lower-bound of 0.5 times the expected soil property, and an upper-bound of 2.0 times expected property.

Stiffness of tower wall footings

For many shear wall footings, the span-to-depth ratios are such that most of the load is transferred from the walls directly to the soil by compression struts. In such cases, the footing can be modelled using uncracked section properties or even considered to be rigid in comparison to the soil below the footing. As the footing becomes more slender, cracking will be more prevalent. For foundation mats and pile caps, ATC 72-1 recommends that the effective flexural rigidity $E_c I_e$ be taken as 0.3 times the gross section properties, or the fully-cracked transformed-section properties be used, and that the effective shear rigidity $G_c A_{ve}$ be taken as 0.3 times gross section properties, or smaller if the shear stress exceeds $0.25 \sqrt{f'_c}$ in MPa units.

Shear stiffness of tower walls

The theoretical upper limit on the shear rigidity of a concrete wall is the uncracked shear rigidity $G_c A_{ve} = 1.0 \, G_c A_{vg} = 0.4 \, E_c A_{vg}$. Given that a small amount of diagonal cracking will significantly reduce the shear stiffness, $G_c A_{ve} = 0.5 \, G_c A_{vg}$ can be used as a safe upper-bound (UB) shear rigidity for Case 2A and 2B. For a concrete shear wall with well distributed horizontal and vertical reinforcement, which provides good diagonal crack control, a safe lower-bound (LB) shear rigidity for Case 1, is $G_c A_{ve} = 0.1 \, G_c A_{vg}$. When the applied shear force in Case 2A and 2B is significantly larger than the cracking shear (accounting for the axial compression in the wall), or the applied shear in Case 1 is significantly less than the nominal shear strength, a refined shear rigidity can be calculated as described in Ref. 21.11.

Concrete diaphragms

Normally concrete slabs are modelled as infinitely rigid diaphragms as their in-plane stiffness is high compared to the lateral stiffness of walls and columns at floor levels above grade. Below grade, the stiffness of walls are significantly higher, particular perimeter basement walls, which are very long. In this case, the small deformations of the diaphragms will be significant and the diaphragm must be modelled as elastic elements. A linear model with a reduced effective stiffness to account for cracking is usually appropriate (even when nonlinear response history analysis is used) as the diaphragms are designed to remain elastic under the design forces.

As the span-to-depth ratio of the diaphragms is usually very small, the shear stiffness is of greatest importance. The same upper-bound (UB) shear rigidity used for the tower walls $G_c A_{ve} = 0.5 \, G_c A_{vg}$ is also appropriate for the diaphragms. The lower-bound shear rigidity depends on the amount of reinforcement that is provided in the diaphragm. If well distributed reinforcement is provided to control diagonal cracking, the same lower bound (LB) shear rigidity $G_c A_{ve} = 0.1 \, G_c A_{vg}$ can be used for diaphragms in Case 1, while a smaller lower-bound $G_c A_{ve} = 0.05 \, G_c A_{vg}$ should be used if it is not known what reinforcement will be provided in the diaphragm. Note that the design forces that dictate the required quantity of reinforcement in the diaphragms is determined from Case 2A analysis where an upper-bound effective stiffness of the diaphragm is used. The recommended flexural rigidity of diaphragms, based on ATC 72-1, are as follows, upper-bound (UB): $E_c I_e = 0.5 E_c I_g$, lower-bound (LB): $E_c I_e = 0.2 E_c I_g$.

Other walls
The shear stiffnesses used for the tower walls can also be used for the perimeter foundation walls. Upper-bound (UB) shear rigidity for Case 2A and 2B is $G_c A_{ve} = 0.5 G_c A_{vg}$ and lower-bound (LB) shear rigidity for Case 1 is $G_c A_{ve} = 0.1 G_c A_{vg}$. The flexural stiffnesses used for the diaphragms can also be used for the perimeter foundation walls. Upper-bound (UB) flexural rigidity for Case 2A and 2B is $E_c I_e = 0.5 E_c I_g$ and lower-bound (LB) flexural rigidity for Case 1 is $E_c I_e = 0.2 E_c I_g$.

Lateral passive soil pressure on perpendicular foundation walls
To determine the maximum reverse shear force in the tower walls, additional horizontal (compression only) soil springs can be added to represent the passive resistance of the soil against the foundation walls that are perpendicular to the shear force in the tower walls in Case 2B. These springs should be omitted or the stiffness significantly reduced for Case 1 and Case 2A. In many structures the stiffness of soil passive resistance is small compared to the stiffness of diaphragms and the in-plane stiffness of the below grade perimeter walls, allowing the horizontal lateral soil springs to be omitted also from Case 2B.[21.10]

Design of floor diaphragms
The following recommendations are from ATC 72-1. The diaphragm located at the base of the plastic hinge (e.g., top of podium perimeter walls or at grade level) will likely transfer more force than any other diaphragms below the plastic hinge. The analysis will confirm this fact. Thus this structural slab may need to be thicker than other floors in the building, and the openings should be located so they do not interrupt critical load paths. Typically a floor slab is designed first for gravity loads and subsequently checked for in-plane diaphragm forces. The slab reinforcement utilized for resisting gravity loads should not be considered for resisting in-plane diaphragm forces. Reinforcement in excess of what is needed to resist the typical gravity load combinations can be used to resist diaphragm forces. A portion of all such reinforcement in the top and bottom of the slab should be continuous, and all lap splices should be Class B. Excess capacity of the slab reinforcement that can be used to help resist in-plane diaphragm forces results from the load factors for gravity loads in combination with earthquake forces being smaller than specified for gravity loads alone. Slab reinforcement used to resist diaphragm and collector forces should be positioned so that the resultant of the tensile forces is near the mid-depth of the slab to minimize eccentricity, which can induce additional slab bending moments. [21.10] The design of slabs for diaphragm forces can be efficiently accomplished using the squat wall provisions in Clause 21.5.10 by treating the diaphragm as a horizontal shear wall.

N21.5.3 Minimum wall thickness
Instability (buckling) of thin walls is a very undesirable failure mode and must be prevented by ensuring the walls have sufficient thickness depending on the unsupported vertical length ℓ_u. As walls are damaged from cyclic loading, the possibility of a stability failure increases. Thus larger thicknesses are required within the plastic hinge region compared to outside the plastic hinge regions; and larger thicknesses are required for walls designed using a larger ductility-based force reduction factor R_d.

When certain conditions are met as given in Clause 21.5.3.3, a smaller wall thickness is acceptable. Fig. N21.5.3 (a) illustrates how a reduced thickness is acceptable where the concrete compression strains are calculated to be less than 0.0035/2. For simple rectangular walls with low axial compressions, the required depth of compression may be small enough to enable the remainder of the wall to provide sufficient restraint to the small highly compressed regions (Fig. N21.5.3 (b)). Certain parts of walls as shown in Fig. N21.5.3(c) provide continuous lateral support of adjacent components. Therefore any part of a wall which is within a distance of $3b_w$ from a line of support is exempted from the slenderness limitation. The shaded part of the flange in Fig. N21.5.3(c) is considered to be too remote to be effectively restrained by the web portion of the wall and hence it needs to comply with the slenderness requirement.

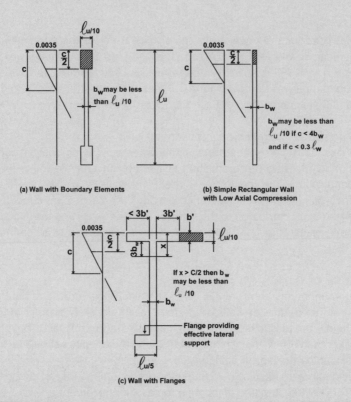

Fig. N21.5.3 Minimum wall thickness in plastic hinge regions of R_d = 3.5 walls

N21.5.4.3 Maximum percentage
The limit is intended to avoid excessive congestion of reinforcement. The reinforcement ratio is calculated using the area of concrete surrounding the concentrated reinforcement.

N21.5.5 Distributed reinforcement
The requirements for distributed reinforcement are summarized in the table below:

	Outside Plastic Hinge Regions	Within Plastic Hinge Regions	
		(R_d ≤ 2.5)	(R_d ≥ 3.5)
Amount (Horiz. & Vert.)	ρ ≥ 0.0025	ρ ≥ 0.0025	ρ ≥ 0.0025
Spacing of Horiz. Reinf.	≤ 500 mm	≤ 400 mm	≤ 300 mm
Spacing of Vert. Reinf.	≤ 500 mm	≤ 500 mm	≤ 500 mm
Ties: when large percentage or large bars used	Column ties (Clause 7.6.5)	Buckling prevention ties (Clause 21.2.8.1)	Buckling prevention ties (Clause 21.2.8.1)
Anchorage of Horiz. Reinf.	See Clause 21.5.5.3	See Clause 21.5.5.3	See Clause 21.5.5.3
			Plus: shear reinf. to develop 1.25 f_y within concen. reinf.

N21.5.5.2 Maximum spacing

The requirements have been relaxed from the previous edition.

N21.5.5.3 Anchorage of horizontal reinforcement

New requirements are introduced that are a function of the expected level of damaged in the wall as reflected by the ductility-based force reduction factor R_d used to design the wall. The requirements for lower ductility walls have generally been tightened, while the requirements for Ductile (R_d = 3.5 or 4.0) walls have been relaxed as only the horizontal reinforcement required for shear resistance is now required to be fully anchored within tied concentrated reinforcement.

N21.5.5.4 Ties for vertical distributed reinforcement

When the percentage of vertical distributed reinforcement is large or the bar sizes used are large, all distributed reinforcement shall be tied with buckling prevention ties (Clause 21.2.8.1) within plastic hinge regions and shall be tied with column ties (Clause 7.6.5) outside plastic hinge regions.

N21.5.6 Concentrated vertical reinforcement

The requirements for concentrated reinforcement are summarized in the table below:

	Outside Plastic Hinge Regions		Within Plastic Hinge	
	($R_d \leq 2.5$)	($R_d \geq 3.5$)	($R_d \leq 2.5$)	($R_d \geq 3.5$)
Where required:	at ends of all walls, including at coupling beams, corners, and junctions			
Min. amount[1] (at least 4 bars)	$A_s \geq 0.00050\, b_w \ell_w$	$A_s \geq 0.00100\, b_w \ell_w$	$A_s \geq 0.00075\, b_w \ell_w$	$A_s \geq 0.00150\, b_w \ell_w$
Max. percentage [2]	0.08			0.06
Ties (detailed as hoops)	Column ties (Clause 7.6.5)		Buckling prevention ties (Clause 21.2.8.1)	
Splice requirements	Min. splice length: $1.5\, \ell_d$			
	Max. amount spliced at same location: 100%			50%
	Min. clear height without splices: none			½ storey height

[1] Amount of reinforcement must also satisfy requirements of Clauses 21.5.2 and 21.5.7.
[2] Maximum bar diameter ≤ 0.1 times wall thickness.

N21.5.6.4 Ties for concentrated reinforcement

All ties for concentrated reinforcement shall be detailed as hoops or seismic crossties over the full height of the wall.

N21.5.6.5 Limited splicing in ductile walls

The requirement to keep at least half the storey height free of lap splices is intended to provide a section of wall with a capacity no greater than that anticipated in the design.

N21.5.7 Ductility of walls

The purpose of this clause is to ensure that flexural walls will have sufficient displacement capacity, which is limited by the compression strain capacity of concrete and the tension strain capacity of reinforcement.

N21.5.7.1.1 Above plastic hinge region

These new requirements have been added to ensure that all walls have sufficient ductility to tolerate some inelastic curvature demands above the plastic hinge region. This is important because the higher mode demands are difficult to determine.

N21.5.7.1.2 Within plastic hinge region

The ductility requirements for walls can be conveniently expressed in terms of a maximum compression strain depth as a portion of the wall length; but is presented in terms of inelastic rotational capacity and inelastic rotational demand in the plastic hinge region in order to provide a physical model rather than a "black box" equation. Eqs. (21-11) and (21-12) are based on a rational model,[21.12] which is briefly described here. Recent studies[21.5] have shown the model gives safe results and that refinements that reduce the requirements for ductility are possible.

Eqs. (21-11) and (21-12) can be combined and rearranged to result in the following equation for the maximum compression strain "depth" in a wall without confinement reinforcement:

$$c/\ell_w \le \frac{1}{1 + 500 \left(\dfrac{\Delta_f R_d R_o}{h_w} \right) \left[\dfrac{1 - \gamma_w/(R_d R_o)}{1 - 0.5\ell_w/h_w} \right]} \le A$$

where A is given in the table below. As h_w / ℓ_w does not have a large influence, the expression can be further simplified by assuming $h_w / \ell_w = 5$, which makes the denominator of the expression within the square brackets equal to 0.90.

Concrete wall system	R_d	R_o	$R_d R_o$	A
Ductile shear wall	3.5	1.6	5.6	0.33
Moderately ductile shear wall	2.0	1.4	2.8	0.40

N21.5.7.2 Inelastic rotational demand at base

The inelastic rotational demand given by Eq. (21-11) is simply the inelastic displacement demand (total displacement minus elastic portion) at the top of the wall divided by the distance from the centre of the plastic hinge in the wall to the top of the wall. The plastic hinge length is assumed to be equal to 1.0 times the wall length ℓ_w. The minimum inelastic rotational demand of 0.004 is to ensure a minimum level of ductility in buildings where the predicted inelastic drift is small.

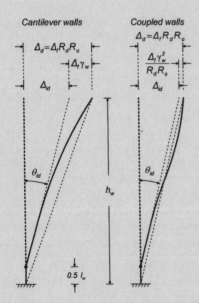

$$\theta_{id} = \frac{(\Delta_f R_o R_d - \Delta_f \gamma_w)}{\left(h_w - \dfrac{\ell_w}{2} \right)} \ge 0.004$$

Design Displacement = $\Delta_f R_o R_d$

Elastic Displacement = $\Delta_f \gamma_w$

Inelastic Displacement = $\Delta_f R_o R_d - \Delta_f \gamma_w$

Fig. N21.5.7.2 Physical explanation of inelastic rotational demands in walls.[21.12]

N21.5.7.3 Inelastic rotational capacity

The inelastic rotation capacity, given by Eq. (21-12), is equal to the total curvature capacity of the wall ε_{cu} / c minus the assumed yield curvature of 0.004 / ℓ_w all times an assumed plastic hinge length 0.5 times the wall length ℓ_w. Note that two different values of plastic hinge length are used – a larger value is used to make a safe estimate of inelastic rotational demand and a smaller value is used to make a safe estimate of inelastic rotation capacity.

$$\theta_{ic} = \left(\frac{\varepsilon_{cu}\ell_w}{2c} - 0.002 \right) \le 0.025$$

$$Plastic\ Hinge\ Length = \frac{\ell_w}{2}$$

$$\theta_{ic} = \frac{\ell_w}{2}\left(\frac{\varepsilon_{cu}}{c} - \frac{\varepsilon_{sy} + \varepsilon_{cy}}{\ell_w} \right)$$

$$\theta_{ic\ max} = \frac{\ell_w}{2}\left(\frac{\varepsilon_{smax}}{\ell_w} \right)$$

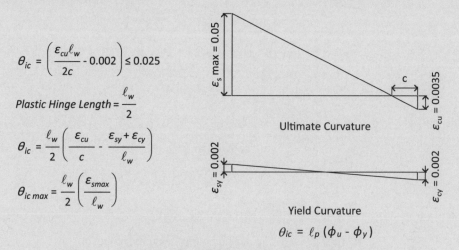

$$\theta_{ic} = \ell_p \left(\phi_u - \phi_y \right)$$

Fig. N21.5.7.3 Inelastic rotational capacity

N21.5.7.4 Compression strain depth in wall

The compression strain depth directly influences the maximum compression strain demand in concrete for a given curvature demand. The two factors that most influence the compression strain depth c are the geometry of the concrete wall cross section and the axial compression force applied to the wall.

N21.5.7.5 Confinement of concrete

When the inelastic rotational demand exceeds the inelastic rotational capacity (compression depth c exceeds the limit), the geometry of the concrete wall can be modified to increase the rotational capacity of the wall (i.e., reduce c). Alternatively, the concrete in the wall can be confined to increase the compression strain capacity of concrete thereby increasing the rotational capacity of the wall. The amount of confinement reinforcement is determined from Clause 21.2.8.2 for the desired compression strain capacity of concrete, which has an upper limit of 0.014.

N21.5.7.6 Simplified procedure for moderately ductile walls

For moderately ductile walls, if the compression strain depth c is less than, the wall will have adequate ductility, i.e., the inelastic rotational capacity will be greater than the inelastic rotational demand, and no further calculations are required. If the compression strain depth c exceeds but is less than, the wall will have sufficient ductility only if is less than.

N21.5.8 Additional requirements for coupled shear walls (R_d = 2.5 or 4.0) and partially coupled shear walls (R_d = 2.0 or 3.5)

Moderately ductile coupled walls and moderately ductile partially coupled walls are new wall systems introduce in the 2014 edition of CSA A23.3. Ductile and moderately ductile coupled walls and partially coupled walls dissipate energy by the formation of plastic hinges in the coupling beams and the base of the walls as shown in Figure N21.2.2.

To simplify the design of coupling beams while at the same time avoiding significant over-strength, the shear forces applied to coupling beams may be redistributed vertically from the linear-elastic distribution as illustrated in Fig. N21.5.8. It has been suggested that the shear in any individual coupling beam should not be reduced by more than 20% from the linear-elastic distribution[21.1] nor should it be reduced below that required for other load cases such as wind. The sum of the resistance over the height of the building must be greater than or equal to the sum of the elastically determined values.

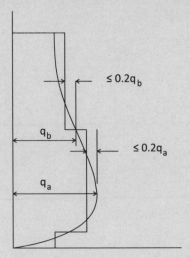

Fig. N21.5.8 Design of coupling beams using redistribution

The coupling beams in a coupled wall system are subjected to large deformation demands, which is why the design forces can be redistributed. Experience has shown that conventionally reinforced beams that are subjected to significant shear stresses can exhibit sliding shear failure at the ends of the beam. Transverse shear reinforcement (stirrups) are not effective in preventing this shear failure mode. Thus Paulay developed the concept of diagonal reinforcement in coupling beams to resist both the bending moments and the shear force (see Ref. 21.1).

N21.5.8.1 Design of coupling beams without diagonal reinforcement

Coupling beams may be designed and detailed as frame members provided the beams satisfy the restrictions of this clause and Clause 21.5.8.4.1(b). They need to be detailed as either moderately ductile beams in accordance to Clause 21.4 or ductile beams in accordance with Clause 21.3 depending on the R_d of the wall system.

The longitudinal reinforcement in coupling beams must be capable of yielding in tension at one end and yielding in compression at the other end. Thus the beam must be long enough (bar diameter small enough) to permit the development of a force equal to $2f_y A_b$ along the length of the beam. The requirement is the same as in Clause 14.4.6.

It is strongly preferred that coupling beams be the same width as the wall and be centered on the wall. When this is not the case, additional design considerations are required. In order for the coupled wall system to dissipate energy, the coupling beams must be capable of undergoing numerous cycles of large inelastic deformations while not failing in an unexpected failure mode due to the geometry of the coupling beam. Due to the large deformation demands on the longitudinal reinforcement, tension stresses over 600 MPa ($1.5f_y$) may develop in Grade 400 reinforcement. This must be considered when ensuring the system has sufficient capacity to prevent an unexpected failure mode due to out-of-plane bending or torsion in the coupling beam or failure of the adjacent wall segments.

N21.5.8.2 Design of coupling beams with diagonal reinforcement

Diagonally reinforced coupling beams cannot be wider than the wall since the diagonal reinforcing bars must be anchored within the wall. The shear and moment in diagonally reinforced coupling beams are resisted entirely by the reinforcement so the limitations on design capacity are usually dictated by the difficulty of placing the diagonal reinforcing through the wall-zone steel at the ends of the wall. Fig. N21.5.8.2 illustrates the design and detailing requirements for diagonal reinforcing. In the case where more than four bars are used in each diagonal, buckling prevention ties in addition to the outside hoop are required. Ties on the diagonal reinforcement are not required where they pass through the inside of buckling prevention ties provided for the concentrated steel adjacent to the opening (see Clause 21.5.8.3.1) and over the last half of the required anchorage.

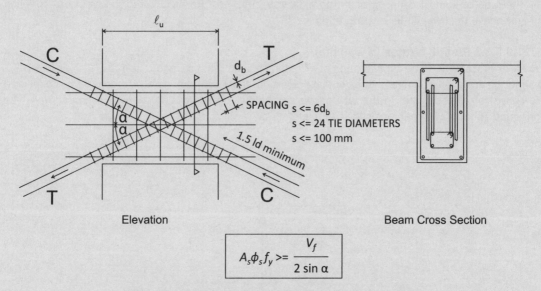

Fig. N21.5.8.2 Diagonal reinforcement in coupling beams

ACI places limitations on the use of shallow angle diagonally reinforced coupling beams based on tests by PCA on small scale specimens. Tests performed on a full-scale specimen[21.13] with shallow diagonal reinforcement showed excellent performance so CSA A23.3 has no such limitation.

ACI 318 permits an alternate arrangement of reinforcement in which the confinement is provided around the entire beam rather than around the individual bundles of diagonal bars. One of the problems observed in the field with this arrangement of reinforcement is that the diagonal bars get inserted into the beam at the wrong angle. This is a serious concern as a small change in angle can significantly influence the shear force and bending moment capacity of a coupling beam. Once a contractor gains experience placing the bundled diagonal bars, they may find it a more expedient method of construction rather than "threading" the individual diagonal bars into the exact location.

N21.5.8.3.1 Concentrated wall reinforcement at coupling beams

As shown in Fig. N21.2.2, coupling beams are expected to yield over the full height of the building, and the yielding of the reinforcement will penetrate into the adjacent wall ends. Thus the ends of the walls require special detailing over the full height. For wall systems designed with $R_d \leq 2.5$, the concentrated reinforcement shall be tied with buckling prevention ties over the plastic hinge region and with hoops spaced according to Clause 7.6.5 over the rest of the height. For wall systems designed with $R_d \geq 3.5$, the concentrated reinforcement shall be tied with buckling prevention ties over the full height.

N21.5.8.3.2 Bending resistance of wall piers

In order to ensure that the plastic hinges form in the coupling beams and not in the walls, the wall at each end of the coupling beam must be stronger than the coupling beams framing into it. This is similar to the requirement for strong columns – weak beams in ductile frames.

The bending capacity of the wall piers is calculated using a net axial load in the wall piers equal to the sum of the axial compression from gravity loads (P_s) and the applied axial tension from the sum of the shear forces due to the nominal capacity of all coupling beams above the section (P_n). To account for the influence of higher modes, the axial tension force P_n in the wall piers is determined by multiplying the factored tension force in the wall piers (from a linear dynamic analysis accounting for higher modes) by the ratio of sum of coupling beam nominal capacities to sum of factored forces in the coupling beams above the level under consideration.

N21.5.8.3.3 Plastic hinges in wall pier

There are cases where the configuration of a building is such that the requirements of Clause 21.5.8.3.2 cannot be achieved at one end of a coupling beam. In that case, the inelastic mechanism is expected to consist of plastic hinges in the wall above and below the beam, and the wall segments must be designed as ductile moment resisting-frame elements.

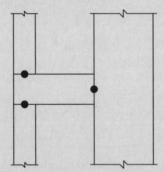

Fig. N21.5.8.3.3 Kinematic mechanism for a weak wall pier

N21.5.8.3.4 Axial forces in wall piers

In order for the assumed energy dissipating mechanism to form in coupled and partially coupled walls, the coupling beams must yield. Clause 21.5.8.3.2 requires sufficient local bending capacity of the wall piers to ensure strong wall piers – weak coupling beams. In addition, the axial capacity of the walls at any height should be sufficient to resist the sum of the coupling beam shear forces required to yield the coupling beams above that height. Due to higher modes, the coupling beam shear forces are not all acting in the same direction at one time. To account for this, the axial forces in the wall piers determined from a linear dynamic analysis of the wall system are increased in proportion to the total overstrength in the coupling beams above the level under consideration.

The coupling beams must be designed to resist the total factored forces including the contribution from accidental torsion; however when calculating the ratio of capacity to factored forces, the contribution from accidental torsion is not to be included in the factored forces. Thus the demand from accidental torsion is in the numerator but not the denominator resulting in a boost to the axial forces in the wall piers. The axial forces in the wall piers are increased to ensure yielding of the coupling beams will still occur when the demand on the coupling beams from the accidental torsion is not present.

The previous requirement (previous Clause 21.6.8.13) that wall segments acting as a tension flange in the flexural mode shall have no shear resistance over the height of the plastic hinge has been removed

Explanatory Notes on CSA A23.3-14

as it was believed to be too severe a requirement. Wide flexural cracks are actually able to transmit shear forces due to the cracks not being perfectly planar, i.e., the cracks have global roughness.

N21.5.8.4.1 General
To ensure a coupled wall system has adequate ductility, the inelastic rotational demands at the base of the walls piers and in the coupling beams must be less than the inelastic rotational capacities.

N21.5.8.4.2 Inelastic rotational demand at base of wall piers
The bending moments from coupling beams cause reverse bending at the top of the wall piers. As a result, the elastic portion of the total displacement is generally much smaller in coupled walls than in cantilever shear walls (See Fig N21.5.7.2). For simplicity, the inelastic rotational demand (inelastic displacement divided by height above plastic hinge) is assumed to be equal to the global drift (total displacement divided by total height of wall).[21.12] That is, replacing the height of the wall above the plastic hinge with the total height of the wall compensates for the assumption that the elastic displacement is zero. While the inelastic displacement is a larger portion of the total displacement in coupled walls, the total displacement demand is greatly reduced by the coupling beams.

N21.5.8.4.3 Inelastic rotational capacity of wall piers
Wall piers with a low degree of coupling will act similar to separate cantilever walls, while walls with a high degree of coupling will act similar to a single solid wall.

N21.5.8.4.4 Inelastic rotational demand on coupling beams
All rotations referred to in this clause are total chord rotations, which are equal to the total relative displacement of the beam-ends divided by the total length of the beam.

Coupling beam rotations are proportional to the difference between wall slope θ_{wall} and floor slope θ_{floor} (see Fig. N21.5.8.4.4), where the latter is equal to the relative axial deformation of walls divided by the horizontal distance between wall centroids. The wall slope associated with maximum coupling beam rotation is much greater than the associated floor slope. Thus, the level of maximum coupling beam rotation occurs near the location of maximum wall slope, which is usually in the lower levels of the coupled walls due to inelastic drift being uniform, and elastic drift reducing with height from coupling beams pulling back on the walls. Due to axial displacement of walls, maximum coupling beam rotations do not necessarily result from maximum wall slopes; however a simplified procedure that gives reasonable results is to assume that the critical wall slope is equal to the maximum global drift, and the corresponding floor slope is equal to zero.[21.14] This approach leads to Eq. (21-15), where ℓ_{cg} is the horizontal distance between centroids of the walls on either side of the coupling beams, and ℓ_u is the clear span of the coupling beam between the walls.

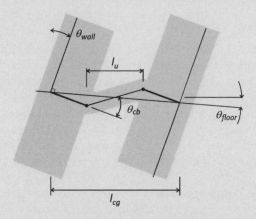

Fig. N21.5.8.4.4 Rotational demands on coupling beams as influenced by wall slope and floor slope.

N21.5.8.4.5 Inelastic rotational capacity of coupling beams

In FEMA 356, the rotational capacity of diagonally reinforced coupling beams is 0.03 and 0.05 for Life Safety and Collapse Prevention performance levels, respectively. For conventionally reinforced coupling beams, the limits are 0.015 and 0.03.

N21.5.9.1

The requirements of Clause 11, Clause 14 and Clauses 21.5.9.2 to 21.5.9.4 must be satisfied for all regions of a concrete wall. In addition, the requirements of Clauses 21.5.9.5 must be satisfied for regions of plastic hinging.

Sliding shear failures during earthquakes have been observed when construction joints are not properly cleaned and roughened. Clause 11.5 provides procedures to determine the factored interface shear resistance of construction joints, which must be greater than the factored seismic shear force applied to the wall.

The following parameters shall be used to calculate the effective normal stress σ in Clause 11.5.4:

N = an equivalent axial compression force accounting for the combined effect of the applied axial compression and any unused vertical reinforcement in the flexural tension end of the wall (see equation below).

A_g = is the total gross area of the wall subjected to the axial compression P_s

A_{vf} = the total area of distributed vertical reinforcement in the shear resisting portion of the wall not considered to be resisting flexural stresses.

$$N = P_s + 2\left(A_s f_y - \frac{M_f}{jd} \right)$$

Where: $A_s f_y$ is the strength of the vertical reinforcement resisting flexural tension, M_f is the applied bending moment; jd is the internal flexural lever-arm.

N21.5.9.2 Shear depth

The effective shear depth d_v is the distance between the flexural compression force and flexural tension force, i.e., the internal flexural lever-arm. Clause 2.3 specifies that d_v be calculated as 0.9 times the effective depth d; but need not be less than 0.72 times the overall member dimension h; however this lower limit is meant for prestressed members and circular sections. A higher lower-bound of $0.8\ell_w$ is appropriate for walls with distributed vertical reinforcement, and is conservative for walls where vertical reinforcement is concentrated at the ends.

N21.5.9.3 Openings in walls

The procedures in Clause 21.5.9.5 assume that the shear force applied to a wall will be resisted by uniform diagonal compression stresses in concrete and uniformly spaced horizontal reinforcement. When there is an opening in the wall, there will be a concentration of diagonal compression stresses around the opening, which may lead to a brittle concrete shear failure. Additional reinforcement beyond what is calculated assuming a uniform stress field will be required, and special care must be taken to detail this reinforcement so that the diagonal compression forces are able to change direction where needed. The strut-and-tie model in Clause 11.4 is an appropriate design tool to ensure that an opening will not be the weak-link in the shear strength of a concrete wall.

N21.5.9.5 Outside plastic hinge regions

The maximum shear resistance is reduced by 20% to account for the fact that walls are subjected to reverse cyclic shear and to account for curvature demands due to higher mode bending moments.

N21.5.9.5.1 General

The design for shear in the plastic hinge region of walls shall meet the requirements of Clause 11.3 – Design for shear in flexural region; except as modified by this clause. Clause 11.3 is based on a truss model for a uniform diagonal compression stress field, plus a concrete contribution representing the shear transmitted across the diagonal cracks by aggregate interlock. The modifications presented below account for the reverse cyclic loading and the formation of a "fan region" at the base of a wall.[21.15]

N21.5.9.5.2 General method for ductile and moderately ductile walls

(a) Clause 11.3.3 limits the maximum shear force in the non-seismic case to $0.25\phi_c f_c' b_w d_v$. Due to the reverse cyclic loading in the plastic hinge region of concrete walls, the flexural compression zone of the wall will become the flexural tension zone during the reverse direction of loading. Thus the flexural compression zone of the wall will be damaged during reverse cyclic loading and less able to resist the concentration of shear that occurs in a "fan region." The inelastic rotation demand is a good indicator of damage in the plastic hinge regions of concrete walls.[21.15] Inelastic rotation is proportional to inelastic curvature and hence directly related to the vertical tensile strains in the plastic hinge region.

(b) In Clause 11, the concrete contribution V_c is a function of the factor β, which in turn is a function of the axial tension strain at the section mid-depth. The axial tension strain is used as an indicator of the diagonal crack widths. As the axial strains become larger, the diagonal crack widths become larger and the diagonal cracks are less able to resist interface shear stresses. The inelastic rotation of the plastic hinge region is used as the indicator of diagonal crack widths in the plastic hinge region. Significantly larger concrete contributions are appropriate in the base of the wall due to the "fan region" that forms (shear is transmitted directly to the flexural compression zone by compression struts.[21.15] When the inelastic rotations are large, the concrete contribution is taken as zero.

(c) The shear resistance provided by transverse shear reinforcement V_s is a function of the angle of inclination of diagonal compression stresses relative to the longitudinal axis of the member θ. The angle θ varies from about 35 to 29 degrees for non-seismic cases. In the design for seismic shear in the plastic hinge regions of walls, θ is considered to be the critical diagonal crack inclination relative to the vertical axis of the wall. The axial compression applied to the wall is the best indicator of the inclination of the critical diagonal crack. When a wall is subjected to larger axial compression, the critical diagonal crack will be steeper (θ will be smaller), and V_s will be larger for the same amount of horizontal reinforcement in the wall.[21.15]

N21.5.9.5.3 Simplified method for moderately ductile walls

As the ductility demands are expected to lower in walls designed with $R_d \le 2.5$, as simplified procedure can be used in in lieu of the requirements of Clause 21.5.9.5.2, which requires the calculation of an inelastic rotational demand. Note that the procedures given in Clause 21.5.9.5.2 are general enough that they will account for the reduced inelastic demands on moderately ductile walls. Specifically, the inelastic rotational demand given by Eq. (21-11) or Eq. (21-14) will be reduced in moderately ductile walls. Thus more efficient designs may result from using Clause 21.5.9.5.2 rather than the simplified limits.

N21.5.9.6 Strut-and-tie models

The limiting compression stress in struts is reduced to account for cyclic loading. Special reinforcement is required to prevent buckling of reinforcement subjected to reverse cyclic loading.

N21.5.10.1 General

Squat walls may not be able to develop an inelastic flexural mechanism prior to developing an inelastic shear mechanism. Thus these walls require special design rules. The procedure presented in Clause 21.5.10 is a complete design procedure for squat walls subjected to reverse cyclic loading. Clause 21.6.3.3 summarizes the requirements that are appropriate for walls subjected to less inelastic demand.

N21.5.10.2 Capacity design

Flexural walls provide a "fuse" that limits the seismic forces induced into a structure. Squat walls may have much more strength than calculations indicate and hence do not provide a well-defined limit on the seismic forces. The squat wall will survive the larger demands. The concern is unexpected failure in other parts of the seismic-force-resisting system such as the diaphragms that are connected to the squat wall. Generally, the deformation of the soil or rock below a squat wall will contribute significantly to the flexibility of the system.

The maximum effective flange width is important for determining the maximum flexural resistance of a wall. The limits given in Clause 14.4.3.3 are also applicable to squat walls.

N21.5.10.4 Reinforcement

The requirements for development and splices of reinforcement, maximum reinforcement ratio of concentrated reinforcement, and maximum diameter of reinforcing bars given in 21.5.4 are also applicable to squat walls.

N21.5.10.5 Distributed reinforcement

The requirements have been relaxed for walls that are subjected to low shear force demands. In a flexural wall the concentrated vertical reinforcement at the tension end and the vertical compression in concrete at the compression end will significantly control diagonal cracking. As these do not exist in squat walls, additional distributed reinforcement is required to control the widths of diagonal cracks.

(b) Poor diagonal crack control may occur if a single layer of reinforcement is offset from the centre of the wall therefore at least two layers of reinforcement is required. When the shear force applied to the wall is higher than the specified limit, significant diagonal cracking is expected.

(d) Extending the horizontal reinforcement into the region of tied vertical reinforcement at the ends of the wall will enhance the anchorage of the horizontal reinforcement thereby permitting yielding of this reinforcement over a longer length.

N21.5.10.6 Concentrated reinforcement

The requirements have been relaxed for walls that are subjected to low shear force demands. Concentrated reinforcement at the ends of walls provides an opportunity to enhance the anchorage of horizontal reinforcement, and protects the end of the wall.

N21.5.10.7 Overturning resistance

In a flexural wall, all vertical reinforcement, including the distributed reinforcement, can be included in the calculation of overturning resistance. The diagonal compression that resists the applied shear force flows to the flexural compression zone, and the size of the flexural compression zone is not significantly influenced by the presence of the diagonal compression. The stress field that forms at the base of a flexural wall is referred to as a "fan region." In a squat wall, the diagonal compression that resists the applied shear force is distributed over much of the wall length. Tension stress is needed in the distributed vertical reinforcement to balance the vertical component of the diagonal compression. As the distributed vertical compression stress in concrete due to shear is not included in the calculation of over-turning resistance, the distributed vertical tension in the reinforcement must also not be included. The length of wall over which the significant vertical compression stresses exist in the concrete varies gradually with the height-to-length ratio of the wall.[21.16] For simplicity, it is assumed that these stresses do not exist when the height-to-length ratio is greater than 1.0, and these stresses exist over the full length of the wall when the height-to-length ratio is less than 1.0.

While plane sections do not remain plane in squat walls, such calculations for the vertical compression stress in concrete and vertical tension stress in reinforcement result in a safe design for the overturning resistance of squat walls.

N21.5.10.8.4 Shear stress
The shear design requirements for squat walls are presented in terms of the average shear stress rather than the shear force, which is used in Clause 11.

N21.5.10.8.5 Maximum shear stress
Clause 11.3.3 limits the maximum shear force for the non-seismic case to $0.25\phi_c f'_c b_w d_v$. Due to damage from reverse cyclic loading in squat walls, the maximum average shear stress must be reduced to avoid diagonal compression failure of concrete in squat walls designed using $R_d = 2.0$. The shear stress limit is increased for conventional squat walls (see Clause 21.6.3.3) and can be further increased if these provisions are used to design a squat wall for non-seismic loading.

N21.5.10.8.6 Distributed horizontal reinforcement
The concrete contribution V_c in Clause 11.3 reflects the shear transmitted across diagonal cracks, which reduces the demand on horizontal reinforcement; but increases the demand on the flexural tension reinforcement as given by Eq. (11-14). In squat walls, any shear on the diagonal cracks will transfer the demand from the horizontal reinforcement to the vertical distributed reinforcement. The calculation for the relative demand on the horizontal and vertical reinforcement can be done without a concrete contribution using Eq. (21-18), and this approach is simpler for squat walls. The effect of including a concrete contribution is similar to using a smaller angle θ.

By choosing the angle θ within the allowable limits, a designer can choose the relative amounts of horizontal and distributed vertical reinforcement. When the vertical compression stress in the wall is small (as is often the case in squat walls), choosing $\theta = 45$ deg. results in $\rho_v = \rho_h$, while choosing $\theta = 30$ deg. results in 65% as much horizontal reinforcement, and 154% as much vertical reinforcement (i.e., the percentage of vertical reinforcement is 2.4 times the percentage of horizontal reinforcement). When there is significant vertical compression stress in the wall, choosing θ smaller than 45 deg. results in less total reinforcement.

Using $\theta = 45$ deg., Grade 400 MPa distributed horizontal reinforcement with a reinforcement ratio = 0.003, provides a factored average shear stress resistance of $\phi_s f_y \rho_h = 1.0$ MPa.

N21.5.10.8.7 Distributed vertical reinforcement
See N21.5.10.8.6 for a discussion about the relative amounts of vertical and horizontal distributed reinforcement.

See N21.5.10.7 for a discussion of the influence of height-to-length ratio on the required amount of distributed vertical reinforcement.

N21.6.1.1
The statement from Clause 21.2.4.3 is repeated here because designers of $R_d = 1.3$ or 1.5 systems may not read other parts of Clause 21.

N21.6.2 Moment-resisting frames
Conventional construction moment-resisting frames are now permitted up to 10 m high (maximum of three stories) in the highest seismic regions in Canada (see N21.2.2). Thus additional requirements have been added.

N21.6.2.4 Shear Resistance of joints in frames

Joints in these frames are expected to have much less inelastic demand than those in moderately ductile or ductile frames and as a consequence the design requirements are not as rigorous. The design forces in the joint (see N21.2.2.1.2) are based on factored moments applied to the joint and are not based capacity design principals and yielding of the columns and beam reinforcement as in ductile and moderately ductile frame joints. The transverse joint reinforcement is minimal and is governed by Clause 7.7. The factored shear resistance of the joint is taken to be the same values as that of a joint in a moderately ductile frame given in Clause 21.4.6.2. These moderately ductile values are allowed, even though the transverse joint reinforcement is minimal, because the non-linear demand on the joint is expected to be low. Hooked and straight bars ending within the joint must satisfy the requirements of Chapter 12 (see Clause 12.11.2) based on f_y of the bar and not based on the calculated stress in the bar even though the joint forces are based on factored moments and not the strength of the reinforcement. This is because: the amount of reinforcement may be governed by other load cases; there is a large uncertainty and scatter in earthquake ground motions which may result in a higher than expected stress in the bar, and; bond failure of the bars degrades the performance of the structure more than an overstress in the concrete joint.

N21.6.3.3 Design of squat shear walls

The general procedure for squat shear walls given in Clause 21.5.10 can be used to design conventional construction squat walls.

N21.6.3.4 Design shear force

In order to preclude a shear failure, flexural overstrength of the wall must be accounted for.

N21.6.3.5 Shear resistance

Clause 11.3.3 limits the maximum shear force for the non-seismic case to $0.25\phi_c f'_c b_w d_v$. Due to damage from reverse cyclic loading, the maximum shear force must be reduced to avoid diagonal compression failure of concrete.

N21.6.3.6 Ductility requirements above potential hinge region

Observations from the 2010 Chile earthquake revealed that thin concrete walls may crush at low compression strains. Experiments[2.17] confirmed the field observations and demonstrated that a cage of light transverse reinforcement was sufficient to prevent premature crushing of the walls.

N21.6.3.7 Additional requirements at base of wall

Conventional construction shear walls are permitted up to a height of 30 m in regions with the highest seismicity in Canada (see N21.2.2). The walls are designed using a ductility force-reduction factor R_d of 1.5 so inelastic action is expected when subjected to the design earthquake motions. The requirements are significantly less than required for moderately ductile walls designed with an R_d = 2.0.

N21.6.4 Two-way slabs without beams

2015 NBCC includes frames with two-way slabs and no beams as a standard seismic-force-resisting system that is only permitted in regions of low seismicity, i.e., $I_E F_a S_a$ (0.2) < 0.35 (see N21.2.2). The requirements are based on ACI 318.

N21.7.1.2 Types of seismic-force-resisting systems

The NBCC specifies three types of seismic-force-resisting systems for tilt-up construction as summarized in Table N21.2.2. Conventional walls and frames do not have any additional design requirement in Clause 21 and are therefore not permitted in regions were $I_E F_a S_a$ (0.2) ≥ 0.35 or $I_E F_a S_a$ (1.0) > 0.3.

Limited Ductility (R_d = 1.5) walls and frames may be designed using the traditional force-based approach. The design requirements are given in Clauses 21.7.1 to 21.7.4. In a large tilt-up building with a flexible

Explanatory Notes on CSA A23.3-14

roof diaphragm, e.g., steel deck diaphragm, the flexibility of the roof diaphragm will increase the period of the building, which will reduce the actual force levels. But the flexible diaphragm will also significantly increase the inelastic displacement demands on the building. As there is no way to explicitly account for the increased displacement demands in a force-based design approach, the influence of the diaphragm flexibility shall not be taken into account when calculating the force demands on a Limited Ductility tilt-up building. The increased design forces due to using a shorter than actual period will compensate for the increased ductility demands due to the flexible diaphragm.

Moderately ductile (R_d = 2.0) walls and frames are designed using a displacement-based approach that explicitly accounts for the increased inelastic displacement demands on wall panels and therefore the influence of the flexible diaphragm may be accounted for in reducing the design force levels.

N21.7.2.2 Out-of-plane shear and bending moment
Category 1 of NBCC Table 4.1.8.18 will typically apply to the design of tilt-up panel elements for out-of-plane forces. C_p = element or component factor; usually taken as 1.0. A_r = element or component force amplification factor; for short period buildings with flexible walls, taken equal to 1.0. R_p = Element or component response modification factor; taken equal to 2.5 for most reinforced tilt-up wall panels.

N21.7.2.4.1 Out-of-plane forces
The design of connections for out-of-plane forces will typically be in accordance NBCC 4.1.8.18.7(e). For category 1 walls that are flexible and with non-ductile connections, C_p = 2.0, A_r = 2.5 and R_p = 1.0.

N21.7.3.1 Strength and ductility of connectors
Chapter 13 of the Cement Association of Canada's Concrete Design Handbook has information about standard tilt-up connectors.

N21.7.5 Additional requirements for Moderately Ductile wall panels (R_d = 2.0)
Additional guidance on how to design tilt-up structures using a displacement-based approach is given in Ref. 21.11.

N21.8 Precast concrete
This clause incorporates the ACI specifications that provide procedures for the testing of systems thereby allowing these systems as well as those that emulate cast-in-place construction to be used. The ACI clauses have been modified to fit the NBCC R_d classification system. Further guidance can be found in the ACI 318 commentary.

N21.9 Structural diaphragms
This clause is a much modified version of ACI 318 Clause 21.9. It was modified to reflect the diaphragm requirements contained in NBCC and to better separate the system types.

N21.9.3 Diaphragm systems
Legible load paths are fundamental to the design of diaphragms. Particular attention should be paid to the provision of adequate collector members.

N21.10 Foundations (R_d = 1.3, 1.5, 2.0, 2.5, 3.5, or 4.0)
Background
It is common to assume a fixed-base foundation for earthquake analysis; however, foundations supporting the seismic-force-resisting system (SFRS) will move under earthquake loading and the resulting displacements, particularly rotations at the base of walls or braced frames, will influence the deflections and drifts of the building. Foundation movements can also change the distribution of forces in the SFRS, such as in shear walls going through below-grade levels. Foundation movements also result in increased demands on the gravity-load resisting structure.

Some of the factors affecting the foundation movements are: the type of soil or rock and the load-displacement relationship of the soil or rock; the type of foundation or footing (e.g., raft, piled or spread footing); whether a footing uplifts at one end due to the applied overturning moment; whether a footing is free to rotate or is restrained in some manner, and; whether a foundation is stronger than the demand from the SFRS (called 'capacity protected'); or is weaker than the SFRS (not capacity protected).

Part 4.1.8 Appendices and Earthquake commentary section in the NBCC 2015 Structural Commentaries also have information on foundations and design for earthquake loading.

A typical soil stress-displacement relationship is shown in Figure N21.10.1. Generally, the relationship is highly non-linear, although for rock it tends towards more of a bi-linear (elastic-plastic) shape. The ultimate stress shown in the plot is not used in design. NBCC ultimate limit state (ULS) design uses a factored ultimate stress or factored resistance that is typically 50% of the actual ultimate stress of the soil or rock. NBCC serviceability limit state (SLS) uses a "working stress" or "specified stress" design stress of about 2/3 of the factored resistance. If a geotechnical report gives an ultimate stress value it is important to clarify if it is the actual ultimate stress or the factored stress to be used for ultimate limit state design.

As the factored resistance of soil or rock is only 50% of the actual resistance, the corollary is that soil or rock has considerable over-strength above the factored resistance and this has implications for footing behaviour, shear and flexural design of footings under applied soil stresses, and for the design forces in the structure. Many soils continue to gain strength at large displacements and do not degrade rapidly at large compression strains like concrete. Footing moment-rotation curves generally have similar nonlinear shapes as the soil load-displacement curves; but have additional nonlinearity due to footing uplift.

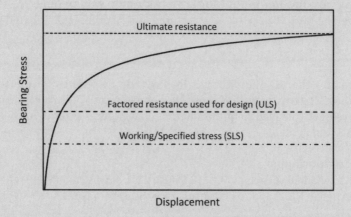

Figure N21.10.1 Typical bearing stress – displacement relationship for soil

The term *foundation* refers to the footing (or raft or pile cap) and the soil it is supported on. Spread footings without soil anchors or piles resist overturning due to the eccentricity of the bearing stress resultant force, which is equal to the total vertical gravity load including the weight of the footing itself. The footing rotation due to an applied overturning moment depends on the shape of the footing, whether or not the footing uplifts, and on the properties of the soil or rock. For spread footings with soil anchor tie-downs, the rotation of the footing at the base of a wall is a function of the soil strength and displacement properties at the toe of the footing and the anchor and structural properties of the soil anchor. A *raft foundation* or *mat foundation* usually involves a thick reinforced concrete slab that is the size of the building it supports or even larger. The rotation at the base of a wall supported on a raft foundation is more a function of the structural properties of the raft than the soil properties. On the other hand, the rotation at the base of a wall supported on a piled foundation is mainly a function of the soil properties and the structural properties of the piles.

In a *capacity-protected foundation*, the factored shear and overturning resistance of the foundation is greater than the maximum demand that can be applied by the SFRS. In a *not capacity-protected (NCP) foundation*, which was previously called a "rocking foundation," the factored overturning resistance of the foundation is less than the maximum possible demand from the SFRS. The foundation is not in static equilibrium when subjected to the maximum force demands; but is in dynamic equilibrium – the foundation will rotate to accommodate the required displacement of the mass similar to a classical rocking system. The term *rocking foundation* is no longer used because there are many differences between NCP foundations and a typical rocking system. Unlike the latter, NCP foundations do not have a well-defined overturning capacity and are not relatively rigid before the uplift causing rocking rotation. NCP foundations can be highly non-linear and can cause significant inelastic yielding of the soil.

A *constrained* or *restrained foundation* is a system where the rotation of the footing and the attached SFRS are in some way restrained from rotating. Examples are raft foundations and spread footings restrained by piles or soil anchors. Another example is a core wall and spread footing at the bottom of several levels of below-grade floor levels where the SFRS wall is attached to adjacent foundation walls by floor slabs. The footing and wall rotation are restrained by the wall interacting with the foundation walls. Note that a footing that is restrained or constrained may still rotate somewhat, although normally the rotations will be small. Constrained foundations are required to be capacity protected, that is, they cannot be designed as not capacity protected (NCP) foundations. Examples of truly unconstrained foundations are walls, braced frames or stiff moment frames attached to a spread footing at grade level where the overturning resistance is provided only by the eccentric gravity loads, and the surrounding attached structure is flexible. In this case the footing and SFRS are free to rotate together. These foundations may be either capacity protected or not capacity protected.

Estimating Foundation Rotations: Non-linear studies[21.18] of walls on unconstrained foundations that were both capacity protected and not-capacity protected and satisfying the requirements of NBCC 2015 and A23.3 indicate that: (i) the shear force and bending moment in the SFRS are often very similar to those calculated using a fixed foundation. Soil over-strength above the factored resistance contributes to this. (ii) For capacity-protected foundations that are unconstrained, the footing rotations can be estimated using linear methods and applying the yield moment capacity to the foundation. (iii) The additional drift ratios in the structure were approximately equal to the footing rotation in radians. (iv) Similar results were observed with not capacity-protected foundations except that linear methods did not give a good estimate of the foundation rotations. (v) Capacity-protected foundations seem to rotate until yielding of the SFRS where the rotation stops and the structure continues to deflect as the hinge undergoes plastic deformation above the footing.

These results suggest the following approach for foundations that are not part of a below-grade structure: (i) Analyze the structure with a fixed base to determine design forces. (ii) Determine the SFRS overturning capacity, which is the maximum demand on the foundation. (iii) Calculate the foundation rotation using either Clause 21.10.3.3.2 or Clause 21.10.3.3.3. (iv) Add the foundation rotations in radians to the drift ratios of the structure calculated using a fixed base.

It is possible to calculate a rotational spring stiffness using the above approach and add it to an analysis model but this approach requires caution as the footing rotation will get multiplied by $R_d R_o$ and that is not how the non-linear model behaved. This approach will lengthen the period resulting in a large increase in the displacements, and reduced structural forces and this is not supported by non-linear analysis. If the approach is used, the design forces should not be reduced.

For foundations that are at the base of a below-grade restraining structure, the principal concern is the effect on the below-grade shear forces in the wall SFRS. Small changes in stiffness of walls and slabs, and small footing rotations can have significant effects on the shear force distribution. See N21.5.2.2.9 for further information.

Some Approaches to Foundation Modeling: For the ULS design of a foundation, the bearing stress in the soil or rock is normally assumed to be uniform and equal to the factored resistance of the soil. This is a statically equivalent bearing stress that normally gives very similar results to the actual bearing stress distribution.[21.19] Raft foundations are often modelled using linear soil springs supporting a linear slab. The soil spring stiffness is provided by the geotechnical engineer, and the effective stiffness of the slab must account for cracking of concrete. A similar approach is used for spread footings with piles or soil anchors.

The behaviour of unconstrained foundations ranges from almost linear to non-linear inelastic. If the footing is capacity protected and does not uplift, the response will likely be fairly linear. If the footing is capacity protected but uplifts, the behaviour may be somewhat non-linear due to some soil yielding. Finally, if the footing is not capacity protected, the behaviour will likely be highly non-linear with the soil pushed well into the non-linear range. Spring stiffnesses are not needed in these cases as footing rotations are given in Clauses 21.10.3.3.2 and 21.10.3.3.3.

N21.10.1 General
The simplified method in Clause 21.10.2 can be used to design foundations that are sufficiently restrained so as to prevent any increased deflection of the SFRS above grade due to foundation movements. The general method in Clause 21.10.3 can be used for all foundations.

N21.10.2 Design of foundations restrained against rotation
When the structure restraining foundation movement has sufficient stiffness and strength to prevent a significant increase in the displacement of the SFRS due to foundation movement, the design of the foundation is simplified as no calculations need to be done for the foundation movements. On the other hand, this implies that there is a statically indeterminate system transmitting the forces from the SFRS to the ground below the structure. One concern is that the load path assumed by the designer may be very different than the actual load distribution and this may result in an expected failure. A common example is when shear walls are interconnected with surrounding foundation walls by below-grade floor diaphragms. The diaphragms will prevent the movement of the foundation from having significant effect on the displacements of the shear walls above grade; but will also cause large shear force reversals in the shear walls. These shear force reversals can cause much larger shear forces than the base shear and a rational analysis must be done in accordance with Clause 21.5.2.2.9 to ensure shear failure will not occur in the shear walls.

N21.10.2.2 Factored resistance
The factored overturning resistance of the foundations satisfying Clause 21.10.2.1 needs to exceed the demand based on the nominal capacity of the SFRS but need not exceed the demand calculated using $R_d R_o = 1.3$. As described in N21.10.3.2.2, the overturning resistance of the foundation due to gravity loads may have little or no overstrength; however as there is a secondary structural system providing restraint to foundation movements, it is expected that system can provide the minimum required overstrength to justify the use of $R_d R_o = 1.3$.

N21.10.2.3 Design of foundation wall restrained by diaphragms
Clause 21.10 applies to R_d values of 1.3 through 4.0, i.e., includes conventional construction, while Clause 21.5.2.2.9 applies only to systems with R_d values of 2.0 or greater. Designers of conventional construction shear walls that are restrained by floor diaphragms are strongly encouraged to use the procedures from Clause 21.5.2.2.9 to ensure that a shear failure will not occur in the shear walls.

N21.10.3.1 General

When a foundation does not meet the limitations given in Clause 21.10.2.1, it must be designed using Clause 21.10.3, which is a general method that can be used for all foundations, including those that meet the limitations given in Clause 21.10.2.1.

N21.10.3.2.1 General

The shear resistance and overturning resistance of foundations are treated separately. In the case of shear resistance, the foundation must be strong enough to resist the demands from the factored gravity loads plus the additional shear force corresponding to the required factored overturning resistance; but the seismic shear force need not exceed the force calculated using $R_d R_o = 1.3$. Here it is assumed that the shear resistance of the walls and the sliding shear resistance of the footings will have sufficient overstrength to justify the $R_d R_o = 1.3$. The requirements for the overturning resistance are more complex and thus are treated in three separate clauses 21.10.3.2.2 to 21.10.3.2.4.

N21.10.3.2.2 Maximum required overturning resistance

NBCC states that structures need not be designed for forces greater than those corresponding to $R_d R_o = 1.0$. NBCC also recognizes that most structural materials have some inherent ductility and minimum over-strength to justify the use of $R_d R_o = 1.3$. NBCC therefore allows the maximum required factored resistances to be based on forces determined using $R_d R_o = 1.3$ when recommended by the appropriate design standard. The expectation is that structures designed this way will perform satisfactorily when subjected to $R_d R_o = 1.0$ force levels. However, for foundations there are two issues that complicate the idea of using an $R_d R_o = 1.3$ force cut-off. Firstly, often the gravity (dead) load on the footing is the main source of overturning resistance and there may be little or no overstrength in the resistance provided by gravity loads. Secondly, while soils typically have bearing resistance over-strengths of about 2.0, the increase in overturning capacity of a footing due to increased bearing resistance of the soil or rock may be very small. The explanation for this follows. An increase in the bearing resistance of soil or rock will increase the lever-arm between the applied vertical gravity load and the equal and opposite vertical reaction force in the soil or rock. In the idealized case of the soil having an infinite bearing capacity (and the concrete in the footing having an infinite strength), the lever-arm will be half the footing length. When soil or rock has a high bearing capacity, the lever-arm may already be 90% of half the footing length. Thus any increase in bearing capacity of soil or rock will result in a small increase in the lever-arm, and hence a small increase in the over-turning capacity of the foundation.

N21.10.3.2.3 Capacity-protected foundations

Whenever possible, the factored overturning resistance of the foundation should satisfy this clause. When a foundation is capacity protected, i.e., when it has a resistance greater than the SFRS, the inelastic action will mostly be in the SFRS, which is preferred for a number of reasons. Systems with capacity-protected foundations are better able to tolerate unexpected larger seismic demands and the foundation movements will have much less influence on the overall deformations of the system.

When a ductile SFRS designed using a large $R_d R_o$ has an overturning capacity that is a small fraction of the elastic demand, the capacity-protected foundation will also have an overturning capacity that is a small fraction of the elastic demand. If the SFRS turns out to have unexpected overstrength, the foundation may become the "weak link" in the system. In that case, the inelastic demands on the foundation may be very large. To reduce the chance of this happening, the foundations with a lower resistance compared to the elastic demand shall have a factored overturning resistance greater than or equal to what is required to resist the factored gravity loads and the *probable* overturning capacity of the SFRS. The wall overstrength factor or the equivalent overstrength factor for other SFRS is included so that the decision to use nominal or probable overturning capacity depends on the actual strength of the SFRS including any overstrength.

N21.10.3.2.4 Not capacity-protected (NCP) foundations

Not capacity-protected is the new terminology used to refer to what was previously called "rocking foundations." The old terminology is no longer used because of the confusion it created. The rotation of a foundation subjected to an overturning moment is commonly referred to as a rocking rotation. Thus the term rocking foundation is sometimes used to refer to any foundation that rotates, which may include any unrestrained foundation. The classical rocking mechanism involves a rigid block on a rigid half-space. The system is rigid until the overturning moment exceeds the overturning resistance provided by the weight of the block, and then the block lifts off (rotates) with a constant overturning resistance. When the overturning moment is reduced, the block returns to the original position. The classical rocking behavior is very different than the behavior of what was previously known as "rocking foundations."

When foundations are made weaker, they reduce the demands on the SFRS; but the total displacements of the structure increases. For example, when a shear wall foundation is made weaker, the maximum overturning moment that can be induced into the base of the wall is reduced and the drifts due to bending of the wall is reduced; however the increased rotation of the weaker foundation will cause the entire wall to rotate as a rigid body, and the total displacements at the top of the building will be larger. Thus the primary concern with designing weaker foundations is ensuring the gravity-load resisting portion of the building, which is connected to the SFRS, is able to tolerate the increased displacements.

Nonlinear analysis of foundations has demonstrated that the amount that the foundation rotation will increase is a function of the absolute overturning capacity of the foundation, reflected in the $R_d R_o$ used to design the foundation; but also the relative overturning capacity of the foundation and the SFRS that is supported by the foundation.[21.20] Thus the factored overturning capacity of the foundation cannot be less than 75% of the nominal overturning capacity of the SFRS or overturning moments calculated using $R_d R_o = 2.0$. This new requirement means that the foundation cannot be designed independent of the SFRS unless the overturning capacity is limited by the maximum required resistance given in Clause 21.10.3.2.2.

N21.10.3.3.1 General

Regardless of the R_d value used to design the structure, the increased displacements of a structure due to foundation movements must be accounted for. Only if the structure restraining foundation movements has sufficient stiffness and strength to prevent a significant increase in displacement of the structure as per Clause 21.10.2.1, can the foundation can be designed according to Clause 21.10.2, and the requirements of this clause do not need to be satisfied.

The following discussion is for *unconstrained foundations*. Foundations constrained by tie-downs or piles require an analysis that includes modeling of the tie-downs or the pile load-deformation relationships, as well as the properties of the foundation and the soil stress-deflection relationships.

N21.10.3.3.2 Movements of capacity-protected foundations

When the factored overturning resistance of a foundation satisfies Clause 21.10.3.2.**2*** (Maximum required overturning resistance) or 21.10.3.2.**3*** (Capacity-protected foundations), the foundation movements may be calculated using the simplified procedures described in this clause (*note: wrong reference clause numbers were indicated in the first printing of CSA A23.3-14).

Estimating the interstorey drift ratios of a building with a flexible foundation by adding the interstorey drift ratios of the building determined using a fixed-base model to an interstorey drift ratio equal to the actual footing rotation (in radians) results in a safe estimate of the interstorey drift ratios. This is because the increased flexibility of the SFRS due to the foundation movements will reduce the demands on the SFRS and hence reduce the deformations of the SFRS.

Explanatory Notes on CSA A23.3-14

Equation 21.22 is a simple equation for estimating foundation rotation (in radians) when the applied overturning moment is sufficiently large to cause the "heel" of the footing to up-lift. It is a simplified version of the procedure summarized below,[21.19] which can be used to make a more accurate estimate:

$$\theta = 0.2\,(1 - v) \left(\frac{q_s}{0.5G_0}\right) \left(\frac{\ell_f}{a_s}\right) \xi_L \cdot \xi_{NL} \qquad \text{Eq. N21.10.1}$$

Where:

v = Poisson's ratio for soil or rock (varies from 0.1 to 0.5; commonly between 0.2 and 0.4);

q_s = magnitude of uniform bearing stress in soil or rock required to resist the applied loads; but shall not exceed the factored bearing resistance;

G_0 = initial shear modulus of soil or rock given by $G_0 = \gamma_s \cdot V_s^2 / 1000$ (Note error in first printing);

ℓ_f = length of footing (perpendicular to axis of rotation).

a_s = length of uniform bearing stress in soil or rock required to resist the applied loads;

ξ_L = nondimensional parameter that accounts for initial linear rotational stiffness of footing. It can be accurately determined from a figure given in Ref. 21.11 or estimated from:

$$\xi_L = \left(1 - 1.5\frac{d_f}{\ell_f}\right)\left(1 - 0.1\frac{\ell_f}{b_f}\right) \geq 0.2 \qquad \text{Eq. N21.10.2}$$

Where the ratios are restricted as follows: $d_f/\ell_f \leq 0.4$ and $\ell_f/b_f \leq 5$;

d_f = depth (thickness) of footing;

b_f = width of footing (parallel to axis of rotation);

ξ_{NL} = nondimensional parameter that accounts for increased nonlinear rotation of foundation due to reduction in shear modulus of soil with increasing soil strains. It can be accurately determined from a figure in Ref. 21.11 or estimated from:

$$\xi_{NL} = 1 + 4\left(\frac{q_s}{q_f} - 0.5\right)\left(\frac{a_s}{b_f}\right)^{1.5} \geq 1.0 \qquad \text{Eq. N21.10.3}$$

Where the ratio is restricted as follows: $0.5 \leq q_s / q_f \leq 1.0$;

q_f = factored bearing resistance of soil or rock, typically 50% of the ultimate bearing capacity at which soil actually yields.

In Eq. 21.22 and Eq. N21.10.1, the effective shear modulus over the linear range of foundation response is assumed to be 50% of the initial shear modulus G_0. To facilitate the use of other values of effective shear modulus, the 0.5 factor is shown in Eq. N21.10.1.

When the size of a footing is just sufficient to provide the required factored overturning resistance, the uniform bearing stress q_s will be equal to the factored bearing resistance q_f, and the length of uniform bearing stress a_s will be known from the footing design calculations. When a footing is made somewhat larger than the minimum size required for strength, these parameters can be calculated as follows:

$$a_s = \ell_f - 2M/P \qquad\qquad\qquad \text{Eq. N21.10.4}$$

$$q_s = P/(a_s \cdot b_f) \qquad\qquad\qquad \text{Eq. N21.10.5}$$

Where:

M = Applied overturning moment;

P = Applied vertical load on the soil or rock, including weight of the footing.

With the procedure above for determining footing rotations, a foundation can be designed for improved performance (reduced rotations) in addition to overturning strength. In one example,[21.19] increasing the size of a footing (the concrete volume) by 10%, reduced the rotations of the footing by 75%, i.e., the rotations of the slightly larger footing was only 25% of the rotations of the slightly smaller footing. The small cost for the increase in footing size will provide significantly improved performance of the building during an earthquake because the reduced footing rotations will result in much less demand on the gravity-load frame attached to the SFRS supported on the footing. The reason for the large reduction in rotation due to a small increase in footing size is because increasing the size of a footing, reduces the required eccentricity of the larger soil reaction force, which combined with the increased footing length, increases the available length of uniform bearing stress a_s and thus reduces the magnitude of the uniform bearing stress q_s. The increase in a_s and decrease in q_s directly reduce the foundation rotation, while the decrease in q_s has the additional effect of reducing ξ_{NL}.

N21.10.3.3.3 Movements of not capacity-protected (NCP) foundations

The rotation of a not capacity-protected (NCP) foundation cannot be determined from an applied overturning moment as the footing movement is the result of the required movement of the structure. That is, the mass of the structure will displace a certain amount depending on the period of the structure and the foundation will rotate to tolerate that movement. The movement of NCP foundations generally have to be determined using a nonlinear dynamic analysis of the structure, and the analysis must account for the increased rotational flexibility of the footing due to the soil strains resulting from the footing movements. NCP foundations are expected to rotate more, sometimes much more, than capacity-protected foundations and should only be used when the gravity-loading resisting structure attached to the SFRS that is supported on the NCP foundation can tolerate the large increase in displacement demands.

The analysis required to accurately determine the movement of an NCP foundation is complex. Such analysis can be avoided by providing a capacity-protected foundation; or by only providing an NCP foundation when the surrounding structure can easily tolerate the increased displacements of the SFRS. In that case, the simple upper-bound estimate of the increased displacements can be used and it will be not be necessary to do the complex dynamic analysis.

In the simple upper-bound (safe) estimate of the increase in displacement of an SFRS due to an NCP foundation, the interstorey drift ratios of the SFRS determined from a fixed-base model (assuming the foundation does not move) are increased at every level, including immediately above the footing, by an interstorey drift ratio equal to the largest of: (a) 50% of the global drift of the structure determined from a fixed-base model; (b) the rotation of the foundation due to the nominal overturning capacity of the SFRS, and; (c) 0.005.

The factored overturning capacity of the foundation may be less than the nominal overturning capacity of the SFRS. In that case, the uniform bearing stress determined from Eq. N21.10.5 (used to calculate the rotation of the foundation due to the nominal overturning capacity of the SFRS in (b) above) may

Explanatory Notes on CSA A23.3-14

be larger than the factored bearing resistance. Note that the factored bearing stress is typically 50% of the ultimate bearing stress.

As indicated by Eq. N21.10.4, the maximum overturning moment that can be resisted by a footing is $P \cdot \ell_f/2$. When the applied overturning moment exceeds this value, the upper limit of 3.0 times the rotation of the foundation when subjected to an overturning moment equal to the factored overturning resistance of the foundation should be used. If this turned out to be a very large rotation, then it would likely be necessary to do a detailed dynamic analysis to make a more accurate estimate of the footing rotation.

N21.10.3.4 Design of footings in NCP foundations

When a foundation is capacity protected by the SFRS, the forces applied to the footing are well defined. Similarly, when a foundation is designed for the maximum required overturning capacity, the foundation design forces can safely be used to design the footing. Only when a foundation is not capacity protected are special considerations needed to determine safe design forces for the footing.

The plan dimensions of the footing, which control the foundation overturning capacity, are determined using the factored bearing capacity of the soil or rock. Overstrength in bearing capacity of soil or rock results in the resultant vertical force being located closer to the "toe" of the foundation. Thus the required amount of flexural reinforcement in the footing must be increased, and the shear design of the footing may need to account for the increased shear span-to-depth ratio of the footing. As the bearing capacity of the soil or rock increases, the capacity of the SFRS may be reached, or footing design forces may reach the upper-bound limit (calculated using $R_d R_o$ equal to 1.3).

NCP footings can have large rotations that can result in large soil strains that mobilize large soil overstrengths, as illustrated in the soil stress-deformation curve in Fig. N21.10.1. This results in a reduction in the size of the soil stress block and movement of the vertical resultant towards the "toe" of the footing, which changes the distribution of shear within the footing along its length and increases the design moment within the footing.

N21.10.4.3

Designers must ensure a complete load path from shear wall zones through the footing into the soil. Fig. N21.10.4.3 illustrates how the strut-and-tie model given in Clause 11.4 may be used to visualize the force flow within a footing. In this case, the shear in the footing is transferred by a compression strut anchored by the 90° hook or mechanical anchorage at the end of the concentrated wall reinforcement (see circle inset). Additional information about anchorage of tension ties is given in Clause 11.4.3.2. It is possible to develop more refined strut and tie models that account for all the reinforcement in the footing and which, in some cases, could allow the development of the tension force in the vertical reinforcement over the depth of the footing. It should be noted that the same principles apply to foundations resisting lateral forces other than seismic forces.

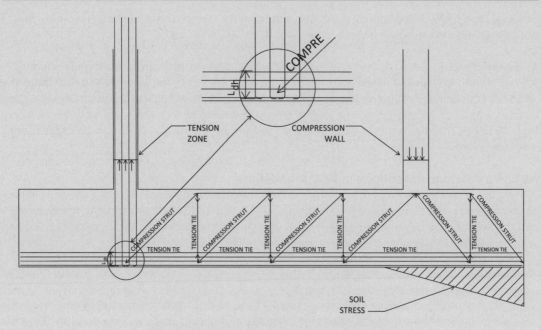

Fig. N21.10.4.3 Flow of forces within a footing.

N21.11 Members not considered part of the seismic-force-resisting system (R_d = 1.5, 2.0, 2.5, 3.5, or 4.0)

Force-based seismic design leads to the approach of identifying a portion of the structure as the seismic-force-resisting system (SFRS), and treating it very differently than the remaining parts of the structure. From a displacement perspective, all parts of the structure must be able to tolerate the same displacement demands that ground motions cause in the structure. Clause 21.11 gives the requirements that ensure that the parts of the structure that are not designed for seismic forces will continue to function and carry the gravity loads during and after the displacement cycles caused by an earthquake.

Structural members covered by this clause include elements of the gravity-load resisting frame, and also members that might be considered part of the SFRS; but are too flexible relative to other members in the SFRS or do not satisfy the dimensional requirements for the SFRS. All members that are not part of the SFRS either need to be flexible (and strong) enough to tolerate the design displacements while remaining elastic or the members must be detailed so that flexural hinging can occur without shear or compression failure.

A simplified approach is to use a linear model of the gravity frame, impose the design displacements (drifts), and calculate the resulting axial forces, shear forces, and bending moments. These must then be added to the forces and bending moments due to the gravity loads. The total axial forces and shear forces must not exceed the factored capacities of the members and sufficient detailing must be provided so that the members have the needed flexural ductility.

N21.11.1.1 Application

The requirements of Clause 21.11 must be satisfied for all structures regardless of the R_d used to design the SFRS. The rationale for this is that an SFRS designed using a low value of R_d could be very flexible thereby causing large demands on the gravity-load frame. The demands on the gravity-load frame will be small when the displacements of the SFRS are small. This will be the case if the seismicity is low (ground displacements are small); or the SFRS is stiff.

N21.11.1.2

Non-structural elements can have a serious effect on structural elements as the structure deflects laterally. Examples are infill block walls that are built tight against columns or up-stand beams (curbs) that are built tight against columns creating the well-known short-column effect (columns with reduced displacement capacity and may fail in shear). Conditions such as these must be accounted for using design and detailing solutions or by ensuring the non-structural elements are sufficiently separated from the structural elements.

N21.11.2.1 General analyses requirements

A linear dynamic analysis can be used to determine an appropriate distribution of strength in the SFRS, i.e., can be used to determine the design forces for the SFRS, and can be used to determine the maximum top displacement of the building when an appropriate average effective stiffness is used in the analysis. Such an analysis cannot however be used to determine the distribution of deformations in the building because it does not account for the concentration of deformations in the inelastic portions of the SFRS. A linear analysis may give very unsafe results for the demands on the gravity-load frame in the building.

When the SFRS is relatively uniform over the height of the building, and meets all the design requirements of Clause 21, the concentration of inelastic deformation is reasonably well known, and thus simplified procedures can be used. For example, a cantilever shear wall designed to Clause 21 will have a concentrated plastic hinge near the base, and the envelope of interstorey drifts given in 21.11.2.2 can be used to make safe estimates of the demands on the gravity-load frame. For coupled-wall systems or moment-resisting frames, the envelopes of interstorey drifts given in N21.11.2.2 can be used.

When the SFRS is highly non-uniform over the height, the simplified envelopes may give unsafe results due to a concentration of inelastic deformations at other elevations of the SFRS. An approach that can be used in that case is to use a nonlinear model of the SFRS, to perform a nonlinear static (push-over) analysis of the building until the top displacement equals the displacement described in 21.11.2.1(a). Note that multiple analyses with different force distributions are required as the envelope of interstorey drifts result from different modes of the SFRS. An alternate to using a nonlinear model of the SFRS, is to use a linear static model with reduced section properties in the portions of the SFRS that are expected to undergo inelastic deformations. Again, the structure must be displaced as described in 21.11.2.1(a) and multiple load distributions are required. Caution is needed with this approach to ensure the zone of reduced section properties and the relative reduction in section properties yields the correct distribution of deformations as will occur in the nonlinear structure.

A final approach that can be used is non-linear response history analysis of the building. If the analysis includes a non-linear model of the gravity frame, then the analysis provides the deformation demands on the gravity frame directly. Appropriate acceptance criteria must be used to ensure the deformation demands on the gravity-frame members are appropriate given the level of detailing. It is very important that nonlinear response history analysis, and in particular the inclusion of the gravity-load frame in the model, is not used to justify reduce deformation demands of the building. Thus the requirements of 21.11.2.1(a) must still be met when using nonlinear response history analysis. Nonlinear response history analysis is a complex process that requires considerable effort and judgement, thus Clause 21.2.2 requires an independent review of such analysis.

A linear model of the gravity frame can be combined with a linear or nonlinear model of the SFRS. The stiffness of the linear gravity-load frame model should be significantly reduced to avoid the frame resisting significant lateral earthquake forces. The calculated forces in the gravity frame must be subsequently corrected. For example, if the stiffnesses of the gravity-load frame members are reduced by a factor of 100, the calculated forces in the members of the gravity-load frame must be increased by a factor of 100 to obtain realistic estimates of the demands on these members.

Whenever a linear model is used for the gravity-load frame, Clause 21.11.3.3.3 and Clause 21.11.3.4.1 can be used to determine whether the force demands on the columns or walls and the beams exceed the appropriate limits that depend on the level of detailing.

Note that all remaining parts of Clause 21.11.3 must be satisfied regardless of what analysis is used to determine the seismic demands. In shear wall buildings, there are additional requirements in Clause 21.11.3.3.2 that the columns and bearing walls must meet over the height of the plastic hinge irrespective of what analysis procedure is used to estimate the interstorey drift demands on the gravity-load frame.

N21.11.2.2 Simplified analysis of shear wall buildings

Figure 21.1 is based on extensive non-linear analyses of cantilever shear wall buildings.[21.5] The simplified interstorey drift envelope provides a simple approach for determining demands on the gravity-load resisting frame when the SFRS is relatively uniform over the height of the building. The interstorey drift ratio at any level is determined by multiplying the global drift ratio Δ/h_w by the ratio given in Fig. 21.1. For example, at the top of a cantilever wall, the interstorey drift ratio is 1.6 times the global drift ratio.

When the SFRS consists of coupled walls or moment-resisting frames, the interstorey drift envelopes to be used are summarized in Fig. N21.11.2.2(a). When the SFRS is a cantilever wall, the interstorey drift ratio is 1.6 times the global drift over the top 25% of the building and reduces linearly to 0.7 times the global drift at the base. When the SFRS is a coupled wall, the interstorey drift ratio is 1.3 times the global drift ratio over the full height of the building. Finally, when the SFRS is a moment-resisting frame, the interstorey drift ratio is 2.0 times the global drift ratio over the bottom 50% of the building height and reduces linearly to 1.0 times the global drift ratio at the top of the building. The interstorey drift envelope for cantilever walls was developed from an extensive study and was adopted into Clause 21. The interstorey drift envelopes for coupled walls and moment-resisting frames are based on a more limited amount of analysis. See Ref. 21.11 for additional information.

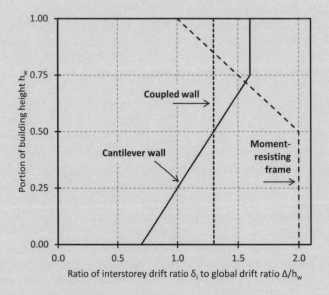

Fig. N21.11.2.2 (a) Envelopes of interstorey drifts for three different types of SFRS[21.11]

As the interstorey drift calculated using the interstorey drift envelopes are specific to a particular gravity frame and not to the structure as a whole, it lends itself to applying it to substructures of each of the gravity frames. When the gravity-load frame is not uniform over the height, for example there is a large horizontal transfer member at one level, simplified analysis of a sub-structure, consisting of a few stories of the gravity-load frame, may be done. The frames must be subjected to the interstorey drifts for that particular elevation of the building as given in the interstorey envelopes. The interstorey drifts are imposed on the frame and the shears, axial forces and bending moments determined. The gravity-load frame can be assessed by looking only at critical portions and without having to analyse the complete structure.

When the gravity-load frame is relatively uniform over the height of the building, the demands on the gravity-load frame can be quickly checked at only a few critical points. The maximum interstorey drift from the envelopes can be used to determine the maximum bending moments and maximum shear forces induced into the columns as described below. The interstorey drifts can also be used to check punching shear resistance of the flat plate floor slabs using 21.11.4.

When the gravity-load resisting frame is uniform over a number of stories, the column/bearing wall drift ratios can be estimated from the interstorey drift ratios knowing only the relative stiffnesses of the columns/bearing walls and floor system. Inherent in this analysis is the assumption that the interstorey drift is uniform over a number of stories. Fig. 21.11.2.2(b) shows the relationship for three cases, where: h_s = the storey height; ℓ_{flr} = the clear span of the floor system.

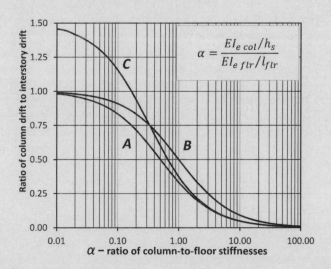

The equation shown in the figure:
$$\alpha = \frac{EI_{e\,col}/h_s}{EI_{e\,flr}/l_{flr}}$$

Fig. N21.11.2.2 (b) Ratio of column-to-building drifts where frame members and building drifts are relatively uniform.[21.21]

Case A is a two-column frame where the interstorey drift ratios are due to the relative lateral displacements of the floors. Case A also provides an approximate solution for the end column in most frames. **Case B** is for an interior column of a multi-column frame where the floor on either side of the column has the same properties. Due to the floor framing in on both sides of the interior column, the column drifts are larger than in Case A. **Case C** is a single column connected directly to a shear wall. Since the shear wall is assumed to be infinitely rigid, the column demands are increased. Note that when the floor rigidity is more than about five times the column rigidity ($\alpha < 0.2$), e.g., due to a stiff floor beam, the column drifts are larger than the building drifts. This happens because of the deflected shape of the beam – the infinitely rigid wall forces the beam to have the same slope at one end, while at the other end; the flexible column is not able to bend the beam in double curvature. Thus the beam is bent in single curvature and this imposes a reverse slope on the column at the floor levels.

When a gravity-load resisting frame includes a long wall, there is an additional magnification of the column drifts that must be included. Due to the portion of the frame made up of solid wall being rigid, column drifts are magnified by an additional factor of $1 + (\ell_w + \ell_c)/2\ell_{flr}$, where ℓ_w = the horizontal length of the wall, ℓ_c = the horizontal dimension of the column and ℓ_{flr} = the clear span of the floor system.

When the column drift ratio δ_{col} has been determined from the building interstorey drift ratio using Fig. 21.11.2.2 (b), the maximum bending moment and shear force applied to the column can be determined from the following well known equations:

$$M = 6EI_{e\,col}/h_s \cdot \delta_{col}$$
Eq. N21.11.1

$$V = 12EI_{e\,col}/h_s^2 \cdot \delta_{col}$$
Eq. N21.11.2

N21.11.3.1 Shear resistance
When a linear model is used for the gravity-load frame, the bending moments induced into the members may be significantly larger than the flexural capacity of the member. Thus the procedures normally used from moment-resisting frames can be used to determine the maximum possible shear demands.

N21.11.3.2 Resistance of members transferring gravity loads
Transfer girders are often used to transfer gravity loads horizontally in a structure. These members may pick up significant additional forces when the gravity-load frame displaces laterally.

N21.11.3.3.1 Limitations on thin bearing walls
Thin concrete bearing walls with a single layer of reinforcement are a cost effective structural member in certain applications. However, such walls may not be able to tolerate cycles of combined in-plane and out-of-plane displacement and therefore must not be used to support significant gravity loads in a structure that is expected to see significant displacements during the design earthquake. The maximum interstorey drift at any point in the structure is used as the indicator of whether or not such thin walls are permitted.

N21.11.3.3.2 Plastic hinge regions of shear wall buildings
(a) The displacements of shear walls can induce demands into gravity-load columns in two different ways. When the bending stiffness of the floor system is significant compared to the columns, interstorey drift of the building induces bending moments and shear forces into the column. The magnitude of the induced bending moments depends on the interstorey drift of the building and the relative column-to-floor stiffness as given in Fig. N21.11.2.2 (b). If a floor system is very flexible, e.g., a very thin flat plate that is significantly cracked, the bending moments induced into the column by interstorey drifts are negligible.

A thin flat plate floor slab may be very flexible in out-of-plane bending; but may have a very high in-plane stiffness and will force the gravity-load columns to experience the same lateral displacement profile as the shear walls at the floor levels. If the shear walls experience significant curvature (the interstorey drift changes significantly from one floor to the next), the column will experience bending as a result of being interconnected to the shear walls by the axially rigid floor slabs, which is the type of column bending that is dealt with in this clause.

If the displacement profile of shear walls and gravity-load columns are the same, then the curvature demands in the two elements will be the same. This clause requires that the curvature capacity of the gravity load columns and bearing walls be sufficient to tolerate the curvature demands in the shear walls. In order to remain flexible enough to tolerate the expecting bending in the plastic hinge zone of the building, the axial compression due to gravity loads must be limited so that the compression strain depth is less than that given by Equation 21.23.

(b) Given the level of damage that is expected in the plastic hinge zone of shear wall buildings, it is prudent to protect all gravity-load columns and bearing walls over this height by providing a minimum level of detailing to increase the chance that these members can tolerate the expected deformations in the plastic hinge zone and continue to support the gravity loads. The specified amount of detailing is considered the minimum that should be provided. Many designers, particularly those with US experience, may choose to provide additional reinforcement to protect this important part of structure and will extend this reinforcement above the plastic hinge zone. The requirement to provide this reinforcement is waived if the maximum global drift is less than 0.005.

N21.11.3.3.3 Design of columns and walls for plastic hinging

When seismic demands on the gravity-load resisting frame are determined using a linear model of the gravity-load frame, the design requirements for the columns and bearing walls are determined by the ratio of the calculated induced bending moment due to the seismic deformation demands to the factored bending resistance of the member M_r. Factored resistances are used to account for the uncertainty in displacement demands. The actual resistance of the members will be larger; but the displacement demands may also be significantly larger due to the variability of the ground motions consistent with the design earthquake motions. While this variability is not normally considered in the design of ductile SFRS members, it must be considered when designing potentially brittle members that may cause collapse of the structure.

Rather than provide design requirements as a function of the ratio of calculated induced bending moment determined from a linear analysis to the factored bending resistance as was done for beams, the approach taken for columns and bearing walls was to provide limits for common members. The limits depend on the axis of bending in walls (strong or weak axis), and the level of applied axial compression. P_s (given in the table) is the axial compression force resulting from factored dead load plus factored live load using earthquake load factors, and must include any additional axial compression induced in the member due to the gravity-load frame being subjected to lateral displacements.

The limits on the calculated induced bending moment determined from a linear analysis are based on test results, reference documents such as FEMA 356 and ASCE 41 and considerable judgment. Note that the effective stiffness that is used for the linear gravity-load frame member will have a significant effect on the calculated induced bending moment. Clause 21.11.2.1 (c) gives the designer the flexibility to choose reasonable (upper-bound) effective stiffness values; however Clause 21.11.3.3.3 specifies that the bending moment induced in walls that are not tied as compression members over the full length shall be determined using the uncracked section properties because of concerns that these members will not have the ductility to tolerate large inelastic curvatures.

N21.11.3.4 Design of gravity-load resisting beams

Much of the discussion given above in N21.11.3.3.3 is also relevant to this clause. For beams, the approach taken was to require increased detailing requirements in the beam depending on the level of the induced bending moments. When the induced bending moments are large, the designer can choose to adjust the geometry of the structure so that the induced bending moments are smaller; or can provide the additional detailing. When the induced bending moment exceeds 5.0 times the factored bending resistance, the geometry of the structure must be modified.

N21.11.4 Design of slab-column connections for seismic drift demands

When the gravity-load frame consists of flat plate floor slabs supported on columns, the inelastic deformation of the gravity-load frame may concentrate in the slab around the columns. The damage in the slab will reduce the punching shear capacity of the slab. Irreparable damage was observed in floor slabs during the Northridge earthquake. The damage was sufficient to result in complete collapse of slabs without sufficient integrity reinforcement.

N21.11.4.1 Reduction of punching shear resistance due to drift demands

Equation 21-24 gives the reduction factor R_E to be applied to the concrete contribution for reinforced concrete slabs given in Clause 13.3.4 and the concrete contribution for prestressed concrete slabs given in Clause 18.12.3.3. When the factored shear stress $v_f = V_f/b_o d$ exceeds the reduced punching shear resistance, transverse shear reinforcement shall be provided in the slab. Note that the shear stress demand is calculated ignoring the additional shear stress due to unbalanced bending moment, as first proposed by Pan and Moehle,[21.22] as the slab is expected to be severely damaged, which will significantly reduce the bending moment that will be transferred from the slab to the column.

When the interstorey drift ratio $\delta_i \leq 0.005$, the reduction factor $R_E = 1.0$, and when the interstorey drift ratio is the maximum value permitted by 2015 NBCC ($\delta_i = 0.025$), the reduction factor $R_E = 0.25$.

Fig. N21.11.4.1 compares Eq. 21.24 with test results from loaded slabs subjected to lateral displacements. All solid data points (close to Eq. 21.24) are from tests on slabs without shear reinforcement. The two results at the top right of the plot are from slabs with shear studs. The slabs with transverse shear reinforcement clearly show a marked increase in drift capacity.

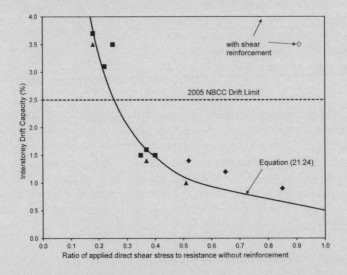

Fig. N21.11.4.1 Comparison for Eq. 21.24 with test data on slabs.

N21.11.4.2 Design of shear reinforcement in slabs

When the concrete contribution to shear strength – reduced to account for damage due to interstorey drift demand on the slab column connection – is not adequate to resist the applied gravity load shear stresses, then either the interstorey drift demand must be reduced by increasing the stiffness of the SFRS, or transverse shear reinforcement must be provided in the slab. This clause specifies the procedure to be used to design shear reinforcement in the slab.

Explanatory Notes on CSA A23.3-14

(a) The same reduction factor R_E given by Eq. 21.24 is used to reduce the total shear strength of a slab with shear reinforcement to account for the damage due to interstorey drift demand. In addition, the concrete contribution used to calculate the shear strength of a slab with shear reinforcement is reduced by 50% from the expressions given in Clauses 13 and 18. Sufficient shear reinforcement must be provided so that the reduced shear strength is greater than the factored shear stress $v_f = V_f/b_o d$ due to gravity load only.

As damage due to interstorey drift will be concentrated in the zone of initial flexural cracking (maximum bending moment) in the slab, only one critical section needs to be considered. That is, a section outside the region defined in 21.11.4.2(d) need not be considered for seismic design; however it may be critical for gravity-load design.

(b) This clause specifies the minimum amount of transverse shear reinforcement.

(c) An arrangement of shear reinforcement that satisfies both the seismic requirements of 21.11.4 and the non-seismic requirements of 13.3 must be provided.

(d) All of the reinforcement design (detailing) rules given in 13.3 must be satisfied. This includes: maximum amount of shear reinforcement to prevent a concrete compression failure as well as spacing, anchorage, and arrangement of shear reinforcement except as multiple sections are not considered, the shear reinforcement must be provided over at least four times the effective depth d of the slab from the zone of initial flexural cracking (maximum bending moment) in the slab.

N22 Plain concrete

N22.1 Scope
Since the structural integrity of plain concrete members depends solely on the properties of the concrete, their use should be limited to: members that are primarily in a state of compression; members that can tolerate random cracks without detriment to their structural integrity; and members where ductility is not an essential feature of design. The standard does not permit the use of plain concrete columns or plain concrete beams.

The minimum concrete strength for plain concrete is not limited to 20 MPa because there is no concern for bond strength and corrosion protection of reinforcement. See Cl. 8.6.1.3. In many circumstances the minimum concrete strength will be governed by the durability provisions of CSA-A23.1. However, even when concrete durability does not restrict the minimum strength it would be normal to use strengths exceeding 15 MPa in order to achieve reasonably homogeneous concrete with adequate cement so that the concrete can be finished satisfactorily. (ACI 318M-14 prescribes a specified compressive concrete strength of structural plain concrete of not less than the larger of 17 MPa and that required for durability).

N22.2 Control joints
Construction joints are a very important design consideration. Control joints are not required if the random cracking resulting from creep, shrinkage and temperature effects will not affect the structural integrity and is otherwise acceptable (e.g. in a continuous wall footing transverse control joints may not be necessary).

Control joints may be made with sheet metal or sheet plastic inserts, "water-stop" inserts, rubber inserts or formed, sawed, or tooled grooves in the concrete surface to cause cracking at the predetermined location. The thickness of the concrete section at these inserts or grooves should be reduced at least 25 percent to make the control joint effective. It is good practice to form joints only part way through the member so that aggregate interlock in the remaining concrete can hold the elements in line. Adjacent elements may be held in line by the use of appropriately aligned, free-sliding dowels protected against corrosion.

N22.3 Design
Plain concrete members are proportioned for adequate strength by using factored forces and by keeping computed stresses within permissible stress limits for all loading conditions.

N22.4 Walls
Eqs. (22-1) has been revised slightly to be consistent with Eq. 14-1. This results in a slightly reduced factored resistance.

N22.6.3
The reduced overall thickness for concrete cast against earth is to allow for unevenness of excavation and for some contamination of the concrete adjacent to the soil.

N22.6.6 Shear resistance
Shear failure in plain concrete will be a diagonal tension failure occurring when the principal tensile stress near the centroidal axis reaches the tensile strength of the concrete. Plain concrete members of usual proportions will be controlled by flexural tensile strength rather than shear strength. For other than rectangular sections the following expression should be used in place of Eq. (22-2).

$$V_r = 0.18 \lambda \phi_c \sqrt{f_c'} \left(\frac{I\,b}{Q} \right)$$

N22.6.6.2.1
The critical sections for shear in plain concrete footings are the same as those shown in Fig. N15.5.2(a) except that d is replaced by h.

N22.8.5(b)
The coefficient for shear is 3/4 rather than 2/3 based on the maximum elastic principal tension stress in a circular section, which is 4/3 times the average.

N23 Tilt-up wall panels

N23.2.7 Sandwich panels
Non-composite sandwich wall panels typically consist of a non-structural outer wythe (outer skin) and a structural inner panel separated by a layer of rigid insulation. The two layers of concrete are connected using proprietary tie systems developed for this specific use. The ties must be designed to resist the weight of the outer wythe and stresses caused during panel lifting. As well, they should be thermally non-conductive and compatible with the concrete material they are cast in, and allow for the two layers of concrete to move independently when subjected to different thermal and shrinkage stresses. Special detailing at panel edges, openings, and embedded metal connectors should allow for the differential movement of the two layers to avoid any bonding, which can cause undesirable cracking of the outer skin. Cracking of the outer skin in non-composite sandwich panels compared to non-sandwich panels can be more prevalent due to the thin concrete section (typically 75 mm), low amount of reinforcement, and the lack of higher axial loads to assist in the closing of cracks. Special concrete mix designs that are low shrinkage or have fibres added to control cracking may also be used to help minimize cracks.

N23.2.9.1
The provision of tension ties is important to hold the walls in place and resist any forces that may be imparted on the walls from other sources. These can include forces induced by foundation settlement, thermal movement, impact, seismic, wind, and fire conditions. Wall panels held at the top by only steel deck, wood decking, or plywood can be susceptible to failure during fire conditions due to the thinness

Explanatory Notes on CSA A23.3-14

of the material and potential for it to fail or lose its strength quickly when exposed to extreme heat from a fire. This can lead to loss of lateral support and the possibility of the walls falling outwards, which could endanger emergency personnel outside the building. The addition of tie struts or continuity ties perpendicular to the wall and connected back to the main roof structure will help to restrain the walls, and in the event of a roof collapse, will work to pull the walls inwards rather than having them fall outwards. The tension ties should be of sufficient size and thickness to be able to maintain some structural strength for the initial duration of the fire. Structural steel ties from channel or angle sections are suitable for this use and can easily be attached to the walls and roof structure. The steel deck, wood decking, or plywood should be directly fastened to the ties.

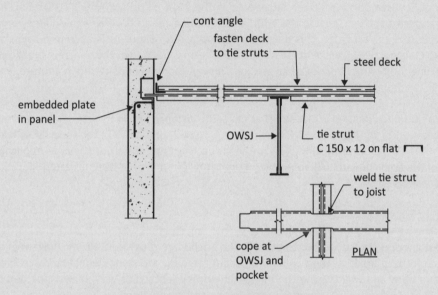

Fig. N23.2.9.1 Tie strut connection

N23.2.9.2
The connection force for tension ties is a minimum and is usually less than out-of-plane wind or seismic loads as determined in the NBCC.

N23.3.1.3
In the version of CSA A23.3-14 appearing in this Handbook, M_r should be replaced with M_f in Equation 23.2. This will be corrected in a later version.

N23.3.1.5
The term $A_{s,eff}$ has been modified from the previous edition and is consistent with changes made in ACI 318. The original term was developed for use in walls with a single layer of reinforcement at the center of the panel. However, this term could overestimate the contribution of axial load in panels with two layers of reinforcement. This revision accounts for cases where the reinforcement is not in the center of the panel.

N23.4.2 Ratio of tributary width to design widths
Panels with large openings can behave differently when subjected to out-of-plane loads. Solid panels or panels with smaller openings are predominately axial loaded vertical members subjected to one-way bending. Panels with large openings can experience two-way bending that should be accounted for by using a more detailed analysis.

ND Annex D Anchorage

ND.1.2

New in the 2014 edition of Annex D is the inclusion of adhesive anchors. The tensile bond strength of adhesive anchors is given in D.6.5. The shear resistance of adhesive anchors is evaluated in accordance with D.7 similar to cast-in-place and post installed anchors. A critical edge distance value C_{ac} for adhesive anchors is given in D.9.7.

ND.3

A number of new symbols have been introduced in the 2014 edition of Annex D. Symbols have been added for adhesive anchors, new to this edition, and other symbols have been modified from the 2004 edition. Note that the term "N_{cpr}" is defined as the factored pullout resistance in tension of a single anchor (see Clause D.6.3.1), while in Clause D.7.3 this term is defined as the concrete breakout capacity in determining the pryout capacity of an anchor. This notation may be revised in a future amendment to the A23.3-14 Standard.

The term "s" has been defined in Clause D.3 as being the distance between individual anchors. However, in the application of the term "s" in Clauses D.6.2.4, D6.4.2, and D.7.5.2, the term "s" is taken as the distance between the outermost anchors in the group resisting tension or shear, as applicable, in the direction of the applied load. In Clause D.7.2.4 the term "s" is taken as the maximum spacing between individual anchors.

ND.4.3.2

The provisions of Annex D are not applicable to plastic hinge regions where concrete cracking is expected to exceed the scope of testing used to develop the anchorage provisions. Plastic hinge regions can be expected to form in areas beyond column or beam faces for a distance equal to twice the member depth and in slabs and walls where the reinforcement is expected to yield in resisting design seismic forces. Anchor reinforcement should be used in any situation where anchors are located in a plastic hinge zone. Sufficient reinforcement must be provided to carry the anchor forces into the concrete member away from the anchor location. Concrete breakout strength should not be used in such cases.

ND.4.3.3

In regions defined by Clause D.4.3.3, unless Clauses D.4.3.5.1 or D.4.3.6.1 apply, anchors are required to satisfy the seismic design requirements of Clause D.4.3 even if seismic loads are not included in the controlling load combination.

ND.4.3.4

Before post installed anchors can be used to resist seismic loads they must first be prequalified in accordance with ACI 355.2 or ACI 355.4 as applicable. Only anchors qualified for use in cracked concrete may be used to resist seismic loads.

ND.4.3.5.2

When the seismic load component exceeds 20% of the total load combination under consideration the additional requirements of Clause D.4.3 apply. In such cases the concrete governed tension resistance of the anchor is required to meet the requirements of Clause D.4.3.5.4. More information can be found in the 2009 NEHRP Recommended Seismic Provisions for New Buildings and Other Structures (FEMA P750).

ND.4.3.5.3

Clause D.4.3.5.3 provides four classes of seismic tension loading on anchors. Option (a) requires that the steel anchor component provides a ductile response to the seismic load. Options (b) and (c) require that the anchor be designed to resist the maximum load applied to it by a yielding or non-yielding attachment respectively. Option (d) requires that the anchor be designed for the maximum load that could be applied to the anchor assuming a conservative seismic response using $R_d R_0 = 1.3$ or in accordance with the anchorage requirements for elements of structures, non-structural components and equipment.

Using D.4.3.5.3 (a) requires that the anchor exhibits clear yielding behaviour and that its interaction in the load path is well understood. A ductile anchor is assumed to exhibit a 14% elongation and an area reduction of not less than 30%. ASTM A36 or A307 steel provides an f_{uta}/f_{ya} ratio of about 1.5. This allows the steel to strain sufficiently before failing in the threaded section. Where other steels are used, testing or calculations should be used to assure similar ductile behaviour. In satisfying D.4.3.5.3(a), the anchor must be configured such that the nominal concrete breakout capacity using $\phi_c = 1.0$ is used to resist the probable resistance of the steel anchor, which is taken as $1.1 \times f_{uta}$ with ϕ_s and R taken as 1.0. The ratio of applied load to material strength is used as a means of ensuring that the failure occurs in the ductile steel anchor rather than in the concrete. The seismic response of the anchor can be heavily influenced by the stretch length provided in the anchor. A stretch length of eight anchor diameters has been found to provide good performance in past seismic events. The use of steel tubes over the anchor stretch length has been found to prevent buckling of the anchor when loaded in compression. More information on ductile anchor response can be found in references D-1 and D-2.

Clause D.4.3.5.3 (b) and (c) require that the anchor resist the maximum load that can be applied by the attachment when yielding (option b), or when non-yielding (option c). Option (c) should be used where the yield behaviour of the element is not well defined. When meeting option (b) the probable strength of the attachment should be used, including the consideration of stress increases due to strain hardening in the member. Ultimate strengths can be assumed to be 50% greater than the specified yield strength and 20% greater than the actual yield strength. The concrete tension breakout resistance is evaluated in accordance with D.4.3.5.4.

Clause D.4.3.5.3(d) provides a maximum upper limit on the load that the attachment can impart to the anchor for a given seismic event. If sufficient anchorage is provided to resist this load level, yielding of the anchor or the attachment is not required.

Additional information on the application of options (a) to (d) in Clause D.4.3.5.3 can be found in the 2009 NEHRP Recommended Seismic Provisions for New Buildings and Other Structures (FEMA P750).

ND.4.3.5.4
This clause is applied to tension loads only. It is assumed under seismic loading that the structure is yielding and that anchors will be in cracked concrete. Clause N.4.3.5.4 further reduces the concrete tension failure resistance in recognition of the increased seismic cracking in the structure. The use of *anchor reinforcement* in accordance with Clause D.6.2.9 negates the need for the reduction in capacity provided by Clause D.4.3.5.4 and no further reduction is required.

ND.4.3.6
Similar to tension loads, seismic shear design requirements are required only where the seismic shear component of the load combination that includes seismic loads exceeds 20% of the total load, and the structure is located in a seismic zone defined by Clause D.4.3.3. The steel component of an anchor cannot provide a sufficient degree of ductility to permit the use of D.4.3.5.3 (a) for shear loads. Clause D.4.3.6.3 provides the three load limiting options for seismic shear loads similar to that provided in D.4.3.5.3 (b) to (d) for tension loads. When resisting seismic shear loads, the concrete anchor shear resistance is determined in accordance with Clause D.7. No reduction similar to D.4.3.5.4 for tension capacity is required for seismic shear anchor capacities.

ND.6.2.4

For the purpose of application to equation D.9, the term "s" means the distance between the outer anchors in tension and not the distance between individual anchors as noted in the notation section of Annex D. See Figure 12.4 of the CAC Concrete Design Handbook for an illustration of the application of the term "S" in Clause D.6.2.4.

ND.6.2.9

More information on anchor reinforcement can be found in reference D-3.

ND.6.4.2

In the case of concrete side face blowout, the concrete failure surface propagates a distance $3\,c_{a1}$ from the centreline of the anchor and not $1.5\,c_{a1}$ as is the case for a standard tension or shear breakout section. As a result equation D.19 uses the term $6\,c_{a1}$ in the denominator to account for overlapping failure sections when determining the blowout capacity of group anchors. Note that the term "s" is taken as the distance between the outer anchors exhibiting the blowout failure and not the distance between individual anchors as noted in the Notation of Annex D. See Figure 12.6 in Chapter 12 of the CAC Concrete Design Handbook.

ND.6.5

Bond strength is applicable only to adhesive anchors. The failure mode of an adhesive anchor may depend on the embedment depth and whether or not a single or group adhesive anchor is being considered. Short embedment depths may produce concrete failures while deeper embedment depths will produce bond failures. The shear strength of adhesive anchors is evaluated in accordance with D.7.

ND.6.5.1

The tension bond strength of an adhesive anchor or group of anchors is calculated in accordance with equations D.20 and D.21[D-3]. The influence of anchor spacing and edge effects are determined by equations D.22 and D.23 and take a form similar to that for mechanical post installed anchors. The concrete breakout area for adhesive anchors is defined by equation D.22 and is dependent on the anchor diameter and the maximum adhesive bond stress. The critical edge distance is assumed unaffected by the presence of cracks. The uncracked bond stress has been used in determining C_{Na} based on research [D-3]. The derivation of equation D.22 is illustrated in Figure D.11.

ND.6.5.2

A unified bond stress model is used to evaluate adhesive anchor bond strengths. This model has been verified by numerical studies and comparison with an international database of testing [D-4]. This model accounts for bond failures between the concrete and the adhesive and between the anchor and the adhesive. Where product-specific information is not available, Table D.2 provides a lower bound bond stress value for use in design. These bond values are based on minimum values obtained for ACI 355.4 qualified adhesive anchors. Table D.2 bond values may be used only within the conditions specified in the table and assume a 21 day concrete age and a minimum concrete strength of 17 MPa. The design performance of adhesive anchors cannot be ensured by establishing a minimum concrete compressive strength at the time of installation in early age concrete. Therefore a minimum concrete age of 21 days at the time of adhesive anchor installation is required. Adhesive anchor performance can be heavily influenced by the quality of the installation. In light of this, the bond stress values obtained from Table D.2 should be selected based on the conditions during installation and not just the in service condition. Additional factors such as concrete temperature, degree of saturation and age can affect the bond strength. Anchor size and the method of drilling will also affect the bond strength. When Table D.2 is used and adhesive anchors support sustained loads, the table bond stress values are to be multiplied by 0.4 before application in Equation D.24 to determine N_{bar}. N_{bar} so determined is then used in D.5.1.3 to resist the factored sustained load on the anchor. Where earthquake loads act in combination with sustained loads, the reduction factors in Table D.2 for both sustained loads and earthquake loads are to be multiplied together.

ND.6.5.4

If side covers are less than c_{Na}, the factor $\Psi_{ed,Na}$ accounts for this effect. This reduction is based on the work of (Fuchs et al. 1995[D-5] and Eligehousen et al. 2006a[D-3]).

ND.7.2.4

In Clause D.7.2.4 the term "s" is taken as the maximum centre-to-centre spacing between individual anchors in the group and is used to calculate the actual reduced breakout area in narrow and thin members. The application of the actual dimension "c_{a1}" in narrow or thin members results in a fictitiously large and un-conservative breakout area.

ND.7.2.8

The modification factor for shear in concrete where $h_a < 1.5c_{a1}$ is based on tests[D-3] which indicate that the resulting concrete breakout capacity is not directly proportional to h_a. The factor $\Psi_{h,V}$ is equal to or greater than 1.0 and aligns the calculated concrete breakout capacity more closely with test results.

ND.7.5.2

The term, "s" as it is used in equation D.39, is taken as the distance between the outer anchors loaded in shear in the same direction as the applied shear force. See Figure D.16 in Annex D. This is similar to the application of the term "s" in Clause D.6.4.2 for tension loads. The factor $\Psi_{ec,V}$ accounts for the unbalanced loading of anchors in shear which can prematurely split the concrete near an edge.

ND.9.4

The lower limit on edge distance values of twice the maximum aggregate size is intended to minimize the effects of possible microcracking, which can result from the drilling of holes for post installed anchors.

ND.9.7

Conservative values of C_{ac} are provided in D.9.7 where critical edge distance values determined in accordance with ACI 355.2 or ACI 355.4 are not available. Research has shown that conditions where $C_{a,min} = 1.5h_{ef}$ may not meet the corner test requirements for post installed expansion and undercut anchors. Adhesive anchors may not meet the corner test requirements as well when $c_{a,min} = c_{na}$.

ND.10

The performance of anchors is highly dependent on the quality of the installation. Cast-in-place anchors should be securely fastened and the concrete around them properly consolidated. Inspection should be provided for the installation of post installed anchors. Adhesive anchors should only be installed by qualified personnel in accordance with the Manufacturers Printed Installation Instructions (MPII). Continuous inspection should be provided when installing adhesive anchors. The performance of post installed anchors may vary significantly for that obtained under ACI 355.2 or ACI 355.4 qualification if proper installation procedures are not followed.

ND.10.2.2

On-site quality control is essential for adhesive anchor performance due to their sensitivity to installation. A proof loading program should be specified where appropriate. The parameters influencing the characteristic bond stress should be documented. These include, but are not limited to, proper installation environment, drilling methods, hole cleaning procedures and anchor type and size range. Hole cleaning is intended to ensure that drilling debris and dust do not impair bond. Site conditions may influence cleaning procedures. Hole cleaning may involve operations to remove drilling debris from the hole with a vacuum or compressed air, mechanical brushing of the hole wall to remove surface dust, and a final step to evacuate any remaining dust or debris, usually with compressed air. In all cases the Manufacturers Printed Installation Instructions (MPII) should be followed.

ND.10.2.3

Installer certification is required for horizontal or upwardly inclined adhesive anchor installation due to the sensitivity of adhesive anchors to these installation conditions. Certification is available through the ACI/CRSI Adhesive Anchor Installation Certification Program or similar program with equivalent requirements.

References

9.1   Council of Tall Buildings and Urban Habitat (CTBUH), 2008. *Recommendations for the seismic design of high-rise buildings*, CTBUH; Chicago, IL.

9.2   Griffis, L.G., Serviceability Limit States Under Wind Load, AISC Engineering, Journal, First Quarter, 1993.

9.3   Kijewski-Correa, T., Pirnia, David J., 2007. "Dynamic Behaviour of Tall Buildings Under Wind: Insights From Full-Scale Monitoring", *The Structural Design of Tall and Special Buildings*, **16**: 471-486.

9.4   Satake, N., Suda, K., Arawaka, T., Sasaki, A. and Tamura, Y, 2003. "Damping evaluation using full-scale data of buildings in Japan", *Journal of Structural Engineering*, **129** (4), 470-477.

9.5   Scanlon, A., and Suprenant, B. A.,2011. "Estimating Two-way Slab Deflections". *Concrete International* **33** (7): 29-34.

9.6   Smith, R.J., Merello, R. and Willford, M.R., 2010. "Intrinsic and supplementary damping in tall buildings", *Proceedings of the Institute of Civil Engineering: Structures and Buildings*, **163** (2): 111-118.

9.7   Grundy, P., and Kabaila, A. (1963): Construction Loads on Slabs with Shored Formwork in Multistory Buildings". *American Concrete Institute Journal, Proceedings,* **60 (**12): 1729-1738. Reprinted in *Concrete International* (2004), **26** (7): 99-112.

9.8   Horvilleur, J., Patel, V. and Young, K., 2006. "Modeling Assumptions for Lateral Analysis", in *ACI SP-240 - Performance-Based Design of Concrete Building for Wind Loads*, American Concrete Institute, Farmington Hills, MI.

10.1   Gergely, P. and Lutz, L.A., "Maximum Crack Width in Reinforced Concrete Beams," Causes, Mechanisms and Control of Cracking in Concrete, SP-20, American Concrete Institute, Detroit, 1968, pp. 87-117.

10.2   Franz, G.L., and Breen, J.E., "Design Proposal for Side Face Crack Control Reinforcement for Large Reinforced Concrete Beams," Concrete International - Design and Construction, October 1980, Vol. 2, No. 10, pp. 29-34.

10.3   Paultre, P, and Légeron, F., "Confinement Reinforcement Design for Reinforced Concrete Columns," ASCE Journal of Structural Engineering, Vol. 134, No. 5, May 2008, pp. 738-749.

10.4   Adebar, P., "Compression failure of thin concrete walls during 2010 Chile earthquake: lessons for Canadian design practice," Canadian Journal of Civil Engineering, Vol. 40, No. 8, August 2013, pp. 711-721.

10.5   Gamble, W.L., and Klinar, J.D., "Tests of High-Strength Concrete Columns with Intervening Floor Slabs," ASCE Journal of Structural Engineering, Vol. 117, No. 5, May 1991, pp. 1462-1476,

10.6   Shu, C-C., and Hawkins, N.M., "Behavior of Columns Continuous through Concrete Floors," ACI Structural Journal, Vol. 89, No.4, July-August 1992, pp. 405-414.

10.7   MacGregor, J.G., Breen, J.E., and Pfrang, E.O., "Design of Slender Concrete Columns," Journal American Concrete Institute, Vol. 67, No. 1, Jan. 1970, pp. 628.

10.8   FIP Recommendations, "Practical Design of Reinforced and Prestressed Concrete Structures," Thomas Telford Ltd., London, 1984

11.1   Kani, M.W., Huggins, M.W. and Wittkopp, R.R., "Kani on Shear in Reinforced Concrete", Department of Civil Engineering, University of Toronto, 1979, 225 pp.

11.2   Vecchio, F.J. and Collins, M.P., "The Modified Compression Field Theory for Reinforced Concrete Elements Subjected to Shear," ACI Journal, Vol. 83, No. 2, Mar.-April 1986, pp. 219-231.

11.3   Fisher, A.W.," Shear Performance of Heavily Reinforced High-Strength Concrete Coupling Beams", MASc Thesis, Department of Civil Engineering, University of Toronto, 2016, 246 pp.

11.4   Perkins, S.M.J.," Shear Behaviour of Deep Reinforced Concrete Members Subjected to Uniform Load," MASc Thesis, Department of Civil Engineering, University of Toronto, 2011, 195 pp.

11.5   Bentz, E.C. and Collins, M.P., "Development of the 2004 CSA A23.3 Shear Provisions for Reinforced Concrete", Canadian Journal of Civil Engineering, Vol. 33, No. 5, May 2006, pp 521-534.

11.6   Masukawa, J.," Degradation of Shear Performance of Beams Due to Bond Deterioration and Longitudinal Bar Cutoffs," PhD Thesis, Department of Civil Engineering, University of Toronto, 2012, 175 pp. plus appendices.

11.7   Loov, R.E. and Patnaik, A.K., "Horizontal Shear Strength of Composite Concrete Beams with a Rough Interface," PCI Journal, Vol. 39, No. 1, Jan.-Feb. 1994, pp. 48-69.

12.1   ACI Committee 408, "Suggested Development, Splice, and Standard Hook Provisions for Deformed Bars in Tension", Concrete International, ACI, V.1, N.7, July 1979, pp. 44-46.

12.2   Orangun, C.O., Jirsa, J.O. and Breen, J.E., "A Reevaluation of Test Data on Development Length and Splices", ACI Journal, Proceedings, V.74, Mar. 1977, pp. 114-122.

12.3   Jirsa, J.O. and Breen, J.E., "Influence of Casting Position and Shear on Development and Splice Length-Design Recommendations", Research Report 242-3F, Center for Transportation Research, Bureau of Engineering Research, The University of Texas at Austin, Nov. 1981.

12.4   Jeanty, P.R., Mitchell, D., and Mirza, M.S., "Investigation of 'Top Bar' Effects in Beams", ACI Structural Journal, V.85, N.3, May-June 1988, pp. 251-257.

12.5   Treece, R.A, "Bond Strength of Epoxy-Coated Reinforcing Bars", Master's thesis, Department of Civil Engineering, The University of Texas at Austin, May, 1987.

12.6   Johnston, D.W., "Bond Characteristics of Epoxy-Coated Reinforcing Bars", Department of Civil Engineering, North Carolina State University, Report No. FHWA/NC/82-002, August, 1982.

12.7   Mathey, R.G. and Clifton, J.R.,"Bond of Coated Reinforcing Bars in Concrete", Journal of Structural Division, ASCE, V. 102, N. ST1, Jan., 1976, pp. 215-228.

21.1   Paulay, T., and Priestley, M.J.N., "Seismic design of reinforced concrete and masonry buildings," John Wiley & Sons Inc., New York, 1992.

Explanatory Notes on CSA A23.3-14

21.2   Adebar, P., Dezhdar, E., "Effective stiffness for linear dynamic analysis of concrete shear walls buildings: CSA A23.3 – 2014," *Proc. of 11th Can. Conf. on Earthquake Eng.*, Victoria, July 2015, 8 pp.

21.3   Paultre, P. and Mitchell, D., "Incorporating High-Strength Concrete in Seismic Provisions of the Canadian Concrete Standard", *Proc. of 13th World Conf. Earthquake Eng.*, Vancouver, BC, Aug. 2004.

21.4   Bohl, A., and Adebar, P., "Plastic Hinge Lengths in High-rise Concrete Shear Walls," *ACI Struct. J.*, V. 108, No. 2, Mar.-Apr. 2011, pp. 148-157.

21.5   Dezhdar, E., Adebar, P., "Estimating Seismic Demands on Concrete Shear Wall Buildings," *Proc. of 11th Can. Conf. on Earthquake Eng.*, Victoria, July 2015, 10 pp.

21.6   Rad, B.R. and Adebar, P., "Seismic Design of High-rise Concrete Walls: Reverse Shear Due to Diaphragms Below Flexural Hinge," *J. Struct. Eng.*, Vol. 135, No. 8, Aug. 2009, pp. 916-924.

21.7   Adebar, P., Dezhdar, E., Yathon, J., "Accounting for Higher Mode Shear Forces in Concrete Wall Buildings: 2014 CSA A23.3, *Proc. of 11th Can. Conf. on Earthquake Eng.*, Victoria, July 2015, 9 pp.

21.8   Ambroise, S., Boiven, Y., Paultre, P. "Parametric study on higher mode amplification effects in ductile RC cantilever walls designed for western and eastern Canada," *Proc. of 2013 CSCE Conf.*, Montreal, 2013.

21.9   Chaallal, O., and Gauthier, D. "Seismic shear demand on wall segments of ductile coupled shear walls." *Can. J. Civ. Eng.*, Vol. 27, No. 3, 2000, pp. 506–522.

21.10   Applied Technology Council, "ATC 72-1: Modeling and Acceptance Criteria for Seismic Design and Analysis of Tall Buildings," Oct. 2010, 242 pp.

21.11   Adebar, P., "Design and Evaluation of Concrete Shear Wall Buildings in Canada," https://www.civil.ubc.ca/adebar/concrete-wall-buildings

21.12   Adebar, P., Mutrie, J., DeVall, R., "Ductility of concrete walls: the Canadian seismic design provision 1984 to 2004, *Can. J. Civ. Eng.*, Vol. 32, No. 6, Dec. 2005, pp. 1124-1137.

21.13   Gonzalez, E., "Seismic Response of Diagonally Reinforced Slender Coupling Beams," M.A.Sc. thesis, Dept. of Civil Eng., University of British Columbia, 2001. 164 pp.

21.14   White, T., and Adebar, P., "Estimating Rotational Demands in High-rise Concrete Wall Buildings," *Proc. of 13th World Conf. on Earthquake Eng.*, Vancouver, Aug. 2004, 15 pp.

21.15   Adebar, P. "Drift capacity of walls accounting for shear: the 2004 Canadian code provisions," Deform. Capacity and Shear Strength of R.C. Members Under Cyclic Loading, *ACI–SP 236*, American Concrete Institute, 2006, pp. 151-170.

21.16   Esfandiari, A., and Adebar, P., "Flexure - Shear Strength Interaction of Squat Shear Walls," *Proc. of 9th US National and 10th Canadian Conf. on Earthquake Eng.*, Toronto, July 2010, 10 pp.

21.17   Adebar, P., "Compression failure of thin concrete walls during 2010 Chile earthquake: lessons for Canadian design practice," *Can. J. Civ. Eng.*, V. 40, No. 8, Aug. 2013, pp. 711-721.

21.18 Bazargani, P., Adebar, P., DeVall, R., Anderson, D.L. "Nonlinear Analysis of Shear Wall Foundation Rocking," *Proc. of 11th Can. Conf. on Earthquake Eng.*, Victoria, July 2015, 10 pp.

21.19 Adebar, P., "Nonlinear rotation of capacity-protected foundations: the 2015 Canadian building code," *Earthquake Spectra*, Vol. 31, No. 4, Nov. 2015. pp. 1885-1907.

21.20 Adebar, DeVall, R., P., Bazargani, P., and Anderson, D. "Seismic Design of Foundations – the 2015 Canadian Building Code," *Proc. of 10th US Nat. Conf. on Earthquake Eng.*, Anchorage, Alaska, July 2014, 10 pp.

21.21 Adebar, P., DeVall, R., and Mutrie, J., "Design of Gravity-Load Resisting Frames for Seismic Displacement Demands," *Proc. of 10th US Nat. Conf. on Earthquake Eng.*, Anchorage, Alaska, July 2014, 10 pp.

21.22 Pan, A., and Moehle, J.P., "Lateral Displacement Ductility of Reinforced Concrete Flat Plates," *ACI Structural Journal*, 86(3), 1989.

D-1   Hoehler, M., and Eligehausen, R., 2008, "Behavior and Testing of Anchors in Simulated Seismic Cracks," *ACI Structural Journal,* V. 105, No.3, May-June, pp. 348-357.

D-2   Vintzileou, E., and Eligehausen, R., 1992, "Behavior of Fasteners under Monotonic or Cyclic Shear Displacements," *Anchors in Concrete: Design and Behavior,* SP-130, American Concrete Institute, Farmington Hills, MI, pp. 181-203.

D-3   Eligehausen R.· Cook, R.; and Appl J., 2006a, "Behavior and Design of Adhesive Bonded Anchors," IICl Structural Journal, V. 103, No.6, Nov.-Dec., pp. 822-831.

D-4   Cook, R. A.; Kunz, 1.; Fuchs, W; and Konz, R. c., 1998, "Behavior and Design of Single Adhesive Anchors under Tensile Load in Uncracked Concrete," ACI Structural Journal, V. 95, No.1, Jan.-Feb., pp. 9-26.

D-5   Fuchs, W; Eligehausen, R.; and Breen, 1., 1995, "Concrete Capacity Design (CCD) Approach for Fastening to Concrete," ACI Structural Journal, V. 92, No.1 , Jan.-Feb. 1995, pp. 73-93. Also discussion, ACI Structural Journal, V.

~NOTES~

INDEX

(Note: Clauses having Explanatory Notes are designated in **bold** type.)

PART II

Chapters

The following thirteen chapters contain design information as well as design examples and design aids on reinforced concrete building structures.

In order to accommodate additional technical material in the new 4th Edition of the CAC Concrete Design Handbook, many design aids that were contained in previous editions of the publication have been relocated to the CAC website. These Design Aids are now available as a free PDF download at www.cement.ca.

By James G. MacGregor
Murat Saatcioglu
Richard J. McGrath
Hélène Dutrisac

General

1.1   Design Method

1.1.1.   General

The objective of structural design and construction is to produce safe, serviceable, economic, durable and aesthetic structures. Each of these attributes will be examined more fully here or in other parts of this Handbook.

Safety - Structures must be able to withstand the loads acting on them during a reasonable lifetime. This is accomplished, first and foremost, by a careful selection of the structural system and a clear understanding of how that system will behave under load. This involves identifying and considering possible failure modes during construction and during the life of the structure. Once the structure is chosen, load factors and resistance factors are used in the proportioning of the members to minimize the risk arising from overloads and understrength elements. Care must be taken to avoid gross errors in the design process and in the construction process.

During its life, the building should have adequate structural integrity to be able to adapt to unforeseen influences and localized damages without major spread of damage or collapse. This is discussed more fully in Section 1.7 of this Handbook. Similarly, building codes require that structures have specified minimum fire resistances so that they will retain their strength long enough for evacuation of occupants and for fire-fighting operations to be carried out. Design for fire is discussed in Section 1.4 of this Handbook.

Serviceability - In addition to having adequate strength, building structures must behave in a satisfactory manner in service. They should not deflect excessively or vibrate excessively and those cracks which occur should not impair the function or the aesthetics of the structure.

Economy - Among other things, a project is judged by its first costs, its lifelong performance and the construction time. In many cases the structure forms a small part of the total cost of a project. Similarly, the cost of concrete and reinforcement form only a fraction of the cost of the structure. For these reasons, optimizing the structure itself may not lead to the most economical project. During the design process, it is essential to consider construction costs and maintenance costs.

Durability - Durable structures survive exposure to the environment and corrosive agents and in doing so, maintenance costs are reduced. Inadequate durability has led to rusting reinforcement, spalling concrete and general deterioration of structures. Section 1.6 of this Handbook reviews the factors affecting durability.

Aesthetics - Buildings and bridges should have an attractive appearance and complement their surroundings. Concrete, as a material, allows a wide range of structural and architectural shapes and a wide range of surface treatments which can be used to develop pleasing buildings and bridges.

1.1.2.   Load and Resistance Factors

The CSA Standard A23.3-14 "Design of Concrete Structures" has adopted the newly revised load factors and load combinations specified in the 2015 edition of the National Building Code of Canada (NBCC). The resistance factors contained in CSA A23.3 Standard are applied to material strengths as noted in Section 1.1.4.

1.1.3. Specified Loads and Effects

1.1.3.1. Definition and Magnitude of Loads

The various loads to be considered in design are defined in Sentence 4.1.2.1.(1) of Division B of the 2015 National Building Code of Canada. The most common loads are:

D = dead load, as specified in Subsection 4.1.4 of the NBCC,
E = earthquake load and effects, as specified in Subsection 4.1.8. of the NBCC,
H = permanent load due to lateral earth pressure, including groundwater,
L = live load, as specified in Subsection 4.1.5. of the NBCC,
P = permanent effects caused by pre-stress,
S = variable load due to snow, including ice and associated rain, as specified in Article 4.1.6.2. of the NBCC, or due to rain, as specified in Article 4.1.6.4. of the NBCC,
T = effects due to contraction, expansion, or deflection caused by temperature changes, shrinkage, moisture changes, creep, ground settlement, or combination thereof, (see Appendix A of the NBCC), and
W = wind load, as specified in Subsection 4.1.7 of the NBCC.

Dead loads - A dead load is a permanent load due to the weight of the building components. Sentence 4.1.4.1.(1) of the NBCC specifies that the dead load for a structural member consists of:

a) the weight of the member itself,
b) the weight of all materials of construction incorporated into the building to be supported permanently by the member,
c) the weight of partitions,
d) the weight of permanent equipment, and
e) the vertical load due to earth, plants and trees.

Dead loads associated with the weight of the member are computed from the specified dimensions and the densities of materials. Tables of the unit mass of construction materials are given in Section 1.8 of this Handbook. Sentences 4.1.4.1(2) through (5) of the NBCC describe the dead load allowance that must be considered for permanent and movable partitions. Note that Sentence 4.1.4.1(5) implies that partition loads are applied in the pattern that gives the largest effect.

Earthquake loads - An earthquake load is a rare load. Earthquake loads and effects are discussed in Chapter 11 of this Handbook.

Lateral earth pressure loads - The NBCC does not indicate whether the earth pressure load should be a high fractile or a mean value. Hydrostatic pressure is normally computed as a mean value for fluids of known density.

Live loads - A live load is a variable load due to intended use and occupancy, including loads due to cranes and the pressure of liquids in containers. Live loads for use and occupancy specified by the NBCC are given in Section 1.8 of this Handbook. These are selected as a high fractile of the loading distributions.

Permanent effects - Permanent effects are caused by pre-stress. Sentence 4.1.3.2.(4) of the NBCC specifies a load factor of 1.0 to prestressing forces and the effects of prestressing. This NBCC Sentence is reproduced in CSA A23.3-14 Annex "C" under C.1.2.4.

Snow loads - The specified loads due to snow, ice and rain also represent a high fractile of the statistical distributions of these loads, typically 2% chance in 50 years that the load will be exceeded in any given year.

T loads - The category of loading (T) differs from the others in that it results from an imposed deformation. Since it is not caused by an external load, the resulting moments, forces and stresses must be self-equilibrating. Their magnitude is a function of the rigidity of the structure. If the structure becomes less rigid due to cracking, the stresses due to T loads will generally decrease. On one hand, this helps the structural engineer since he may be able to count on cracking or creep to dissipate T stresses. On the other hand however, the cracking which is required for this to occur may be unacceptable.

Wind loads - A wind load is a variable load due to wind. Similar to live and snow loads, wind loads represent a high fractile of the statistical distribution, typically a 2% chance in 50 years that the load will be exceeded in any given year.

1.1.3.2. Limit States Design

The 2015 NBCC has retained the limit states design approach. In this approach, designs must satisfy various conditions expressed in terms of limit states. The NBCC includes 3 limit states: ultimate limit states (ULS), serviceability limit states (SLS) and fatigue limit states. The ultimate limit states pertain to those conditions concerning safety and include checks for load-bearing capacity, overturning, sliding and fracture. Serviceability limit states include conditions that reflect the use and occupancy of the building and include deflection, vibration, permanent deformation and local structural damage such as cracking. The fatigue limit states represent failure conditions under repeated loading.

1.1.3.3. Load Factors and Load Combinations

Clause 8.3. of CSA A23.3 refers the designer back to the applicable building code for factored loads and factored load combinations. The 2015 NBCC utilises a "companion load" approach. Tables 4.1.3.2.A and 4.1.3.2.B "Load Combinations for Ultimate Limit States" from the 2015 NBCC are shown below without and with crane loads, respectively.

Table 4.1.3.2.-A
Load Combinations Without Crane Loads for Ultimate Limit States
Forming part of sentence 4.1.3.2.(2) and (5) to (10)
(Reproduced with the permission of the National Research Council of Canada, copyright holder)

Case	Load Combination[1]	
	Principal Loads	**Companion Loads**
1	$1.4D$[2]	–
2	$(1.25D$[3] or $0.9D$[4]$) + 1.5L$[5]	$1.0S$[6] or $0.4W$
3	$(1.25D$[3] or $0.9D$[4]$) + 1.5S$	$1.0L$[6][7] or $0.4W$
4	$(1.25D$[3] or $0.9D$[4]$) + 1.4W$	$0.5L$[7] or $0.5S$
5	$1.0D$[4] $+ 1.0E$[8]	$0.5L$[6][7] $+ 0.25S$[6]

Notes to Table 4.1.3.2.-A
(1) See Sentences 4.1.3.2.(2), (3) and (4).
(2) See Sentence 4.1.3.2.(9).
(3) See Sentence 4.1.3.2.(8).
(4) See Sentence 4.1.3.2.(5).
(5) See Sentence 4.1.3.2.(6).
(6) See Article 4.1.5.5.
(7) See Sentence 4.1.3.2.(7).
(8) See Sentence 4.1.3.2.(10).

Table 4.1.3.2.-B
Load Combinations With Crane Loads for Ultimate Limit States
Forming part of sentence 4.1.3.2.(2), (5) to (8) and (10)
(Reproduced with the permission of the National Research Council of Canada, copyright holder)

Case	Load Combination[1]	
	Principal Loads	**Companion Loads**
1	$(1.25D^{(2)}$ or $0.9D^{(3)}) + (1.5C + 1.0L_{xc})$	$1.0S^{(4)}$ or $0.4W$
2	$(1.25D^{(2)}$ or $0.9D^{(3)}) + (1.5\,L_{xc}^{(5)} + 1.0C)$	$1.0S^{(4)}$ or $0.4W$
3	$(1.25D^{(2)}$ or $0.9D^{(3)}) + 1.5S$	$1.0C + 1.0L_{xc}^{(4)(6)}$
4	$(1.25D^{(2)}$ or $0.9D^{(3)}) + 1.4W$	$1.0C^{(7)} + 0.5L_{xc}^{(4)(6)}$
5	$(1.25D^{(2)}$ or $0.9D^{(3)}) + C_7$	-
6	$1.0D^{(3)} + 1.0E^{(8)}$	$1.0C_d + 0.5L_{xc}^{(4)(6)} + 0.25S^{(4)}$

Notes to Table 4.1.3.2.-B
(1)   See Sentences 4.1.3.2.(2), (3) and (4).
(2)   See Sentence 4.1.3.2.(8).
(3)   See Sentence 4.1.3.2.(5).
(4)   See Article 4.1.5.5.
(5)   See Sentence 4.1.3.2.(6).
(6)   See Sentence 4.1.3.2(7).
(7)   Side thrust due to cranes need not be combined with full wind load.
(8)   See Sentence 4.1.3.2.(10).

Article 4.1.3.2 of the NBCC requires that:

1)   A building and its structural components shall be designed to have sufficient strength and stability so that the factored resistance, ϕR, is greater than or equal to the effect of factored loads, where the effect of factored loads shall be determined in accordance with Sentence 4.1.3.2.(2).

2)   Except as provided in Sentence (3), the effect of factored loads for a building or structural component shall be determined in accordance with the requirements of this Article and the following load combination cases, the applicable combination being that which results in the most critical effect:

    a)   for load cases without crane loads, the load combinations listed in Table 4.1.3.2.-A., and
    b)   for load cases with crane loads, the load combinations listed in Table 4.1.3.2.-B

(See Appendix A of the NBCC.)

3)   Other load combinations that must also be considered are the principal loads acting with the companion loads taken as zero.

4)   Where the effects due to lateral earth pressure H, restraint effects from prestress P and imposed deformation T affect the structural safety, they shall be taken into account in the calculations, with load factors of 1.5, 1.0 and 1.25 assigned to H, P and T respectively. (See Appendix A of the NBCC.)

5)   Except as provided in Sentence 4.1.8.16.(2), the counteracting factored dead load - 0.9D in load combinations 2, 3 and 4 and 1.0D in load combination case 5 in Table 4.1.3.2.-A, and 0.9D in load combination cases 1 to 5 and 1.0D in load combination case 6 in Table 4.1.3.2.-B - shall be used when dead load acts to resist overturning, uplift, sliding, failure due to stress reversal, and to determine anchorage requirements and factored member resistances. (See Appendix A of the NBCC.)

6)   The principal-load factor 1.5 for live loads L in Table 4.1.3.2.-A. and L_{xc} in Table 4.1.3.2.-B. may be reduced to 1.25 for liquids in tanks.

7)   The companion-load factor for live load L in Table 4.1.3.2.-A. and L_{xc} in Table 4.1.3.2.-B. shall be increased by 0.5 for storage areas, and equipment areas and service rooms referred to in Table 4.1.5.3.

8)   Except as provided in Sentence (9), the load factor 1.25 for dead load, D, for soil, superimposed earth, plants and trees in Table 4.1.3.2.-A and 4.1.3.2.-B shall be increased to 1.5, except that when the soil depth exceeds 1.2m, the factor may be reduced to $1+0.6/h_s$, but not less than 1.25, where h_s is the depth of soil in metres supported by the structure.

9)   A principal-load factor of 1.5 shall be applied to the weight of saturated soil used in load combination case 1 of Table 4.1.3.2.-A.

10) Earthquake load, E, in load combinations cases 5 of Table 4.3.1.2.-A, and case 6 of Table 4.1.3.2.-B, includes horizontal earth pressure due to earthquake determined in accordance with Sentence 4.1.8.16.(7).

11) Provision shall be made to ensure adequate stability of a structure as a whole, and adequate lateral, torsional and local stability of all structural parts.

12) Sway effects produced by vertical loads acting on the structure in its displaced configuration shall be taken into account in the design of buildings and their structural members.

1.1.3.4. Effect of Factored Loads

Clause 8.3.2 of CSA Standard A23.3-14 uses the term "effect of factored loads" to refer to the moments, axial forces, shears, and torques calculated for the combinations of factored loads specified in the applicable building code.

For problems which do not involve second-order effects (slenderness or PΔ effects in columns or frames), the analysis can either be based on factored loads, giving factored load effects directly, or on unfactored loads, giving unfactored load effects which must then be factored when they are combined. On the other hand, when second-order effects are significant, these effects are affected by the magnitude of the loads and hence the loads must be factored prior to carrying out the analysis.

The symbols M_f, V_f, P_f, T_f, etc. refer to moments, shears, axial forces and torques due to the factored loads. Thus, the subscript "f" signifies a load effect due to factored loads.

1.1.4.   Factored Resistance

The 2014 edition of the CSA A23.3 Standard has retained the same method of expressing resistance factors as in the 2004 edition, where the resistance factor is applied to the material strength, $\phi_c f'_c$, or $\phi_s f_y$, rather than to the nominal resistance, ϕM_n, ϕV_n, etc.

Resistance factors account for a number of factors causing variability in strengths. These include:

a)   variability in the strengths of concrete and reinforcement,
b)   variability in dimensions,
c)   approximations in the design equations,
d)   mode of failure, brittle or ductile and the resulting warning of failure.

The resistance factor for steel, ϕ_s, accounts for variability of the strength of reinforcement and to a lesser extent the variability in d, etc. resulting from placement tolerances for reinforcement. Similarly, the variability of the strength of concrete and dimensions of concrete are reflected in the resistance factor for concrete, ϕ_c. The brittle nature of failures initiated by failure of the concrete and the higher variability of design equations for failure initiated by failure of the concrete (the shear V_c, for example) were accounted for by using a higher safety index when evaluating the value of ϕ_c than for ϕ_s.

1.1.4.1. Values of Resistance Factors

A23.3 Clauses 8.4.2 and 8.4.3 give the values of the resistance factors:

8.4.2 - The factored concrete strengths used in checking ultimate limit states shall be taken as $\phi_c f'_c$ and $\phi_c \sqrt{f'_c}$ where $\phi_c = 0.65$, except for precast concrete conforming to A23.3 Clause 16.1.3 where ϕ_c may be taken as 0.70.

8.4.3 - The factored force in reinforcing bars, tendons, and structural shapes shall be taken as the product of the resistance factor, ϕ, and the respective steel force as specified in other Clauses of this Standard, where

    ϕ_s = for reinforcing bars
    ϕ_p = for prestressing tendons
    ϕ_a = for structural steel

Clause 16.1.3 of CSA Standard A23.3 permits the use of $\phi_c = 0.70$ for precast elements manufactured and erected in accordance with the requirements of CSA Standard A23.4.

1.1.4.2. Use of Resistance Factors

The resistance factors ϕ_c, ϕ_s, ϕ_p, and ϕ_a are included in the equations for calculating the factored resistances, M_r, V_r, P_r, T_r, etc. The subscripts "r" in these notations refer to "factored resistance".

When concrete is used in compression, its strength is taken as $\phi_c f'_c$. In defining the equivalent rectangular stress block, Clause 10.1.7 states that a concrete stress of $\alpha_1 \phi_c f'_c$ shall be used. When properties related to the concrete tensile strength are used in calculations, as in the calculation of V_c in Clause 11.3, the tensile strength is taken as a function of $\phi_c \sqrt{f'_c}$.

Clauses 8.4.3 and 8.5.3.2 require that when determining the factored resistance of bars and tendons, the resistance factor, ϕ_s be applied to the bar force, $\phi_s A_s f_y$ or $\phi_s A_s E_s \varepsilon_s$, regardless of whether the steel has yielded or not. The reason for this is that ϕ_s takes into account deviation in the location of the reinforcement and uncertainty in the prediction of resistance as well as variability in yield strength.

In addition to ϕ_c, ϕ_s and ϕ_p, a member resistance factor ϕ_m is used in slender column calculations in Clause 10.15 and for certain brittle members in Clause 21.

Resistance factors ϕ_s, ϕ_c and ϕ_p are not included in equations giving empirical limits, such as Eq. 10.28 in Clause 10.18.2 or in the equations in Clause 12. In the latter case, it was recognized that the equations in Clause 12 were empirical in nature and implicitly included a safety margin. The expression for the modulus of elasticity of concrete in Clause 8.6.2.2 does not include ϕ_c. When E_c is used in stability calculations in Clause 10.15 and 10.16, the variability of EI and P_c is taken into account using a member resistance factor ϕ_m. Fig. 1 illustrates the use of resistance factors in analysis of plane sections.

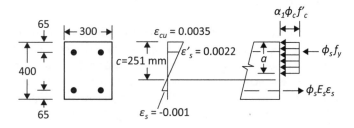

Fig. 1.1 Plane section analysis

1.2 Structural Concrete

1.2.1. General

The performance of reinforced concrete structures is significantly influenced by the quality of concrete. Structural concrete is affected by the properties of constituent materials and the proportions in which they are mixed. Requirements for proportioning and producing quality concrete as well as acceptance tests for the constituent materials are specified in CSA Standards A23.1 and A23.4 for cast-in-place and precast concrete, respectively.

Fig. 1.2 illustrates the typical range in proportions of materials used in producing concrete. The mass density of concrete is dependent on the aggregates, which constitute 60-80 percent of the total volume. Fine aggregates consisting of natural or manufactured sand, and coarse aggregates consisting of crushed stone, gravel or air-cooled iron blast-furnace slag are used to produce "Normal Density Concrete" with a mass density of about 2400 kg/m³. Low density aggregates are used to produce "Structural Low-Density Concrete" with a mass density not exceeding 1850 kg/m³. Sometimes, normal density fine aggregate is mixed with low density coarse aggregate to produce "Structural Semi-Low-Density Concrete" having a mass density between 1850 and 2150 kg/m³. Occasionally, high density aggregates are used to produce "High-Density Concrete" for special applications.

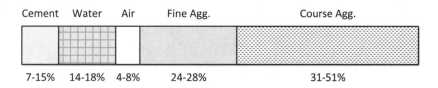

Fig. 1.2 Typical proportions of constituent materials by absolute volume – air entrained concrete

In a properly mixed concrete, each particle of aggregate is coated with cement and water paste. Cement, in the presence of water, hydrates and hardens, binding the aggregate particles, to form a solid rocklike mass. The quality of cement paste largely depends on the water-cement ratio. Excess water in the paste reduces concrete quality in terms of strength, watertightness, abrasion resistance and durability.

Six types of Portland cement and four types of Portland-limestone cement (PLC) conforming to CSA Standard A3001 are available for structural use. Types GU, General Use Portland Cement and GUL, General Use Portland-limestone Cement are used in general concrete construction when the special properties or the other types are not required. The cement types and their effects on concrete are summarized in Table 1.1. Portland-limestone cement has the advantage of producing 10% less CO_2 emissions during manufacturing than regular Portland cement and is a more environmentally friendly cement product.

1.2.2.   Strength and Elastic Modulus

One of the most important properties of structural concrete is its compressive strength. Other properties of concrete, required in structural design, can approximately be expressed in terms of compressive strength f_c'. Therefore, the structural engineer is required to specify f_c' on the drawings or in related specifications. Unless otherwise specified, f_c' is based on the 28-day strength. Generally the concrete strengths used in structural applications vary between 20 MPa and 50 MPa. Higher strength concretes may be used for special applications and in prestressed concrete constructions.

Low-density concrete can be used for structural purposes only if the 28 day strength is in excess of 20 MPa. If the structural low-density concrete is to be used for earthquake resistant design, the maximum concrete strength is limited to 30 MPa by Clause 21.2.6.2 of CSA Standard A23.3.

Concrete strength is usually determined by testing either 100 X 200 mm cylinders or 150 X 300 mm cylinders under axial compression. Two cylinders are tested at 28 days, and the average of the two results is used as f_c' provided that neither of the cylinders shows a sign of defect. The specimens are prepared in accordance with CSA Test Method A23.2-3C and tested in accordance with CSA Test Method A23.2-9C.

Typical stress-strain relationships obtained from standard cylinder tests are shown in Fig. 1.3. Test results indicate that the ultimate concrete strain recorded at failure varies from 0.003 to as high as 0.008. However, CSA Standard A23.3 limits the maximum usable compressive strain conservatively to 0.0035.

The modulus of elasticity is another important property of concrete that is often used in structural design to compute deformations. Generally, the modulus of elasticity is a secant modulus based on the stress and strain at about 50% of f_c'. CSA Standard A23.3 provides an empirical equation for concrete modulus of elasticity based on the secant modulus. Accordingly,

$$E_c = \left(3300 + \sqrt{f_c'} + 6900\right)\left(\frac{\gamma_c}{2300}\right)^{1.5} \tag{1.8}$$

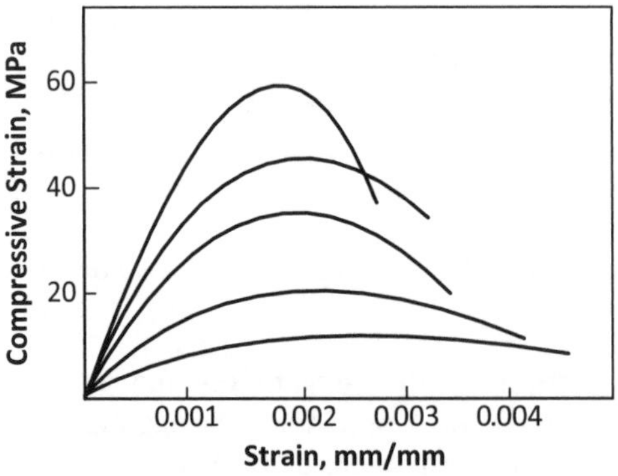

Fig. 1.3 Concrete stress-strain relationships obtained from standard cylinder tests

where γ is the mass density of concrete in kg/m³ and f_c' is the compressive strength of concrete in MPa. The above equation is provided for values of γ_c between 1500 and 2500 kg/m³. For normal density concrete with strengths between 20 and 40 MPa, E_c may be taken as $4500\sqrt{f_c'}$, where f_c' is in MPa.

1.2.3. Creep and Shrinkage

Creep of concrete is defined as the time dependent increase in strain under sustained loading. Other time dependent deformations are generally attributed to shrinkage and temperature changes in concrete.

Creep is usually expressed in terms of the creep coefficient C_t, defined as the ratio of creep strain ε_{cr} to initial immediate strain ε_i. Creep strain increases with time at a decreasing rate. This is illustrated in Fig. 1.4.

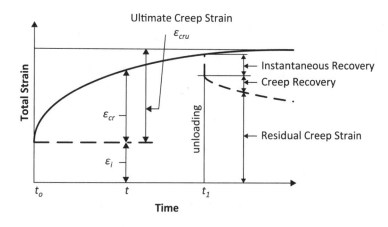

Fig. 1.4 Variation of creep with time

A commonly accepted procedure to determine the creep coefficient is to follow the ACI Committee 209 recommendation[*]. The following expression given by ACI Committee 209 is applicable to normal, semi-low and low-density concretes.

$$C_t = \frac{t^{0.6}}{10 + t^{0.6}} C_u Q_{cr} \qquad (1.9)$$

where t is time in days after loading, and C_u is the ultimate creep coefficient and varies between 1.30 and 4.15. In the absence of specific creep data for local aggregates and conditions, the average value suggested for C_u is 2.35.

The above equation was developed for sustained compressive stress not exceeding 50% of concrete strength. It consists of an expression for creep under standard conditions multiplied by the correction factor Q_{cr} to modify for non-standard conditions. The standard conditions and the correction factor Q_{cr} are specified in Table 1.2.

Shrinkage is the decrease in the volume of hardened concrete with time. Unlike creep, shrinkage is independent of externally applied loads. The decrease in volume is mainly attributed to the moisture loss caused by drying and hydration as well as the chemical changes that result in the carbonation of cement hydration products.

Shrinkage strains start taking place immediately after exposing concrete to a drying environment. Fig. 1.5 illustrates the variation of shrinkage with time. According to ACI Committee 209, the shrinkage strain ε_{sh} is determined using the expression given in Equation 1.10. This expression is applicable to normal, semi-low and low-density concretes.

---

[*] "Prediction of Creep, Shrinkage, and Temperature Effects in Concrete Structures", Reported by ACI Committee 209, Report No. ACI 209R-92. American Concrete Institute, Special Publication SP-76, 1982, pp. 143-300.

$$\varepsilon_{sh} = \frac{t}{C_s + t}\varepsilon_{shu}P_{sh}$$

(1.10)

where t is time in days starting immediately after the initial wet curing. C_s is equal to 35 if the concrete is moist cured for 7 days, and 55 if steam cured for 1-3 days. ε_{shu} is the ultimate shrinkage strain. In the absence of specific shrinkage data for local conditions, the average value of ε_{shu} suggested for use is 0.00078 mm/mm. P_{sh} is a correction factor for conditions that are other than the standard conditions specified in Table 1.2. The values of P_{sh} can be obtained from the same table.

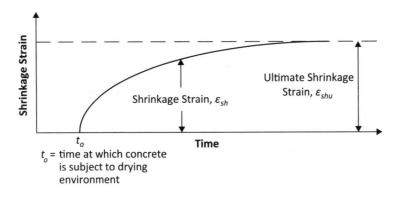

Fig. 1.5 Variation of shrinkage strain with time

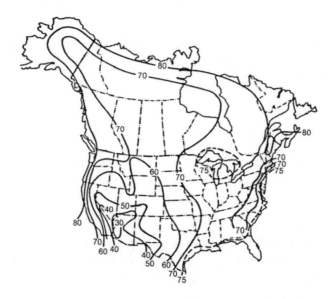

Fig. 1.6 Annual average ambient relative humidity (%)
(Reproduced from CPCI Metric Design Manual)

Concrete creep and shrinkage are both sensitive to environmental factors such as relative humidity and temperature. The effect of relative humidity on creep and shrinkage is empirically considered in Eqs. (1.9) and (1.10) through correction factors Q_{cr} and P_{sh}. The effect of temperature is usually considered to be less important than relative humidity. The expressions for creep and shrinkage given in this section are based on concrete temperature of 23 ± 2°C. It has been shown that structures exposed to high temperature for an extended period of time experience higher creep strains. At 50°C, creep strain is approximately two to three times the creep strain at 19° to 24°C. Where temperature effects may be a significant design factor, it is recommended that an in-depth determination be made to establish more exact values of creep and shrinkage.

The creep coefficient and shrinkage strain given by Eqs. (1.9) and (1.10) are meant for unreinforced, unrestrained concrete. In reinforced concrete members, time-dependent deformations are restrained by the reinforcement. While the procedure described in this section provides acceptable results for lightly reinforced members, its application to most reinforced concrete members is questionable. A proper adjustment to these values is recommended to account for the effect of reinforcement. Empirical equations are available for this purpose.

Long term deformations due to creep and shrinkage can be several times the initial deformation. According to CSA Standard A23.3, the total deflection, including long term effects, can be as high as 3.0 times the immediate initial deflection, depending on the percentage of reinforcement and the time for which deflection is computed.

Shrinkage strain alone is in the order of 0.0002 to 0.0008 mm/mm. In reinforced concrete structures with commonly used percentages of reinforcement, the shrinkage strain is in the range of 0.0002 to 0.0003 mm/mm.

Example

A prestressed concrete beam with an 8.0 m span and a 400 mm by 600 mm rectangular cross-section is pretensioned using 15 - 11mm 7-wire Grade 1860 strands. The steel stress after transfer is 1300 MPa. If the beam is prestressed immediately after seven days of moist curing, determine the shortening in the beam 60 days after the moist curing, when it is erected for a structure in Calgary. Use the following concrete properties:

Concrete strength at 7 days	: 30 MPa
Air content	: 5%
Slump	: 100 mm
Fine aggregate	: 670 kg/m³
Coarse aggregate	: 1000 kg/m³
Type GU cement	: 400 kg/m³

Solution

i. Elastic concrete strain (ε_i):

$A_{ps} = (15)\,(74.2) = 1113\ mm^2$
$P_o = (1300)\,(1113) = 1447 \times 10^3\ N$
$P_o/A = 1447 \times 10^3/(400 \times 600) = 6.0\ MPa$
$E_c = 4500\sqrt{30} = 24648\ MPa$
$\varepsilon_i = 6.0\ /\ 24648 = 243 \times 10^{-6}\ mm/mm$

ii. Creep and shrinkage modification factors, from Table 1.2:

Age at loading: 7 days, moist cured

$Q_a = 1.00$

Relative humidity: 70% for Calgary from Fig. 1.6

$Q_h = 0.80$
$P_h = 0.70$

Ratio of fine to total aggregate:

$$\frac{670}{670 + 1000} = 0.40$$

$Q_f = 0.98$
$P_f = 0.86$

Volume surface ratio: $\dfrac{(400)(600)}{2(400) + 2(600)} = 120mm$

$Q_r = 0.75$
$P_r = 0.69$

Slump: 100 mm

$Q_s = 1.08$
$P_s = 1.05$

Air %: 5

$Q_v = 1.00$
$P_v = 1.00$

Cement content: 400 kg/m³

$P_c \quad = 0.99$
$Q_{cr} \quad = Q_a\, Q_h\, Q_f\, Q_r\, Q_s\, Q_v$
$\qquad = (1.00)\,(0.80)\,(0.98)\,(0.75)\,(1.08)\,(1.00)$
$\qquad = 0.635$
$P_{sh} \quad = P_c\, P_h\, P_f\, P_r\, P_s\, P_v$
$\qquad = (0.99)\,(0.70)\,(0.86)\,(0.69)\,(1.05)\,(1.00)$
$\qquad = 0.432$

iii.   Creep strain (ε_{cr})

$\varepsilon_{cr} = \varepsilon_i C_t$

$$C_t = \frac{t^{0.6}}{10 + t^{0.6}} C_u\, Q_{cr} \qquad\qquad\qquad\text{(from Eq. 1.9)}$$

$C_u = 2.35$ \hfill (average value)

$$C_t = \frac{(60)^{0.6}}{10 + (60)^{0.6}} (2.35)(0.635) = 0.80$$

$\varepsilon_{cr} = (243 \times 10^{-6})(0.80) = 194 \times 10^{-6}$ mm/mm

iv. Shrinkage strain (ε_{sh}):

$$\varepsilon_{sh} = \frac{t}{C_s + t}\,\varepsilon_{shu}\,P_{sh}$$

(from Eq. 1.10)

$C_s = 35$

(moist cured for 7 days)

$\varepsilon_{shu} = 0.00078$ mm/mm

(average value)

$$\varepsilon_{sh} = \frac{60}{35 + 60}(0.00078)(0.432) \ = 213 \times 10^{-6} \text{ mm/mm}$$

v. Total shortening due to creep and shrinkage

Total strain $= \varepsilon_{cr} + \varepsilon_{sh}$
$= 194 \times 10^{-6}$ mm/mm $+ 213 \times 10^{-6}$ mm/mm $= 407 \times 10^{-6}$ mm/mm

Total shortening $= (407 \times 10^{-6})(8000) = 3.3$ mm

1.2.4. Concrete Durability

The durability of concrete is affected by exposure conditions and the presence of chemical constituents and impurities that may react with cement. Severe weather, causing freeze-thaw cycles, may fracture the concrete. Air voids, if present in concrete, relieve the pressure caused by frozen water in concrete. Therefore, air-entrainment producing 5 to 8 percent air is strongly recommended for concretes subjected to severe exposure conditions. De-icing agents are known to accelerate freeze-thaw cycles. CSA Standard A23.1-14, Clause 4.1.1 provides specific requirements for durability.

Another harmful exposure condition is the soil or ground water that may have high sulphate content. The use of Type MS or Type HS cement, depending on the sulphate concentration, is recommended for protection against sulphate attack. Table 1.1 provides guidelines in selecting the cement type against sulphate action.

Certain chemical constituents and impurities that may be present in mixing water and aggregates are also potential sources of hazard to concrete. In some areas, the chemical composition of aggregate is such that it reacts with alkalies in cement, producing abnormal expansion and cracking. CSA Standard A23.1-14 should be consulted for the selection of mixing water and aggregates that are free of deleterious substances and organic impurities.

Structural engineers are also concerned with the durability of reinforced concrete and protection of reinforcement in concrete against corrosive environments. Calcium chloride, sometimes used as an accelerating admixture, is a potential corrosion hazard to prestressing tendons. Concrete cover requirements for different exposure conditions and the protection of reinforcement against corrosive environments are discussed in Section 1.6.

1.3   Reinforcing and Prestressing Steel

1.3.1.   General

The design requirements for non-prestressed reinforcement and prestressing tendons are specified in CSA Standards A23.3 and A23.1. These requirements include a minimum specified yield strength, a minimum ultimate tensile strength, ductility, and a sufficient bendability for hooks.

Non-prestressed reinforcement consists of deformed bars, deformed wire reinforcement and welded wire fabric, fabricated using smooth or deformed wires. Plain reinforcing bars may be used for spirals, and if smaller than 10 mm in diameter, may also be used for stirrups and ties.

Prestressing steel consists of high strength smooth wire, seven-wire strands and high-strength alloy bars.

1.3.2.   Strength and Elastic Modulus

Reinforcement is classified on the basis of its minimum specified strength for structural purposes. In the case of non-prestressed reinforcement, minimum specified yield strength, f_y in MPa defines the grade of steel. Hot-rolled deformed and plain billet-steel reinforcing bars conforming to CSA Standard G30.18-09 are produced in grades 400 and 500. Weldable low alloy steel bars conforming to CSA Standard G30.18-09 are also produced in grades 400 and 500.

Cold-drawn wires and welded wire fabric are produced with minimum specified yield strengths ranging between 450 and 515 MPa depending on the use, size and whether the wire is deformed or smooth. Mechanical properties of wires and welded wire fabric are discussed in section 1.3.4.

Typical stress-strain relationships for hot-rolled bars and cold-drawn wires are shown in Fig.1.7.

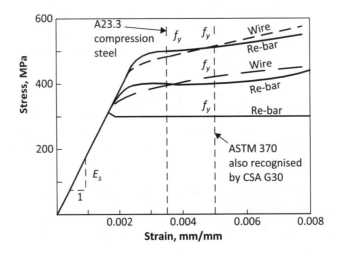

Fig. 1.7 Typical stress-strain curves for reinforcing steel

CSA Standard A23.3 provides certain design limitations with respect to reinforcement strength. These limitations are summarized below.

i.   In general, the value of f_y to be used in design calculations is limited to 500 MPa except for prestressing steel (See Clause 8.5.1.). Except fot Clause 21.2.8.2, the requirements of Clause 21 were developed for Grade 400 reinforcement. It is noted that the use of higher yield strength steel will generally reduce ductility (see Clause 21.2.7.1.2).

ii.   If the compression reinforcement has a yield strength in excess of 400 MPa, the design calculations will be based on either the value of 400 MPa, or the stress corresponding to a strain of 0.0035. (See Clause 8.5.2.)

iii.   In earthquake resistant design, when reinforcement conforming to CSA Standard G30.18-09 is used for members subjected to flexure and axial forces, the reinforcement strength is required to be closely controlled. Accordingly, the actual yield strength determined by mill tests is not permitted to exceed the specified minimum yield strength by more than 125 MPa for grade 400W and 500W reinforcement. Furthermore, the ultimate tensile strength of reinforcement is required to be at least 1.15 times the actual yield strength.

Steel grades for tendons depend on the minimum tensile strength, f_{pu} in MPa. Grades and properties of prestressing wires, strands and bars are listed in Tables 1.3 and 1.4.

High strength steels, used in prestressed concrete construction, do not have definite yield points. Typical stress-strain relationships are shown in Fig. 1.8. Yield strengths as specified by ASTM A416/A416M, ASTM A421/A421M, ASTM A722/A722M are indicated in the same figure.

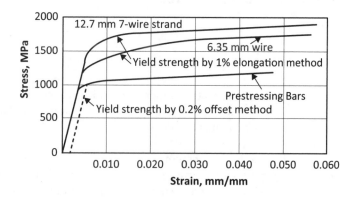

Fig. 1.8 Typical stress-strain curves for prestressing tendons

The elastic modulus of steel, E_s, is typically 200,000 MPa. For non-prestressed reinforcement, E_s is specified by CSA Standard A23.3 to be 200,000 MPa. For prestressing tendons, E_s is required to be determined by tests or supplied by the manufacturer. Typical values will range from 190,000 to 200,000 MPa.

1.3.3. Reinforcing Bar Properties

The standard reinforcing bar sizes and their properties are given in Table 1.5. Specifications for deformations on bars, bendability requirements and the related test procedures are given in CSA Standard G30.18-09 for hot-rolled steel bars and weldable low alloy steel reinforcement. Table 1.6 and 1.7 summarize the tensile and bond test requirements for reinforcing bars. Steel grades and stress-strain characteristics are discussed in Section 1.3.2.

1.3.4.   Properties of Wire and Welded Wire Fabric

Specifications for deformed steel wire for concrete reinforcement are given in ASTM A496. At the present time, the Metric wire sizes are soft converted from Imperial units. Therefore, wire sizes are expressed in terms of soft converted cross-sectional area in mm^2 prefixed with letters MW or MD for smooth and deformed wires respectively. Tensile and bend test requirements for smooth and deformed steel wire are summarized in Tables 1.8 and 1.9.

Wire reinforcement is generally used in the form of welded wire fabric, consisting of a series of longitudinal and transverse wires welded together to form a mesh. Fabrication requirements, mechanical properties and the test procedures for welded wire fabric are specified in ASTM A185 and ASTM A497/A497M. Table 1.10 gives the sizes that are currently used in Canada.

1.3.5.   Properties of Prestressing Steel

The standard tendon sizes and their properties are given in Tables 1.3 and 1.4. Specifications for prestressing wires, strands and bars are outlined in ASTM A416/A416M, ASTM A421/A421M, ASTM A722/A722M. Steel grades and stress-strain characteristics of prestressing tendons are discussed in Section 1.3.2.

1.4   Requirements for Fire Resistance

1.4.1.   Introduction

1.4.1.1. General

CSA Standard A23.3 does not cover any aspect of design concerning fire resistance. In fact, Clause 1.2 of the Standard reminds designers that all designs must be carried out in accordance with the fire resistance requirements of the applicable building code.

In the design of structures, building code requirements for fire resistance are sometimes overlooked. Such omissions may require costly measures to rectify. For example, slab thicknesses designs which are adequate to satisfy CSA Standard A23.3 provisions may not be sufficient to provide the necessary fire resistance. Similarly, cover to reinforcement may need to be increased for fire design purposes.

The purpose of this section is to make the reader aware of the importance of first examining the fire resistance provisions of the governing building code before proceeding with the structural design.

The field of fire technology is highly involved and complex and it is not the intent here to deal with the chemical or physical characteristics of fire, nor with the behaviour of structures in real fire situations. Rather, the goal is to present some basic information as an aid to designers in establishing those fire protection features of construction which may impact their structural design work.

1.4.1.2. Definitions

Fire resistance generally refers to the property of a material or assembly to withstand fire or give protection from it; as applied to elements of buildings, it is characterized by the ability to confine a fire or to continue to perform a given structural function, or both.

Fire resistance rating is defined in NBCC 2015 as the time in minutes or hours that a material or assembly of materials will withstand the passage of flame and transmission of heat when exposed to fire under specified conditions of test and performance criteria, or as determined by extension or interpretation of information derived therefrom as prescribed in this Code.

1.4.1.3. Test Criteria for Fire Resistance

The fire resistance rating of building components is determined in accordance with ULC Standard CAN/ULC-S101-14, Standard Methods of Fire Endurance Tests of Building Construction and Materials. During these tests, a building assembly such as a portion of a floor, wall, roof or column is subjected to increasing temperatures that vary with time as shown in Fig. 1.9. Floor and roof specimens are exposed to the test fire from beneath, beams from the bottom and sides, walls from one side and columns from all sides.

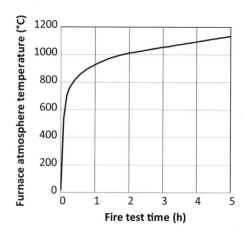

Fig. 1.9 Standard time-temperature curve

The standard time-temperature curve approximates the conditions which would pertain during a fire within a moderate size compartment having a relatively small amount of ventilation and a fire load of about 50 kg of combustibles per square metre, per hour of fire.

The end of the test is reached and the fire endurance of the specimen is established when any one of the conditions noted below first occurs.

For floor and roof assemblies and for bearing walls and partitions:

1) The temperature of the unexposed surface rises an average of 140°C above its initial temperature or 180°C at any location. In addition, walls must sustain a hose stream test.

2) Cotton waste placed on the unexposed side of a wall, floor or roof system is ignited through cracks or fissures developed in the specimen.

3) The test assembly fails to sustain the full specified load required by CSA Standard A23.3. Additional criteria limiting the reinforcing steel temperature to 593°C also apply in the case of certain restrained and all unrestrained floors, roofs and beams tested restrained.

Though the complete requirements of ULC S101 and the conditions of acceptance are much too detailed for inclusion in this chapter, experience shows that the fire resistance of concrete floor/roof assemblies and walls is usually governed by heat transmission (item 1), and columns and beams by failure to sustain the applied loads (item 3), or beam reinforcement fails to meet the temperature rise criterion (item 3).

1.4.1.4. NBCC Requirements

Most NBCC requirements for fire resistance are set forth in Part 3 of Division B of the Code, "Use and Occupancy". Part 9, "Housing and Small Buildings", also contains similar requirements. For design of buildings under Part 9, fire ratings can be determined from the construction specifications presented in Table A-9.10.3.1.-A and A-9.10.3.1.-B.

Fire ratings must be provided for major structural assemblies as prescribed in subsection 3.2.2 of the NBCC. In addition, such assemblies may be required to possess a fire resistance rating on the basis of the major occupancy separations of Subsection 3.1.3, the spatial separation requirements of Subsection 3.2.3 or other fire separation requirements listed throughout Subsections 3.3 to 3.5 of the NBCC. Rules governing the determination of the fire resistance rating of a specific assembly are given in NBCC Subsection 3.1.5.

Subsection 3.1.5 requires that fire resistance ratings be determined on the basis of results of tests conducted in conformance with ULC S101. It also provides that assemblies may be assigned a rating according to Appendix "D" of the NBCC. It should be noted that the ratings contained in Appendix "D" of the NBCC apply strictly to assemblies and structural members of generic materials for which there exist nationally recognized standards. Appendix "D" does not apply to assemblies of materials or structural members whose fire performance depends on proprietary information or where specifications do not meet all Appendix "D" provisions.

In practice, the designer has three options namely:

a)   rate an assembly in accordance with Appendix "D" of the NBCC.
b)   use an existing ULC listing for the specific assembly for which the rating is required.

Note: Relatively few reinforced concrete assemblies are included in ULC listings. While these should be used where applicable, the discussion included in this Section is aimed at the determination of fire resistance ratings, in accordance with Appendix "D", Fire Performance Ratings.

The third option is known as:

c)   "Rational Design"

Rational design, or analytical procedures for determining fire resistance, refers to an engineering method of calculating the duration that a structural element can be subjected to a standard fire exposure while performing its function, both structurally and as a barrier to heat. As the calculations used in this method are based on ULC S101 test criteria, they may be acceptable to an authority having jurisdiction under the alternate solution provisions of the Compliance Requirements of the NBCC. It should be emphasized, however, that because no standard for rational design is currently referenced in NBCC, specific prior approval must be obtained from the authority having jurisdiction for the use of rational design methods to establish fire ratings. Further detailed discussion of rational design techniques is beyond the scope of this brief Section and the reader is referred to Reference (7) for further information.

1.4.2.   Factors Which Influence Fire Resistance

1.4.2.1. General

In order to recognize all of the factors which influence the fire resistance rating which may be assigned to a building construction assembly, on the basis of Appendix "D", a thorough knowledge and understanding of that document is obviously necessary.

For the purposes of this brief Section, the following are the main factors applicable to reinforced concrete assemblies which influence their fire resistance rating.

1.4.2.2. Concrete Type

Concrete is considered to be one of the most highly fire resistive structural materials used in construction. Nonetheless, the properties of concrete and reinforcing steel change significantly in the high temperatures of fire. Strength and the modulus of elasticity are reduced, the coefficient of expansion increases, and creep and stress relaxations are considerably higher.

Two basic types of normal weight concretes are recognized in Appendix "D" of the NBCC, namely:

- Type S concrete, in which the coarse aggregate is granite, quartzite, siliceous gravel or other dense materials containing at least 30% quartz, chert or flint; and

- Type N concrete, in which the coarse aggregate is limestone, calcareous gravel, traprock, sandstone, blast furnace slag or similar dense material containing not more than 30% quartz, chert or flint.

Appendix "D" of the NBCC recognizes five different types of low-density concretes. Structural Low-Density concrete, as defined in CSA Standard A23.3, generally corresponds with:

- Type L40S concrete, in which the fine aggregate is sand and the coarse aggregate is low-density material and the sand does not exceed 40% of the total volume of all of the aggregate.

The compressive strength of concrete during fire exposure mainly depends upon the aggregate it contains. Generally speaking, for structural concretes, the behaviour of Types N and L40S concrete is superior to that of Type S concrete. As these differences are recognized in the assignment of fire resistance ratings, the designer must clearly specify which aggregate type should be used in critical assemblies.

1.4.2.3. Member Dimensions

Other factors being equal, the fire resistance rating of an assembly is proportional to its thickness or overall cross section. In the case of slab-like members, such as floors, roofs or walls, sufficient thickness must be provided to achieve the desired rating without violation of the temperature limit on the unexposed surface of the assembly. It should be noted that, in the case of hollow core or voided cross sections and ribbed slabs, the "equivalent thickness" of the slab must be used. This is computed in accordance with the rules given in Appendix "D" of the NBCC. For beams and columns, dimensionally larger cross sections take longer to heat up, as compared to smaller members. Larger cross sections thus suffer less average concrete strength loss than smaller ones for a given period of fire endurance.

1.4.2.4. Reinforcing Steel

As is the case with concrete, reinforcement loses strength at high temperatures. Hot rolled reinforcing steel used for deformed bars retains its strength longer at elevated temperatures than the cold drawn steel used for prestressing tendons. As the ability of a member to carry load depends largely upon the tensile strength of its reinforcement, its fire resistance rating depends upon the type of reinforcing steel it contains, the temperature the steel reaches and the level of stress required in the steel.

1.4.2.5. Cover to Reinforcement

The rate at which heat reaches the reinforcement of a member and hence the loss of strength of the steel, is inversely proportional to the concrete cover provided. Designers should bear in mind that the covers specified in CSA Standard A23.1 for various members and exposures may not be sufficient to meet the requirements of Appendix "D" of the NBCC to provide the necessary fire resistance rating.

1.4.2.6. Restraint and Continuity

The provisions of Appendix "D" of the NBCC generally only apply to the rating of simply supported assemblies. In that document it is stated that:

"It is known that both edge restraint of a floor or roof and end restraint of a beam can significantly extend the time before collapse in a standard test", and also that:

"In a restrained condition the floor, roof or beams would probably have greater fire resistance (than that set forth in this Chapter), but the extent of this increase can be determined only by reference to behaviour in a standard test."

Thus, unless the designer has access to specific test data for restrained or continuous reinforced concrete slabs or beams, or is prepared to undertake rational design computations and have them approved as discussed previously, the benefits of restraint or continuity cannot be utilized. It must, however, be emphasized that in the case of a slab-like member whose fire resistance rating is governed by temperature rise on its unexposed surface and hence the thickness of the slab, no increase in rating can be obtained by rational design, even though the slab may be restrained or continuous.

1.4.2.7. Protected Construction

Appendix "D" of the NBCC includes detailed provisions to enable the assessment of the contribution of plaster of gypsum wall board finish to the fire resistance of masonry or concrete. In addition, ULC data covering the use of sprayed fireproofing or special fire retardant mastics is also available. While consideration of protected construction is beyond the scope of this Section, information on the subject is readily available.

1.4.2.8. Column Eccentricities

The A23.3 Standard requires that a minimum eccentricity of $(15 + 0.03h)$ mm be assumed in the design of columns. This equates to a load level equivalent to approximately 90% of the full theoretical factored resistance of the column. As the eccentricity of the applied load increases, the calculated factored resistance of the column decreases in accordance with the load/moment interaction diagram. The fire ratings for reinforced concrete columns provided in Appendix D of the NBCC apply to all columns designed in accordance with CSA Standard A23.3-14.

1.4.3.   Design Examples

1.4.3.1. General

The following examples illustrate the determination of fire resistance ratings in accordance with Appendix "D" of the NBCC 2015. Only those provisions of the code document needed to work the examples have been reproduced here. The numbering used for these is that of the original 2015 document.

Designers should refer to that edition of the NBCC which is referenced in the provincial building code governing the building under design for complete information on the assignment of fire resistance ratings to assemblies under consideration.

1.4.4. General Concrete and Masonry Provisions of Appendix "D" of the 2015 NBCC

(Reproduced with the permission of the National Research Council of Canada, copyright holder)

D-1.3. Concrete

D-1.3.1 Aggregates in Concrete

Low density aggregate concretes generally exhibit better fire performance than natural stone aggregate concretes. A series of tests on concrete masonry walls, combined with mathematical analysis of the test results, has allowed further distinctions between certain low density aggregates to be made.

D-1.4. Types of Concrete

D-1.4.1. Description

1) For purposes of this Appendix, concretes are described as Types S, N, L, L_1, L_2, L4OS, $L_1$2OS or $L_2$2OS as described in (2) to (8).

2) Type S concrete is the type in which the coarse aggregate is granite, quartzite, siliceous gravel or other dense materials containing at least 30% quartz, chert or flint.

3) Type N concrete is the type in which the coarse aggregate is cinders, broken brick, blast furnace slag, limestone, calcareous gravel, trap rock, sandstone or similar dense material containing not more than 30% of quartz, chert or flint.

4) Type L concrete is the type in which all the aggregate is expanded slag, expanded clay, expanded shale or pumice.

5) Type L_1 concrete is the type in which all the aggregate is expanded shale.

6) Type L_2 concrete is the type in which all the aggregate is expanded slag, expanded clay or pumice.

7) Type L4OS concrete is the type in which the fine portion of the aggregate is sand and low density aggregate in which the sand does not exceed 40% of the total volume of all aggregates in the concrete.

8) Type $L_1$2OS and Type $L_2$2OS concretes are the types in which the fine portion of the aggregate is sand and low density aggregate in which the sand does not exceed 20% of the total volume of all aggregates in the concrete.

D-1.4.2. Determination of Ratings

Where concretes are described as being of Type S, N, L, L_1 or L_2, the rating applies to the concrete containing the aggregate in the group that provides the least fire resistance. If the nature of an aggregate cannot be determined accurately enough to place it in one of the groups, the aggregates shall be considered as being in the group that requires a greater thickness of concrete for the required fire resistance.

D-1.4.3. Description of Aggregates

1)   The descriptions of the aggregates in Type S and Type N concretes apply to the coarse aggregates only. Coarse aggregate for this purpose means that retained on a 5 mm sieve using the method of grading aggregates described in CSA-A23.1/A23.2, "Concrete Materials and Methods of Concrete Construction / Test Methods an Standard Practices for Concrete".

2)   Increasing the proportions of sand as fine aggregate in low density concretes requires increased thicknesses of material to produce equivalent fire-resistance ratings. Low density aggregates for Type L and Types L-S concretes used in loadbearing components shall conform to ASTM C330, "Lightweight Aggregates for Structural Concrete".

3)   Non-loadbearing low density components of vermiculite and perlite concrete, in the absence of other test evidence, shall be rated on the basis of the values shown for Type L concrete.

D-1.6.   Equivalent Thickness

D-1.6.1. Method of Calculating

1)   The thickness of solid-unit masonry and concrete described in this Appendix shall be the thickness of solid material in the unit or component thickness. For units that contain cores or voids, the Tables refer to the equivalent thickness determined in conformance with (2) to (10).

2)   Where a plaster finish is used, the equivalent thickness of a wall, floor, column or beam protection shall be equal to the sum of the equivalent thicknesses of the concrete or masonry units and the plaster finish measured at the point that will give the least value of equivalent thickness.

3)   Except as provided in (5), the equivalent thickness of a hollow masonry unit shall be calculated as equal to the actual overall thickness of a unit in millimetres multiplied by a factor equal to the net volume of the unit and divided by its gross volume.

4)   Net volume shall be determined using a volume displacement method that is not influenced by the porous nature of the units.

5)   Gross volume of a masonry unit shall be equal to the actual length of the unit multiplied by the actual height of the unit multiplied by the actual thickness of the unit.

6)   Where all the core spaces in a wall of hollow concrete masonry or hollow-core precast concrete units are filled with grout, mortar, or loose fill materials such as expanded slag, burned clay or shale (rotary kiln process), vermiculite or perlite, the equivalent thickness rating of the wall shall be considered to be the same as that of a wall of solid units, or a solid wall of the same concrete type and the same overall thickness.

7)   The equivalent thickness of hollow-core concrete slabs and panels having a uniform thickness and cores of constant cross section throughout their length shall be obtained by dividing the net cross-sectional area of the slab or panel by its width.

8)   The equivalent thickness of concrete panels with tapered cross sections shall be the cross section determined at a distance of 2 t or 150 mm, whichever is less, from the point of minimum thickness, where t is the minimum thickness.

9) Except as permitted in (10), the equivalent thickness of concrete panels with ribbed or undulating surfaces shall be

a) t_a for s less than or equal to 2 t,
b) $t + (4 t/s - 1)(t_a-t)$ for s less than 4 t and greater than 2 t, and
c) t for s greater than or equal to 4 t

where

t = minimum thickness of panel,
t_a = average thickness of panel (unit cross-sectional area divided by unit width), and
s = centre to centre spacing of ribs or undulations.

10) Where the total thickness of a panel described in (9), exceeds 2 t, only that portion of the panel which is less than 2 t from the nonribbed surface shall be considered for the purpose of the calculations in (9).

1.4.5. Masonry and Concrete Walls

1.4.5.1. Applicable Provisions of Appendix "D"

(Reproduced with the permission of the National Research Council of Canada, copyright holder)

SECTION D-2   Fire-Resistance Ratings

D-2.1   Masonry and Concrete Walls

D-2.1.1. Minimum Equivalent Thickness for Fire-Resistance Rating

The minimum thicknesses of unit masonry and monolithic concrete walls are shown in Table D-2.1.1. Hollow masonry units and hollow-core concrete panels shall be rated on the basis of equivalent thickness as described in D-1.6.

Table D-2.1.1.
Minimum Equivalent Thicknesses[1] of Unit Masonry and
Monolithic Concrete Walls Loadbearing and Non-Loadbearing, mm

Type of Wall	Fire-Resistance Rating						
	30 min	45 min	1 h	1.5 h	2h	3h	4h
Solid brick units (80% solid and over), actual overall thickness	63	76	90	108	128	152	178
Cored brick units and hollow tile units (less than 80% solid), equivalent thickness	50	60	72	86	102	122	142
Solid and hollow concrete masonry units, equivalent thickness							
Type S or N concrete[2]	44	59	73	95	113	142	167
Type $L_1$20S concrete	42	54	66	87	102	129	152
Type L_1 concrete	42	54	64	82	97	122	143
Type $L_2$20S concrete	42	54	64	81	94	116	134
Type L_2 concrete	42	54	63	79	91	111	127

Type of Wall	Fire-Resistance Rating						
	30 min	45 min	1 h	1.5 h	2h	3h	4h
Monolithic concrete and concrete panels, equivalent thicknesses							
Type S concrete	60	77	90	112	130	158	180
Type N concrete	59	74	87	108	124	150	171
Type L40S or Type L concrete	49	62	72	89	103	124	140

Notes to Table D-2.1.1:

(1)   See definition of equivalent thickness in D-1.6.

(2)   Hollow concrete masonry units made with Type S or N concrete shall have a minimum compressive strength of 15 MPa base on net area, as defined in CAN/CSA-A165.1, "Concrete Block Masonry Units"

D-2.1.2. Applicability of Ratings

1)   Ratings obtained as described in D-2.1.1. apply to either loadbearing or non-loadbearing walls, except for walls described in (2) to (6).

2)   Ratings for walls with a thickness less than the minimum thickness prescribed for load-bearing walls in this Code apply to non-loadbearing walls only.

3)   Masonry cavity walls (consisting of 2 wythes of masonry with an air space between) that are loaded to a maximum allowable compressive stress of 380 kPa have a fire resistance at least as great as that of a solid wall of a thickness equal to the sum of the equivalent thicknesses of the 2 wythes.

4)   Masonry cavity walls that are loaded to a compressive stress exceeding 380 kPa are not considered to be within the scope of this Appendix.

5)   A masonry wall consisting of 2 types of masonry units, either bonded together or in the form of a cavity wall, shall be considered to have a fire-resistance rating equal to that which would apply if the whole of the wall were of the material that gives the lesser rating.

6)   A non-loadbearing cavity wall made up of 2 precast concrete panels with an air space or insulation in the cavity between them shall be considered to have a fire-resistance rating as great as that of a solid wall of a thickness equal to the sum of the thicknesses of the 2 panels.

D-2.1.3. Framed Beams and Joists

Beams and joists that are framed into a masonry or concrete fire separation shall not reduce the thickness of the fire separation to less than the equivalent thickness required for the fire separation.

D-2.1.4. Credit for Plaster Thickness

On monolithic walls and walls of unit masonry, the full plaster finish on one or both faces multiplied by the factor shown in Table D-1.7.1. shall be included in the wall thickness in Table D-2.1.1., under the conditions and using the methods described in D-1.7.

D-2.1.5. Walls Exposed to Fire on Both Sides

1) Except as permitted in (2), portions of loadbearing reinforced concrete walls, which do not form a complete fire separation and thus may be exposed to fire on both sides simultaneously, shall have minimum dimensions and minimum cover to steel reinforcement in conformance with D-2.8.2 to D-2.8.5.

2) A concrete wall exposed to fire from both sides as described in (1) has a fire-resistance rating of 2 h if the following conditions are met:

a) its equivalent thickness is not less than 200 mm,
b) its aspect ratio (width/thickness) is not less than 4.0,
c) the minimum thickness of concrete cover over the steel reinforcement specified in (d) is not less than 50 mm,
d) each face of the wall is reinforced with both vertical and horizontal steel reinforcement in conformance with either Clause 10 or Clause 14 of CSA A23.3, "Design of Concrete Structures,"
e) the structural design of the wall is governed by the minimum eccentricity (15 + 0.03h) specified in Clause 10.15.3.1. of CSA A23.3, "Design of Concrete Structures," and
f) the effective length of the wall, kl_u, is not more than 3.7 m

where
k = effective length factor obtained from CSA A23.3, "Design of Concrete Structures,"
l_u = unsupported length of the wall in metres.

1.4.5.2. Determination of the Fire Resistance Rating of a Ribbed Panel Wall

Given:

The section of wall panel shown. Type L40S concrete.

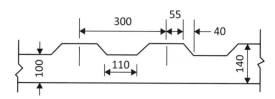

Problem:

Determine the fire resistance rating of the wall.

Solution:

Determine equivalent thickness per D-1.6.1.(9)

t = 100 mm

$$t_a = \frac{(100 \times 300) + (150 \times 40)}{300} = 120\,mm$$

s = 300 mm

As total thickness of panel does not exceed 2t, D-1.6.1. (10) does not apply.
As s is less than 4t and greater than 2t, expression (b) of D-1.6.1. (9) applies and:

$$\text{Equivalent thickness} = 100 + \left(\frac{4(100)}{300} - 1\right)(120 - 100) = 106.6\,mm$$

From NBCC Table D-2.1.1, 106.6 mm > 103 mm of L40S concrete and qualifies for a 2 hour fire resistance rating.

1.4.6.   Reinforced and Prestressed Floor and Roof Slabs

1.4.6.1. Applicable Provisions of NBCC Appendix "D"

(Reproduced with the permission of the National Research Council of Canada, copyright holder)

D-2.2.   REINFORCED AND PRESTRESSED CONCRETE FLOOR AND ROOF SLABS

D-2.2.1 Assignment of Rating

1)   Floors and roofs in a fire test are assigned a fire-resistance rating which relates to the time that an average temperature rise of 140°C or a maximum temperature rise of 180°C at any location is recorded on the unexposed side, or the time required for collapse to occur, whichever is the lesser. The thickness of concrete shown in Table D-2.2.1.-A. shall be required to resist the transfer of heat during the fire resistance period shown.

Table D-2.2.1.-A.
Minimum Thickness of Reinforced and Prestressed Concrete Floor or Roof Slabs, mm

Type of Concrete	Fire-Resistance Rating						
	30 min	45 min	1 h	1.5 h	2 h	3 h	4 h
Type S concrete	60	77	90	112	130	158	180
Type N concrete	59	74	87	108	124	150	171
Type L40S or Type L concrete	49	62	72	89	103	124	140

2) The concrete cover over the reinforcement and steel tendons shown in Table D-2.2.1.-B. shall be required to maintain the integrity of the structure and prevent collapse during the same period.

Table D-2.2.1.-B.
Minimum Concrete Cover over Reinforcement in Concrete Slabs, mm

Type of Concrete	Fire-Resistance Rating						
	30 min	45 min	1 h	1.5h	2 h	3 h	4 h
Type S, N, L40S or L concrete	20	20	20	20	25	32	39
Prestressed concrete slabs Type S, N, L40S or L concrete	20	25	25	32	39	50	64

D-2.2.2. Floors with Hollow Units

The fire resistance of floors containing hollow units may be determined on the basis of equivalent thickness as described in D-1.6.

D-2.2.3. Composite Slabs

1) For composite concrete floor and roof slabs consisting of one layer of Type S or N concrete and another layer of Type L40S or L concrete in which the minimum thickness of both the top and bottom layers is not less than 25 mm, the combined fire-resistance rating may be determined using the following expressions:

a) when the base layer consists of Type S or N concrete,

$$R = 0.00018t^2 - 0.00009dt + (8.7/t)$$

b) when the base layer consists of Type L40S or L concrete,

$$R = 0.0001t^2 - 0.0002dt - 0.0001d^2 + (6.4/t)$$

where
  R = fire resistance of slab, h,
  t = total thickness of slab, mm, and
  d = thickness of base layer, mm.

2) If the base course described in (1) is covered by a top layer of material other than Type S, N, L40S or L concrete, the top course thickness may be converted to an equivalent concrete thickness by multiplying the actual thickness by the appropriate factor listed in Table D-2.2.3.-A. This equivalent concrete thickness may be added to the thickness of the base course and the fire-resistance rating calculated using Table D-2.2.1.-A.

Table D-2.2.3.-A. Multiplying Factors for Equivalent Thickness		
Top Course Material	**Base Slab Normal Density** **Concrete (Type S or N)**	**Base Slab Low Density** **Concrete (Type L40S or L)**
Gypsum wallboard	3	2.25
Cellular concrete (mass density 400 - 560 kg/m³)	2	1.5
Vermiculite and perlite concrete (mass density 560 kg/m3 or less)	1.75	1.5
Portland cement with sand aggregate	1	0.75
Terrazzo	1	0.75

3) The minimum concrete cover under the main reinforcement for composite floor and roof slabs with base slabs of less than 100 mm thick shall conform to Table D-2.2.3.-B. For base slabs 100 mm or more thick, the minimum cover thickness requirements of Table D-2.2.1.-B. shall apply.

Table D-2.2.3.-B
Minimum Concrete Cover under Bottom Reinforcement in composite Concrete Slabs, mm

Base Slab Concrete Type	Fire-Resistance Rating						
	30 min	45 min	1h	1.5h	2h	3h	4h
Reinforced Concrete							
Type S, N, L40S or L	15	15	20	25	30	40	55
Prestressed concrete							
Type S	20	25	30	40	50	65	75
Type N	20	20	25	35	45	60	70
Type L40S or L	20	20	25	30	40	50	60

4) Where the top layer of a 2-layer slab is less than 25 mm thick, the fire-resistance rating of the slab shall be calculated as though the entire slab were made up of the type of concrete with the lesser fire resistance.

D-2.2.4. Contribution of Plaster Finish

1) The contribution of plaster finish securely fastened to the underside of concrete may be taken into account in floor or roof slabs under the conditions and using the methods described in D-1.7.

2) Plaster finish on the underside of concrete floors or roofs may be used in lieu of concrete cover referred to in D-2.2.1.(2) under the conditions and using the methods described in D-1.7.

1

D-2.2.5. Concrete Cover

1) In prestressed concrete slab construction, the concrete cover over an individual tendon shall be the minimum thickness of concrete between the surface of the tendon and the fire-exposed surface of the slab, except that for ungrouted ducts the assumed cover thickness shall be the minimum thickness of concrete between the surface of the duct and the bottom of the slab. For slabs in which several tendons are used, the cover is assumed to be the average of those of individual tendons, except that the cover for any individual tendon shall be not less than half of the value given in Table D-2.2.1.B. nor less than 20 mm.

2) Except as provided in (3), in post-tensioned prestressed concrete slabs, the concrete cover to the tendon at the anchor shall be not less than 15 mm greater than the minimum cover required by (1). The minimum concrete cover to the anchorage bearing plate and to the end of the tendon, if it projects beyond the bearing plate, shall be 20 mm.

3) The requirements of (2) do not apply to those portions of slabs not likely to be exposed to fire, such as the ends and tops.

D-2.2.6. Minimum Dimensions for Cover

Minimum dimensions and cover to steel tendons of prestressed concrete beams shall conform to D-2.10.

1.4.6.2. Determination of the Fire Resistance Rating of a Hollow Core Slab

Given:

The section of prestressed concrete hollow core slab shown.

Type N concrete slab, Type L40S topping. Cross sectional area of 1200 mm wide slab, from product literature = 134,000 mm². 12.7 mm diameter strand.

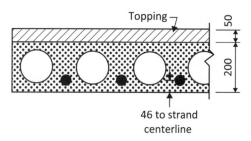

Problem:

Determine the fire resistance rating of the section, both without the topping and topped.

Solution:

a) Untopped Section

Determine equivalent thickness of slab per D-1.6.1.(7)

Equivalent thickness = $\dfrac{\text{net cross-sectional area}}{\text{panel width}}$ = 134,000 / 1200 = 112 mm

The rating for transfer of heat, per NBCC Table D-2.2.1.-A, Type N concrete is 1½ hours (+).

The rating for structural integrity, per NBCC Table D-2.2.1.-B, Type N concrete

Concrete cover to strand = 46 - 12.7 / 2 mm

$\qquad\qquad\qquad\qquad$ = 39.65 mm > 39 mm

∴ Rating for this cover is 2 hours.

However, as transfer of heat governs, rating is 1½ hours.

b) Topped Section

As the base layer is Type N concrete and the topping Type L40S concrete, D-2.2.3.(1)(a) governs, and

$R = 0.00018t^2 - 0.00009dt + (8.7/t)$

t = total equivalent thickness of slab = 112 + 50 = 162 mm

d = equivalent thickness of base slab = 112 mm

Thus $R = 0.00018(162)^2 - 0.00009(112)(162) + \dfrac{8.7}{162}$

$\qquad$ = 4.72 - 1.63 + .05
$\qquad$ = 3.14 hours

However, by the provisions of D-2.2.3(3), the minimum cover thickness of NBCC Table D-2.2.1.B governs.

Thus, for 39 mm cover, a rating of 2 hours applies to the topped section.

1.4.7.   Reinforced Concrete Columns

1.4.7.1. Applicable Provisions of Appendix "D"

(Reproduced with the permission of the National Research Council of Canada, copyright holder)

D-2.8.   Reinforced Concrete Columns

D-2.8.1 Minimum Dimensions

Minimum Dimensions for reinforced concrete columns and minimum concrete cover for vertical steel reinforcement are obtained from NBCC D-2.8.2. to D-2.8.5., taking into account the type of concrete, the effective length of the column and the area of the vertical reinforcement.

D-2.8.2. Method

  1)   The minimum dimension, t, in millimetres, of a rectangular reinforced concrete column shall be equal to

a)   75 f(R + 1) for all Types L and L40S concrete,
b)   80 f(R + 1) for Type S concrete when the design condition of the concrete column is defined in the second and fourth columns of Table D-2.8.2.,
c)   80 f(R + 0.75) for Type N concrete when the design condition of the concrete is defined in the second and fourth columns of Table D-2.8.2, and
d)   100 f(R + 1) for Types S and N concrete when the design condition of the concrete column is defined in the third column of Table D-2.8.2.

   where
       f = the value shown in Table D-2.8.2.,
       R = the required fire-resistance rating in hours,
       k = the effective length factor obtained from CSA A23.3, "Design of Concrete Structures"
       h = the unsupported length of the column in metres, and
       ρ = the area of vertical reinforcement in the column as a percentage of the column area.

Table D-2.8.2
Values of Factor f[1]

Overdesign Factor[2]	Values of Factor f to be Used in Applying Article D-2.8.2.		
	Where kh is not more than 3.7 m	Where kh is more than 3.7 m but not more than 7.3 m	
		t is not more than 300 mm, ρ is not more than 3%[3]	All other cases[4]
1.00	1.0	1.2	1.0
1.25	0.9	1.1	0.9
1.50	0.83	1.0	0.83

Notes to Table D-2.8.2.:
(1)   For conditions that do not fall within the limits described in Table D-2.8.2., further information may be obtained from Reference (7) in D-6.1.
(2)   Overdesign factor is the ratio of the calculated load carrying capacity of the column to the column strength required to carry the specified loads determined in conformance with CSA A23.3, "Design of Concrete Structures".
(3)   Where the factor f results in a t greater than 300 mm, the appropriate factor f for "All other cases" shall be applicable.
(4)   Where ρ is equal to or less than 3% and the factor f results in a t less than 300 mm, the minimum thickness shall be 300 mm.

2) The diameter of a round column shall be not less than 1.2 times the value t determined in (1) for a rectangular column.

D-2.8.3. Minimum Thickness of Concrete Cover

1) Where the required fire-resistance rating of a concrete column is 3 h or less, the minimum thickness in millimetres of concrete cover over vertical steel reinforcement shall be equal to 25 times the number of hours of fire resistance required or 50 mm, whichever is less.

2) Where the required fire-resistance rating of a concrete column is greater than 3 h, the minimum thickness in millimetres of concrete cover over vertical steel reinforcement shall be equal to 50 plus 12.5 times the required number of hours of fire resistance in excess of 3 h.

3) Where the concrete cover over vertical steel required in (2) exceeds 62.5 mm, wire mesh reinforcement with 1.57 mm diameter wire and 100 mm openings shall be incorporated midway in the concrete cover to retain the concrete in position.

D-2.8.4. Minimum Requirements

The structural design standards may require minimum column dimensions or concrete cover over vertical steel reinforcement differing from those obtained in D-2.8.2.(1) and D-2.8.2.(2). Where a difference occurs, the greater dimension shall govern.

D-2.8.5. Addition of Plaster

The addition of plaster finish to the concrete column may be taken into account in determining the cover over vertical steel reinforcement by applying the multiplying factors described in D-1.7. The addition of plaster shall not, however, justify any decrease in the minimum column sizes shown.

D-2.8.6. Built-In Columns

The fire-resistance rating of a reinforced concrete column that is built into a masonry or concrete wall so that not more than one face may be exposed to the possibility of fire at one time may be determined on the basis of cover to vertical reinforcing steel alone. In order to meet this condition, the wall shall conform to D-2.1. for the fire-resistance rating required.

1.4.7.2. Determination of the Fire Resistance of a Reinforced Concrete Column

Given:

300 × 300 mm column, Type S concrete
Column height = 3650 mm
Maximum specified load = 1200 kN
Concrete strength f_c' = 35 MPa
Steel strength f_y = 400 MPa
Percentage steel, ρ = 4%
Effective length factor k = 1.0

Problem:

Determine the fire resistance rating of the column.

Solution:

Maximum specified (unfactored) load capacity of column, taking slenderness into account and an eccentricity corresponding to 15 + 0.03h is 1660 kN.

*Note that eccentricity is within CSA Standard A23.3 limit for concentric loading.

Overdesign factor = 1660/1200 = 1.33, use overdesign factor = 1.25

∴ f factor from NBCC Table D-2.8.2 for kh = 3.65m is 0.9.

From D-2.8.2.(1)(b)

$t \geq 80 f (R + 1)$

Substituting t = 300 and f = 0.9 into this equation yields a fire-resistance rating of 3.16 hrs.

1.4.8. Reinforced Concrete Beams

1.4.8.1. Applicable Provisions of Appendix "D"

(Reproduced with the permission of the National Research Council of Canada, copyright holder)

D-2.9. Reinforced Concrete Beams

D-2.9.1. Minimum Cover Thickness

The minimum thickness of cover over principal steel reinforcement in reinforced concrete beams is shown in Table D-2.9.1 for fire-resistance ratings from 30 min to 4h where the width of the beam or joist is at least 100 mm.

Table D-2.9.1.
Minimum cover to Principal Steel Reinforcement in Reinforced Concrete Beams, mm

Type of Concrete	Fire-Resistance Rating						
	30 min	45 min	1h	1.5h	2h	3h	4h
Type S, N or L	20	20	20	25	25	39	50

> ### D-2.9.2. Maximum Rating
>
> No rating over 2 h may be assigned on the basis of Table D-2.9.1. to a beam or joist where the average width of the part that projects below the slab is less than 140 mm, and no rating over 3 h may be assigned where the average width of the part that projects below the slab is less than 165 mm.
>
> ### D-2.9.3. Beam Integrated in Floor or Roof Slab
>
> For the purposes of these ratings, a beam may be either independent of or integral with a floor or roof slab assembly.
>
> ### D-2.9.4. Minimum Thickness
>
> Where the upper extension or top flange of a joist or T-beam in a floor assembly contributes wholly or partly to the thickness of the slab above, the total thickness at any point shall be not less than the minimum thickness described in Table D-2.2.1.-A. for the fire-resistance rating required.
>
> ### D-2.9.5. Effect of Plaster
>
> The addition of plaster finish to a reinforced concrete beam may be taken into account in determining the cover over principal reinforcing steel by applying the multiplying factors described in D-1.7.

1.4.8.2. Determination of the Fire Resistance of a Reinforced Concrete Beam

Given:

The section of reinforced concrete beam and slab shown:

Type S concrete

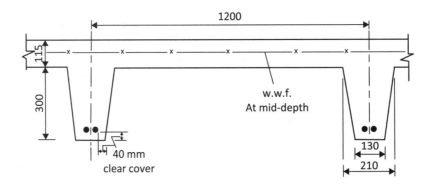

Problem:

Determine the fire resistance of the section.

Solution:

a) Determine the fire resistance of the beam section.

For 40 mm cover, from NBCC Table D-2.9.1, Type S concrete,

Maximum rating = 3 hours
Width of beam, average = 170 mm
From D-2.9.2, 170 mm > 165 mm ∴ Rating of 3 hours is justified for the beam

b) Determine the fire resistance of the slab.

From Table D-2.2.1.-A, for 115 mm of Type S concrete the rating to resist transfer of heat is 1½ hours.

From NBCC Table D-2.2.1.-B, for a clear cover of 55 mm, a structural rating in excess of 4 hours is achieved.
∴ heat transmission governs

Check to determine whether, by the provisions of D-1.6.1.(9), an increased equivalent thickness can be assumed.

t = 115 mm
s = 1200 mm
4t = 460 mm

Because s exceeds 4t, no increased equivalent thickness can be assumed.

Thus, the total assembly qualifies for a 1½ hour rating.

1.4.9. Prestressed Concrete Beams

1.4.9.1. Applicable Provisions of Appendix "D"

(Reproduced with the permission of the National Research Council of Canada, copyright holder)

D-2.10. Prestressed Concrete Beams

D-2.10.1. Minimum Cross-Sectional Area and Thickness of Cover

The minimum cross-sectional area and thickness of concrete cover over steel tendons in prestressed concrete beams for fire-resistance ratings from 30 min to 4 h are shown in Table D-2.10.1.

Table D-2.10.1.

Minimum Thickness of Concrete Cover over Steel Tendons in Prestressed Concrete Beams, mm[1]

Type of Concrete	Area of Beam cm²	Fire-Resistance Rating						
		30 min	45 min	1h	1.5h	2h	3h	4h
Type S or N	260 to 970	25	39	50	64	-	-	-
	Over 970 to 1940	25	26	39	45	64	-	-
	Over 1940	25	26	39	39	50	77	102
Type L	Over 970	25	25	25	39	50	77	102

Note to Table D-2.10.1.:

(1)   Where the thickness of concrete cover over the tendons exceeds 64 mm, a wire mesh reinforcement with 1.57 mm diameter wire and 100 mm by 100 mm openings shall be incorporated in the beams to retain the concrete in position around the tendons. The mesh reinforcement shall be located midway in the cover.

D-2.10.2. Minimum Cover Thickness

The cover for an individual tendon shall be the minimum thickness of concrete between the surface of the tendon and the fire-exposed surface of the beam, except that for ungrouted ducts the assumed cover thickness shall be the minimum thickness of concrete between the surface of the duct and the surface of the beam. For beams in which several tendons are used, the cover is assumed to be the average of the minimum cover of the individual tendons. The cover for any individual tendon shall be not less than half the value given in Table D-2.10.1. nor less than 25 mm.

D-2.10.3. Applicability of Ratings

The ratings in Table D-2.10.1. apply to a beam that is either independent of or integral with a floor or roof slab assembly. Minimum thickness of slab and minimum cover to steel tendons in prestressed concrete slabs are contained in D-2.2.

D-2.10.4. Effect of Plaster

The addition of plaster finish to a prestressed concrete beam may be taken into account in determining the cover over steel tendons by applying the multiplying factors described in D-1.7.

D-2.10.5 Minimum Cover

1)   Except as provided in (2), in unbonded post-tensioned prestressed concrete beams, the concrete cover to the tendon at the anchor shall be not less than 15 mm greater than the minimum required away from the anchor. The concrete cover to the anchorage bearing plate and to the end of the tendon, if it projects beyond the bearing plate, shall be not less than 25 mm.

2)   The requirements in (1) do not apply to those portions of beams not likely to be exposed to fire (such as the ends and the tops of flanges of beams immediately below slabs).

1.4.9.2. Determination of the Fire Resistance Rating of a Prestressed Concrete Beam

Given:

The section of prestressed concrete T-beam shown, Type S concrete, 8-12.7 mm diameter strand. Bottom cover to lowest strand, 40 mm.

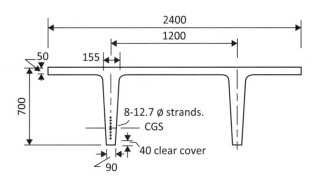

Problem:

Determine the structural fire resistance of the beam section.

Solution:

Area of stem = $\dfrac{90 + 155}{2}(700 - 50)\,\text{mm}^2 = 79625\ \text{mm}^2$

Concrete cover to bottom strand of group = 40 mm

Distance from bottom of stem to CGS

$= 40 + 4 \times 12.7 = 90.8\ \text{mm}$

Width of stem at CGS = $90 + \left(\left(\dfrac{155 - 90}{650}\right) \times 90.8\right) = 99.1\ \text{mm}$

∴ Clear side cover at CGS = $\dfrac{99.1 - 12.7}{2} = 43.2$

Minimum individual strand, bottom cover = 40 mm

Minimum individual strand, side cover
$= 45 - (12.7/2) = 38.65\ \text{mm}$

Fire resistance rating, based on side cover of centroid of strand group (from D-2.10.2 and Table D-2.10.1)

$= ¾$ hour (39 mm < 43.2 mm)

Check: Minimum cover to critical bottom tendon is greater than (39/2) = 19.5 mm and 25 mm

1.4.9.3. Single Prestressed Concrete T-Beam, Tapered Flanges

Given:

The section of flange of prestressed concrete T-beam shown. Type N concrete beam and topping.

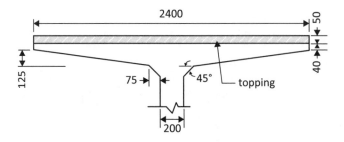

Problem:

Determine the fire resistance rating of the flange for heat transmission.

Solution:

The provisions of Subsection D-1.6.1.(8) apply.

Thickness at edge of flange = 50 + 40 = 90 mm = t

2t = 180 mm > 150 mm

∴ Determine thickness at 150 mm from edge

Slope is 125 mm in 1025 mm

At 150 mm, t = 90 + (125/1025) × 150 = 90 + 18 = 108 mm

From Table D-2.2.1.A (see Section 1.4.6.1), for Type N concrete, the fire-resistance rating is 1½ hours.

1.4.10. Reference Publications

(1) **Design Manual** - Canadian Precast Prestressed Concrete Institute, PO Box 24058, Hazeldean, Ottawa Ontario, Canada K2M 2C3

(2) CRSI - Reinforced Concrete Fire Resistance; Concrete Reinforcing Steel Institute, 933 N. Plum Grove Road, Schaumburg, Illinois, 60195

1.5   Sound Transmission

1.5.1.   Introduction

The sound transmission requirements of the NBCC are specified in Part 5 of the Code. The NBCC has traditionally specified a Sound Transmission Class (STC) rating of 50 between a dwelling unit and all other areas of a building. An STC rating of 55 is specified between a dwelling unit and an elevator shaft or refuse chute. The STC rating is a measure of the sound attenuation measured directly through a wall or floor and is determined in accordance with ASTM E413 "Classification for Rating Sound Insulation". ASTM E413 requires that measurements be carried out in accordance with ASTM E90 and ASTM E336. To facilitate compliance with these ASTM Standards, STC ratings were included in the NBCC in Table A-9.10.3.1.(A) for a variety of wall assemblies, and Table A-9.10.3.1.(B) for floors, ceilings and roofs. The designer simply checked to see that these tables listed an appropriate STC rating for the construction being used on the project. If a matching assembly did not provide the required STC rating the designer was required to modify the construction to one conforming to an appropriate assembly contained in the tables.

1.5.2.   ASTC Sound Transmission System

In 2015 the NBCC has introduced the an "Apparent Sound Transmission Class" (ASTC) rating system. The ASTC system provides a better estimate of the actual sound transmission measured between units, taking into account flanking transmission through connections between adjacent walls and between walls and floors. As a result, the ASTC value will always be equal to or less than the STC value. The ASTC system has been adapted from European practice, which is the source of much of the original data on ASTC ratings used for concrete construction in the 2015 NBCC. Additionally, the ASTC system provides for greater flexibility in determining sound attenuation between a wider variety of assemblies when introducing new materials and elements with known acoustical properties in the construction. This allows the designer to utilize a greater variety of assemblies beyond those prescribed in Tables A-9-10.3.1(A) and (B). The new ASTC system can be used to entirely replace the existing STC rating system, or it can be used in combination with the STC rating system to meet the sound transfer requirements of the Code.

1.5.3.   Meeting the Sound Transfer Requirements of the 2015 NBCC

Part 5 of the 2015 NBCC provides two compliance paths for sound transfer between a dwelling unit and other areas of a structure. The compliance paths are noted below:

a)   Provide an STC rating of 50 using Tables 9.10.3.1.-A and 9.10.3.1.-B, or
b)   Provide an ASTC rating of 47 using the methods provided in Part 5.

The provision of an STC rating of 55 rather than an ASTC rating is still required between a dwelling unit and an elevator shaft or refuse chute as there are currently no ASTC metrics that address noise generated by elevators.

In meeting compliance path (a) noted above, the construction must also meet the additional requirements of Article 9.11.1.4. This ensures that the construction conforms to the assumptions used in the ASTC method.

In meeting compliance path (b) both a simplified and detailed procedure is provided. The NRC publication "Guide to Calculating Airborne Sound Transmission in Buildings" contains background information on the concepts and procedures used in determining ASTC ratings. Worked examples are also included for the major construction materials. This free publication is available on the NRC website.

Additional information on sound transmission in various forms of concrete construction can be found in the Canadian Precast/Prestressed Concrete Institute's Design Manual (4th Edition).

1.6   Special Requirements for Corrosive Environments

1.6.1.   Introduction

In common with other construction materials, unprotected or improperly designed concrete will suffer corrosion if exposed to an environment in which certain chemically aggressive agents are present.

The following provides information on means of minimizing or preventing loss of serviceability* and damage to concrete which may be exposed to commonly occurring corrosive environments.

1.6.2.   De-Icer Salt Environment

CSA Standard A23.1 (Clause 4.1.1 and Table 2) requires that concrete subject to applications of de-icing chemicals be designated as Exposure Classes 'C-XL, and C-1 to C-4', which implies a low water/cementing materials ratio, a high content of entrained air and other mix design controls. CSA A23.1 Clause 6 and Table 17 provide requirements for concrete cover to reinforcement where the concrete is exposed to chlorides. It should be borne in mind that specified minimum covers are the minimum anywhere in the member. Reveals, architectural grooving and chamfers at joints, which may reduce the cover to less than acceptable minimum amounts, should not be ignored. Increased cover may also be required for fire resistance. For information on this subject, see Subsection 1.4 of this Handbook.

1.6.3.   Sea Water Environment

CSA Standard A23.1, Clause 4 contains requirements for concrete in sea water environments. Deterioration problems due to the presence of salts in the air may occur in structures located within a kilometre of the ocean, particularly if covers to reinforcement are small or concrete properties inadequate.

Sea water contains significant amounts of sulphates and chlorides. Although sulphates in sea water are capable of attacking concrete, the presence of chlorides inhibits the expansive reaction that is characteristic of attack by sulphates in groundwaters or soils. Calcium sulphoaluminate, the reaction product of sulphate attack, is more soluble in a chloride solution and can be more readily leached out of the concrete, thus causing less destructive expansion. This is the major factor explaining observations from a number of sources that the performance of concretes in sea water with Portland cements having tricalcium aluminate (C_3A) contents as high as 10%, and sometimes greater, have shown satisfactory durability, providing the permeability of the concrete is low.

Maximum permissible water/cement ratio for the submerged portions of a structure should not exceed 0.45 by mass. For portions in the splash zone and above, maximum permissible water/cement ratios should not exceed 0.40 by mass. Water/cement ratios as high as 0.50 by mass may be used for submerged areas provided the C_3A content of the Portland cement does not exceed 8%.

Cements meeting the requirements of CSA Standard A3001 and meeting the C_3A requirement noted above (that is, not more than 10%) are acceptable. In the case of blended cements, this limitation applies to the Portland cement clinker used in the blended cement.

Calcium chloride should not be used as an admixture in reinforced concrete to be exposed to sea water.

In addition to the proper selection of cement and adherence to the requirements, other requirements for quality concrete such as adequate air entrainment, low slump, low permeability, adequate consolidation, uniformity, adequate clear cover over reinforcement, and sufficient curing to develop

---

* For example, 1h parking structures, leakage of chloride-laden water onto parked cars constitutes an unserviceable condition.

the potential properties of the concrete are essential for securing economical and durable concrete exposed to sea water.

References:

CSA Standard A23.1-14, Concrete Materials and Methods of Concrete Construction
CSA Standard A3000-13, Cementitious Materials Compendium
ACI Publication SP-65, Performance of Concrete in Marine Environment

1.6.4. Sulphate Soils and Groundwater Exposure

CSA Standard A23.1, Clause 4 contains requirements for concrete that will be exposed to sulphate soils and groundwaters.

Sulphate attack on concrete can occur where soil and groundwater have a high sulphate content and where measures to prevent sulphate attack (such as those contained in CSA Standard A23.1) have not been taken. The attack is confined to concrete that is cool and moist, such as foundations and slabs on ground. It usually causes an expansion of the concrete because of the formation of solids as a result of chemical action. The amount of this expansion in some cases has been higher than 0.1% and the accompanying disruptive effect within the concrete can result in extensive cracking and deterioration.

When using Portland-limestone cement in a sulphate exposure environment, a maximum water/cement ratio of 0.40 is required by CSA A23.1-14 Standard. The concrete mix design must also pass the CSA A3004-13 C8 test for expansion at both 5°C and 23°C. Such concrete must also contain at least the minimum levels of SCM specified in A23.1 Table 3.

References:

CSA Standard A23.1-14, Concrete Materials and Methods of Concrete Construction
ACI Publication SP-77, Sulphate Resistance of Concrete

1.6.5. Sewage and Waste Water Treatment Exposure

While sanitary engineering structures are considered to be "special structures" within the context of CSA Standard A23.3, the requirements of that Standard are generally valid for their structural design, provided that special consideration is given to control of cracking. ACI 350-01/350R-01, Code Requirements for Environmental Engineering Concrete Structures and Commentary, contains detailed recommendations for loadings to be used for the limitations of concrete and steel stresses at service loads and for the design of joints in such structures.

Specifications for concrete mix design and for construction should be drawn up to provide for dense, impermeable concrete which will be resistant to naturally occurring or commonly used chemicals and have a smooth, well formed surface finish. Recommendations towards obtaining these properties are also set forth in ACI 350R.

Generally speaking, additional protection against corrosion should not be necessary, provided the design and construction meet the requirements outlined above. Certain areas within water treatment plants or domestic sewage plants where chemically aggressive agents may be present, may require the use of protective coatings or linings. Industrial waste treatment plants will probably require the use of chemically resistant surface coatings, depending on the particular wastes being processed. Information on commonly occurring chemicals and advice on types of protective coatings is included in ACI 350R.

Reference:

ACI 350-01/350R-01 Code Requirements for Environmental Engineering Concrete Structures and Commentary

1.6.6. Chemical Attack of Concrete

Parts of some concrete structures, mainly for industrial uses, must be designed for exposure to chemicals, oils, food products and other solid, liquid or gaseous substances which may or may not cause corrosion of concrete.

To determine the effect that most such products or substances will have on exposed concrete surfaces, and for recommendations on protective coatings, the reader is referred to the following publications:

References:

Effects of Substances on Concrete and Guide to Protective Treatment; Portland Cement Association (IS001.T)

ACI 515.1R-79 (Revised 1985), A Guide to the Use of Waterproofing, Dampproofing, Protective and Decorative Barrier Systems for Concrete

1.7   Structural Integrity

1.7.1. Definition

A structure is said to have structural integrity if localized damage or failure of a structural member which may be initiated by an abnormal event does not lead to collapse of a disproportionately large part of the structure. Thus, the failure of one element should not lead to a "progressive collapse" or "incremental collapse" of the rest of the structure.

This definition is difficult to quantify. The extent of damage that is expected or acceptable is a function of the magnitude and extent of the overload causing the failure, the tributary area of the member which fails, the structural system and a host of other details. Thus, a multistorey concrete building with 16 to 20 main floor columns should have enough structural integrity to remain standing if one or two of the columns were destroyed in an explosion. However, a building having only two vertical supports would not have structural integrity unless its supports were designed to resist loads and forces of the magnitude created by the explosion.

1.7.2. Types of Incremental Collapse Observed in Reinforced Concrete Buildings

One of the most prominent cases of incremental collapse of a concrete structure occurred when a gas explosion blew two exterior walls out of a corner apartment on the 18th floor of a 22 storey precast building with walls and floors consisting of precast panels (Ronan Point, Canning Town, England). The loss of support of the floors above, caused this floor to collapse. The falling debris then caused all the floors and walls below to collapse progressively.

Progressive collapse failures are rare in continuously reinforced cast-in-place concrete structures. Formerly, a possible exception to this statement involved failure originating due to a punching shear failure at a column to slab connection in a flat plate. The portion of the slab supported by this connection could have then dropped, increasing the shear and moment at adjacent columns, causing them to fail. When this happened, the slab fell onto the slab below, causing it to fail as well. This progressed vertically down the building, causing each lower slab to fail in turn. Such failures could have been initiated by premature form removal, formwork fires, inadequate slab thickness or insufficient slab column reinforcement. The 2014 edition of CSA Standard A23.3 addresses this situation by means of Clause 13.10.6.

Other examples of incremental collapse involve buildings which collapsed when a column or wall was removed by a vehicle collision, a chemical, gas or bomb explosion or similar event. Still others involve collapses which occurred when a floor member failed and, in doing so, displaced its support horizontally so that other floor members were pulled off their supports.

Precast structures or other structures with friction connections between walls and floors are particularly susceptible to such damage. References (1) and (2) review a number of buildings which have developed incremental collapses.

1.7.3.   Basic Requirements of NBCC and CSA Standard A23.3

Section 4.1.1.3(1) of the 2015 National Building Code of Canada includes structural integrity as a requirement for structural design:

4.1.1.3(1) - Buildings and their structural members and connections including formwork and falsework, shall be designed to have sufficient structural capacity and structural integrity to resist safely and effectively resist all loads, effects of loads and influences that may reasonably be expected, having regard to the expected service life of buildings, and shall in any case satisfy the requirements of this Section.

Further information can be found in the Commentary entitled Structural Integrity in the "User's Guide - NBC 2015, Structural Commentaries (Part 4 of Division B)." Appendix 'D' of the NBCC provides information on fire - performance ratings.

Clause 8.1.5 of CSA Standard A23.3 restates the NBCC requirement as follows:

8.1.5 - Consideration shall be given to the robustness of the overall structural system to minimize the likelihood of a progressive type at collapse.

This is followed by notes which state:

1) Provisions for structural integrity are required for two-way slabs (Clause 13.10.6), precast concrete structures (Clause 16.5), and tilt-up structures (Clause 23.2.9).

2) The requirements in this Standard generally provide a satisfactory level of structural integrity for most concrete structures for buildings. It is possible that supplementary provisions for structural integrity will be needed for mixed or unusual structural systems or for structures exposed to severe loads such as vehicle impacts or explosions. For further guidance, refer to Commentary B in the NRCC's User's Guide to Part 4 of the National Building Code of Canada.

Clause 16.5, entitled Structural Integrity, states:

In buildings where precast concrete elements constitute a portion of the structural system, all structural elements shall be effectively tied together.

A Note to Clause 16.5.2.1 gives a series of references providing guidance on design for structural integrity in precast buildings.

It should be noted that the governing NBCC requirement calls for buildings to be capable of resisting loads and effects of loads and influences that may "reasonably be expected". This clearly implies that only "accidental" abnormal events are to be considered. It must be recognized that well placed explosives or certain "acts of god" can bring down most structures. The Code does not require that buildings usually be designed to have structural integrity to resist collapse due to events like sabotage. Nonetheless, even such abnormal events might reasonably be expected under certain special circumstances and hence, in those specific cases, are worthy of consideration. For example, in countries where civil strife is the norm, sabotage of structures such as police stations is not unusual.

1.7.4.   Design for Adequate Structural Integrity

As stated in the Notes to Clause 8.1.5 of CSA Standard A23.3, most cast-in-place buildings designed in accordance with the Standard will possess a satisfactory level of structural integrity. This statement assumes that the layout of the structural systems and interaction between structural members will normally ensure a robust and stable design with sufficient redundancy. On this basis, no quantitative evaluation of structural integrity should be necessary insofar as the ordinary design conditions are concerned, which includes the effect of overloads during construction or those occurring in service which may cause localized failures. Thus, normally, only a general review of the structural system of such buildings will be needed to assess its likely failure modes. This review should ensure that no progressive collapse will result from any localized failures.

The Notes to Clause 8.1.5 do, however, state that compliance with the requirement may need supplementary provisions to ensure structural integrity in the case of:

a)   precast concrete structures (as stated in Clause 16.5),
b)   for mixed or unusual structural systems and
c)   for structures exposed to severe overloads, such as those due to vehicle impact or chemical explosion.

This subsection will therefore review the basic concepts which may be employed in the design of those buildings whose unusual layout or structural system does not result in a robust and stable design and where sufficient redundancy is absent, or in the design of those other relatively uncommon structures which may reasonably be expected to suffer accidental overloads.

In suggesting these rules of good practice, it must be recognized that definitive guidance for all cases cannot be provided. Just as there are so many ways that a localized failure might be initiated - gas explosions, vehicular collision, flooding, foundation failure, corrosion, fire or just understrength materials - and there are so many different types of structural systems involving different types of potential failures in each of those systems, no one set of rules can be universally applicable.

Four different design strategies are discussed in the structural integrity literature (see for example Ref. (3)):

1.   **Control of events causing abnormal loads.** An example would be placing energy absorbing devices adjacent to columns supporting the floor and walls of a building adjacent to a high speed roadway so that the energy from a vehicle colliding with the column is dissipated before it strikes the pier. Other examples would be control of building explosions by avoiding the use of natural gas stoves or heating or the relocation of a high-risk building from an area immediately downstream of a suspect dam. In many cases, however, this type of strategy is impractical and even when it is employed, the structure should be resistant to progressive collapse resulting from other causes.

2.   **Design to resist abnormal loads.** An abnormal load is one that is not normally considered in the design of the particular type of structure under consideration such as gas explosion, vehicle impact, etc. If the abnormal load or event can be defined and if loss of a particular member in a structure due to that abnormal event would lead to a progressive collapse, then that member should be able to resist the particular abnormal event or load. In general, this is not a satisfactory design strategy. In some cases, however, such as when the structural integrity of a building depends on, say, less than four columns, it may be the only practical strategy to employ. (See Subsection 1.7.5.)

3.   **Design for alternate load paths in the damaged structure.** In this design process, the designer imagines that a column, beam or other member has been removed from the structure and then checks whether the structure can bridge the gap without collapsing. Design is carried out at service load levels to ensure the structure can support the dead load, a third to a half of the live load, the wind load exceeded about once a month, plus any debris resulting from the failure. The structure is permitted to undergo a considerable amount of localized collapse and deformation, provided the damage does not spread progressively. For this to occur, the structure must have a good floor plan with proper layout of walls and columns and be well tied together horizontally and vertically. (See Subsection 1.7.6.)

4.   **Design using specified loads and local resistance details.** In this design strategy, the designer does not postulate any particular mode of failure. Instead, a minimum structural resistance is provided along with a minimum amount of reinforcement to tie various parts of the structure. In addition, consideration is given to providing strong points in the building to anchor the tie forces. (See Subsection 1.7.7.)

In summary, the first of these scenarios is generally outside the structural engineer's control. The second, third and fourth methods will be discussed further - not to provide hard and fast rules, but rather to form a basis for approaching the problems of progressive collapse.

1.7.5.   Design to Resist Abnormal Loads

Adoption of this design strategy is generally less desirable and less economical than either design for alternate load paths or design for specified loads and local resistance details, but for some buildings it cannot be avoided. Where the integrity of the structure depends entirely on one or two structural elements, these elements cannot be assumed to be removed or relied upon to anchor tie forces. Thus if the removal of such an element by an abnormal event that may reasonably be expected would initiate progressive collapse, that element must be designed to remain functional when the abnormal event occurs. The problem with this strategy is that all reasonably foreseeable abnormal events have to be anticipated and their effect assessed.

Assessment of the magnitude of accidental loads is discussed in the reference publications, in particular those adopted in Great Britain, which primarily address gas explosion.

In conclusion, design to resist abnormal loads should normally only be considered as a last resort. In cases when this strategy is employed, the designer should have rationalize, for the building in question, the magnitude of the loads which may reasonably be anticipated. It should be emphasized that the loadings suggested above are only provided to suggest the order of magnitude which these loads and forces may assume.

1.7.6.   Design for Alternate Load Paths

The basic method of designing for structural integrity is to design a structure in such a way that it can bridge over the gap left when a structure component is removed.

Two examples are shown in Figs. 1.10 and 1.11. In the first, a wall has failed due to an internal explosion, poor construction, vehicle impact (if on the main floor) or some similar cause. The remaining structure should be able to bridge over the gap. For this to occur, the walls above the lost wall must act as cantilevers to support the loads formerly supported by the missing wall. This requires horizontal tension resistance in the floors, effective vertical ties from floor to floor above the gap and effective ties to transfer the overturning moments generated in the rest of the building. This resistance may involve large deformations in the vicinity of the damaged area, but the extent of damage should be limited.

The floor in the storey below the damaged area should be able to support the weight of any debris which falls onto it. Since this could exceed the conventional capacity of the floor, the floor would be allowed to deflect 100 to 200, or even 300 millimetres under this load, until it carried the load by a catenary action, or carried load in the perpendicular direction, or both. For this to occur, tie forces must be developed in various directions as shown in Fig. 1.11.

It should be emphasized that these actions are accomplished with a load factor greater than 1.0 against total collapse under the loadings expected to occur before the building can be repaired or at least propped up. Typical load combinations to be considered would be

$$R_f (D + 0.5L + 0.2W)$$
$$R_f (D - 0.3W)$$

where R_f is the factored resistance and D, L and W are the specified dead, live and wind loads.

The following are a number of ways in which the necessary load resistance might be developed in a damaged structure:

1. **Good Floor Plan** - The use of a systematic floor plan with a proper layout of walls and columns is probably the most important single step in achieving structural integrity. Such things as number, location and continuity of lateral load resisting elements should be an arrangement of longitudinal spline walls to support and reduce the span of the cross-walls.

2. **Beam Action of Walls** - Walls can be used to span over an opening if sufficient tying steel is provided at the top and bottom of walls to allow them to act as beams with the slabs above and below possibly acting as flanges.

3. **Tensile Action of Floor Slabs** - When an interior support is removed, the floor span will increase. In this case, the sagging of the slab will stretch the reinforcement until the slab carries the load as a membrane. Such a structure can carry very large loads at large deflections provided the tensile forces are adequately anchored in the surrounding structure and provided that shear failures will not occur.

4. **Changing Direction of Span of Floor or Roof Slab** - The membrane action discussed in the preceding paragraph may occur in the original direction of the span or in some other direction if the shrinkage and temperature reinforcement can be counted on to act as membrane reinforcement.

5. **Strong Points** - In some designs, certain elements may need to be strengthened to carry the abnormal loads in order to complete an alternate path. Sometimes, a return or flange on a wall will allow it to be used as a strong point, especially when tension tie forces must be mobilized at right angles to the wall.

6. **Adequate Diaphragm Action** - Diaphragms should be reinforced with tension tie members around their perimeters and around notches and discontinuities to allow adequate load distribution.

7. **Lines of Weakness** - Occasionally, it will be desirable to provide lines of weakness to limit the spread of damage. The effect of such weak areas on other load paths should be carefully examined.

When using this strategy, designers should consider the effect of removal, one at a time, of:

*   one span of any floor or roof element,

*   one column or hanger in any one storey, except that in a multi-column structure, the loss of resistance of a column need not be considered, providing all columns are designed to resist abnormal loads as discussed in 1.7.5, or

*   one length of bearing wall panel for any storey equal to 1½ times the storey height, unless the panels are prefabricated, when this length shall equal the panel length.

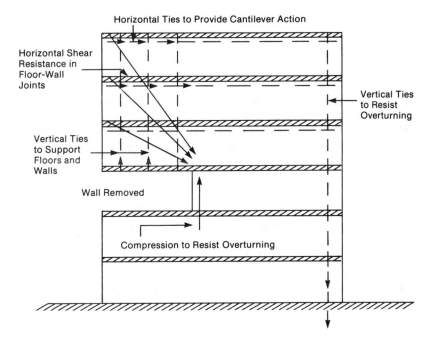

Fig. 1.10 Development of alternate load path

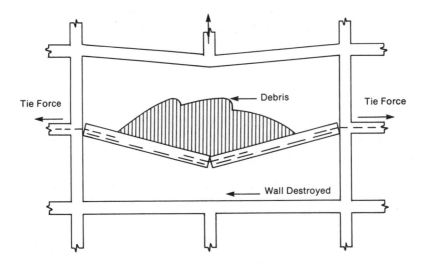

Fig. 1.11 Catenary action of floor slab

1.7.7. Design Using Specified Loads and Local Resistance Details

This design process is an attempt to provide alternate load paths without consideration of specific damage scenarios and specific load paths. This "deemed to satisfy" method is relatively well developed for precast panel buildings, much less so for cast-in-place buildings.

(a) Precast Buildings

Figure 1.12 shows the types of ties required to develop overall structural integrity in a precast structure, the longitudinal ties, often placed in the joints between floor planks, ensure that the floor can develop membrane or catenary action to span over broken wall panels or to support heavy debris loading. The transverse ties, generally placed in the horizontal joints between the walls above and below a floor, serve to tie a series of wall panels together and act as tension flanges if these walls have to cantilever or bridge over a missing support. The peripheral ties act as tension flanges for the diaphragm action of the floors and to provide anchorage of the longitudinal and transverse ties. They also help create an edge member in case a corner loses support. Vertical ties are provided to keep the walls above a damaged support from falling and to serve as a tension tieback to resist overturning moments. Specific recommendations concerning tie forces are contained in References (4), (5), and (6).

It is important that the ties be ductile to enable them to survive the movements associated with local damage. The ties must be designed and detailed so that the connections can undergo deformations, resist impact from falling debris, and in some cases undergo load reversals.

(b) Cast-in-place Buildings

Cast-in-place concrete buildings have continuity and redundancy that produce an inherent structural integrity. CSA Standard A23.3 recognizes this and, with one exception, does not require any particular details for structural integrity in cast-in-place construction. The exception involves punching shear in column-slab joints in flat-plates. Clause 13.11.5 requires special reinforcement through the column at the bottom of the slab. This reinforcement is not intended to prevent shear failures from occurring. Once such a failure has occurred, however, the slab is prevented from dropping to the floor below.

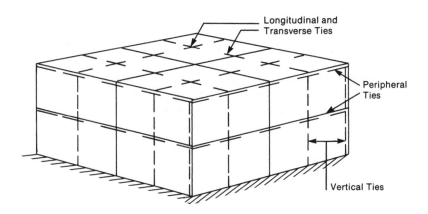

Fig. 1.12 Ties required in a precast building

1.7.8.   References

(1) Allen, D.E. and Shriever, W.R., "Progressive Collapse, Abnormal Loads and Building Codes", Structural Failures: Modes, Causes, Responsibilities, American Society of Civil Engineers, 1973, pp 21-47.

(2) Taylor, D.A., "Progressive Collapse", Canadian Journal of Civil Engineering, Vol. 2, No. 4, Dec. 1975, pp 517-529.

(3) Breen, J.E., "Developing Structural Integrity in Bearing Wall Buildings", Journal of the Prestressed Concrete Institute, Vol. 25, No. 1, Jan.-Feb. 1980, pp 42-73; Closure, Vol. 25, No. 4, July-Aug. 1980, pp 146-152.

(4) PCI Committee on Precast Bearing Wall Buildings, "Consideration for the Design of Precast Bearing Wall Buildings to Withstand Abnormal Loads", Journal of the Prestressed Concrete Institute, Vol. 21, No. 2, March/April 1976, pp 18-51.

(5) Fintel, M., Schultz, D.M. and Iqbal, M., "Report 2, Philosophy of Structural Response to Normal and Abnormal Loads", Design and Construction of Large-Panel Concrete Structures, Portland Cement Association, Skokie, Illinois, PCA Publication EB092D, August 1976, 133 pp.

(6) Schultz, D.M., "Report 6, Design Methodology", Design and Construction of Large-Panel Concrete Structures, Portland Cement Association, Skokie, Illinois, PCA Publication EB096D, March 1979, 112 pp.

(7) Andrew Buchanan, *Structural Design for Fire Resistance*, May 2001, John Wiley and Sons Inc., 448 pages.

1.8   Structural Loads

Loads for use in structural design are specified in the National Building Code of Canada. Dead loads include the weight of structural and non-structural members including all construction materials that are supported permanently. Tables 1.11 and 1.12 contain dead loads due to commonly used construction materials. Live loads, based on intended use and occupancy, are tabulated in Table 1.13. For live loads due to snow, rain, wind, earthquake an other effects, users are referred to the National Building Code of Canada.

1.9   Green Building Design

Today, developers and owners are asking engineers and architects to design their projects in the most environmentally responsible way possible. Currently LEED Canada V4.0 is the most frequently used building rating system for determining the environmental impact of a building. LEED stands for Leadership in Energy and Environmental Design. LEED Canada V4.0 was adapted from the US Green Building Council's LEED-NC 4.0 rating system and was tailored for the Canadian climate and construction practices. It is designed for new construction and major renovations.

The LEED rating system evaluates project performance from a whole-building, whole-life perspective, encouraging healthy, high-quality performance with reduced environmental impact. This is done by awarding points for certain performance criteria that a project meets. The five principal LEED categories are as follows:

1) Sustainable Sites
2) Water Efficiency
3) Energy and Atmosphere
4) Materials and Resources
5) Indoor Environmental Quality

An additional category called Innovation & Design Process, allows designers to provide solutions not captured in the 5 standard categories. Graduated LEED ratings of Certified, Silver, Gold and Platinum are awarded based on the number of points achieved by the design.

General information on concrete products, applications and sustainability can be found at www.rediscoverconcrete.ca.

1.10   Beam Diagrams

Beam diagrams for single span beams with different support and loading conditions are provided in Table 1.14. The application of these diagrams can be extended to cases where more than one loading condition can be superimposed.

Bending moments and support reactions for continuous beams with equal spans are given in Tables 1.15, 1.16 and 1.17. These figures cover either uniformly distributed loads or concentrated loads at centres or at third points. Pattern loading, for design purposes, is also included.

Table 1.18 provides approximate moments and shears for continuous beams and one-way slabs as noted in CSA A23.3 Table 9.1. The use of Table 1.18 is limited to beams with approximately equal spans, where the longer of the two adjacent spans is not greater than the shorter by more than 20 percent.

1.11   Sectional Properties

Geometric properties of various sections that may be required in a structural design process are given in Table 1.19. For sectional areas and moments of inertia and centroid of 'T' sections see Chapter 6.

1.12   Frame Constants

Frames constants (Tables 1.20 through 1.24) are available on the CAC website at www.cement.ca.

The majority of concrete construction consists of prismatic members between the supporting elements. However, one of the advantages of using concrete as a construction material is that it can be molded into any geometric shape. Sometimes the structural engineer makes use of this advantage and increases the cross section within a member where needed. This results in a change in stiffness and the distribution of moments. Furthermore, concrete members, monolithically cast with the adjoining members, have end regions that are integral parts of the adjoining members. These end regions are generally considered to have very high stiffness and affect the distribution of moments. Tables 1.20 through 1.24 contain frame constants for non-prismatic members and members with one or two infinitely stiff end regions. The stiffness factors included in the tables are used to determine member stiffness K. (K = kEI/L).

Table 1.1: Cement types and their effect on concrete

CSA Cement Types		Type GU or GUL General use	Type MS Moderate sulfate resistance	Type MH or MHL Moderate heat of hydration	Type HE or HEL High early strength	Type LH or LHL Low heat of hydration	Type HS High sulfate resistance
Heat of hydration, 7-day maximum (kJ/kg)		-	-	300	-	275	-
Compressive strength (MPa) †	1 day	-	-	-	13.5	-	-
	3 day	14.5	14.5	14.5	24.0	8.5	14.5
	7 day	20.0	20.0	20.0	-	-	20.0
	28 day	26.5	26.5	26.5	-	25.0	26.5
	91 day	-	-	-	-	33.0	-
Type of cement to be used when Water-soluble Sulphate (SO4) in the soil sample, ††	> 2.0	HS, HSb, HSLb or HSe					
	0.20 - 2.0	HS, HSb, HSLb or HSe					
	0.10 - 0.20	MS, MSb, MSe, MSLb, LH, LHb,HS, HSb, HSLb, or HSe					
Type of cement to be used when Sulphate (SO4) in groundwater (mg/L) ††	> 10,000	HS, HSb, HSLb or HSe					
	1500 - 10,000	HS, HSb, HSLb or HSe					
	150 - 1500	MS, MSb, MSe, MSLb, LH, LHb,HS, HSb, HSLb, or HSe					

†   The values set forth in Table 1.1 reflect the minimum mortar cube strengths required by CSA Standard A3001-13 and are not necessarily representative of concrete strengths. Factors such as variations in water-cement ratios, aggregate type and quantity, concrete admixtures used and curing will have a very significant effect on concrete strength at any age. These variables may also alter the strength relationship in the concrete between types of cement used.

††   See CSA A23.1 Table 3 for additional requirements applicable to the different cement types included in each category.

Table 1.2: Creep and shrinkage modification factors for non-standard conditions

$$Q_{cr} = Q_a\, Q_h\, Q_f\, Q_r\, Q_s\, Q_v$$
$$P_{sh} = P_c\, P_h\, P_f\, P_r\, P_s\, P_v$$

Age at loading days	Q_a	
	moist cured	steam cured
1	1.25	1.00
7	1.00	0.94
20	0.87	0.85
60	0.77	0.76

Relative humidity (%)	Q_h	P_h
40	1.00	1.00
60	0.87	0.80
80	0.73	0.60
100	0.60	0.00

Ratio of fine to total aggr.	Q_f	P_f
0.30	0.95	0.72
0.40	0.98	0.86
0.50	1.00	1.00
0.70	1.05	1.04

Volume surface ratio (mm)	Q_r	P_r
38	1.00	1.00
75	0.82	0.84
150	0.70	0.59
250	0.67	0.37

Slump (mm)	Q_s	P_s
50	0.95	0.97
70	1.00	1.00
125	1.15	1.09

Air (%)	Q_v	P_v
≤ 6	1.00	1.00
8	1.18	1.01
10	1.36	1.03

	Cement content (kg/m³)		
	225	300	410
P_c	0.89	0.93	1.00

Notes:
- Standard conditions produce modification factors of 1.0.
- Volume – surface ratio of a rectangular member having a X b cross-section is ab/(2a + 2b).
- Ratio of fine aggregate to total aggregate is expressed as the ratio of the weights.
- For average ambient relative humidity, see Fig. 1.6.

Table 1.3: Properties of prestressing wires and seven-wire strands

Tendon type	Grade f_{pu} MPa	Size designation	Nominal diameter mm	Nominal area mm²	Nominal mass kg/m
Prestressing wire	1550	8	8.00	50.27	0.394
	1620	7	7.00	38.48	0.302
	1650	6	6.35	31.67	0.248
	1720	6	6.35	31.67	0.248
		7	7.00	38.48	0.302
		8	8.00	50.27	0.394
	1760	7	7.00	38.48	0.302
Seven wire strand	1720	6	6.35	23.2	0.182
		8	7.95	37.4	0.294
		9	9.53	51.6	0.405
		11	11.13	69.7	0.548
		13	12.70	92.9	0.730
		15	15.24	138.7	1.094
	1760	16	15.47	148.4	1.173
	1860	9	9.53	54.8	0.432
		11	11.13	74.2	0.582
		13	12.70	98.7	0.775
		13 Special	12.7	107.7	0.819
		15	15.24	140.0	1.109

Table 1.4: Properties of plain and deformed prestressing

Tendon type	Grade f_{pu} MPa	Nominal diameter mm	Nominal area mm²	Nominal mass kg/m
Plain prestressing bars	1030	19	284	2.23
		22	387	3.04
		25	503	3.97
		28	639	5.03
		32	794	6.21
		36	955	7.52
	1100	19	284	2.23
		22	387	3.04
		25	503	3.97
		28	639	5.03
		32	794	6.21
		36	955	7.52
Deformed prestressing bars	1030	26	551	4.48
		32	804	6.54
		36	1018	8.28
	1080	15	177	1.46
		20	314	2.56
	1100	26	551	4.48
		32	804	6.54

Table 1.5: Properties of deformed reinforcing bars

Bar designation	Nominal dimensions			Mass per unit length kg/m
	Diameter mm	Area mm²	Perimeter mm	
10M	11.3	100	35.5	0.785
15M	16.0	200	50.1	1.570
20M	19.5	300	61.3	2.355
25M	25.2	500	79.2	3.925
30M	29.9	700	93.9	5.495
35M	35.7	1000	112.2	7.850
45M	43.7	1500	137.3	11.775
55M	56.4	2500	177.2	19.625

Notes:
1. Bar numbers are based on the rounded off nominal diameter of the bars.
2. Nominal dimensions are equivalent to those of a plain round bar having the same mass per metre as the deformed bar.
3. Both Billet Steel Bars and Weldable Low Alloy Steel Bars are produced in the above standard sizes. However, all sizes may not be available; manufacturers should be consulted to verify availability.

Table 1.6: Tensile test requirements for hot-rolled deformed carbon steel bars conforming to CSA G30.18-09 (reproduced from CSA G30.18-09 – Table 4)

	Grade			
	400R	**500R**	**400W**	**500W**
Min. tensile strength, MPa	540*	675*	540*	625*
Min. yield strength, MPa	400	500	400	500
Max. yield strength, MPa	–	–	525	625
Min. elongation in 200mm, % Bar designation number				
10M	10	9	13	12
15M or 20M	10	9	13	12
25M	9	8	13	12
30M or 35M	8	7	12	10
45M or 55M	7	6	12	10

* And not less than 1.15 times the actual yield strength.

Table 1.7: Bend test requirements for hot-rolled deformed carbon steel bars conforming to CSA G30.18-09 (reproduced from CSA G30.18-09 – Table 5)

		Diameter of pin			
Bar designation number	**Degrees of bending**	**Grade 400R**	**Grade 500R**	**Grade 400W**	**Grade 500W**
10M or 15M	180	3 – 1/2d	5d	3d	4d
20M or 25M	180	5d	5d	4d	4d
30M or 35M	180	7d	7d	6d	6d
45M or 55M (Grade R)	90	9d	9d	–	–
45M or 55M (Grade W)	180	–	–	8d	8d

Note: d = nominal diameter of specimen.

Table 1.8: Tensile and bend test requirements for deformed wires conforming to ASTM A496-07

Material	Min. tensile strength (MPa)	Min. yield strength (MPa)	Bend test (180°)
Wires	585	515	–
Wire fabric	550	485	–
D6 and smaller	–	–	Bend around a pin the diameter of which is twice the diameter of the specimen.
Larger than D6	–	–	Bend around a pin the diameter of which is four times the diameter of the specimen.

Table 1.9: Tensile test requirements for wires conforming to ASTM A497-07

Use	Minimum tensile strength (MPa)	Minimum yield strength (MPa)	Weld shear strength (MPa)
D45 through D4	550	480	240
Under D4	550	480	

Table 1.10: Properties of welded wire fabric

Designation*	Wire diameter mm	Wire cross-sectional area Long. mm²	Transv. mm²	Mass per unit area kg/ m²	Cross-sectional area Per metre width Long. mm²	Transv. mm²
152 X 152 MW 9.1 X MW 9.1	3.40	9.1	9.1	1.04	59.8	59.8
152 X 152 MW 11.1 X MW 11.1	3.76	11.1	11.1	1.26	73.0	73.0
152 X 152 MW 13.3 X MW 13.3	4.12	13.3	13.3	1..50	87.5	87.5
152 X 152 MW 18.7 X MW 18.7	4.88	18.7	18.7	2.11	123.0	123.0
152 X 152 MW 25.8 X MW 25.8	5.74	25.8	25.8	2.91	170.0	170.0
152 X 152 MW 34.9 X MW 34.9	6.67	34.9	34.9	3.95	230.0	230.0
152 X 152 MW 47.6 X MW 47.6	7.79	47.6	47.6	5.38	313.0	313.0
102 X 102 MW 9.1 X MW 9.1	3.40	9.1	9.1	1.52	89.2	89.2
102 X 102 MW 11.1 X MW 11.1	3.76	11.1	11.1	1.83	109.0	109.0
102 X 102 MW 13.3 X MW 13.3	4.12	13.3	13.3	2.18	130.0	130.0
102 X 102 MW 18.7 X MW 18.7	4.88	18.7	18.7	3.07	183.0	183.0
102 X 102 MW 25.8 X MW 25.8	5.74	25.8	25.8	4.23	253.0	253.0
51 X 51 MW 3.2 X MW 3.2	2.03	3.2	3.2	1.03	62.8	62.8
51 X 51 MW 5.6 X MW 5.6	2.69	5.6	5.6	1.80	110.0	110.0
51 X 51 MW 9.1 X MW 9.1	3.40	9.1	9.1	2.94	178.0	178.0

* The first two numbers give the spacing in mm, and the second two give the size of wire.

Table 1.11: Dead loads for floors, ceilings, roofs and walls

	Load (kN/ m²)
Floorings:	
Normal density concrete topping, per 10mm of thickness	0.24
Semi-low density concrete (1900 kg/m³) topping, per 10mm	0.19
Low density concrete (1500 kg/m³) topping, per 10mm	0.15
22mm hardwood floor on sleepers, clipped to concrete without fill	0.24
40mm terrazzo floor finish directly on slab	0.95
40mm terrazzo floor finish on 25mm mortar bed	1.49
25mm terrazzo floor finish on 50mm concrete bed	1.79
20mm ceramic or quarry tile on 12mm mortar bed	0.80
20mm ceramic or quarry tile on 25mm mortar bed	1.06
8mm linoleum or asphalt tile directly on concrete	0.06
8mm linoleum or asphalt tile on 25mm mortar bed	0.59
20mm mastic floor	0.45
Hardware flooring, 22mm thick	0.19
Subflooring (softwood), 20mm thick	0.13
Asphaltic concrete, 40mm thick	0.90
Ceilings:	
12.7mm gypsum board	0.10
15.9mm gypsum board	0.12
19mm gypsum board directly on concrete	0.24
20mm plaster directly on concrete	0.26
20mm plaster on metal lath furring	0.40
Suspended ceilings, add	0.10
Acoustical tile	0.05
Acoustical tile on wood furring strips	0.15
Mechanical duct allowance	0.19
Roofs:	
Five-ply felt and gravel (or slag)	0.31
Three-ply felt and gravel (or slag)	0.27
Five-ply felt composition roof, no gravel	0.20
Three-ply felt composition roof, no ravel	0.15
Asphalt strip shingles	0.15
Slate, 8mm thick	0.57
Gypsum, per 10mm of thickness	0.08
Insulating concrete, per 10mm	0.06

	Load (kN/m²)		
	Unplastered	One side Plastered	Both sides plastered
Walls (Brick, Concrete Block or Tile)			
100mm brick wall	1.86	2.10	2.33
200mm brick wall	3.77	4.00	4.24
300mm brick wall	5.59	5.83	6.06
100mm hollow normal density concrete block	1.37	1.61	1.84
150mm hollow normal density concrete block	1.67	1.90	2.14
200mm hollow normal density concrete block	2.11	2.34	2.58
250mm hollow normal density concrete block	2.50	2.74	2.97
300mm hollow normal density concrete block	2.94	3.18	3.38
100mm hollow low density block or tile.................................	1.08	1.31	1.55
150mm hollow low density block or tile.................................	1.28	1.51	1.75
200mm hollow low density block or tile.................................	1.62	1.85	2.09
250mm hollow low density block or tile.................................	1.91	2.15	2.38
300mm hollow low density block or tile.................................	2.26	2.49	2.73
100mm brick 100mm hollow normal density block backing	3.24	3.47	3.71
100mm brick 200mm hollow normal density block backing	3.97	4.21	4.44
100mm brick 300mm hollow normal density block backing	4.81	5.04	5.28
100mm brick 100mm hollow low density block backing..........	2.94	3.18	3.41
100mm brick 200mm hollow low density block backing..........	3.48	3.72	3.95
100mm brick 300mm hollow low density block backing..........	4.12	4.36	4.59

	Load (kN/m²)
Walls (Others):	
Windows, glass, frame and sash	0.38
100mm stone..	2.59
Steel or wood studs, lath, 20mm plaster	0.86
Steel or wood studs, lath, 15.9mm gypsum board each side	0.28
Steel or wood studs, 2 layers 12.7mm gypsum board each side	0.44
Exterior stud walls with brick veneer..	2.30

1

General

Table 1.12 Minimum design loads for materials

Material	Load (kN/m³)	Material	Load (kN/m³)
Bituminous products:		Lead	111.6
Asphaltum	12.7	Lime	
Graphite	21.2	Hydrate, loose	5.0
Paraffin	8.8	Hydrated, compacted	7.1
Petroleum, crude	8.6	Masonry, ashlar:	
Petroleum, refined	7.9	Granite	25.9
Petroleum, benzine	7.2	Limestone, crystalline	25.9
Petroleum, gasoline	6.6	Limestone, oolitic	21.2
Pitch	10.8	Marble	27.2
Tar	11.8	Sandstone	22.6
Brass	82.7	Masonry, brick:	
Bronze	86.7	Hard (low absorption)	20.4
Cast-stone masonry (cement, stone, sand)	22.6	Medium, (Medium absorption)	18.1
Cement, portland, loose	14.1	Soft (high absorption)	15.7
Ceramic Tile	23.6	Masonry, rubble mortar:	
Charcoal	1.9	Granite	24.0
Cinder fill	9.0	Limestone, crystalline	23.1
Cinders, dry, in bulk	7.1	Limestone, oolitic	21.7
Coal:		Marble	24.5
Anthracite, piled	8.2	Sandstone	21.5
Bituminous piled	7.4	Mortar, hardened:	
Lignite, piled	7.4	Cement	20.4
Peat, dry, piled	3.6	Lime	17.3
Concrete, plain:		Particleboard	7.1
Cinder	17.0	Plywood	5.7
Expanded-slag aggregate	15.7	Riprap (not submerged):	
Haydite (burned-clay aggregate)	14.1	Limestone	13.0
Slag	20.7	Sandstone	14.1
Stone (including gravel)	22.6	Sand:	
Vermiculite and perlite aggregate		Clean and dry	14.1
nonload-bearing	4.0-8.0	River, dry	16.7
Other light aggregate, loadbearing	11.0-16.5	Slag:	
Concrete, reinforced:		Bank	11.0
Cinder	17.4	Bank, screenings	17.0
Slag	21.7	Machine	15.1
Stone (including gravel)	23.6	Sand	8.2
Copper	87.4	Slate	27.0
Cork, compressed	2.3	Steel, cold-drawn	76.8
Earth (not submerged):		Stone, quarried, piled:	
Clay, dry	10.0	Bassalt, granite, gneiss	15.1
Clay, damp	17.3	Limestone, marble, quartz	14.9
Clay and gravel, dry	15.7	Sandstone	12.9
Silt, moist, loose	12.3	Shale	14.5
Silt, moist packed	15.1	Greenstone, hornblende	16.8
Silt, flowing	17.0	Terra cotta, architectural:	
Sand and gravel, dry, loose	15.7	Voids filled	18.9
Sand and gravel, dry, packed	17.3	Voids unfilled	11.3
Sand and gravel, wet	18.9	Tin	72.1
Earth, (submerged):		Water:	
Clay	12.6	Fresh	9.8
Soil	11.0	Sea	10.1
River mud	14.1	Wood, seasoned:	
Sand or gravel	9.4	Ash commercial white	6.4
Sand or gravel, and clay	10.2	Cypress, southern	5.3
Gravel, dry	16.3	Fir, Douglas, coast region	5.3
Gypsum, loose	11.0	Hem fir	4.4
Gypsum wallboard	7.9	Oak, commercial reds and whites	7.4
Ice	9.0	Pine, southern yellow	5.8
Iron:		Redwood	4.4
Cast	70.4	Spruce, red, white and Stitka	4.6
Wrought	75.4	Western hemlock	5.0
		Zinc, rolled sheet	70.6

Table 1.13: Live loads for floors or roofs due to use and occupancy
(Reproduced with the permission of the National Research Council of Canada, copyright holder)

NBCC Table 4.1.5.3.
Specified Uniformly Distributed Live Loads on an Area of Floor/Roof
Forming Part of Sentence 4.1.5.3.(1)

Use of Area of Floor or Roof	Minimum Specified Load, kPa
Assembly Areas	
a) Except for those areas listed under b), c), d) and e), assembly areas with or without fixed seats including	
Arenas[1], auditoria, churches, dance floors, dining areas[2] foyers and entrance halls, grandstands[1], reviewing stands and bleachers, gymnasia, lecture halls[1], museums, promenades, rinks, stadia[1], *theatres* and other areas with similar uses	4.8
b) Classrooms and courtrooms with or without fixed seats[1]	2.4
c) Portions of assembly areas with fixed seats that have backs for the following uses:	
Arenas, grandstands and stadia	2.9
d) Portions of assembly areas with fixed seats that have backs for the following uses:	
Churches, lecture halls[1] and *theatres*	2.4
e) Vomitories, *exits*, lobbies and corridors[1,6]	4.8
Attics[1]	
Accessible by a stairway in *residential occupancies* only	1.4
Having limited accessibility so that there is no storage of equipment or material	0.5
Balconies	
Exterior	4.8
Interior and *mezzanines* that could be used by an assembly of people as a viewing area[1]	4.8
Interior and *mezzanines* other than above	(3)
Corridors, lobbies and aisles[1]	
Other than those listed below	4.8
Not more than 1200 mm in width and all upper floor corridors of residential areas only of apartments, hotels and motels (that cannot be used by an assembly of people as a viewing area)[1]	(1)(3)
Equipment areas and *service rooms* including	
Generator rooms	
Mechanical equipment exclusive of elevators	
Machine rooms	3.6(4)
Pump rooms	
Transformer vaults	
Ventilating or air-conditioning equipment	
Exits and fire escapes	4.8
Factories	6.0(4)

1

General

Use of Area of Floor or Roof	Minimum Specified Load, kPa
Footbridges	4.8
Garages for	
Vehicles not exceeding 4 000 kg gross weight	2.4
Vehicles exceeding 4 000 kg but not exceeding 9 000 kg gross weight	6.0
Vehicles exceeding 9 000 kg gross weight	12.0[1]
Kitchens (other than residential)	4.8
Libraries	
Stack rooms	7.2
Reading and study rooms	2.9
Office areas (not including record storage and computer rooms) located in	
Basement and *first storey*	4.8
Floors above *first storey*	2.4
Operating rooms and laboratories	3.6
Patient's bedrooms	1.9
Recreation areas that cannot be used for assembly purposes including	

Billiard rooms
  Bowling alleys
  Pool rooms
	3.6

Residential areas (within the scope of Article 1.3.3.2. of Division A)	
Sleeping and living quarters in apartments, hotels, motels, boarding schools and colleges	1.9
Residential areas (within the scope of Article 1.3.3.3. of Division A)	
Bedrooms	1.9
Other areas	1.9
Stairs within *dwelling units*	1.9
Retail and wholesale areas	4.8
Roofs	1.0[1][5]
Sidewalks and driveways over areaways and *basements*	12.0 [1][5]
Storage areas	4.8[4]
Toilet areas	2.4
Underground slabs with earth cover	[5]
Warehouses	4.8[4]

NBCC Notes to Table 4.1.5.3.:
(1)   See Note A-Table 4.1.5.3.
(2)   See Article 4.1.5.6.
(3)   See Article 4.1.5.4.
(4)   See Sentence 4.1.5.1.(1).
(5)   See Article 4.1.5.5.

Table 1.14:   Beam Diagrams

Simple Beam — uniformly distributed load

$R = V$ .... $= \dfrac{w\ell}{2}$

V_x .... $= w\left(\dfrac{\ell}{2} - x\right)$

M max. (at centre) .... $= \dfrac{w\ell^2}{8}$

M_x .... $= \dfrac{wx}{2}(\ell - x)$

Δmax. (at centre) .... $= \dfrac{5\,w\ell^4}{384\,EI}$

Δ_x .... $= \dfrac{wx}{24\,EI}(\ell^3 - 2\ell x^2 + x^3)$

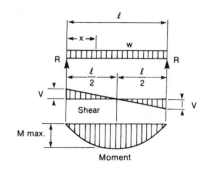

Simple Beam — load increasing uniformly to one end

$R_1 = V_1$ .... $= \dfrac{w\ell}{6}$

$R_2 = V_2$ .... $= \dfrac{w\ell}{3}$

V_x .... $= \dfrac{w\ell}{6} - \dfrac{wx^2}{2\ell}$

M max. $\left(\text{at } x = \sqrt{\dfrac{\ell}{3}} = 0.5774\ell\right)$ .... $= \dfrac{w\ell^2}{9\sqrt{3}} = 0.06415w\ell^2$

M_x .... $= \dfrac{wx}{6\ell}(\ell^2 - x^2)$

Δmax. $\left(\text{at } x = \ell\sqrt{1 - \sqrt{\dfrac{8}{15}}} = 0.5193\ell\right)$ ...... $0.00652\dfrac{w\ell^4}{EI}$

Δ_x .... $= \dfrac{wx}{360\,EI\ell}(3x^4 - 10\ell^2x^2 + 7\ell^4)$

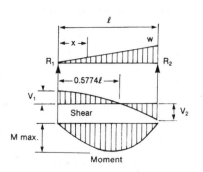

Simple Beam — load increasing uniformly to centre

$R = V$ .... $= \dfrac{w\ell}{4}$

$V_x \left(\text{when } x < \dfrac{\ell}{2}\right)$ .... $= \dfrac{w}{4\ell}(\ell^2 - 4x^2)$

M max. (at centre) .... $= \dfrac{w\ell^2}{12}$

$M_x \left(\text{when } x < \dfrac{\ell}{2}\right)$ .... $= \dfrac{w\ell x}{2}\left(\dfrac{1}{2} - \dfrac{2x^2}{3\ell^2}\right)$

Δmax. (at centre) .... $= \dfrac{w\ell^4}{120\,EI}$

Δ_x .... $= \dfrac{wx}{960\,EI\,\ell}(5\ell^2 - 4x^2)^2$

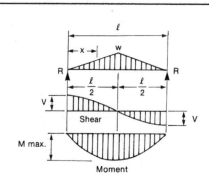

Note:
w: Distributed load per unit length. In the case of triangular distribution, w represents the maximum intensity of load per unit length.
P: Concentrated load.

Table 1.14: (Continued)

Simple Beam — uniform load partially distributed

$R_1 = V_1$ (max. when a < c) .... $= \dfrac{wb}{2\ell}(2c + b)$

$R_2 = V_2$ (max. when a > c) .... $= \dfrac{wb}{2\ell}(2a + b)$

V_x (when x > a and < (a + b)) .... $= R_1 - w(x - a)$

M max. $\left(\text{at } x = a + \dfrac{R_1}{w}\right)$ .... $= R_1\left(a + \dfrac{R_1}{2w}\right)$

M_x (when x < a) .... $= R_1 x$

M_x (when x > a and < (a + b)) .... $= R_1 x - \dfrac{w}{2}(x - a)^2$

M_x (when x > (a + b)) .... $= R_2(\ell - x)$

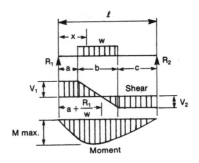

Beam fixed at both ends — symmetrical trapezoidal load

$R = V$ .... $= \dfrac{w\ell}{2}\left(1 - \dfrac{a}{\ell}\right)$

M_1 .... $= -\dfrac{w\ell^2}{12}\left(1 - 2\dfrac{a^2}{\ell^2} + \dfrac{a^3}{\ell^3}\right)$

M_2 .... $= \dfrac{w\ell^2}{24}\left(1 - 2\dfrac{a^3}{\ell^3}\right)$

M_x (when x < a) .... $= M_1 + R_1 x - \dfrac{wx^3}{6a}$

M_x (when a < x < ℓ − a) .... $= M_1 + R_1 x - \dfrac{wa}{2}\left(x - \dfrac{2}{3}a\right)$
$ - \dfrac{w}{2}(x - a)^2$

Note: When a = ℓ/2 loading is triangular

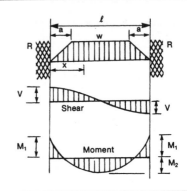

Simple Beam — concentrated load at any point

$R_1 = V_1$ (max. when a < b) .... $= \dfrac{Pb}{\ell}$

$R_2 = V_2$ (max. when a > b) .... $= \dfrac{Pa}{\ell}$

M max. (at point of load) .... $= \dfrac{Pab}{\ell}$

M_x (when x < a) .... $= \dfrac{Pbx}{\ell}$

Δmax. $\left(\text{at } x = \sqrt{\dfrac{a(a + 2b)}{3}} \text{ when a > b}\right)$ $= \dfrac{Pab(a + 2b)\sqrt{3a(a + 2b)}}{27\,EI\ell}$

Δa (at point of load) .... $= \dfrac{Pa^2 b^2}{3\,EI\ell}$

Δ_x (when x < a) .... $= \dfrac{Pbx}{6\,EI\ell}(\ell^2 - b^2 - x^2)$

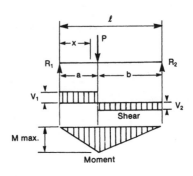

Note:
w: Distributed load per unit length. In the case of triangular distribution, w represents the maximum intensity of load per unit length.
P: Concentrated load.

Table 1.14: (Continued)

Beam fixed at both ends — uniformly distributed loads

$$R = V \quad \ldots\ldots\ldots\ldots\ldots\ldots\ldots\ldots\ldots\ldots\ldots\ldots\ldots = \frac{w\ell}{2}$$

$$V_x \quad \ldots\ldots\ldots\ldots\ldots\ldots\ldots\ldots\ldots\ldots\ldots\ldots = w\left(\frac{\ell}{2} - x\right)$$

$$M \text{ max. (at ends)} \quad \ldots\ldots\ldots\ldots\ldots\ldots = -\frac{w\ell^2}{12}$$

$$M_1 \text{ (at centre)} \quad \ldots\ldots\ldots\ldots\ldots\ldots\ldots = \frac{w\ell^2}{24}$$

$$M_x \quad \ldots\ldots\ldots\ldots\ldots\ldots\ldots\ldots\ldots\ldots\ldots = \frac{w}{12}(6\ell x - \ell^2 - 6x^2)$$

$$\Delta \text{max. (at centre)} \quad \ldots\ldots\ldots\ldots\ldots = \frac{w\ell^4}{384\,EI}$$

$$\Delta_x \quad \ldots\ldots\ldots\ldots\ldots\ldots\ldots\ldots\ldots\ldots = \frac{wx^2}{24\,EI}(\ell - x)^2$$

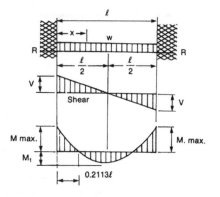

Beam fixed at both ends — concentrated load at any point

$$R_1 = V_1 \text{ (max. when } a < b) \quad \ldots\ldots\ldots = \frac{Pb^2}{\ell^3}(3a + b)$$

$$R_2 = V_2 \text{ (max. when } a > b) \quad \ldots\ldots\ldots = \frac{Pa^2}{\ell^3}(a + 3b)$$

$$M_1 \text{ (max. when } a < b) \quad \ldots\ldots\ldots = -\frac{Pab^2}{\ell^2}$$

$$M_2 \text{ (max. when } a > b) \quad \ldots\ldots\ldots = -\frac{Pa^2b}{\ell^2}$$

$$M_a \text{ (at point of load)} \quad \ldots\ldots\ldots\ldots = \frac{2Pa^2b^2}{\ell^3}$$

$$M_x \text{ (when } x < a) \quad \ldots\ldots\ldots\ldots = R_1 x - \frac{Pab^2}{\ell^2}$$

$$\Delta \text{max.} \left(\text{when } a > b \text{ at } x = \frac{2a\ell}{3a+b}\right) \ldots\ldots = \frac{2Pa^3b^2}{3\,EI(3a+b)^2}$$

$$\Delta_a \text{ (at point of load)} \quad \ldots\ldots\ldots\ldots = \frac{Pa^3b^3}{3\,EI\ell^3}$$

$$\Delta_x \text{ (when } x < a) \quad \ldots\ldots\ldots\ldots\ldots = \frac{Pb^2x^2}{6\,EI\ell^3}(3a\ell - 3ax - bx)$$

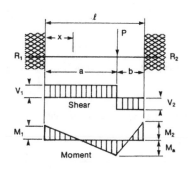

Beam fixed at both ends — uniform load partially distributed

$$M_1 \quad \ldots\ldots\ldots\ldots\ldots\ldots\ldots\ldots = \frac{w}{12\ell^2}\left[(\ell - a)^3(\ell + 3a) - c^3(4\ell - 3c)\right]$$

$$M_2 \quad \ldots\ldots\ldots\ldots\ldots\ldots\ldots\ldots = \frac{w}{12\ell^2}\left[(\ell - c)^3(\ell + 3c) - a^3(4\ell - 3a)\right]$$

$$R_1 = V_1 \quad \ldots\ldots\ldots\ldots\ldots\ldots\ldots = \frac{1}{\ell}\left[M_1 - M_2 + wb\left(c + \frac{b}{2}\right)\right]$$

$$R_2 = V_2 \quad \ldots\ldots\ldots\ldots\ldots\ldots\ldots = \frac{1}{\ell}\left[M_2 - M_1 + wb\left(a + \frac{b}{2}\right)\right]$$

$$M_x \text{ (when } x < a) \quad \ldots\ldots\ldots\ldots = R_1 x - M_1$$

$$M_x \text{ (when } a < x < (a + c)) \quad \ldots\ldots\ldots = R_1 x - M_1 - \frac{w}{2}(x - a)^2$$

$$M_x \text{ (when } x > (a + c)) \quad \ldots\ldots\ldots = R_2(\ell - x) - M_2$$

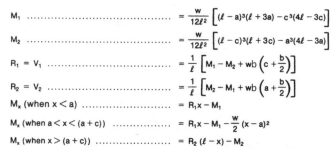
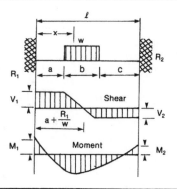

Note:
w: Distributed load per unit length. In the case of triangular distribution, w represents the maximum intensity of load per unit length.
P: Concentrated load.

Table 1.14:   (Continued)

Beam fixed at both ends — load increasing uniformly to one end

$R_1 = V_1$ .... $= \dfrac{3wl}{20}$

$R_2 = V_2$ .... $= \dfrac{7wl}{20}$

V_x .... $= \dfrac{3wl}{20} - \dfrac{wx^2}{2l}$

M_1 .... $= -\dfrac{wl^2}{30}$

M_2 .... $= -\dfrac{wl^2}{20}$

M_x .... $= \dfrac{3wlx}{20} - \dfrac{wl^2}{30} - \dfrac{wx^3}{6l}$

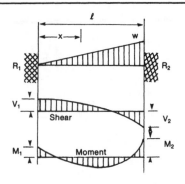

Beam fixed at one end, supported at other — uniformly distributed load

$R_1 = V_1$ .... $= \dfrac{3wl}{8}$

$R_2 = V_2 \text{ max.}$ .... $= \dfrac{5wl}{8}$

V_x .... $= R_1 - wx$

$M \text{ max.}$ .... $= -\dfrac{wl^2}{8}$

$M_1 \left(\text{at } x = \dfrac{3}{8}l\right)$ .... $= \dfrac{9}{128} wl^2$

M_x .... $= R_1 x - \dfrac{wx^2}{2}$

$\Delta \text{ max.} \left(\text{at } x = \dfrac{l}{16}(1+\sqrt{33}) = 0.4215l\right)$. $= \dfrac{wl^4}{185\,EI}$

Δ_x .... $= \dfrac{wx}{48\,EI}(l^3 - 3lx^2 + 2x^3)$

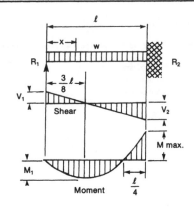

Beam fixed at one end, supported at other — concentrated load at any point

$R_1 = V_1$ .... $= \dfrac{Pb^2}{2l^3}(a + 2l)$

$R_2 = V_2$ .... $= \dfrac{Pa}{2l^3}(3l^2 - a^2)$

$M_1 \text{ (at point of load)}$ .... $= R_1 a$

$M_2 \text{ (at fixed end)}$ .... $= -\dfrac{Pab}{2l^2}(a + l)$

$M_x \text{ (when } x < a)$ .... $= R_1 x$

$M_x \text{ (when } x > a)$ .... $= R_1 x - P(x - a)$

$\Delta \text{max.} \left(\text{when } a < 0.414l \text{ at } x = l\,\dfrac{l^2 + a^2}{3l^2 - a^2}\right) = \dfrac{Pa}{3\,EI}\dfrac{(l^2 - a^2)^3}{(3l^2 - a^2)^2}$

$\Delta \text{max.} \left(\text{when } a > 0.414l \text{ at } x = l\sqrt{\dfrac{a}{2l + a}}\right) = \dfrac{Pab^2}{6\,EI}\sqrt{\dfrac{a}{2l + a}}$

$\Delta a \text{ (at point of load)}$ .... $= \dfrac{Pa^2 b^3}{12\,EIl^3}(3l + a)$

$\Delta x \text{ (when } x < a)$ .... $= \dfrac{Pb^2 x}{12\,EIl^3}(3al^2 - 2lx^2 - ax^2)$

$\Delta x \text{ (when } x > a)$ .... $= \dfrac{Pa}{12\,EIl^3}(l - x)^2 (3l^2 x - a^2 x - 2a^2 l)$

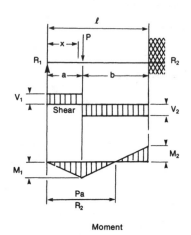

Note:
w: Distributed load per unit length. In the case of triangular distribution, w represents the maximum intensity of load per unit length.
P: Concentrated load.
Moments are positive if they cause compression in the top of the beam.

Table 1.14: (Continued)

Cantilever Beam — uniformly distributed load

$R = V$ .... $= w\ell$

V_x .... $= wx$

M max. (at fixed end) .... $= -\dfrac{w\ell^2}{2}$

M_x .... $= \dfrac{wx^2}{2}$

Δ max. (at free end) .... $= \dfrac{w\ell^4}{8\,EI}$

Δ_x .... $= \dfrac{w}{24\,EI}\,(x^4 - 4\ell^3 x + 3\ell^4)$

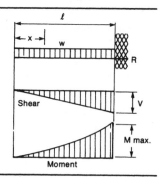

Cantilever Beam — load increasing uniformly to fixed end

$R = V$ .... $= \dfrac{w\ell}{2}$

V_x .... $= \dfrac{wx^2}{2\ell}$

M max. (at fixed end) .... $= -\dfrac{w\ell^2}{6}$

M_x .... $= \dfrac{wx^3}{6\ell}$

Δ max. (at free end) .... $= \dfrac{w\ell^4}{30\,EI}$

Δ_x .... $= \dfrac{w}{120\,EI\ell}\,(x^5 - 5\ell^4 x + 4\ell^5)$

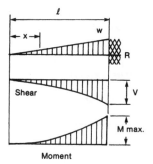

Cantilever Beam — concentrated load at any point

$R = V$ .... $= P$

M max. (at fixed end) .... $= -Pb$

M_x (when $x > a$) .... $= P\,(x - a)$

Δ max. (at free end) .... $= \dfrac{Pb^2}{6\,EI}\,(3\ell - b)$

Δa (at point of load) .... $= \dfrac{Pb^3}{3\,EI}$

Δ_x (when $x < a$) .... $= \dfrac{Pb^2}{6\,EI}\,(3\ell - 3x - b)$

Δ_x (when $x > a$) .... $= \dfrac{P\,(\ell - x)^2}{6\,EI}\,(3b - \ell + x)$

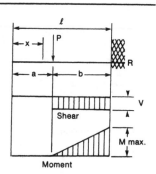

Note:
w: Distributed load per unit length. In the case of triangular distribution, w represents the maximum intensity of load per unit length.
P: Concentrated load.
Moments are positive if they cause compression in the top of the beam.

Table 1.14: (Continued)

Beam overhanging one support — uniformly distributed load

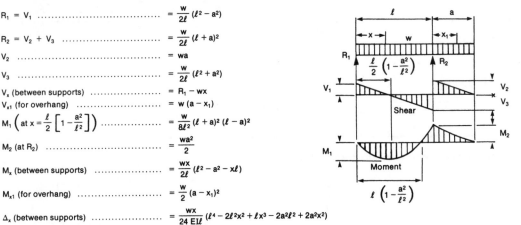

$R_1 = V_1$ .... $= \dfrac{w}{2\ell}(\ell^2 - a^2)$

$R_2 = V_2 + V_3$ .... $= \dfrac{w}{2\ell}(\ell + a)^2$

V_2 .... $= wa$

V_3 .... $= \dfrac{w}{2\ell}(\ell^2 + a^2)$

V_x (between supports) .... $= R_1 - wx$

V_{x1} (for overhang) .... $= w(a - x_1)$

$M_1\left(\text{at } x = \dfrac{\ell}{2}\left[1 - \dfrac{a^2}{\ell^2}\right]\right)$ .... $= \dfrac{w}{8\ell^2}(\ell + a)^2(\ell - a)^2$

M_2 (at R_2) .... $= \dfrac{wa^2}{2}$

M_x (between supports) .... $= \dfrac{wx}{2\ell}(\ell^2 - a^2 - x\ell)$

M_{x1} (for overhang) .... $= \dfrac{w}{2}(a - x_1)^2$

Δ_x (between supports) .... $= \dfrac{wx}{24\,EI\ell}(\ell^4 - 2\ell^2 x^2 + \ell x^3 - 2a^2\ell^2 + 2a^2 x^2)$

Δ_{x1} (for overhang) .... $= \dfrac{wx_1}{24\,EI}(4a^2\ell - \ell^3 + 6a^2 x_1 - 4ax_1^2 + x_1^3)$

Beam overhanging one support — uniformly distributed load on overhang

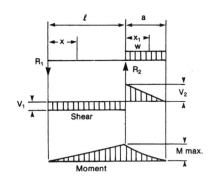

$R_1 = V_1$ .... $= \dfrac{wa^2}{2\ell}$

$R_2 = V_1 + V_2$ .... $= \dfrac{wa}{2\ell}(2\ell + a)$

V_2 .... $= wa$

V_{x1} (for overhang) .... $= w(a - x_1)$

M max. (at R_2) .... $= \dfrac{wa^2}{2}$

M_x (between supports) .... $= \dfrac{wa^2 x}{2\ell}$

M_{x1} (for overhang) .... $= \dfrac{w}{2}(a - x_1)^2$

Δmax. $\left(\text{between supports at } x = \dfrac{\ell}{\sqrt{3}}\right)$ ... $= \dfrac{wa^2\ell^2}{18\sqrt{3}\,EI} = 0.03208\,\dfrac{wa^2\ell^2}{EI}$

Δmax. (for overhang at $x_1 = a$) .... $= \dfrac{wa^3}{24\,EI}(4\ell + 3a)$

Δ_x (between supports) .... $= \dfrac{wa^2 x}{12\,EI\ell}(\ell^2 - x^2)$

Δ_{x1} (for overhang) .... $= \dfrac{wx_1}{24\,EI}(4a^2\ell + 6a^2 x_1 - 4ax_1^2 + x_1^3)$

Note:
w: Distributed load per unit length. In the case of triangular distribution, w represents the maximum intensity of load per unit length.
P: Concentrated load.
Moments are positive if they cause compression in the top of the beam.

Table 1.14: Beam Diagrams

Beam overhanging one support — concentrated load at end of overhang

$R_1 = V_1$ .... $= \dfrac{Pa}{\ell}$

$R_2 = V_1 + V_2$ .... $= \dfrac{P}{\ell}\,(\ell + a)$

V_2 .... $= P$

M max. (at R_2) .... $= Pa$

M_x (between supports) .... $= \dfrac{Pax}{\ell}$

M_{x1} (for overhang) .... $= P\,(a - x_1)$

Δmax. $\left(\text{between supports at } x = \dfrac{\ell}{\sqrt{3}}\right)$ ... $= \dfrac{Pa\ell^2}{9\sqrt{3}\,EI} = 0.06415\dfrac{Pa\ell^2}{EI}$

Δmax. (for overhang at $x_1 = a$) .... $= \dfrac{Pa^2}{3\,EI}\,(\ell + a)$

Δ_x (between supports) .... $= \dfrac{Pax}{6\,EI\ell}\,(\ell^2 - x^2)$

Δ_{x1} (for overhang) .... $= \dfrac{Px_1}{6\,EI}\,(2a\ell + 3ax_1 - x_1^2)$

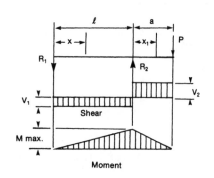

Note:
w: Distributed load per unit length. In the case of triangular distribution, w represents the maximum intensity of load per unit length.
P: Concentrated load.
Moments are positive if they cause compression in the top of the beam.

Table 1.15:   Moments and Reactions in Continuous Beams Uniformly Distributed Loads

Moment : Coefficient × wℓ²	w: Uniform load per unit length
Reaction: Coefficient × wℓ	ℓ : Length of one span

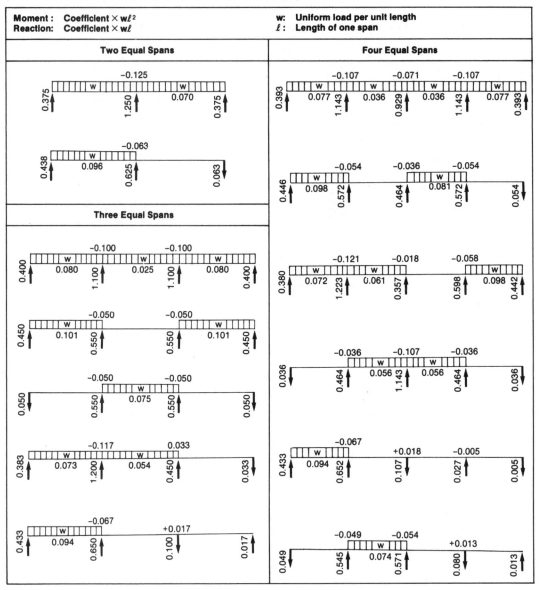

Table 1.16: Moments and Reactions in Continuous Beams Central Point Loads

Moment : Coefficient × Pℓ
Reaction: Coefficient × P

P: Concentrated load
ℓ : Length of one span

Two Equal Spans

0.313 | 0.156 | −0.188 | 1.375 | 0.156 | 0.313

0.406 | 0.203 | −0.094 | 0.688 | 0.094

Three Equal Spans

0.350 | 0.175 | −0.150 | 1.150 | 0.100 | −0.150 | 1.150 | 0.175 | 0.350

0.425 | 0.213 | −0.075 | 0.575 | −0.075 | 0.575 | 0.213 | 0.425

0.075 | −0.075 | 0.575 | 0.175 | −0.075 | 0.575 | 0.075

0.325 | 0.163 | −0.175 | 1.300 | 0.138 | −0.050 | 0.425 | 0.050

0.400 | 0.200 | −0.100 | 0.725 | +0.025 | 0.150 | 0.025

Four Equal Spans

0.339 | 0.170 | −0.161 | 1.214 | 0.116 | −0.107 | 0.893 | 0.116 | −0.161 | 1.214 | 0.170 | 0.339

0.420 | 0.210 | −0.080 | 0.607 | −0.054 | 0.446 | 0.183 | −0.080 | 0.607 | 0.080

0.319 | 0.160 | −0.181 | 1.335 | 0.146 | −0.027 | 0.286 | −0.087 | 0.647 | 0.207 | 0.413

0.054 | −0.054 | 0.446 | 0.143 | −0.161 | 1.214 | 0.143 | −0.054 | 0.446 | 0.054

0.400 | 0.200 | −0.100 | 0.728 | +0.027 | 0.161 | −0.007 | 0.040 | 0.007

0.074 | −0.074 | 0.567 | 0.173 | −0.080 | 0.607 | +0.020 | 0.121 | 0.020

Table 1.17: Moments and Reactions in Continuous Beams Point Loads at Third Points of Span

Moment : Coefficient $\times P\ell$ P: Total concentrated load on one span
Reaction: Coefficient $\times P$ ℓ : Length of one span

Two Equal Spans

$\frac{P}{2}$ $\frac{P}{2}$ −0.167 $\frac{P}{2}$ $\frac{P}{2}$
0.333   0.111   1.333   0.111   0.333

$\frac{P}{2}$ $\frac{P}{2}$ −0.083
0.417   0.139   0.667   0.083

Three Equal Spans

$\frac{P}{2}$ $\frac{P}{2}$ −0.133 $\frac{P}{2}$ $\frac{P}{2}$ −0.133 $\frac{P}{2}$ $\frac{P}{2}$
0.367   0.122   1.133   0.033   1.133   0.122   0.367

$\frac{P}{2}$ $\frac{P}{2}$ −0.067   −0.067 $\frac{P}{2}$ $\frac{P}{2}$
0.433   0.145   0.567   0.567   0.145   0.433

−0.067 $\frac{P}{2}$ $\frac{P}{2}$ −0.067
0.067   0.567   0.100   0.567   0.067

$\frac{P}{2}$ $\frac{P}{2}$ −0.156 $\frac{P}{2}$ $\frac{P}{2}$ −0.045
0.345   0.115   1.267   0.085   0.433   0.045

$\frac{P}{2}$ $\frac{P}{2}$ −0.089   +0.022
0.411   0.137   0.700   0.133   0.022

Four Equal Spans

$\frac{P}{2}$ $\frac{P}{2}$ −0.143 $\frac{P}{2}$ $\frac{P}{2}$ −0.096 $\frac{P}{2}$ $\frac{P}{2}$ −0.143 $\frac{P}{2}$ $\frac{P}{2}$
0.357   0.119   1.190   0.056   0.905   0.056   1.190   0.119   0.357

$\frac{P}{2}$ $\frac{P}{2}$ −0.072   −0.048 $\frac{P}{2}$ $\frac{P}{2}$ −0.072
0.428   0.143   0.596   0.452   0.111   0.596   0.072

$\frac{P}{2}$ $\frac{P}{2}$ −0.161 $\frac{P}{2}$ $\frac{P}{2}$ −0.024   −0.078 $\frac{P}{2}$ $\frac{P}{2}$
0.340   0.113   1.298   0.097   0.309   0.631   0.141   0.423

−0.048 $\frac{P}{2}$ $\frac{P}{2}$ −0.143 $\frac{P}{2}$ $\frac{P}{2}$ −0.048
0.048   0.453   0.087   1.190   0.087   0.453   0.048

$\frac{P}{2}$ $\frac{P}{2}$ −0.089   +0.024   −0.006
0.411   0.137   0.702   0.143   0.036   0.006

$\frac{P}{2}$ $\frac{P}{2}$ −0.066   −0.071   +0.018
0.066   0.560   0.099   0.595   0.107   0.018

Table 1.18:   Approximate Moments and Shears for Continuous Beams and One-Way Slabs

> **w : Factored load per unit length**
> ℓ_n: **Clear span length**
> ℓ_a: **Average length of adjacent clear spans**

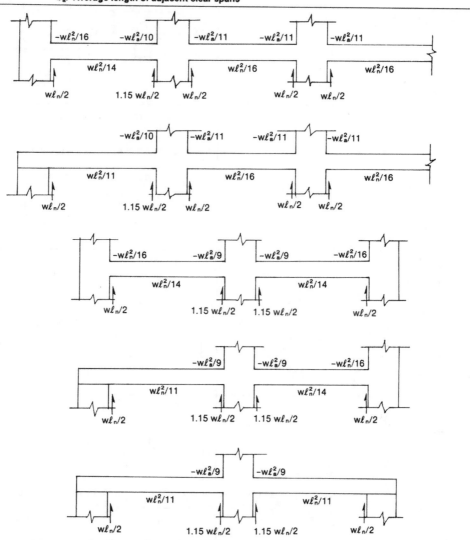

Notes:

1. This figure is applicable to prismatic members loaded with uniformly distributed load where the ratio of factored live load to factored dead load is not greater than 2.0, and the span lengths approximately equal, with the longer of the two adjacent spans not greater than the shorter by more than 20 per cent.

2. If the exterior support is a spandrel or girder, the negative moment at the interior face of exterior support is $w\ell_n^2/24$.

3. For slabs with spans not exceeding 3 m or beams with the ratio of the sum of the column stiffnesses to the beam stiffness exceeds eight at each end, the negative moment at all supports can be taken equal to $w\ell_n^2/12$.

Table 1.19: Sectional Properties

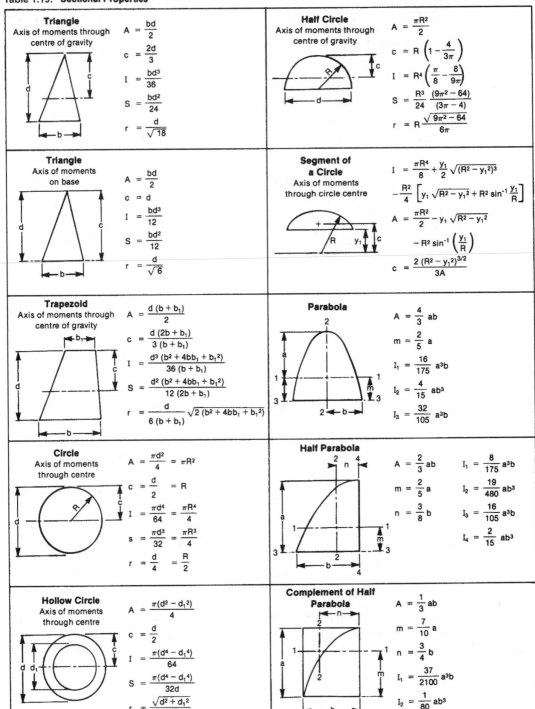

Triangle
Axis of moments through centre of gravity

$A = \dfrac{bd}{2}$

$c = \dfrac{2d}{3}$

$I = \dfrac{bd^3}{36}$

$S = \dfrac{bd^2}{24}$

$r = \dfrac{d}{\sqrt{18}}$

Half Circle
Axis of moments through centre of gravity

$A = \dfrac{\pi R^2}{2}$

$c = R\left(1 - \dfrac{4}{3\pi}\right)$

$I = R^4\left(\dfrac{\pi}{8} - \dfrac{8}{9\pi}\right)$

$S = \dfrac{R^3}{24}\dfrac{(9\pi^2 - 64)}{(3\pi - 4)}$

$r = R\dfrac{\sqrt{9\pi^2 - 64}}{6\pi}$

Triangle
Axis of moments on base

$A = \dfrac{bd}{2}$

$c = d$

$I = \dfrac{bd^3}{12}$

$S = \dfrac{bd^2}{12}$

$r = \dfrac{d}{\sqrt{6}}$

Segment of a Circle
Axis of moments through circle centre

$I = \dfrac{\pi R^4}{8} + \dfrac{y_1}{2}\sqrt{(R^2 - y_1^2)^3}$
$\quad - \dfrac{R^2}{4}\left[y_1\sqrt{R^2 - y_1^2} + R^2\sin^{-1}\dfrac{y_1}{R}\right]$

$A = \dfrac{\pi R^2}{2} - y_1\sqrt{R^2 - y_1^2}$
$\quad - R^2\sin^{-1}\left(\dfrac{y_1}{R}\right)$

$c = \dfrac{2(R^2 - y_1^2)^{3/2}}{3A}$

Trapezoid
Axis of moments through centre of gravity

$A = \dfrac{d(b + b_1)}{2}$

$c = \dfrac{d(2b + b_1)}{3(b + b_1)}$

$I = \dfrac{d^3(b^2 + 4bb_1 + b_1^2)}{36(b + b_1)}$

$S = \dfrac{d^2(b^2 + 4bb_1 + b_1^2)}{12(2b + b_1)}$

$r = \dfrac{d}{6(b + b_1)}\sqrt{2(b^2 + 4bb_1 + b_1^2)}$

Parabola

$A = \dfrac{4}{3}ab$

$m = \dfrac{2}{5}a$

$I_1 = \dfrac{16}{175}a^3b$

$I_2 = \dfrac{4}{15}ab^3$

$I_3 = \dfrac{32}{105}a^3b$

Circle
Axis of moments through centre

$A = \dfrac{\pi d^2}{4} = \pi R^2$

$c = \dfrac{d}{2} = R$

$I = \dfrac{\pi d^4}{64} = \dfrac{\pi R^4}{4}$

$s = \dfrac{\pi d^3}{32} = \dfrac{\pi R^3}{4}$

$r = \dfrac{d}{4} = \dfrac{R}{2}$

Half Parabola

$A = \dfrac{2}{3}ab$

$m = \dfrac{2}{5}a$

$n = \dfrac{3}{8}b$

$I_1 = \dfrac{8}{175}a^3b$

$I_2 = \dfrac{19}{480}ab^3$

$I_3 = \dfrac{16}{105}a^3b$

$I_4 = \dfrac{2}{15}ab^3$

Hollow Circle
Axis of moments through centre

$A = \dfrac{\pi(d^2 - d_1^2)}{4}$

$c = \dfrac{d}{2}$

$I = \dfrac{\pi(d^4 - d_1^4)}{64}$

$S = \dfrac{\pi(d^4 - d_1^4)}{32d}$

$r = \dfrac{\sqrt{d^2 + d_1^2}}{4}$

Complement of Half Parabola

$A = \dfrac{1}{3}ab$

$m = \dfrac{7}{10}a$

$n = \dfrac{3}{4}b$

$I_1 = \dfrac{37}{2100}a^3b$

$I_2 = \dfrac{1}{80}ab^3$

Reproduced from the 'Metric Design Manual' with the permission of CPCI.

Table 1.19: (Continued)

Square Axis of moments through centre 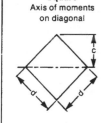	$A = d^2$ $c = \dfrac{d}{2}$ $I = \dfrac{d^4}{12}$ $S = \dfrac{d^3}{6}$ $r = \dfrac{d}{\sqrt{12}} = 0.288675\,d$
Rectangle Axis of moments on diagonal 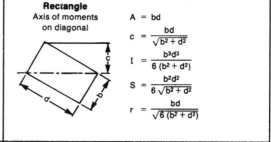	$A = bd$ $c = \dfrac{bd}{\sqrt{b^2 + d^2}}$ $I = \dfrac{b^3 d^3}{6\,(b^2 + d^2)}$ $S = \dfrac{b^2 d^2}{6\sqrt{b^2 + d^2}}$ $r = \dfrac{bd}{\sqrt{6\,(b^2 + d^2)}}$
Square Axis of moments on base 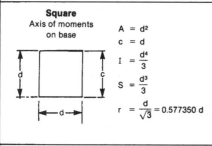	$A = d^2$ $c = d$ $I = \dfrac{d^4}{3}$ $S = \dfrac{d^3}{3}$ $r = \dfrac{d}{\sqrt{3}} = 0.577350\,d$
Rectangle Axis of moments any line through centre of gravity 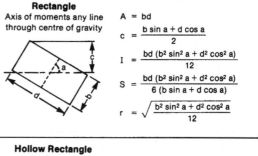	$A = bd$ $c = \dfrac{b\sin a + d\cos a}{2}$ $I = \dfrac{bd\,(b^2 \sin^2 a + d^2 \cos^2 a)}{12}$ $S = \dfrac{bd\,(b^2 \sin^2 a + d^2 \cos^2 a)}{6\,(b\sin a + d\cos a)}$ $r = \sqrt{\dfrac{b^2 \sin^2 a + d^2 \cos^2 a}{12}}$
Square Axis of moments on diagonal 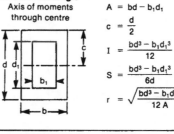	$A = d^2$ $c = \dfrac{d}{\sqrt{2}} = 0.707107\,d$ $I = \dfrac{d^4}{12}$ $S = \dfrac{d^3}{6\sqrt{2}} = 0.117851\,d^3$ $r = \dfrac{d}{\sqrt{12}} = 0.288675\,d$
Hollow Rectangle Axis of moments through centre	$A = bd - b_1 d_1$ $c = \dfrac{d}{2}$ $I = \dfrac{bd^3 - b_1 d_1^3}{12}$ $S = \dfrac{bd^3 - b_1 d_1^3}{6d}$ $r = \sqrt{\dfrac{bd^3 - b_1 d_1^3}{12\,A}}$
Rectangle Axis of moments through centre 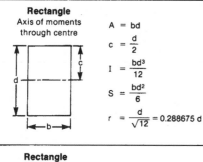	$A = bd$ $c = \dfrac{d}{2}$ $I = \dfrac{bd^3}{12}$ $S = \dfrac{bd^2}{6}$ $r = \dfrac{d}{\sqrt{12}} = 0.288675\,d$
Equal Rectangles Axis of moments through centre of gravity	$A = b\,(d - d_1)$ $c = \dfrac{d}{2}$ $I = \dfrac{b\,(d^3 - d_1^3)}{12}$ $S = \dfrac{b\,(d^3 - d_1^3)}{6d}$ $r = \sqrt{\dfrac{d^3 - d_1^3}{12\,(d - d_1)}}$
Rectangle Axis of moments on base	$A = bd$ $c = d$ $I = \dfrac{bd^3}{3}$ $S = \dfrac{bd^2}{3}$ $r = \dfrac{d}{\sqrt{3}} = 0.577350\,d$
Unequal Rectangles Axis of moments through centre of gravity 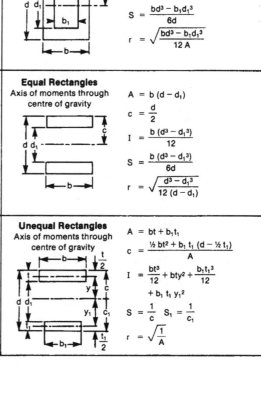	$A = bt + b_1 t_1$ $c = \dfrac{\frac{1}{2}bt^2 + b_1 t_1\,(d - \frac{1}{2}t_1)}{A}$ $I = \dfrac{bt^3}{12} + bty^2 + \dfrac{b_1 t_1^3}{12}$ $\quad + b_1 t_1 y_1^2$ $S = \dfrac{1}{c} \quad S_1 = \dfrac{1}{c_1}$ $r = \sqrt{\dfrac{1}{A}}$

Table 1.19:   (Continued)

Parabolic Fillet in Right Angle

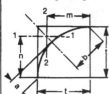

$$a = \frac{t}{2\sqrt{2}}$$

$$b = \frac{t}{\sqrt{2}}$$

$$A = \frac{1}{6} t^2$$

$$m = n = \frac{4}{5} t$$

$$I_1 = I_2 = \frac{11}{2100} t^4$$

*Half Ellipse

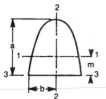

$$A = \frac{1}{2} \pi ab$$

$$m = \frac{4a}{3\pi}$$

$$I_1 = a^3 b \left(\frac{\pi}{8} - \frac{8}{9\pi} \right)$$

$$I_2 = \frac{1}{8} \pi ab^3$$

$$I_3 = \frac{1}{8} \pi a^3 b$$

*Quarter Ellipse

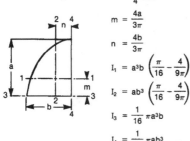

$$A = \frac{1}{4} \pi ab$$

$$m = \frac{4a}{3\pi}$$

$$n = \frac{4b}{3\pi}$$

$$I_1 = a^3 b \left(\frac{\pi}{16} - \frac{4}{9\pi} \right)$$

$$I_2 = ab^3 \left(\frac{\pi}{16} - \frac{4}{9\pi} \right)$$

$$I_3 = \frac{1}{16} \pi a^3 b$$

$$I_4 = \frac{1}{16} \pi ab^3$$

*To obtain properties of half circles, quarter circle and circular complement, substitute $a = b = R$.

*Elliptic Complement

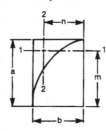

$$A = ab \left(1 - \frac{\pi}{4} \right)$$

$$m = \frac{a}{6 \left(1 - \frac{\pi}{4} \right)}$$

$$n = \frac{b}{6 \left(1 - \frac{\pi}{4} \right)}$$

$$I_1 = a^3 b \left[\frac{1}{3} - \frac{\pi}{16} - \frac{1}{36 \left(1 - \frac{\pi}{4} \right)} \right]$$

$$I_2 = ab^3 \left[\frac{1}{3} - \frac{\pi}{16} - \frac{1}{36 \left(1 - \frac{\pi}{4} \right)} \right]$$

Regular Polygon
Axis of moments through centre

n = Number of sides

$$\phi = \frac{180°}{n}$$

$$a = 2\sqrt{R^2 - R_1^2}$$

$$R = \frac{a}{2 \sin \phi}$$

$$R_1 = \frac{a}{2 \tan \phi}$$

$$A = \frac{1}{4} na^2 \cot \phi = \frac{1}{2} nR^2 \sin 2\phi = nR_1^2 \tan \phi$$

$$I_1 = I_2 = \frac{A(6R^2 - a^2)}{24} = \frac{A(12R_1^2 + a^2)}{48}$$

$$r_1 = r_2 = \sqrt{\frac{6R^2 - a^2}{24}} = \sqrt{\frac{12R_1 + a^2}{48}}$$

Beams and Channels
Transverse force oblique through centre of gravity

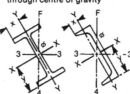

$$I_3 = I_x \sin^2 \phi + I_y \cos^2 \phi$$

$$I_4 = I_x \cos^2 \phi + I_y \sin^2 \phi$$

$$f_b = M \left[\frac{y}{I_x} \sin\phi + \frac{x}{I_y} \cos\phi \right]$$

where M is bending moment due to force F.

Angle
Axis of moments through centre of gravity

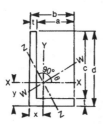

Z-Z is axis of minimum I

$$\tan 2\theta = \frac{2K}{I_y - I_x}$$

$$A = t(b + c) \qquad x = \frac{b^2 + ct}{2(b + c)} \qquad y = \frac{d^2 + at}{2(b + c)}$$

K = Product of Inertia about X-X & Y-Y

$$= \pm \frac{abcdt}{4(b + c)}$$

$$I_x = \frac{1}{3} \left[t(d - y)^3 + by^3 - a(y - t)^3 \right]$$

$$I_y = \frac{1}{3} \left[t(b - x)^3 + dx^3 - c(x - t)^3 \right]$$

$$I_z = I_x \sin^2\theta + I_y \cos^2\theta + K \sin 2\theta$$

$$I_w = I_x \cos^2\theta + I_y \sin^2\theta - K \sin 2\theta$$

K is negative when heel of angle, with respect to c.g., is in 1st or 3rd quadrant, positive when in 2nd or 4th quadrant.

By Murat Saatcioglu

Design for Flexure

2.1   Introduction

The majority of structural members used in practice are subjected to flexural stresses caused by bending moments. Flexural stresses often occur in combination with other types of stresses caused by axial force, shear, and torsion. Typical examples of flexure dominant members include beams and slabs, although the concepts and design aids presented in this chapter also apply to other members that are subjected flexure, including structural walls, retaining walls and footings.

Flexural design is performed in two stages. The first stage involves sectional design, including sections that are subjected to highest negative and positive bending moments. The second stage involves member design, including determination of bar lengths. Length of reinforcement and locations of cut-off points are affected by provisions specified for development length and splice length requirements, as discussed in Chapter 3.

Flexural design of a reinforced concrete section should conform to the Limit States Design provisions of CSA A23.3-14. Accordingly, the ultimate limit state expressed below should be satisfied to meet the required strength.

Moment Resistance ≥ Factored Moment

$$M_r \geq M_f$$

Factored moments are obtained by structural analysis under factored loads. Load factors and load combinations are discussed in Chapter 1.

2.2   Moment Resistance (M_r)

Moment resistance M_r is obtained by computing the flexural strength of a section, with resistance factors ϕ_c and ϕ_s applied to concrete cylinder strength f'_c and steel yield strength f_y, respectively. The material resistance factor for concrete, ϕ_c is 0.65 as per Clause 8.4.2 of CSA A23.3-14, and may be taken as 0.70 for precast elements produced in manufacturing plants prequalified in accordance with CSA A23.4. In this chapter, all design aids and examples are produced for the general case of $\phi_c = 0.65$. The material resistance factor for reinforcing steel, ϕ_s is 0.85, as specified in Clause 8.4.3 of CSA A23.3-14.

The flexural strength is computed from internal forces that can be established by a plane section analysis. Accordingly, plane sections of a reinforced concrete member before bending are assumed to remain plane after bending. Furthermore, perfect bond is assumed between the concrete and reinforcing steel. These assumptions lead to a linear distribution of strains across the section depth, with strains in steel and concrete proportional to their distances from the neutral axis. The corresponding stress distribution is obtained from material stress-strain relationships. This leads to a parabolic stress distribution for concrete in compression. Concrete in tension is ignored without affecting the flexural resistance significantly. Internal forces in concrete and steel are then computed from the stress distribution, with due considerations given to the area of concrete and reinforcement. An iterative approach may have to be employed until the neutral axis location that satisfies force equilibrium is established. This procedure is referred to as strain compatibility analysis. The moment resistance is computed for a specific strain distribution that corresponds to a given load stage. Complete response of a section can be established if the analysis is carried out for different load stages and corresponding strain conditions. This is usually done in the form of a moment-curvature relationship (M-ϕ), as illustrated in Fig. 2.1.

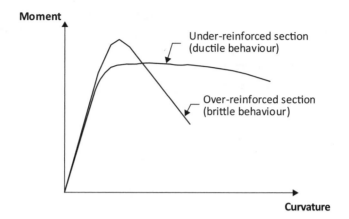

Fig. 2.1 Moment curvature relationship

While the plane section analysis is a powerful tool for establishing the characteristics of sectional response, only one point on the M-ϕ relationship, i.e. the maximum moment resistance, is of interest for design purposes. CSA A23.3-14 defines the strain condition corresponding to the maximum moment resistance in Clause 10.1.3. This condition is illustrated in Fig. 2.2. Accordingly, the maximum strain at the extreme compression fibre is assumed to be 0.0035 when the factored moment resistance is attained. CSA A23.3-14 also defines an equivalent rectangular stress block to represent the parabolic distribution of compression in concrete, simplifying the design process significantly.

The rectangular stress block, with the parameters given in the standard, is applicable to the limiting strain condition, which is used to compute the maximum resistance of a section. The following expressions define the parameters of the rectangular stress distribution, which spreads over a depth of $a = \beta_1 c$ from the extreme compression fibre, with a constant intensity of $\alpha_1 \phi_c f_c'$.

$$\alpha_1 = 0.85 - 0.0015 f_c' \geq 0.67 \tag{2.1}$$

$$\beta_1 = 0.97 - 0.0025 f_c' \geq 0.67 \tag{2.2}$$

Reinforced concrete sections in flexure exhibit different modes of failure depending on the percentage of steel in the section. Sections with small percentage of steel develop yielding of reinforcement in tension, prior to crushing of concrete in compression. These sections are referred to as "under-reinforced" sections. Members designed to have under-reinforced sections deflect excessively prior to concrete crushing, exhibiting ductile behaviour with prior warning of an imminent failure. Sections with excessive tension steel may not develop yielding of reinforcement prior to concrete crushing. These members deflect very little until failure, and the failure is usually brittle, explosive and unexpected. These sections are referred to as "over-reinforced" sections.

The amount of tension steel that causes simultaneous onset of concrete crushing and tension steel yielding is referred to as "balanced reinforcement" and the section is referred to as "balanced section." Fig. 2.2 shows the strain condition for each type of behaviour. Ductile behaviour of an under-reinforced section and brittle behaviour of an over-reinforced section are illustrated in Fig. 2.1. It is preferable to design under-reinforced sections. Tension reinforcement, approximately equal to 50% of balanced reinforcement is usually believed to be economically optimum steel content, also producing ductile behaviour.

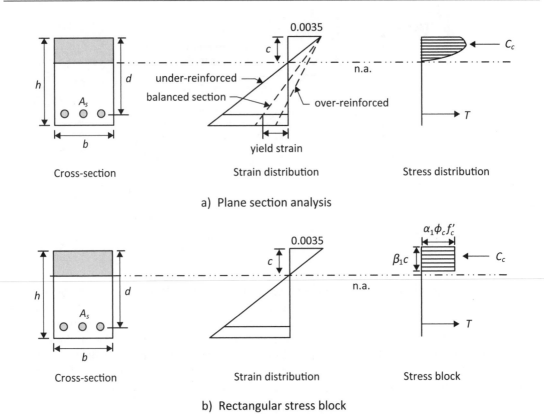

a) Plane section analysis

b) Rectangular stress block

Fig. 2.2 Flexural analysis of reinforced concrete sections

2.2.1. Limit of *c/d* for Yielding of Tension Reinforcement

Computation of factored moment resistance M_r may require strain compatibility analysis as described above. If the section is under-reinforced, however, the tension steel yields prior to the attainment of the strain condition defined in A23.3 for the computation of factored moment resistance. Hence, the internal tensile force in reinforcement becomes known, and the iterative procedure that is usually required for strain compatibility analysis is not needed. This simplifies the computation of M_r. The limiting strain condition for yielding of tension reinforcement is the same as the strain condition for balanced section. This limiting condition is expressed in Clause 10.5.2 of CSA A23.3-14 in terms of c/d ratio for balanced section. Accordingly, flexural members without axial load shall be design such that Eq. 2.3 is satisfied. This condition ensures the yielding of tension reinforcement prior to the crushing of concrete, which is desirable for ductile behaviour.

$$\frac{c}{d} \leq \frac{0.0035}{0.0035 + \varepsilon_y} = \frac{700}{700 + f_y} \tag{2.3}$$

2.2.2. Minimum Reinforcement

Reinforcement in concrete is not effective until after cracking. The flexural capacity of an uncracked concrete section is primarily provided by concrete alone. Plain concrete members, on the other hand, fail rapidly as soon as the cracking moment M_{cr} is reached. Reinforced sections with very little reinforcement may behave similar to plain concrete sections, and may not be able to sustain M_{cr} upon cracking. Hence, a minimum amount of tension reinforcement may be necessary to provide adequate post-cracking strength as indicated in Eq. 2.4. This requirement may be waved when the factored moment resistance M_r is at least one-third greater than the factored moment M_f.

$$M_r \geq 1.2\, M_{cr} \tag{2.4}$$

where;

$$M_{cr} = \frac{f_r I}{y_t} \tag{2.5}$$

and;

$$f_r = 0.6\lambda\sqrt{f_c'} \tag{2.6}$$

"I" is the moment of inertia of section about the centroidal axis, and y_t is the distance between the section centroid and the extreme tension fibre. In lieu of the computation of cracking moment, the following expression may be used [Clause 10.5.1.2] to ensure that the section has the minimum required area of tension reinforcement.

$$A_{s,min} = \frac{0.2\sqrt{f_c'}}{f_y} b_t h \tag{2.7}$$

where, b_t is the width of the tension zone of the section. For T-beams with the flange in tension, b_t need not exceed 2.5 b_w for beams with a flange on both sides of the web, and 1.5 b_w for beams with a flange on one side of the web (L-beams).

The minimum reinforcement for slabs is intended to provide control of cracking due to shrinkage and temperature. It also provides minimum reinforcement to keep the cracked concrete together. A minimum area of $0.002A_g$, in each direction, is found to be adequate for this purpose [Clause 7.8]. However, this minimum area may have to be increased for exposure conditions that necessitate further crack control. The maximum spacing of minimum reinforcement in slabs is limited to the smaller of 500 mm or five times the slab thickness, with sufficient length to develop yield strength as per Clause 12.

2.2.3. Rectangular Sections with Tension Reinforcement

Factored moment resistance M_r for rectangular sections with tension reinforcement is computed from the internal force couple illustrated in Fig. 2.2. The depth of rectangular concrete stress block is determined from equilibrium of internal forces, especially for under-reinforced sections where the tension force in steel is readily available. This helps define the internal lever arm and the moment resistance.

$$C_c = T \tag{2.8}$$

$$\alpha_1 \phi_c f_c'\, ab = A_s \phi_s f_y \tag{2.9}$$

$$a = \frac{\phi_s A_s f_y}{\alpha_1 \phi_c f_c' b} \tag{2.10}$$

$$M_r = A_s \phi_s f_y \left(d - \frac{a}{2}\right) \tag{2.11}$$

Substituting "a" from Eq. 2.10, and expressing the area of steel in terms of reinforcement ratio, $\rho = A_s/bd$;

$$M_r = bd^2 \left[1 - \frac{\phi_s \rho f_y}{2\alpha_1 f_c' \phi_c}\right] \rho \phi_s f_y \tag{2.12}$$

$$M_r = K_r bd^2 10^{-6} \text{ kN·m} \tag{2.13}$$

where, M_r is expressed in kN·m, and b and d are expressed in mm. The resistance factor K_r, given in Eq. 2.14, is dependent on material properties and related coefficients, and reinforcement ratio ρ.

$$K_r = \left[1 - \frac{\phi_s \rho f_y}{2\alpha_1 f_c' \phi_c}\right] \rho \phi_s f_y \text{ MPa} \tag{2.14}$$

The required ρ can be computed for different material properties and values of K_r, and can be tabulated as a design aid. Table 2.1 was generated in this manner, and it can be used to compute the factored resistance of a rectangular section with tension reinforcement. It can also be used for design. In this case the factored resistance M_r should at least be equal to the factored moment, M_f. Therefore, K_r is solved from Eq. 2.13 after substituting M_f in place of M_r. Table 2.1 can then be entered with K_r to read the required reinforcement ratio ρ.

2.2.4. Rectangular Sections with Compression Reinforcement

Flexural members are usually designed for tension reinforcement. Any requirement for an increase in capacity can be accommodated by an increase in tension reinforcement and/or section size. However, sometimes the cross-sectional dimensions may be limited by architectural and/or other functional requirements. The additional moment resistance required in such sections may be provided by placing additional reinforcement in compression and tension regions of the beam. The additional steel results in an internal force couple, increasing the flexural capacity. Fig. 2.3 illustrates the components of moment resistance provided in a rectangular section with compression reinforcement.

The compression reinforcement becomes effective in sections where they are needed. A lightly reinforced section requires little concrete in the compression zone to maintain equilibrium. The neutral axis of such a section approaches the extreme compression fibre. Hence, any reinforcement in the compression zone becomes ineffective. In most under-reinforced sections the extension of positive tension reinforcement into the negative compression zone usually does not contribute significantly to the negative moment resistance. Designers usually ignore the presence of bar extension into the compression zone or detailing reinforcement that may be present in the compression zone. A heavily reinforced section, on the other hand, requires a larger compression zone to maintain equilibrium, with neutral axis moving away from the extreme compression fibre. The reinforcement placed near the extreme compression fibre becomes fully effective when the section attains its capacity at 0.0035 fibre strain. When the required moment resistance can not be provided with heavy use of tension reinforcement, the designer may make use of the extension of tension reinforcement from nearby sections into the compression zone, provided that the development length and lap length requirements of CSA A23.3-14 are met.

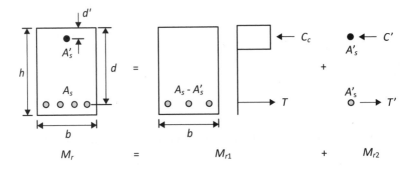

Fig. 2.3 Rectangular section with compression reinforcement

It is clear from the foregoing discussion that compression reinforcement is most effective when the neutral axis approaches the section centroid. The compression reinforcement placed in such a section usually yields when the section reaches its capacity (ε_c = 0.0035). If the compression reinforcement does not yield, it is usually very close to yielding. Hence, it is reasonable to assume, for design purposes, that the compression steel does yield at the limiting strain condition. This simplifies the design process considerably.

The moment resistance of a rectangular section with compression reinforcement can be obtained from the following expressions.

$$M_r = M_{r1} + M_{r2} \tag{2.15}$$

$$M_{r1} = K_r bd^2 \tag{2.16}$$

$$M_{r2} = A'_s \phi_s f_y (d - d') \tag{2.17}$$

$$M_{r2} = K'_r bd^2 \tag{2.18}$$

where;

$$K'_r = \rho' \phi_s f_y \left[1 - \frac{d'}{d} \right] \tag{2.19}$$

$$\rho' = \frac{A'_s}{bd} \tag{2.20}$$

Substituting Eqs. 2.16 and 2.18 into 2.15 yields;

$$M_r = (K_r + K'_r)bd^2 10^{-6} \tag{2.21}$$

where M_r is expressed in kN·m, K_r and K'_r are expressed in MPa, and b and d are expressed in mm. K_r is given in Eq. 2.14, and is based on the reinforcement ratio $\rho = (A_s - A'_s)/bd$. It can also be obtained from Table 2.1. The resistance factor K'_r can be obtained from Table 2.2 in terms of the compression reinforcement ratio ρ', and d'/d ratio.

2.2.5. T-Sections

Most concrete structures are built monolithically with slabs and beams cast together. Fig. 2.4 illustrates a typical reinforced concrete slab system where the floor slab and the supporting beams together provide flexural resistance to applied loading. The resulting structural system includes T-beams, each consisting of a rectangular beam section forming the web, and the slab near the web forming the flange. The slab width near the web, considered to be effective in contributing to load resistance, is referred to as the "effective flange width". The effective flange width, b_f, is defined in CSA A23.3-14 as illustrated in Table 2.4, and should be used in computing the sectional resistance.

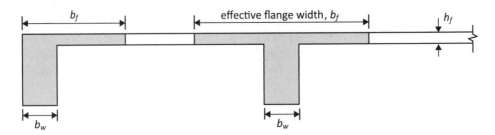

Fig. 2.4 T and L Beams

Although the T-beam example given above is a direct consequence of monolithic construction, T shaped concrete cross-sections are sometimes produced intentionally because of their superior performance in positive bending. These sections provide increased area of compression concrete in the flange, with reduced dead load associated with reduced area of tension concrete in the web. Single T's and double T's are commonly used in the precast industry.

The flange width in most T-sections is significantly wider than the web width. Therefore, the amount of tension reinforcement placed in the web can easily be equilibrated by part of the flange concrete compressed near the extreme compression fibre. This implies that the neutral axis falls within the flange. In fact, in most practical applications it is difficult to create a situation where the neutral axis falls below the flange, since this may require excessive tension force and associated reinforcement that could not be placed in the web without creating construction problems. Therefore, most T-sections behave as rectangular sections with flange width equal to the equivalent width of a rectangular section. T-sections in negative bending also behave as rectangular beams with web width equal to the equivalent width of a rectangular section, while the flange concrete is subjected to tension. However, sections with relatively narrow and thin flanges, subjected to positive bending, may require part of the web concrete below the flange to be compressed to equilibrate heavy tension steel that may be present in the web. In such cases the neutral axis lies within the web, forming concrete compression zone that has a T-shape. These sections are said to behave as T-sections.

The limiting condition for T-section behaviour occurs when the flange concrete is fully compressed. This condition can either be expressed in terms of the limiting area of tension reinforcement, or the limiting thickness of flange. The following inequalities define conditions for T-section behaviour.

$$A_s \phi_s f_y > \alpha_1 \phi_c f_c' \, h_f b_f \tag{2.22}$$

$$A_s > \frac{\alpha_1 \phi_c f_c' \, h_f b_f}{\phi_s f_y} \tag{2.23}$$

$$h_f < \frac{A_s \phi_s f_y}{\alpha_1 \phi_c f_c' b_f} \tag{2.24}$$

Fig. 2.5 illustrates the T-beam behaviour. The moment resistance of this section is provided by two internal force couples; one formed by the compression concrete in the overhangs and the corresponding tension steel (M_{rf}, A_{sf}), and the other by the compression in web concrete and the corresponding tension steel (M_{rw}, A_{sw}). Each moment component represents moment resistance of a rectangular section with tension reinforcement. Hence, the design aids prepared for rectangular sections can be used to find moment resistance of a section exhibiting T-beam behaviour. Consequently, Table 2.1 can be used with $\rho_f = A_{sf}/(b_f - b_w)d$ to determine M_{rf}, and with $\rho_w = A_{sw}/b_w d$ to find M_{rw}.

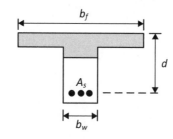

T-section behaviour

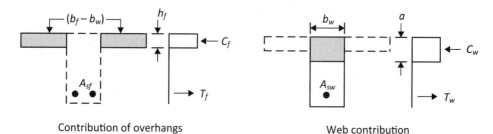

Contribution of overhangs   Web contribution

Fig. 2.5 T-section behaviour

$$M_r = M_{rf} + M_{rw} \tag{2.25}$$

where;

$$M_{rf} = K_{rf}(b_f - b_w)d^2 \tag{2.26}$$

with; $\rho_f = \dfrac{A_{sf}}{(b_f - b_w)d}$

$$M_{rw} = K_{rw}bd^2 \tag{2.27}$$

with; $\rho_w = \dfrac{A_{sw}}{b_w d}$

$$A_{sf} = \frac{\alpha_1 \phi_c f'_c (b_f - b_w)h_f}{\phi_s f_y} \tag{2.28}$$

$$\rho_f = \frac{\alpha_1 \phi_c f'_c h_f}{\phi_s f_y d} \tag{2.29}$$

$$A_{sw} = A_s - A_{sf} \tag{2.30}$$

$$\rho_w = \frac{A_{sw}}{b_w d} \tag{2.31}$$

Table 2.3 contains the values of ρ_f for different material strengths and h_f/d ratios.

2.2.6.   Joist Construction

Concrete floor joist is another example of a flexural member with a "T" cross-section. Regularly spaced joists, in one or two directions, result in increased redundancy in the structural system, allowing redistribution of loads. Therefore, a monolithically cast joist system is considered to have significant ductility. Certain provisions of CSA A23.3-14 specifically apply to joist construction. Joist construction, not meeting the geometric limitations specified in Table 2.5 [Clause 10.4.1] shall be designed as slabs and beams.

2.3   Placement of Reinforcement

Flexural reinforcement is placed with due considerations given to the spacing of reinforcement and crack control. The crack control is achieved by using well distributed reinforcement. It is usually preferable to use sufficient number of small size bars, as opposed to fewer bars of larger size, while also respecting the spacing requirements. These requirements are discussed in the following sections.

2.3.1.   Spacing of Longitudinal Reinforcement

Longitudinal reinforcement should be placed such that the spacing between the bars allow proper placement of concrete. The minimum spacing requirement for beam reinforcement is shown in Table 2.6. The maximum bar spacing in walls and one-way slabs, other than the joist construction illustrated in Table 2.5, is 3 times the member thickness or 500 mm, whichever is smaller [Clause 7.4.1.2].

2.3.2.   Crack Control

Beams reinforced with few large size bars may experience cracking between the bars, even if the required area of tension reinforcement is provided and the sectional capacity is achieved. Crack widths in these members may exceed what is usually regarded as acceptable limits of cracking for various exposure conditions. The crack width limitation is specified in CSA A23.3-14 in terms of the quantity "z" given below:

$$z = f_s \, (d_c A)^{1/3} \tag{2.32}$$

where; z = 30 000 N/mm for interior exposure and 25 000 N/mm for exterior exposure. The crack control is checked under service loads. Hence, the tensile stress in reinforcement f_s can be determined from the strain compatibility analysis presented earlier in Sec. 2.2. Because the strain condition is different than that at maximum factored resistance, the rectangular stress block defined in Sec. 2.2 can not be used. This may require the use of a parabolic stress distribution for concrete, and an iterative strain compatibility analysis to establish the stress in reinforcement. Alternatively, CSA A23.3-14 permits the use 60% of the yield strength f_y as an estimate of stress in steel under service loads. The other terms used in Eq. 2.32 are defined in Table 2.7. In calculating d_c and A, the effective clear concrete cover need not be taken greater than 50 mm. For epoxy coated bars, the "z" valued computed by Eq. 2.32 should be multiplied by 1.2. The crack control requirement described in this section may not be sufficient for structures subjected to very aggressive exposure conditions or for structures designed to be watertight.

2.3.3.   Skin Reinforcement

In deep flexural members, the crack control provided by the above procedure may not be sufficient to control cracking near the mid-depth of the section, between the neutral axis and the tension concrete controlled by main flexural reinforcement. For members with a depth $h > 750$ mm, skin reinforcement with a total area of A_{sk} should be provided along the exposed side faces.

$$A_{sk} = \rho_{sk} A_{cs} \tag{2.33}$$

where; ρ_{sk} = 0.008 for interior exposure and 0.010 for exterior exposure. The area of concrete, A_{cs}, to be controlled by skin reinforcement is defined in Table 2.8. The maximum spacing of skin reinforcement is limited to 200 mm, [Clause 10.6.2]. The contribution of skin reinforcement to flexural resistance may be included in design if the stress in steel is computed from a strain compatibility analysis.

2.3.4. Tension Reinforcement in T-Beam Flanges

The flexural resistance of T-shaped sections is discussed in Sec. 2.2.5. These sections behave as rectangular beams when subjected to negative bending. While the required reinforcement ratio may be computed using the web width "b_w", the placement of reinforcement should not be limited to the same width. Hence, CSA A23.3-14 calls for some distribution of tension reinforcement within the flange. Accordingly, part of the reinforcement is to be placed over a width of each overhang equal to 1/20 of the beam span, or the width defined in Table 2.9, whichever is smaller. The area of this reinforcement should not be less than 0.4% of the gross area of overhanging flange.

2.4 Design Examples

Example 2.1   Analysis of a Rectangular Beam with Tension Reinforcement

Compute moment resistance M_r for the rectangular section shown in the figure using f'_c = 30 MPa and f_y = 400 MPa.

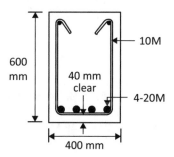

Example 2.1

1. Calculate effective depth d:

    $d = 600 - 40 - 11.3 - (19.5 / 2) = 539$ mm

2. Calculate reinforcement ratio ρ:

    $\rho = A_s / bd = (4 \times 300) / (400 \times 539) = 0.0056 = 0.56\%$

3. Determine K_r corresponding to $\rho = 0.56\%$ from Table 2.1:

    $K_r = 1.8$ MPa

4. Calculate resisting moment M_r:

    $M_r = K_r bd^2 \times 10^{-6} = 1.8\,(400)\,(539)^2 \times 10^{-6} = 209$ kN·m

Example 2.2   Design of a Rectangular Beam with Tension Reinforcement

Design the rectangular beam shown in the figure for a factored moment of M_f = 415 kN·m. Use normal density concrete with f'_c = 40 MPa, f_y = 400 MPa, and maximum aggregate size of 25 mm. The beam is to be built in a non-corrosive environment, having interior exposure.

2

Design for Flexure

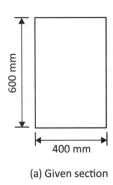

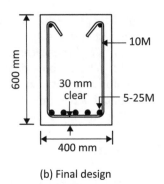

(a) Given section   (b) Final design

Example 2.2

1. Estimate effective depth d, assuming 25M bars for flexural reinforcement and 10M stirrups for transverse reinforcement. Select a clear cover of 30 mm from Table 2.6 (for non-corrosive environment, interior exposure).

   $d = 600 - 30 - 11.3 - (25.2 / 2) = 546$ mm

2. Calculate resistance factor K_r : For design; $M_r \geq M_f = 415$ kN·m

   $K_r = M_r \times 10^6 / bd^2 = 415 \times 10^6 / (400) (546)^2 = 3.48$ MPa

3. Determine reinforcement ratio ρ from Table 2.1: $\rho = 1.13\%$

4. Determine required tension reinforcement:

   $A_s = \rho bd = 0.0113 \times 400 \times 546 = 2468$ mm^2
   No. of 25M bars required; 2468 / 500 = 4.94
   Select 5 – 25M bars

5. Check the minimum steel requirement:

   $M_r \geq 1.2\, M_{cr}$
   $M_r = 415$ kN·m for 5 – 25M bars
   $M_{cr} = 0.6\, \lambda \sqrt{f_c'}\ I/c_t$ (Eq. 2-5 and 2-6)
   $I = bh^3 / 12 = (400) (600)^3 / 12 = 7.2 \times 10^9$ mm^4
   $c_t = 600 / 2 = 300$ mm; $\lambda = 1.0$ (normal density concrete)
   $M_{cr} = 0.6\,(1.0)\sqrt{40}\,(7.2 \times 10^9\,) / (300) = 91 \times 10^6$ N·mm
   $M_r = 415$ kN·m > 1.2 (91) = 109 kN·m   OK

   Note: Eq. 2-7 may be used in lieu of Eq. 2-5.

   $A_{smin} = 0.2 \sqrt{f_c'}\ b_t h / f_y$ (Eq. 2-7)
   $A_{smin} = 0.2\sqrt{(40)}(400) (600) / (400) = 759$ mm^2
   $A_s = 5 (500) = 2500 > 759$ mm^2 OK

6. Check minimum bar spacing:

$s = [400 - 2\,(30) - 2\,(11.3) - 5\,(25.2)] / 4 = 48$ mm

From Table 2.6; $s \geq 1.4\,d_b = 1.4\,(25.2) = 35$ mm   OK
                        $s \geq 1.4\,a_{max} = 1.4\,(25) = 35$ mm   OK
                        $s \geq 30$ mm   OK

7. Check maximum bar spacing as governed by crack control:

Compute quantity "z" from Eq. 2-32 or Table 2.7: $z = f_s(d_c A)^{1/3}$

Note: For calculation of A and d_c clear cover need not be taken greater than 50 mm.

From Table 2.7; $y = h - d = 600 - 546 = 54$ mm;

$A = 2yb/5 = 2\,(54)\,(400) / 5 = 8640$ mm^2
$f_s = 0.6\,f_y = 0.6\,(400) = 240$ MPa; $d_c = 600 - 546 = 54$ mm
$z = 240\,(54 \times 8640)^{1/3} = 18\,614$ N/mm
$z = 18\,614$ N/mm $< 30\,000$ N/mm (interior exposure)   OK

8. Check if skin reinforcement is needed:

$h \leq 750$ mm no skin reinforcement is needed.

9. Final design: Use 5 – 25M bars as longitudinal tension reinforcement with 10M stirrups and 30 mm clear cover for the stirrup steel.

Example 2.3   Analysis of a Rectangular Beam with Tension and Compression Reinforcement

Calculate the flexural resistance of the beam shown in the figure using $f'_c = 30$ MPa and $f_y = 400$ MPa.

1. Compute moment resistance provided by steel couple, M'_r from Table 2.2 :

Note : Total moment resistance = $M_r + M'_r$

$\rho' = A'_s / bd = (2 \times 700) / (600 \times 330) = 0.0071$; $d'/d = 65 / 330 = 0.20$
From Table 2.2; $M'_r = K'_r\,bd^2 \times 10^{-6}$ kN·m, and for $\rho' = 0.71\%$,
$K'_r = 1.93$ MPa; $M'_r = 1.93\,(600)\,(330)^2 \times 10^{-6} = 126$ kN·m

Note: $M'_r = 126$ kN·m is found assuming that the compression steel is yielding. In this example the compression steel does not yield but develops a significant compressive stress as indicated in Section 2.2.4. The assumption of the yielding of compression steel in this example results in less than 1% difference in moment capacity. Where very high percentage of compression reinforcement is used, the designer may wish to verify this assumption and use the appropriate level of stress in the compression reinforcement.

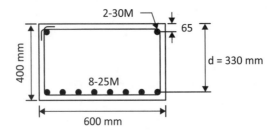

Example 2.3

2. Compute the moment resistance provided by tension reinforcement $(A_s - A'_s)$ from Table 2.1:

$\rho = (A_s - A'_s) / bd = (8 \times 500 - 2 \times 700) / (600) (330) = 0.0131$
From Table 2.1; $M_r = K_r bd^2 \times 10^{-6}$ kN·m, and for $\rho = 1.31$ %,
$K_r = 3.83$ MPa; $M_r = 3.83 (600) (330)^2 \times 10^{-6} = 250$ kN·m

3. Total moment resistance of section:

$M_r + M'_r = 250 + 126 = 376$ kN·m

Example 2.4   Design of a Rectangular Beam with Tension and Compression Reinforcement

Design the rectangular beam section shown in the figure for a factored moment of $M_f = 700$ kN·m using $f'_c = 30$ MPa, $f_y = 400$ MPa and maximum aggregate size = 25 mm. The beam is to be built as part of a parking structure located in Ottawa, with a limited cross-sectional size due to functional requirements.

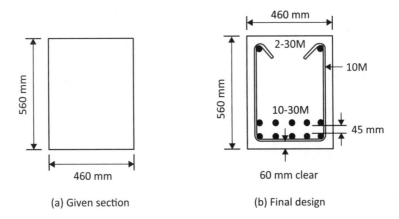

Example 2.4

1. Determine concrete cover for corrosive environment from Table 2.6:

    Select 60 mm clear cover to stirrups.

2. Estimate effective depth d assuming 30M bars for longitudinal reinforcement and 10M stirrups.

    $d = 560 - 60 - 11.3 - (29.9 / 2) = 474$ mm

3. Determine the required tension reinforcement from Table 2.1 :

   For design; $M_r \geq M_f = 700$ kN·m.
   For $M_r = 700$ kN·m; $K_r = M_r \times 10^6 / (bd^2) = 700 \times 10^6 / [(460)\,(474)^2] = 6.77$ MPa

   There is no ρ value given in Table 2.1 for $K_r = 6.77$ MPa indicating that the section can not be designed to behave in a ductile manner (under-reinforced) unless compression reinforcement is used. Try using compression reinforcement.

4. Determine the required compression reinforcement from Table 2.2:

   Provide maximum tension reinforcement given in Table 2.1.
   For $f'_c = 30$ MPa; select $\rho = 2.63$ %, and read corresponding $K_r = 6.4$ MPa

   Moment resistance provided by this reinforcement; $M_r = K_r\, bd^2 \times 10^{-6}$
   $M_r = 6.4\,(460)\,(474)^2 \times 10^{-6} = 661$ kN·m

   Remaining moment resistance to be provided by compression reinforcement;
   $M'_r = M_f - M_r = 700 - 661 = 39$ kN·m
   $K'_r = M'_r \times 10^6 / bd^2 = 39 \times 10^6 / (460)\,(474)^2 = 0.38$ MPa

   Compute d' based on assumed compression bar size of 15M;
   $d' = 60 + 11.3 + (16 / 2) = 79$ mm
   $d' / d = 79 / 474 = 0.17$; from Table 2.2; $\rho' = 0.14$ %
   $A'_s = \rho'\, bd = 0.0014\,(460)\,(474) = 305$ mm^2
   Use 2 – 15M with $A'_s = 400$ mm^2 and $d' = 79$ mm.

5. Determine required tension reinforcement:

   $\rho + \rho' = 2.63 + 0.14 = 2.77$; $A_s = 0.0277\,(460)\,(474) = 6040$ mm^2
   Use 9 – 30M bars with $A_s = 6300$ mm^2.

   Note: 9 – 30M bars can not be placed within $b = 460$ mm in a single row without violating the cover and/or minimum spacing limitations specified in Table 2.6. Therefore, use double layers of reinforcement and revise the design.

6. Revise d:

   Revise "d" based on double layers of 30M bars and 45 mm clear spacing between the two layers:
   $d = 560 - 60 - 11.3 - 29.9 - 45 / 2 = 436$ mm

   Note: More reinforcement will be needed since "d" is reduced.

7. Determine the required compression reinforcement from Table 2.2:

   Provide maximum tension reinforcement given in Table 2.1.
   For $f'_c = 30$ MPa; select $\rho = 2.63$ %, and read corresponding $K_r = 6.4$ MPa

   Moment resistance provided by this reinforcement; $M_r = K_r\, bd^2 \times 10^{-6}$
   $M_r = 6.4\,(460)\,(436)^2 \times 10^{-6} = 560$ kN·m

Remaining moment resistance to be provided by the compression reinforcement;

$M_r' = M_f - M_r = 700 - 560 = 140$ kN·m

$K_r' = M_r' \times 10^6 / bd^2 = 140 \times 10^6 / (460) (436)^2 = 1.60$ MPa

$d' / d = 79 / 436 = 0.18$; from Table 2.2 read $\rho' = 0.57$ %

$A_s' = \rho' bd = 0.0057 (460) (436) = 1143$ mm² (required)

Use 2 – 30M with $A_s' = 1400$ mm² (provided)

Note: The effect of the change in d' from 79 mm to 86 mm, because of the use of 30M top reinforcement instead of 15M initially assumed, is negligible and is compensated in the extra steel area provided.

8. Determine required tension reinforcement:

$\rho + \rho' = 2.63 + 0.57 = 3.20$; $A_s = 0.0320 (460) (436) = 6418$ mm²

Use 10 – 30M bars in two layers (5 – 30M in each layer), with $A_s = 7000$ mm²

9. Check spacing of tension reinforcement from Table 2.6:

$s = [460 - 2 (60) - 2 (11.3) - 5 (29.9)] / 4 = 42$ mm

42 mm $= 1.4 b_d = 1.4 (29.9) = 42$ mm

$> 1.4 a_{max} = 1.4 (25) = 35$ mm

> 30 mm

Note: This section is heavily reinforced in the tension region and hence is not likely to violate minimum steel and crack control requirements.

Final design is illustrated in the figure.

Example 2.5   Analysis of a T-Section in Positive Bending Behaving as a Rectangular Section

Compute positive bending resistance of the T-beams shown below using $f_c' = 40$ MPa and $f_y = 400$ MPa. The beams are continuous with a span length of 9.0 m.

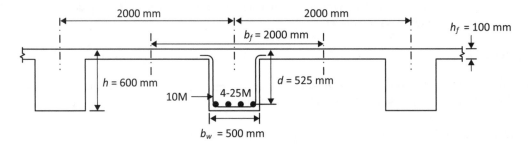

Example 2.5

1. Determine the effective flange width b_{eff} from Table 2.4:

Overhanging flange width $b_T' \leq 12 \, h_f = 12 (100) = 1200$ mm

$\leq \ell / 10 \ = 9000 / 10 = 900$ mm

$\leq x$ or $y = 750$ mm

$b_T' = 750$ mm governs. $b_{eff} = 2 (750) + (500) = 2000$ mm

2. Determine if the section behaves as a T-section:

Condition for T-section behaviour: Use either Eq. 2-23 or Eq. 2-24.
For T-section behaviour Eq 2-23 gives; $A_s > (\alpha_1 \phi_c f'_c h_f b_f) / (\phi_s f_y)$
α_1 can be obtained from Table 2.1
$A_s = 4\,(500) = 2000\ mm^2 < [(0.79)\,(0.65)\,(40)\,(100)\,(2000)] / [(0.85)\,(400)] = 12\,082\ mm^2$
Therefore, the section behaves as a rectangular section, $b = b_f$

Alternatively, for T-section behaviour from Eq. 2-24; $h_f < (A_s\,\phi_s\,f_y)/(\alpha_1\,\phi_c\,f'_c\,b_f)$
$h_f = 100 > [(2000)\,(0.85)\,(400)] / [(0.79)\,(0.65)\,(40)\,(2000)] = 17\ mm$
Hence, rectangular section behaviour.

3. Compute moment resistance M_r from Table 2.1:

$\rho = A_s / bd = 2000 / (2000 \times 525) = 0.0019$
From Table 2.1 for $\rho = 0.19$; $K_r = 0.63$ MPa

$M_r = K_r\,bd^2 \times 10^{-6} = 0.63\,(2000)\,(525)^2 \times 10^{-6} = 347\ kN\cdot m$

Example 2.6   Analysis of an L-Section in Positive Bending Behaving as a T-Section

Compute factored moment resistance M_r of the L-section shown in the figure using $f'_c = 30$ MPa and $f_y = 400$ MPa.

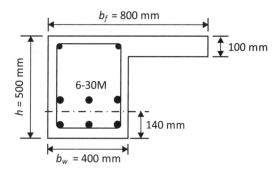

$b_f = 800$ mm

100 mm

$h = 500$ mm

6-30M

140 mm

$b_w = 400$ mm

Example 2.6

1. Determine if the section behaves as a T-section:

Condition for T-section behaviour from Eq. 2-24; $h_f < (A_s \phi_s f_y)/(\alpha_1 \phi_c f'_c b_f)$
$h_f = 100\ mm < (6 \times 700 \times 0.85 \times 400) / (0.81 \times 0.65 \times 30 \times 800) = 113\ mm$
Therefore, the section behaves as a T-section, and the moment resistance consists of two components; M_{rf} and M_{rw}.

2. Compute moment resistance provided by the overhanging flange, M_{rf}:

Determine ρ_f from Table 2.3: For $d/h_f = 360 / 100 = 3.6$ read $\rho_f = 1.31\ \%$
Determine K_{rf} from Table 2.1 using $\rho = \rho_f = 1.31\ \%$; $K_{rf} = 3.83$ MPa
$M_{rf} = K_{rf}\,(b_f - b_w)\,d^2 \times 10^{-6} = (3.83)\,(800 - 400)\,(360)^2 \times 10^{-6} = 199\ kN\cdot m$

3. Compute moment resistance provided by the web, M_{rw} :

$A_{sf} = \rho_f (b_f - b_w) d = 0.0131 \, (800 - 400) \, (360) = 1886$ mm^2
$A_{sw} = A_s - A_{sf} = 6 \times 700 - 1886 = 2314$ mm^2
$\rho_w = A_{sw} / b_w d = 2314 / (400 \times 360) = 0.0161 = 1.61$ %

Determine K_{rw} from Table 2.1 using $\rho = \rho_w = 1.61$ %; $K_{rw} = 4.52$ MPa
$M_{rw} = K_{rw} b_w d^2 \times 10^{-6} = (4.52) \, (400) \, (360)^2 \times 10^{-6} = 234$ kN·m

4. Total moment resistance, M_r :

$M_r = M_{rf} + M_{rw} = 199 + 234 = 433$ kN·m

Example 2.7   Design of a T-Section in Positive Bending

Design the T-section shown in the figure for a factored positive moment of $M_f = 1500$ kN·m considering $f'_c = 30$ MPa, $f_y = 400$ MPa, clear cover to stirrups = 40 mm, interior exposure condition and maximum aggregate size $a_{max} = 25$ mm.

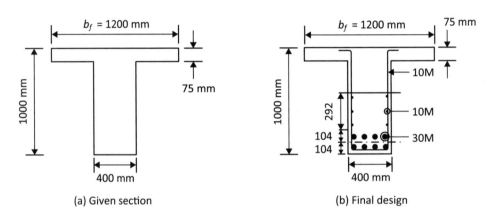

(a) Given section   (b) Final design

Example 2.7

1. Estimate the effective depth d, assuming two layers of 30M bars with 45 mm spacing between the layers, and 10M stirrups.

$d = 1000 - 40 - 11.3 - 29.9 - 45 / 2 = 896$ mm

2. Determine the reinforcement ratio ρ from Table 2.1 assuming rectangular section behaviour:

$M_r \geq M_f;$ $K_r = M_r \times 10^6 / bd^2 = (1500 \times 10^6) / (1200) \, (896)^2 = 1.56$ MPa
From Table 2.1 $\rho = 0.48$ %

3. Verify if the beam behaves as a rectangular section using Eq 2-23 :

$(\alpha_1 \phi_c f'_c h_f b_f)/(\phi_s f_y) = (0.81 \times 0.65 \times 30 \times 75 \times 1200) / (0.85 \times 400) = 4181$ mm^2
$A_s = \rho bd = 0.0048 \, (1200) \, (896) = 5161$ mm$^2 > 4181$ mm^2
Therefore, the section behaves as a T-section, and hence must be designed as a T-section.

4. Compute the area of tension steel A_{sf} associated with moment resistance of the overhangs from Table 2.3:

for $d/h_f = 896 / 75 = 11.9$; read $\rho_f = 0.39$ %
$A_{sf} = \rho_f (b_f - b_w)d = 0.0039 (1200 - 400) (896) = 2796$ mm^2

Moment resistance provided by $\rho_f = 0.0039$ from Table 2.1;
$K_{rf} = 1.27$ MPa; $M_{rf} = K_{rf} (b_f - b_w)d^2 \times 10^{-6} = 1.27 (1200 - 400) (896)^2 \times 10^{-6} = 816$ kN·m

5. Compute the area of tension steel A_{sw} associated with web resistance from Table 2.1 :

Moment resistance to be provided by web steel; $M_{rw} = M_f - M_f = 1500 - 816 = 684$ kN·m
$K_{rw} = M_{rw} \times 10^6 / b_w \, d^2 = (684 \times 10^6) / [(400) (896)^2] = 2.13$ MPa
From Table 2.1; $\rho_w = 0.68$ % $= 0.0068$; $A_{sw} = \rho_w \, b_w d = 0.0068 (400) (896) = 2437$ mm^2

6. Total tension steel:

$A_s = A_{sf} + A_{sw} = 2796 + 2437 = 5233$ mm^2
Use $8 - 30$M bars in two rows, with $A_s = 8 \times 700 = 5600$ mm^2

7. Check minimum spacing of reinforcement using Table 2.6:

$s = [400 - 2 (40) - 2 (11.3) - 4 (29.9)] / 3 = 59$ mm

From Table 2.6; $s \geq 1.4 \, d_b = 1.4 (29.9) = 42$ mm   OK
                    $s \geq 1.4 \, a_{max} = 1.4 (25) = 35$ mm   OK
                    $s \geq 30$ mm   OK

8. Check minimum reinforcement ratio:

Use Eq. 2-7; $A_{smin} = 0.2 \sqrt{f'_c} \, b_t \, h / f_y = 0.2 \sqrt{30} (400) (1000)/(400) = 1095$ mm^2
$A_s = 5600 > 1095$ mm^2 OK

9. Check maximum bar spacing as governed by crack control:

Compute quantity "z" from Eq. 2-32 or Table 2.7: $z = f_s (d_c A)^{1/3}$
Note: For calculation of A and d_c clear cover need not be taken greater than 50 mm. From Table 2.7;

$y = h - d = 1000 - 896 = 104$ mm;
$A = 2yb_w/8 = 2 (104) (400) / 8 = 10\,400$ mm^2;
$f_s = 0.6 f_y = 0.6 (400) = 240$ MPa;
$d_c = 40 + 11.3 + 29.9 / 2 = 66$ mm
$z = 240 (66 \times 10\,400)^{1/3} = 21\,171$ N/mm
$z = 21\,171$ N/mm $< 30\,000$ N/mm (interior exposure)   OK

10. Check if skin reinforcement is needed:

$h > 750$ mm. Therefore, skin reinforcement, as illustrated in Table 2.8 is needed. Area of skin reinforcement on each side;
$A_{sk} / 2 = 0.008 \, A_{cs} / 2 = 0.008 (2x)[(h/2) - 2 (h - d)]$
Assuming 10M bars will be used, $x = 40 + 11.3 + 11.3 / 2 = 57$ mm $\leq b_w / 4 = 100$ mm
$A_{sk} / 2 = (0.008) (2) (57)[(500 - 2 (1000 - 896)] = 266$ mm^2

Provide 3 – 10M bars along each side face, uniformly placed within distance $[(h/2) - 2(h - d)] = 500 - 2(1000 - 896) = 292$ mm. Note that the spacing of bars does not exceed the maximum value of 200 mm. Total $A_{sk} = 6(100) = 600$ mm^2 (for two side faces).

Note: The contribution of skin reinforcement to flexural resistance is ignored. Final design is illustrated in the figure.

Table 2.1 Reinforcement ratio ρ (%) for rectangular sections with tension reinforcement $f_y = 400$ MPa

2

Design for Flexure

$$M_r = K_r\,bd^2 \times 10^{-6}\ \text{kN·m};$$

$$K_r = \left[1 - \frac{\rho\,\phi_s f_y}{2\alpha_1\phi_c f_c'}\right]\rho\,\phi_s f_y\,;$$

$$\rho = \frac{A_s}{bd}$$

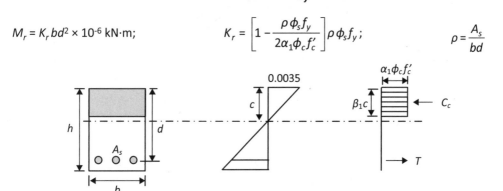

f_c' (MPa)	20	25	30	35	40	45	50	55	60
α_1 :	0.82	0.81	0.81	0.80	0.79	0.78	0.78	0.77	0.76
β_1 :	0.92	0.91	0.90	0.88	0.87	0.86	0.85	0.83	0.82
ρ_{bal} :	1.83	2.24	2.63	3.00	3.34	3.67	3.98	4.27	4.55
K_r					ρ (%)				
0.5	0.15	0.15	0.15	0.15	0.15	0.15	0.15	0.15	0.15
0.6	0.18	0.18	0.18	0.18	0.18	0.18	0.18	0.18	0.18
0.7	0.21	0.21	0.21	0.21	0.21	0.21	0.21	0.21	0.21
0.8	0.24	0.24	0.24	0.24	0.24	0.24	0.24	0.24	0.24
0.9	0.28	0.27	0.27	0.27	0.27	0.27	0.27	0.27	0.27
1.0	0.31	0.31	0.30	0.30	0.30	0.30	0.30	0.30	0.30
1.1	0.34	0.34	0.34	0.33	0.33	0.33	0.33	0.33	0.33
1.2	0.38	0.37	0.37	0.37	0.36	0.36	0.36	0.36	0.36
1.3	0.41	0.40	0.40	0.40	0.40	0.39	0.39	0.39	0.39
1.4	0.44	0.44	0.43	0.43	0.43	0.43	0.42	0.42	0.42
1.5	0.48	0.47	0.46	0.46	0.46	0.46	0.46	0.45	0.45
1.6	0.51	0.50	0.50	0.49	0.49	0.49	0.49	0.49	0.48
1.7	0.55	0.54	0.53	0.53	0.52	0.52	0.52	0.52	0.52
1.8	0.58	0.57	0.56	0.56	0.55	0.55	0.55	0.55	0.55
1.9	0.62	0.61	0.60	0.59	0.59	0.58	0.58	0.58	0.58

Table 2.1 (Cont'd)

f'_c (MPa)	20	25	30	35	40	45	50	55	60
K_r					ρ (%)				
2.0	0.66	0.64	0.63	0.62	0.62	0.62	0.61	0.61	0.61
2.1	0.69	0.68	0.67	0.66	0.65	0.65	0.65	0.64	0.64
2.2	0.73	0.71	0.70	0.69	0.69	0.68	0.68	0.68	0.67
2.3	0.77	0.75	0.73	0.73	0.72	0.71	0.71	0.71	0.70
2.4	0.81	0.79	0.77	0.76	0.75	0.75	0.74	0.74	0.74
2.5	0.85	0.82	0.81	0.79	0.79	0.78	0.78	0.77	0.77
2.6	0.89	0.86	0.84	0.83	0.82	0.81	0.81	0.80	0.80
2.7	0.93	0.90	0.88	0.86	0.85	0.85	0.84	0.84	0.83
2.8	0.98	0.94	0.91	0.90	0.89	0.88	0.88	0.87	0.87
2.9	1.02	0.98	0.95	0.93	0.92	0.92	0.91	0.90	0.90
3.0	1.06	1.02	0.99	0.97	0.96	0.95	0.94	0.94	0.93
3.1	1.11	1.06	1.03	1.01	0.99	0.98	0.98	0.97	0.97
3.2	1.15	1.10	1.06	1.04	1.03	1.02	1.01	1.00	1.00
3.3	1.20	1.14	1.10	1.08	1.06	1.05	1.04	1.04	1.03
3.4	1.25	1.18	1.14	1.12	1.10	1.09	1.08	1.07	1.07
3.5	1.30	1.22	1.18	1.15	1.14	1.12	1.11	1.11	1.10
3.6	1.35	1.26	1.22	1.19	1.17	1.16	1.15	1.14	1.13
3.7	1.40	1.31	1.26	1.23	1.21	1.19	1.18	1.17	1.17
3.8	1.46	1.35	1.30	1.27	1.25	1.23	1.22	1.21	1.20
3.9	1.51	1.40	1.34	1.31	1.28	1.27	1.25	1.24	1.23
4.0	1.57	1.45	1.38	1.35	1.32	1.30	1.29	1.28	1.27
4.1	1.63	1.49	1.43	1.39	1.36	1.34	1.32	1.31	1.30
4.2	1.69	1.54	1.47	1.43	1.40	1.38	1.36	1.35	1.34
4.3	1.76	1.59	1.51	1.47	1.44	1.41	1.40	1.38	1.37
4.4	1.83	1.64	1.56	1.51	1.47	1.45	1.43	1.42	1.41
4.5		1.69	1.60	1.55	1.51	1.49	1.47	1.45	1.44
4.6		1.75	1.65	1.59	1.55	1.53	1.51	1.49	1.48
4.7		1.80	1.69	1.63	1.59	1.56	1.54	1.53	1.51
4.8		1.85	1.74	1.67	1.63	1.60	1.58	1.56	1.55
4.9		1.91	1.79	1.72	1.67	1.64	1.62	1.60	1.59

Table 2.1 (Cont'd)

f'_c (MPa)	20	25	30	35	40	45	50	55	60
K_r					ρ (%)				
5.0		1.97	1.84	1.76	1.71	1.68	1.66	1.64	1.62
5.1		2.03	1.88	1.81	1.75	1.72	1.69	1.67	1.66
5.2		2.09	1.93	1.85	1.80	1.76	1.73	1.71	1.69
5.3		2.16	1.99	1.90	1.84	1.80	1.77	1.75	1.73
5.4		2.23	2.04	1.94	1.88	1.84	1.81	1.79	1.77
5.5			2.09	1.99	1.92	1.88	1.85	1.82	1.80
5.6			2.15	2.04	1.97	1.92	1.89	1.86	1.84
5.7			2.20	2.08	2.01	1.96	1.93	1.90	1.88
5.8			2.26	2.13	2.06	2.00	1.97	1.94	1.92
5.9			2.32	2.18	2.10	2.05	2.01	1.98	1.95
6.0			2.38	2.23	2.15	2.09	2.05	2.02	1.99
6.1			2.44	2.28	2.19	2.13	2.09	2.06	2.03
6.2			2.50	2.33	2.24	2.17	2.13	2.10	2.07
6.3			2.57	2.39	2.29	2.22	2.17	2.14	2.11
6.4			2.63	2.44	2.33	2.26	2.21	2.18	2.15
6.5				2.50	2.38	2.31	2.25	2.22	2.19
6.6				2.55	2.43	2.35	2.30	2.26	2.23
6.7				2.61	2.48	2.40	2.34	2.30	2.26
6.8				2.67	2.53	2.44	2.38	2.34	2.30
6.9				2.73	2.58	2.49	2.43	2.38	2.34
7.0				2.79	2.63	2.54	2.47	2.42	2.39
7.1				2.85	2.68	2.58	2.52	2.46	2.43
7.2				2.91	2.74	2.63	2.56	2.51	2.47
7.3				2.98	2.79	2.68	2.61	2.55	2.51
7.4					2.85	2.73	2.65	2.59	2.55
7.5					2.90	2.78	2.70	2.64	2.59
7.6					2.96	2.83	2.74	2.68	2.63
7.7					3.02	2.88	2.79	2.72	2.68
7.8					3.08	2.93	2.84	2.77	2.72
7.9					3.14	2.99	2.89	2.81	2.76

2

Design for Flexure

Table 2.1 (Cont'd)

f_c' (MPa)	20	25	30	35	40	45	50	55	60
K_r					ρ (%)				
8.0					3.20	3.04	2.93	2.86	2.80
8.1					3.26	3.09	2.98	2.91	2.85
8.2					3.33	3.15	3.03	2.95	2.89
8.3						3.20	3.08	3.00	2.94
8.4						3.26	3.13	3.05	2.98
8.5						3.32	3.18	3.09	3.02
8.6						3.38	3.24	3.14	3.07
8.7						3.44	3.29	3.19	3.12
8.8						3.50	3.34	3.24	3.16
8.9						3.56	3.40	3.29	3.21
9.0						3.62	3.45	3.34	3.25
9.1							3.51	3.39	3.30
9.2							3.56	3.44	3.35
9.3							3.62	3.49	3.40
9.4							3.68	3.54	3.45
9.5							3.74	3.59	3.49
9.6							3.80	3.65	3.54
9.7							3.86	3.70	3.59
9.8							3.92	3.76	3.64
9.9							3.98	3.81	3.69
10.0								3.87	3.75
10.5								4.16	4.01
11.0									4.29

Table 2.2 Compression reinforcement ratio ρ' (%); f_y = 400 MPa

$$M'_r = K'_r bd^2 \times 10^{-6} \text{ kN·m};$$

$$K'_r = \left[1 - \frac{d'}{d}\right] \rho' \phi_s f'_y$$

$$\rho = \frac{A'_s}{bd}$$

d'/d:	0.05	0.10	0.15	0.20	0.25
K'_r			ρ' (%)		
0.20	0.06	0.07	0.07	0.07	0.08
0.40	0.12	0.13	0.14	0.15	0.16
0.60	0.19	0.20	0.21	0.22	0.24
0.80	0.25	0.26	0.28	0.29	0.31
1.00	0.31	0.33	0.35	0.37	0.39
1.20	0.37	0.39	0.42	0.44	0.47
1.40	0.43	0.46	0.48	0.51	0.55
1.60	0.50	0.52	0.55	0.59	0.63
1.80	0.56	0.59	0.62	0.66	0.71
2.00	0.62	0.65	0.69	0.74	0.78
2.20	0.68	0.72	0.76	0.81	0.86
2.40	0.74	0.78	0.83	0.88	0.94
2.60	0.80	0.85	0.90	0.96	1.02
2.80	0.87	0.92	0.97	1.03	1.10
3.00	0.93	0.98	1.04	1.10	1.18
3.20	0.99	1.05	1.11	1.18	1.25
3.40	1.05	1.11	1.18	1.25	1.33
3.60	1.11	1.18	1.25	1.32	1.41
3.80	1.18	1.24	1.31	1.40	1.49
4.00	1.24	1.31	1.38	1.47	1.57

Table 2.3 Reinforcement ratio, ρ_f (%) that balances concrete in overhang(s) of T or L beams; f_y = 400 MPa

$$\rho_f = \frac{\alpha_1 \phi_c f'_c h_f}{\phi_s f_y d} \qquad M_{rf} = \rho_f (b_f - b_w) d \phi_s f_y \left(d - \frac{h_f}{2}\right) \quad \text{or;}$$

$$M_{rf} = K_{rf}(b_f - b_w)d^2 \times 10^{-6} \text{ kN·m} \; (K_{rf} \text{ to be obtained from Table 2.1})$$

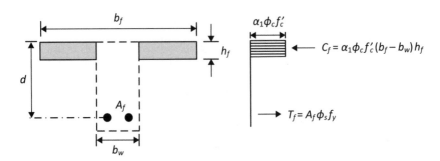

f'_c (MPa)	20	25	30	35	40	45	50	55	60
d/h_f					ρ_f (%)				
3.00	1.05	1.29	1.54	1.78	2.01	2.24	2.47	2.69	2.91
4.00	0.78	0.97	1.15	1.33	1.51	1.68	1.85	2.02	2.18
5.00	0.63	0.78	0.92	1.07	1.21	1.35	1.48	1.61	1.74
6.00	0.52	0.65	0.77	0.89	1.01	1.12	1.23	1.35	1.45
7.00	0.45	0.55	0.66	0.76	0.86	0.96	1.06	1.15	1.25
8.00	0.39	0.49	0.58	0.67	0.76	0.84	0.93	1.01	1.09
9.00	0.35	0.43	0.51	0.59	0.67	0.75	0.82	0.90	0.97
10.00	0.31	0.39	0.46	0.53	0.60	0.67	0.74	0.81	0.87
11.00	0.29	0.35	0.42	0.49	0.55	0.61	0.67	0.73	0.79
12.00	0.26	0.32	0.38	0.44	0.50	0.56	0.62	0.67	0.73
13.00	0.24	0.30	0.36	0.41	0.46	0.52	0.57	0.62	0.67
14.00	0.22	0.28	0.33	0.38	0.43	0.48	0.53	0.58	0.62
15.00	0.21	0.26	0.31	0.36	0.40	0.45	0.49	0.54	0.58

Table 2.4 Effective flange width in T and L-sections

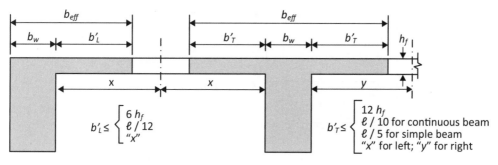

$$b'_L \leq \begin{cases} 6\,h_f \\ \ell\,/\,12 \\ \text{``}x\text{''} \end{cases}$$

$$b'_T \leq \begin{cases} 12\,h_f \\ \ell\,/\,10 \text{ for continuous beam} \\ \ell\,/\,5 \text{ for simple beam} \\ \text{``}x\text{'' for left; ``}y\text{'' for right} \end{cases}$$

where ℓ is the beam span length

Table 2.5 Concrete joist construction

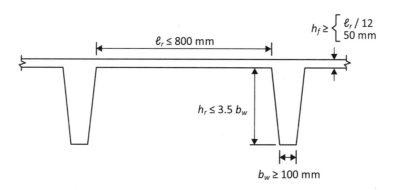

$$h_f \geq \begin{cases} \ell_r\,/\,12 \\ 50 \text{ mm} \end{cases}$$

$\ell_r \leq 800$ mm

$h_r \leq 3.5\,b_w$

$b_w \geq 100$ mm

Table 2.6 Spacing and cover requirements for beam reinforcement

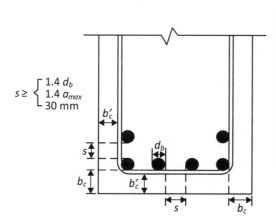

$$s \geq \begin{cases} 1.4\,d_b \\ 1.4\,a_{max} \\ 30 \text{ mm} \end{cases}$$

a_{max} = max. aggregate size

	Minimum cover (b_c or b'_c)		
Exposure[1]	Not Exposed[2]	Exposed[3]	Exposed[4]
Beams and girders	30 mm 1.0 d_b 1.0 a_{max}	40 mm 1.5 d_b 1.5 a_{max}	60 mm 2.0 d_b 2.0 a_{max}
Slabs	20 mm 1.0 d_b 1.0 a_{max}	40 mm 1.5 d_b 1.5 a_{max}	60 mm 2.0 d_b 2.0 a_{max}

[1] See CSA A23.1 for detailed description of exposure conditions.

[2] Concrete remaining dry within the vapour barrier of the building envelope.

[3] Concrete exposed to freeze-thaw cycles and/or sulphate.

[4] Concrete exposed to chlorides or; manure and/or silage gases and liquids. Increase to 75 mm if permanently exposed to earth.

Table 2.7 Crack control requirement

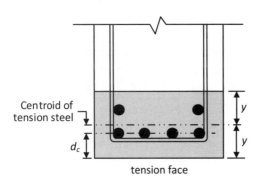

$$z = f_s \, (d_c A)^{1/3}$$

$$A = \frac{\text{shaded area}}{\text{number of bars}}$$

f_s may be taken as $0.6 \, f_y$

In calculating d_c and A, the clear cover need not be taken greater than 50 mm.

$$z \leq \begin{cases} 25\,000 \text{ N/m (exposed)} \\ 30\,000 \text{ N/m (not exposed)} \end{cases}$$

For epoxy coated bars, multiply the permissible "z" by 1.2.

Centroid of tension steel

tension face

Table 2.8 Skin reinforcement

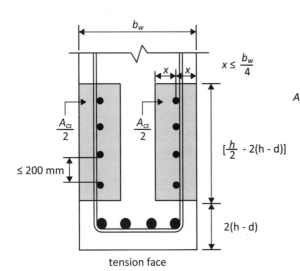

$$x \leq \frac{b_w}{4}$$

$$\left[\frac{h}{2} - 2(h - d)\right]$$

$$2(h - d)$$

≤ 200 mm

tension face

$$\text{Area of skin reinforcement in each strip when } h > 750 = \begin{cases} 0.008 \dfrac{A_{cs}}{2} & \text{for interior exposure} \\ 0.010 \dfrac{A_{cs}}{2} & \text{for exterior exposure} \end{cases}$$

A_{cs} : total shaded area

Table 2.9 Tension reinforcement in overhangs

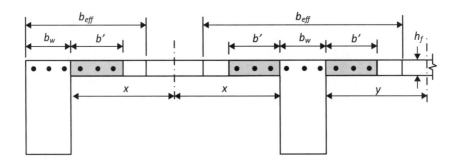

$$b' \leq \begin{cases} 12 \, h_f \text{ for T-section, 6 for L-section} \\ \ell \,/\, 20 \\ \text{"}x\text{" or "}y\text{", whichever is applicable} \end{cases}$$

ℓ = beam span length

Area of flange steel within width $b' \geq 0.004 \, b'h_f$

3

By Robert E. Loov
Tel Rezansoff

Development and Splices of Reinforcement

3.1   Introduction

A strength related failure should not occur at an anchorage or a splice, just as connections in steel construction, and joint details or shear and torsion resistance in concrete construction should not be the weak link when ensuring adequate strength and ductility. Development and splice lengths are intended to have sufficient over-strength to decrease the probability of a bond related failure before failure occurs in a more ductile flexure mode.

For small concrete covers and deformed reinforcement, failures in development or lap splices occur when the concrete confining the reinforcement splits away. This is due to the radial bursting component of the bearing force between reinforcement deformations and the surrounding concrete in straight bar anchorages, and additional lateral bursting forces imposed on the concrete with hooked anchorages or the cross wires in welded wire reinforcement. In flexure, prying of the reinforcement on the confining concrete also occurs because of beam curvature, and dowel action at transverse crack locations.

A bond splitting failure can be prevented by providing sufficient confinement to the reinforcement along its anchorage length using a combination of concrete confinement and confinement provided by stirrups, ties and spirals that intercept bond splitting cracks. Features that improve confinement, such as the restraint provided to bars from adjoining members framing into a common joint, or to stirrup hooks from a slab placed integrally with a beam, require careful attention to detail and construction to ensure realization of the expected strength. Care is also needed to ensure that the hooks used in transverse reinforcement provide positive confinement to the longitudinal bars.

As in previous CSA A23.3 Standards, design for development uses empirical equations with full (unfactored) specified material strengths. The coefficients used in the equations are chosen to provide the required factor of safety without the use of the material factors ϕ_c and ϕ_s.

The requirements for development and splicing of reinforcement are unchanged from A23.3-04.

3.2   Development Tension

3.2.1.   General

(a) Detailed approach
Equation (12-1) in Clause 12.2.2 accounts for factors that affect the tension development length of deformed bars or wire or deformed welded wire reinforcement. The benefit of concrete confinement provided by cover and bar spacing, and transverse tie and stirrup reinforcement placed to intercept potential bond splitting cracks, is explicitly included. There is a limit to the total confinement that is effective. Bond failure changes from splitting of the confining concrete, to a pullout failure with crushing of the concrete in front of the reinforcement deformations in a heavily confined anchorage. The total confinement provided by concrete and transverse reinforcement up to an equivalent 2.5 bar diameters of concrete cover, is considered to be effective in preventing splitting bond failures. Additional confinement does not increase pullout strength.

Epoxy coating, used as corrosion protection for reinforcement, has a detrimental influence on bond development. A coating modification factor k_2, is required by Clause 12.2.4 to increase anchorage length when bars are epoxy coated. The reduction in bond resistance is particularly severe when smaller concrete cover and bar spacing is used.

The applicability of the empirical equations used for anchorage of reinforcement in high performance concretes has not been adequately investigated. The maximum concrete compressive strength that is permitted for calculating bond strength is therefore limited to

$f'_c = 64$ MPa ($\sqrt{f'_c} \leq 8$ MPa in Clause 12.1.2).

3

For development of deformed welded wire reinforcement in tension, the ℓ_d calculated for deformed wires by Clause 12.2 is modified by factors from Clause 12.7.2 that recognize the anchorage provided by the cross wires.

If heavier confinement is available, the use of Equation (12-1) may be justified to reduce anchorage lengths. Using design aids, only a little extra design effort is needed to apply this detailed approach.

(b) Simple approach
As an alternate to the direct calculation and inclusion of the confinement available to an anchorage carrying tension, Table 12-1 permits a simpler approach for obtaining ℓ_d when the minimum concrete cover of d_b and principal reinforcement clear spacing of $1.4d_b$ are provided. These are the minimum values specified in CSA Standard A23.1-14 (see Annex A of A23.3).Two coefficients are provided in Table 12-1, depending on the confinement available.

3.2.2.   Design Aids

Design aids, in the form of tables and figures, are provided at the end of Chapter 3.

(a) Simple approach – Table 12-1
Table 3.1 provides development lengths for 400 MPa standard deformed reinforcing bars while Table 3.11 provides development lengths for Grade 515 deformed wire when heavier confinement exists. The factor k_4 for bar size is included in both tables. The development length must be multiplied by the appropriate values of k_1, k_2, and k_3. For lighter confinement, satisfying "Other cases" in Table 12-1, lengths in Tables 3.1 and 3.11 are multiplied by 1.33. After applicable factors are applied, the development length must not be less than 300 mm, except when used to calculate tension lap splice lengths.

(b) Detailed approach – Equation (12-1)
Table 3.2 provides development lengths for deformed reinforcing bars made of Grade 400 steel based on a confinement index "C.I." which is the sum of the non-dimensionalized confinements provided by the concrete, d_{cs}/d_b as obtained from Tables 3.3(a), (b) & (c), and by the transverse reinforcement K_{tr}/d_b obtained from Table 3.5.

Tables 3.3(a), (b), and (c) (as well as Tables 3.4(a), (b), and (c)) have been revised slightly to recognize that the bars adjacent to the vertical part of the stirrups slide down till they lie on the horizontal part of the stirrup. For a 10M stirrup bent around a 4 d_b pin this point is located 20 mm from the inside vertical face of the stirrup. Thus any bar with a diameter less than 40 mm will shift toward the centre. The reduced width available for the bars is b_w - 2(c+20), where c is the cover to the inside face of the stirrup.

(c) Welded wire reinforcement
Development lengths for common sizes of deformed and smooth welded wire reinforcement (WWR) are given in Tables 3.12 and 3.13 respectively.

3.2.3.   Design Examples

A simple example using deformed welded wire reinforcement is given in Example 3.5.

3.3   Standard Hooks in Tension

3.3.1.   General

The development length of a standard hook is the total length of the hook plus the straight lead-in distance required up to the critical section to develop the full specified yield strength of the reinforcing bar. The basic hook development length ℓ_{hb} before multiplying by applicable modification factors is given by the equation in Clause 12.5.2 for Grade 400 reinforcement. Epoxy coated standard hooks in tension have a single penalty factor of 1.2. (Clause 12.5.3(f))

Minimum bend diameters for standard hooks (Clause 6.6.2 and Table 16 of Annex A), recognize the better ductility available with weldable grade reinforcing bars.

3.3.2.   Design Aids

Basic hook development lengths ℓ_{hb} for standard deformed bars are shown in Table 3.6 for f_y = 400 MPa. The dimensions of the hook to satisfy CSA Standard A23.1-14, as excerpted in Annex A of CSA A23.3, are illustrated in Table 3.7.

Heavy confinement is necessary for hook development since large bursting and splitting forces are imposed by the hook into the concrete over a relatively short distance. For standard hooks at the ends of members, either the side cover, or the top or bottom cover over the hook must be used to enclose the hook as specified in Clause 12.5.4. Illustrations explaining the hook confinement required by Clause 12.5.4 are shown in Figure 3.1. The use of extra reinforcement, larger covers, and larger covers coupled with enclosure within ties or stirrups permit the use of modifiers which reduce the required hook development length. Factors that may be applied when good confinement is provided are shown in Figure 3.1.

The development length ℓ_{dh} is obtained by multiplying the basic hook development length ℓ_{hb} by modifying factors for structural low-density concrete, for epoxy-coated reinforcement and for f_y > 400 MPa. The 1.3 factor required for straight "top" horizontal reinforcement is not required as a modifier for hook development lengths.

3.4   Tension Lap Splices

3.4.1.   General

Tension lap splice lengths governed by Clause 12.15, are calculated by multiplying the development length by a splice "Class" factor which considers the excess bar area provided at the location of the splice, and the percentage of the bars spliced at the same location. The largest required lap is a Class B splice with a factor of 1.3 when more than 50% of the bars are spliced at the same location or the reinforcing area provided at the splice location is less than twice the required area (Clause 12.15.2 and 12.17.3.2.)

3.4.2.   Design Aids

Splice lengths, which are multiplied by the Class factor to give the lap length for deformed bars and wire in tension, are obtained in the same fashion as outlined in Sections 3.2.2 (a) & (b). The only difference is that for the "Detailed Approach" using Equation (12-1); Tables 3.4, rather than Tables 3.3, are used to obtain the confinement index provided by the concrete, where the extra beam width needed by the contacting spliced bars along the lap is accounted for. The reduction in development length based on excess reinforcement (Clause 12.2.5) is not used for calculating splice lengths, nor is the minimum development length of 300 mm specified in Clause 12.2.1. However, after application of the Class factor, Clause 12.15.1 requires a lap length of at least 300 mm.

Tensile lap splice lengths for welded wire reinforcement are obtained by using Tables 3.12 and 3.13, based on Clauses 12.18 & 12.19, as defined in Figures N12.18 and N12.19.

3.5   Development of Shear Reinforcement and Ties

The ends of deformed bar and wire stirrup legs must be anchored around longitudinal reinforcement using 135° hooks as specified in Clauses 12.13 & 7.1.2, unless a pair of stirrups, meeting the requirements of Clause 12.13.5 for lap splicing of straight legs (no hooks) is placed to form a single closed unit. A 90° hook is permitted if the concrete cover over the hook is restrained against spalling (Clause 7.1.2). Stirrups and ties made of 15M and smaller diameter deformed bars and wire are considered to be fully anchored by a standard stirrup or tie hook around longitudinal reinforcement, with no requirement for a straight lead-in length. In stirrups and ties made with smaller bars and wire, requirements are specified separately for 90° and 135° hooks (Annex A, Clause 6.6.2.4 of A23.1).

Stirrups and ties made with 20M and 25M bars require a minimum lead-in distance of $0.33 \, \ell_d$ measured from mid depth of the member as specified in Clause 12.13.2 (b) and illustrated in Figure N12.13.2. Minimum bends in stirrups and ties made with 20M and 25M bars are the same as standard hooks (Clauses 7.1.2 & 12.13.2(b)).

Hooked ends are not required on stirrups made with smooth welded wire reinforcement if the cross-wires of the reinforcement, running in the longitudinal direction of the member, meet the spacing and location requirements of Clauses 12.13.2 (c) & (d) as illustrated in Figure N12.13.2(c). The provision for single leg stirrups Clause 12.13.2 (d) also applies to deformed welded wire reinforcement.

Between anchored ends, each bend in the continuous portion of a stirrup must enclose a longitudinal bar (Clause 12.13.3).

Ties in columns may use a 90° hook if $f'_c \le 50$ MPa. (Clause 7.1.2) The required spacing of ties in concrete with compressive strength exceeding 50 MPa is 0.75 of the values specified for lower strength concrete (Clause 7.6.5.2).

For cross ties (Clause 7.1.3), at least one end must have a bend of at least 135°, while the other end can have a 90° hook to facilitate placing. The position of the 90° hook between successive cross ties must alternate to provide an average confinement to each longitudinal bar on the basis of alternating 135° hooks and the less effective 90° hooks.

3.5.1.   Design Aids

The overall depth h that is required to provide the necessary straight embedment, in addition to the hook anchorage at the ends of 20M and 25M stirrup legs (Clause 12.13.2(b)) is given in Table 3.8. Illustrations showing the anchorages necessary for web reinforcement are given in Figures N12.13.2, N12.13.2 (c), and N12.13.5.

3.6   Development in Compression

Development of deformed bars in compression is assisted by the end bearing of the bar on the concrete. The development length is also reduced because the bond is not weakened by the transverse flexural tensile cracking that occurs in tensile development zones. Compression reinforcement must be confined inside spirals or ties in compression members (Clauses 7.6.4 & 7.6.5); and inside stirrups or ties for beams and girders (Clause 7.6.6). Modifiers for excess reinforcement area and for enclosure within a spiral or within closely spaced ties can be used to reduce the required development length (Clause 12.3.3).

The modified development length cannot be less than 200 mm (Clause 12.3.1) and hooks cannot be used for compression development (Clause 12.5.5).

3.6.1.   Design Aids

Compression development lengths for standard deformed reinforcing bars are provided in Table 3.9.

3.7   Compression Lap Splices

Compression lap splicing of 45M and 55M bars is prohibited, unless these bars are lapped with 35M or smaller bars (Clauses 12.14.2.1, 12.16.2, & 15.9.2.4). Modification factors for reducing the usual lap length apply for the improved confinement provided by special ties and spirals (Clauses 12.17.3.4 & 5, and Fig N12.17.3.4).

3.7.1.   Splices in Columns

All columns are designed as beam-columns because some loading conditions may produce tension in column reinforcement, so the reinforcement in each face of a column is required to develop a minimum tensile resistance. It may be possible to achieve sufficient tensile resistance at splice locations by staggering compression butt (end bearing) splices so that some reinforcement is continuous to develop tension. Alternately, compression lap splices may be sufficient to develop the required tensile resistance. Otherwise, tensile splicing is necessary. The tensile resistance requirements for column reinforcement are defined in Clause 12.17 and are illustrated in Figure 3.2.

3.8   Bundled Bars

Bundled bars may be used in columns and beams so that reinforcement can be fit into limited space. The details of bundled bar requirements are covered in Clause 7.4.2. Clause 12.4 covers development and Clause 12.14.2.2 deals with lap splicing. Bars may be bundled in groups of 2, 3 or 4 bars, with no more than two bars in any one plane. For spacing and cover (including crack control requirements), the unit of bundled bars is treated as a single bar with a diameter that provides the same area as all the bars in the bundle.

3.8.1.   Bundled Bars in Beams

Only bars 35M and smaller may be bundled in beams and girders (Clause 7.4.2.2). A typical flexural design utilizing bundled bars, where individual bars in the bundle are terminated with reducing moment, is illustrated in Figure 3.3. Clause 7.4.2.3 requires the cutoff locations of individual bars to be staggered. Clause 12.4 requires a 33% increase in development length for an individual bar in a 4-bar bundle, a 20% increase in a 3-bar bundle, and a 10% increase for a 2-bar bundle. Therefore, to achieve the design yield strength, bar 1 requires a tensile development length of $1.33\ell_d$, where ℓ_d is the single bar development length from Table 3.1 or Table 3.2. Similarly, bar 2 requires a development length of $1.2\,\ell_d$.

Clause 12.4 of A23.3 addresses only the development of an individual bar in a bundle, and does not specify requirements for the simultaneous development of more than one bar in a bundle. The two bars of each bundle that extend into the support in Figure 3.3 require a development length based on the size of an equivalent bar with the same area as the two actual bars, if the recommendations of

ACI Committee 408, 1979 report (References, Chapter 12, Citation 12.1) are followed. Clause 11.3.9.5 requires that the terminating tensile reinforcement be capable of developing a substantial tensile resistance at the inside face of the support bearing area.

3.8.2. Splicing of Bundled Bars

For tension and compression lap splicing of individual bars in a bundle, Clause12.14.2.2 requires that there be no overlap of the individual bar splices. This requires the cutoff points of the individual bars to be staggered if the full strength is to be developed. The intent of Clause 12.14.2.2 is illustrated in Figure 3.4(a) where the full strength splicing of a two bar bundle is achieved through the introduction of a separate "splice bar," to produce a 3 bar bundle along the total staggered splice length. In any splice length region (A to B, B to C or C to D), load transfer occurs between only two bars, thereby meeting the requirement that "individual bar splices within a bundle shall not overlap."

Bundled bar arrangements in columns, and the tensile resistances that can be developed with full strength compressive butt splices (end bearing or compression mechanical device), are summarized in Figure 3.4(b). In many columns, the required tensile resistance is only a fraction of the compressive strength of the reinforcement (Clause 12.17) as illustrated in Figure 3.2. Full mechanical connection for tension or welding can be used if a larger tensile resistance is necessary with unstaggered splices.

3.9 Development of Cut Off and Continuing Reinforcement

Clause 11.3.9.5 is intended to ensure that sufficient tensile force can be developed in tensile reinforcement that extends into a simple support, an exterior support of a continuous span, or near the free end of a cantilever supporting a concentrated load, where termination of the member does not permit reinforcement to be extended into a "continuing" span. Diagonal flexural-shear cracking increases the tensile force in the longitudinal reinforcement above that predicted on the basis of bending alone, and the horizontal component of the compressive strut force that must be picked up by the longitudinal bars must be capable of being developed through sufficient anchorage beyond the inside face of the bearing area.

Figure N12.11.3 illustrates the embedment requirements necessary to limit flexural bond stresses in positive moment tension reinforcement at locations where moment is rapidly increasing (high shears), as required by Clause 12.11.3. This requirement applies to points of zero moment, i.e.; the supports of simply supported beams and the points of inflection in continuous construction. The flexural bond provision, however, is waived by Clause 12.11.3 if the positive moment reinforcement terminates in a standard hook or equivalent mechanical anchorage that provides full development beyond the centerline of the simple support.

It may be economical to reduce the total flexural reinforcing steel provided in slabs, beams and girders by using different lengths of bars so that the flexural resistance, M_r, provided follows the factored moments, M_f, applied. For beams and girders, Figures N12.10.3, N12.12 & N12.13.4 provide an overview of the embedment requirements to be satisfied for cutoff and continuing reinforcement to ensure development of the bars required at critical sections.

For flat plates and slabs, Clause13.10.8 and Figure 13.1 provide a guide for choosing bar lengths and cutoff locations. To ensure integrity against progressive collapse, a minimum area of bottom flexural reinforcement must be effectively continuous through the column or support as specified in Clause 13.10.6.

Whether web reinforcement is designed by the "Simple Method" of Clause 11.3.6.3 or the "General Method" of Clause 11.3.6.4, the build-up of force in the flexural reinforcement must include the affect of shear as specified in Clause 11.3.9 and illustrated in Figure N12.10.3.

3.9.1. Design Examples

Examples 3.3 and 3.4 illustrate the design for cut off and continuing reinforcement to ensure adequate development of the reinforcement when web reinforcement is designed by the "Simplified Method" of Clause 11.3.6.3.

3.10   Design Examples and Design Aids

Design Examples 3.1 through 3.5 presented on the following pages utilize several of the design aids (Tables 3.1 through 3.13 located at the end of Chapter 3).

Example 3.1:   Hooked Anchorage
Design negative moment reinforcement for the 150 mm slab and check anchorage into the 200 mm wall for:

A. $M_f(neg)$ = 25 kN·m per m of slab width using normal density concrete.

B. $M_f(neg)$ = 20 kN·m per m of slab width using structural low-density concrete.

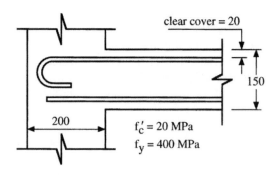

Figure Ex. 3.1 Hooked anchorages

Solution and comments:

A. M_f (neg) = 25 kN·m/m   normal density concrete

Assume 10M bars d = 150 − 20 − 10/2 = 125 mm

$$K_r = \frac{M_f}{bd^2} = 25 \times 10^6/(1000(125^2)) = 1.60 \text{ MPa}$$

ρ = 0.51%   Table 2.1

$s \le A_b/(\rho d)$ = 100/(0.0051(125)) = 157 mm   use s = 150 mm

Anchorage:

ℓ_{hb}(10M) = 220 mm for f_y = 400 MPa and f'_c = 20 MPa   Table 3.6

Modifiers: Large cover (because hook is embedded in wall)   0.7   Clause 12.5.3(b)
$\ell_{dh} = \ell_{hb}(0.7) = 220(0.7) = 154$ mm

Minimum hook length   Clause 12.5.1
$\ell_{dh} \geq 0.8d_b = 8(10) = 80$ mm
$\ell_{dh} \geq 150$ mm

Embedment available = 200 – 20 = 180 mm if the cover to the face of the wall is also 20 mm.
180 mm > 154 mm   therefore O.K.

B. $M_f(neg)$ =20 kN·m/m using structural low-density concrete.

$$K_r = \frac{M_f}{bd^2} = 20\times10^6/(1000(125^2)) = 1.28 \text{ MPa}$$

$\rho = 0.38 + 0.8(0.41 - 0.38) = 0.40\% = 0.004$ Interpolate in Table 2.1

$s = A_b/(\rho d) = 100/(0.004(125)) = 200$ mm   try s = 200 mm

Anchorage:
ℓ_{hb}(10M) = 220 mm for f_y = 400 MPa and f'_c = 20 MPa   Table 3.6

Modifiers: Large cover (because hook is embedded in wall)   0.7   Clause 12.5.3(b)
Structural low-density concrete   1.3   Clause 12.5.3(e)

$\ell_{dh} = \ell_{hb}(0.7)(1.3) = 220(0.7)(1.3) = 200$ mm
200 mm > 180 mm   Therefore N.G.

The anchorage for the hook would be satisfactory if the area of steel provided were greater than
the area required.   Clause 12.5.3(d)

Reduce spacing $s = 200(180/200) = 180$ mm   Use s = 180 mm

Example 3.2: Tensile Lap Splices

The beam section illustrated has $b \times h = 400 \times 600$ mm, is made of normal density concrete with
f'_c = 25 MPa, and uses uncoated, grade 400 deformed reinforcement. The effective depth, d, is 545 mm.
All three 30M bars are lap spliced in the same high stress region. 10M stirrups spaced at 200 mm
confine the lap length. Compare the required lap length for the simple approach using Table 12-1 with
the detailed approach using Clause 12.2.2.

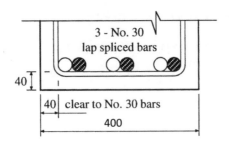

Figure Ex. 3.2 Tensile lap splices

A. Simple approach

Table 12-1 and Table 3.1
Check bar spacing and cover
For clear cover = 40 mm to 30M bars, and b_w = 400 mm, a maximum of 3 pairs of contact spliced
30M bars can be placed with clear spacing ≥1.4d_b and 30 mm   Table 3.4(a)

To use 0.45 coefficient, check for minimum stirrups by Equation 11-1 in Clause 11.2.8.2

$$s \leq \frac{A_v f_y}{0.06\sqrt{f'_c}\, b_w} = \frac{2(100)(400)}{0.06\sqrt{25}(400)} = 667 \text{ mm}$$ Equation 11-1

200 mm < 667 mm   O.K.
∴ Use the 0.45 coefficient in the equation for ℓ_d

ℓ_d = 1080 mm   Table 3.1
All bars spliced at same location therefore use a class B splice.   Clause 12.15.2
ℓ_s = 1.3 ℓ_d = 1.3(1080) = 1404 mm   use 1410 mm

B. Detailed approach

Total confinement index $C.I. = \dfrac{d_{cs}}{d_b} + \dfrac{K_{tr}}{d_b} = 1.83 + 0.85\left(\dfrac{100}{200}\right) = 2.26$ Tables 3.4(a) and 3.5

$$\ell_d = 980 + \frac{2.26 - 2.20}{2.5 - 2.2}(860 - 980) = 956 \text{ mm}$$ Interpolate in Table 3.2

For a class B splice ℓ_s = 1.3(956) = 1243 mm   Use 1250 mm

In this example, the detailed approach results in a splice length that is approximately 11% shorter.

Example 3.3: Development of Flexural Reinforcement in a Cantilever beam

A cantilever beam, illustrated in Figure Ex. 3.3 with $b \times h = 400 \times 500$ mm and a length of 3500 mm, supports a total factored uniformly distributed load $w_f = 36.5$ kN/m. Material properties are $f'_c = 25$ MPa (Structural low-density concrete) and $f_y = 400$ MPa. Using a clear cover of 60 mm on the 10M vertical stirrups results in a design requiring four 25M bars with a flexural resistance $M_r = 240$ kN·m for the maximum factored negative moment of $M_f = 224$ kN·m at the face of the support. The 10M stirrups are spaced at 200 mm.

A. Calculate the cutoff location for the two centre 25M bars labelled "B" with $M_r = 130$ kN·m for the two remaining 25M bars.

$Y = L - X + EXT$; provided $L - X \geq \ell_d$ for bars "B".

$$X = \sqrt{\frac{2M_{r2}}{w_f}} = \sqrt{\frac{2(130)}{36.5}} = 2.67 \ m$$

$EXT = d_v \cot \theta$	Clause 11.3.9.1
$d = 500 - 60 - 10 - 25/2 = 417$ mm	
$d_v = 0.9d = 0.9(417) = 375$ mm	
Assume Simplified shear design $\therefore \theta = 35°$	Clause 11.3.6.3
$EXT = 375 \cot 35 = 536$ mm	
$Y = 3500 - 2670 + 536 = 1366$ mm	(provided bars "B" can be developed)

B. Check Development and Cutoff Location
(a) Short bars "B"
Clear cover to 25M bars = 60 + 10 = 70 mm
Check for minimum stirrups

$$s \leq \frac{A_v f_y}{0.06 \sqrt{f'_c} b_w} = \frac{2(100)(400)}{0.06 \sqrt{25}(400)} = 667 \ mm$$

Equation (11-1)

200 mm < 667 mm	O.K. to use 0.45 coefficient
ℓ_d prior to introduction of modification factors is 900 mm	Table 3.1

Modification factors:
Top bars $d > 300$ mm	$k_1 = 1.3$
Structural low density concrete	$k_3 = 1.3$

$\ell_d = 1.3(1.3)(900) = 1521$ mm
$Y = \ell_d + EXT = 1521 + 536 = 2057$ mm

A more detailed calculation based on the C.I. provides a shorter length.
For calculation of K_{tr} consider that only 2 of the 4 bars are being developed at this location.

$$C.I. = \frac{d_{cs}}{d_b} + \frac{K_{tr}}{d_b} = 2.50 + 1.52 \left(\frac{100}{200} \right) = 3.26$$

Tables 3.3(c) and 3.5

$C.I.$ is limited to 2.5 ℓ_d without modification factors = 740 mm

Table 3.2

$\ell_d = 1.3(1.3)(740) = 1251$ mm
Increase Y
$Y' = \ell_d + EXT = 1251 + 536 = 1787$ mm   Use $Y' = 1790$ mm

If this beam is subjected to exterior exposure, 2 - 25M bars might be inadequate to prevent z from exceeding 25 kN/mm in the region of highest stress. Bars B may have to be extended to a location where the stress in bars A will be low enough to satisfy Eq. 10-6.

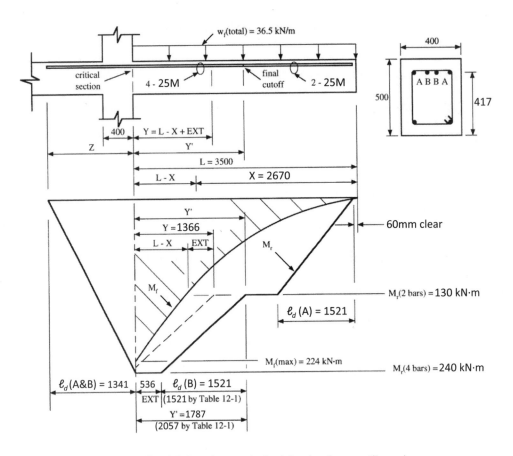

Figure Ex. 3.3 Development of reinforcing in a cantilever beam

(b) Long bars
As above $\ell_d = 1.3(1.3)(900) = 1521$ mm   O.K.
(A shorter development length can be calculated using Table 3.2 with C.I. from Tables 3.3(c) and 3.5 but there is no need to do so.) The moment is changing slowly in this region so the longer length causes no problems.

C.   Anchorage of all four bars to left of column

Assume there is no load on beam to left of column so that anchorage is needed from the right face of the column.

An $\ell_d = 1521$ mm as computed above could be used. However, a more detailed calculation based on the C.I. could be used if a shorter length might be worthwhile.

$$C.I. = \frac{d_{cs}}{d_b} + \frac{K_{tr}}{d_b} = 1.96 + 0.76 \left(\frac{100}{200}\right) = 2.34 \leq 2.50 \qquad \text{Tables 3.3(c) and 3.5}$$

$$\ell_d = 1.3(1.3)\left(840 + \frac{2.34 - 2.2}{2.5 - 2.2}(740 - 840)\right) = 1341 \text{ mm} \qquad \text{Interpolate in Table 3.2}$$

3

D. Check development of the stirrups

No check is necessary for 10M or 15M stirrups. A 135° hook around corner bars is adequate.
Clause 12.13.2(a)

Example 3.4: Development and Cutoffs in a simply supported beam

A simply supported beam in Figure Ex. 3.4 rests on 800 mm wide masonry pilasters over a clear span of 10 m. Although anchored, the beam is not integral with its supports. The uniformly distributed loading on the beam is 22 kN/m dead (including self-weight) and 25 kN/m live. Using f'_c = 30 MPa normal density concrete with f_y = 400 MPa, select the flexural reinforcement and choose cutoff locations. Assume a cover of 40 mm to 10M stirrups.

A. Design the flexural reinforcement:

Determine span length

$$\ell = \ell_n + h = 10000 + 750 \leq \ell_n + W = 10000 + 800 \quad \ell = 10750 \text{ mm} \qquad \text{Clause 9.2.2.3}$$

$$w_f = 1.25(22) + 1.5(25) = 65 \text{ kN/m}$$

$$M_f = 65.0 \frac{10.75^2}{8} = 939 \text{ kN·m}$$

Assuming 10M stirrups and 35M bars d = 750 – 40 – 10 – 35/2 = 682 mm

$$\text{Required } K_r = \frac{M_f}{bd^2} = \frac{0.939}{0.50(0.682)^2} = 4.04 \text{ MPa·}$$

$\rho \approx 1.40\%$ Table 2.1

$A_s = 0.014(500)(682) = 4774 \text{ mm}^2$

Number of 35M bars required = 4774/1000 = 4.8   Use 5 – 35M bars

$\rho = 5(1000)/(500(682)) = 0.0147$ $K_r = 4.2$ Table 2.1
$M_{r5} = K_r bd^2 = 4.2(0.5)(0.682^2) = 0.977 \text{ MN·m}$

Check bar spacing from Table 3.3(a)
For b_w = 500 mm   5 – 35M bars O.K. in one layer

B. Determination of bar cutoff locations

Consider possible location for terminating the two bars labelled "B"
With 2 bars cut off, ρ for the remaining bars is 3(1000)/(500(682)) = 0.0088 = 0.88%
$K_r = 2.75$ Table 2.1

M_r for the remaining 3 bars is therefore;

$$M_{r3} = 2.75(0.5)(0.682^2) = 0.640 \text{ MN·m}$$

Locate point where 3 bars are adequate a distance X from the centreline

$$X = \frac{\ell}{2}\sqrt{\frac{M_f - M_{r3}}{M_f}} = \frac{10750}{2}\sqrt{\frac{939 - 640}{939}} = 3033 \text{ mm}$$

The required extension is EXT = d_v cot θ   Clause 11.3.9.1
$d_v = 0.9d = 0.9(682) = 614$ mm
Assume Simplified shear design   ∴ θ = 35°   Clause 11.3.6.3
EXT = 614 cot 35 = 877 mm

Total length of bars "B" $\ell_B = 2(3033 + 877) = 2(3910) = 7820$ mm   Use ℓ_B =7820 mm

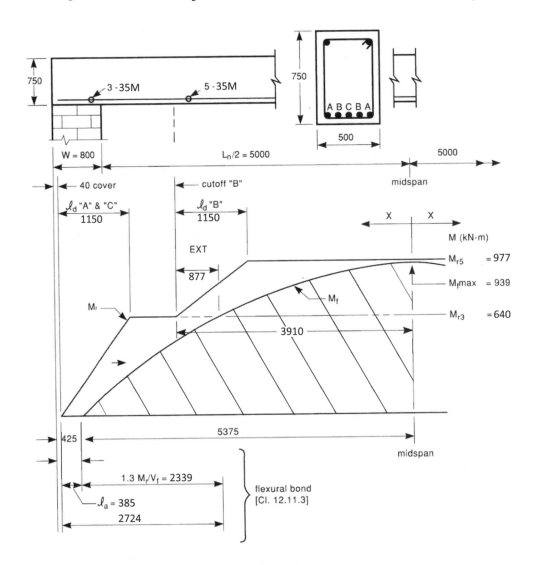

Fig. Ex. 3.4: Development of reinforcement in a simply supported beam

C. Check for adequate anchorage of 3 bars at support

Because these bars are close to full length, it doesn't seem worthwhile to terminate bar "C". Bars "A" and "C" should be full length. Assume 40 mm cover to end of bars.

ℓ_A = 10 000 + 2(800 – 40) = 11 520 mm

D. Check flexural bond at support

Clause 12.11.3

V_f = 65(10.75/2) = 349 kN

$$\ell_d \leq \frac{1.3 M_{r3}}{V_f} + \ell_a \quad \text{where } \ell_a = 800 - 40 - 750 \ / \ 2 = 385 \text{ mm}$$

$$\ell_d \leq \frac{1.3(640)}{0.349} + 385 = 2769 \text{ mm}$$

ℓ_d = 1150 mm

Table 3.1

ℓ_d = 1150 mm < 2769 mm

∴ O.K.

Example 3.5: Development of Deformed Welded Wire Reinforcement (WWR)

Find the development length for MD47.6 × MD47.6 WWR with a 152 × 152 mm grid and f_y = 485 MPa to be used as temperature and shrinkage reinforcement in structural low-density concrete with f'_c = 20 MPa. More than 300 mm of concrete is placed below the WWR.

Solution:

Table 3.12

For "top" wire and low density concrete k_1 = 1.3, and k_3 = 1.3

From upper left corner of Table 3.12 the development length for MD47.6 WWR in 20 MPa concrete with both k_1 and k_3 = 1.3 is 260 mm.

Table 3.1 Tension development length, ℓ_d (mm) for heavier confined deformed reinforcing bars with f_y = 400 MPa, for normal density concrete.

$$\ell_d = 0.45\,k_1 k_2 k_3 k_4\,\frac{f_y}{\sqrt{f'_c}}\,d_b$$

f'_c	Bar Size							
MPa	10M	15M	20M	25M	30M	35M	45M	55M
20	320	480	640	1010	1210	1410	1810	2210
25	290	430	580	900	1080	1260	1620	1980
30	260	390	530	820	990	1150	1480	1810
35	240	370	490	760	910	1060	1370	1670
40	230	340	460	710	850	1000	1280	1570
45	210	320	430	670	800	940	1210	1480
50	200	310	410	640	760	890	1150	1400
55	190	290	390	610	730	850	1090	1330
60	190	280	370	580	700	810	1050	1280
≥ 64	180	270	360	560	680	790	1010	1240

Clear cover and clear spacing of bars must be at least $1.0d_b$ and $1.4d_b$, respectively.   [Cl. 12.2.3]

Member must contain at least minimum stirrups or ties within length ℓ_d or   [Cl. 7.6.5, 11.2.8.2]

for slabs, walls, shells or folded plates
    have clear spacing between bars being developed not less than $2d_b$.   [Table 12.1]

Table gives development lengths for $k_1 = k_2 = k_3 = 1.0$.

Multiply development lengths in this table by k_1, k_2, and k_3 when these differ from 1.0.
(The product $k_1 k_2$ need not be taken greater than 1.7)   [Cl. 12.2.4]

k_1 = 1.3 for horizontal reinforcement placed in such a way that more than 300 mm of fresh concrete is cast in the member below the development length or splice.

k_2 = 1.5 for epoxy-coated reinforcement with clear cover less than $3d_b$, or with clear spacing between bars being developed less than $6d_b$.
    = 1.2 for all other epoxy-coated reinforcement

k_3 = 1.3 for structural low-density concrete
    = 1.2 for structural semi-low-density concrete

For $f_y \neq 400$ MPa, multiply development length by $f_y/400$.

For "Other cases" with lighter confinement, multiply the above lengths by 1.33.   [Table 12.1]

After application of all modification factors, the development length must not be less than 300 mm.   [Cl. 12.2.1]

Table 3.2 Development lengths (mm) for deformed reinforcing bars with f_y = 400 MPa before factors k_1 to k_3 are applied, for different confinement indices (C.I.)

Application	C.I.	f'_c	10M	15M	20M	25M	30M	35M	45M	55M
	1.5	20	550	730	820	1370	1600	1960	2290	3120
		25	490	650	740	1230	1430	1750	2040	2790
If no stirrups considered along development length then the following cover and spacing are required for this C.I.: Minimum clear cover = $1.0d_b$ Minimum bar spacing = $2.25d_b$		30	450	600	670	1120	1310	1600	1870	2540
		35	410	550	620	1040	1210	1480	1730	2360
		40	390	520	580	970	1130	1390	1620	2200
		45	370	490	550	910	1070	1310	1520	2080
		50	350	460	520	870	1010	1240	1450	1970
		55	330	440	500	830	960	1180	1380	1880
		60	320	420	480	790	920	1130	1320	1800
	1.5	≥ 64	310	410	460	770	890	1100	1280	1740
	1.8	20	460	610	690	1140	1330	1630	1900	2600
		25	410	550	610	1020	1190	1460	1700	2320
If no stirrups considered along development length then the following cover and spacing are required for this C.I.: Minimum clear cover = $1.3d_b$ Minimum bar spacing = $2.7d_b$		30	370	500	560	930	1090	1330	1560	2120
		35	350	460	520	860	1010	1230	1440	1960
		40	320	430	480	810	940	1150	1350	1840
		45	300	410	460	760	890	1090	1270	1730
		50	290	390	430	720	840	1030	1200	1640
		55	280	370	410	690	800	980	1150	1570
		60	260	350	400	660	770	940	1100	1500
	1.8	≥ 64	260	340	380	640	750	910	1060	1450
	2.2	20	370	500	560	940	1090	1340	1560	2130
		25	330	450	500	840	980	1190	1390	1900
If no stirrups considered along development length then the following cover and spacing are required for this C.I.: Minimum clear cover = $1.7d_b$ Minimum bar spacing = $3.3d_b$		30	310	410	460	760	890	1090	1270	1740
		35	280	380	420	710	820	1010	1180	1610
		40	260	350	400	660	770	940	1100	1500
		45	250	330	370	620	730	890	1040	1420
		50	240	320	350	590	690	840	990	1340
		55	230	300	340	560	660	810	940	1280
		60	220	290	320	540	630	770	900	1230
	2.2	≥ 64	210	280	310	520	610	750	870	1190
	2.5	20	330	440	490	820	960	1180	1370	1870
		25	290	390	440	740	860	1050	1230	1670
If no stirrups considered along development length then the following cover and spacing are required for this C.I.: Minimum clear cover = $2.0d_b$ Minimum bar spacing = $3.75d_b$		30	270	360	400	670	780	960	1120	1530
		35	250	330	370	620	730	890	1040	1410
		40	230	310	350	580	680	830	970	1320
		45	220	290	330	550	640	780	910	1250
		50	210	280	310	520	610	740	870	1180
		55	200	260	300	500	580	710	830	1130
		60	190	250	290	480	550	680	790	1080
	2.5	≥ 64	180	250	280	460	540	660	770	1050

The table gives development lengths for $k_1 = k_2 = k_3 = 1.0$.
Multiply development lengths by k_1, k_2, and k_3 when these differ from 1.0.   [Table 3.1]
The confinement Index, $C.I. = d_{cs}/d_b$ from Table 3.3 or 3.4, plus K_{tr}/d_b from Table 3.5
For $f_y \neq 400$ MPa, multiply development length by $f_y/400$
After application of all modification factors, development length must not be less than 300 mm.

Table 3.3(a) Concrete confinement index d_{cs}/d_b for n deformed bars with a clear cover of 40 mm spaced uniformly across a stem width b_w (mm)

b_w	n	15M	20M	25M	30M	35M	b_w	n	15M	20M	25M	30M	35M
200	2	2.50	2.50	2.10	1.78		700	7	2.50	2.50	2.10	1.83	1.64
250	2	2.50	2.50	2.10	1.83	1.64		8	2.50	2.50	2.10	1.83	
	3	2.50	2.17	1.73				9	2.50	2.42	1.93	1.61	
300	3	2.50	2.50	2.10	1.83	1.64		10	2.50	2.15	1.72		
	4	2.50	2.00	1.60				11	2.50	1.93			
	5	2.00						12	2.34	1.76			
350	3	2.50	2.50	2.10	1.83	1.64		13	2.15				
	4	2.50	2.50	2.04	1.70		750	8	2.50	2.50	2.10	1.83	1.64
	5	2.50	1.92					9	2.50	2.50	2.10	1.75	
	6	2.04						10	2.50	2.33	1.87		
400	4	2.50	2.50	2.10	1.83	1.64		11	2.50	2.10	1.68		
	5	2.50	2.33	1.87				12	2.50	1.91			
	6	2.49	1.87					13	2.33	1.75			
	7	2.07						14	2.15				
450	4	2.50	2.50	2.10	1.83	1.64		15	2.00				
	5	2.50	2.50	2.10	1.83		800	8	2.50	2.50	2.10	1.83	1.64
	6	2.50	2.20	1.76				9	2.50	2.50	2.10	1.83	1.62
	7	2.44	1.83					10	2.50	2.50	2.01	1.68	
	8	2.10						11	2.50	2.27	1.81		
500	5	2.50	2.50	2.10	1.83	1.64		12	2.50	2.06	1.65		
	6	2.50	2.50	2.03	1.69			13	2.50	1.89			
	7	2.50	2.11	1.69				14	2.32	1.74			
	8	2.41	1.81					15	2.16				
	9	2.11						16	2.01				
550	6	2.50	2.50	2.10	1.83	1.64	850	9	2.50	2.50	2.10	1.83	1.64
	7	2.50	2.39	1.91				10	2.50	2.50	2.10	1.80	
	8	2.50	2.05	1.64				11	2.50	2.43	1.95	1.62	
	9	2.39	1.79					12	2.50	2.21	1.77		
	10	2.12						13	2.50	2.03	1.62		
600	6	2.50	2.50	2.10	1.83	1.64		14	2.50	1.87			
	7	2.50	2.50	2.10	1.78			15	2.32	1.74			
	8	2.50	2.29	1.83				16	2.16				
	9	2.50	2.00	1.60				17	2.03				
	10	2.37	1.78				900	10	2.50	2.50	2.10	1.83	1.64
	11	2.13						11	2.50	2.50	2.08	1.73	
650	7	2.50	2.50	2.10	1.83	1.64		12	2.50	2.36	1.89		
	8	2.50	2.50	2.02	1.68			13	2.50	2.17	1.73		
	9	2.50	2.21	1.77				14	2.50	2.00	1.60		
	10	2.50	1.96					15	2.48	1.86			
	11	2.36	1.77					16	2.31	1.73			
	12	2.14						17	2.17				
								18	2.04				

Values are included only if a clear spacing of $1.4d_b$ and 30 mm is available between bars.
Values are included only if the value of z is less than 25 kN/mm for exterior exposure

Table 3.3(b) Concrete confinement index d_{cs}/d_b for n deformed bars with a clear cover of 50 mm spaced uniformly across a stem width b_w (mm)

b_w	n	15M	20M	25M	30M	35M
200	2	2.50	2.00	1.60		
250	2	2.50	2.50	2.50	2.17	
	3	2.44	1.83			
300	2	2.50	2.50			
	3	2.50	2.50	2.13	1.78	
	4	2.37	1.78			
350	3	2.50	2.50	2.50	2.17	1.93
	4	2.50	2.33	1.87		
	5	2.33	1.75			
400	3	2.50	2.50	2.50	2.17	
	4	2.50	2.50	2.31	1.93	1.65
	5	2.50	2.17	1.73		
	6	2.31	1.73			
450	3	2.50	2.50			
	4	2.50	2.50	2.50	2.17	1.93
	5	2.50	2.50	2.07	1.72	
	6	2.50	2.07	1.65		
	7	2.30	1.72			
500	4	2.50	2.50	2.50	2.17	
	5	2.50	2.50	2.40	2.00	1.71
	6	2.50	2.40	1.92	1.60	
	7	2.50	2.00	1.60		
	8	2.29	1.71			
550	4	2.50	2.50	2.50		
	5	2.50	2.50	2.50	2.17	1.93
	6	2.50	2.50	2.19	1.82	
	7	2.50	2.28	1.82		
	8	2.50	1.95			
	9	2.28	1.71			
600	4	2.50	2.50			
	5	2.50	2.50	2.50	2.17	1.93
	6	2.50	2.50	2.45	2.04	1.75
	7	2.50	2.50	2.04	1.70	
	8	2.50	2.19	1.75		
	9	2.50	1.92			
	10	2.27	1.70			
650	5	2.50	2.50	2.50	2.17	
	6	2.50	2.50	2.50	2.17	1.93
	7	2.50	2.50	2.27	1.89	1.62
	8	2.50	2.43	1.94	1.62	
	9	2.50	2.13	1.70		
	10	2.50	1.89			

b_w	n	15M	20M	25M	30M	35M
700	5	2.50	2.50	2.50		
	6	2.50	2.50	2.50	2.17	1.93
	7	2.50	2.50	2.49	2.07	1.78
	8	2.50	2.50	2.13	1.78	
	9	2.50	2.33	1.87		
	10	2.50	2.07	1.66		
	11	2.49	1.87			
750	5	2.50	2.50			
	6	2.50	2.50	2.50	2.17	
	7	2.50	2.50	2.50	2.17	1.93
	8	2.50	2.50	2.32	1.94	1.66
	9	2.50	2.50	2.03	1.69	
	10	2.50	2.26	1.81		
	11	2.50	2.03	1.63		
	12	2.46	1.85			
800	6	2.50	2.50	2.50	2.17	
	7	2.50	2.50	2.50	2.17	1.93
	8	2.50	2.50	2.50	2.10	1.80
	9	2.50	2.50	2.20	1.83	
	10	2.50	2.44	1.96	1.63	
	11	2.50	2.20	1.76		
	12	2.50	2.00	1.60		
	13	2.44	1.83			
850	6	2.50	2.50	2.50		
	7	2.50	2.50	2.50	2.17	1.93
	8	2.50	2.50	2.50	2.17	1.93
	9	2.50	2.50	2.37	1.97	1.69
	10	2.50	2.50	2.10	1.75	
	11	2.50	2.37	1.89		
	12	2.50	2.15	1.72		
	13	2.50	1.97			
	14	2.43	1.82			
900	6	2.50	2.50			
	7	2.50	2.50	2.50	2.17	
	8	2.50	2.50	2.50	2.17	1.93
	9	2.50	2.50	2.50	2.11	1.81
	10	2.50	2.50	2.25	1.88	1.61
	11	2.50	2.50	2.03	1.69	
	12	2.50	2.30	1.84		
	13	2.50	2.11	1.69		
	14	2.50	1.95			
	15	2.41	1.81			

3

Development and Splices

Values are included only if a clear spacing of $1.4d_b$ and 30 mm is available between bars.
Values are included only if the value of z is less than 25 kN/mm for exterior exposure.

Table 3.3(c) Concrete confinement index d_{cs}/d_b for n deformed bars with a clear cover of 70 mm spaced uniformly across a stem width b_w (mm)

b_w	n	15M	20M	25M	30M	35M	b_w	n	15M	20M	25M	30M	35M
250	2	2.50	2.33	1.87			700	5	2.50	2.50	2.50	2.50	
300	2	2.50	2.50	2.50	2.50			6	2.50	2.50	2.50	2.31	1.98
	3	2.50	2.00	1.60				7	2.50	2.50	2.31	1.93	1.65
350	2	2.50	2.50					8	2.50	2.48	1.98	1.65	
	3	2.50	2.50	2.27	1.89	1.62		9	2.50	2.17	1.73		
	4	2.50	1.89					10	2.50	1.93			
400	3	2.50	2.50	2.50	2.44	2.10		11	2.31	1.73			
	4	2.50	2.44	1.96	1.63		750	5	2.50	2.50	2.50		
	5	2.44	1.83					6	2.50	2.50	2.50	2.50	2.17
450	3	2.50	2.50	2.50				7	2.50	2.50	2.50	2.11	1.81
	4	2.50	2.50	2.40	2.00	1.71		8	2.50	2.50	2.17	1.81	
	5	2.50	2.25	1.80				9	2.50	2.38	1.90		
	6	2.40	1.80					10	2.50	2.11	1.69		
	7	2.00						11	2.50	1.90			
500	3	2.50	2.50					12	2.30	1.73			
	4	2.50	2.50	2.50	2.37	2.03	800	5	2.50	2.50			
	5	2.50	2.50	2.13	1.78			6	2.50	2.50	2.50	2.50	
	6	2.50	2.13	1.71				7	2.50	2.50	2.50	2.30	1.97
	7	2.37	1.78					8	2.50	2.50	2.36	1.97	1.69
	8	2.03						9	2.50	2.50	2.07	1.72	
550	4	2.50	2.50	2.50	2.50			10	2.50	2.30	1.84		
	5	2.50	2.50	2.47	2.06	1.76		11	2.50	2.07	1.65		
	6	2.50	2.47	1.97	1.64			12	2.50	1.88			
	7	2.50	2.06	1.64				13	2.30	1.72			
	8	2.35	1.76				850	6	2.50	2.50	2.50		
	9	2.06						7	2.50	2.50	2.50	2.48	2.13
600	4	2.50	2.50	2.50				8	2.50	2.50	2.50	2.13	1.82
	5	2.50	2.50	2.50	2.33	2.00		9	2.50	2.50	2.23	1.86	
	6	2.50	2.50	2.24	1.87	1.60		10	2.50	2.48	1.99	1.65	
	7	2.50	2.33	1.87				11	2.50	2.23	1.79		
	8	2.50	2.00	1.60				12	2.50	2.03	1.62		
	9	2.33	1.75					13	2.48	1.86			
	10	2.07						14	2.29	1.72			
650	4	2.50	2.50				900	6	2.50	2.50	2.50		
	5	2.50	2.50	2.50	2.50	2.24		7	2.50	2.50	2.50	2.50	2.29
	6	2.50	2.50	2.50	2.09	1.79		8	2.50	2.50	2.50	2.29	1.96
	7	2.50	2.50	2.09	1.74			9	2.50	2.50	2.40	2.00	1.71
	8	2.50	2.24	1.79				10	2.50	2.50	2.13	1.78	
	9	2.50	1.96					11	2.50	2.40	1.92	1.60	
	10	2.32	1.74					12	2.50	2.18	1.75		
	11	2.09						13	2.50	2.00	1.60		
								14	2.46	1.85			

Values are included only if a clear spacing of $1.4d_b$ and 30 mm is available between bars.
Values are included only if the value of z is less than 25 kN/mm for exterior exposure.

Table 3.4(a) Concrete confinement index d_{cs}/d_b for n pairs of contacting deformed bars lap spliced in tension with a clear cover of 40 mm, spaced uniformly across a stem width b_w.

b_w	n	15M	20M	25M	30M	35M	b_w	n	15M	20M	25M	30M	35M
200	2	2.22					750	5	2.50	2.50	2.10	1.83	1.64
250	2	2.50	2.50	2.10				6	2.50	2.50	2.10	1.83	1.60
300	2	2.50	2.50	2.10	1.83	1.64		7	2.50	2.50	2.02		
	3	2.50	2.00					8	2.50	2.24	1.64		
350	2	2.50	2.50	2.10	1.83	1.64		9	2.50	1.88			
	3	2.50	2.50	2.07				10	2.37				
	4	2.50	1.67				800	6	2.50	2.50	2.10	1.83	1.64
400	2	2.50	2.50	2.10	1.83	1.64		7	2.50	2.50	2.10	1.74	
	3	2.50	2.50	2.10	1.83	1.64		8	2.50	2.48	1.83		
	4	2.50	2.22	1.60				9	2.50	2.08			
450	3	2.50	2.50	2.10	1.83	1.64		10	2.50	1.78			
	4	2.50	2.50	2.04				11	2.29				
	5	2.50	1.92				850	6	2.50	2.50	2.10	1.83	1.64
	6	2.13						7	2.50	2.50	2.10	1.83	
500	3	2.50	2.50	2.10	1.83	1.64		8	2.50	2.50	2.02		
	4	2.50	2.50	2.10	1.83			9	2.50	2.29	1.68		
	5	2.50	2.33	1.70				10	2.50	1.96			
	6	2.50	1.73					11	2.50	1.70			
	7	2.04						12	2.22				
550	4	2.50	2.50	2.10	1.83	1.64	900	7	2.50	2.50	2.10	1.83	1.64
	5	2.50	2.50	2.03				8	2.50	2.50	2.10	1.71	
	6	2.50	2.07					9	2.50	2.50	1.85		
	7	2.41						10	2.50	2.15			
600	4	2.50	2.50	2.10	1.83	1.64		11	2.50	1.87			
	5	2.50	2.50	2.10	1.83			12	2.42				
	6	2.50	2.40	1.76			950	7	2.50	2.50	2.10	1.83	1.64
	7	2.50	1.89					8	2.50	2.50	2.10	1.83	
	8	2.29						9	2.50	2.50	2.02		
650	5	2.50	2.50	2.10	1.83	1.64		10	2.50	2.33	1.72		
	6	2.50	2.50	2.03				11	2.50	2.03			
	7	2.50	2.17					12	2.50	1.79			
	8	2.50	1.76					13	2.35				
	9	2.19					1000	7	2.50	2.50	2.10	1.83	1.64
700	5	2.50	2.50	2.10	1.83	1.64		8	2.50	2.50	2.10	1.83	1.63
	6	2.50	2.50	2.10	1.78			9	2.50	2.50	2.10	1.69	
	7	2.50	2.44	1.80				10	2.50	2.50	1.87		
	8	2.50	2.00					11	2.50	2.20	1.61		
	9	2.47	1.67					12	2.50	1.94			
	10	2.12						13	2.50	1.72			
								14	2.29				

Values are provided only if a clear spacing of $1.4d_b$ and 30 mm is available between bars.

Table 3.4(b) Concrete confinement index d_{cs}/d_b for n pairs of contacting deformed bars lap spliced in tension with a clear cover of 50 mm, spaced uniformly across a stem width b_w.

b_w	n	15M	20M	25M	30M	35M	b_w	n	15M	20M	25M	30M	35M
250	2	2.50	2.33	1.60			750	5	2.50	2.50			
300	2	2.50	2.50					6	2.50	2.50	2.45	1.91	
	3	2.50	1.67					7	2.50	2.50	1.93		
350	3	2.50	2.50	1.80				8	2.50	2.14			
	4	2.22						9	2.50	1.79			
400	3	2.50	2.50	2.47	1.89			10	2.27				
	4	2.50	2.00				800	5	2.50				
	5	2.06						6	2.50	2.50	2.50	2.13	
450	3	2.50	2.50					7	2.50	2.50	2.16	1.67	
	4	2.50	2.50	1.87				8	2.50	2.38	1.75		
	5	2.50	1.75					9	2.50	2.00			
500	3	2.50						10	2.50	1.70			
	4	2.50	2.50	2.31	1.78			11	2.20				
	5	2.50	2.17				850	5	2.50				
	6	2.40						6	2.50	2.50	2.50		
550	4	2.50	2.50	2.50				7	2.50	2.50	2.38	1.85	
	5	2.50	2.50	1.90				8	2.50	2.50	1.94		
	6	2.50	1.93					9	2.50	2.21	1.62		
	7	2.26						10	2.50	1.89			
600	4	2.50	2.50					11	2.42				
	5	2.50	2.50	2.23	1.72		900	6	2.50	2.50			
	6	2.50	2.27	1.65				7	2.50	2.50	2.50	2.04	
	7	2.50	1.78					8	2.50	2.50	2.13	1.65	
	8	2.16						9	2.50	2.42	1.78		
650	4	2.50						10	2.50	2.07			
	5	2.50	2.50	2.50	2.00			11	2.50	1.80			
	6	2.50	2.50	1.92				12	2.34				
	7	2.50	2.06				950	6	2.50				
	8	2.48	1.67					7	2.50	2.50	2.50		
	9	2.08						8	2.50	2.50	2.32	1.81	
700	5	2.50	2.50	2.50				9	2.50	2.50	1.95		
	6	2.50	2.50	2.19	1.69			10	2.50	2.26	1.66		
	7	2.50	2.33	1.71				11	2.50	1.97			
	8	2.50	1.90					12	2.50	1.73			
	9	2.36					1000	6	2.50				
								7	2.50	2.50	2.50		
								8	2.50	2.50	2.50	1.97	
								9	2.50	2.50	2.12	1.64	
								10	2.50	2.44	1.81		
								11	2.50	2.13			
								12	2.50	1.88			

Values are included only if a clear spacing of $1.4d_b$ and 30 mm is available between bars.
Values are included only if $z \le 25$ kN/mm for exterior exposure.

Table 3.4(c) Concrete confinement index d_{cs}/d_b for n pairs of contacting deformed bars lap spliced in tension with a clear cover of 70 mm, spaced uniformly across a stem width b_w.

b_w	n	15M	20M	25M	30M	35M
300	2	2.50	2.50	1.87		
350	3	2.50	1.83			
400	3	2.50	2.50	1.93		
	4	2.37				
450	3	2.50	2.50	2.50		
	4	2.50	2.11			
	5	2.17				
500	3	2.50	2.50			
	4	2.50	2.50	1.96		
	5	2.50	1.83			
	6	2.04				
550	4	2.50	2.50	2.40	1.85	
	5	2.50	2.25	1.63		
	6	2.49	1.67			
600	4	2.50	2.50	2.50		
	5	2.50	2.50	1.97		
	6	2.50	2.00			
	7	2.33				
650	4	2.50	2.50			
	5	2.50	2.50	2.30	1.78	
	6	2.50	2.33	1.71		
	7	2.50	1.83			
	8	2.22				
700	5	2.50	2.50	2.50	2.06	
	6	2.50	2.50	1.97		
	7	2.50	2.11			
	8	2.50	1.71			
	9	2.14				
750	5	2.50	2.50	2.50		
	6	2.50	2.50	2.24	1.73	
	7	2.50	2.39	1.76		
	8	2.50	1.95			
	9	2.42				
	10	2.07				

b_w	n	15M	20M	25M	30M	35M
800	5	2.50	2.50			
	6	2.50	2.50	2.50	1.96	
	7	2.50	2.50	1.98		
	8	2.50	2.19	1.60		
	9	2.50	1.83			
	10	2.32				
	11	2.02				
850	5	2.50				
	6	2.50	2.50	2.50		
	7	2.50	2.50	2.20	1.70	
	8	2.50	2.43	1.79		
	9	2.50	2.04			
	10	2.50	1.74			
	11	2.24				
900	6	2.50	2.50	2.50		
	7	2.50	2.50	2.42	1.89	
	8	2.50	2.50	1.98		
	9	2.50	2.25	1.65		
	10	2.50	1.93			
	11	2.47	1.67			
	12	2.18				
950	6	2.50	2.50			
	7	2.50	2.50	2.50	2.07	
	8	2.50	2.50	2.17	1.68	
	9	2.50	2.46	1.82		
	10	2.50	2.11			
	11	2.50	1.83			
	12	2.38				
	13	2.13				
1000	6	2.50				
	7	2.50	2.50	2.50		
	8	2.50	2.50	2.36	1.84	
	9	2.50	2.50	1.98		
	10	2.50	2.30	1.69		
	11	2.50	2.00			
	12	2.50	1.76			
	13	2.31				
	14	2.09				

Values are included only if a clear spacing of $1.4d_b$ and 30 mm is available between bars.
Values are included only if z ≤ 25 kN/mm for exterior exposure.

3

Development and Splices

Table 3.5 Transverse reinforcing confinement index K_{tr}/d_b for 2 legged 10M vertical stirrups with f_{yt} = 400 MPa placed at a spacing s = 100 mm, and providing confinement to n equally spaced main reinforcing bars or pairs of lapspliced bars, across the member width.

s (mm)	n	15M	20M	25M	30M	35M	45M	55M
100	2	2.54	1.90	1.52	1.27	1.09	0.85	0.69
	3	1.69	1.27	1.02	0.85	0.73	0.56	0.46
	4	1.27	0.95	0.76	0.63	0.54	0.42	0.35
	5	1.02	0.76	0.61	0.51	0.44	0.34	0.28
	6	0.85	0.63	0.51	0.42	0.36	0.28	0.23
	7	0.73	0.54	0.44	0.36	0.31	0.24	0.20
	8	0.63	0.48	0.38	0.32	0.27	0.21	0.17
	9	0.56	0.42	0.34	0.28	0.24	0.19	0.15
	10	0.51	0.38	0.30	0.25	0.22	0.17	0.14
	11	0.46	0.35	0.28	0.23	0.20	0.15	0.13
	12	0.42	0.32	0.25	0.21	0.18	0.14	0.12
	13	0.39	0.29	0.23	0.20	0.17	0.13	0.11
	14	0.36	0.27	0.22	0.18	0.16	0.12	0.10
	15	0.34	0.25	0.20	0.17	0.15	0.11	0.09
100	16	0.32	0.24	0.19	0.16	0.14	0.11	0.09

Transverse reinforcing confinement index: $\dfrac{K_{tr}}{d_b} = \dfrac{A_{tr}\,f_{yt}}{10.5\,n\,s\,d_b}$ [Cl. 12.2.2]

Modifiers for stirrup area, A_{tr}:

    Modifier for stirrup size: Multiply by 2 for 15M, 3 for 20M and 5 for 25M

    Modifier for number of legs: Multiply by number of legs and divide by 2
                                                                  (Where n ≥ number of legs)

Modifier for yield strength f_{yt} ≠ 400 MPa: Multiply by f_{yt} /400

Modifier for spacing, s: Multiply by 100 and divide by s

Table 3.6 Tension development lengths, ℓ_{hb}, (mm) using standard hooks for deformed bars with f_y = 400 MPa, for normal density concrete.   [Clause 12.5.2]

f'_c MPa	Bar Size							
	10M	15M	20M	25M	30M	35M	45M	55M
20	220	340	450	560	670	780	1010	1230
25	200	300	400	500	600	700	900	1100
30	180	270	370	460	550	640	820	1000
35	170	250	340	420	510	590	760	930
40	160	240	320	400	470	550	710	870
45	150	220	300	370	450	520	670	820
50	140	210	280	350	420	490	640	780
55	130	200	270	340	400	470	610	740
60	130	190	260	320	390	450	580	710
≥ 64	130	190	250	310	380	440	560	690

The development length is the out to out dimension including the hook and the straight length to the critical section.

Hooks must satisfy the dimensions for standard hooks.   [Table 3.7]

Special fabrication is required for bends greater than 90° for 45M and 55M bars with steel grades of 400R and 500R.   [Annex A, Table 16]

The basic hook development length shall be multiplied by the following factors to obtain the development length ℓ_{dh}:   [Cl. 12.5.3]
(a) For bars with $f_y \neq 400$ MPa $f_y/400$
(b) For 35M or smaller bars where the side cover (normal to the plane of the hook) is at least 60 mm, and for 90° hooks where the cover on the bar extension beyond the hook is at least 50 mm
0.7   [Fig. 3.1(a)]
(c) For 35M or smaller bars where the hook is enclosed vertically or horizontally within at least three ties or stirrup ties spaced along a length at least equal to the inside diameter of the hook at a spacing not greater than $3d_b$, where d_b is the nominal diameter of the hooked bar.
0.8   [Fig. 3.1(b)]

(d) Where anchorage or development for f_y is not specifically required for reinforcing exceeding that required by analysis. $A_{y\ required}/A_{y\ provided}$

(e) For structural low-density concrete   1.3

(f) For epoxy-coated reinforcement   1.2

The minimum development length, ℓ_{dh}, shall be not less than $8d_b$ or 150 mm, whichever is greater.
[CL. 12.5.1]
If both covers "A" and "B" are less than 60 mm then ties or stirrups defined by Fig 3.1(b) must be provided, but the 0.8 modifier does not apply.
[Cl. 12.5.4]

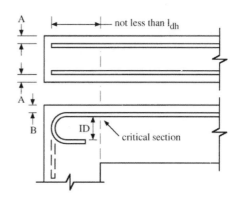

Table 3.7 Detailing and estimating dimensions (mm) for standard hooks for deformed reinforcing bars.

Standard hooks are defined in Clause 6.6.2 and Table 16 of CSA A23.1 (See A23.3 Annex A)

Bar	300R				400R or 500R				400W or 500W			
	180° Hook			90° Hook	180° Hook			90° Hook	180° Hook			90° Hook
Size	ID	J	G	A or G	ID	J	G	A or G	ID	J	G	A or G
10M	60	80	130	180	70	90	140	180	60	80	130	180
15M	90	120	170	250	100	130	180	260	90	120	170	250
20M					120	160	220	310	100	140	200	300
25M					150	200	280	400	150	200	280	400
30M					250	310	400	510	200	260	350	490
35M					300	370	480	610	250	320	430	590
45M					450	540	680	790	400	490	630	770
55M					600	710	900	1030	550	660	850	1010

The dimensions provided use the minimum diameters (ID) permitted and the nominal bar diameters rather than the bar numbers.

Add the additional hook dimension G to the detailing dimension to estimate the total bar length.

For 180° hooks: $G = (4d_b \geq 60 \text{ mm}) + \pi(\text{ID} + d_b)/2 - \text{ID}/2 - d_b$

For 90° hooks: $G = A = 12d_b + \text{ID}/2 + d_b$

Special fabrication is required for bends exceeding 90° for 45M and 55M bars.

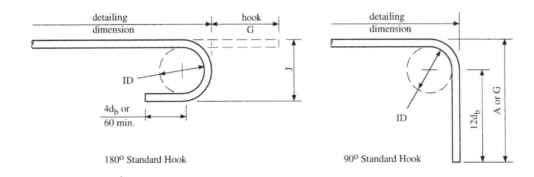

180° Standard Hook   90° Standard Hook

Table 3.8 Minimum depth, *h*, (mm) to provide anchorage for 20M and 25M deformed bar stirrups for shear, with hooks and bends placed around longitudinal reinforcement for vertical or bottom placed, uncoated stirrups in normal density concrete.

Cover to Stirrups		30 mm		40 mm		60 mm	
Bar Size		20M	25M	20M	25M	20M	25M
f'_c (MPa)	s	≥60 mm	≥65 mm	≥75 mm	≥80 mm	≥95 mm	≥100 mm
20		490	720	510	740	550	780
25		440	650	460	670	500	710
30		410	600	430	620	470	660
35		380	560	400	580	440	620
40		360	530	380	550	420	590
45		340	500	360	520	400	560
50		330	480	350	500	390	540
55		320	460	340	480	380	520
60		310	440	330	460	370	500
≥64		300	430	320	450	360	490

A centre-to-centre spacing smaller than listed does not provide the necessary confinement assumed in calculating minimum h.

Hooks must satisfy the dimensions for standard hooks. [Table 3.7]

The table gives beam depths for $k_1 = k_2 = k_3 = 1.0$.
For a conservative approximation, multiply beam depths in this table by k_1, k_2, and k_3
when these differ from 1.0. [Cl. 12.2.4]

k_2 = 1.5 for epoxy-coated stirrups with clear cover less than $3d_b$, or
with clear spacing between stirrups less than $6d_b$.
= 1.2 for all other epoxy-coated stirrups

k_3 = 1.3 for structural low-density concrete
= 1.2 for structural semi-low-density concrete

For $f_y ≠ 400$ MPa, multiply depths by $f_y/400$.

For "Other cases" with lighter confinement, multiply depths by 1.33. [Table 12.1]

3

Development and Splices

Table 3.9 Compression development lengths, ℓ_{db}, for deformed reinforcing bars with $f_y = 400$ MPa, for normal density concrete.   [Cl. 12.3.1]

$\ell_{db} \geq 0.24\, d_b f_y \,/\, \sqrt{f_c'}$ and $\ell_{db} \geq 0.044\, d_b f_y$

f_c'	Bar Size							
MPa	10M	15M	20M	25M	30M	35M	45M	55M
20	210	320	430	540	640	750	970	1180
25	190	290	380	480	580	670	860	1060
≥ 30	180	260	350	440	530	620	790	970

The development length ℓ_d is the product of ℓ_{db} from the above table and the following factors:

(a) Reinforcement in excess of that required by analysis $\qquad\qquad$ $A_{s,required}/A_{s,provided}$
(b) Enclosure within spiral reinforcement of not less than 6 mm diameter and a pitch no more than 100 mm or within 10M ties in conformance with Clause 7.6.5 and spaced at not more than 100 mm $\qquad\qquad$ 0.75

Also $\ell_d \not< 200$ mm

Table 3.10 Compression lap splice lengths, ℓ_s, (mm) for deformed reinforcing bars with $f_y = 400$ MPa, for normal density concrete   [Cl. 12.16.1]

$\ell_s = 0.073\,(400)\, d_b$

Confinement	Bar Size					
	10M	15M	20M	25M	30M	35M
Usual	290	440	580	730	880	1020
Columns with special ties	240	360	480	610	730	850
Spiral column	220	330	440	550	660	770

Modification factors:

Columns with special ties: $\qquad\qquad\qquad\qquad\qquad\qquad\qquad\qquad\qquad\qquad$ [Cl. 12.17.3.4]
When ties are provided so that the effective tie area (A_{te}) along the splice in each direction (the legs perpendicular to dimension h) satisfies $A_{te} \geq 0.0015hs$, as illustrated in Fig N12.17.3.4 and Clause N12.17.3.4) $\qquad\qquad$ 0.83

Spiral column: $\qquad\qquad\qquad\qquad\qquad\qquad\qquad\qquad\qquad\qquad\qquad\qquad\qquad$ [Cl. 12.17.3.5]
When the lap splice is confined within a spirally reinforced compression member $\qquad\qquad$ 0.75

45M and 55M bars may be lap spliced with 35M or smaller bars in a compression splice. When bars of different sizes are lap spliced in compression, the splice length shall be the larger of the development length of the larger bar from Table 3.9 or the splice length of the smaller bar from Table 3.10.
$\qquad\qquad\qquad\qquad\qquad\qquad\qquad\qquad\qquad$ [Cls. 12.14.2.1, 12.16.2 and 15.8.2.4]

The minimum lap length is 300 mm.

Table 3.11 Tension development lengths, ℓ_d (mm) for confined deformed wire with f_y = 515 MPa for normal density concrete.

$$\ell_d = 0.45\, k_1 k_2 k_3 k_4 \frac{f_y}{\sqrt{f_c'}}\, d_b$$

f_c'	Wire Size, (Area, mm²)						
MPa	MD25.8	MD32.3	MD38.7	MD45.2	MD51.6	MD58.1	MD64.5
20	240	270	290	310	340	360	380
25	210	240	260	280	300	320	340
30	190	220	240	260	270	290	310
35	180	200	220	240	250	270	280
40	170	190	210	220	240	250	270
45	160	180	190	210	220	240	250
50	150	170	180	200	210	230	240
55	140	160	180	190	200	210	230
60	140	150	170	180	190	210	220
≥ 64	130	150	160	180	190	200	210

Clear cover and clear spacing of bars must be at least $1.0 d_b$ and $1.4 d_b$, respectively.

Member must contain at least minimum stirrups or ties within length ℓ_d or,
for slabs, walls, shells, or folded plates have a clear spacing not less than $2 d_b$ between bars being developed.

The table gives development lengths for $k_1 = k_2 = k_3 = 1.0$ and $k_4 = 0.8$.

Multiply development lengths in this table by k_1, k_2, and k_3 when these differ from 1.0.   [Cl. 12.2.4]
(The product $k_1 k_2$ need not be taken greater than 1.7)

k_1 = 1.3 for horizontal reinforcement placed in such a way that more than 300 mm of fresh concrete is cast in the member below the development length or splice.
k_2 = 1.5 for epoxy-coated reinforcement with clear cover less than $3 d_b$, or with clear spacing between bars being developed less than $6 d_b$.
   = 1.2 for all other epoxy-coated reinforcement
k_3 = 1.3 for structural low-density concrete
   = 1.2 for structural semi-low-density concrete

For $f_y \neq 515$ MPa, multiply development length by $f_y/515$

The minimum permissible size of deformed wire is MD25   [Clause 3.1.3(d)]

For "Other cases" of Table 12.1 multiply the above lengths by 1.33

After application of all modification factors, the development length must not be less than 300 mm

Table 3.12 Tension development lengths, ℓ_d and lap splice lengths, ℓ_s for deformed welded wire reinforcement (WWR) with f_y = 485 MPa

$$\ell_d = 0.45\, k_1 k_2 k_3 k_4 k_5 \frac{f_y}{\sqrt{f'_c}} d_b \geq 200 \qquad\qquad \ell_s = 1.3\,\ell_d \geq 200$$

Development Length, ℓ_d					Splice Length, ℓ_s									
Wire Size	f'_c				Wire Size	d_b mm	f'_c							
	20	25	30	≥ 35			20	25	30	35	40	45	50	≥ 55
Top bars and low-density concrete k_1 and k_3 = 1.3														
MD47.6	260	230	210	200	MD47.6	7.79	340	300	280	260	240	220	210	200
MD34.9	220	200	200		MD34.9	6.67	290	260	240	220	200	200	200	
≤ MD25.7	200				MD25.7	5.74	250	220	200	200				
					MD18.7	4.88	210	200						
					≤ MD13.3	4.12	200							
Top bars and semi-low-density concrete k_1 = 1.3, k_3 = 1.2														
	20	25	≥ 30				20	25	30	35	40	45	≥ 50	
MD47.6	240	210	200		MD47.6	7.79	310	280	250	240	220	210	200	
MD34.9	210	200			MD34.9	6.67	270	240	220	200	200	200		
≤ MD25.7	200				MD25.7	5.74	230	210	200					
					≤ MD18.7	4.88	200	200						
Top bars or low-density concrete $k_1\, k_3$ = 1.3														
	≥ 20						20	25	30	≥ 35				
≤ MD47.6	200				MD47.6	7.79	260	230	210	200				
					MD34.9	6.67	220	200	200					
					≤ MD25.7	5.74	200							
Bottom bars in semi-low-density concrete k_1 = 1.0, k_3 = 1.2														
	≥ 20						20	25	≥ 30					
≤ MD47.6	200				MD47.6	7.79	240	210	200					
					MD34.9	6.67	210	200						
					≤ MD25.7	5.74	200							
Bottom bars in normal density concrete $k_1 = k_3$ = 1.0														
	≥ 20						≥ 20							
≤ MD47.6	200				≤ MD47.6	7.79	200							

The number in the wire size is the cross-sectional area of each of the longitudinal wires.

Tabulated values are based on uncoated wires with k_2 = 1.0, k_4 = 0.8 and k_5 = (485 − 240)/485 = 0.505.
[Cl. 12.7.2]
Factor, k_5, does not govern for standard mesh sizes.)

The development length, ℓ_d, for welded deformed welded wire reinforcement is measured from the end of the wire. At least one cross wire must be within the development length and not less than 50 mm from the critical section. [Cl. 12.7.2]

The lap length, ℓ_s, for welded deformed wire reinforcement is measured between the ends of the wires of each sheet. The overlap of the end cross wires must be ≥ 50 mm. [Cl. 12.18.1]

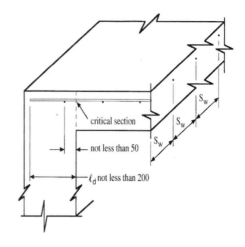

Table 3.13 Tension development lengths, ℓ_d and lap splice lengths, ℓ_s for smooth welded wire reinforcement (WWR) with f_y = 450 MPa

Designation	≤ MW11.1	≤ MW35.5	≤ MW71.0	≤ MW116
Diameter (mm)	≤ 3.80	≤ 6.73	≤ 9.50	≤ 12.17
s_w (mm)	51 X 51	102 X 102	152 X 152	203 X 203
ℓ_d (mm)	150	150	200	250
ℓ_s (mm)	150	230	300	380

The number in the designation is the cross-sectional area of the longitudinal wires (mm²)

As welded wire reinforcement has small diameters, the minimum development lengths, ℓ_d, and minimum splice lengths, ℓ_s, based on cross wire spacing, control for the sizes tabulated for all k_3 and $f'_c \geq 20$ MPa.   [Cl.12.8 and 12.19]

For larger wires the equation $\ell_d = 3.3 k_3 \dfrac{A_w}{s_w} \dfrac{f_y}{\sqrt{f'_c}}$ will govern.

The development length, ℓ_d, for smooth welded wire reinforcement is measured starting from the outer cross wire. At least two cross wires must be within the development length with the closer wire not less than 50 mm from the critical section.
The minimum development length is 150 mm.   [Cl. 12.8]

The splice length, ℓ_s, for smooth welded wire reinforcement is measured between the outermost cross wires of each sheet.   [Cl. 12.19.2]

The splice length may be less than the values tabulated above when the ratio $A_{s,provided}/A_{s,required}$ is greater than 2.0 as illustrated in Figure N12.19, with a minimum of 50 mm.   [Cl. 12.19.3]

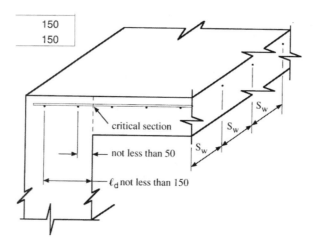

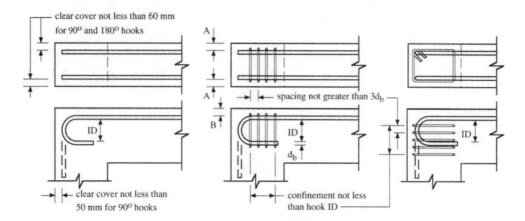

For 35M or smaller bars
Modification factor = 0.7

For 35M bars or smaller where either clear cover "A" or clear cover "B" is at least 60 mm, and at least 3 ties or stirrups with s ≯ 3d$_b$ enclose the hook over a distance not less than ID. As shown, the ties may be placed vertically or horizontally.

(a) Large concrete cover is provided
(Clause 12.5.3(b))

(b) Enclosure within ties or stirrups
(Clause 12.5.3(c))

Fig. 3.1 Modification Factors for Improved Confinement to Standard Hooks

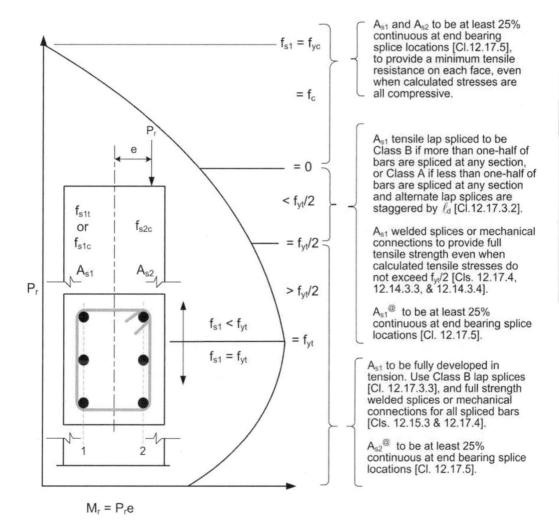

A_{s1} and A_{s2} to be at least 25% continuous at end bearing splice locations [Cl.12.17.5], to provide a minimum tensile resistance on each face, even when calculated stresses are all compressive.

A_{s1} tensile lap spliced to be Class B if more than one-half of bars are spliced at any section, or Class A if less than one-half of bars are spliced at any section and alternate lap splices are staggered by ℓ_d [Cl.12.17.3.2].

A_{s1} welded splices or mechanical connections to provide full tensile strength even when calculated tensile stresses do not exceed $f_{yt}/2$ [Cls. 12.17.4, 12.14.3.3, & 12.14.3.4].

$A_{s1}{}^{@}$ to be at least 25% continuous at end bearing splice locations [Cl. 12.17.5].

A_{s1} to be fully developed in tension. Use Class B lap splices [Cl. 12.17.3.3], and full strength welded splices or mechanical connections for all spliced bars [Cls. 12.15.3 & 12.17.4].

$A_{s2}{}^{@}$ to be at least 25% continuous at end bearing splice locations [Cl. 12.17.5].

$M_r = P_r e$

[@] Different loading conditions may produce moment reversal to switch the roles of A_{s1} and A_{s2}

Typical Notation

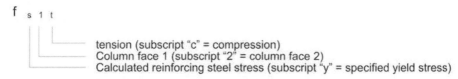

tension (subscript "c" = compression)
Column face 1 (subscript "2" = column face 2)
Calculated reinforcing steel stress (subscript "y" = specified yield stress)

A_{s1} = reinforcing steel area in column face 1 (subscript "2" = face 2)

Fig. 3.2 Special Splice Requirements for Columns (Clause 12.17)

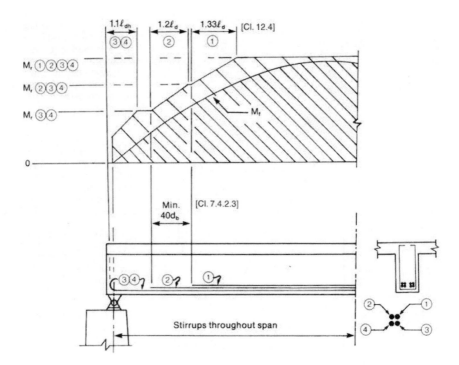

Fig. 3.3 Bundled Bars in Flexural Members

A two bar bundle is spliced in compression or tension to maintain the full strength of $2A_bf_y$, by providing staggered splices and a separate splice bar. With the splice bar, the arrangement becomes a 3 bar bundle, requiring a 20% increase in the individual bar splice length to $1.2\ell_s$ [Cl. 12.14.2.2]. Force transfer between spliced bars is assumed to occur linearly along the required splice length of $1.2\ell_s$.

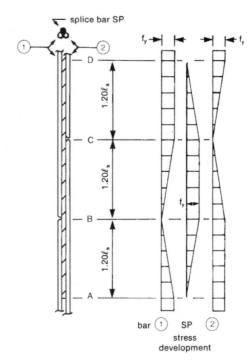

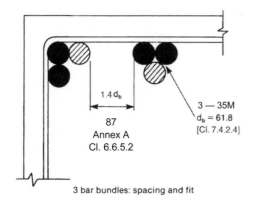

3 bar bundles: spacing and fit

(a) Bundled bar splices for full strength in tension or compression.

		Splice Bar			
	bundle configuration	⊛	⊛	⊛	⊛
	continuing bars in bundle	4	3	3	2
A	length of splice bar	*	$2(1.33\ell_s)$	$2(1.33\ell_s)$	$2(1.20\ell_s)$
	tensile resistance (%)~	0	33	33	50
B	length of splice bar	*	$4(1.33\ell_s)$	$4(1.33\ell_s)$	$3(1.20\ell_s)$
	tensile resistance (%)~	75	100	100	100

A All bars butt spliced at same location (no tensile strength).
B Butt splice locations staggered.
 * Splice bar not permitted — Makes a 5 bar bundle.
~ % of area of continuing bars.

(b) Bundled bar lap splices for tensile resistance in columns.

Fig. 3.4   Bundled Bar Splices [Cl. 12.14.2.2]

4

Michael P. Collins
Denis Mitchell
Evan C. Bentz

4

Shear and Torsion

Shear and Torsion

4.1   Introduction

Members subjected to shear and/or torsion may develop diagonal cracks. Unless these members contain appropriate amounts of properly detailed transverse and longitudinal reinforcement, these cracks can result in the premature and perhaps sudden failure of the members. Avoiding such failures is the objective of shear and torsion design.

The shear and torsion chapter of CSA standard A23.3-14 specifies two different methods of designing for shear: the sectional method appropriate for typical flexural regions and the strut-and-tie method appropriate for regions near discontinuities. Detailed comments on the individual code clauses of these two methods have been given in the "Explanatory Notes" section of this handbook. This chapter will give an overview of the two methods, background information helpful in understanding the methods, together with detailed design examples illustrating the application of both methods.

4.2   Sectional Design Method

The sectional design method is based on the "modified compression field theory" (MCFT) (Refs. 4.1, and 4.2). This theory captures the essential features of the behaviour of cracked reinforced concrete without considering all of the details. It uses the requirements of equilibrium and compatibility combined with experimentally determined stress-strain relationships for cracked concrete to predict the load-deformation behaviour of reinforced concrete elements.

The cracked web of a reinforced concrete beam transmits shear stress in a relatively complex manner. As the load is increased, new cracks open and some pre-existing cracks close. The cracks have rough surfaces capable of transmitting considerable shear stresses. The local stresses in both the concrete and the reinforcement vary from point to point, with high reinforcement stresses but low concrete tensile stresses occurring at crack locations. The MCFT considers the stresses and strains averaged over distances larger than the crack spacing in addition to the local stresses which occur at crack locations. These local stresses often govern the maximum shear capacity of the element.

To conveniently solve the equilibrium, compatibility and stress-strain relationships of the MCFT, a computer program is required. Response is such a program and enables the strains, stresses and deflections caused when loads are applied to a reinforced concrete member to be determined. This program is available in Ref. 4.3. As an example of the capabilities of this program, Fig. 4.1 compares the predicted and observed load-deformation response of a specimen representing a strip cut from a four-metre-thick one-way slab (Ref. 4.4). It can be seen that the overall load-deformation response of this large specimen is predicted accurately.

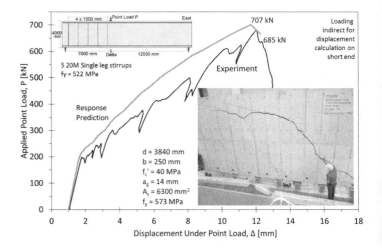

Fig. 4-1 Observed and predicted load-deformation response of large test specimen

While the MCFT is capable of accurately predicting the complete load-deformation response of a member loaded in moment, shear and axial load, for shear design it is typically only the maximum shear capacity of a section that is required. It has proved possible to develop relatively simple equations from the MCFT which are capable of predicting this capacity (Ref. 4.5). These equations form the basis of the sectional design method specified in Clause 11.3.

The factored shear strength, V_r, of a non-prestressed section with a web width of b_w and an effective shear depth of d_v ($d_v = 0.9d$) is expressed as:

$$V_r = V_c + V_s \leq 0.25\phi_c f_c' b_w d_v$$

$$V_r = \phi_c \lambda \beta \sqrt{f_c'} \cdot b_w d_v + \phi_s \frac{A_v}{s} f_y d_v \cot\theta \tag{4-1}$$

where β represents the ability of cracked concrete to transmit shear by aggregate interlock stresses and θ is the angle of inclination of the diagonal compressive stresses. Both of these parameters are functions of the longitudinal strain, ε_x, at the mid-depth of the section and are given as:

$$\beta = \frac{0.40}{(1+1500\varepsilon_x)} \cdot \frac{1300}{(1000+s_{ze})} \tag{4-2}$$

$$\theta = 29° + 7000\,\varepsilon_x \tag{4-3}$$

and $\quad \varepsilon_x = \dfrac{M_f / d_v + V_f}{2E_s A_s} \tag{4-4}$

where A_s is the area of longitudinal reinforcement on the flexural tension side of the member and s_{ze} is the effective crack spacing. If the member contains at least minimum stirrups, the value of s_{ze} is taken as 300 mm. For members without stirrups, s_{ze} is related to the crack spacing parameter s_z and the aggregate size a_g, as $s_{ze} = 35s_z/(15 + a_g)$, but $s_{ze} \geq 0.85s_z$. The crack spacing parameter s_z is the longitudinal crack spacing at mid-depth of the member between transverse cracks. As can be seen in Fig. 4-1 and Fig. 4-2, the spacing of the transverse cracks is much greater at mid-depth than it is at the flexural tension face.

For members without intermediate layers of crack control reinforcement, s_z is taken as d_v.

Note that the equation for β consists of the product of a strain effect, governed by ε_x, and a size effect governed by s_{ze}. Thus the shear strength of a member decreases as the longitudinal strain increases and, for members without stirrups, the shear stress at failure decreases as the member depth increases. For members with stirrups an increase in ε_x also causes an increase in θ which decreases $\cot\theta$ and, hence, decreases shear capacity.

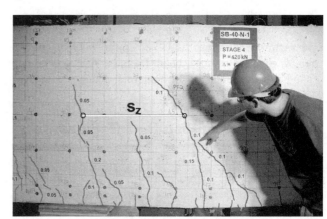

Fig. 4-2 Observed crack pattern in 1.5 metre deep slab not containing transverse reinforcement

If Eq. 4-4 indicates a reasonably high value of ε_x, it is possible that the capacity of the member may be dictated by yielding of the longitudinal reinforcement on flexural tension side. This yielding can be checked from Eq. 11-14 of the code. Thus:

$$A_s f_y \geq \frac{M_f}{d_v} + (V_f - 0.5V_s)\cot\theta \tag{4-5}$$

As an example of the use of these equations, the strength of the member described in Fig. 4-1 will be calculated. As it is desired to make the best estimate of the actual member strength, the capacity reduction factor ϕ_c will be taken as unity. In the experiment the member failed at a section about 5.5 m from the east support when the point load reached 685 kN. At this location and at this load the shear force equalled 348 kN (96 kN due to self-weight and 252 kN due to the point load) while the bending moment equalled 2279 kN·m (891 kN·m due to self-weight and 1388 kN·m due to the point load). From Eq. 4-4 the strain ε_x is calculated as $(2279 \times 10^6/3456 + 348 \times 10^3)/(2 \times 200{,}000 \times 6300) = 0.400 \times 10^{-3}$. From Eq. 4-2 the parameter β is calculated as the product of the strain effect which is $0.40/(1 + 1500 \times 0.400 \times 10^{-3}) = 0.2500$ and the size effect which is $1300/(1000 + 35 \times 3456/(15 + 14)) = 0.2514$ giving $\beta = 0.06285$. The predicted shear strength from Eq. 4-1 is thus: $0.06285 \times$ sqrt. $40 \times 250 \times 3456 = 343$ kN. Because the shear for which the strain ε_x was calculated, 348 kN, is very close to the predicted failure shear, 343 kN, no further iterations are required to determine the failure shear predicted by the CSA method.

It should be emphasized that in the design of new members, no iteration is required to determine ε_x. If the longitudinal reinforcement has been chosen and the design values of M_f, and V_f are known, ε_x can be directly calculated from Eq. 4-4. With ε_x known, β and θ are calculated from Eqns. 4-2 and 4-3 and then the required quantity of stirrups, A_v/s can be found from Eq. 4-1.

Alternatively, for the design of members where f_c' does not exceed 60 MPa and f_y does not exceed 400 MPa and where the axial tension is insignificant, the value of ε_x may be taken as 0.85×10^{-3}. In this case, Eq. 4-1 becomes

$$V_r = 0.18 \cdot \phi_c \lambda \sqrt{f_c'} \cdot b_w d_v + 1.43 \phi_s \frac{A_v}{s} f_y d_v \leq 0.25 \phi_c f_c' b_w d_v \tag{4-6}$$

while for the design of members without stirrups, constructed using concrete with at least 20 mm aggregate, Eq. 4-1 becomes:

$$V_r = \frac{230}{1000 + d_v} \cdot \phi_c \lambda \sqrt{f_c'} \cdot b_w d_v \tag{4-7}$$

Equations 4-5, 4-6 and 4-7 are the main equations of the 2014 simplified method.

The sectional design method is illustrated with the shear design of a thick one-way slab (Example 4.1), a heavily loaded coupling beam (Example 4.2), a large beam (Example 4.3), a column (Example 4.4), a spandrel beam subjected to shear, torsion and moment (Example 4.5), and a spandrel beam supporting a two-way slab (Example 4.6).

4.3   Design of Disturbed Regions

The manner in which the resisting compressive stresses flow in a beam determines the different regions that need to be considered in design. These different regions are illustrated in Fig. 4.3 and are described below.

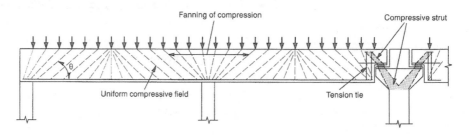

Fig. 4-3 Regions of Uniform Compressive Fields and Disturbed Regions

a) Regions of uniform compressive fields. In these regions the principal compressive stress trajectories can be approximated by a series of parallel lines at an angle of θ from the longitudinal axis of the beam, and the shear stress may be assumed to be uniformly distributed over the effective shear depth, d_v. These regions can be designed using the sectional design method.

b) Regions of fanning of compressive stresses. These disturbed regions are characterized by radiating compressive stresses near supports and in regions where the shear changes sign. These regions can also be designed using the sectional design approach.

c) Regions of compressive struts and tension ties. The flow of the forces in these disturbed regions can be visualized as struts of unidirectional compressive stresses together with ties provided by reinforcing bars. It is appropriate to design these regions using the strut-and-tie method.

The strut-and-tie model described in Clause 11.4 utilizes concepts from plasticity and truss models (Refs. 4.6, 4.7 and 4.8) developed in Europe, together with compatibility concepts from the MCFT to determine the crushing strength of the struts (Ref. 4.1 and 4.9).

The geometry of the truss, which consists of concrete compressive struts and reinforcing tension ties, is determined by following the flow of the forces from the loading points to the support reactions. The intersection of the struts with the ties or the support reactions delineate the nodal regions of multi directionally compressed concrete. Once the geometry of the truss is known the forces in the struts and ties can usually be determined by statics. The items to be checked in the design procedure with reference to the deep beam shown in Fig. 4.4 are listed below.

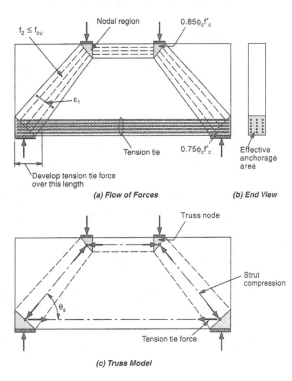

(a) Flow of Forces

(b) End View

(c) Truss Model

Fig. 4-4 Strut-and-Tie Truss Model for a Deep Beam

i. Choose bearing areas at the loading points and the support reactions such that the nodal region stresses are not exceeded.

ii. Determine the geometry of the truss by first locating the nodes of the truss at the points of intersection of the forces meeting at the nodal regions (see Fig. 4.4c). Solve for the forces in the members of the truss.

iii. Choose the tie reinforcement such that the factored resistance equals or exceeds the tie force required.

iv. Distribute the tie reinforcement such that the stress calculated by dividing the tie force by the effective area of concrete surrounding the tie reinforcement is less than the stress limit for the nodal region anchoring the tie. The effective area of concrete has the same centroid as the tie reinforcement (see Fig. 4.4b).

v. Check that the tie can develop the required tensile force at the location where the centroid of the tie crosses the edge of the strut (see Fig. 4-4a). If the embedment length is not sufficient then hooks or mechanical anchorages should be provided in accordance with the requirements of Clause 12.

vi. Check that the compressive stress, f_2, in the strut is less than the crushing limit, f_{cu}. The compressive stress, f_2, is determined by dividing the strut force by the width and the thickness of the strut. Since the compressive strut is crossed by a tie near the support nodal region (see Fig. 4.4a) then f_{cu} must be reduced to account for the presence of the principal tensile strain, ε_1. Figure N11.4.2.3 describes the variation of the crushing strength of the strut as a function of θ_s.

vii. Provide uniformly distributed pairs of well anchored reinforcing bars in the vertical and horizontal directions to control diagonal cracking and to improve the ductility of the deep beam (Clause 11.4.5).

The application of the strut-and-tie model is demonstrated in the design of a thick footing not containing shear reinforcement (Example 4.7), a deep beam subjected to concentrated loads (Example 4.8), a corbel (Example 4.9) and a beam with dapped ends (Example 4.10).

4.4　　References

4.1　　Vecchio, F.J., and Collins, M.P., "The Modified Compression Field Theory for Reinforced Concrete Elements Subjected to Shear," ACI Journal, Vol. 83, No. 2, Mar. Apr. 1986, pp. 219-231.

4.2　　Collins, M.P., Mitchell, D., Adebar, P.E., Vecchio, F.J., "A General Shear Design Method," ACI Structural Journal, Vol. 93, No. 1, Jan.-Feb. 1996, pp. 36-45.

4.3　　*http://www.ecf.utoronto.ca/~bentz/r2k.htm* last accessed Jan. 2016.

4.4　　Collins, M.P., Bentz, E.C., Quach, P.T. and Proestos, G.T. "The Challenge of Predicting the Shear Strength of Very Thick Slabs", ACI Concrete International, Vol. 37, No. 11, Nov. 2015, pp. 29-37.

4.5　　Bentz, E.C. and Collins, M.P., "Development of the 2004 CSA A23.3 Shear Provisions for Reinforced Concrete," Canadian Journal of Civil Engineering, Vol. 33, No. 5, May 2006, pp 521-534.

4.6　　Schlaich, J., Schäfer, K., and Jennewein, M., "Towards a Consistent Design of Reinforced Concrete Structures," PCI Journal, Vol. 32, No. 3, May June 1987, pp. 74-150.

4.7　　Marti, P., "Basic Tools of Reinforced Concrete Beam Design," ACI Journal, Vol. 82, No. 1, Jan. Feb. 1985, pp. 46-56.

4.8　　Nielsen, M.P., Limit Analysis and Concrete Plasticity, Prentice Hall Inc., Englewood Cliffs, N.J., 1984, 420 pp.

4.9　　Collins, M.P., and Mitchell, D., "A Rational Approach to Shear Design – The 1984 Canadian Code Provisions" Journal of the American Concrete Institute, Vol. 83, No. 6, Nov.-Dec. 1986, pp. 925-933.

4.5   Design Examples

Example 4.1   Design of Thick One-Way Slab

It is desired to construct a one-way slab without stirrups to span 16 m between two 400 mm thick bearing walls and carry a superimposed specified live of 20 kN/m² due to soil overburden. Design the slab. Use $f_c' = 30$ MPa, $a_g = 20$ mm and $f_y = 400$ MPa.

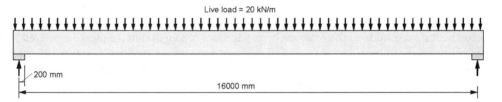

Live load = 20 kN/m

200 mm

16000 mm

1. Estimate required slab thickness

    From Table 9-2, CSA A23.3, deflections need not be calculated if the slab thickness exceeds $\ell_n/20 = (16\,000 - 400)/20 = 780$ mm. Try a total thickness of 800 mm.

2. Calculate the factored loads

    Taking a 1 m wide strip of slab and using a thickness of 800 gives:

    $w_f = 1.25D + 1.5L = 1.25 \cdot 0.8 \cdot 24 + 1.5 \cdot 20 = 24 + 30 = 54$ kN/m

3. Design longitudinal reinforcement at midspan

    The factored moment at midspan is $M_f = w_f\ell^2/8 = (54 \cdot 16^2)/8 = 1728$ kN·m

    In order to choose a trial area of reinforcement we will assume a flexural lever arm equal to $0.9d$. Assuming a cover to the bottom bars of 40 mm and assuming that 30M bars are used for the principal reinforcement, the effective depth d is $800 - 40 - 30/2 = 745$ mm. Hence, the required area of reinforcement is about

    $A_s = 1728 \cdot 10^6/(0.9 \cdot 745 \cdot 0.85 \cdot 400) = 7580$ mm²

    The minimum amount of flexural reinforcement required for this slab (Clause 7.8.1) is

    $A_s = 0.002 \cdot 800 \cdot 1000 = 1600$ mm²

    Try 30M at a spacing of 90 mm, giving $A_s = 7778$ mm². The stress block depth, a is

    $$a = \frac{\phi_s A_s f_y}{\phi_c \alpha_1 f_c' b} = \frac{0.85 \cdot 7778 \cdot 400}{0.65 \cdot 0.805 \cdot 30 \cdot 1000} = 168\,\text{mm}$$

    Hence, the factored moment resistance is

    $M_r = \phi_s A_s f_y(d - a/2) = 0.85 \cdot 7778 \cdot 400 \cdot (745 - 168/2) = 1748$ kN·m

    Since $M_r > M_f$ the flexural capacity is sufficient.

    Check the c/d limit (Clause 10.5.2). The c/d ratio must be less than or equal to $700/(700 + f_y) = 0.636$. The flexural stress block factor $\beta_1 = 0.97 - 0.0025\,f_c' = 0.895$. For this slab $c = a/\beta = 168/0.895 = 188$ mm and $c/d = 188/745 = 0.252 < 0.636$.

    Provide minimum reinforcement in the slab in the direction perpendicular to the span. Provide 25M bars at a spacing of 300 mm, giving $A_s = (1000/300) \cdot 500 = 1667$ mm²/m.

4. Check the shear strength by the simplified method

    For this simply supported, uniformly loaded slab we will first check the shear strength at a location
    a distance d_v from the face of the support. The value of d_v is taken as $0.9d = 671$ mm. At this
    location:

    $$V_f = (8 - 0.2 - 0.671) \times 54 = 385 \text{ kN}$$

    $$M_f = (0.671 + 0.2) \times 54 \times 8 - 54 \times (0.671 + 0.2)^2/2 = 356 \text{ kN·m}$$

    In the Simplified Method of shear design (Clause 11.3.6.3), the predicted shear capacity is not
    affected by the magnitude of the moment or the amount of longitudinal reinforcement and hence
    V_c for nonprestressed members is predicted to remain constant along the length of the member.
    Because of this the critical section for shear will occur near the end of the beam where the factored
    shear force has its maximum value. Checking the shear capacity at this location:

    $$V_r = V_c = \frac{230}{1000 + d_v} \phi_c \lambda \sqrt{f_c'} \, b_w d_v = \frac{230}{1000 + 671} 0.65 \times 1.0 \sqrt{30} \times 1000 \times 671 = 329 \text{ kN}$$

    As $V_r < V_f$, the shear capacity, as calculated by the simplified method, is inadequate. Therefore if
    the design is to be continued using the simplified method, it will be necessary to increase the depth
    of the slab. The simplified method assumes that $\varepsilon_x = 0.85 \times 10^{-3}$ which is appropriate for sections
    where the stress in the longitudinal reinforcement is close to the yield stress. Near the supports
    of this simple span beam, however, the moment is low and, hence, the simplified method will be
    rather conservative. Because of this, it is worthwhile to investigate the shear capacity using the
    general method before deciding whether a thicker slab is required.

5. Check the shear strength by the general method

    The shear strength determined by the general method depends on ε_x, which, in turn, is a function of
    the amount of longitudinal reinforcement and the magnitude of the applied moment. When using
    the general method to investigate the shear strength of a uniformly loaded simple span beam, it is
    found that the critical section will occur d_v from the face of the support or at a location somewhat
    further into the span. For this slab, the value of ε_x calculated at d_v from the face of the support is:

    $$\varepsilon_x = \frac{M_f/d_v + V_f}{2E_s A_s} = \frac{356 \times 10^6 /671 + 385 \times 10^3}{2 \times 200000 \times 7778} = 0.294 \times 10^{-3}$$

    For this slab with only one layer of longitudinal reinforcement made from concrete with 20 mm
    aggregate, the crack spacing parameter, s_{ze} is equal to $d_v = 671$ mm. Thus:

    $$\beta = \frac{0.4}{(1 + 1500\varepsilon_x)} \times \frac{1300}{(1000 + s_{ze})} = \frac{0.4}{(1 + 1.5 \times 0.294)} \times \frac{1300}{(1000 + 671)} = 0.216$$

    Hence:

    $$V_r = V_c = \phi_c \lambda \beta \sqrt{f_c'} \, b_w d_v = 0.65 \times 1.0 \times 0.216 \times \sqrt{30} \times 1000 \times 671 = 516 \text{ kN}$$

    As V_r exceeds V_f the shear strength is adequate at this location. Note that V_r is 34% higher than V_f
    at this location.

    To investigate whether the shear strength might be more critical at a higher moment location, the
    above calculations will be repeated for a section which is 10% of the span length from the centre
    of the support. At this location, $M_f = 622$ kN·m, and $V_f = 346$ kN. The strain ε_x is calculated as
    $0.41 \cdot 10^{-3}$ and $V_r = 461$ kN. Thus at this location the shear strength is 33% higher than the factored
    shear which is slightly more critical than for the section at d_v from the face of the support. Because
    of these large margins, it not necessary to check other locations along the span.

6. Check tensile capacity of longitudinal reinforcement at end support

From Clause 11.3.9.5 the reinforcement must be capable of resisting a tensile force of $V_f \cot\theta$. As noted in 11.3.6.4 (d), the value of ε_x used to calculate θ may be that calculated at d_v from the face of the support, i.e. $\varepsilon_x = 0.294 \times 10^{-3}$. Thus by Eq. 11-12, $\theta = 29° + 7000 \times 0.294 \times 10^{-3} = 31.1°$. Thus the tensile force that must be resisted by the longitudinal reinforcement is equal to $385/\tan(31.1°) = 639$ kN. For 30M bars with a clear spacing of 60 mm between bars the development length from Table 12-1 is

$$\ell_d = 0.45 k_1 k_2 k_3 k_4 \frac{f_y}{\sqrt{f_c'}} d_b = 0.45 \times 1.0 \times 1.0 \times 1.0 \times 1.0 \cdot \frac{400}{\sqrt{30}} 30 = 986 \text{mm}$$

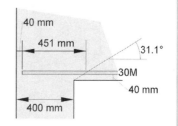

The length available for developing the tension in the longitudinal bars is illustrated in the figure and is equal to 451 mm. Hence, if all of the bars are continued into the support, the tensile capacity at the location specified in Clause 11.3.9.5 and shown in the figure is $(451/986) \cdot 0.85 \cdot 400 \cdot 7778 = 1210$ kN. As 1210 kN considerably exceeds the required force of 639 kN, consider reducing the number of bars going into the support.

7. Choose bar cut-offs

If every fourth bar is to be terminated before reaching the supports, this will reduce both the moment and shear capacities in the regions near the ends of the slab. To account for the cracking and associated tensile strains that develop near bar cut-offs in flexural tension zones ε_x is increased by 50% (Clause 11.3.6.4). Using a spreadsheet and the equations for ε_x, θ, and F_{lt}, the impact of this reduction in capacities may be readily determined. At a location of 1.1 m from the centreline of support V_f is 372.6 kN and M_f is 442.5 kN·m. If the bars are cutoff at this location then $A_s = 5833$ mm² and ε_x is:

$$\varepsilon_x = 1.5 \times \frac{M_f / d_v + V_f}{2 E_s A_s} = 1.5 \times \frac{442.5 \times 10^6 / 671 + 372.6 \times 10^3}{2 \times 200000 \times 5833} = 0.663 \times 10^{-3}$$

$$\beta = \frac{0.4}{(1 + 1500 \varepsilon_x)} \times \frac{1300}{(1000 + s_{ze})} = \frac{0.4}{(1 + 1.5 \times 0.663)} \times \frac{1300}{(1000 + 671)} = 0.156$$

Hence:

$$V_r = V_c = \phi_c \lambda \beta \sqrt{f_c'} b_w d_v = 0.65 \times 1.0 \times 0.156 \times \sqrt{30} \times 1000 \times 671 = 372.6 \text{kN}$$

Therefore, if the bars are to be cutoff, the cutoff location should be no more than 1.1 m from the centreline of support where V_r will just equal V_f.

The influence of the reduction in area of longitudinal reinforcement near the support on the factored shear resistance of the slab is shown in the figure below. It can be seen that at the bar cut-off location, the shear resistance of the slab has been reduced by about 10% due to the reduction in the area of the longitudinal reinforcement and by about an additional 13% decrease due to the localized increase of strain at the bar cut-off. However, even after allowing for these significant decreases, the shear capacity of the slab is still satisfactory at all locations along the span.

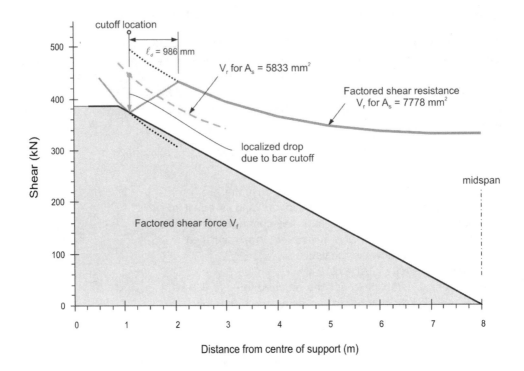

The figure below compares the force which must be resisted by the longitudinal reinforcement with the capacity of this reinforcement accounting for bar cut-offs and development length. For this slab, the choice of the bar cut-off location is controlled by the need to provide sufficient shear resistance rather than by the need for sufficient longitudinal force in the bottom bars. Because only one-quarter of the bottom bars are cutoff at a location only 1.1 m from the centreline of the support a practical solution would be to continue all the bars into the support region.

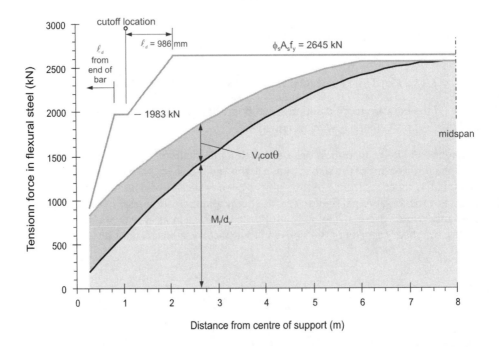

Example 4.2   Design of Coupling Beam

The lintel beams in coupled shear walls will be subjected to significant shear forces when the building is resisting wind. Further, it is often desired to keep these lintel beams shallow so that the floor-to-floor height of the building can be minimized. Because of this, the specified upper limit on shear capacity will sometimes govern the size of lintel beams.

The overall structural analysis on a building with 1250 mm long coupling beams has predicted a factored shear force in a particular coupling beam of V_f =1250 kN with corresponding end moments of M_f = ±800 kN·m. The cross section of the beam is 500 mm by 500 mm, f_c' = 50 MPa, a_g = 20 mm and f_y = 400 MPa. Design the required reinforcement and check section size.

1. Design flexural reinforcement

As the required cover is 30 mm and assuming that 15M bars will be used for the stirrups, a strain compatibility analysis indicates that with 7 – 35M bars top and bottom, the factored moment capacity will be M_r = 867 kN·m. As shown in the figure, the depth of compression at maximum capacity will be 122 mm and the effective flexural depth d = 413 mm.

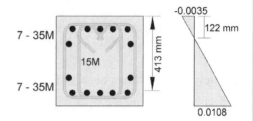

2. Check maximum shear capacity

The effective shear depth, d_v, of this section will be 0.9d = 372 mm. If the cover does not spall b_w will be 500 mm while if the cover concrete must be neglected to account for spalling in accordance with Clause 11.2.10.5 then b_w = 500 – 2 × 30 – 15 = 425 mm. If spalling is neglected then from Clause 11.3.3,

$$V_{r,max} = 0.25\phi_c f_c' b_w d_v + V_p = 0.25 \cdot 0.65 \cdot 50 \cdot 500 \cdot 372 + 0 = 1511 \text{ kN}$$

If, however, spalling must be accounted for then $V_{r,max}$ = 1511 × 425/500 = 1284 kN.
Thus even if the cover spalls the section size is large enough to resist the required 1250 kN of shear. Because the applied shear is very high, being 97% of the maximum permitted shear if cover spalling is taken into account and 83% of the maximum permitted shear if cover spalling is neglected, it will be assumed that cover spalling will need to be taken into account.

3. Design stirrups

When using the simplified method of Clause 11.3.6.3, to design the required stirrups, the basic shear strength equation can be expressed as shown in Eq. 4-6 of the introduction to this chapter as:

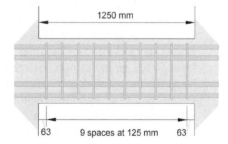

$$V_r = 0.18 \cdot \phi_c \lambda \sqrt{f_c'} \cdot b_w d_v + 1.43 \phi_s \frac{A_v}{s} f_y d_v$$

Because V_r must equal or exceed 1250 kN

$$0.18 \cdot 0.65 \cdot 1 \cdot 7.07 \cdot 425 \cdot 372 + 1.43 \cdot 0.85 \cdot (A_v/s) \cdot 400 \cdot 372 > 1250 \times 10^3 \text{ N}$$

$$A_v/s > 6.19 \text{ mm}^2/\text{mm}$$

If the stirrups have four legs of 15M, A_v = 4 · 200 = 800 mm² then, $s \leq$ 129 mm. A spacing of 125 mm is selected. The resulting stirrup layout is shown in the figure.

Note that because V_s provides more than 90% of the required shear resistance for this heavily loaded beam, reducing b_w to account for spalling has increased the required amount of stirrups by only 2%. That is the required value of A_v/s has gone from 6.06 mm²/mm to 6.19 mm²/mm. Thus while cover spalling does not significantly increase the demand on the stirrups it does very seriously reduce the shear at which diagonal crushing of the concrete will occur before yielding of the stirrups. Thus spalling reduces the maximum shear this section can resist, irrespective of the amount of stirrups provided, from 1511 kN to 1284 kN.

4. Check capacity of longitudinal reinforcement

As the walls at the ends of the lintel beam will introduce direct compression into the flexural compression face of the beam, Clause 11.3.9.4 states that "the area of longitudinal reinforcement on the flexural tension side of the member need not exceed the area required to resist the maximum moment acting alone." Because the moments will reverse direction when the direction of the wind forces change and due to the short length of the lintel beam, both the top and bottom longitudinal reinforcement will be continuous along the length of the beam and will be anchored into the walls at each end to be fully developed at the face of the wall.

Example 4.3   Design of Large Beam

The beam shown below is simply supported by 300 mm thick reinforced masonry walls and is subjected to a specified live load of 50 kN/m and a dead load of 40 kN/m (including the weight of the beam). Design the required longitudinal and transverse reinforcement to safely resist the moments and shears.

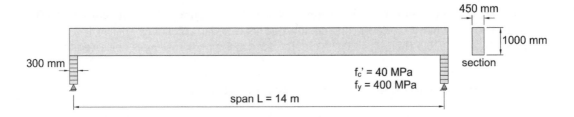

450 mm

1000 mm

section

300 mm

$f_c' = 40$ MPa
$f_y = 400$ MPa

span L = 14 m

1. Design flexural reinforcement required at midspan

The maximum factored moment, M_f, at midspan is $w_f L^2/8 = 125 \times 14^2/8 = 3062$ kN·m. For this large beam it is appropriate to use 35M bars for flexural tension reinforcement. If the required cover is 30 mm and 15M bars are used for the stirrups, layers of five 35M bars can be placed across the 450 mm width of the beam with the lowest layer being centred 65 mm from the bottom face. Note that because the overall depth of the beam exceeds 750 mm Clause 10.6.2 requires "skin reinforcement" to control crack widths near mid-depth. The large depth also results in the need for minimum shear reinforcement throughout the length of the beam. See Clause 11.2.8.1(b). The chosen reinforcement at mid-span has twelve 35M bars in three layers as the primary flexural tension reinforcement, one

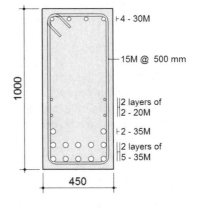

4 - 30M

15M @ 500 mm

2 layers of 2 - 20M

2 - 35M

2 layers of 5 - 35M

450

layer of four 30M bars as flexural compression reinforcement to increase the flexural lever arm and two layers of two 20M bars as skin reinforcement. See figure above of section near mid-span. The six layers of reinforcement are at 65, 150, 235, 335, 435 and 936 mm from the bottom face. The centroid of the reinforcement on the "flexural tension side" of the member (see Figure 11.2 of

A23.3) is 848 mm from top surface of the beam. Hence d equals 848 mm and d_v equals 763 mm. The factored flexural resistance, M_r, of this section was calculated using the general principals described in Clause 10.1 which can be conveniently applied using program Response (Ref. 4.3). It was determined that M_r at midspan for the section described above was 3120 kN·m, which is 2% higher than the value of M_f at this location, 3062 kN·m.

2.   Choose bar cut-off locations

Shear causes additional tension in the longitudinal reinforcement which influences the locations where the area of longitudinal reinforcement can be reduced. Clause 11.3.9.1 permits this effect to be accounted for by extending the flexural tension bars a distance of $d_v \cot\theta$ beyond the location where the bars could be cut-off if only the tension due to flexure was considered. With the simplified method of Clause 11.3.6.3 the angle θ can be taken as 35° and hence $d_v \cot\theta$ will be 763 × 1.423 which is 1090 mm. In addition, Clause 11.2.13 requires that the reduction in shear capacity caused by terminating longitudinal reinforcement in flexural tension zones be taken into account. See Fig. N11.3.6.4(c).

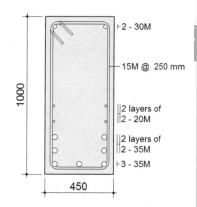

Based primarily on the bending moment diagram shown in the figure on the next page the following cut-off locations were chosen. Two of the four 30M flexural compression bars were terminated at 4.50 m from the centre of the support. This reduces M_r from 3120 kN·m to 2950 kN·m. At 2.80 m from the centre of the support three of the five 35M flexural tension bars in the second layer of bars are terminated. This further reduces M_r to 2470 kN·m and changes d from 848 mm to 847 mm. Finally, at 1.80 m from the centre of the support two of the five 35M bars in the first layer of bars are terminated, reducing M_r to 2015 kN·m and d to 826 mm which changes d_v to 743 mm and $d_v \cot\theta$ to 1061 mm. The resulting cross-section of the beam near the supports is shown in the figure above.

The Design Bending Moment Diagram on the next page shows how the above arrangement of longitudinal bar cut-offs results in factored flexural capacities, M_r, which exceed the factored applied moments, M_f, at all locations along the length of the beam. Note that the development length for the 35M flexural tension bars is 996 mm and the development length for the 30M flexural compression bars is 578 mm.

3.   Design stirrups

The stirrups are designed with the aid of the Design Shear Force Diagram shown in the figure below. The simplified method accounts for the reduction in shear capacity at a location where flexural tension bars are terminated by reducing the calculated shear strength by 15% for a distance of $d_v/2$ on each side of the cut-off. Near the end of the beam, where the shear is high, d_v equals 743 mm. At $d_v/2$ from the cut-off closest to the support, the factored shear force equals 650 plus 0.5 × 0.743 × 125.0 = 696 kN. Because of the bar cut-off the factored shear resistance at this location must equal or exceed, not 696 kN but rather 696/0.85 = 819 kN. As can be seen in the diagram this demand actually exceeds that at the section d_v from the face of the support which is 763 kN.

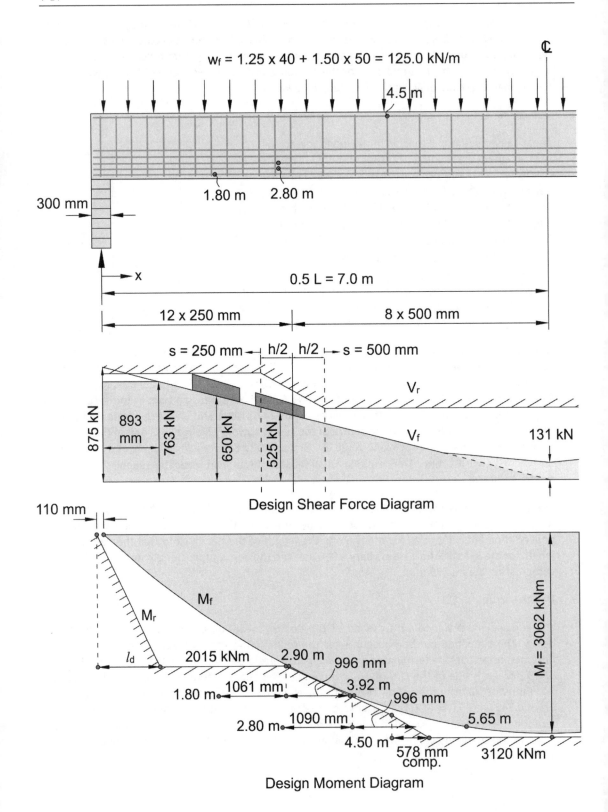

$w_f = 1.25 \times 40 + 1.50 \times 50 = 125.0$ kN/m

4.5 m

300 mm

1.80 m   2.80 m

→ x

0.5 L = 7.0 m

12 x 250 mm   8 x 500 mm

s = 250 mm → h/2   h/2 ← s = 500 mm

875 kN   893 mm   763 kN   650 kN   525 kN V_r

V_f 131 kN

Design Shear Force Diagram

110 mm

M_f

M_r

l_d

2015 kNm   2.90 m   996 mm

1.80 m   1061 mm   3.92 m

1090 mm   996 mm

2.80 m   5.65 m

4.50 m   578 mm   3120 kNm
          comp.

$M_f = 3062$ kNm

Design Moment Diagram

At cut-off locations Clause 11.2.13.3 requires that stirrup spacing, s, not exceed $0.35d_v$ which in this case is $0.35 \times 743 = 260$ mm. With s equal to 250 mm the shear resistance is:

$$V_r = 0.18 \cdot \phi_c \lambda \sqrt{f_c'} \cdot b_w d_v + 1.43 \phi_s \frac{A_v}{s} f_y d_v$$

$$V_r = 0.18 \cdot 0.65 \cdot 1 \sqrt{40} \cdot 450 \cdot 743 + 1.43 \cdot 0.85 \frac{400}{250} 400 \cdot 743 = 247.4 + 578.0 = 825 \, kN$$

As 825 kN exceeds 819 kN the stirrups spacing of 250 mm is appropriate at this critical location.

Away from cut-off locations the maximum permitted spacing of the stirrups is $0.70d_v$ which equals $0.70 \times 763 = 534$ mm. If s equals 500 mm

$$V_r = 0.18 \cdot 0.65 \cdot 1 \sqrt{40} \cdot 450 \cdot 763 + 1.43 \cdot 0.85 \frac{400}{500} 400 \cdot 763 = 254.1 + 296.8 = 551 \, kN$$

The change in stirrup spacing from 250 mm to 500 mm is made at three metres (12 × 250 mm) from the centre of the support. Based on Clause 11.3.7 the shear resistance changes linearly from 825 kN to 551 kN over a length equal to h centred on this location where the spacing actually changes. It can be seen from the Design Shear Force Diagram that this arrangement of stirrups provides an appropriate shear resistance along the span of the beam.

4. Check tensile capacity of longitudinal reinforcement at end support

From Clause 11.3.9.5, the longitudinal reinforcement on the flexural tension side of the member at the support must be capable of resisting a tensile force, F_{lt}, given by

$$F_{lt} = (V_f - 0.5V_s)\cot\theta = (763 - 0.5 \cdot 578)\cot 35° = 677 \, kN$$

For 35M bars in regions with stirrups, the development length from Table 12-1 is

$$\ell_d = 0.45 k_1 k_2 k_3 k_4 \frac{f_y}{\sqrt{f_c'}} d_b = 0.45 \cdot 1 \cdot 1 \cdot 1 \cdot 1 \frac{400}{\sqrt{40}} 35 = 996 \, mm$$

Considering only the seven 35M bars anchored at the end of the beam, the centroid of these bars is located 138 mm above the bottom face. Thus the effective embedment length of these bars is

$300 - 40 + 138 \cot 35° = 457$ mm. The tensile force that these bars can resist is thus:

$T = 7 \times 1000 \times 0.85 \times 400 \times$
$457/996 = 1092$ kN

As 1092 kN exceeds 677 kN the anchorage of the longitudinal bars at the end supports is satisfactory and the design is now complete.

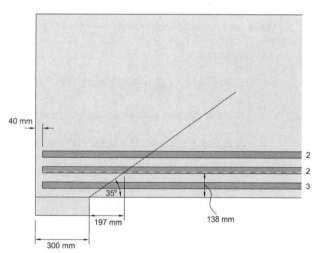

4

Shear and Torsion

Example 4.4   Design of Column for Shear

The ties in the ground storey columns of a high-rise building have been dimensioned to satisfy the column detailing requirements of Clause 7.6.5. Under wind loading, the leeward exterior columns are subjected to compression and the windward exterior columns are subjected to a tension. The two loading cases and the details of these columns are shown below.   Check if the tie reinforcement is adequate for shear and if necessary, adjust the tie spacing.

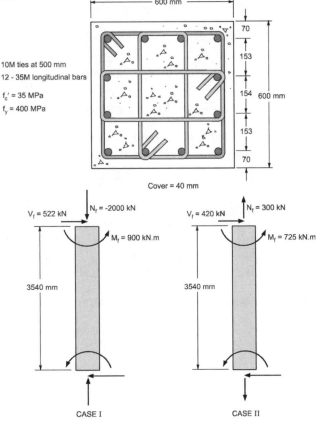

10M ties at 500 mm
12 - 35M longitudinal bars

$f_c' = 35$ MPa
$f_y = 400$ MPa

Cover = 40 mm

1.   Determine factored loads at critical section

For columns with a regular array of longitudinal steel A_s is the area of the bars in one-half of the column cross section.   Hence, $A_s = 6 \cdot 1000 = 6000$ mm² and the centroid of these 6 bars is located at a distance x from the tension face, where

$$x = \frac{70 \cdot 4000 + 223 \cdot 2000}{6000} = 121 \text{mm}$$

CASE I   CASE II

Therefore, $d = 600 - 121 = 479$ mm, and the effective shear depth $d_v = 0.9d = 0.9 \cdot 479 = 431$ mm.

At the critical section, d_v from the ends of the column, the factored loads are:

a)   Case I $V_f = 522$ kN $N_f = -2000$ kN $M_f = 900 - 522 \cdot 0.431 = 675$ kN·m

b)   Case II $V_f = 420$ kN $N_f = +300$ kN $M_f = 725 - 420 \cdot 0.431 = 544$ kN·m

2.   Check that the section is large enough to resist the required shear

$$V_{max} = 0.25\phi_c f_c' b_w d_v = 0.25 \times 0.65 \times 40 \times 400 \times 452.3 = 1176 \text{ kN} > V_f = 522 \text{ kN}$$

as the factored shear force that must be resisted, V_f, is less than the maximum possible shear resistance, $V_{r,max}$, the section size is adequate.

3.   Determine required tie spacing for Case I

For this member, subjected to an axial force of -2000 kN, the longitudinal strain, ε_x, from Eq. 11-13 of Clause 11.3.6.4 is:

$$\varepsilon_x = \frac{M_f/d_v + 0.5N_f + V_f}{2A_s E_s} = \frac{675 \cdot 10^6 / 431 + 0.5 \cdot (-2000 \cdot 10^3) + 522 \cdot 10^3}{2 \cdot 200000 \cdot 6000} = 0.453 \cdot 10^{-3}$$

As this column will contain at least minimum ties, s_{ze} = 300 mm and substituting this into Eq. 11-11 gives:

$$\beta = \frac{0.4}{1+1500\varepsilon_x} \cdot \frac{1300}{(1000+s_{ze})} = \frac{0.4}{1+1500\cdot0.453\cdot10^{-3}} \cdot \frac{1300}{(1000+300)} = 0.238$$

Substitition into Eq. 11-12 produces: θ = 29° + 7000ε_x = 29° + 7000 · 0.453 · 10^{-3} = 32.2°

Thus from Eq. 11-6 $V_c = \phi_c\lambda\beta\sqrt{f_c'}b_wd_v = 0.65\cdot1.0\cdot0.238\cdot\sqrt{35}\cdot600\cdot431 = 237\,kN$

The shear to be carried by the ties is thus equal to V_s = 522 − 237 = 285 kN. From Eq. 11-7 the required spacing is:

$$s \le \frac{\phi_s A_v f_y d_v \cot\theta}{V_s} = \frac{0.85\cdot4\cdot100\cdot400\cdot431\cdot\cot32.2°}{285\cdot10^3} \le 327\,mm$$

4.   Determine required tie spacing for Case II

With an axial tension of 300 kN, ε_x is equal to:

$$\varepsilon_x = \frac{544\cdot10^6/431+0.5\cdot(+300\cdot10^3)+420\cdot10^3}{2\cdot200000\cdot6000} = 0.763\cdot10^{-3}$$

With s_{ze} = 300 mm:

$$\beta = \frac{0.4}{1+1500\cdot0.763\cdot10^{-3}} \cdot \frac{1300}{(1000+300)} = 0.186$$

and: θ = 29° + 7000ε_x = 29° + 7000 · 0.763 · 10^{-3} = 34.3°

$$V_c = \phi_c\lambda\beta\sqrt{f_c'}b_wd_v = 0.65\cdot1.0\cdot0.186\cdot\sqrt{35}\cdot600\cdot431 = 185\ kN$$

The shear to be carried by the ties is thus equal to V_s = 420 − 185 = 235 kN. Hence

$$s \le \frac{0.85\cdot4\cdot100\cdot400\cdot431\cdot\cot34.3°}{235\cdot10^3} \le 366\,mm$$

Note that the load case with high axial compression and high shear is more critical than the load case with axial tension and shear.

5.   Check maximum spacing requirements.

Clause 11.3.8.3 reduces the maximum stirrup spacing by one-half if:

$V_f > 0.125\lambda\phi_c f_c'b_wd_v$ = 0.125 × 1.0 × 0.65 × 35 × 600 × 431 = 735 kN

As the maximum applied shear is less than this value, the maximum tie spacing is that given by Clause 11.3.8.1 namely 600 mm or 0.7d_v = 0.7 · 431 = 302 mm.

The minimum amount of shear reinforcement from Clause 11.2.8.2 requires a spacing of

$$s \le \frac{A_v f_y}{0.06\sqrt{f_c'}\cdot b_w} = \frac{4\cdot100\cdot400}{0.06\sqrt{35}\cdot600} \le 751\,mm$$

6.   Final choice of tie spacing

The tie spacing is governed by the maximum spacing for shear reinforcement. Thus use a tie spacing of 300 mm.

Example 4.5   Design of Spandrel Beam Supporting Balcony Slab

The balcony slab shown below is subjected to a specified live load of 3 kN/m² and, its own self weight. Design the longitudinal and transverse reinforcement required in the spandrel beam. Assume the beam is fully fixed against rotation at the column faces. Note that in this example the torsion is required for equilibrium and hence it is not a function of the torsional stiffness of the spandrel beam.

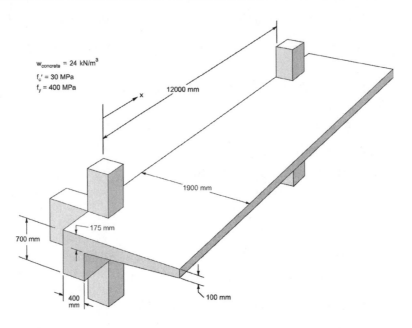

$w_{concrete} = 24$ kN/m³
$f_c' = 30$ MPa
$f_y = 400$ MPa

12000 mm

1900 mm

175 mm

700 mm

400 mm

100 mm

1. Determine loads acting on spandrel beam

   Take a 1 m length of slab and beam.

   $w_f = 1.25D + 1.50L = 1.25 \cdot (6.72$
   $+ 1.35 + 3.60) + 1.50 \cdot 5.70$
   $= 23.14$ kN/m

   $D_1 = 0.4 \cdot 0.7 \cdot 24 = 6.72$ kN/m

   $D_2 = 0.5 \cdot 1.5 \cdot 0.075 \cdot 24 = 6.72$ kN/m

   $D_3 = 1.5 \cdot 0.10 \cdot 24 = 3.60$ kN/m

   $m_f = 1.25 \cdot [1.35 \cdot (0.20 + 0.50) + 3.60 \cdot (0.20 + 0.75)]$
   $+ 1.5 \cdot 5.70 \cdot (0.95 - 0.20) = 11.87$ kN·m/m

   $\frac{1900}{2}$

   $L = 1 \times 1.9 \times 3 = 5.70$ kN/m

   500

   D_3

   $\frac{1500}{2}$

   200

   D_1

   D_2

2. Determine M_f, T_f, V_f along spandrel.

   See figure below

3. Check if torsion is significant

   From Clause 11.2.9.1

   $$T_{cr} = (A_c^2 / p_c) \cdot 0.38\lambda\phi_c\sqrt{f_c'} = \frac{(400 \cdot 700)^2}{2 \cdot (400 + 700)} \cdot 0.38 \cdot 1.0 \cdot 0.65 \cdot \sqrt{30} \cdot 10^{-6} = 48.2 \, \text{kN} \cdot \text{m}$$

   As T_f will exceed $0.25T_{cr}$, which is 12.1 kN·m, torsion must be considered.

4.   Determine section parameters b_w, d_v, A_{oh}, p_h

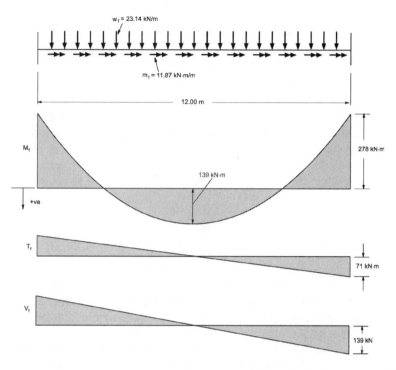

4

Shear and Torsion

Assume cover = 40 mm. Also assume that 25M longitudinal bars and 10M closed stirrups will be used.

b_w = 400 mm

d = 700 – 40 – 10 – 25/2 = 637.5 mm d_v = 0.9d = 0.9 · 637.5 = 574 mm

A_{oh} = 310 · 610 = 189 · 10³ mm² p_h = 2 · (310 + 610) = 1840 mm

5.   Design of closed stirrups near support

At critical section d_v from the face of the support

V_f = 139 – 23.14 · 0.574 = 125.7 kN

T_f = 71 – 11.87 · 0.574 = 64.2 kN·m

$$M_f = -278 + \left(\frac{139 + 125.7}{2}\right)0.574 = -202 \, \text{kN·m}$$

The maximum shear stress limit is checked by Eq. 11-19 of Clause 11.3.10.4.

$$\sqrt{\left(\frac{V_f}{b_w d_v}\right)^2 + \left(\frac{T_f p_h}{1.7 A_{oh}^2}\right)^2} \le 0.25 \lambda \phi_c f_c'$$

$$\sqrt{\left(\frac{125.7 \times 10^3}{400 \times 574}\right)^2 + \left(\frac{64.2 \times 10^6 \times 1840}{1.7 \cdot \left(189 \times 10^3\right)^2}\right)^2} \le 0.25 \cdot 1.0 \cdot 0.65 \cdot 30$$

$$\sqrt{(0.547)^2 + (1.945)^2} \le 4.88$$

$$2.02 \le 4.88 \text{ MPa}$$

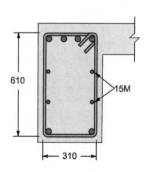

610

15M

310

Since this condition is satisfied, the cross section is large enough to carry the combined shear and torsion.

Design the member with the simplified method whereby $\beta = 0.18$ and $\theta = 35°$ by Clause 11.3.6.3.

The shear carried by the concrete is:

$$V_c = \phi_c \lambda \beta \sqrt{f_c'} b_w d_v = 0.65 \cdot 1.0 \cdot 0.18 \cdot \sqrt{30} \cdot 400 \cdot 574 \cdot 10^{-3} = 147.1 \, \text{kN}$$

As $V_c > V_f$, no stirrups are required to resist the shear in this beam. Had they been required, the parameter A_v/s would have been calculated by Clause 11.3.5 to provide the required stirrup area for shear.

The amount of closed stirrups required for torsion, from Eq. 11-17 of Clause 11.3.10 is:

$$\frac{A_t}{s} = \frac{T_r}{2 A_o \phi_s f_y \cot \theta}$$

where $A_o = 0.85 A_{oh}$. Hence:

$$\frac{A_t}{s} = \frac{64.2 \cdot 10^6}{2 \cdot 0.85 \cdot 189 \cdot 10^3 \cdot 0.85 \cdot 400 \cdot \cot 35°} = 0.412 \, \text{mm}^2/\text{mm}$$

Thus while for this example stirrups are not needed for shear, they are required for resisting the applied torsion. According to Clause 11.3.10.1, the transverse reinforcement required shall be equal to the sum of that required for shear and the coexisting torsion, See Figure N11.3.10.1 in the explanatory notes. Recognizing that the term A_v is the area of two stirrup legs and A_t is the area of a single leg, the required spacing of the 10M closed stirrups can be found from:

$$\frac{A_t}{s} + 0.5 \frac{A_v}{s} = 0.412 + 0.5 \cdot 0.0 = 0.412 \, \text{mm}^2/\text{mm} \qquad \text{Hence:} \qquad s \leq \frac{100}{0.412} = 243 \, \text{mm}$$

Clause 11.3.8.3 states that for all sections where $T_f > 0.25 T_{cr}$ the spacing of transverse reinforcement shall not exceed 300 mm nor $0.35 d_v = 0.35 \cdot 574 = 201$ mm.

The maximum spacing required to satisfy the minimum transverse reinforcement requirements of Clause 11.2.8.2 is:

$$s \leq \frac{A_v f_y}{0.06 \sqrt{f_c'} \cdot b_w} = \frac{2 \cdot 100 \cdot 400}{0.06 \sqrt{30} \cdot 400} \leq 609 \, \text{mm}$$

Therefore, provide closed 10M stirrups at a spacing of 200 mm at this location.

6. Determine where wider stirrup spacing can be used

   From step 5 it is clear that the stirrup spacing in this example is controlled by the maximum spacing of a 10M closed stirrup in regions where $T_f > 0.25 T_{cr}$. To allow wider stirrup spacing near the centre of the spandrel beam, determine where this condition no longer applies. That is, determine where the applied factored torsion is less than 12.1 kN·m. From the applied torsion diagram, this can be seen to occur 5 metres from the face of the supports where the torsion will equal $71 - 5 \cdot 1.87 = 11.65$ kN·m. Hence for a region about 2 m long near midspan the spacing of the closed stirrups will be increased from 200 mm to 400 mm.

7. Design of longitudinal reinforcement at support face

   Torsion will increase the need for longitudinal reinforcement, even at sections of maximum moment. Torsion is resisted by diagonal compressive stresses that spiral around all faces of the section, which increases the demand for tensile capacity in the longitudinal reinforcement. In addition, the support reactions resisting torsion do not introduce direct compression into the flexural compression face of the member.

At the support face: V_f = 139 kN T_f = 71 kN·m M_f = 278 kN·m

From Clauses 11.3.9.2 and 11.3.10.6, the required tension force in the longitudinal reinforcement on the flexural tension side is:

$$F_{lt} = \frac{M_f}{d_v} + \cot\theta \sqrt{\left(V_f - 0.5V_s\right)^2 + \left(\frac{0.45 p_h T_f}{2A_o}\right)^2}$$

$$= \frac{278 \cdot 10^6}{574} + \cot 35° \sqrt{\left(139 \cdot 10^3 - 0.5 \cdot 0.0\right)^2 + \left(\frac{0.45 \cdot 1840 \cdot 71 \cdot 10^6}{2 \cdot 189 \cdot 10^3}\right)^2}$$

$$= 484 \cdot 10^3 + 297.9 \cdot 10^3 = 782 \, kN$$

Therefore the required area of the fully developed longitudinal reinforcement in the top half of the beam is

$$A_s \geq \frac{782 \cdot 10^3}{0.85 \cdot 400} = 2300 \, mm^2$$

With an overall depth of 700 mm, this spandrel beam is just below the size where longitudinal skin reinforcement is required for crack control by Clause 10.6.2. However, for such large beams subjected to torsion, it is good practice to provide some of the required longitudinal reinforcement as bars distributed down the sides. In this case use two intermediate layers each containing two 15M bars. Near the top face of the beam use 4 – 25M bars. Hence in the top half of the beam

A_s = 4 · 500 + 2 · 200 = 2400 mm²

At the bottom face of the beam, at the support, the compression from the flexure dominates and hence, we need only satisfy the requirements of Clause 12.11.1 that one-fourth of the bottom steel extend into the support.

In order to verify that the longitudinal reinforcement will yield, we will calculate the depth of compression, c, required to balance the total tensile force required, T = 782 kN. In calculating the stress block depth, a, the stress block factor $\alpha_1 = 0.85 - 0.0015 f_c' = 0.805$. Hence,

$$a = \frac{F_{lt}}{\alpha_1 \phi_c f_c' b} = \frac{782 \cdot 10^3}{0.805 \cdot 0.65 \cdot 30 \cdot 400} = 124 \, mm$$

The stress block factor $\beta_1 = 0.97 - 0.0025 f_c' = 0.895$ and therefore the depth of compression, $c = a/\beta_1 = 124/0.895 = 139$ mm. The ratio $c/d = 139/637 = 0.218$ which is less than the yield limit given in Clause 10.5.2 as $700/(700 + f_y) = 0.636$. Therefore the longitudinal reinforcement will yield.

8. Determine required reinforcement at point of contraflexure

The point of contraflexure is located 2.54 m from the face of the support. At this location:

V_f = 80.2 kN T_f = 41.0 kN·m M_f = 0 kN·m

The required tension force at this location is therefore:

$$F_{lc} = F_{lt} \geq \frac{0}{574} + \cot 35° \sqrt{\left(80.2 \cdot 10^3 - 0.5 \cdot 0.0\right)^2 + \left(\frac{0.45 \cdot 1840 \cdot 41 \cdot 10^6}{2 \cdot 189 \cdot 10^3}\right)^2} \geq 172.0 \, kN$$

This tensile force is required for both the top and bottom halves of the beam, see Clauses 11.3.9.3 and 11.3.10.6. The area of longitudinal reinforcement required for both the top and bottom halves of the beam is thus:

$$A_s \geq \frac{172.0 \cdot 10^3}{0.85 \cdot 400} = 506 \, mm^2$$

Hence provide 2 – 25M bars, top and bottom, to support the stirrups, plus the 2 – 15M distributed bars in each half. Thus $A_s = 2 \cdot 500 + 2 \cdot 200 = 1400 \, mm^2$.

Note that Clause 11.2.7 requires that the diameter of the longitudinal bars in the corners of the closed hoops required for torsion not be less than $s/16 = 200/16 = 12.5$ mm.

These bars will also satisfy the requirements of Clause 12.12.2 that at least one-third of the total tension reinforcement must extend beyond the point of inflection.

9. Determined required longitudinal reinforcement at midspan

    At midspan the factored moment is 139 kN·m. We will estimate the required reinforcement assuming a lever arm of $0.9d = 574$ mm. Hence, the required force is $139/0.574 = 242$ kN and the required $A_s = 242 \cdot 10^3/(0.85 \cdot 400) = 712 \, mm^2$. Therefore use 2 – 25M bars.

    A check of the flexural capacity is carried out below.

    $$a = \frac{\phi_s A_s f_y}{\alpha_1 \phi_c f_c' b} = \frac{0.85 \cdot 1000 \cdot 400}{0.805 \cdot 0.65 \cdot 30 \cdot 400} = 54 \, mm$$

    $$M_r = \phi_s A_s f_y (d - a/2) = 0.85 \cdot 1000 \cdot 400 \cdot (637 - 54/2) = 207 \, kN·m \geq M_f$$

    $$c/d = \frac{(54/0.895)}{637} = 0.095 \leq 0.636$$

10. Bar cut-off locations

    The figure shows the variations of required tensile force in the longitudinal reinforcement, as well as the factored resistance of the reinforcement provided. For this beam, with closed stirrups, the tensile development length for the bottom bars (from Table 12-1) is:

    $$\ell_d = 0.45 k_1 k_2 k_3 k_4 \frac{f_y}{\sqrt{f_c'}} d_b$$

    $$= 0.45 \cdot 1 \cdot 1 \cdot 1 \cdot 1 \frac{400}{\sqrt{30}} 25$$

    $$= 822 \, mm$$

    For the top bars $\ell_d = 1.3 \cdot 822 = 1068$ mm.

    The bar cut-offs are illustrated in the figure. In determining the factored tensile resistance of the steel, it has been assumed that the bar force varies linearly over the development length.

    Note that because the bar cut-off locations are not in flexural tension zones Clause 11.2.13 does not apply.

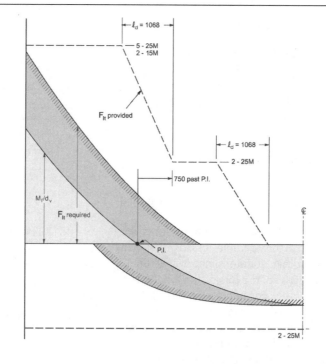

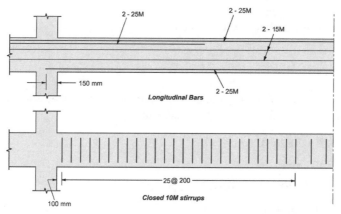

Example 4.6 Torsional Design of Spandrel Beam in Two-Way Slab

The analysis of a two-way slab has resulted in a calculated factored moment at the edge of the slab of 17.57 kN·m/m. This moment causes torsions in the spandrel beams as shown in the figure. Note that each spandrel beam has a clear span of 7100 mm. In addition, the spandrel beam has a factored moment, M_f, at the face of the column, of 135.3 kN·m, while the factored shear, d_v from the face of the column, is 83.5 kN.

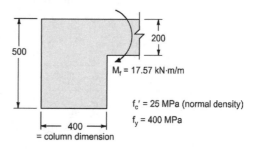

M_f = 17.57 kN·m/m

f_c' = 25 MPa (normal density)
f_y = 400 MPa

400
= column dimension

1. Determine if torsion is significant

The cracking torque, T_{cr}, from Clause 11.2.9.1 is:

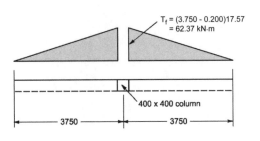

$T_f = (3.750 - 0.200)17.57$
$= 62.37$ kN·m

$$T_{cr} = \left(A_c^2 / p_c\right) \cdot 0.38\lambda\phi_c\sqrt{f_c'}$$

$$= \frac{(400 \cdot 500)^2}{2 \cdot (400 + 500)} 0.38 \cdot 1.0 \cdot 0.65 \cdot \sqrt{25} \cdot 10^{-6}$$

$$= 27.4 \text{ kN} \cdot \text{m}$$

400 x 400 column

3750   3750

Since T_f exceeds $0.25T_{cr} = 6.85$ kN·m, torsion must be considered.

2. Adjust torsion diagram to account for redistribution

When a reinforced concrete beam cracks in torsion, there is a considerable loss of torsional stiffness. In statically indeterminate structures, where the magnitude of the torsion is a function of the torsional stiffness, considerable redistribution occurs after torsional cracking. Because of this, Clause 11.2.9.2 permits the maximum torsion at the face of the support to be reduced to $0.67T_{cr}$ provided that appropriate adjustments are made to the moments in adjoining members. The resulting torsions are illustrated in the adjoining figure.

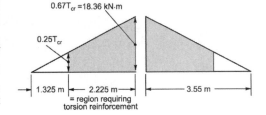

$0.67T_{cr} = 18.36$ kN·m

$0.25T_{cr}$

1.325 m | 2.225 m | 3.55 m
= region requiring torsion reinforcement

3. Check if section size is adequate

Determine required cross-sectional properties. Assuming 10M closed stirrups, 20M longitudinal bars, and a clear cover of 30 mm for interior exposure gives

$d = 500 - 30 - 10 - 20/2 = 450$ mm

$d_v = 0.9 \cdot 450 = 405$ mm

$A_{oh} = (500 - 60 - 10)(400 - 60 - 10) = 141\,900$ mm²

$p_h = 2(430 + 330) = 1520$ mm

V_f at a distance d_v from the face of the support is 83.5 kN. T_f at d_v from the face of the support is:

$$T_f = \frac{(3.55 - 0.405)}{3.55} \cdot 18.36 = 16.27 \text{ kN} \cdot \text{m}$$

Checking the maximum combined shear and torsion with Eq. 11.19 of Clause 11.3.10.4(b):

$$\sqrt{\left(\frac{V_f}{b_w d_v}\right)^2 + \left(\frac{T_f p_h}{1.7 A_{oh}^2}\right)^2} \leq 0.25\lambda\phi_c f_c'$$

$$\sqrt{\left(\frac{83.5 \cdot 10^3}{400 \cdot 405}\right)^2 + \left(\frac{16.27 \cdot 10^6 \cdot 1520}{1.7 \cdot (141900)^2}\right)^2} \leq 0.25 \cdot 1.0 \cdot 0.65 \cdot 25$$

$$\sqrt{(0.515)^2 + (0.723)^2} \leq 4.06$$

$$0.89 \leq 4.06 \text{ MPa}$$

Therefore the section size is adequate.

4. Design of transverse reinforcement for shear and torsion

As this design will be performed with the simplified method, from Clause 11.3.6.3, $\beta = 0.18$, $\theta = 35°$. At the section d_v from the face of the support, the required amount of closed stirrups for torsion can be calculated from Clause 11.3.10.3 as:

$$\frac{A_t}{s} = \frac{T_r}{2A_o\phi_s f_y \cot\theta} = \frac{16.27\cdot10^6}{2\cdot0.85\cdot141900\cdot0.85\cdot400\cdot\cot35°} = 0.1389\,\text{mm}^2/\text{mm}$$

From Clause 11.3.5.1, the shear carried by the concrete, V_c, is:

$$V_c = \phi_c\lambda\beta\sqrt{f_c'}\cdot b_w d_v = 0.65\cdot1\cdot0.18\cdot\sqrt{25}\cdot400\cdot405 = 94.8\,\text{kN}$$

As V_f is less than V_c, no shear reinforcement is required to satisfy the strength requirement.

Hence the total amount of closed stirrups required to provide the required shear and torsional strengths is:

$$\frac{A_t}{s} + 0.5\frac{A_v}{s} = 0.1389 + 0.5\cdot0.0 = 0.1389\,\text{mm}^2/\text{mm}$$

The required spacing of 10M closed stirrups is therefore 100/0.1389 = 720 mm.

Clause 11.2.8.1(c) requires that a minimum amount of transverse reinforcement be provided. The required spacing of 10M closed stirrups is:

$$s \le \frac{A_v f_y}{0.06\sqrt{f_c'}\cdot b_w} = \frac{2\cdot100\cdot400}{0.06\sqrt{25}\cdot400} \le 667\,\text{mm}$$

As the factored torsion exceeds $0.25T_{cr}$, Clause 11.3.8.3 indicates that the maximum stirrup spacing shall not exceed 300 mm or $0.35d_v = 0.35\cdot405 = 142$ mm. Therefore, provide stirrups at 140 mm.

According to Clause 11.2.9, no stirrups are required when the factored torque is less than $0.25T_{cr}$. This occurs at a distance of 2.225 m from the face of the column (see figure).

5. Design of longitudinal reinforcement

The factored moment at the face of the column

$M_f = 135.3$ kN·m, $\qquad T_f = 18.36$ kN·m, and $\qquad V_f = 83.5$ kN.

Checking the demand on the longitudinal reinforcement:

$$F_{lt} \ge \frac{M_f}{d_v} + \cot\theta\sqrt{\left(V_f - 0.5V_s\right)^2 + \left(\frac{0.45p_h T_f}{2A_o}\right)^2}$$

$$\ge \frac{135.3\cdot10^6}{405} + \cot35°\sqrt{\left(83.5\cdot10^3 - 0.5\cdot0.0\right)^2 + \left(\frac{0.45\cdot1520\cdot18.36\cdot10^6}{2\cdot141900}\right)^2}$$

$$\ge 334\times10^3 + 135\times10^3$$

$$\ge 469\,\text{kN}$$

Thus the reinforcement on the flexural tension side must be able to resist a force of 469 kN. This requires an area of reinforcement of:

$$A_s \ge \frac{469\times10^3}{0.85\times400} = 1379\,\text{mm}^2$$

Hence use 3 – 25M as flexural tension reinforcement. From Clause 11.3.9.3 it can be determined that the flexural compression force is larger than the component due to torsion and shear. Provide 2 – 20M bars to anchor stirrup legs.

Note: The design of the spandrel beam assumed redistribution of moments after torsional cracking. This gives reduced torsions in the spandrel beam and therefore, the moments in the design strips perpendicular to the spandrel must be adjusted accordingly. That is, the end moments should be reduced and the positive moment increased.

Example 4.7   Design of a Thick Footing Not Containing Shear Reinforcement

The footing shown below supports two 750 mm thick reinforced concrete walls. The centre-to-centre distance between the two walls is 8.0 m while as a first estimate the cross section of the footing is chosen 1300 mm thick and 2.75 m wide. The factored axial load, P_f, at the base of the wall is 2890 kN. The specified concrete compressive strength, f_c', is 35 MPa and the specified yield strength of the reinforcing steel is 400 MPa. The nominal maximum size of coarse aggregate is 20 mm. The footing has been designed for flexure and contains 24 – 30M top headed bars (100 mm diameter circular heads) and 9 – 15M headed bottom bars (50 mm diameter circular heads). The clear cover on the heads of the headed bars is 50 mm.

Design the footing to resist the factored forces without using shear reinforcement.

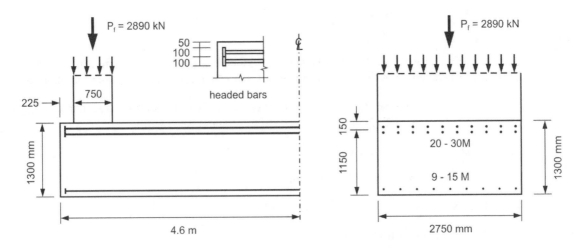

Initial design with 1300 mm thick footing

The shear capacity of the footing can be calculated by using either the CSA sectional design method or the CSA strut-and-tie method. The former corresponds to the initiation of slip on the critical shear crack while the latter corresponds to a state of redistributed internal forces after significant cracking has occurred.

1.   Calculate sectional shear capacity of 1300 mm thick footing

The sectional design procedure of Clause 11.3.6 will first be used to calculate the shear resistance. It is assumed that the soil reaction is uniformly distributed across the bottom face of the footing, and thus the upward load per unit length along the footing is:

$$w_f = \frac{2890}{4.6} = 628\,\text{kN/m}$$

The critical section will be located either at a distance d_v from the inner face of the wall or if the loads within this distance contribute more than 20% of the shear then the critical section needs to be taken at $0.5d_v$ from the face (see Clause 11.3.2). The effective shear depth d_v is taken as $0.9d = 0.9 \times 1150 = 1035$ mm. The distance from the end of the footing to the section d_v from the inner face of the wall is $225 + 750 + 1035 = 2010$ mm. At this section:

$$V_f = 2890 - 628 \times 2.01 = 1628 \text{ kN}$$

The distance from the end of the footing to the inner face of the wall is $225 + 750 = 975$ mm. At this section, the factored shear is:

$$V_f = 2890 - 628 \times 0.975 = 2278 \text{ kN}$$

Thus the ratio of the shear at the face to the shear at d_v from the face is $2278/1628 = 1.40$. As this ratio exceeds 1.2 the loads applied within distance d_v increase the magnitude of the shear at the face by more than 20% and hence the critical section will be taken at $0.5d_v$ from the face (Clause 11.3.2.2). At this section the shear is:

$$V_f = 2890 - 628 \times (0.975 + 1.035/2) = 1953 \text{ kN}$$

The distance from the point of zero shear to the face of the wall is 3.625 m. Note that because $3625/1035 = 3.50$ is greater than 2.0, Clause 11.3.6.2 for "special member types" cannot be used for this footing.

Using the "simplified method" of Clause 11.3.6.3, the value of β is given as:

$$\beta = \frac{230}{1000 + d_v} = \frac{230}{1000 + 1035} = 0.113$$

For this footing without transverse reinforcement:

$$V_r = V_c = \phi_c \lambda \beta \sqrt{f_c'} b_w d_v = 0.65 \times 1.0 \times 0.113 \times \sqrt{35} \times 2750 \times 1035 \times 10^{-3} = 1237 \text{ kN}$$

Because $V_r = 1237$ kN is less than $V_f = 1953$ kN the sectional shear capacity of the footing determined by the sectional design approach is insufficient. It is noted that even if the "general method" of Clause 11.3.6.4 were used the sectional shear capacity will still be insufficient.

Recalling that the shear resistance of a member is the larger of the shear determined from the sectional model and the shear determined from the strut-and-tie model, see Fig. N11.1.2(b), the next step is to check whether the strut-and-tie approach will produce higher factored shear resistance than the sectional approach.

2. Strut-and-tie capacity of 1300 mm thick footing

The 2014 CSA standard permits the use of the strut-and-tie model (see figure below). The dashed lines represent compressive struts and the solid line represents the tension tie. In this model the lever arm of the internal longitudinal forces at the midspan section is assumed to be $d_v = 1035$ mm. The uniform soil reaction on the bottom face of the footing is represented by a statically equivalent system of 6 point loads of 458.1 kN and a load of 141.3 kN on the short cantilevering part of the footing. The 141.3 kN load is relatively small and located very close to the column, and hence it is not included in the strut-and-tie model.

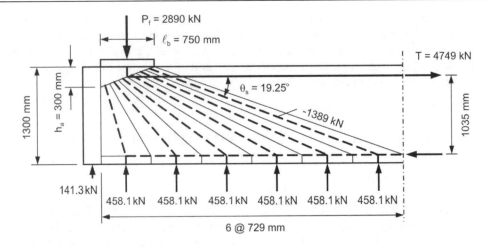

Strut-and-tie model for initial design with 1300 mm thick footing

The factored bending moment at midspan is:

M_f = 2890 × 4.0 − 628 × 4.6 × 4.6/2 = 4915 kN·m

The factored tension force in the top reinforcement is:

$T_f = M_f/d_v$ = 4915 × 10³/1035 = 4749 kN

The dimensions of the triangular nodal region under the column are determined based on the width of the column and the distance from the top face of the footing to the centroid of the top reinforcement (tie). These dimensions are used to determine the effective anchorage area. The maximum stress in the nodal region occurs on vertical planes and equals 4749 × 1000/(300 × 2750) = 5.75 MPa which is much less than the code limit of 0.75$\phi_c m f_c'$ = 0.75 × 0.65 × 1.0 × 35 = 17.1 MPa for node regions anchoring a one-direction tie.

The inclined face of the node region is divided into six equal segments which correspond to the six tributary areas on the bottom face of the footing. It is assumed that the point loads of 458.1 kN are transmitted to the nodal zone by direct struts that form a compression fan. The strut closest to the midspan of the footing is critical as it carries the largest compressive force of 1389 kN and has the smallest angle with respect to the tie. The dashed centreline of this strut intersects the inclined nodal face 1/12 of h_a below the top face. The horizontal projection of this strut centreline can be determined as: H = 6 × 729 − 729/2 − (11/12) × 750 = 3322 mm

The vertical projection of this strut is V = 1035 + 150 − (1/12) × 300 = 1160 mm

Hence the angle between the strut and the tie, θ_s, is 19.25°.

The nominal strength of the strut is obtained as follows:

Where the strut cross-sectional area is:

$$A_{cs} = \frac{l_b \times \sin\theta_s + h_a \times \cos\theta_s}{6} b = \frac{750 \times \sin 19.25° + 300 \times \cos 19.25°}{6} 2750 = 243100 \, \text{mm}^2$$

The strain in the tie near the strut:

$$\varepsilon_s = \frac{T_f}{E_s A_s} = \frac{4749 \times 1000}{200000 \times 20 \times 700} = 1.696 \times 10^{-3}$$

The strain perpendicular to the strut is:

$\varepsilon_1 = \varepsilon_s + (\varepsilon_s + 0.002)\cot^2\theta_s = 1.696 \times 10^{-3} + (1.696 \times 10^{-3} + 2 \times 10^{-3})\cot^2 19.25° = 32.0 \times 10^{-3}$

The strut compression strength is:

$$f_{cu} = \frac{f_c'}{0.8 + 170\varepsilon_1} = \frac{35}{0.8 + 170 \times 32.0 \times 10^{-3}} = 5.61\,\text{MPa} < 0.85 f_c' = 29.75\,\text{MPa}$$

The simplified expression from Eq. (11-24) assumes that the tension reinforcement yields and hence gives a lower value of 5.21 MPa for f_{cu}. The higher value will be used.

The factored strut capacity is: $= \phi_c A_{cs} f_{cu} = 0.65 \times 243100 \times 5.61 \times 10^{-3} = 886$ kN

Because this factored strut resistance of 886 kN is less than the required factored resistance of 1389 kN the strut capacity is insufficient.

To increase the capacity, it is decided to increase the thickness of the footing from 1300 mm to 1600 mm as shown in the figure below and to repeat the strut-and-tie calculations.

3. Strut-and-tie capacity of 1600 mm thick footing

The effective depth to the centroid of the top reinforcement is 1600 − 150 = 1450 mm and hence d_v is 0.9 × 1450 = 1305 mm (see figure below).

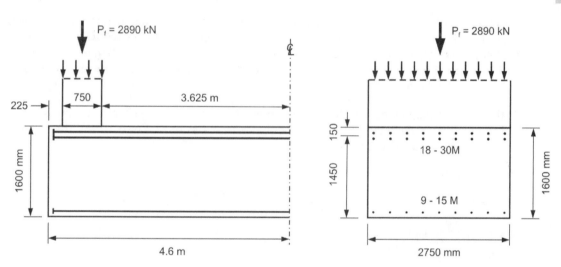

(a) Final details

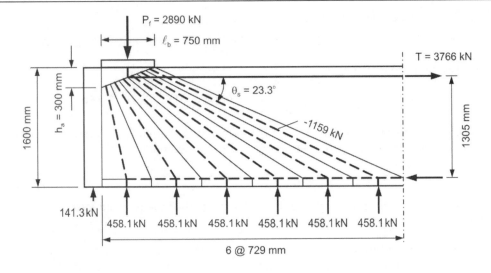

(b) Strut-and-tie model

Final design with 1600 mm thick footing

The required tension force in the top reinforcing can be found from the moment at midspan which equals 4915 kN·m. Hence the required tension force in the top steel is 4915 × 1000/1305 = 3766 kN. The required reinforcement area is thus 3766 × 1000/(0.85 × 400) = 11 077 mm². Hence use 18 − 30M bars (area of 12 600 mm²). Note that two layers of tension reinforcement are used to increase the dimensions of the nodal zone.

As the depth of the footing is increased, the compressive force in the critical strut decreases to 1159 kN and the angle between the strut and the tie increases to 23.3°(see figure). The nominal strength of the critical strut is obtained as follows:

The strut cross-sectional area is:

$$A_{cs} = \frac{l_b \times \sin\theta_s + h_a \times \cos\theta_s}{6}b = \frac{750 \times \sin 23.3° + 300 \times \cos 23.3°}{6} \times 2750 = 262300\,\text{mm}^2$$

Strain in the tie near the strut:

$$\varepsilon_s = \frac{T_f}{E_s A_s} = \frac{3766 \times 1000}{200000 \times 18 \times 700} = 1.494 \times 10^{-3}$$

Strain perpendicular to the strut:

$$\varepsilon_1 = \varepsilon_s + (\varepsilon_s + 0.002)\cot^2\alpha_s = 1.494 \times 10^{-3} + (1.494 \times 10^{-3} + 2 \times 10^{-3})\cot^2 23.3° = 20.3 \times 10^{-3}$$

Strut compression strength:

$$f_{cu} = \frac{f_c'}{0.8 + 170\varepsilon_1} = \frac{35}{0.8 + 170 \times 20.3 \times 10^{-3}} = 8.23\,\text{MPa} < 0.85 f_c' = 29.75\,\text{MPa}$$

The factored strut capacity is: $= \phi_c A_{cs} f_{cu} = 0.65 \times 262300 \times 8.23 \times 10^{-3} = 1403$ kN

Because this factored strut resistance of 1403 kN exceeds the required factored resistance of 1159 kN the strut capacity is sufficient and so the design of the footing is adequate. Hence use a footing thickness of 1600 mm.

Example 4.8   Design of a Deep Beam Subjected to Concentrated Loads

Design the reinforcement for the laterally supported transfer girder shown below. Use $f_c' = 25$ MPa and $f_y = 400$ MPa.

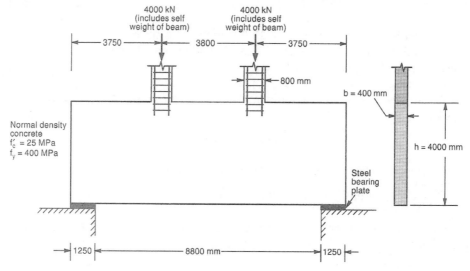

1. Check bearing stresses at supports and loading points

    Support reaction   = 4000 kN

    Bearing stress: = 4000 · 1000/(400 · 1250) = 8.00 MPa

    Allowable bearing stress: = 0.75 · 0.65 · 1.0 · 25 = 12.19 MPa   (Clause 11.4.4.1(b) tension tie present)

    Bearing stress < Allowable   OK

    Bearing stress at loading point = 4000 · 1000 / (400 · 800) = 12.50 MPa

    Allowable bearing stress   = 0.85 · 0.65 · 1.0 · 25 = 13.81 MPa (Clause 11.4.4.1(a))

    Bearing stress < Allowable   OK

2. Calculate required tension in tie of truss

    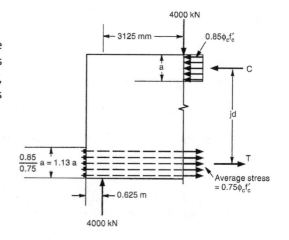

    Due to the presence of the tension tie, the maximum nodal zone stress at the support is $0.75\phi_c f_c'$ by Clause 11.4.4.1(b). Since $C = T$, the depth over which the tie reinforcement is distributed is

    $$\frac{0.85}{0.75}a = 1.133a$$

    Therefore the lever arm

    $$jd = h - a/2 - 1.133a/2 = h - 1.067a$$

    Equating the external moment with the internal moment, we have

    $$4000 \cdot 10^3 \cdot 3125 = C \cdot jd = 0.85 \cdot 0.65 \cdot 25 \cdot a \cdot 400 \cdot (4000 - 1.067a) \qquad \therefore\ a = 694 \text{ mm}$$

    Hence: $C = T = 0.85 \cdot 0.65 \cdot 25 \cdot 400 \cdot 694 \cdot 10^{-3} = 3834$ kN

3. Choose reinforcement for tension tie

    Required area

    $$A_s \geq \frac{3834 \cdot 10^3}{0.85 \cdot 400} = 11280\,\text{mm}^2$$

    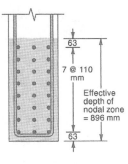

    Provide 24 − 25M bars, A_s = 24 · 500 = 12 000 mm². The minimum
    size over which to distribute this steel is 1.13 · 694 = 784 mm. If the
    24 bars are placed in 8 layers of 3 bars, as shown in the figure, the
    effective nodal zone depth will be 896 mm. As the tension tie depth
    is somewhat greater than assumed, the lever arm will be somewhat
    reduced.

    $jd = 4000 - 0.5 \cdot 720 - 0.5 \cdot 896 = 3192$ mm

    Required tie force = 4000 · 3125 / 3192 = 3916 kN. This causes a stress in the tie of

    $$= \frac{3916 \cdot 10^3}{24 \cdot 500} = 326\,\text{MPa} \leq \phi_s f_y = 0.85 \cdot 400 = 340\,\text{MPa}$$

    Note that as the development length for 25M bars is 900 mm, the tensile tie can be transferred to
    the nodal zone within the 1250 mm bearing length.

4. Sketch idealized truss model

    The idealized truss model is shown in the figure below.

    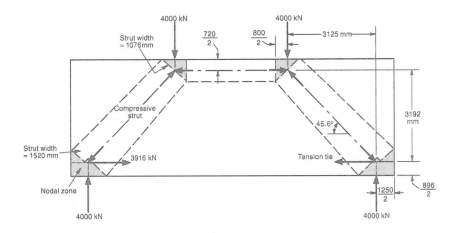

5. Check for compressive strut crushing

    The force in the strut is 4000/sin45.6° = 5598 kN

    At the top of the strut the compressive stress is

    $$f_2 = \frac{5598 \cdot 10^3}{400 \cdot 1075} = 13.01\,\text{MPa}$$

    Since no tension ties cross the strut in this region (i.e., ε_1 is about zero) the permissible compressive
    stress near the top of the strut is calculated by Clause 11.4.2.3 as

    $\phi_c f_{cu} = \phi_c 0.85 f_c' = 0.65 \times 0.85 \times 25 = 13.8$ MPa

Since $f_2 < \phi_c f_{cu}$, the compressive stresses at the top of the strut are acceptable.

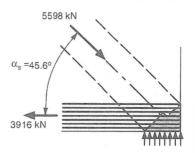

5598 kN

$\alpha_s = 45.6°$

3916 kN

At the bottom of the strut the stress in the strut is

$$f_2 = \frac{5598 \cdot 10^3}{400 \cdot 1520} = 9.21 \, \text{MPa}$$

The compressive strut in this region is crossed by a tension tie and therefore the limiting stress, f_{cu} is reduced. Since the tie is resisting a stress of 326 MPa the tensile strain in the reinforcing bars is 1.63×10^{-3}. Thus the principal tensile strain from Eq. 11-23 of Clause 11.4.2.3 is

$$\varepsilon_1 = \varepsilon_s + (\varepsilon_s + 0.002)\cot^2\theta_s = 0.00163 + (0.00163 + 0.00200)\cot^2 45.6° = 0.00511$$

And the limiting stress in the strut from Eq. 11-22 is therefore

$$\phi_c f_{cu} = \frac{\phi_c f_c'}{0.8 + 170\varepsilon_1} = \frac{0.65 \cdot 25}{0.8 + 170 \cdot 0.00511} = 9.74 \, \text{MPa}$$

As $f_2 < \phi_c f_{cu}$, the compressive stresses at the bottom of the strut are also acceptable.

6. Calculate minimum shear reinforcement required for crack control and ductility

Using 10M U-stirrups, $A_v = 2 \cdot 100 = 200 \, \text{mm}^2$

Required spacing of transverse reinforcement by Clause 11.4.5 is:

$$s \leq \frac{200}{0.002 \cdot 400} = 250 \, \text{mm} \leq 300 \, \text{mm}$$

Provide 10M U-stirrups at 250 mm.

To satisfy the minimum longitudinal requirements of Clause 11.4.5, provide pairs of 10M longitudinal bars at 250 mm centres.

7. Summarize design

To provide some restraint against vertical splitting at the ends of the beam, 10M horizontal U-bars have been added as shown.

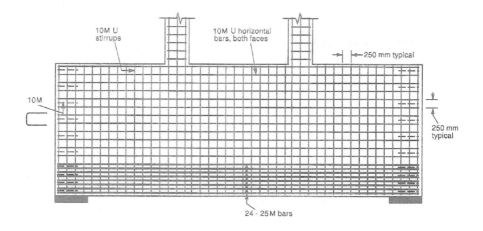

10M U stirrups

10M U horizontal bars, both faces

250 mm typical

10M

250 mm typical

24 - 25M bars

Example 4.9   Design of Corbel for Exterior Column

As shown in the figure, a corbel projecting from a 350 mm × 350 mm column supports a precast girder that is to be constructed in a prequalified precast plant. The corbel is subjected to a vertical specified dead load of 80 kN and a vertical specified live load of 100 kN. Calculations indicate that due to restraint of beam creep and shrinkage deformations, a horizontal force of 35 kN will develop. Design the corbel assuming $f_c' = 35$ MPa and $f_y = 400$ MPa (weldable).

1. Determine factored loads

    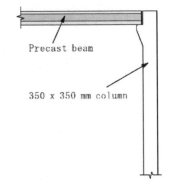

    Precast beam

    Vertical factored load:

    $$V_f = \alpha_D D + \alpha_L L = 1.25 \times 80 + 1.5 \times 100 = 250 \text{ kN}$$

    Horizontal factored load:

    350 x 350 mm column

    $$N_f = \alpha_T T = 1.25 \times 35 = 44 \text{ kN} \geq 0.2 V_f = 50 \text{ kN}$$

    The second limitation is specified in Clause 11.6.4 and, in this case, controls so $N_f = 50$ kN.

2. Determining bearing plate dimensions

    Assume that bearing plate extends across a width of 350 – (2 × 40) = 270 mm. Use $\phi_c = 0.70$ for this column and corbel constructed in a prequalified precast plant (Clause 16.1.3). By Clause 11.4.4.1(b), the minimum width of the bearing plate is

    $$= \frac{V_f}{0.75 \phi_c f_c' b} = \frac{250 \times 10^3}{0.75 \times 0.70 \times 35 \times 270} = 50.4 \text{ mm}$$

    Use a 270 × 75 × 25 mm bearing plate.

3. Choose corbel dimensions

    Choose an overall corbel depth at column face of 500 mm. If required reinforcement with this depth turns out to be excessive, this dimension may have to be increased.

    Choose the depth at the free end of the corbel to ensure that the depth at the outside of the bearing area is at least 0.5 × 500 mm = 250 mm to satisfy Clause 11.6.3.

    The external dimensions chosen for the corbel are summarized in the adjacent figure.

    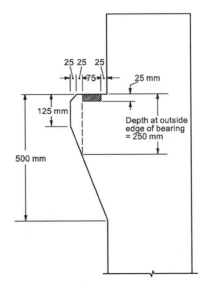

4. Determine geometry of strut-and-tie model

To allow for load eccentricities and erection tolerances, consider the vertical load to be placed 25 mm towards edge of corbel from centre of bearing plate. See Clause 16.4.4.3.

The assumed compressive strut, tension tie and nodal zone model for the corbel is shown. To clarify the geometry of the assumed truss, a separate line drawing of the truss is also given.

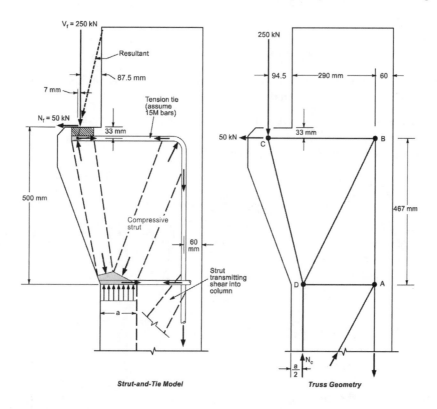

Strut-and-Tie Model   **Truss Geometry**

Nodes A and B are located at the intersections of the centrelines of the tension ties. Node C is located at the intersection of the centreline of the upper tension tie and the line of action of the resultant applied load. Node D is located at the intersection of the centreline of the lower tension tie and the centreline of the vertical compressive strut below the corbel. The location of this strut centreline is found by calculating the strut width "a".

The compressive force in the strut, N_c, can be found by taking moments about Node A

$$250 \times 384.5 + 50 \times 467 = N_c \times (290 - a/2)$$

As the stress on the nodal zone at D is to be limited by Clause 11.4.4.1(b) to:

$$0.75\phi_c f_c' = 0.75 \times 0.70 \times 35 = 18.4 \text{ MPa} \qquad \text{and} \qquad a = \frac{N_c \times 10^3}{18.4 \times 350}$$

Solving these two equations gives $N_c = 471$ kN $\qquad a = 73$ mm

This fixes the geometry of the truss and means that member CD has a horizontal projection of $94.5 + 73/2 = 131$ mm, while member BD has a horizontal projection of $290 - 73/2 = 253.5$ mm.

5. Determine forces in truss by statics

Member	CD	CB	BD	BA	DA
Force (kN)	-260	+120	-251	+221	+50

Positive indicates tension and negative is compression

6. Design of tension ties

The area of reinforcement required for tension tie CB is $\quad = \dfrac{120 \times 1000}{0.85 \times 400} = 353 \, \text{mm}^2$

The area, A_{st}, of the primary tensile tie reinforcement must satisfy the minimum reinforcement requirements of Clause 11.6.6 such that

$$A_{st} \geq 0.04 \frac{f'_c}{f_y} bd = 0.04 \times \frac{35}{400} \times 350 \times 467 = 572 \, \text{mm}^2$$

The minimum reinforcement requirement controls.

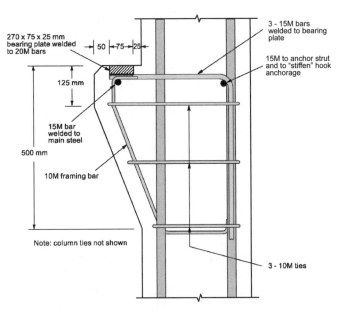

Hence, use 3 – 15M bars
  ($A_{st} = 3 \times 200 = 600 \, \text{mm}^2$).

Having to increase the tie reinforcement to satisfy the minimum reinforcement requirement indicates that the 500 mm depth of the corbel could have been reduced.

Although tie BA has a larger tension, it must be appreciated that the longitudinal reinforcement in the column, 2 – 30M bars on the tension face, will have been designed to resist this longitudinal tensile force. Hence, continue the 3 – 15M bars for a sufficient distance down the column to fully develop these bars.

The area of reinforcement required for tension tie DA is $\quad = \dfrac{50 \times 1000}{0.85 \times 400} = 147 \, \text{mm}^2$

Hence, use one additional 10M column tie at location DA.

7. Design of nodal zones

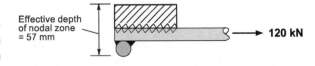

The width "a" of nodal zone D was chosen in Step 4 to satisfy the stress limits on this nodal zone. The longitudinal column bars and the column ties will assist in anchoring the tension ties in nodal zones D, A and B. To anchor tension tie CB in nodal zone C, weld the 3 – 15M bars to the bearing plate and also weld a 15M cross bar to these bars as shown in the figure.

To satisfy the nodal zone stress limits, Clause 11.4.4.2(b), the tension tie reinforcement must engage an effective depth of concrete at least equal to

$$= \frac{120 \times 10^3}{0.75 \times 0.70 \times 35 \times 270} = 24\,mm \le 57\,mm \qquad\qquad OK$$

8. Checking compressive struts

Compressive strut DC intersects tension tie CB at an angle of 74.3°. The tensile strain in tie CB is about $1.0 \cdot 10^{-3}$ and hence from Eq. 11-23, ε_1 is about $1.2 \cdot 10^{-3}$. For this low strain, f_{cu} is $0.85\phi_c f_c'$. Since this exceeds the stress checked for in the nodal zone, the compressive stresses in strut DC will not be critical.

Compressive strut DB intersects tension tie BA at an angle of 28.5°. The tensile strain in tie BA is

$$\varepsilon_s = \frac{221 \times 10^3}{200000 \times (2 \times 700 + 3 \times 200)} = 0.553 \times 10^{-3}$$

Hence: $\varepsilon_1 = 0.553 \times 10^{-3} + (0.553 \times 10^{-3} + 2 \times 10^{-3})\cot^2 28.5° = 9.21 \times 10^{-3}$

Thus: $f_{cu} = \dfrac{35}{0.8 + 170 \times 9.21 \times 10^{-3}} = 14.79\,MPa$

Strut DB is anchored by the 15M and 30M reinforcing bars at B. If in accordance with Fig. 11.5(a) we conservatively take ℓ_a as $16 \cdot 15 = 240$ mm then the thickness of the strut is $240\sin28.5° = 115$ mm. From Clause 11.4.2.1, the strength of the strut is then $\phi_c f_{cu} A_{cs} = 0.70 \times 14.79 \times 115 \times 350 = 417$ kN as 417 kN > 251 kN the strength of strut DB is adequate.

9. Check minimum reinforcement requirements

The minimum area, A_{st}, of the primary tensile tie reinforcement has been chosen to satisfy Clause 11.6.6.

To satisfy Clause 11.6.5, provide additional closed stirrups of area $A_{st}/2 = 300$ mm² over a depth of $2/3 \cdot 467 = 311$ mm. Use $2 - 10M$ closed stirrups.

10. Summarize design

The final details of the corbel are shown on the figure.

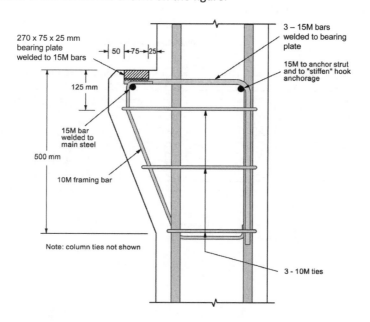

270 x 75 x 25 mm bearing plate welded to 15M bars

50 ⊢75→ 25

125 mm

15M bar welded to main steel

500 mm

10M framing bar

Note: column ties not shown

3 – 15M bars welded to bearing plate

15M to anchor strut and to "stiffen" hook anchorage

3 - 10M ties

Example 4.10 Design of Beam With Dapped End

The beam shown below is subjected to a factored uniform load of 127 kN/m over a span of 6.3 m and a factored axial tension of 80 kN. Design the reinforcement for this beam that is to be constructed in a prequalified precast plant. The factored loading includes an allowance for the self-weight of the beam.

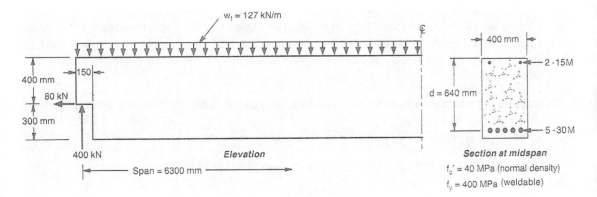

Elevation

Section at midspan

$f_c' = 40$ MPa (normal density)

$f_y = 400$ MPa (weldable)

1. Design flexural reinforcement at midspan

    Taking the axis of the beam to be on the line of the axial force, the factored moment at midspan is $M_f = 127 \times 6.3^2/8 = 630$ kN·m. If the tension reinforcement consists of 5 – 30M bars as shown above, the depth of the compressive stress block at the factored moment resistance, accounting for the tension of 80 kN, is

    $$a = \frac{\phi_s A_s f_y - N_f}{\alpha_1 \phi_c f_c' b} = \frac{0.85 \times 5 \times 700 \times 400 - 80 \times 10^3}{0.79 \times 0.70 \times 40 \times 400} = 125.5 \,\text{mm}$$

    so that $M_r = 0.79 \times 0.70 \times 40 \times 125.5 \times 400 \times (400 - 125.5/2) \times 10^{-6}$
    $+ 0.85 \times 400 \times 5 \times 700 \times (300 - 60) \times 10^{-6} = 660.1$ kN·m

    As $M_r > M_f$, the flexural reinforcement is OK at midspan.

2. Identify design regions of beam

    The design regions of the beam and some important components of the load carrying path are identified in the figure below.

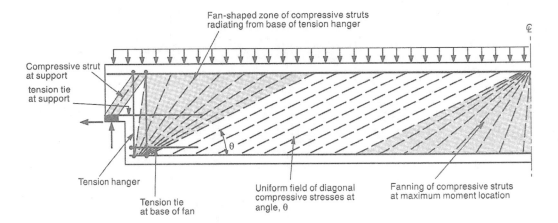

3.   Determine bearing area at support

Assuming that a 320 mm long steel angle across the width of the beam is to be used at the support, the required bearing length by Clause 11.4.4.1(b) is:

$$\ell_b = \frac{V_f}{0.75\phi_c f'_c b} = \frac{400 \times 10^3}{0.75 \times 0.70 \times 40 \times 320} = 60 \, \text{mm}$$

Provide a 100 × 100 × 16 mm thick angle

4

Shear and Torsion

4.   Determine geometry of strut and tie model

A strut-and-tie model of one-half the beam is shown below. This truss was designed to reasonably approximate the flow of forces in the beam. This included providing a tension hanger BC near the face of the dap, anchoring the horizontal tie AD by two diagonal compressive struts, and modelling the fanning action at midspan and near the supports.

The specific geometry for this strut-and-tie model was chosen in the following manner. The bottom chord of the truss was located along the centreline of the bottom longitudinal reinforcement. The top chord was located at the level of the centroid of the compressive force due to flexure, at midspan. Nodes B and C, which define the centreline of the hanger, were located just far enough

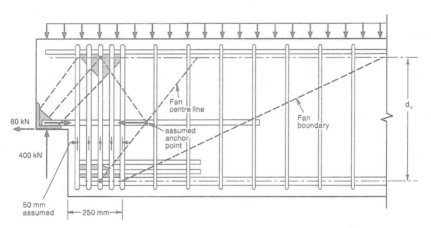

Strut and Tie Model

from the face of the dap to distribute the tension steel in the hanger over a region large enough to establish a nodal zone capable of resisting the applied strut and tie forces. Near the supports and at midspan, narrower "frames" were used to model the steeper angle of the fanning compressive stresses in these regions.

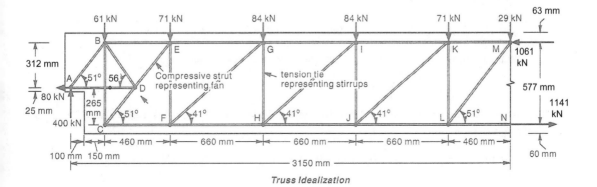

Truss Idealization

5. Determine forces in truss by statics

Member	Force (kN)
AB	-513
DB	-328
AD	401
CB	611
CD	-781
DE	-434

Member	Force (kN)
BE	-137
CF	487
EF	268
EG	-407
FG	-407
FH	794

Member	Force (kN)
GH	184
GI	-713
HI	-280
HJ	1004
IJ	100
IK	-924

Member	Force (kN)
JK	-152
JL	1118
KL	29
KM	-1038
LM	-37
LN	1141

Positive indicates tension, negative compression.

6. Design of tension ties.

The following areas of reinforcement are required for the tension ties.

Tie AD: $A_s = \dfrac{401 \times 10^3}{0.85 \times 400} = 1179\,mm^2$ Use 5 – 20M bars

Hanger CB: $A_s = \dfrac{611 \times 10^3}{0.85 \times 400} = 1797\,mm^2$ Use 5 – 15M closed stirrups

Tie CF: $A_s = \dfrac{487 \times 10^3}{0.85 \times 400} = 1432\,mm^2$ 5 – 30M OK but need to check anchorage

The forces in tension ties EF, GH, IJ, and KL determine the amount of shear reinforcement required in these regions (bands).

Stirrup Band EF: Tie force = 268 kN

Capacity of 10M closed stirrup is 2 × 100 × 0.85 × 400 = 68 kN. Therefore 268/68 = 3.94 stirrups are required over a width of 660 mm.

$$s \le \frac{660}{3.94} = 167\,mm$$

Check minimum shear reinforcement requirements from Clause 11.2.8.2

$$s \le \frac{A_v f_y}{0.06\sqrt{f_c'}\,b_w} = \frac{2 \times 100 \times 400}{0.06 \times \sqrt{40} \times 400} = 527\,mm$$

Check maximum spacing requirements. The shear force at which the basic stirrup spacing limits of Clause 11.3.8.1 must be halved if

$$V_f \ge 0.125 \lambda \phi_c f_c' b_w d_v = 0.125 \times 1.0 \times 0.65 \times 40 \times 400 \times (0.9 \times 640) = 749\text{ kN}$$

As the maximum V_f is less than this value, the maximum stirrup spacing is

$$s \le 0.7 d_v = 0.7 \times (0.9 \times 640) = 403\text{ mm}$$

The crack control requirements for strut-and-tie designs in Clause 11.4.5 also limit the stirrup spacing to: $s \le 300$ mm

For stirrup band EF, therefore, the strength criterion governs. Use $s = 150$ mm.

Stirrup Band GH: Tie force = 184 kN

184/68 = 2.71   10M closed stirrups are required over 660 mm, or $s \leq 244$ mm. Thus strength controls, use $s = 240$ mm.

Stirrup Band IJ: Tie force = 100 kN

100/68 = 1.47   10M closed stirrups are required over 660 mm, or $s \leq 449$. Crack control reinforcement governs, so select $s = 300$ mm

Stirrup Band KL: Tie force = 29 kN

Crack control reinforcement governs, select $s = 300$ mm

7.   Design of nodal zones

Nodal Zone A: The 100 mm horizontal leg length of the angle was chosen to satisfy the nodal stress limit in Step 3.

The required depth of the nodal zone from Clause 11.3.4.1(b) $= \dfrac{(401-80)\times 10^3}{0.75\times 0.70\times 40\times 320} = 48\,\text{mm}$

Thus the 100 mm provided by the angle is sufficient.

Nodal Zone B: Because of a concern about spalling of the concrete cover, neglect the concrete outside of the anchoring tie reinforcement. The required width of the nodal zone by Clause 11.4.4.1(b) is:

$= \dfrac{611\times 10^3}{0.75\times 0.70\times 40\times 320} = 91\,\text{mm}$

A spacing of 50 mm between the 5 – 15M closed stirrups will provide a nodal zone width of at least 4 × 50 + 15 = 215 mm, which is conservative.

Nodal Zone C: This zone anchors two tension ties. Clause 11.4.4.1(c) requires a width of

$= \dfrac{611\times 10^3}{0.65\times 0.70\times 40\times 320} = 105\,\text{mm}$ Thus, 215 mm still OK.

The require depth of the nodal zone to resist the tension in tie CF is: $= \dfrac{487\times 10^3}{0.65\times 0.70\times 40\times 320} = 84\,\text{mm}$

To provide this nodal zone depth, provide 2 – 15M horizontal U-bars with 50 mm spacing above the layer of 30M bars.

Also check the anchorage of tension tie CF in Nodal Zone C. As the 30M bars emerge from Nodal Zone C, they can resist a tensile force of approximately

$= \dfrac{215}{\ell_d}\times \phi_s A_s f_y = \dfrac{215}{854}\times 0.85\times 3500\times 400\times 10^{-3} = 300\,\text{kN}$

The 2 – 15M U-bars will be capable of resisting a tension of = 0.85 × 2 × 2 × 200 × 400 = 272 kN

Hence the total tensile capacity at the face of the nodal zone is = 300 + 272 = 572 kN

As 573 kN > 487 kN, the anchorage of the tension reinforcement at node C is OK.

Extend the 15M bars at least ℓ_d (= 455 mm) beyond the nodal zone and far enough for the 5 – 30M bars to be capable of carrying the 487 kN tie force on their own (i.e., 352 mm from the end of the 30M bars).

Although the addition of the 15M U-bars will raise the location of node C somewhat, this secondary effect will be neglected.

8.   Checking compressive struts

As the compressive strut CD-DE represents a fan-shaped region of radiating struts and as the nodal zone stresses at the base of the fan have been checked, further checks are not required.

Check compressive stress in struts which meet at Node B. See drawing below.

Assuming the nodal zone is to be in equilibrium under a "hydrostatic" stress condition, the length of the faces of the nodal zone will be proportional to the loads applied to these faces and the faces will be perpendicular to the loads. Hence, the lengths of the compressive strut bearing surfaces at Nodal Zone B are

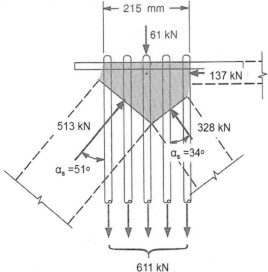

$$\ell_{AB} = \frac{513}{611+61} \times 215 = 164 \, mm$$

$$\ell_{DB} = \frac{328}{611+61} \times 215 = 105 \, mm$$

$$\ell_{EB} = \frac{137}{611+61} \times 215 = 44 \, mm$$

Thus the stress in all struts at Nodal Zone B (neglecting the concrete cover) equals:

$$f_2 = \frac{(611+61) \times 10^3}{215 \times 320} = 9.77 \, MPa$$

As the line of action of strut DB is closest to that of tie CB, strut DB will have the lowest diagonal crushing strength.

The average tensile strain in tie CB can be estimated as

$$\varepsilon_s = \frac{611 \times 10^3}{10 \times 200 \times 0.85 \times 200 \times 10^3} = 1.80 \times 10^{-3}$$

From Clause 11.4.2.3, the strain, ε_1, perpendicular to the strut will be:

$$\varepsilon_1 = \varepsilon_s + (\varepsilon_s + 0.002)\cot^2\theta_s = 0.00180 + (0.00180 + 0.002)\cot^2 34° = 0.01015$$

The diagonal crushing strength is

$$\phi_c f_{cu} = \frac{\phi_c f_c'}{0.8 + 170 \times \varepsilon_1} = \frac{0.70 \times 40}{0.8 + 170 \times 0.01015} = 11.09 \, MPa$$

As $f_2 < \phi_c f_{cu}$, the compressive stress in the strut is OK.

The other struts meeting at Node B will have the same compressive stress but smaller values of ε_1. Hence they will not be critical.

9.   Other detailing considerations

To improve crack control and ductility, provide a minimum amount of horizontal reinforcement parallel to the primary tensile tie reinforcement in the region above the support. If the dapped end were treated as a bracket, the required area of such additional reinforcement would be (Clause 11.6.5) $= 0.5 \times A_s = 0.5 \times 5 \times 300 = 750 \, mm^2$

Use 2 – 15M horizontal U-bars distributed over two-thirds of the effective depth. Extend these bars at least ℓ_d beyond face of dap. To improve the support conditions for the highly stressed compressive struts AB and DB, use two additional 15M top longitudinal bars in the region of Node B.

10. Summarize design

The final details of the dap ended beam are shown in the figure below.

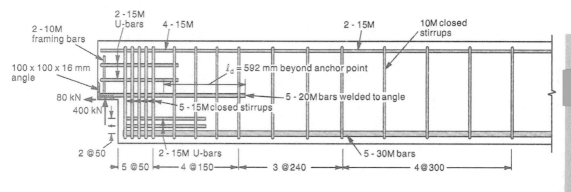

5

By Scott Alexander

Slabs

5

Slabs

5.1   Introduction

Reinforced concrete slabs span either one-way or two-way, depending upon their support conditions. A slab supported so that it deforms in a barrel shape, with bending primarily about one axis, is a one-way slab. A slab that bends in two directions is a two-way slab. There are many variations of two-way slabs, three of which are shown in Fig. 5.1.

One-way slabs are essentially wide beams and are designed following the same principles. The behaviour of two-way slabs is more complex. They are more indeterminate than one-way systems. A detailed prediction of their behavior, especially in the vicinity of column supports, would require complex analysis; however, such an analysis is not usually needed for design. Provisions for the design of two-way slabs are provided in Clause 13 and Annex B of the Standard.

In Clause 3.1, the Standard provides criteria that define a **regular two-way slab system**. The vast majority of two-way slabs satisfy this definition. The designer needs to be mindful of these criteria since many of the provisions in Clause 13 apply only to regular two-way slabs.

Slabs must have sufficient strength to carry loads safely. Slabs should also meet serviceability expectations, meaning they should not deflect or crack excessively. Barring blunder, providing sufficient strength in a slab rarely poses a difficult design problem. The success or failure of a design is almost always judged on the basis of serviceability.

The designer should be mindful of architectural features that may make the floor system more sensitive to deflection or cracking. Non-structural partition walls that are not tied at the ceiling may rotate out of plumb if they are located along a line of inflection. Brittle floor coverings may require special control of deflection. The slab may have to meet a tight tolerance with respect to flatness. In these situations, it is prudent to assume a levelling compound will be used and increase the design dead load accordingly.

The design of any slab system may be divided into the following steps:

1) select slab thickness;
2) obtain design moments;
3) choose flexural reinforcement;
4) check shear capacity;
5) design beams and/or other elements (if any).

These steps are not independent and indeed may not be completed in the order listed. For example, it is usual to make at least a preliminary evaluation of shear capacity when selecting slab thickness. Nevertheless, these steps correspond to the grouping of the design calculations and are used as the major divisions in the remainder of this chapter and in the design examples.

Design examples are presented to assist in interpreting the provisions of specific clauses of the Standard. It should be pointed out that each example is an incomplete design in that only portions of the slab system are considered. Computations described in other chapters of this Handbook are usually omitted.

5.2   Selecting Slab Thickness

5.2.1.   General

For a given span and support configuration, the slab thickness is the primary factor affecting deflection and shear strength. In some instances, fire resistance requirements may govern both the cover and slab thickness.

The slab thickness is usually chosen by one of two methods. The first is to select a thickness that is equal to or greater than the minimum thickness specified the Standard. The second is to select a trial thickness and compute the expected deflections.

For one-way slabs the minimum thickness is specified in Table 9.2. For regular two-way slabs, the minimum thickness is given in Clause 13.2. Slabs close to these minimums should be chosen with caution since they are, as the name implies, minimally acceptable for typical dimensions and loading. They require good workmanship and shoring practice. For many designs the appropriate thickness will be greater than the minimum thickness given in the Standard.

Both Table 9.2 and Clause 13.2 give minimum thickness as a function of span, independent of loading. The origin of these provisions is in Working Stress Design. The presumption is that every element is designed to satisfy working stress limits, in both compression and tension, at full service load. It then follows that the extreme fibre strains at full service load, in both compression and tension, are also controlled. A structure designed for a larger load will have more reinforcement so that it satisfies the same stress limits, and hence, same strain limits, under full service load. The combination of limited maximum strains and a specified depth controls maximum curvature. Specifying thickness as a fraction of the span, with some accounting for changes in boundary conditions, effectively limits instantaneous deflection under full service load to some fraction of the span.

Deflection limits in Table 9.3 apply to either live load deflection or to long-term total deflection occurring after the attachment of non-structural elements. Limiting the ratio of span to depth (S/D) controls instantaneous curvature under total load. Long-term deflection includes creep deflection, which depends upon sustained load and time. Where live load and sustained load are consistent fractions of total load, limiting S/D can provide a reliable control on deflection. Meeting a specified S/D may not provide the desired deflection control where there is an unusual distribution between live and dead load or between transient and sustained load.

Deflection calculations are mandatory for slabs that do not meet minimum thickness requirements or do not satisfy the limitations for regular two-way slabs given in Clause 3.1. The trial thickness is revised as required until the calculated deflections satisfy the maximum permissible values given in Clause 9 of the Standard. Examples of deflection calculations are given in Chapter 6 of this Handbook.

The trial thickness should be evaluated for shear strength. At this stage of the design, especially for two-way slabs without beams, only a preliminary check for shear capacity can be made since the moments to be transferred by eccentricity of shear are yet to be determined.

The increments used to adjust thickness are a matter of designer judgment, local practice, and forming convenience. One consideration will be the availability of "high chairs" for the top layers of reinforcement. In the examples of this Chapter an increment of 10 mm is used.

5.2.2.   One-Way Slabs

For one-way slabs not supporting or attached to partitions or other construction likely to be damaged by large deflections, Table 9-2 of the Standard gives minimum thickness as a fraction of the clear span, ℓ_n, for different support conditions. If the slab is supporting construction likely to be damaged by large deflections, calculations are required to show that expected deflections, including time effects, will be satisfactory for the specific application.

For one-way slabs in buildings, it would be unusual for shear capacity to govern. Nonetheless, it should be checked.

5.2.3. Two-way Slabs

Clause 13.2 contains provisions for the minimum thickness of regular two-way slab systems as defined in Clause 3.1. The geometric limitations of a regular two-way slab system are a necessary prerequisite for applying the provisions of Clause 13.2. Deflection calculations are required for two-way slabs that cannot be classified as regular or for slabs that do not meet the minimums specified in Clauses 13.2.3 through 13.2.6.

For **slab panels with beams on all sides**, the deflection, and hence minimum thickness, depends upon both the panel aspect ratio and the relative stiffness of the beams in the two directions. If beams in one direction are significantly stiffer than in the other, even for columns located on an essentially square grid, the slab will tend to act as a one-way slab spanning between the stiffer beams. Equation 13-3 gives the minimum thickness as a function of the longer clear span, ℓ_n, the panel aspect ratio, β, and the mean beam stiffness ratio, α_m. The beam stiffness ratio, α, is the ratio of the moment of inertia of the beam to that of the slab; the mean beam stiffness, α_m, is the average value of α for the beams along the four panel edges. The maximum effective value of α_m is limited to 2.0. Recognizing the approximations needed to develop Eqn. 13-3, a simplified method of determining the beam moment of inertia, Eqn. 13-4, is provided to ease the calculation of α.

For **slabs with drop panels or slab bands**, Clause 13.2.4 accounts for variations in the size of the drop panel. Note that slab bands are defined in Clause 3.1 as continuous extensions of drop panels. The significance of this is that slab bands need not meet the minimum requirements for shear reinforcement in beams. Nevertheless, Clause 13.2.6 requires that the thickness of the slab band itself also satisfy the span to depth requirements for beams listed in Table 9.2. This additional stipulation is required for the lateral distribution of moments in 13.11.2.4 and 13.11.2.5.

The minimum specified thickness for **slabs without drop panels** (flat plates and slabs with column capitals only) is given in Clause 13.2.3. Such slabs have no interior beams and may or may not have edge beams.

The thickness of two-way slabs without beams may also be governed by the shear capacity of the slab at the supports. This is especially true for slabs supported on columns without capitals or drops and at exterior columns where significant moment and shear are transferred between the slab and column. Thus, although the slab thickness is generally selected for deflection considerations, it is prudent to make a preliminary shear capacity check before proceeding to the next design step. At this early stage of design, the total loading on the slab is known and the corresponding value of the factored shear force at each column, V_f, can be determined but the moments to be transferred are unknown and their effects can only be estimated. One approach is to multiply the average factored shear stress by a factor (suitable values given below) that approximates the effect of moment transfer and compare this increased shear stress to the factored shear stress resistance.

interior column	1.2
edge column	1.6

5.3 Slab Moments

5.3.1. General

For one-way slabs, it is usual to consider a strip of unit width spanning perpendicular to the supports and to analyze this strip for moments and shears as a continuous beam. When the loading and geometry satisfy the requirements of Clause 9.3.3, design moments and shears may be obtained directly from the coefficients given therein.

There are many techniques that may be used to analyze and design two-way slabs. Clause 13.5.1 states "A slab may be designed by any procedure satisfying conditions of equilibrium and compatibility with the supports, provided that it is shown that the factored resistance at every section is at least equal to the effects of the factored loads, and that all serviceability conditions, including specified limits on deflections, are met." The Standard explicitly addresses analyses based on Elastic Plate Theory and on the Theorems of Plasticity. In addition, it provides details for modeling slab-column structures as elastic frames and it retains the Direct Design Method. Appendix B provides an analysis for two-way slabs with stiff supports on all sides.

An important distinction needs to be made between different analysis methods. While a one-way slab is constrained to carry all load by bending in one direction, a two-way slab may carry load by bending in two directions as well as by torsion or twisting. The designer may choose a method of analysis for a two-way slab that fully satisfies equilibrium without relying on torsion. The resulting bending moments are the design moments. Examples of such analyses are plane frame analogies, the Direct Design Method, and most typical applications of the strip method. Alternatively, the designer may also choose an analysis, such as elastic finite element, that relies on torsion to satisfy equilibrium. In this case, the torsional moments cannot be ignored. The design moments must account for both bending and torsion.

5.3.2. Elastic Plate Theory

Finite difference or finite element techniques may be used to perform an elastic analysis of a two-way slab. All such analyses require some system of orthogonal coordinate axes, say x and y, to describe the slab. The designer chooses the coordinate axes to be parallel to the flexural reinforcement. The analysis provides values of moment intensity (moment per unit width) at various points on the slab. At each point, there are three components of moment intensity; two bending, m_x and m_y, and one from torsion, m_{xy}.

Torsional moments are non-zero whenever the principal bending axes are not parallel to the coordinate axes, x and y. By itself, a torsional moment will cause the two-way slab to deflect into a saddle shape, with the axes of bending skew to the coordinate axes. The saddle shape means that the slab is subject to negative bending about one skew axis in combination with positive bending about the other skew axis. Since the reinforcement is parallel to the coordinate axes, it follows that a torsional moment by itself will require both top and bottom reinforcement to resist the skew negative and positive bending. This is reflected in the expressions for design moment in Clause 13.6.4 in which both the negative and positive design moments are increased by torsion. The corner reinforcement of Clause 13.12.5 is another example of reinforcing for torsional moments.

It is usually desirable to define bands within which the flexural reinforcement is uniformly spaced. The provisions in 13.6.4 produce design moment intensities at points on the slab. At any section across the width of the slab, the design moment intensities may vary substantially. Clause 13.6.5 provides a rule for defining reinforcing bands that will not place undue demands on ductility.

In column-supported slabs, shears are high in the vicinity of the column and the moments in the slab vary sharply, with peak values at the column face. If the finite difference or finite element mesh is too coarse

5

Slabs

near the column, these peaks may be greatly reduced and the total design moment underestimated. On the other hand, the shears are low near midspan and the variation in moments is gradual. A fine mesh here is unnecessary and may greatly increase run time of the numerical model. It is generally adequate to provide a relatively coarse mesh over most of the slab, reserving the finer mesh for within about 4 slab thicknesses of the column face.

Regardless of the meshing strategy, it is good practice to investigate whether the solution is mesh-size dependent. The designer should check whether reducing the mesh size affects the solution significantly. If it does, the mesh is too coarse and should be refined.

Classical elastic theory for isotropic thin plates has features that make it attractive for design. It satisfies conditions of equilibrium and compatibility at every point in the slab and provides a complete description of the deflected shape. For circular slabs, found in many silo or tank structures, there are published closed-form solutions for many practical load cases. Modelling of more varied structures can be done using finite element or finite difference.

The accuracy of the results, particularly with respect to deflection, depends upon the accuracy of the material properties and boundary conditions. One aspect warrants further discussion.

Flexural cracking of a slab results in a significant reduction in bending stiffness in the cracked regions. The change in bending stiffness affects both deflection and the distribution of bending moments. For slabs with reinforcing ratios near minimum, the un-cracked and fully-cracked stiffness will differ by a factor of 5 or more. Tensile stresses resulting from restraint of shrinkage and thermal strains introduce uncertainty in predicting the flexural cracking load for a slab (Scanlon, 1999). A reasonable way to account for the effect of restraint stresses is to reduce the effective modulus of rupture used in calculating the cracking moment. Clause 9.8.2.3 of the Standard reduces the modulus of rupture by a factor of 2 for the calculation of the cracking moment.

5.3.3.   Theorems of Plasticity

The Standard permits the analysis of a two-way slab to be based on either the upper or lower bound theorems of plasticity. An upper bound technique produces an estimate of the failure load of a slab that is greater than or equal to the correct failure load. Hence, the upper bound method approaches the correct solution from the "unsafe" side. A lower bound technique will always produce an estimate of failure load that is less than or equal to the correct failure load. Hence, the lower bound technique approaches the correct answer from the "safe" side. The most common upper and lower bound techniques used for two-way slabs are the yield line method (Park and Gamble, 2000) and the strip method (Hillerborg, 1975; 1996), respectively. These methods address the flexural strength of the slab only; neither addresses the shear strength.

In the yield line method, the factored moments are obtained by satisfying equilibrium for an assumed folding (collapse) mechanism. Because it is based on an assumed collapse mechanism, a yield line analysis addresses only ultimate strength. It provides no check on serviceability. The validity of the answer depends on finding the governing folding mechanism. Except in the simplest cases, finding the governing folding mechanism can be a far from trivial problem. Failing to find the correct folding mechanism will result in the slab being under-designed. There is no way of bounding the magnitude of the error.

With the strip method, the designer assumes a set of load paths that will carry all load to the supports of the slab. Each load path is analyzed for the load it is assumed carry and is reinforced accordingly. As is pointed out by Hillerborg (1996), load paths that are reasonably close to the elastic distribution can be analyzed elastically, providing a reasonable estimate of deflection.

5.3.4.   Elastic Frame Analogies

The concept behind the use of elastic frame analogies is that satisfactory values for average design moments and shears can be obtained by considering design strips (see Fig. 5.2) located along the support lines and bounded by the centre lines of the adjacent panels. These design strips are then analyzed as elastic plane frames. For gravity loading, the frame analysis may be simplified to consider only one level of slab at a time by assuming that the far ends of column supports are fixed against rotation. Simmonds (1999) provides a description and history of the development of elastic frame analogies.

In a conventional plane frame analysis it is assumed that all members meeting at a joint undergo the same rotation. In a column-supported slab, the column provides only local restraint to the slab. As a result, across the full width of the design strip, the average rotation of the slab will not usually match the rotation of the column. For the case of gravity loading, the effective column stiffness is reduced to account for this added degree of flexibility between the slab and the column. The Standard provides two methods, prismatic and non-prismatic modelling, for estimating this reduced stiffness but it should be emphasized that these are for gravity loading only.

The note to Clause 13.8.1.1 states that a frame analogy may be used for slabs that do not satisfy the definition of regular two-way slabs. In principle, this includes unbraced frames under lateral load. Here the rotation of the column will exceed the average rotation of the slab. A frame analogy for lateral load would require softening of the properties for the slab (beam) members. The Standard contains no guidance for selecting these properties.

The use of elastic frame analogies is restricted to regular two-way slabs for two reasons. First, the definition of the design strips assumes that support lines and adjacent panels are readily identifiable. This is the case for slab systems supported on columns aligned to create essentially rectangular panels. Second, recommendations for assigning stiffness values to the members of the frame and the provisions for the lateral distribution of the design moments at the critical sections were all derived assuming rectangular panels.

Once the effective geometry of the frame has been selected using either prismatic or non-prismatic members, it is analyzed elastically for a number of defined patterned loadings to obtain the maximum effects at all critical sections in the slab and supporting members (see Fig. 5.3). When the live load is uniformly distributed and does not exceed three-quarters of the specified dead load, slab moments can be obtained assuming full factored design load on the entire slab system. This implies that pattern loadings are not required to compute unbalanced moments transferred at interior supports for this case.

The moments obtained from the analysis of the analogous frame are average values over the width of the design strip. The lateral distribution of these average design moments is addressed in Clause 13.11.

Non-prismatic modelling

Non-prismatic modelling of member stiffness uses the concept of an attached torsional member (see Fig. 5.4) to reduce the stiffness of the column. This approach, originally called the 'Equivalent Frame Method', was developed at the time when the only practical method for analyzing an elastic frame was by the 'moment distribution' procedure. Thus recommendations for assigning member stiffness to determine stiffness and carry-over-factors were made with that procedure in mind. The effective column stiffness is determined from the sum of the flexibilities of the attached torsional member and the column.

With this procedure, the frame is modelled using member centrelines. As a result, the moments obtained at the beam member ends should be reduced to obtain the design moments at the critical sections at the face of supports. To use this method for electronic computation requires writing a special program that incorporates use of attached torsional members. The program ADOSS™: Analysis and Design of Slab Systems (currently spSlab) is a PCA/StructurePoint software program that incorporates this procedure.

Prismatic Modelling

Today virtually every design office has a computer program for the elastic analysis of frames that is based on the direct stiffness method. So that these programs can be used for the analysis of slab systems, the Standard contains coefficients for reducing the effective stiffness of 'prismatic' column members. If the frame is modelled using only centreline dimensions, then centreline moments at the ends of the beam members must be reduced to obtain design moments at the critical sections as required with 'non-prismatic' modelling. However, with little effort, the designer may introduce joints at the critical sections to obtain design moments directly.

5.3.5. Direct Design Method

Over time the 'Direct Design Method' has gradually been reduced from a complete design method to a specialized simple elastic frame analogy that provides average design moments at the critical sections. The lateral distribution of the average design moments is addressed in Clause 13.11.

The same design strip is used for the Direct Design Method as was used for the elastic frame analogy except that the columns are not included explicitly. Column dimensions are considered by using clear spans. The essence of the method is to distribute the total factored moment in each span of the frame to the critical sections using a set of coefficients. To ensure that the coefficients are applicable, additional restraints on the slab geometry are imposed. The unbalanced moments in interior columns and walls are determined from an expression involving partial loading on adjacent spans.

For slabs meeting the geometric requirements for use of the Direct Design Method, the curtailment of reinforcement may be obtained from Fig. 13-1 of the Standard.

5.3.6. Two-way Slabs with Stiff Supports

It is not uncommon for slab panels to be supported on all sides by walls or beams of sufficient stiffness that their curvature under load is much smaller than that required for the adjacent slab to develop significant moment. Thus, for determining slab moments and shears, the panel boundaries may be considered as non-deflecting. One possible approach is to treat each panel separately with moments determined from tabulated coefficients obtained from classical plate theory. For continuous slab systems, any difference in negative moments in adjacent panels at their common support can be distributed. This is the basis for the method given in Appendix B of the Standard and is illustrated in Example 5.5.

Some criterion is required in the case of slabs with beams on all sides to determine whether the beam may be considered stiff. Appendix B defines a beam as stiff when the ratio $b_w h_b^3/(\ell_n h_s^3)$ is at least 2.0. Hence the determination as to whether the beam is stiff requires prior knowledge of the slab thickness, h_s. It should be noted that this ratio is different than the mean beam stiffness ratio, α_m, used previously. Nevertheless, a reasonable trial slab thickness can be obtained using Eqn. 13-3 in Clause 13.2.5 of the Standard with $\alpha_m = 2.0$. This trial thickness should not be less than the perimeter of the panel divided by 160 in the case of fully continuous slabs or the perimeter of the panel divided by 140 in the case of slabs discontinuous on one or more edges.

The procedure described in Appendix B also uses the terms "middle" and "column" strips but the definitions are different from those used for reinforcement distribution in slabs analyzed using frame analogies. When the panel boundaries are prevented from deflecting, the larger moments are in the central portions of the panel or "middle" strips. Coefficients for determining design moments in these strips are given. The two portions of the slab outside this central half are referred to as "column" strips even though there may only be wall supports. Moments in these strips are determined from the "middle" strip moments. When slabs are designed using Appendix B, all other requirements of the Standard, such as area of minimum reinforcement, etc. apply.

5.4   Slab Reinforcement

5.4.1.   General

For all slabs, sufficient flexural reinforcement is required at each section to resist the factored moments at that section. The minimum area of reinforcement required in each direction is $0.002\ A_g$; however, for exposure conditions where crack control is essential, this minimum area of reinforcement must be increased (Clause 7.8.2). A general comment is that it is often beneficial to assess the flexural resistance provided by minimum reinforcement at an early stage in the design. In many cases, minimum reinforcement will satisfy the flexural requirements of the entire slab or at least large fractions of it. This allows the designer to focus attention on those regions that are most critical.

Clause 13.10.5 deals with reinforcement at discontinuous edges of a slab. Both top and bottom reinforcement should extend to the free edge. It is good practice to enclose the free edge of a slab with U-bars to control cracking from twisting moments. This and other slab reinforcing details are discussed in Rogowsky (1999).

Other requirements pertain specifically to either one-way or two-way slabs and are discussed separately.

5.4.2.   One-way Slabs

For solid one-way slabs, flexural reinforcement must be spaced not further than 3 times the slab thickness or 500 mm and cut-off points and development lengths are computed as for beams. In addition, to limit width of flexural cracks, spacing of the principal flexural reinforcement at critical sections shall be such that the crack control parameter, z, (Clause 10.6.1) does not exceed 30 000 N/mm for interior exposure and 25 000 N/mm for exterior exposure. Perpendicular to the span, minimum reinforcement must not be spaced further than 5 times the slab thickness or 500 mm.

Where the slab is considered as a T-beam flange and the principal reinforcement in the slab is parallel to that beam, Clause 10.5.3.2 requires flexural reinforcement perpendicular to this beam in the top of the slab. This clause uses the phrase "clear distance between the webs of the T-beams". Here the term "T-beams" refers to the beams supporting the slab. The clear distance between the webs corresponds to the clear span of the one-way slab.

5.4.3.   Two-way Slabs

Most methods of analyzing two-way slabs (finite difference and finite element methods being exceptions) provide average design moments across critical sections. Since the intensity of bending across these critical sections is generally not uniform, it follows that the distribution of the bending moments and hence the flexural reinforcement should not be uniform. Clauses 13.12 and 13.11 provide criteria for laterally distributing design moments in slabs with and without interior beams, respectively. The objective is to assign a greater fraction of the design moment to sections that have either greater flexural stiffness or greater curvature.

The provisions for the lateral distribution of design moments in slabs without interior beams, Clause 13.11, allow the designer to exercise some judgment in the placing of slab reinforcement. For a slab with no interior beams and rectangular panels, midspan bending for the long span will be more uniform than it is for the short span. As a result, bottom reinforcement for the long span should be more uniformly spaced than bottom steel for the short span.

For negative moment in slabs without beams or slab bands, the lateral distribution coefficients at interior columns place some top reinforcement in the middle strip. The Standard does not specify how this reinforcement should be distributed across the middle strip nor is there a universally accepted practice. Rogowsky (1999) discusses this issue in some depth. ACI distributes the reinforcement uniformly over the middle strip, consistent with an elastic distribution of moment. There are two problems with this. First, the elastic distribution of moment is based on an elastic distribution of curvature while the area of reinforcement provided is based on the reinforcement reaching yield. The negative curvatures in the middle strip will not be great enough to fully mobilize the middle strip reinforcement. Second, the middle strip top reinforcement is awkward to support since it is not part of a two-way reinforcing mat. Rogowsky (1999) recommends placing middle strip negative reinforcement where middle strip negative curvatures are larger, near the boundary between the middle strip and the column strip. This is consistent with lateral distribution guidelines in Hillerborg (1996). Where it is needed, reinforcement proportioned for crack control should be placed in the middle strip.

Clauses 13.11.2.4 and 13.11.2.5 provide guidance for the lateral distribution of reinforcement in slabs with slab bands. Perpendicular to the slab band, between 85% and 95% of the design moment is distributed uniformly over the entire design strip. The remaining 5% to 15% that is placed within a width b_b centred on the column is in addition to the uniformly distributed moment.

Clause 13.10 provides additional requirements for placement of slab reinforcement. Clauses 13.10.2 through 13.10.4 as well as 13.11.2.7 ensure a minimum amount of top reinforcement in close proximity to the column (within a width b_b centred on the column).

Unless beams containing shear reinforcement are provided in all spans framing into the column, integrity reinforcement is required to prevent progressive collapse. Clause 13.10.6 presents general requirements in terms of the total area of anchored bottom reinforcement on all faces of the periphery of the column.

Clause 13.10.9 requires top reinforcement at all free slab edges. Clearly, wherever a slab cantilevers beyond the face of support there is a need to provide at least minimum reinforcement throughout the entire cantilevering section to resist the cantilever moment. What may not be as obvious is the desirability of some top reinforcement at any free edge. Point loads near a free edge generate local negative moments in the slab about an axis parallel to the free edge. As well, hooking the top reinforcement, as required by 13.10.5.2, provides reinforcement for the effects of torsional moments at the free edge.

5.5   Shear and Moment Transfer

For slabs, two shear failure modes are considered in design. One-way or beam shear failure occurs when the slab fails in shear across its full width, as in a wide beam. Two-way shear failure, sometimes called perimeter or punching shear failure, is a localized shear failure of the slab in close proximity to a concentrated load or support. Figure 5.5 shows tributary areas and critical sections for both one and two-way shear calculations for a column-supported slab. The resistances under one-way and two-way shear are given in Clauses 11.3 and 13.3, respectively.

Unless it is subjected to a significant concentrated load, a one-way slab is checked for one-way shear only. Two-way slabs are also checked for one-way shear although this is rarely critical. For a two-way slab supported by beams, the designer typically checks one-way shear on a strip of unit width spanning perpendicular to the beam. For a one-way shear check on a two-way slab without beams, the slab is treated as a wide beam with shear distributed between column and middle strips in proportion to the design negative moment assigned to each strip.

Two-way shear strength in two-way slabs at interior and edge column supports is evaluated by comparing a factored shear stress computed at a critical section to a factored shear stress resistance. The critical section for two-way shear surrounds the support or concentrated load. It is located so that its perimeter is a minimum but it need not be closer than $d/2$ from the face of the support or edge of concentrated load. Examples of critical sections are given in the Explanatory Notes to Clause 13.3.3. The factored shear resistance is a function of the concrete compressive strength and the shape and size of the support (Clause 13.3.4).

At interior and edge column-slab connections, the factored shear stress is computed from Eqn. 13-9 and includes terms for unbalanced factored moments transferred to the support about the centroidal axes of the critical section. The centroidal axes to be used are parallel and perpendicular to the design strips framing into the column. Expressions for evaluating b_o, γ_v, e and J at interior, edge, and corner columns for use in Eqn. 13-9 are illustrated in Fig. 5.6. These terms are functions of c_1, c_2 and d only.

Eqn. 13-9 can be rewritten in the form:

$$v_f = kv_f + k_1 M_1 + k_2 M_2$$

Design charts for estimating the coefficients k, k_1 and k_2 can be obtained as a free download from the Cement Association of Canada website.

The Explanatory Notes for Clause 13.3 illustrate the critical sections for shear for square, rectangular, circular, and L-shaped columns. Although the critical section is defined for all, the parameter J, usually described as being analogous to a polar moment of inertia, is undefined for non-rectangular column supports.

Equation 13-9 may also be applied to corner column-slab connections; however, the Standard permits an alternative analysis in which the average shear stress on a critical section located $d/2$ from the support is limited to the one-way value defined in Eqn. 13-10.

Some judgment is required when assigning values for V_f, M_1 and M_2 in Eqn. 13-9. Clause 13.3.5.5 indicates that the values used should be from a "consistent loading". For an interior column, the maximum factored shear force, V_f, occurs with all adjacent panels loaded whereas the maximum values of the unbalanced moments occur with selected partial loadings. Thus maximum values for all three terms cannot occur simultaneously and the consistent loading that would result in the sum of all three terms being a maximum is not easily determined. For an interior column, it is suggested that a satisfactory value of v_f can be obtained by adding the full V_f term to one of the unbalanced moment terms to obtain the larger sum. For an edge column, the maximum value of v_f will occur when both adjacent panels are loaded. Thus, for equal spans, the unbalanced moment about an axis perpendicular to the edge may be neglected.

To address scale effect in two-way shear, Clause 13.3.4.3 provides a multiplier to be applied whenever the slab thickness exceeds 300 mm.

5.6   References

[1]   Hillerborg, A., Strip Method of Design, Veiwpoint Publications, The Cement and Concrete Association, Wexham Springs, Slough, 1975, 256 pp.

[2]   Hillerborg, A., Strip Method Design Handbook, Chapman and Hall, London, UK, 1996, 302 pp.

[3]   Park, R. and Gamble, W., Reinforced Concrete Slabs, John Wiley and Sons, Inc., New Yory, N.Y., 2000, 716 pp.

[4]   Rogowsky, D., "Detailing for Serviceability," The Design of Two-Way Slab Systems, SP-183, Editor T.C. Schaeffer, American Concrete Institute, 1999, pp. 131-144.

[5]   Scanlon, A., "Design and Construction of Two-Way Slabs for Deflection Control," The Design of Two-Way Slab Systems, SP-183, Editor T.C. Schaeffer, American Concrete Institute, 1999, pp. 145-160.

[6]   Simmonds, S., "Concept and Background of Elastic Frame Analogies for Two-Way Slab Systems," The Design of Two-Way Slab Systems, SP-183, Editor T.C. Schaeffer, American Concrete Institute, 1999, pp. 1-16.

5.7   Examples

The following design examples are presented to assist in interpreting provisions in the Standard. They are incomplete designs in that only portions of the slab system are considered. Computations described elsewhere in this Handbook are generally omitted.

Previous editions of the CAC Concrete Design Handbook provided graphic design aids for estimating the beam stiffness ratio, α, and the parameters described above for shear and moment transfer, k, k_1, and k_2. To reduce the size of the handbook, these design aids have been omitted; however, they are available electronically as a free download from the Cement Association of Canada website.

The first four examples deal with two-way slab variations that have the same column layout and the same design strip widths. The fifth example presents the design of an edge-supported two-way slab using the method presented in Appendix B. The sixth example demonstrates the calculation of design moments using the results of an elastic plate analysis (13.6). Finally, the seventh example is a one-way slab and beam system with the same column layout as the first four examples.

For all examples, the specified design strength of the concrete, f_c' is 25 MPa (α_1 = 0.81) and the specified yield strength of the reinforcement, f_y , is 400 MPa. The density (unit weight) of reinforced concrete is assumed to be 24 kN/m³.

Example 1 Two-way Slab without Beams (Flat Plate)

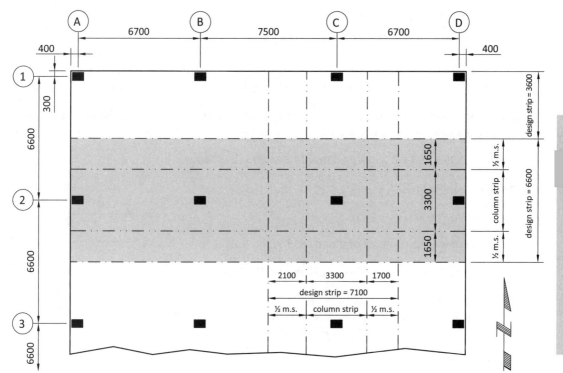

The sketch above shows a plan view of a portion of a typical floor in an apartment building. All columns measure 400 mm by 600 mm. The slab projects 100 mm beyond the exterior column face to support wall panels and assist with shear transfer. The slab supports a service live load of 1.9 kN/m² and a fixed partition allowance of 1.0 kN/m². The slab projection supports exterior cladding panels weighing 2.4 kN/m.

Step 1 – Select Slab Thickness

a)   Deflection requirements (13.2.3)

Interior Panel (E-W direction governs)

$\ell_n = 7500 - 300 - 300 = 6900$ mm

$$h_s \geq \frac{\ell_n\left(0.6 + \frac{f_y}{1000}\right)}{30} = \frac{6900 \times 1}{30} = 230 \text{ mm}$$

Exterior Panel (N-S direction governs)

$\ell_n = 6600 - 200 - 200 = 6200$ mm

$$h_s \geq 1.1 \times \frac{\ell_n\left(0.6 + \frac{f_y}{1000}\right)}{30} = \frac{1.1 \times 6200 \times 1}{30} = 227 \text{ mm}$$

Try $h_s = 250$ mm

Effective depths using 15 M bars with 25 mm clear cover

flexure (outer layer): $d_{max} = 250 - 25 - 8 = 217$ mm

flexure (inner layer): $d_{min} = 250 - 25 - 15 - 8 = 202$ mm

shear (centre of mat): $d = 250 - 25 - 15 = 210$ mm

Factored loading:

Load combination 1 (See Annex C)

$1.4 \times (0.25 \text{ m} \times 24 \text{ kN/m}^3 + 1.0 \text{ kN/m}^2) = 9.8 \text{ kN/m}^2$

Load combination 2

$1.5 \times 1.9 \text{ kN/m}^2 + 1.25 \times (0.25\text{m} \times 24 \text{ kN/m}^3 + 1.0 \text{ kN/m}^2) = 11.6 \text{ kN/m}^2$ →   Governs

Loading at free edge: area of 100 mm overhang is not subject to live load but self-weight should be included in dead load of cladding panels.

$W_{CLAD} = 1.25 \times (2.4 + 0.1 \text{ m} \times 0.25 \text{ m} \times 24 \text{ kN/m}^2) = 3.75 \text{ kN/m}$

b)   Preliminary shear check

i) Interior column at C2

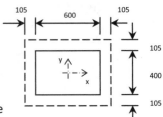

Shear perimeter (see sketch) defined in 13.3.3.

$b_o = 2 \times (400 \text{ mm} + 600 \text{ mm} + 2 \times 210 \text{ mm}) = 2840 \text{ mm}$

To account for the effect of unbalanced moment, the ratio of the resisting shear stress, v_r, to the average shear stress from the factored shear acting alone, v_f, should be at least 1.2.

v_r is the lesser of:

$$\left(1+\frac{2}{\beta_c}\right)0.19\lambda\phi_c\sqrt{f_c'} = \left(1+\frac{2}{1.5}\right)0.19\times1\times0.65\times5 \text{ MPa}=1.44 \text{ MPa} \qquad (13\text{-}5)$$

$$\left(\frac{\alpha_s d}{b_o}+0.19\right)\lambda\phi_c\sqrt{f_c'} = \left(\frac{4\times210}{2840}+0.19\right)\times1\times0.65\times5 \text{ MPa}=1.58 \text{ MPa} \qquad (13\text{-}6)$$

$$0.38\lambda\phi_c\sqrt{f_c'} =0.38\times1\times0.65\times5 \text{ MPa}=1.23 \text{ MPa} \qquad (13\text{-}7)$$

$$v_{f,ave} =\frac{V_f}{b_o d}=\frac{7.1\times6.6\times11.6 \text{ kN/m}^2}{2840\times210}=0.911 \text{ MPa}$$

$$\frac{v_r}{v_{f,ave}} = 1.35 > 1.2 \text{ proceed} \qquad\qquad\qquad \text{(see section 5.2.3)}$$

ii) Edge columns at C1 and D2

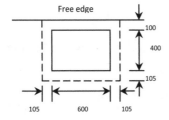

Column at C1

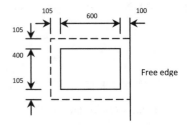

Column at D2

C1 (see sketch): $b_o = 2 \times (400 + 100 + 105) + 600 + 210 = 2020$ mm

$$v_{f,ave} = \frac{V_f}{b_o d} = \frac{(3.3\,\text{m}+0.2\,\text{m})\times 7.1\,\text{m}\times 11.6\ \text{kN/m}^2 + 7.1\,\text{m}\times 3.75\ \text{kN/m}}{2020\times 210} = 0.74\ \text{MPa}$$

$v_r = 1.23$ MPa $\dfrac{v_r}{v_{f,ave}} = 1.66 > 1.6$ proceed (see section 5.2.3)

D2 (see sketch): $b_o = 2 \times (600 + 100 + 105) + 400 + 210 = 2220$ mm

$$v_{f,ave} = \frac{V_f}{b_o d} = \frac{(3.35\,\text{m}+0.3\,\text{m})\times 6.6\,\text{m}\times 11.6\ \text{kN/m}^2 + 6.6\,\text{m}\times 3.75\ \text{kN/m}}{2220\ \text{mm}\times 210\ \text{mm}} = 0.65\ \text{MPa}$$

$v_r = 1.23$ MPa $\dfrac{v_r}{v_{f,ave}} = 1.88 > 1.6$ proceed

iii)   Corner column D1

The critical section for shear is located $d/2$ from the face of support (see sketch at right). The average stress on this section under vertical shear alone is limited to the one-way value for slabs. (13.3.6)

$$V_c = \phi_c \lambda \beta \sqrt{f'_c} \times b_o d_v$$

$\beta_d = 0.21$ (Clause 11.3.6.2)

$b_o = 400 + 600 + 210 + 200 = 1410$ mm

$d_v = \max(0.72h; 0.9d) = \max(180; 189) = 189$ mm

$V_c = 0.65 \times 1 \times 0.21 \times 5 \times 1410 \times 189 = 182$ kN

$$V_f = \left(\frac{6.7}{2}+0.3\right)\left(\frac{6.6}{2}+0.2\right)11.6\,\text{kN/m}^2 + \left(\frac{6.7}{2}+\frac{6.6}{2}+0.45+0.35\right)\times 3.75\,\text{kN/m} = 176\,\text{kN}$$

All preliminary shear checks are satisfactory.

Use $h_s = 250$ mm

Step 2 – Design Moments

Consider a design strip along gridline 2. Since the limitations of (13.9.1) are satisfied, use Direct Design Method.

Clause 13.9.3.3 permits up to 15% redistribution of moments calculated by the Direct Design Method provided that the total static moment, M_o, is unchanged. In this case the numerically larger negative moments at B and C are reduced with appropriate adjustment to the positive moment between B and C. Note that the positive moment has been increased 15.6%. There are two factors that justify this. First, the difference between 15% and 15.6% is not significant. Second and more important, distributing moment from negative to positive creates a plastic demand on the negative moment region. It is the negative moment region that requires ductility, not the positive moment region.

	A			**B**			**C**			**D**	
ℓ_n		6100			6900			6100			(mm)
M_o (13.9.2.2)		356			456			356			(kN·m)
%M_o (13.9.3)	0.26	0.52	0.70	0.65	0.35	0.65	0.70	0.52	0.26		
M_{DES}	-93	185	-249	-296	160	-296	-249	185	-93		(kN·m)
Adjusted M_{DES}	-93	185	-249	-271	185	-271	-249	185	-93		(kN·m)

Column D1

Step 3 – Select Reinforcement

Assume 15 M bars: place N-S reinf. in inner layer

E-W reinf. in outer layer

Approximate moment resistance per bar (E-W design strips):

$$M_{r\,bar} \approx \phi_s A_{bar} f_y \times 0.9 d_{max} = \frac{0.85 \times 200 \times 400 \times 0.9 \times 217}{10^6} = 13.28\,kN \cdot m$$

Minimum Reinforcement

$$A_{s\,min} = 0.002 A_g = 0.002 \times 250\,mm \times 1000\,mm/m = 500\,mm^2/m$$

Use 15 M at 400 c/c

Moment resistance with minimum reinforcement (E-W design strips)

$$m_{r\,min} = \frac{\phi_s A_{smin} f_y}{s}\left(d_{min} - \frac{\phi_s A_{smin} f_y}{2\alpha_1 \phi_c f_c's} \right)$$

$$= \frac{0.85 \times 200 \times 400}{400}\left(217 - \frac{0.85 \times 200 \times 400}{2 \times 0.81 \times 0.65 \times 25 \times 400} \right) \times \frac{1}{10^3} = 35.8\,kN \cdot m/m$$

Positive moment (bottom) reinforcement

(13.11.2.2) requires that between 55% and 65% of the positive moment in all spans be taken by the column strips, leaving 45% to 35% to be taken by the middle strips. This puts the column strip design positive moment between 102 kN·m and 120 kN·m. The corresponding design moments for the middle strip are 83 kN·m and 65 kN·m. Design moment intensity in the column strip ranges from 30.9 kN·m/m to 36.4 kN·m/m. The corresponding design moment intensity in the middle strip ranges from 25.1 kN·m/m to 19.7 kN·m/m.

The resistance provided by minimum reinforcement, 35.8 kN·m/m, falls within the range of column strip design moment intensities and exceeds the range of middle strip design moment intensities. Minimum reinforcement will provide sufficient resistance for all for all spans.

Check Maximum spacing (13.10.4)

Positive moment reinforcement: $s \le 3h_s$ but not to exceed 500 mm   OK

Use 15 M at 400 c/c bottom East-West

Negative moment (top) reinforcement: Column at C2

Design top East-West mat to be centred on column.

Total negative design moment: M_{DES} = 271 kN·m

Minimum total number of bars in top mat: $\dfrac{271\,kN \cdot m}{13.28\,kN \cdot m/bar} = 20.4\,bars$ ⇒   say 21 bars

At least one third of these bars are to be placed within a width b_b (13.11.2.7).

Requires 7 bars within width b_b

From Clause 3.2: $b_b = c_2 + 3h_s = 400 + 3 \times 250 = 1150$ mm $\Rightarrow$ say 1000 mm

Check moment transfer: for Direct Design, minimum unbalanced moment is (13.9.4)

$$M_f = 0.07\left[\left(w_{df} + 0.5w_{lf}\right)\ell_{2a}\ell_n^2 - w'_{df}\ell'_{2a}\left(\ell'_n\right)^2\right]$$
$$= 0.07\left[\left(8.75 + \frac{2.85}{2}\right)6.6 \times 6.9^2 - 8.75 \times 6.6 \times 6.1^2\right] = 73.4 \text{ kN·m}$$

Fraction to be transferred by flexural reinforcement within width b_b (13.10):

$$\gamma_f = 1 - \gamma_v = \cfrac{1}{1 + \cfrac{2}{3}\sqrt{\cfrac{b_1}{b_2}}} = \cfrac{1}{1 + \cfrac{2}{3}\sqrt{\cfrac{810}{610}}} = 0.566$$

This would require $\dfrac{41.5 \text{kN·m}}{13.28 \text{kN·m/bar}} = 3.1$ bars

Requires 4 bars within width b_b. Does not govern

Use 21 – 15 M bars. Place 7 bars in band 1000 wide centred on column

Remaining 14 bars spaced at 200 c/c

Check bars required in column strip (13.11.2.2):   from 0.70×21 bars = 14.7 bars

to 0.90×21 bars = 18.9 bars

# of bars provided in column strip $= 7 + \dfrac{3300 - 1000}{200} = 18.5$ bars   OK

The intent here is that the spacing of top bars continues at 200 c/c into each half middle strip until the total number of bars is provided. This leaves the central part of each middle strip without top reinforcement. Depending upon the sensitivity to slab cracking of the intended use and occupancy, crack control reinforcement may be required throughout the negative moment region of the middle strips. While curvature at factored load in these regions will not generally be sufficient to yield the reinforcement, curvature at service load may be sufficient to crack the concrete.

Negative moment (top) reinforcement: Edge column at D2 and free edge of slab

From Direct Design on gridline 2, moment at face of support is 93 kN·m. 100% of this is to be transferred by reinforcement within width b_b. As before, b_b is 1150 mm.

Reinforsment required $= \dfrac{93 \text{kN·m}}{13.28 \dfrac{\text{kN·m}}{\text{bar}}} = 7$ bars

Use 7 – 15 M bars in band 1000 wide centred on column

The Standard calls for at least minimum top reinforcement perpendicular to the free edge of the slab (13.10.9). Close free edge with 180° U-bars to provide reinforcement for edge shear resulting from torsional moments at free edge.

Use 15 M bars U-bars at 400 c/c at all slab edges

Structural Integrity (13.10.6)

$$V_{se} = 7.1 \times 6.6 \times (1.9 + 1 + 0.25 \times 24) = 417 \text{ kN}$$
$$\Sigma A_{sb} = \frac{2 \times V_{se}}{fy} = \frac{2 \times 562 \times 10^3}{400} = 2810 \text{ mm}^2$$

Place 2 – 15 M bars from bottom flexural steel through column in each direction. These bars must be continuous through the column. Add 1 – 15 M extra bottom bar through column East-West and 1 – 15 M extra bottom bar through column North-South. Hence, $\Sigma A_{sb} = 12 \times 200$ mm² = 2400 mm². These extra bars must lap $2\ell_d$ with the bottom mat on either side of the column.

Step 4 – Check Shear

Interior column-slab connection at C-2

With the Direct Design Method, it is reasonable to check shear with moment acting about only one axis (x or y). Maximum vertical shear transfer and maximum moment transfer do not occur simultaneously.

For the East-West design strip (bending about the y-axis of the critical section shown above):

$c_1 = 600$ mm; $c_2 = 400$ mm

$b_1 = c_1 + d = 600 + 210 = 810$ mm; $b_2 = c_2 + d = 400 + 210 = 610$ mm

$$J = \frac{b_1^3 \times d + d^3 \times b_1}{6} + \frac{b_2 \times d \times b_1^2}{2}$$

$$= \frac{810^3 \times 210 + 210^3 \times 810}{6} + \frac{610 \times 210 \times 810^2}{2} = 61.87 \times 10^9 \text{ mm}^4$$

$$e = \frac{b_1}{2} = 405 \text{ mm}$$

From previous calculations:

$$\frac{V_f}{b_o d} = 0.911 \text{ MPa} \qquad\qquad M_f = 73.4 \text{ kN·m}$$

$$\gamma_v = 1 - \gamma_f = 1 - 0.566 = 0.434 \qquad v_r = 1.23 \text{ Mpa}$$

For moment about one axis only, Eqn. 13.9 simplifies to:

$$v_f = \frac{V_f}{b_o d} + \frac{\gamma_v M_f e}{J}$$

$$v_f = 0.911 \text{MPa} + \frac{0.434 \times 73.4 \times 10^6 \times 405}{61.87 \times 10^9} = 1.12 \text{MPa} \qquad\qquad V_f < V_r \qquad\qquad \text{OK}$$

For the North-South design strip (bending about the x-axis of the critical section shown above):

$c_1 = 400$ mm; $c_2 = 600$ mm

$b_1 = c_1 + d = 400 + 210 = 610$ mm; $b_2 = c_2 + d = 600 + 210 = 810$ mm

$$J = \frac{b_1^3 \times d + d^3 \times b_1}{6} + \frac{b_2 \times d \times b_1^2}{2} = \frac{610^3 \times 210 + 210^3 \times 610}{6} + \frac{810 \times 210 \times 610^2}{2} = 40.53 \times 10^9 \text{ mm}^4$$

$$e = \frac{b_1}{2} = 305 \text{ mm}$$

$$M_f = 0.07\left[\left(8.75 + \frac{2.85}{2}\right)7.1 \times 6.2^2 - 8.75 \times 7.1 \times 6.2^2\right] = 27.2 \text{ kN·m}$$

$$\gamma_v = 1 - \frac{1}{1 + \frac{2}{3}\sqrt{\frac{610}{810}}} = 0.366$$

$$v_f = 0.911 \text{MPa} + \frac{0.366 \times 34.9 \times 10^6 \times 305}{40.53 \times 10^9} = 0.99 \text{MPa} \qquad\qquad V_f < V_r \qquad\qquad \text{OK}$$

Edge column-slab connection at D-2

Consider moment about axis parallel to free edge. Equation 13.9 requires that moments be defined at the centroid of the critical section. Many analysis packages provide moments at the centroid of the column. The Direct Design Method gives moments at the face of the support. In either case, additional calculations are required to determine the moment to be used in Eqn. 13.9. With reference to the sketches at right:

$$e = \frac{805^2}{2 \times 805 + 610} = 292 \, \text{mm}$$

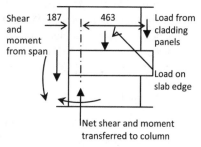

Plan

5

Slabs

From **Step 2**, the factored moment at the face of column support is 93 kN·m. The shears from span C-D, from the edge strip of slab between columns, and from the cladding panels loading the edge are, respectively:

$$V_{SPAN} = 3.05 \, \text{m} \times 6.6 \, \text{m} \times 11.6 \, \text{kN/m}^2 = 233.5 \, \text{kN}$$

$$V_{EDGE} = 0.6 \, \text{m} \times 6.6 \, \text{m} \times 11.6 \, \text{kN/m}^2 = 45.9 \, \text{kN}$$

$$V_{CLAD} = 6.6 \, \text{m} \times 3.75 \, \text{kN/m} = 24.8 \, \text{kN}$$

These shears have been overestimated a little. It would be reasonable to deduct load applied within the critical section. Also, the tributary area of an edge column does not extend to the midpoint of the span, as is usually assumed.

The net shear and moment acting at the centroid of the critical section are:

$$V_f = 233.5 + 45.9 + 24.8 = 304.2 \, \text{kN·m}$$

$$M_f = 93 + 233.5 \times 0.187 - 45.9 \times (0.3 - 0.187) - 24.8 \times 0.463$$

$$= 93 + 44 - 5.2 - 11.5 = 120.3 \, \text{kN·m}$$

Geometric properties of the critical section for shear are:

$$b_1 = 805 \, \text{mm}; \qquad b_2 = 610 \, \text{mm};$$

$$b_o = 2220 \, \text{mm}$$

$$J = 2\left(\frac{b_1^3 \times d}{3} + \frac{d^3 \times b_1}{12}\right) - b_o d e^2$$

$$= 2\left(\frac{805^3 \times 210}{3} + \frac{210^3 \times 805}{12}\right) - 2220 \times 210 \times 292^2 = 34.53 \times 10^9 \, \text{mm}^4$$

$$\gamma_v = 1 - \frac{1}{1 + \frac{2}{3}\sqrt{\frac{805}{610}}} = 0.434$$

From preliminary shear check:

$$v_r = 1.23 \, \text{MPa}$$

$$v_f = \frac{304.2 \times 10^3}{2220 \times 210} + \frac{0.434 \times 120.3 \times 10^6 \times 292}{34.53 \times 10^9} = 1.10 \, \text{MPa} \qquad v_f < v_r \qquad \text{OK}$$

Edge column-slab connection at C-1

$b_1 = 605$ mm; $b_2 = 810$ mm; $b_o = 2020$ mm

$e = 181.2$ mm; $J = 18.01 \times 10^9$ mm⁴; $\gamma_v = 0.366$

$V_{SPAN} = 255.3$ kN; $V_{EDGE} = 32.9$ kN; $V_{CLAD} = 26.6$ kN

$M_{face} = 0.26 \times 11.6 \times 7.1 \times \dfrac{6.2^2}{8} = 116.6$ kN·m; $M_f = 122$ kN·m

$$v_f = \frac{315 \times 10^3}{2020 \times 210} + \frac{0.366 \times 122 \times 10^6 \times 181}{18.01 \times 10^9} = 1.19 \text{ MPa} \qquad V_f < V_r \qquad\qquad \text{OK}$$

Example 2 Two-way Slab with Drop Panels

Consider a floor with the same column layout as Example 1 that supports a higher live load of 3.6 kN/m², a partition load of 1.0 kN/m², and an additional mechanical services load of 1.0 kN/m². From the preliminary shear check in Example 1 we know that a 250 mm thick flat plate will not be satisfactory.

Try drop panels.

Step 1 – Select Slab Thickness

a)   Deflection requirements (13.2.4)

For economy, the projection of a drop panel below the underside of the slab, Δ_h, should be compatible with the forming system. In the past this usually meant being modular in some way with dimension lumber. While the importance of dimension lumber may have diminished, it is still important to understand the forming system that is likely to be used and choose dimensions accordingly. Here the dimension Δ_h will be taken as the lumber dimension plus the thickness of one sheet of plywood (19 mm). Economical choices for Δ_h are:

38 + 19 = 57mm or 89 + 19 = 108 mm: Try $\Delta_h = 57$mm

The value of x_d/ℓ_n is not known at this point. The upper limit is ¼. A reasonable preliminary estimate is ⅙.

Interior Panel

$$h_s \geq \frac{\ell_n\left(0.6 + \dfrac{f_y}{1000}\right)}{30} - \frac{2x_d}{\ell_n}\Delta_h = \frac{6900}{30} - \frac{2}{6} \times 57 = 211 \text{ mm} \qquad \text{Try:} \qquad h_s = 220 \text{ mm}$$

$h_d = 277$ mm

Effective depths (to centre of mat) for shear using 15 M bars with 25 mm clear cover

> at column face: $d = 277 - 25 - 15 = 237$ mm
> at face of drop: $d = 220 - 25 - 15 = 180$ mm

Factored loading:

1.5 × 3.6 kN/m² + 1.25 × (0.22m × 24 kN/m³ + 2.0 kN/m²) = 14.5 kN/m²

b) Preliminary shear check

i) column at C3

Shear perimeter defined in 13.3.3.

$b_o = 2 \times (400 \text{ mm} + 600 \text{ mm} + 2 \times 237 \text{ mm}) = 2948 \text{ mm}$

The final dimensions of the drop have not been decided but can be estimated as roughly ⅓ of the spans.

V_f = factored uniformly distributed load + factored weight of drop projection

$$= 7.1 \times 6.6 \times 14.5 \, \text{kN} \Big/ \text{m}^2 + 0.057 \times \frac{7.1}{3} \times \frac{6.6}{3} \times 24 \, \text{kN} \Big/ \text{m}^2 \times 1.25 = 688 \text{ kN}$$

$$v_f = \frac{V_f}{b_o d} = \frac{688 \text{kN}}{2948 \times 237} = 0.985 \text{ MPa} \qquad \frac{v_r}{v_f} = 1.25 > 1.2 \text{ proceed} \qquad \text{(see section 5.2.3)}$$

c) Size drop panel

Re-arranging Equation 13.2,

$$x_d = \frac{\frac{\ell_n}{30} - h_s}{2\Delta_h} \times \ell_n = \frac{230 - 220}{2 \times 57} \times 6900 = 605 \, (\text{east} - \text{west}); \qquad 2 \times 605 + 600 = 1810 \text{ mm}$$

$$= \frac{230 - 220}{2 \times 57} \times 6200 = 544 \, (\text{north} - \text{south}); \qquad 2 \times 544 + 400 = 1488 \text{ mm}$$

Choose drop panel measuring 2000 × 2000.

Check shear around perimeter of drop. For a large shear perimeter, the resisting shear stress given by (13-6) will govern.

$$v_r = \left(\frac{\alpha_s d}{b_o} + 0.19 \right) \lambda \phi_c \sqrt{f_c'} = \left(\frac{4 \times 180}{4 \times (2000 + 180)} + 0.19 \right) \times 1 \times 0.65 \times 5 \text{MPa} = 0.886 \text{ MPa}$$

$$v_f = \frac{(7.1 \times 6.6 - 2.0 \times 2.0) \times 14.5 \, \text{kN} \Big/ \text{m}^2 \times 10^3}{4 \times (2000 + 180) \times 180} = 0.396 \text{ MPa} < v_r \qquad \text{OK}$$

Use h_s = 220 mm; h_d = 277 mm; drop measures 2000 × 2000

Step 2 – Design Moments

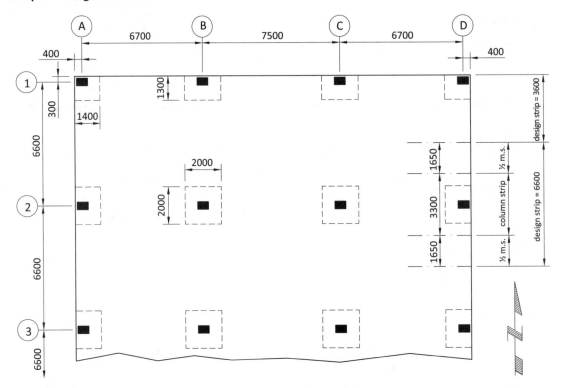

Consider a design strip along gridline 2. Since the limitations of (13.9.1) are satisfied, use Direct Design Method.

	A			B			C			D	
ℓ_n			6100			6900			6100		(mm)
M_o (13.9.2.2)			445			570			445		(kN·m)
$\%M_o$ (13.9.3)	0.26	0.52	0.70	0.65	0.35	0.65	0.70	0.52	0.26		
M_{DES}	-116	231	-312	-370	201	-370	-312	231	-116		(kN·m)

Step 3 – Select Reinforcement

Assume 15 M bars: place N-S reinf. in inner layer

E-W reinf. in outer layers

slab (outer layer): $d_{max} = 220 - 25 - 8 = 187$ mm

slab (inner layer): $d_{min} = 220 - 25 - 15 - 8 = 172$ mm

Approximate moment resistance per bar (E-W design strips):

$$M_{r\,bar} \approx \phi_s A_{bar} f_y \times 0.9 d_{min} = \frac{0.85 \times 200 \times 400 \times 0.9 \times 187}{10^6} = 11.44 \text{ kN·m}$$

Minimum Reinforcement (in slab)

$A_{s\,min} = 0.002 A_g = 0.002 \times 220 \text{ mm} \times 1000 \text{ mm/m} = 440 \text{ mm}^2/\text{m}$

Use 15 M at 400 c/c

Moment resistance with minimum reinforcement (E-W design strips)

$$m_{rmin} = \frac{\phi_s A_{smin} f_y}{s}\left(d_{min} - \frac{\phi_s A_{smin} f_y}{2\alpha_1 \phi_c f'_c s}\right)$$

$$= \frac{0.85 \times 200 \times 400}{400}\left(187 - \frac{0.85 \times 200 \times 400}{2 \times 0.81 \times 0.65 \times 25 \times 400}\right) \times \frac{1}{10^3} = 30.7\,\text{kN·m/m}$$

Positive moment (bottom) reinforcement

(13.11.2.3) requires that 55% to 65% of the positive moment in all spans be taken by the column strips. This leaves 45% to 35% of the positive moment to be taken by the middle strips.

	A		B		C		D	
M_{DES}	231		200		231			(kN·m)
$m_{DES\ col.\ st.}$	38.5 to 45.5		33.3 to 39.4		38.5 to 45.5			(kN·m/m)
$m_{DES\ mid.\ st.}$	31.5 to 24.5		27.3 to 21.2		31.5 to 24.5			(kN·m/m)

The resistance provided by minimum reinforcement, 30.7 kN·m/m, is not sufficient for the column strips but does satisfy the requirements of the middle strips. Try 15 M at 400 c/c bottom and add bars in column strip as required.

Spans AB and CD

$$m_{r\ col.st.}\,(\text{required}) = \frac{231\,\text{kN·m} - 3.3\,\text{m} \times 30.7\,\text{kN·m/m}}{3.3\,\text{m}} = 39.3\,\text{kN·m/m}$$

Deficit within width of column strip (3.3 m) = 3.3 × (39.3 − 30.7) = 28.4 kN·m

$$\frac{28.4}{11.44} = 2.5 \text{ additional bars} \quad \Rightarrow \quad \text{Add } 3 - 15 \text{ M bottom in column strip of spans AB and CD}$$

Note that this calculation makes use of the approximate moment resistance provided by a single bar determined in Step 3. That approximate moment resistance is based on an assumed internal lever arm of 0.9d. The reader may wish to confirm whether this is a safe assumption.

Span BC

The 30.7 kN·m/m provided by minimum reinforcement in the middle strip exceeds the maximum middle strip design moment. As a result, column strip reinforcement needs to resist only the minimum column strip design moment.

$$m_{r\ col.\ st.}\,(\text{required}) = 33.3\,\text{kN·m/m}$$

Deficit within width of column strip (3.3 m) = 3.3 × (33.3 − 30.7) = 8.58 kN·m

$$\frac{8.58}{11.44} = 0.75 \text{ additional bars} \quad \Rightarrow \quad \text{Add } 1 - 15 \text{ M bottom in column strip of spans BC}$$

Check Maximum spacing (13.10.4)

Positive moment reinforcement: $s \le 3h_s$ but not to exceed 500 mm   OK

Use 15 M at 400 c/c bottom East-West

Add 3 – 15 M bottom in column strip of spans AB and CD

Add 1 – 15 M bottom in column strip of spans BC

Negative moment (top) reinforcement: Column at C3

Design top East-West mat to be centred on column.

Effective depth of reinforcement for negative moment

In drop   East-West (outer layer): $d_{max} = 277 - 25 - 8 = 244$ mm

Outside drop

The slab adjacent and in close proximity to the drop will act more like the flange of a T-beam, with the drop serving as the stem, than simply a slab. Bars in this zone will have a flexural depth larger than that of the slab alone. For the purpose of selecting reinforcement, ignoring this T-beam behavior errs on the safe side.

East-West (outer layer): $d_{max} = 220 - 25 - 8 = 187$ mm

Approximate moment resistance per bar **in drop** (E-W design strip):

$$M_{r\,bar} \approx \phi_s A_{bar} f_y \times 0.9 d_{max} = \frac{0.85 \times 200 \times 400 \times 0.9 \times 244}{10^6} = 14.93 \text{ kN·m}$$

Approximate moment resistance per bar **outside drop** (E-W design strip):

From previous calculation, $M_{r\,bar} = 11.44$ kN·m

Total negative design moment: $M_{DES} = 370$ kN·m

Require moment resistance for $370\!\big/\!_3 = 123$ kN·m within width b_b.

$b_b = c_2 + 3h_s = 400 + 3 \times 277 = 1231$ mm

Try extending same spacing throughout column strip.

# of bars in column strip $= \dfrac{123}{14.93} \times \dfrac{3300}{1231} = 22.1 \quad \Rightarrow \quad$ Try 24 – 15 M bars in column strip

# of bars in drop $= \dfrac{2000}{3300} \times 24 = 14.5$ bars

# of bars outside of drop $= \dfrac{1300}{3300} \times 24 = 9.5$ bars

Moment resistance provided in column strip $= 14.5 \times 14.93 + 9.5 \times 11.44 = 325$ kN·m

Moment to be carried by middle strip $= 370 - 325 = 45$ kN·m

# of bars in middle strip $= \dfrac{45}{11.44} = 3.9 \qquad \Rightarrow \qquad$ Try 2 – 15 M in each half middle strip

These middle strip bars are provided for factored load and are simply an extension of the column strip top mat into the middle strip. Crack control reinforcement may be needed throughout the negative moment region of the middle strip.

Check resistance provided

Moment in column strip: $0.75 \times 370 = 278 \le 325 \le 0.9 \times 370 = 333$ \qquad\qquad OK

Use 30 – 15 M bars top. Place 24 in column strip and 2 in each half middle strip

Example 3 Two-way Slab with Slab Bands

This example is the same as Example 2 except that slab bands will be used in lieu of drop panels.

Use edge beam on perimeter (same depth as slab bands)

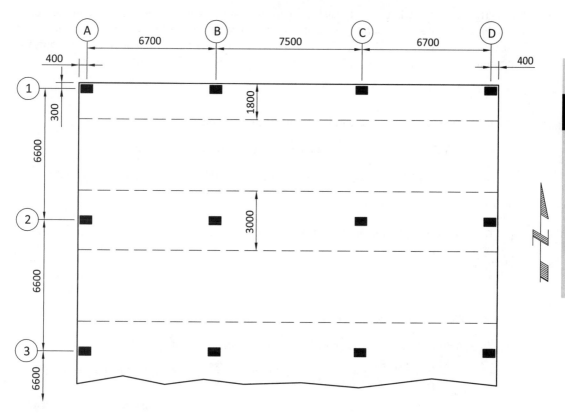

Step 1 – Select Slab Thickness

a) Deflection requirements (13.2.4)

Choose slab bands running east to west. Minimum thickness to satisfy Table 9.2 (13.2.6)

$$h_{band\,min} = \frac{6100}{18} = 339 \text{ (end span)} \qquad \rightarrow \qquad \text{Governs}$$

$$h_{band\,min} = \frac{6900}{21} = 329 \text{ (interior span)} \qquad \Rightarrow \qquad \text{Try } h_{band} = 350 \text{ mm}$$

By definition a slab band is an extended drop panel; however, as a drop panel, the slab band is very deep. The difference between the band thickness and the slab thickness, Δ_h, is likely to exceed the slab thickness. Since, for the purposes of Equation 13.2, Δ_h cannot be taken larger than the slab thickness, a preliminary estimate of slab thickness is based on Eqn. 13.2 with Δ_h equal to h_s. In the spanning direction of the slab band the term x_d/ℓ_n would take its maximum value of 0.25; however, Clause 13.2.4 requires that the lower value be used in Eqn. 13.2. Assume $x_d/\ell_n = 0.2$.

$$h_s \geq \frac{1}{1 + 2\frac{x_d}{\ell_n}} \times \left(\frac{\ell_n}{30}\right) = \frac{1}{1.4} \times \left(\frac{6900}{30}\right) = 164 \text{ mm} \qquad \Rightarrow \qquad \text{Try } h_s = 175 \text{ mm}$$

b) Width of slab band

$0.2\ell_n = 0.2 \times 6200 = 1240;$ $2 \times 1240 + 400 = 2880$ mm

Try width of slab band to be 3000.

Note: The slab band will cause the slab to behave as a one-way element spanning in the north-south direction. The projection of the slab band beyond the face of the column is 1300 mm. The clear span of the slab is $6200 - 2 \times 1300 = 3600$. For a one-way slab with one end continuous, the minimum thickness by Table 9.2 is 150 mm, consistent with the slab thickness selected here.

c) Preliminary shear check

Factored loading (averaging slab band over entire panel is conservative) :

1.5×3.6 kN/m² $+ 1.25 \times (0.175\text{m} \times 24$ kN/m³ $+ 2.0$ kN/m²$) = 13.15$ kN/m²

1.25×0.175 m $\times 3.0/6.6 \times 24$ kN/m³ $= 2.39$ kN/m²   (slab band projection below slab)

$w_f = 13.15 + 2.39 = 15.5$ kN/m²

$V_f = 6.6$ m $\times 7.1$ m $\times 15.5$ kN/m² $= 726$ kN

Assume 15 M bars.

$d = 350 - 25 - 15 = 310$ mm

$b_o = 2 \times (400 + 600 + 2 \times 310) = 3240$ mm

Since $d > 300$ mm, shear resistance modified for scale effect (13.3.4.3)

$$V_r = \frac{3240 \times 310 \times 1.23\,\text{MPa}}{10^3} \times \frac{1300}{1000 + 310} = 1226 \text{ kN}; \qquad \frac{V_r}{V_f} = 1.69 > 1.2 \quad \text{OK (see section 5.2.3)}$$

Use Slab band running east-west

$h_s = 175$ mm; $h_{band} = 350$ mm; width of band = 3000mm

Step 2 – Design Moments

For moments in span parallel to slab band, the design process is much the same as it is for a slab with drop panels. Consider instead part of the design strip perpendicular to the slab band on gridline C. Use Direct Design Method.

	1				**2**			**3**	
ℓ_n			6200				6200		(mm)
M_o (13.9.2.2)			529				529		(kN·m)
%M_o (13.9.3)		0.26	0.52	0.70		0.65	0.35	0.65	
M_{DES}		-138	275	-370		-344	185	-344	(kN·m)

Step 3 – Select Reinforcement (perpendicular to slab band)

Assume 15 M bars: place N-S bottom reinforcement in outer layer

                                        place N-S top reinforcement in outer layer

Negative Moment

Check (13.10.7): distance from edge of band to face of support (1300 mm) is more than 4 times the projection of the slab band (175 mm). **Full depth of slab band can be used for negative moment.**

At slab band: $d_{max} = 350 - 25 - 8 = 317$ mm

Approximate negative moment resistance per bar:

$$M_{r\,bar} \approx \phi_s A_{bar} f_y \times 0.9 d_{min} = \frac{0.85 \times 200 \times 400 \times 0.9 \times 317}{10^6} = 19.4 \text{ kN} \cdot \text{m}$$

$$\text{\# of bars required} = \frac{370}{19.4} = 19.1 \qquad \Rightarrow \qquad \text{say 20 bars}$$

Of these, between 5% (1 bar) and 15% (3 bars) are added within width b_b. The remainder is uniformly distributed across the entire design strip (13.11.2.5).

$$b_b = 600 + 3 \times 350 = 1650 \text{ mm}$$

Use 15 M at 400 c/c top. Add 2 – 15 M in width b_b

$$\frac{7100}{400} = 17.75 \text{ spaces} \quad \text{uniformly distributed plus 2 additional bars within } b_b$$

$$\text{\# of bars provided} = 19 + 2 = 21 \qquad\qquad \text{OK}$$

Positive Moment

In slab: $d_{max} = 175 - 25 - 8 = 142$ mm

Approximate positive moment resistance per bar:

$$M_{r\,bar} \approx \phi_s A_{bar} f_y \times 0.9 d_{min} = \frac{0.85 \times 200 \times 400 \times 0.9 \times 142}{10^6} = 8.7 \text{ kN} \cdot \text{m}$$

$$\text{\# of bars required} = \frac{275}{8.7} = 31.6 \qquad\qquad \Rightarrow \qquad \text{Try 15 M at 200 c/c}$$

$$\text{\# of bars in design strip} = \frac{7100}{200} = 35.5 \quad \Rightarrow \qquad \text{say 35 bars}$$

Check

$$M_r = 35 \times 0.85 \times 200 \times 400 \times \left(142 - \frac{35 \times 0.85 \times 200 \times 400}{2 \times 0.81 \times 0.65 \times 25 \times 7100} \right) \times \frac{1}{10^6} = 308 \text{ kN} \cdot \text{m}$$

$$M_r \cong M_f \qquad\qquad \text{OK}$$

Use 15 M at 200 c/c

Example 4 Two-way Slab with Beams between All Supports

This slab has the same column layout as the three preceding examples but supports a higher service live load of 4.8 kN/m² and a superimposed dead load of 1.6 kN/m². A two-way slab and beam system will be used.

Step 1 – Select Slab Thickness (13.2.5)

Consider the interior panel bounded by gridlines B, C, 2, and 3.

$$\beta = \frac{6900}{6600} = 1.04 ; \qquad \text{assume } \alpha_m = 2;$$

$$h_s \geq \frac{\ell_n}{30 + 4\beta\alpha_m} = \frac{6900}{30 + 4 \times 1.04 \times 2} = 180 \qquad \Rightarrow \qquad \text{Try } h_s = 200 \text{ mm}$$

Size beam

Table 9.2.   interior span: $h \geq \dfrac{6900}{21} = 320$

exterior span: $h \geq \dfrac{6200}{18} = 344 \qquad \rightarrow \qquad$ Governs

Try $h = 400$ mm

Determine required width of beam.

$$\alpha = \frac{I_b}{I_s} \qquad \text{(by definition)}$$

$$= \frac{b_w}{\ell_2} \times 2.5 \times \left(\frac{h}{h_s}\right)^3 \times \left(1 - \frac{h_s}{h}\right) \qquad \text{(combine with Equation 13-4)}$$

The required beam width b_w to provide an average value of α equal to 2 (i.e. $\alpha_m = 2$) is estimated as:

$$b_w = \frac{\alpha_m \times \ell_{2average}}{2.5 \times \left[\left(\frac{h}{h_s}\right)^3 - \left(\frac{h}{h_s}\right)^2\right]} = \frac{2 \times \left(\dfrac{7100 + 6600}{2}\right)}{2.5 \times \left[2^3 - 2^2\right]} = 1370 \text{ mm}$$

The average value of I_2 is appropriate because α_m is averaged for the four beams that define the panel.

Try $b_w = 1400$ mm for interior beams, $b_w = 800$ mm for perimeter beams.

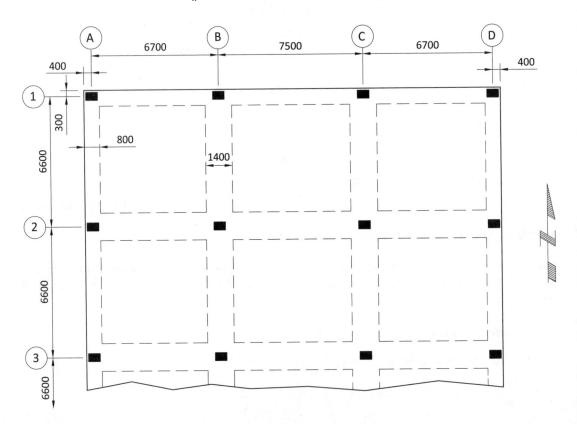

Step 2 – Design Moments

Loading

$$w_f = 1.5 \times 4.8 + 1.25 \times (0.2 \times 24 + 1.6) = 15.2 \text{ kN/m}^2$$

Beam stem: $1.25 \times 1.4 \times 0.2 \times 24 = 8.4 \text{ kN/m}$

	A			**B**			**C**			**D**	
ℓ_n		6100			6900			6100			(mm)
M_o (13.9.2.2)		506			647			506			(kN·m)
%M_o (13.9.3)	0.16	0.59	0.70	0.65	0.35	0.65	0.70	0.59	0.16			
M_{DES}	-81	299	-354	-421	227	-421	-354	299	-81			(kN·m)

Step 3 – Select Reinforcement

Span AB

$$\alpha_1 = \frac{1400}{6600}\left(\frac{400}{200}\right)^3 \times 2.5 \times \left(1 - \frac{200}{400}\right) = 2.12$$

Portion of design moment resisted by beam (13.12.2.1)

$$\frac{\alpha_1}{0.3 + \alpha_1}\left(1 - \frac{\ell_2}{3\ell_1}\right) = \frac{2.12}{0.3 + 2.12}\left(1 - \frac{6600}{3 \times 6700}\right) = 0.59$$

Slab moment $M_{slab\ DES} = (1 - 0.59) \times M_{DES} = 0.41 M_{DES}$

Span BC

Portion of design moment resisted by beam (13.12.2.1)

$$\frac{\alpha_1}{0.3 + \alpha_1}\left(1 - \frac{\ell_2}{3\ell_1}\right) = \frac{2.12}{0.3 + 2.12}\left(1 - \frac{6600}{3 \times 7500}\right) = 0.62$$

Slab moment $M_{slab\ DES} = (1 - 0.62) \times M_{DES} = 0.38 M_{DES}$

Reinforcement for slab moments may be uniformly distributed over width of slab.

Step 4 – Shear Check (in slab)

$d = 200 - 25 - 15 = 160 \text{ mm}$ (to middle of mat)

d_v is larger of: $0.9d = 144 \text{ mm}$ or

$0.72h_s = 144 \text{ mm}$

Consider a 1 meter wide strip (i.e. $b_w = 1 \text{ m}$):

$$V_r = \beta\phi_c\sqrt{f_c'}\,b_w d_v$$
$$= 0.21 \times 0.65 \times 5 \times 1000 \times 144 = 98.3 \text{ kN}$$

$V_f = 15.2 \times (2.6 - 0.144) \times 1 = 37.3 \text{ kN}$

$V_r > V_f$ OK

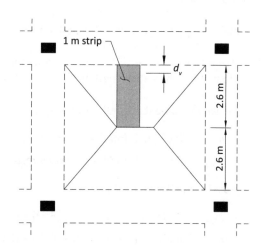

Example 5 Two-way Slab with Stiff Supports (Annex B)

The roof of a storage facility supports a factored live (combination of snow and use and occupancy) load of 4.4 kN/m² and a factored superimposed dead load of 1.8 kN/m². Note that Annex B considers only live and dead loads. The roof slab is supported on all sides by stiff beams or masonry block walls.

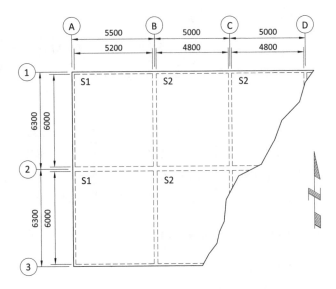

Step 1 – Select Slab Thickness

Deflection requirements
(13.2.5 and Annex B)

Corner panel S1 governs (smallest value of β combined with longest spans):

$$\beta = \frac{6000}{5200} = 1.15$$

assume $\alpha_m = 2$;   Equation 13.2: $h_{s\,min} = \dfrac{6000\left(0.6 + \frac{400}{1000}\right)}{(30 + 4 \times 2 \times 1.15)} = 153\,mm$

Annex B does not explicitly state whether the perimeter of the panel is based on clear span dimensions or some other. Clear span dimensions are used here.

(B.3.1) $h_{s\,min} = \dfrac{\text{perimeter}}{140} = \dfrac{2 \times (6000 + 5200)}{140} = 160\,mm$ $\Rightarrow$ Try $h_s = 160$ mm

Loading

$w_{lf} = 4.4$ kN/m²

$w_{df} = 1.8 + 1.25 \times (0.16 \times 24) = 6.6$ kN/m²

$w_f = 4.4 + 6.6 = 11$ kN/m²

Step 2 – Design Moments

Middle strip moments

Panel S1; $\ell_a / \ell_b = 5200/6000 = 0.84 \approx 0.85$; Case 4 (continuous on two adjacent sides).

With regard to the aspect ratio of the panel, one could use $\ell_a / \ell_b = 0.84$ and interpolate moment factors. It is debateable whether the method warrants this level of precision.

Negative moment at continuous edge (B.3.4):

$m_{a\,neg} = 0.066\,(11)\,(5.2)^2 = 19.63$ kN·m/m

$m_{b\,neg} = 0.034\,(11)\,(6.0)^2 = 13.46$ kN·m/m

Positive moments (B.3.5)

$m_{a\,pos} = [0.043 \times (4.4) + 0.036 \times (6.6)] \times (5.2)^2 = 11.54$ kN·m/m

$m_{b\,pos} = [0.023 \times (4.4) + 0.019 \times (6.6)] \times (6.0)^2 = 8.16$ kN·m/m

The remaining middle strip moments are as shown in the sketch below. Negative moments at discontinuous edges are taken as ¾ of the positive moment (B.3.8). Bending moments in column strips are ⅔ of the adjacent middle strip (B.3.5). At all outside corners, special corner reinforcement to satisfy (13.12.5) is required (B.3.9). This special corner reinforcement matches the maximum positive moment in the panel.

The difference in negative moment at gridline B is not great enough to require balancing (B.3.10); nevertheless, they are balanced here to illustrate the process. Note that since the negative moments have been balanced, the positive moment in panel 1 requires adjustment.

$$m_{BA\,neg} = 19.63 - \frac{\frac{1}{5200}}{\frac{1}{5200} + \frac{1}{4800}} \times (19.63 - 19.01) = 19.33\,\text{kN·m/m}$$

$$m_{BC\,neg} = 19.01 + \frac{\frac{1}{4800}}{\frac{1}{5200} + \frac{1}{4800}} \times (19.63 - 19.01) = 19.33\,\text{kN·m/m}$$

$$m_{AB\,pos} = 11.54 + \frac{(19.63 - 19.331)}{2} = 11.69\,\text{kN·m/m}$$

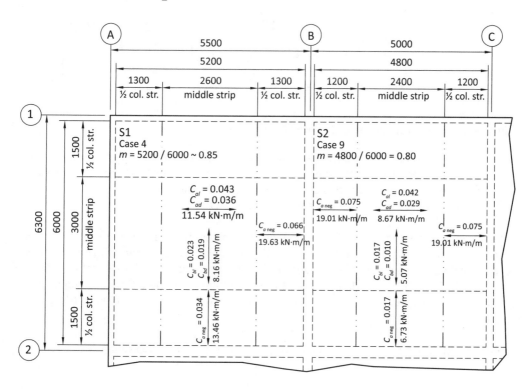

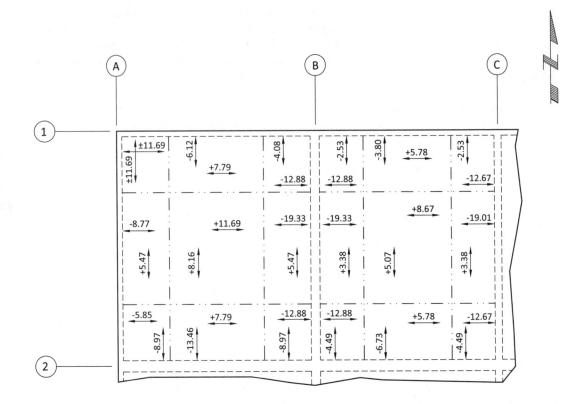

Steps 3 and 4 – Select Reinforcement and Check Shear

The procedure for selecting reinforcement is essentially the same as has been shown in earlier examples. Special attention should be given to the placing order so that reinforcement for the larger bending moments is given the larger flexural depth. As a general rule, it is usually economical to place minimum bottom reinforcement in both directions and add bars as required.

Bar cut-offs are not addressed in Annex B. These can be determined from flexural demands considering the effect of patterned loading. Maximum distance to the point of inflection occurs with minimum load in a panel and maximum load in the adjacent panel. In no case should bar cut-offs be less than indicated for column strips in Figure 13.1. For slabs satisfying the edge support stiffness criteria of Annex B, the larger bending moments occur in the middle strips (as defined by Annex B). The column strip bar cut-offs in Figure 13.1 are appropriate.

The procedure for checking shear is the same as was illustrated in step 4 of example 4 (two-way slab with beams).

Example 6 Design Using Elastic Plate Theory (13.6)

The slab shown at right is continuous over two interior columns (500 × 500) and is simply-supported on the edges. It is 200 mm thick and supports a total factored load of 12 kN/m². Determine the design moments and lateral distribution for reinforcement crossing the section indicated.

From an elastic analysis, values of m_x, m_y, and m_{xy} are determined for each point on a regular grid covering the entire slab. Since the section in question will be crossed by reinforcement in the y-direction, we require values of m_y and m_{xy} along the section. These results are plotted below.

Determine Design Moments (13.6.4)

The distribution of m_y and m_{xy} are shown as dashed lines in the lower figure. The distributions of design moments, $m_{yDES}(pos)$ and $m_{yDES}(neg)$, form an envelope offset by the absolute value of m_{xy} above and below m_y. The region filled with horizontal dashes is the negative design moment envelope and the region filled with vertical dashes is the positive design moment envelope.

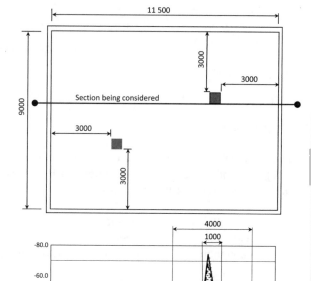

Note that non-zero torsional moments in the slab at the edge supports cause both negative and positive design moments, even though the value of m_y is zero.

Lateral Distribution (13.6.5)

Minimum reinforcement

$$\frac{0.2}{100} \times 200 \times 1000 = 400 \; \frac{mm^2}{m}$$

Use 15 M at 500 c/c

Assume minimum effective depth for reinforcement.

$$d = 200 - 25 - 15 - 8 = 152 \text{ mm}$$

Moment resistance at minimum:

$$\frac{0.85 \times 200 \times 400}{500}\left(152 - \frac{0.85 \times 200 \times 400}{2 \times 0.81 \times 0.65 \times 25 \times 500}\right) = 20.0 \text{kN} \cdot \text{m/m}$$

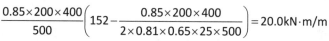

This is sufficient for all positive moment (bottom) reinforcement in y-direction.

Use 15 M at 500 c/c bottom throughout

Total negative moment at column = shaded area = 133 kN·m. The maximum negative design moment is 70 kN·m/m.

Place reinforcement in bands (i.e uniform spacing). Extend top mat to uncracked concrete. From (13.2.7)

$$m_{cr} = \frac{h_s^2}{6} \times \frac{f_r}{2} = \frac{200^2}{6} \times 0.3\sqrt{25} = 10 \text{ kN} \cdot \text{m/m}$$

Region with design moment exceeding 10 kN·m/m is approximately 4 m wide (see sketch). Required average moment resistance is 133 kN·m / 4 m = 33.25 kN·m.

Minimum required moment intensity in the band over the column = $\frac{70}{1.5} = 46.7 \text{ kN} \cdot \text{m/m}$ (13.6.5(b)).

Concentrated band over column is needed. Try 1 meter wide band with concentrated reinforcement.

Try 15 M at 200 c/c.

$$m_r = \frac{0.85 \times 200 \times 400}{200}\left(152 - \frac{0.85 \times 200 \times 400}{2 \times 0.81 \times 0.65 \times 25 \times 200}\right) = 47.3 \text{kN} \cdot \text{m/m} \qquad \text{OK}$$

Try 15 – 15 M at 300 top for remainder of 4 meter wide strip.

$$m_r = \frac{0.85 \times 200 \times 400}{300}\left(152 - \frac{0.85 \times 200 \times 400}{2 \times 0.81 \times 0.65 \times 25 \times 300}\right) = 32.5\,\text{kN·m/m}$$

**Use 16 – 15 M top: band of 6 bars at 200 c/c over column;
remaining bars at 300 c/c on either side**

Check   1 m × 47.3 kN·m + 3 m × 32.5 kN·m/m = 145 kN·m >133 kN·m   OK

Example 7 One-way Slab

An alternative slab and beam system supported by the same column grid as was used in Examples 1 through 4 is shown below. The slab supports a live load of 4.8 kN/m² and a superimposed dead load of 1.6 kN/m². Assume an exterior exposure.

Because the ratio of the long to short clear spans of the slab panels is 2 or more, the behaviour of the slab panels is essentially one-way, spanning in the short direction. One design approach is to use Appendix B with $m = 0.5$. An alternative to this is to design the slab as a continuous one-way beam.

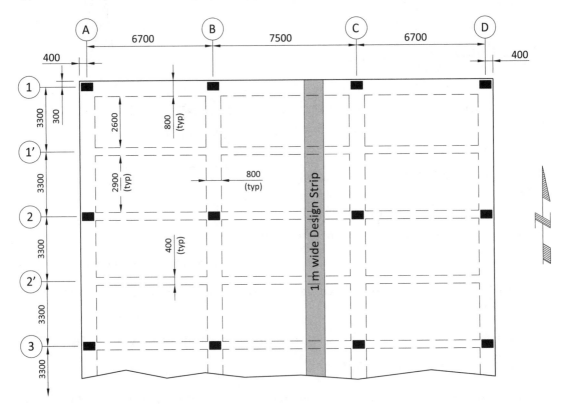

Step 1 – Slab Thickness (9.8.2.1)

Deflection requirements (Table 9-2)

Exterior span 1-1' $h_{s\,min} = \ell_n/24 = 2600/24 = 108\,\text{mm}$

Interior span $h_{s\,min} = \ell_n/28 = 2900/28 = 104\,\text{mm}$ $\Rightarrow$ Try $h_s = 125$ mm (approaching minimum thickness permitted)

5

Slabs

Step 2 – Design Moments

Factored Loading $w_f = 1.5 \times 4.8 + 1.25 \times (0.125 \times 24 + 1.6) = 12.95$ kN/m²

For design strip 1 metre wide, $w_f = 12.95$ kN/m

Limitations for use of Clause 9.3.3 are satisfied; use coefficients in Clause 9.3.3.

Step 3 – Select Reinforcement

Assume 10 M reinforcement.

Minimum Reinforcement

$0.02 \times 125 \times 1000 = 250$ mm²/m

$\Rightarrow$ Try 10 M at 400 c/c

Check crack control (Clause 10.6.1)

At least minimum reinforcement will be provided for bottom steel in both directions. The principal reinforcement in the North-South direction will be in the outside layer. The reinforcement in the non-spanning East-West direction is more critical for crack control.

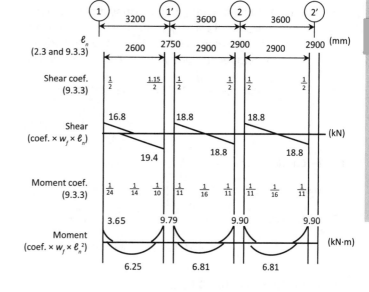

$d_c = 25 + 10 + 5 = 40$ mm

For $s = 400$ mm

$A = 400 \times 2 \times 40 = 32000$ mm²

$f_s = 0.6 \times 400 = 240$ MPa

$z = f_s \times \sqrt[3]{d_c A} = 240 \times \sqrt[3]{40 \times 32000} = 26060$ N/mm

For an exterior exposure, z should be less than 25,000. This suggests that a spacing of 400 mm is too large. Revise spacing to 350 mm ($A = 28,000$).

$z = 240 \times \sqrt[3]{40 \times 28000} = 24{,}920$ N/mm

Resisting moment at minimum reinforcement:

$d = 125 - 25 - 5 = 95$ mm

$$m_{rmin} = \frac{\phi_s A_{smin} f_y}{s} \left(d_{min} - \frac{\phi_s A_{smin} f_y}{2\alpha_1 \phi_c f'_c s} \right)$$

$$= \frac{0.85 \times 100 \times 400}{350} \left(95 - \frac{0.85 \times 100 \times 400}{2 \times 0.81 \times 0.65 \times 25 \times 350} \right) \times \frac{1}{10^3} = 8.87 \text{ kN·m/m}$$

This is adequate for all bottom steel requirements and for top steel on gridline 1. For top steel at interior supports try $s = 300$ mm.

$$m_r = \frac{0.85 \times 100 \times 400}{300}\left(95 - \frac{0.85 \times 100 \times 400}{2 \times 0.81 \times 0.65 \times 25 \times 300}\right) \times \frac{1}{10^3} = 10.3\,\text{kN·m/m}$$

This is sufficient at all interior supports.

Use 10 M at 350 c/c bottom each way

10 M at 350 c/c top North-South at perimeter beam

10 M at 300 c/c top North-South at interior beams

Transverse reinforcement over girders spanning parallel to slab is governed by (10.5.3.2). Purpose of reinforcement is to control cracking from local bending and address flexural shear in flanges of T-beam. In region of negative moment for the T-beam, the full thickness of the slab (top flange) is in tension. It is appropriate to consider amount of reinforcement needed per meter of slab.

$$A_{s\,min} = \frac{0.2\sqrt{f_c'}}{f_y}b_t h = \frac{0.2 \times 5}{400} \times 1000 \times 125 = 313\,\text{mm}^2/\text{m}$$

Use 10 M at 300 c/c top East-West over all girders

Step 4 – Check Shear

d_v is larger of:

0.9d = 85.5 mm   or $0.72h_s$ = 90 mm   → Governs; d_v = 90 mm

$V_r = \beta\lambda\phi_c\sqrt{f_c'}b_w d_v = 0.21 \times 1 \times 0.65 \times 5 \times 1000 \times 86.4 = 59.0\,\text{kN} > V_f$ OK

Step 5 – Design Supporting Beams

Beams and girders designed for vertical reaction from slab, self-weight of beam stem, and any other loads applied directly to beams. Edge beams must also be designed for torsion corresponding to negative support moments assumed in slab design.

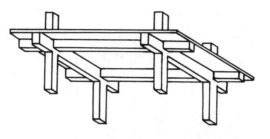

(a) 2-way slab with beams

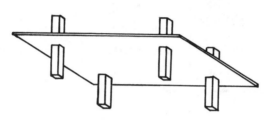

(b) 2-way slab without beams
(flat plate)

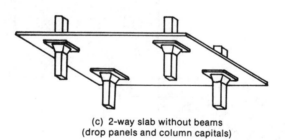

(c) 2-way slab without beams
(drop panels and column capitals)

Fig. 5.1 Types of 2-way Slabs

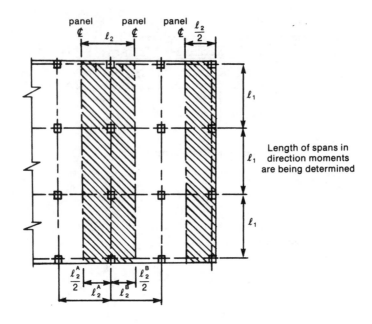

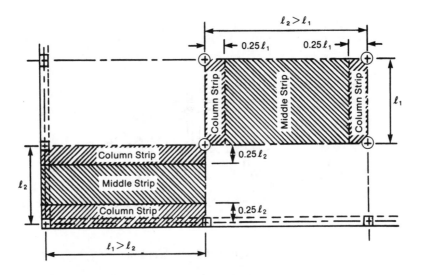

Fig. 5.2 Design Strips for Use with Direct Design and Elastic Frame Analogies

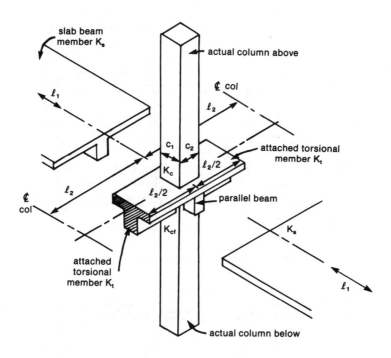

Fig. 5.3 Equivalent Column and Attached Torsional Members

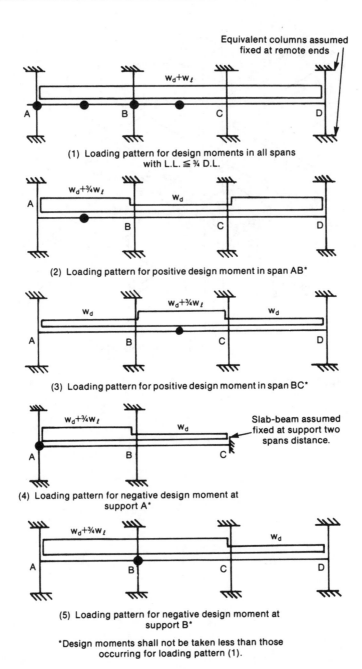

Equivalent columns assumed
fixed at remote ends

$w_d + w_\ell$

A   B   C   D

(1) Loading pattern for design moments in all spans
with L.L. $\leq$ ¾ D.L.

$w_d + ¾w_\ell$ w_d

A   B   C   D

(2) Loading pattern for positive design moment in span AB*

w_d $w_d + ¾w_\ell$ w_d

A   B   C   D

(3) Loading pattern for positive design moment in span BC*

$w_d + ¾w_\ell$ w_d

Slab-beam assumed
fixed at support two
spans distance.

A   B   C

(4) Loading pattern for negative design moment at
support A*

$w_d + ¾w_\ell$ w_d

A   B   C   D

(5) Loading pattern for negative design moment at
support B*

*Design moments shall not be taken less than those
occurring for loading pattern (1).

Fig. 5.4 Partial Frame and Loading Patterns for Elastic Frame Analogies

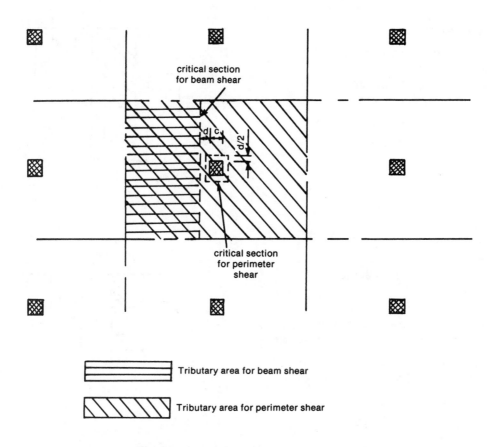

5

Slabs

Fig. 5.5 Critical Sections for Shear in Slabs

INTERIOR COLUMN

$A = 2d(c_1 + c_2 + 2d)$

$e = (c_1 + d)/2$

$J = (c_1 + d)d^3/6 + (c_1 + d)^3d/6$
$\quad + d(c_2 + d)(c_1 + d)^2/2$

$\gamma_v = 1 - \dfrac{1}{1 + \dfrac{2}{3}\sqrt{\dfrac{c_1 + d}{c_2 + d}}}$

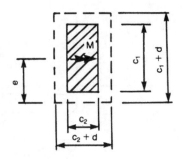

EDGE COLUMN

$A = d(2c_1 + c_2 + 2d)$

$e_1 = (c_1 + d/2)^2/(2c_1 + c_2 + 2d)$

$e_2 = (c_2 + d)/2$

$J_1 = [(c_1+d/2)d^3 + (c_1+d/2)^3d]/6$
$\quad + (c_2+d)d[e_1]^2 + 2(c_1+d/2)d[(c_1+d/2)/2 - e_1]^2$

$J_2 = [(c_2+d)d^3 + (c_2+d)^3d]/12 + 2(c_1+d/2)d[e_2]^2$

$\gamma_{v1} = 1 - \dfrac{1}{1 + \dfrac{2}{3}\sqrt{\dfrac{c_1 + d/2}{c_2 + d}}}$

$\gamma_{v2} = 1 - \dfrac{1}{1 + \dfrac{2}{3}\sqrt{\dfrac{c_2 + d}{c_1 + d/2}}}$

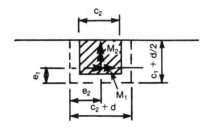

CORNER COLUMN

$A = d(c_1 + c_2 + d)$

$e = (c_1 + d/2)^2/[2(c_1 + c_2 + d)]$

$J = [(c_1+d/2)d^3 + (c_1+d/2)^3d]/12$
$\quad + (c_2+d/2)de^2 + (c_1+d/2)d[(c_1+d/2)/2 - e]^2$

$\gamma_v = 1 - \dfrac{1}{1 + \dfrac{2}{3}\sqrt{\dfrac{c_1 + d/2}{c_2 + d/2}}}$

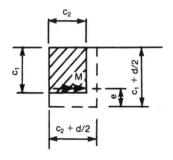

Fig. 5.6 Geometric Expressions for Shear-Moment Transfer

6

By F. Michael Bartlett

Deflections

6

Deflections

6.1   Introduction

The need to verify that deflections of concrete members and structures satisfy Serviceability Limit State criteria developed when the design process evolved from Working Stress Design to Ultimate Strength Design in the mid '60s. The use of higher strength concretes and steels allowed Ultimate Limit States to be satisfied using shallower, material-efficient members that are inherently more likely to exhibit excessive short- and long-term deflections. In A23.3-14, the deflection criteria are presented in Clause 9.8, with additional provisions for two-way slabs in Clause 13.2. Deflections are computed for specified values of applied loads, accounting for the duration of each type of load.

The American Concrete Institute Committee 435 report "Control of Deflection in Concrete Structures" (ACI 435, 2000), although dated, remains an excellent resource. It lists, for example, the broad range of factors that influence deflections, including: time-varying material properties of concrete; flexural cracking at specified loads or due to prior construction loads; temperature changes; and, long-term effects due to shrinkage and creep. It also cautions that "the magnitude of actual deflections in concrete structural elements...   ... can only be estimated within a range of 20 – 40 percent accuracy". It is difficult to quantify these factors, given their inherent variability, so excessive reliance should not be placed on computed deflection values, whether calculated using the relatively simple methods presented in A23.3-14 or using proprietary state-of-the-art software.

Table 9.3 "Maximum permissible computed deflections" in A23.3-14 provides various deflection limitations for floor and roof construction attached to, or supporting, non-structural elements that are likely or not likely to be damaged by large deflections. The deflection limit is presented as a fraction of the effective span length, ℓ_n, which is conventionally taken as the clear span length between faces of supporting elements for monolithic construction. It is often sufficient to verify that the deflection occurring after the installation of non-structural elements is not excessive. In some instances, however, the total deflection may be critical, impacting the installation of long solid millwork units or some types of flooring.

This chapter will explore the two methods permitted in A23.3-14 for deflection control in one- and two-way construction. Under certain circumstances, deflection criteria are deemed to be satisfied without further calculation if the member depth exceeds specified minimum limits that are proportional to the span length. Otherwise approximate calculations based on linear-elastic theory with modifications to account for flexural cracking and time-dependent effects must be carried out, with the computed result compared with the limits given in Table 9.3.

The chapter concludes with an updated list of references that designers may wish to consult for further background on the calculation of flexural deflections of structural concrete members.

6.2   Deflection Control by Span-to-Depth Ratios

Deflection controls were not required in historical Working-Stress-Design-based standards because controlling the maximum stresses permitted under working loads effectively controls the maximum curvatures at the critical section. This effectively controls maximum deflection, expressed as a ratio of the effective span length, ℓ_n.

To illustrate this, consider a member with a rectangular cross section designed to resist a maximum applied moment M_{max} by limiting the steel stress to an allowable value, f_s. The strain diagram is linear, with zero strain at a distance kd from the extreme compression fibre, where kd is approximately ⅜ d for a beam and smaller for a lightly-reinforced slab. The corresponding curvature, ϕ_{max}, is therefore

$$\phi_{max} = \frac{f_s}{E_s} \frac{1}{(d-kd)} \approx \frac{8f_s}{5E_s d}$$

If the beam is simply supported, the maximum deflection is

$$\Delta = \frac{5w\ell^4}{384EI} = \frac{5M_{max}\ell^2}{48EI} = \frac{5\phi_{max}\ell^2}{48} = (\text{from the equation for } \phi_{max} \text{ above}) \frac{f_s \ell^2}{6E_s d}$$

If a deflection limit $(\Delta/\ell)_{max}$ is desired, then the corresponding minimum thickness h_{min} is

$$h_{min} = \frac{f_s}{6E_s} \frac{h}{d} \frac{1}{(\Delta/\ell)_{max}} \ell$$

Substituting representative values: $f_s = 0.6f_y = 240$ MPa; $E_s = 200\,000$ MPa; $h/d = 1.15$; and, $(\Delta/\ell)_{max} = 1/240$, one obtains

$$h_{min} = \frac{240}{6\times200000}1.15\frac{1}{(1/240)}\ell = \frac{\ell}{18.1}$$

which is close to the slightly more stringent value, $\ell_n/16$, specified for simply supported beams in Table 9.2 of A23.3-14. A one-way slab is lightly reinforced and would have a smaller value of k, and perhaps a larger representative h/d and so a different minimum thickness requirement.

Although controlling deflections by satisfying minimum member thicknesses is clearly rational, there are a number of shortcomings and simplifications that cloud this approach. Flexural reinforcement is now usually proportioned to satisfy Ultimate Limit States, not allowable stress limits, so the reinforcement stresses in service will be higher for members that resist predominantly dead loads. Patterned live load configurations on multi-span continuous beams are ignored. Most significantly, deflections due to high sustained loads are ignored: these increase the curvature without appreciably changing the reinforcement stresses in service.

6.2.1. One Way Construction (Non-prestressed)

Values in Table 9.1 of A23.3-14 "for construction **not** supporting partitions or other elements likely to be damaged by large deflections" (*emphasis added*) are shown for one-way slabs and for beams and ribbed one-way slabs in Tables 6.1(a) and 6.1(b), respectively. Essentially identical values have appeared in ACI 318-71 and subsequent editions. A minimum thickness table first appeared in ACI 318-63: previous editions did not require the computation of deflections. The original ACI 318-63 values are consistent with those in A23.3 Table 9.1 if corrected for the different reinforcing steel yield strengths that were most commonly available, i.e., 280 MPa (40 ksi) in 1963 compared to 400 MPa subsequently. The limitation that the tabulated values are "limited to elements **not** supporting partitions or other elements likely to be damaged by large deflections" first appeared in ACI 318-71.

Tables 6.1(a) and 6.1(b) also show the recommended minimum thickness requirements for members not supporting deflection-sensitive elements and for members supporting deflection-sensitive elements as proposed by ACI Committee 435 (2000). The latter may provide a useful tool for selecting a preliminary member depth to check subsequently using the more detailed procedures. Bischoff and Veysey (2011) have recently investigated minimum thickness requirements.

6

Deflections

Table 6.1(a)
Minimum thickness requirements for deflections not to be computed:
one-way slabs

Support condition	Not supporting deflection-sensitive elements		Supporting deflection-sensitive elements
	A23.3-14 Table 9.1	ACI 435R-95 (2000)	ACI 435R-95 (2000)
Simply supported	$\ell_n/20$	$\ell_n/18$	$\ell_n/12$
One end continuous	$\ell_n/24$	$\ell_n/23$	$\ell_n/15$
Both ends continuous	$\ell_n/28$	$\ell_n/28$	$\ell_n/19$
Cantilever	$\ell_n/10$	$\ell_n/7$	$\ell_n/5$

Table 6.1(b)
Minimum thickness requirements for deflections not to be computed:
beams or ribbed one-way slabs

Support condition	Not supporting deflection-sensitive elements		Supporting deflection-sensitive elements
	A23.3-14 Table 9.1	ACI 435R-95 (2000)	ACI 435R-95 (2000)
Simply supported	$\ell_n/16$	$\ell_n/14$	$\ell_n/10$
One end continuous	$\ell_n/18$	$\ell_n/18$	$\ell_n/13$
Both ends continuous	$\ell_n/21$	$\ell_n/21$	$\ell_n/16$
Cantilever	$\ell_n/8$	$\ell_n/5.5$	$\ell_n/4$

6.2.2. Two-way Construction (Non-prestressed)

Deflections of two-way slab systems need not be computed if the slab thickness equals or exceeds the minimum thicknesses specified in A23.3-14 Clauses 13.2.3 (for slabs without drop panels), 13.2.4 (slabs with drop panels), 13.2.5 (slabs with beams between all supports), or 13.2.6 (slab bands). These minimum values apply whether or not the slab is supporting partitions or other construction likely to be damaged by large deflections.

Excessive deflections of two-way slabs present a serious serviceability problem that is not easily remedied, particularly after the installation of non-structural elements and mechanical services. It is preferable, therefore, to err on the side of thicker rather than thinner two-way slabs.

6.3   Instantaneous Deflection Computations

The total deflection of a concrete member is the combination of instantaneous deflections that occur at the time of load application plus long-term deflections due to shrinkage and due to creep under sustained loads. These issues will be addressed separately in Sections 6.3 and 6.4, respectively.

6.3.1. Beams and One-way Slabs (Non-prestressed)

Flexural cracking of a concrete beam or slab causes a reduction of rigidity that varies along the length of the member from a minimum at the cracked cross sections to a greater value between cracks. It is conventional to account for this "tension stiffening" effect by computing an effective moment of inertia, I_e, for the member based on ratio of the moment due to the applied load, M_a, to the cracking moment, M_{cr}.

Tables 6.2(a) and 6.2(b) summarize the equations necessary to compute the section properties of rectangular and T-beam cross sections, respectively. Equations are provided for the gross moment of inertia, I_g and the moment of inertia of the cracked section, I_{cr}.

Table 6.2(a)
Properties of gross and cracked cross sections: rectangular beam

Condition	Figure	Equations
Uncracked		Moment of Inertia of Gross Section, I_g: $$I_g = \frac{1}{12} = b\,h^3$$ Cracking Moment, M_{cr}: $$M_{cr} = \frac{f_r I_g}{y_t}$$ where $\quad y_t = \dfrac{h}{2}$
Cracked – no Compression Steel		Moment of Inertia of Cracked Transformed Section, I_{cr}: $$I_{cr} = \frac{1}{3}b(kd)^3 + nA_s(d-kd)^2$$ where $\quad kd = \dfrac{\sqrt{2dB+1}-1}{B}$ and $\quad B = \dfrac{b}{n\,A_s}$
Cracked – with Compression Steel		Moment of Inertia of Cracked Transformed Section, I_{cr}: $$I_{cr} = \frac{1}{3}b(kd)^3 + nA_s(d-kd)^2 + (n-1)A_s'(kd-d')^2$$ where $$kd = \dfrac{\sqrt{2dB\left(1+\dfrac{rd'}{d}\right)+(1+r)^2}-(1+r)}{B}$$ and $\quad r = \dfrac{(n-1)A_s'}{n\,A_s}$

Table 6.2(b)

Properties of gross and cracked cross sections: T- beam

Condition	Figure	Equations
Uncracked		Moment of Inertia of Gross Section, I_g: $$I_g = C_T b h^3$$ where $$C_T = \frac{4A_r\left(1 - \dfrac{h_f}{h}\right)^2 + \left(1 + A_r \dfrac{h_f}{h}\right)^2}{12\dfrac{b}{b_w}(1 + A_r)}$$ and $$A_r = \frac{h_f}{h}\left(\frac{b}{b_w} - 1\right)$$ Cracking Moment, M_{cr}: a) Tension at bottom face: $$M_{cr} = \frac{f_r I_g}{y_{tb}}$$ where $$\frac{y_{tb}}{h} = \frac{\dfrac{b}{b_w}\left(\dfrac{h_f}{h}\right)\left(1 - \dfrac{1}{2}\dfrac{h_f}{h}\right) + \dfrac{1}{2}\left(1 - \dfrac{h_f}{h}\right)^2}{\dfrac{b}{b_w}\left(\dfrac{h_f}{h}\right) + \left(1 - \dfrac{h_f}{h}\right)}$$ b) Tension at top face: $$M_{cr} = \frac{f_r I_g}{y_{tt}}$$ where $y_{tt} = h - y_{tb}$

Condition	Figure	Equations
Cracked – no Compression Steel		Moment of Inertia of Cracked Transformed Section, I_{cr}, for $kd \geq h_f$: a) Tension at bottom face: $$I_{cr} = \frac{(b-b_w)h_f^3}{12} + \frac{b_w(kd)^3}{3}$$ $$+ (b-b_w)h_f\left(kd - \frac{h_f}{2}\right)^2 + nA_s(d-kd)^2$$ where $$kd = \frac{\sqrt{C(2d+h_f f)+(1+f)^2}-(1+f)}{C}$$ and $\quad f = \dfrac{h_f(b-b_w)}{nA_s}$ and $\quad C = \dfrac{b_w}{nA_s}$ b) Tension at top face: same as rectangular section with width $b = b_w$
Cracked – with Compression Steel		The presence of compression steel typically has a negligible impact on location of neutral axis or associated cracked moment of inertia and above equations can be used.

A23.3-14 uses an equation originally proposed by Branson (1963), A23.3 Eq. 9-1, to compute I_e:

$$I_e = I_{cr} + (I_g - I_{cr})\left(\frac{M_{cr}}{M_a}\right)^3 \leq I_g$$

The A23.3 procedure requires computing the cracking moment, M_{cr}, using a reduced modulus of rupture, $f_r = 0.3\sqrt{f_c'}$, that reflects:

1) presence of tension due to restrained shrinkage that reduces the applied moment that causes flexural cracking; and

2) unconservative errors created because the Branson Equation is based on an incorrect mechanical model (Bischoff, 2007).

The requirement to compute M_{cr} based on half the modulus of rupture, which had previously required only when computing deflections of two-way slabs, was therefore extended to beams and one-way slabs in the 2009 Supplement to A23.3.

The impact of various methods for computing I_e is illustrated in Fig. 6.1, which shows the variation of I_e/I_g for a range of reinforcing steel ratios. The methods shown are:

1) A23.3-04, which uses the Branson Equation with no reduction in the modulus of rupture, i.e., $f_r = 0.6 \sqrt{f_c'}$;

2) A23.3-04-S09, which uses the Branson Equation with a modulus of rupture of $0.3 \sqrt{f_c'}$;

3) an equation proposed by Bischoff (2007) with no reduction in the modulus of rupture;

4) the Bischoff Equation with a modulus of rupture of $0.4\sqrt{f_c'}$; and,

5) the provisions of Australian Standard A3600-2009.

The reinforcement ratio in beam or ribbed one-way slab typically exceeds 0.8%: in this case M_a/M_{cr} is typically sufficiently large that I_e approaches I_{cr} as accurately predicted by all methods. For one-way slabs with reinforcement ratios between 0.4 and 0.8%, the effective moment of inertia computed accounting for the 2009 revisions to A23.3 is between 40% and 90% of that obtained using the 2004 provisions. Application of the Bischoff Equation with a cracking moment based on two-thirds the modulus of rupture, as recommended by Scanlon and Bischoff (2008), yields very similar values for the range of reinforcement ratios investigated. The provisions of AS3600-2009 also give very similar values.

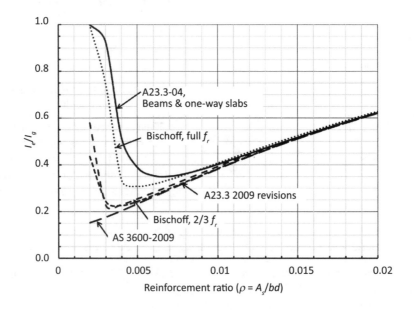

Fig. 6.1 Variation of I_e/I_g with reinforcement ratio

6.3.1.1. Deflection Computation using Effective Moment of Inertia, I_e

Three methods are presented herein for computing flexural deflections that typically give similar results. An example calculation illustrating the application of each method is presented in the next section.

A23.3 Clause 9.8 Procedure using an Average Moment of Inertia

The deflection, Δ, is:

$$\Delta = K\left(\frac{5}{48}\right)\frac{M\ell_n^2}{E_c I_e}$$

where M is the support moment for a cantilever or the midspan moment for simple or continuous beams, and E_c is the elastic modulus of concrete, taken as (A23.3-14 Clause 8.6.2.2):

$$E_c = \left(3300\sqrt{f'_c} + 6900\right)\left(\frac{\gamma_c}{2300}\right)^{1.5}$$

for concretes with densities, γ_c, between 1500 and 2500 kg/m³, or, for normal density concretes (A23.3-14 Clause 8.6.2.3):

$$E_c = 4500\sqrt{f'_c}$$

Values of K are shown in Table 6.3(a). For continuous beams, a weighted average of the I_e values at the middle, left end, and right end of the span is computed using the equation shown in Table 6.3(b).

Table 6.3(a)
Values of K for deflection computation

Displacement boundary condition	K
Cantilevers (fixed end)*	2.40
Simply supported beams	1.00
Beams fixed at both ends	0.60
Beams fixed at one end, simply supported at the other	
— Midspan deflection	0.80
— Maximum deflection (when using maximum moment)	0.74
Continuous spans	$1.20 - 0.20\, M_o/M_m$ where $M_o = w\,\ell_n^2/8$ and M_m is the net midspan moment

Notes to Table 6.3(a)
*Deflection due to rotation at the cantilever support must also be included.

Table 6.3(b)
Equations for weighted average I_e for continuous spans

Displacement boundary condition	Equation	Note
One end continuous	$I_e = 0.85\, I_{em} + 0.15\, I_{ec}$ where I_{em} is the value of I_e at midspan, and I_{ec} is the value of I_e at the continuous support	A23.3-14 Eq. 9.4
Both ends continuous	$I_e = 0.70\, I_{em} + 0.15\,(I_{e1} + I_{e2})$ where I_{e1} is the value of I_e at the left support, and I_{e2} is the value of I_e at the right support	A23.3-14 Eq. 9.3
Column-supported end span where exterior column provides partial fixity	$I_e = 0.75\, I_{em} + 0.25\, I_{ec}$ where I_{ec} is the value of I_e at the continuous (interior) support	

6

Deflections

The effective moment of inertia, I_e, must be computed using a value of M_a equal to "the maximum moment in the member at the load stage at which deflection is computed or any previous load stage" (A23.3-14 Clause 3.2). As described further in Section 6.3.2, depending on the shoring and reshoring schedule adopted, the maximum M_a may occur during construction. A new note to Clause 9.8.2.3 states that "If construction loadings are unknown, M_a may be computed as the moment due to specified dead and live loads for the computation of instantaneous and long-term deflections." If M_a is increased by applied live load, then the total dead and live load deflection is computed for the total M_a and the increased dead load deflection is computed by subtracting the live load deflection from this total.

Curvature-based Method

If the curvature distribution for a beam subjected to uniformly distributed loads is assumed parabolic along the length of the member, the midspan deflection can be approximated as:

$$\Delta = \left(\frac{\ell_n^{\,2}}{96} \right) \left(\phi_1 + 10\phi_m + \phi_2 \right)$$

where ϕ_1, ϕ_m and ϕ_2 are the curvatures at the left support, midspan, and right support, respectively, computed as $\phi = M_a/EI_e$. This equation emphasises the sensitivity of the total deflection to the curvature at midspan and the relative insensitivity of the total deflection to the curvatures at the left and right supports. Further detail concerning this approximation is presented by Ghali (1993).

This method is similar to that previously presented: both require computation of the applied moments and effective moments of inertia at the support(s) and at midspan of a continuous beam. In the first method, a weighted average I_e is computed to compute the deflection; in the second method, the deflection is computed using weighted curvature values.

Discretize Member and Compute Moment, I_e and Curvature for each Segment

The effective moment of inertia computed using Branson's 3th power equation, presented above, is intended to represent an averaged moment of inertia that accounts for regions where the beam is uncracked and its rigidity is represented by the gross moment of inertia. Analysis of a discretized member will account explicitly for these uncracked regions because the effective moments of inertia are computed based on the applied moments at each segment. It is therefore necessary to reduce further the effective moment of inertia in the cracked regions. Branson (1963) recommended the following 4th power equation for this purpose:

$$I_e = I_{cr} + (I_g - I_{cr}) \left(\frac{M_{cr}}{M_a} \right)^4 \leq I_g$$

This procedure is laborious using manual calculations but is readily executed on an electronic spreadsheet. It can be used to provide independent insight concerning the "inner workings" of proprietary structural analysis software. The applied moments are computed at the ends (or an average value is computed at the middle) of each segment, and the associated the effective moments of inertias are computed. The curvature of each element can then be computed, using the equation presented above, and any available standard method, such as the moment-area method, can be used to compute the deflections from the curvatures.

6.3.1.2. Design Example 1: Instantaneous Deflection of Two-span One-way Slab

Fig. 6.2(a) shows the span, reinforcement, and loading for an idealized two-span one-way slab. The slab depth is 200 mm and the effective depth of the reinforcement, both at midspan and over the centre support, is 170 mm. Since the supports are idealized, $\ell_n = \ell$ for each span. The 200 mm thickness is less the minimum thickness specified in A23.3-14 Table 9.2 for a one-way slab with one end continuous of $\ell_n/24$, or (6000 mm/24 =) 250 mm, so deflections must be computed.

The specified concrete compressive strength, f_c', is 30 MPa and this value is assumed relevant for the time of load application. It will be further assumed that the bending moments sustained during construction are equal to those due to the specified dead and live loads, and so the latter may be used for the computation of M_a.

Required:

Compute the maximum instantaneous deflection due to a dead load of 4.8 kN/m on both spans plus a live load of 4.8 kN/m on one span only.

Solution:

1. **Determine the critical M_a values at the span and centre support sections.**

   From the beam diagrams presented in Chapter 1 of the Concrete Design Handbook, the specified dead load on both spans causes:

   - End reaction of $0.375\ W_D\ \ell_n = (0.375 \times 4.8 \times 6 =)$ 10.8 kN,

   - Negative moment at centre support of $-0.125\ W_D\ \ell_n^2 = (-0.125 \times 4.8 \times 6^2 =)$ -21.6 kN·m.

   Similarly, the specified live load on the left span causes:

   - End reaction of $0.438\ W_L\ \ell_n = (0.438 \times 4.8 \times 6 =)$ 12.6 kN,

   - Negative moment at centre support of $-0.063\ W_L\ \ell_n^2 = (-0.063 \times 4.8 \times 6^2 =)$ -10.9 kN·m.

   The total end reaction is (10.8 + 12.6 =) 23.4 kN, so the shear force is zero at (23.4/(4.8 + 4.8) =) 2.44 m from the left end where the maximum positive span moment is 28.6 kN·m. The moment at the centre support is (-21.6 -10.9 =) -32.5 kN·m.

   The values shown in Fig. 6.2(c) differ slightly from these because they account for the effect of slight moment redistribution due to cracking from the positive moment region to the negative moment region.

2. **Compute concrete material properties, cracking moment, and cracked section properties.**

   For $f_c' = 30$ MPa, $E_c = 4500\sqrt{30} = 24\,650$ MPa   and $f_r = 0.6\sqrt{30} = 3.29$ MPa

   For a metre width of slab, $I_g = (1000 \times 200^3/12 =) 666.7 \times 10^6$ mm⁴   so

   $$M_{cr} = \frac{0.5 f_r I_g}{y_t} = \frac{0.5 \times 3.29 \times 666.7 \times 10^6}{0.5 \times 200} = 10.95 \times 10^6 \text{ N·mm} = 10.95 \text{ kN·m}$$

   As shown in Fig. 6.2(c), the computed M_a values exceed M_{cr} in the regions of the middle of the left span, and at the support, so effective moments of inertia must be computed for these regions.

   Calculation of the cracked section properties requires application of the various equations shown in Table 6.2(a). The detailed calculations are shown for the support region and the results for the span region are summarized in Table 6.4(a) using a modular ratio, $n = E_s/E_c = 200\,000\ /\ 24\,650 = 8.11$.

Table 6.4(a)
Design example 1: cracked section properties.

Centre cupport section	Span section
$B = \dfrac{b}{n\,A_s} = \dfrac{1000}{8.11 \times 1000} = 0.123\,\text{mm}^{-1}$	$B = 0.154\,\text{mm}^{-1}$
$kd = \dfrac{\sqrt{2dB+1}-1}{B} = \dfrac{\sqrt{2 \times 170 \times 0.123 + 1}-1}{0.123} = 45.0\,\text{mm}$	$kd = 40.9\,\text{mm}$
$I_{cr} = \dfrac{1}{3}b(kd)^3 + nA_s(d-kd)^2$ $= \dfrac{1}{3}1000 \times (45.0)^3 + 8.11 \times 1000 \times (170 - 45.0)^2 = 157.2 \times 10^6\,\text{mm}^4$	$I_{cr} = 131.0 \times 10^6\,\text{mm}^4$

3(a).   For Method 1 compute effective moment of inertia for the span and support sections.

These are summarized in Table 6.4(b).

Table 6.4(b)
Design example 1: effective moments of Inertia

Centre support section	Span section
$M_a = -32.5$ kN·m	$M_a = 28.6$ kN·m
$I_e = \left(\dfrac{M_{cr}}{M_a}\right)^3 I_g + \left[1 - \left(\dfrac{M_{cr}}{M_a}\right)^3\right] I_{cr}$ $= \left(\dfrac{10.95}{32.5}\right)^3 666.7 \times 10^6 + \left[1 - \left(\dfrac{10.95}{32.5}\right)^3\right] 152.7 \times 10^6$	
$= 172.4 \times 10^6\,\text{mm}^4$	$I_e = 161.1 \times 10^6\,\text{mm}^4$

4(a).   For Method 1, compute average effective moment of inertia and deflection

With one end continuous:

$$I_e = 0.85\,I_{em} + 0.15\,I_{ec} = 0.85 \times 161.1 \times 10^6 + 0.15 \times 172.4 \times 10^6 = 162.8 \times 10^6\,\text{mm}^4$$

For $M_o = w\,\ell_n^2/8 = (4.8 + 4.8) \times 6^2/8 = 43.2$ kN·m   and $M_m = 28.6$ kN·m

$$K = 1.20 - 0.20\,M_o/M_m = 1.20 - 0.20\,(43.2/28.6) = 0.897$$

Thus $\Delta = K\left(\dfrac{5}{48}\right)\dfrac{M\,\ell_n^2}{E_c\,I_e} = 0.897\left(\dfrac{5}{48}\right)\dfrac{28.6 \times 10^6 \times 6000^2}{24650 \times 162.8 \times 10^6} = 24.0\,\text{mm}$

3(b).   For Method 2, compute effective moment of inertia for the span and support sections

This step is identical to Step 3(a).

4(b).   For Method 2, compute span and support curvatures and deflection

At the left (pinned) support, $M = 0$ so $\phi_m = 0$.

In the span region, $\phi_m = \dfrac{M_{am}}{E_c\, I_{em}} = \dfrac{28.6 \times 10^6}{24650 \times 161.2 \times 10^6} = 7.20 \times 10^{-6}$ mm^{-1}

At the middle support, $\phi_2 = \dfrac{M_{a2}}{E_c\, I_{e2}} = \dfrac{-32.5 \times 10^6}{24650 \times 172.4 \times 10^6} = -7.65 \times 10^{-6}$ mm^{-1}

Thus

$$\Delta = \left(\frac{\ell_n^{\,2}}{96}\right)\!\left(\phi_1 + 10\phi_m + \phi_2\right) = \left(\frac{6000^2}{96}\right)\!\left(0 + 10 \times 7.20 - 7.65\right) \times 10^{-6} = 24.1\,\text{mm}$$

3(c).   For Method 3, compute effective moment of inertia for each segment of discretized beam

Fig. 6.3(b) shows the discretization assumed for the analysis, with 500 mm segments in the positive moment regions and 250 mm segments in the negative moment regions. The segment lengths in the positive moment region of the left span have been adjusted manually to have the location of the maximum deflection correspond to the right end of the 666 mm segment.

Fig. 6.3(c) shows the resulting bending moment diagram: it differs slightly from that computed in Step 1 because the non-uniform effective moment of inertia along the length of the member requires a different negative moment at the centre support to satisfy the displacement boundary conditions. In other words, cracking of the member has caused a redistribution of the total static moment between the positive and negative moment regions. The magnitudes of the cracking moment are also shown in this figure: the beam is cracked in the positive moment region of the left span, then uncracked near the point of inflection in the left span, then cracked in the negative moment region near the center support, then uncracked for the remainder of the right span.

The moment, $M(x)$, at a distance x from the end support for the left span is given by the equation

$$M(x) = R_A x - (W_D + W_L)\, x^2 = 23.23\, x - 4.8\, x^2$$

where x is in m and $M(x)$ is in kN·m. For the right span, for x between 6 and 12 m, $M(x)$ is given by

$$M(x) = R_A x - (W_D + W_L)\, \ell_n\, (x - 0.5\, \ell_n) + R_B\, (x - \ell_n) - 0.5\, W_D\, (x - \ell_n)^2$$

$$= 23.23\, x - 57.6\, (x - 3) + 54.33\, (x - 6) - 2.4\, (x - 6)^2$$

The distribution of effective moment of inertia along the member is shown in Fig. 6.2(d). For the maximum positive moment in the left span, $M_a = 27.83$ kN·m, the associated effective moment of inertia is

$$I_e = I_{cr} + \left(\frac{M_{cr}}{M_a}\right)^4 (I_g - I_{cr}) = \left[131.0 + \left(\frac{10.95}{27.83}\right)^4 (666.7 - 131.0)\right] \times 10^6 = 143.9 \times 10^6 \text{ mm}^4$$

or 1.098 I_{cr}. Similarly at the interior support, where $M_a = -33.39$ kN·m, the effective moment of inertia is

$$I_e = \left[157.2 + \left(\frac{10.95}{33.39}\right)^4 (666.7 - 157.2)\right] \times 10^6 = 163.1 \times 10^6 \text{ mm}^4$$

or 1.038 I_{cr}. Fig. 6.2(d) shows that, for this rather fine-mesh discretization of the beam, the effective moment of inertia very rapidly approaches the cracked moment of inertia in the cracked regions.

6

Deflections

4(c).   For Method 3, compute the curvature distribution along the span and the deflection

Fig. 6.2(e) shows the curvature distribution along the span. The curvatures are very small in the uncracked regions near the left support, at the inflection point of the left span, and in the uncracked region of the right span. The magnitudes of curvature computed are slightly higher than those obtained in Step 4(b) for Method 2, because Method 3 uses the Branson 4th power equation so the effective moments of inertia are smaller.

The deflected shape is shown in Fig. 6.2(f). The maximum deflection is 22.2 mm.

The analysis was repeated assuming that the full live load had previously been applied to the right span only. Thus when the load is moved to the left span only, the distribution of rigidity is as shown for the left span in Fig. 6.2(d) but is now symmetric about the centre support. The maximum defection due to the dead load on the right span increases for this case, but the maximum deflection in the left span due to combined specified dead and live load remains relatively unchanged at 21.8 mm.

5.   Comparison of results for Methods 1, 2 and 3.

Table 6.4(c) presents a comparison of the deflections computed using Methods 1, 2 and 3. For this example, they are remarkably similar.

Table 6.4(c)
Design example 1: comparison of computed deflections

Method	Deflection (mm)
1: Weighted average moment of inertia	24.0
2: Computed from maximum span and support curvature	24.1
3: Discretized beam analysis using Branson's 4th power equation for I_e	22.2

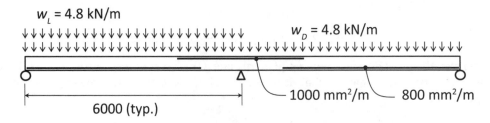

$w_L = 4.8$ kN/m

$w_D = 4.8$ kN/m

1000 mm²/m   800 mm²/m

6000 (typ.)

(a) Span, reinforcement, loading

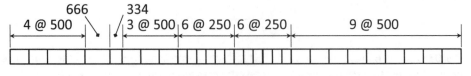

666   334

4 @ 500   3 @ 500 , 6 @ 250 , 6 @ 250   9 @ 500

(b) Discretization

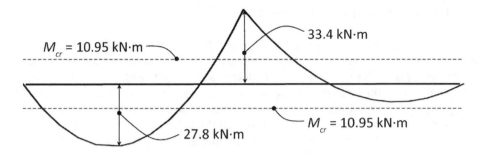

$M_{cr} = 10.95$ kN·m

33.4 kN·m

$M_{cr} = 10.95$ kN·m

27.8 kN·m

(c) Bending moments

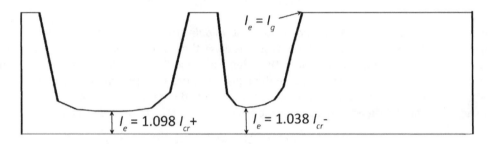

$I_e = I_g$

$I_e = 1.098\ I_{cr}+$

$I_e = 1.038\ I_{cr}-$

(d) Effective moment of inertia

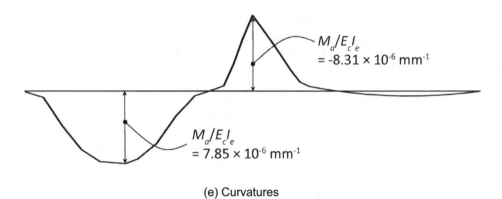

$M_a/E_cI_e = -8.31 \times 10^{-6}$ mm^{-1}

$M_a/E_cI_e = 7.85 \times 10^{-6}$ mm^{-1}

(e) Curvatures

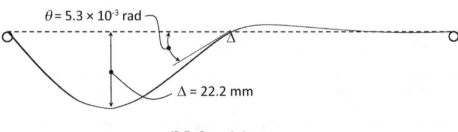

$\theta = 5.3 \times 10^{-3}$ rad

Δ

$\Delta = 22.2$ mm

(f) Deflected shape

Fig. 6.2 Design example 1: instantaneous deflection of 2-span one-way slab.

6.3.2. Two-way Slabs (Non-prestressed)

The procedures and equations derived in Section 6.3.1 for one-way construction can be used to computed deflections for two-way slab systems by idealizing them as equivalent frames as shown schematically in Fig. 6.3. Fig. 6.3(a) shows deflections due to bending in the x- direction only: there is no deflection along the column lines parallel to the y axis. The deflection at midspan of the middle strip, Δ_{mx}, is less than the deflection at the column strip, Δ_{cx}, because the middle strip bending moments per unit width of slab have smaller magnitudes than the column strip moments. Similarly, Fig. 6.3(b) shows deflections due to bending in the y- direction only and the deflections from these two cases are combined to yield the overall deflected shape due to combined bending shown in Fig. 6.3(c). The total deflection at midspan of the column strips is either Δ_{cx} or Δ_{cy}, as shown, and the deflection, Δ_{mp}, at the midpanel of the slab is:

$$\Delta_{mp} = \Delta_{mx} + \Delta_{cy} = \Delta_{my} + \Delta_{cx}$$

The end and midspan moments in the column and middle strips may be computed for the specified applied loads at Serviceability Limit States by scaling down the factored moments used to proportion the reinforcement at the Ultimate Limit State. The column and middle strip deflections may then computed for these end and midspan moments using the equations presented for one-way construction. Values of K obtained from Table 6.3(a) for continuous spans should determined taking M_o as the total static moment of the strip, instead of the total static moment due to the total load w, i.e.:

$$M_o = \frac{1}{2} \left| M_{1s} + M_{2s} \right| + M_{ms}$$

where M_{1s}, M_{2s} and M_{ms} are the end moments applied to the ends and at midpanel of the strip, respectively.

Similarly, if computing deflections from curvatures, the values ϕ_1, ϕ_m and ϕ_2 should be computed using the bending moments and moments of inertia of the column strips to determine the column strip deflections and using the bending moments and moments of inertia of the middle strip to determine the middle strip deflection.

For irregular panel layouts and non-uniform loading conditions, computer-based procedures based on the finite element method can be used to compute deflections. It is essential to confirm that the software accounts the effect of cracking on the moment of inertia appropriately: neglecting cracking will often markedly underestimate the deflections. It may be prudent to develop independently an analysis similar to that shown in Fig. 6.2 to determine whether proprietary software:

1) correctly identifies the regions where the applied moment exceeds the cracking moment computed using the reduced modulus of rupture, $0.5\,f_r$;

2) correctly computes the effective moment of inertia using the Branson 4th-power equation; and,

3) correctly redistributes the total static moment between the midpanel and the ends to account for the effect of cracking.

It is emphasized that a finite element or other type of analysis that does not include the effect of reduced stiffness due to cracking is likely to underestimate deflections significantly.

Deflection limits specified in A23.3-14 Table 9.3 also apply to two-way construction. Several deflections in each two-way slab panel should be investigated, namely, the column strip, middle strip, and mid-panel deflections. Effective span lengths to be used are the column strip span for column strip deflection, middle strip span for middle strip deflection, and length of span measured diagonally between columns for mid-panel deflection.

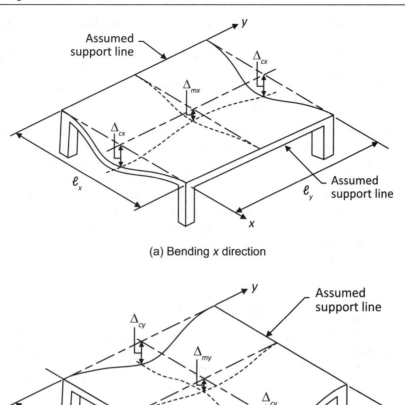

(a) Bending x direction

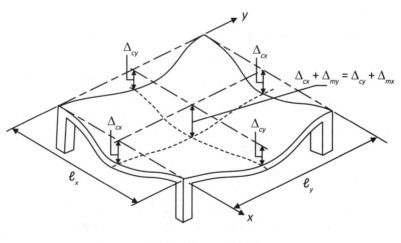

(b) Bending y direction

(c) Bending combined

Fig. 6.3 Deflection analysis of two-way slab using equivalent frame idealization

6.3.2.1. Effect of Construction Loads on Cracking & Effective Moment of Inertia, I_e

The effective moment of inertia, I_e, for the midspan and end cross-sections of column and middle strips can be computed using the expressions given in Tables 6.2(a) and (b). If reinforcement is present near the compression face of the member, it should be verified that it is in compression because lightly reinforced slabs often have neutral axes that are very close to the extreme compression fibre.

Normal construction procedures may induce loads in the slab at an early age that can equal or exceed the specified service dead and live loads. Grundy and Kabaila (1963, reprinted 2004) present a simple analytical method when the load of the newly placed slab is transferred by shoring to several lower supporting floors: the lowest supporting slab can be subjected to a maximum load of 2.25 times the slab weight if two tiers of shoring are used or 2.36 times the slab weight if three tiers of shoring are used. Scanlon and Suprenant (2011) show that construction using flying forms with two tiers of reshores beneath subjects the newly cast slab to its own weight at a very young age, when the forms are "flown", and subjects lower supporting slabs to maximum loads of 1.33 times the slab weight. Further guidance may be found in Monette and Gardner (2015).

These high construction loads may cause irreversible cracking that reduces the effective moment of inertia, even for deflections due to the slab self-weight, and so increases the instantaneous deflection. It is for this reason that the applied moment M_a used to compute I_e is defined in A23.3-14 Clause 3.2 as "maximum moment in the member at the stage at which deflection is computed **or at any previous loading stage**" (*emphasis added*). It is also for this reason that the note to Clause 9.8.2.3 has been revised to state "If construction loadings are unknown, M_a may be computed as the maximum due to specified dead and live loads for the computation of instantaneous and long-term deflections."

6.3.2.2. Design Example 2: Instantaneous Deflection of 2-way Slab System

Fig. 6.4(a) shows the plan of a flat plate system. The slab depth is 180 mm and the assumed effective depth of the reinforcement, for positive and negative bending in both directions, is 150 mm. The specified concrete compressive strength, f_c', is 30 MPa and this value is assumed relevant for the time of load application. It will be further assumed that the bending moments due to the specified dead and live loads exceed those that may have occurred during construction, and so govern the computation of M_a. The specified steel yield strength, f_y, is 400 MPa.

The specified applied loads are:

1) slab self weight of (24 kN/m³ × 180 mm × 10^{-3} m/mm =) 4.32 kPa;
2) superimposed dead load due to partitions of 1.0 kPa;
3) superimposed dead load due to the exterior wall of 4.4 kN/m; and,
4) live load of 2.4 kPa.

The live load may be reduced slightly accounting for the tributary area: for Panel A-B-2-3, the tributary area, B, is (5.5 m × 5.5 m =) 30.25 m², so the live load reduction factor is

$$0.3 + \sqrt{\frac{9.8}{B}} = 0.3 + \sqrt{\frac{9.8}{30.25}} = 0.87$$

so the reduced live load, accounting for tributary area, is (0.87 × 2.4 kPa =) 2.09 kPa. (Explanatory Note N8.2 discusses the application of tributary-area-based live-load reduction factors to two-way slab systems.)

Fig. 6.4(b) shows schematically the reinforcement for Panel A-B-2-3, sized at Ultimate Limit States. The factored panel load is (q_f = 1.25 q_D + 1.5 q_L = 1.25 (4.32 kPa + 1.0 kPa) +1.5 (2.09 kPa) =) 9.78 kPa, and the factored wall load is (1.25 × 4.4 kN/m =) 5.5 kN/m.

The slab system meets the requirements for design by the Direct Design Method of A23.3-14 Clause 13.9.

In the East-West direction, the total design moment along Column Lines 2 or 3, per A23.3-14 Eq. 13-23, is:

$$M_o = \frac{q_f \ell_{2a} \ell_n^2}{8} = \frac{9.78 \times 5.5 \times 5.05^2}{8} = 171.5 \text{ kN·m}$$

The distribution factors for an exterior span of a slab without beams, from A23.3-14 Table 13.1, are: 0.26 M_o exterior negative factored moment at Column Line A, which is all assigned to the column strip; 0.70 M_o interior negative factored moment at Column Line B, of which 75% is assigned to the column strip; and 0.52 M_o positive factored moment at the middle of Span A-B, of which 60% is assigned to the column strip. Minimum steel of 0.002 A_g must also be provided in accordance with A23.3-14 Clause 7.8.1: this governs for all cases except the top steel in the column strip at Column Line B, where 10 – № 15 bars are required as shown. Using № 15 bars, slightly more steel is needed to satisfy the maximum reinforcement spacing of 500 mm given in A23.3-14 Clause 7.8.3.

In the North-South direction, the total design moment along Column Line B is:

$$M_o = \frac{q_f \ell_{2a} \ell_n^2}{8} = \frac{9.78 \times 5.75 \times 5.20^2}{8} = 190.1 \text{ kN·m}$$

The distribution factors for an interior span, A23.3-14 Clause 13.9.3.1, are: 0.65 M_o negative factored moment at the faces of the supports at Column Lines 1 and 2, of which 75% is assigned to the column strip; and 0.35 M_o positive factored moment at the middle of Span 1-2, of which 60% is assigned to the column strip. Minimum steel of 0.002 A_g again governs for all cases except the top steel in the column strip at Column Lines 2 and 3, where 10 – № 15 bars are required as shown.

Similarly, in the North-South direction, the total design moment along Column Line A is must include the superimposed dead load of the wall:

$$M_o = \frac{(q_f \ell_{2a} + w_f) \ell_n^2}{8} = \frac{(9.78 \times 3.0 + 5.5) \times 4.9^2}{8} = 104.6 \text{ kN·m}$$

The distribution of this total interior span moment to positive and negative moments and to column and middle strips is identical to that for Column Line B as presented above. Minimum steel of 0.002 A_g governs for all cases except the top steel in the column strip at Column Lines 2 and 3, where 6 – № 15 bars are required as shown.

Required:

Compute the maximum instantaneous deflection of Panel A-B-2-3.

Solution:

1. **Determine if deflection computations are required.**

    A23.3-14 Clause 13.3.2 indicates that deflection calculations are not required if the slab thickness, h_s, satisfies:

    $$h_s \geq \frac{\ell_n (0.6 + f_y / 1000)}{30} = \frac{\ell_n (0.6 + 400 / 1000)}{30} = \frac{\ell_n}{30}$$

    where ℓ_n is the longer clear span and this value must be increased by 10% because there is a discontinuous edge at Column Line A. Thus, for $\ell_n = 5200$ mm, $h_s \geq 1.1 \times 5200/30 = 191$ mm and, because the actual slab thickness is only 180 mm, a deflection check is necessary.

2.   Compute concrete material properties, cracking moment, and specified loads.

For $f_c' = 30$ MPa, $E_c = 4500\sqrt{30} = 24\ 650$ MPa and $f_r = 0.6\sqrt{30} = 3.29$ MPa. For this value of E_c, $n = E_s/E_c = 200\ 000/24\ 650 = 8.11$.

For a metre width of slab, $I_g = (1000 \times 180^3/12 =)\ 486. \times 10^6$ mm^4/m so

$$M_{cr} = \frac{0.5 f_r I_g}{y_t} = \frac{0.5 \times 3.29 \times 486 \times 10^6}{0.5 \times 180} = 8.87 \times 10^6\,\text{N·mm/m} = 8.87\ \text{kN·m/m}$$

The specified panel load is $(q_s = q_D + q_L = (4.32\ \text{kPa} + 1.0\ \text{kPa}) + 2.09\ \text{kPa} =)\ 7.41$ kPa, and the specified wall load is 4.4 kN/m.

3.   Compute deflections of column and middle strips in the East-West Frame, Column Lines 2 & 3

Moments will be assigned to the critical sections of the column and middle strips using the coefficients of the Direct Design Method. The total specified moment along Column Lines 2 or 3, per A23.3-14 Eq. 13-23, is:

$$M_{os} = \frac{q_s \ell_{2a} \ell_n^2}{8} = \frac{7.41 \times 5.5 \times 5.05^2}{8} = 129.8\ \text{kN·m}$$

The exterior negative moment at Column Line A is 0.26 M_o, or $(-0.26 \times 129.8 =)$ -33.8 kN·m, and 100% of this moment is assigned to the column strip. For the column strip width of 2.75 m, as shown in Fig. 6.4(b), the cracking moment, M_{cr}, is (8.87 kN·m/m × 2.75 m =) 24.4 kN·m. Thus the magnitude of the applied moment exceeds the cracking moment and an effective moment of inertia must be computed.

The gross moment of inertia, I_g, is (486.0 × 10^6 mm^4/m × 2.75 m =) 1337 × 10^6 mm^4. For 6 – № 15 bars, $A_s = 1200$ mm^2, so

$$B = \frac{b}{n\,A_s} = \frac{2750}{8.11 \times 1200} = 0.283\,\text{mm}^{-1}$$

$$kd = \frac{\sqrt{2dB+1}-1}{B} = \frac{\sqrt{2 \times 150 \times 0.283 + 1} - 1}{0.283} = 29.2\,\text{mm}$$

and

$$I_{cr} = \frac{1}{3}b(kd)^3 + nA_s\,(d-kd)^2 = \frac{1}{3} \times 2750 \times (29.2)^3 + 8.11 \times 1200 \times (150 - 29.2)^2 = 164.8 \times 10^6\ \text{mm}^4$$

Thus

$$I_e = \left(\frac{M_{cr}}{M_a}\right)^3 I_g + \left[1 - \left(\frac{M_{cr}}{M_a}\right)^3\right] I_{cr} = \left(\frac{24.4}{33.8}\right)^3 1337 \times 10^6 + \left[1 - \left(\frac{24.4}{33.8}\right)^3\right] 164.8 \times 10^6 = 605.6 \times 10^6\ \text{mm}^4$$

The East-West middle strip between Column Lines 2 and 3 is assigned zero external negative moment, so it does not crack, and $I_e = I_g = (486.0 \times 10^6$ mm^4/m × 2.75 m =) 1337 × 10^6 mm^4.

Table 6.5(a) summarizes similar calculations for the East-West Frame analysis concerning the moments due to specified loads, and effective moments of inertia for the column and middle strips at the middle of span A-B, where the applied moment is 0.52 M_{os}, or 67.5 kN·m, and at Column Line B, where the applied moment is 0.70 M_{os}, or -90.9 kN·m. In all cases, the strip width is 2.75 m, so $I_g = 1337 \times 10^6$ mm^4, and $M_{cr} = 24.4$ kN·m.

Table 6.5(a)
Applied moments and effective moments of inertia, East-West frame analysis

Location		Column Line A		Midspan A-B		Column Line B	
Moment fraction	%	26%		52%		70%	
Moment	(kN·m)	-33.8		67.5		-90.9	
Strip	—	column	middle	column	middle	column	middle
Moment fraction	%	100%	0%	60%	40%	75%	25%
Moment	(kN·m)	-33.8	0	40.5	27.0	-68.2	-22.7
$\lvert M \rvert > M_{cr}$?	—	Yes	No	Yes	Yes	Yes	No
A_s	mm²	1200	1200	1200	1200	2000	1200
I_{cr}	10^6 mm⁴	164.8	164.8	164.8	164.8	253.6	164.8
I_e	10^6 mm⁴	605.6	1337.	420.9	1029.	303.3	1337.

3 (a). Compute the average effective moment of inertia and deflection for the column strip

Use Method 1 as described in Section 6.3.1.1. For both ends continuous:

$I_e = 0.70\, I_{em} + 0.15\,(I_{e1} + I_{e2}) = 0.70 \times 420.9 \times 10^6 + 0.15 \times (605.6 + 303.3) \times 10^6 = 431 \times 10^6$ mm⁴

For $M_o = 0.5\,\lvert M_{1s} + M_{2s}\rvert + M_{ms} = 0.5\,\lvert\text{-}33.8 - 68.2\rvert + 40.5 = 91.5$ kN·m

$$K = 1.20 - 0.20\, M_o/M_{ms} = 1.20 - 0.20\,(91.5/40.5) = 0.748$$

Thus

$$\Delta = K\left(\frac{5}{48}\right)\frac{M\,\ell_n^{\,2}}{E_c\,I_e} = 0.748\left(\frac{5}{48}\right)\frac{40.5 \times 10^6 \times 5050^2}{24650 \times 431 \times 10^6} = 7.6\,\text{mm}$$

3 (b). Compute the average effective moment of inertia and deflection for the middle strip

Here only one end is continuous:

$I_e = 0.85\, I_{em} + 0.15\, I_{ec} = 0.85 \times 1029 \times 10^6 + 0.15 \times 1337 \times 10^6 = 1075 \times 10^6$ mm⁴

For $M_o = 0.5\,\lvert M_{1s} + M_{2s}\rvert + M_{ms} = 0.5\,\lvert 0 - 22.7\rvert + 27.0 = 38.4$ kN·m

$$K = 1.20 - 0.20\, M_o/M_{ms} = 1.20 - 0.20\,(38.4/27.0) = 0.916$$

Thus

$$\Delta = K\left(\frac{5}{48}\right)\frac{M\,\ell_n^{\,2}}{E_c\,I_e} = 0.916\left(\frac{5}{48}\right)\frac{27.0 \times 10^6 \times 5050^2}{24650 \times 1075 \times 10^6} = 2.5\,\text{mm}$$

4. Compute deflections of column and middle strips in the North-South frame

This requires three steps:

1) computation of the moments in the North-South Frame at Column Line A and the column strip deflection;

2) computation of the moments in the North-South Frame at Column Line B and the column strip deflection; and

3) computation of the total middle strip moments as the sum of those from the middle strips of both North-South frames and compute the middle strip deflection.

6

Deflections

4.1   Analysis of North-South Frame at Column Line A

Following the same procedure as used for the East-West Frame, the total specified moment along Column Line A, is:

$$M_{os} = \frac{(q_s \ell_{2a} + w_{wall})\ell_n^2}{8} = \frac{(7.41 \times 3.0 + 4.4) \times 4.9^2}{8} = 79.9 \text{ kN·m}$$

For this interior panel, the negative moment at Column Lines 2 and 3 is 0.65 M_{os}, or (-0.65 × 79.9 =) -51.9 kN·m, and 75% of this moment is assigned to the column strip. For the column strip width of 1.625 m, as shown in Fig. 6.4 (b), the cracking moment, M_{cr}, is (8.874 kN·m/m × 1.625 m =) 14.42 kN·m. Thus the magnitude of the applied moment exceeds the cracking moment and an effective moment of inertia must be computed.

The gross moment of inertia, I_g, is (486.0 × 10⁶ mm⁴/m × 1.625 m =) 789.8 × 10⁶ mm⁴.
For 6 – № 15 bars, $A_s = 1200$ mm², so

$$B = \frac{b}{n A_s} = \frac{1625}{8.11 \times 1200} = 0.167 \text{mm}^{-1}$$

$$kd = \frac{\sqrt{2dB+1}-1}{B} = \frac{\sqrt{2 \times 150 \times 0.167 + 1} - 1}{0.167} = 36.8 \text{mm}$$

and

$$I_{cr} = \frac{1}{3}b(kd)^3 + nA_s(d-kd)^2 = \frac{1}{3} \times 1625 \times (36.8)^3 + 8.11 \times 1200 \times (150-36.8)^2 = 151.7 \times 10^6 \text{ mm}^4$$

Thus

$$I_e = \left(\frac{M_{cr}}{M_a}\right)^3 I_g + \left[1 - \left(\frac{M_{cr}}{M_a}\right)^3\right] I_{cr} = \left(\frac{14.4}{38.9}\right)^3 789.8 \times 10^6 + \left[1 - \left(\frac{14.4}{38.9}\right)^3\right] 151.7 \times 10^6 = 184.1 \times 10^6 \text{ mm}^4$$

Table 6.5(b) summarizes similar calculations for the Column Line A North-South Frame analysis concerning the moments due to specified loads in the column and middle strips. Effective moments of inertia are shown for the column strip regions only because the middle strips are also assigned moments from the Column Line B North-South Frame. At the middle of span 1-2, the applied moment is 0.35 M_{os}, or 28 kN·m.

Table 6.5(b)
Moments and effective moments of inertia, North-South frame at column Line A

Location		Column Lines 1 and 2		Midspan 1-2	
Moment fraction	%	65%		35%	
Moment	(kN·m)	-51.9		28.0	
Strip	—	column	middle	column	middle
Moment fraction	%	75%	25%	60%	40%
Moment	(kN·m)	-38.9	-13.0	16.8	11.2
$|M| > M_{cr}$?	—	Yes	—	Yes	—
A_s	mm²	1200	—	600	—
I_{cr}	10⁶ mm⁴	151.7	—	84.3	—
I_e	10⁶ mm⁴	184.1	—	532.2	—

4.1 (a). Compute the average effective moment of inertia and deflection for the column strip

For both ends continuous:

$I_e = 0.70\, I_{em} + 0.15\, (I_{e1} + I_{e2}) = 0.70 \times 532.2 \times 10^6 + 0.15 \times (184.1 + 184.1) \times 10^6 = 427.7 \times 10^6 \text{ mm}^4$

For $M_o = 0.5\, |M_{1s} + M_{2s}| + M_{ms} = 0.5\, |{-38.9} - 38.9| + 16.8 = 55.7$ kN·m

$$K = 1.20 - 0.20\, M_o/M_{ms} = 1.20 - 0.20\,(55.7/16.8) = 0.536$$

Thus

$$\Delta = K\left(\frac{5}{48}\right)\frac{M\,\ell_n^2}{E_c\,I_e} = 0.536\left(\frac{5}{48}\right)\frac{16.8\times 10^6 \times 4900^2}{24650\times 427.7\times 10^6} = 2.1\,\text{mm}$$

4.2   Analysis of North-South Frame at Column Line B

The total specified moment along Column Line B, is:

$$M_{os} = \frac{(q_s \ell_{2a})\ell_n^2}{8} = \frac{(7.41\times 5.75)\times 5.2^2}{8} = 143.9 \text{ kN·m}$$

The calculations follow those already shown and are summarized in Table 6.5(c). Effective moments of inertia are shown for the column strip regions only because the middle strips are also assigned moments from the Column Line A North-South Frame. The column strip width is 2.75 m so, as for the East-West frame, $I_g = 1337 \times 10^6 \text{ mm}^4$, and $M_{cr} = 24.4$ kN·m.

Table 6.5(c)
Moments and effective moments of inertia, North-South frame at column Line B

Location		Column Lines 1 and 2		Midspan 1-2	
Moment fraction	%	65%		35%	
Moment	(kN·m)	-93.6		50.4	
Strip	—	column	middle	column	middle
Moment fraction	%	75%	25%	60%	40%
Moment	(kN·m)	-70.2	-23.4	30.2	20.2
$\lvert M \rvert > M_{cr}$?	—	Yes	—	Yes	—
A_s	mm²	2000	—	1200	—
I_{cr}	10^6 mm⁴	253.6	—	164.9	—
I_e	10^6 mm⁴	299.2	—	781.3	—.

4.2 (a). Compute the average effective moment of inertia and deflection for the column strip

For both ends continuous:

$I_e = 0.70\, I_{em} + 0.15\, (I_{e1} + I_{e2}) = 0.70 \times 781.3 \times 10^6 + 0.15 \times (299.2 + 299.2) \times 10^6 = 636.7 \times 10^6 \text{ mm}^4$

For $M_o = 0.5\, |M_{1s} + M_{2s}| + M_{ms} = 0.5\, |{-70.2} - 70.2| + 30.2 = 100.4$ kN·m

$$K = 1.20 - 0.20\, M_o/M_{ms} = 1.20 - 0.20\,(100.4/30.2) = 0.536$$

Thus

$$\Delta = K\left(\frac{5}{48}\right)\frac{M\,\ell_n^2}{E_c\,I_e} = 0.536\left(\frac{5}{48}\right)\frac{30.2\times 10^6 \times 5200^2}{24650\times 636.7\times 10^6} = 2.9\,\text{mm}$$

6

Deflections

4.3   Analysis of North-South Middle Strip between Column Lines A and B

The width of this middle strip, as shown in Fig. 6.5(b), is 2750 mm, so from previous calculations, $I_g = 1337 \times 10^6$ mm⁴, $M_{cr} = 24.4$ kN·m, and, because the steel area is 1200 mm² in both the positive and negative moment regions, $I_{cr} = 164.9 \times 10^6$ mm⁴. The clear span length will be assumed equal to the average of clear span lengths at Column Lines A and B, 5050 mm. The moments resisted by the middle strip are the sum of the full middle strip moment from Column Line A and, because there are two half middle strips on each side of Column Line B, half the middle strip moment from Column Line B as determined in the previous two steps.

The applied moment and effective moment of inertia calculations summarized in Table 6.5(d).

Table 6.5(d)
Moments and effective moments of inertia, middle strip of North-South frame

Location		Column Lines 1 and 2	Midspan 1-2
Moment from Column Line A	(kN·m)	-13.0	11.2
Moment from Column Line B	(kN·m)	0.5 × -23.4 = -11.7	0.5 × 20.2 = 10.1
Total Middle Strip Moment	(kN·m)	-24.7	21.3
$|M| > M_{cr}$?	—	Yes (just!)	No
I_e	10⁶ mm⁴	1298	1337

4.3 (a). Compute the average effective moment of inertia and deflection for the middle strip

For both ends continuous:

$I_e = 0.70\, I_{em} + 0.15\,(I_{e1} + I_{e2}) = 0.70 \times 1337 \times 10^6 + 0.15 \times (1298 + 1298) \times 10^6 = 1325 \times 10^6$ mm⁴

For $M_o = 0.5\,|M_{1s} + M_{2s}| + M_{ms} = 0.5\,|-24.7 - 24.7| + 21.3 = 46.0$ kN·m

$$K = 1.20 - 0.20\, M_o/M_{ms} = 1.20 - 0.20\,(46.0/21.3) = 0.768$$

Thus

$$\Delta = K\left(\frac{5}{48}\right)\frac{M\,\ell_n^{\,2}}{E_c\, I_e} = 0.768\left(\frac{5}{48}\right)\frac{21.3\times10^6 \times 5050^2}{24650\times1325\times10^6} = 1.3\,\text{mm}$$

5. Compute total deflection at middle of Panel A-B-1-2

The various column and middle strip deflection computed are as shown in Table 6.5(e).

Table 6.5(e)
Computed column and middle strip deflections

	East-West frame	North-South frame	
	Column Line 2 or 3	Column Line A	Column Line B
Column Strip Deflection (mm)	7.6	2.1	2.9
Middle Strip Deflection (mm)	2.5	1.3	

The total deflection of the middle of the panel is therefore:

- the average column strip deflection of the East-West frame plus the middle strip deflection of the North-South frame, i.e., (7.6 mm + 1.3 mm =) 8.9 mm; or

- the average column strip deflection of the North-South frame plus the middle strip deflection of the East-West frame, i.e., (0.5 × (2.1 mm + 2.9 mm) + 2.5 mm =) 5.0 mm.

It is prudent to assume the larger value of 8.9 mm in this case, although the average value, 6.9 mm, is also reasonable.

6. Reflection on the results obtained

The results shown in Table 6.5(e) are clearly imperfect because, as is clear from Fig. 6.3, the deflection at the middle of the panel must have a single value irrespective of the procedure used to compute it! The observed difference is due to inaccuracies of the various coefficients used in the Direct Design Method to assign the total static moment to the negative and positive moment regions and further to assign the moment transversely to the column and middle strips.

The distribution factors for static moment, A23.3-14 Clause 13.9.3, are expressed as single values but the transverse distribution factors, A23.3-14 Clause 13.11, are typically expressed as ranges. To reconcile the difference between the deflections obtained, the East-West column strips should be assigned the minimum permissible fraction of the total moment and the North-South column strips should be assigned the maximum permissible fraction of the total moment.

This example was reanalyzed with:

- the fraction of the East-West positive moment assigned to the column strip reduced from 60% to 55%, the minimum permitted by A23.3-14 Clause 13.11.2.2;
- the fraction of the North-South positive moment assigned to the column strip increased from 60% to 65%, the maximum permitted by A23.3-14 Clause 13.11.2.2; and
- all negative moment fractions maintained, with 100% assigned to the column strip at exterior supports and 75% assigned to the column strip at interior supports.

These minor changes have no impact on the selection of flexural reinforcement at Ultimate Limit States. They do, however, favourably impact the various column and middle strip deflections as shown in Table 6.5(f).

Table 6.5(f)
Revised computed column and middle strip deflections

	East-West frame	North-South frame	
	Column Line 2 or 3	Column Line A	Column Line B
Column Strip Deflection (mm)	6.0	2.9	3.9
Middle Strip Deflection (mm)	3.5	1.1	

Thus the recomputed total deflection at the midspan of the panel is:

- the average column strip deflection in the East-West frame plus the middle strip deflection of the North-South frame, i.e., (6.0 mm + 1.1 mm =) 7.1 mm, or
- the average column strip deflection in the North-South frame plus the middle strip deflection of the East-West frame, i.e., (0.5 × (2.9 mm + 3.9 mm) + 3.5 mm =) 6.9 mm.

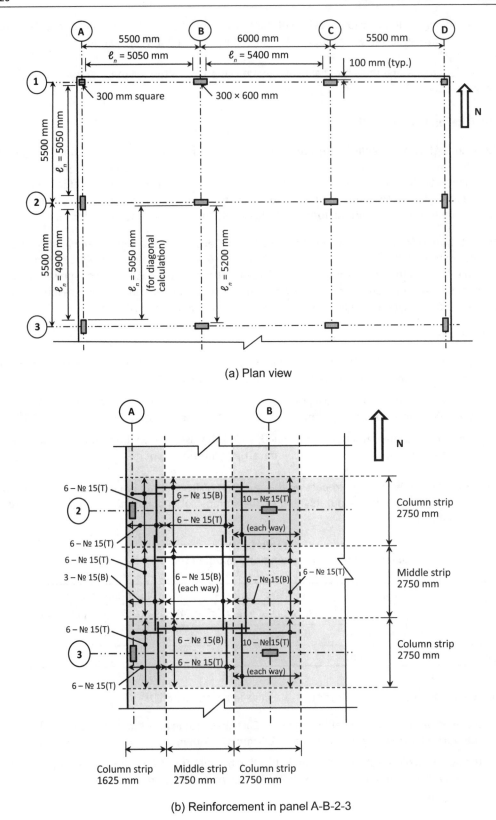

(a) Plan view

(b) Reinforcement in panel A-B-2-3

Fig. 6.4 Design example 2: instantaneous deflection of exterior panel of two-way slab.

6.4   Long-Term Deflection Computations

Instantaneous deflections of concrete flexural elements are increased due to additional long-term deflections caused by shrinkage and by creep due to sustained applied loads. Figure 6.5 shows the deflection time history of a typical concrete element:

- the instantaneous deflection due to the self weight of the member, $\Delta_{i,SW}$, that occurs when the forms are "flown" when the concrete is assumed to be one week old.

- the increase of the self-weight deflection due to shrinkage and creep, until the superimposed dead load is applied when the concrete is assumed to be three months old.

- the instantaneous deflection due to the superimposed dead load, $\Delta_{i,SDL}$.

- the additional deflections due to shrinkage and creep under the sustained self-weight and superimposed dead loads.

- the instantaneous deflection due to the sustained live load, $\Delta_{i,SLL}$, assumed applied when the concrete is nine months old. The sustained live load is often assumed to be 20 to 25% of the total live load for residential or office buildings: this fraction can be much higher for storage facilities including warehouses and libraries.

- the additional deflections due to shrinkage and creep under the sustained self-weight, superimposed dead and sustained live loads.

- the instantaneous deflection due to the instantaneous live load $\Delta_{i,ILL}$.

Table 9.3 of A23.3-14 often requires that the deflection to be considered must be "that part of the total deflection occurring after the attachment of non-structural elements likely to be damaged by large deflections". As is clear from Fig. 6.5, this can be in the order of half of the total deflection and is primarily due to the long-term deflection caused by the sustained self-weight, superimposed dead, and live loads.

Both the total deflection and the deflection occurring after the attachment of non-structural elements are sensitive to the loading history of the member. If the instantaneous portion of the live load is applied at the end of the service life of the member, the initial deflections due to sustained applied loads and the long-term increases of these deflections loads will be relatively small. If the instantaneous portion of the live load is applied at the beginning of the service life of the member, or if construction loadings subject the member to large moments, then the initial deflections and associated long-term deflection increases due to sustained loads will be much greater. Unless the loading history can be accurately forecast, it is prudent to assume that the construction loadings will cause applied moments that equal approximately those due to the specified dead and live loads.

Clause 9.8.2.5 of A23.3-14 allows the total deflection to be computed as

$$\Delta_t = \left[1 + \frac{S_t}{1 + 50\rho'} \right] \Delta_i$$

where Δ_t is the total (i.e., instantaneous plus long-term) deflection, S_t is the factor for creep deflections due to loads sustained for a duration t, ρ' is the compression steel reinforcement ratio, A_s'/ bd, and Δ_i is the instantaneous deflection. If steel at the compression face has insufficient development length for compression reinforcement it does not qualify as compression steel for this calculation.

Fig. 6.6 shows the variation of S_t with load duration and Table 6.6 gives equations to compute S_t, for loading durations between 1 week (i.e., 0.25 months) and 5 years (i.e., 60 months).

Table 6.6
Equations for S_t: long-term deflection factor under sustained loads

Range of load duration, t (months)	Equation for S_t (note: t in *months*)
0.25 to 12	$S_t = 0.683 + 0.289\,\ln(t)$
12 to 60	$S_t = 0.474 + 0.373\,\ln(t)$
greater than 60	$S_t = S_\infty = 2.0$

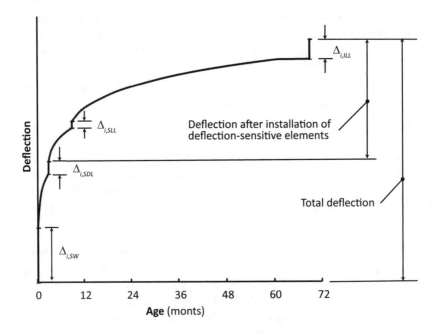

Fig. 6.5 Time history of flexural deflections for a typical concrete beam or slab

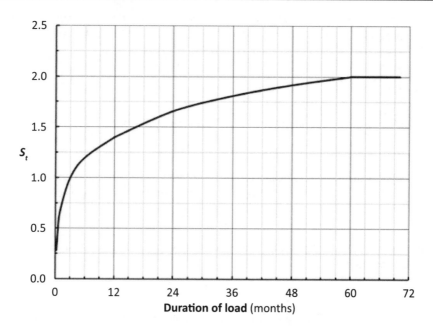

Fig. 6.6 Variation of S_t with load duration

Frequently, only that part of the total deflection that occurs after the installation of deflection-sensitive non-structural elements must be computed. As is clear from Fig. 6.5, this is the sum of long-term deflection due to self weight, superimposed dead, and sustained live loads, and the instantaneous deflection due to instantaneous and sustained live loads. It may not be necessary to include the instantaneous deflection due to the weight of the partitions themselves because:

1) they may not be sensitive to small deflections that occur immediately after their installation; and,

2) they are likely present and so causing the member to deflect before they are actually installed. In this case, as has been shown by Zhou and Kokai (2010):

$$\Delta_\infty - \Delta_{ti} = \left[\frac{S_\infty - S_{ti}}{1 + 50\rho'} \right] \Delta_{i,SW} + \left[\frac{S_\infty}{1 + 50\rho'} \right] \Delta_{i,SDL} + \left[1 + \frac{S_\infty}{1 + 50\rho'} \right] \Delta_{i,SLL} + \Delta_{i,ILL}$$

where S_∞ is the S value for an infinite load duration (i.e., $S_\infty = 2.0$) and S_{ti} is the S value for the load duration until ti, the time of installation of the deflection sensitive elements.

6.4.1. Creep and Shrinkage Warping Deflections Computed Separately

The long-term deflection of a concrete member is caused by creep of the concrete in compression, which is stress dependent, and shrinkage, which is not. If a member is reinforced on one face only, the reinforcement will restrain shrinkage at that face, causing curvatures and associated "shrinkage warping". These curvatures increase the deflection irrespective of the magnitude of the sustained load. In the previous edition of the CAC Concrete Design Handbook (CAC 2006), Professors A. Scanlon and N. J. Gardner presented the following method to account for the long-term creep and shrinkage effects independently.

The total long-term deflection, Δ_t, is:

$$\Delta_t = \Delta_{cr} + \Delta_{sh}$$

where Δ_{cr} is the creep deflection and Δ_{sh} is the deflection due to shrinkage warping. The total creep deflection (i.e., instantaneous plus long-term deflection) depends on the instantaneous deflection, Δ_i:

$$\Delta_{cr} = \left[1 + \frac{0.85 C_t}{1 + 50 \rho'}\right]\Delta_i$$

where $C_t = 0.8\, S_t$.

The shrinkage deflection is independent of the instantaneous deflection:

$$\Delta_{sh} = K_{sh}\, \phi_{sh}\, \ell_n^2$$

where K_{sh} accounts for the boundary displacement conditions using the values shown in Table 6.7 and ℓ_n is the clear span length. The curvature due to the restrained shrinkage, ϕ_{sh}, is computed as

$$\phi_{sh} = \frac{A_{sh}\, \varepsilon_{sh}}{h}$$

where h is the depth of the section and ε_{sh} is a measure of the shrinkage that has occurred at the time the deflection is computed:

$$\varepsilon_{sh} = \frac{S_t}{2.0}\, 400 \times 10^{-6}$$

The term A_{sh} is obtained from Table 6.8. The steel percentages used to determine A_{sh} correspond to those at the support section of cantilevers or the midspan section of simple and continuous spans. For T-beams, use $\rho = 100\,(\rho + \rho_w)/2$ to compute A_{sh}, where $\rho_w = A_s /(b_w d)$.

Table 6.7
Values of K_{sh} for shrinkage deflection computation

Displacement boundary condition	K_{sh}
Cantilevers	0.500
Simply supported beams	0.125
Beams continuous at both ends	0.065
Beams fixed at one end, simply supported at the other	0.090

Table 6.8
Values of A_{sh} for calculating shrinkage curvature*

ρ \ ρ'	0.00	0.25	0.50	0.75	1.00	1.25	1.50	1.75	2.00	2.25	2.50	2.75	3.00
0.25	0.44	0.00	-	-	-	-	-	-	-	-	-	-	-
0.50	0.56	0.31	0.00	-	-	-	-	-	-	-	-	-	-
0.75	0.64	0.45	0.25	0.00	-	-	-	-	-	-	-	-	-
1.00	0.70	0.55	0.39	0.22	0.00	-	-	-	-	-	-	-	-
1.25	0.75	0.63	0.49	0.35	0.20	0.00	-	-	-	-	-	-	-
1.50	0.80	0.69	0.57	0.45	0.32	0.18	0.00	-	-	-	-	-	-
1.75	0.84	0.74	0.64	0.57	0.42	0.30	0.17	0.00	-	-	-	-	-
2.00	0.88	0.79	0.69	0.64	0.50	0.39	0.28	0.16	0.00	-	-	-	-
2.25	0.92	0.83	0.74	0.69	0.56	0.47	0.37	0.26	0.15	0.00	-	-	-
2.50	0.95	0.87	0.79	0.74	0.62	0.53	0.44	0.35	0.25	0.14	0.00	-	-
2.75	0.98	0.91	0.83	0.79	0.67	0.59	0.51	0.42	0.33	0.24	0.13	0.00	-
3.00	1.00	0.94	0.87	0.83	0.72	0.64	0.57	0.49	0.40	0.32	0.23	0.13	0.00
3.25	1.00	0.97	0.90	0.87	0.76	0.69	0.62	0.54	0.47	0.39	0.31	0.22	0.12
3.50	1.00	1.00	0.94	0.90	0.80	0.74	0.67	0.60	0.52	0.45	0.37	0.29	0.32
3.75	1.00	1.00	1.00	0.94	0.84	0.78	0.71	0.64	0.58	0.52	0.44	0.36	0.28
4.00	1.00	1.00	1.00	1.00	0.88	0.81	0.75	0.69	0.62	0.56	0.49	0.42	0.35

Notes to Table 6.8
* $\rho = 100 A_s/(bd)$ $\rho' = 100A_s'/(bd)$. When $\rho' > \rho$, interchange ρ' and ρ to obtain corresponding solution in opposite direction.

6.4.2.   Design Examples

6.4.2.1. Design Example 3: Total Deflection of Two-span One-way Slab

In Design Example 1, the total maximum instantaneous deflection of the left span of a two-span one-way slab member subjected to a uniformly distributed dead load of 4.8 kPa and a uniformly distributed live load on the left span only of 4.8 kPa was computed to be 22.0 mm.

Assume that:

1)   deflection-sensitive non-structural elements are installed when the member is 1.5 months old; and,

2)   25% of the live load is sustained and applied when the member is 6 months old.

Required:

Compute that part of the total deflection occurring after the installation of the non-structural elements. Are the requirements of A23.3-14 Table 9.3 satisfied if the non-structural elements are

a)   likely to be or

b)   not likely to be damaged by large deflections?

Solution:

1.   **Determine deflections due to dead load, instantaneous and transient live loads.**

The previously obtained deflection of 22 mm was determined assuming that construction loadings had created cracking that is similar in nature to that due to specified dead and live loads applied when the concrete has reached its 28-day specified strength of 30 MPa. The EI values used to compute the instantaneous dead and live load deflections are therefore identical, and the various deflections can be obtained by scaling.

The deflection due to the dead load, in this case entirely the self weight of the slab is

$$\Delta_{i,SW} = \frac{w_{SW}}{w_{SW}+w_L}\Delta_i = \frac{4.8\,\text{kPa}}{4.8\,\text{kPa}+4.8\,\text{kPa}} \times 22\,\text{mm} = 11\,\text{mm}$$

Similarly, the instantaneous live load deflection is 11 mm, of which 25% is due to the sustained live load, $\Delta_{i,SLL} = 0.25 \times 11 = 2.8$ mm, and the remaining 75% is due to the instantaneous live load, $\Delta_{i,ILL} = 8.2$ mm.

2.   **Determine deflection that occurs after installation of deflection-sensitive elements.**

Here $S_\infty = 2.0$ and $S_{1.5} = 0.683 + 0.289\,ln(1.5) = 0.800$

Thus, from

$$\Delta_\infty - \Delta_{ti} = \left[\frac{S_\infty - S_{ti}}{1+50\rho'}\right]\Delta_{i,SW} + \left[\frac{S_\infty}{1+50\rho'}\right]\Delta_{i,SDL} + \left[1+\frac{S_\infty}{1+50\rho'}\right]\Delta_{i,SLL} + \Delta_{i,ILL}$$

for $\rho' = 0$, and $\Delta_{i,SDL} = 0$, this becomes

$$\Delta_\infty - \Delta_{1.5} = \left[\frac{2-0.8}{1+50\times0}\right]\times11\,\text{mm} + \left[\frac{2}{1+50\times0}\right]\times0\,\text{mm} + \left[1+\frac{2}{1+50\times0}\right]\times2.8\,\text{mm} + 8.2\,\text{mm}$$

$$= 13.2 + 0 + 8.4 + 8.2\,\text{mm} = 29.8\,\text{mm}$$

3.   **Compare with deflection limits specified in A23.3-14 Table 9.3:**

For "floor construction supporting non-structural elements likely to be damaged by large deflections" the limit is $\ell_n/480$ or $6000/480 = 12.5$ mm. The slab **does not satisfy** this requirement.

For "floor construction supporting non-structural elements not likely to be damaged by large deflections" the limit is $\ell_n/240$ or $6000/240 = 25$ mm. The slab **does not satisfy** this requirement.

4.   **Next steps**

The total deflection due to sustained and instantaneous live load is 16.6 mm, which exceeds the 12.5 mm limit for "elements likely to be damaged by large deflections". It will therefore be necessary to increase the slab thickness, increase the reinforcement or prestress the slab to satisfy this requirement.

On the other hand, the slab is close to adequate if the elements are not likely to be damaged by large deflections. If the installation of the deflection-sensitive elements can be delayed until the slab is 7 months old, $S_7 = (0.683 + 0.289 \times ln\,(7) =) 1.24$, the increase of deflection due to the slab self weight is $[(2 - 1.24) \times 11 =]\ 8.3$ mm, and the total deflection is $(8.3 + 8.4 + 8.2 =)\ 24.9$ mm, which is just satisfactory. Alternatively, consider increasing the slab thickness, increasing the reinforcement, or prestressing the slab.

6.4.2.2. Design Example 4: Total Deflection of 2-way Slab System

In Design Example 2, the total maximum instantaneous deflection of edge panel A-B-2-3 in a two-way flat plate system, subjected to specified self-weight of 4.32 kPa, a partition load of 1.0 kPa, an exterior wall load of 4.4 kN/m, and a live load after tributary area reduction of 2.09 kPa was computed to be 7.1 mm.

Assume that:

1) the partitions are deflection-sensitive and are installed when the slab is 3 months old; and,

2) 20% of the live load is sustained and applied when the slab is 9 months old.

Required:

Compute that part of the total deflection occurring after the installation of the non-structural partitions. Are the requirements of A23.3-14 Table 9.3 satisfied if the partitions are

a) likely to be or

b) not likely to be damaged by large deflections?

Solution:

1. **Determine instantaneous deflections due to dead load, instantaneous and transient live loads.**

   The deflections summarized in Table 6.5(e) were determined assuming that construction loads caused cracking similar to that due to the specified dead and live loads applied when the concrete has reached its 28-day specified strength of 30 MPa. The EI values used to compute the instantaneous dead and live load deflections are therefore identical, and the various deflections can be obtained by scaling.

   The total specified load on the interior column and middle strips is a uniformly distributed load of $4.32 + 1.0 + 2.09 = 7.41$ kPa. The deflection due to the self-weight of the slab is therefore $(4.32/7.41 =)\ 58.3\%$ of the total deflection, that due to the partition load is $(1.0/7.41) = 13.5\%$ of the total, and that due to the live load is $(2.09/7.41 =)\ 28.2\%$ of the total. The deflection due to the sustained live load is $(0.2 \times 28.2\% =)\ 5.6\%$ of the total, and that due to the instantaneous live load is $(0.8 \times 28.2\% =)\ 22.6\%$ of the total.

   The total specified load on the exterior North-South Frame at Column Line A is a line load due to the uniformly distributed loads of $(7.41\ \text{kPa} \times 1.625\ \text{m}) = 12.0$ kN/m, plus the wall load of 4.4 kN/m, giving a total of 16.4 kN/m. The deflection due to the self weight of the slab is therefore $(4.32 \times 1.625/16.4 =)\ 42.7\%$ of the total deflection, that due to the partition and wall load is $[(1.0 \times 1.625 + 4.4)/16.4 =]\ 36.7\%$ of the total deflection, and that due to the specified live load is $(2.09 \times 1.625/16.4 =)\ 20.7\%$ of the total deflection. The deflection due to the sustained live load is $(0.2 \times 20.7\% =)\ 4.1\%$ of the total deflection and that due to the instantaneous live load is $(0.8 \times 20.7\% =)\ 16.6\%$ of the total deflection.

6

Deflections

Table 6.9(a) summarizes the instantaneous deflections in the column and middle strips due to self weight, superimposed dead load, sustained live load and instantaneous live load. The total values are taken directly from Table 6.5(e). The values are shown to the nearest hundredths of a millimetre to limit rounding errors: this is overly precise given that calculated concrete deflections are generally only accurate to within +/− 20% of the true values!

Table 6.9(a)
Instantaneous deflections due to self-weight, superimposed dead, and live loads

	East-West frame	North-South frame	
	Column Line 2 or 3	**Column Line A**	**Column Line B**
Total Column Strip Deflection (mm)	6.0	2.9	3.9
Self-weight, $\Delta_{i,SW}$ (mm)	× 0.583 = **3.50**	× 0.427 = **1.24**	× 0.583 = **2.27**
Superimposed dead, $\Delta_{i,SDL}$ (mm)	× 0.135 = **0.81**	× 0.367 = **1.06**	× 0.135 = **0.53**
Sustained live, $\Delta_{i,SLL}$ (mm)	× 0.056 = **0.34**	× 0.041 = **0.12**	× 0.056 = **0.22**
Instantaneous live, $\Delta_{i,ILL}$ (mm)	× 0.226 = **1.36**	× 0.166 = **0.48**	× 0.226 = **0.88**
Total Middle Strip Deflection (mm)	3.5	1.1	
Self-weight, $\Delta_{i,SW}$ (mm)	× 0.583 = **2.04**	× (0.583 + 0.427)/2 = **0.56**	
Superimposed dead, $\Delta_{i,SDL}$ (mm)	× 0.135 = **0.47**	× (0.135 + 0.367)/2 = **0.28**	
Sustained live, $\Delta_{i,SLL}$ (mm)	× 0.056 = **0.20**	× (0.056 + 0.041)/2 = **0.05**	
Instantaneous live, $\Delta_{i,ILL}$ (mm)	× 0.226 = **0.79**	× (0.226 + 0.166)/2 = **0.22**	

2. **Determine deflection that occurs after installation of deflection-sensitive elements.**

Here $S_\infty = 2.0$ and $S_3 = 0.683 + 0.289\,I_n(3.0) = 1.00$

Thus, for $\rho' = 0$, the governing equation is:

$$\Delta_\infty - \Delta_{ti} = [2 - 1]\Delta_{i,SW} + [2]\Delta_{i,SDL} + [1 + 2]\Delta_{i,SLL} + \Delta_{i,ILL} = \Delta_{i,SW} + 2\Delta_{i,SDL} + 3\Delta_{i,SLL} + \Delta_{i,ILL}$$

For the East-West column strip on Column Line 2 or 3:

$$\Delta_\infty - \Delta_{ti} = \Delta_{i,SW} + 2\Delta_{i,SDL} + 3\Delta_{i,SLL} + \Delta_{i,ILL} = 3.5 + 2 \times 0.81 + 3 \times 0.34 + 1.36 = 7.48 \text{ mm}$$

Similarly, for the East-West middle strip on Column Line 2 or 3:

$$\Delta_\infty - \Delta_{ti} = 2.04 + 2 \times 0.47 + 3 \times 0.20 + 0.79 = 4.36 \text{ mm}$$

For the North-South column strip on Column Line A:

$$\Delta_\infty - \Delta_{ti} = 1.24 + 2 \times 1.06 + 3 \times 0.12 + 0.48 = 4.21 \text{ mm}$$

For the North-South column strip on Column Line B:

$$\Delta_\infty - \Delta_{ti} = 2.27 + 2 \times 0.53 + 3 \times 0.22 + 0.88 = 4.86 \text{ mm}$$

For the North-South middle strip between on Column Lines A and B:

$$\Delta_\infty - \Delta_{ti} = 0.56 + 2 \times 0.28 + 3 \times 0.05 + 0.22 = 1.48 \text{ mm}$$

These values are summarized in Table 6.9(b).

Table 6.9(b)
Long-term column and middle strip deflections

	East-West frame	North-South frame	
	Column Line 2 or 3	Column Line A	Column Line B
Column Strip Deflection (mm)	7.48	4.21	4.86
Middle Strip Deflection (mm)	4.36	1.48	

Thus the recomputed total deflection at the midspan of the panel is:

- the average column strip deflection in the East-West frame plus the middle strip deflection of the North-South frame, i.e., (7.48 mm + 1.48 mm =) 8.96 mm, say 9.0 mm or

- the average column strip deflection in the North-South frame plus the middle strip deflection of the East-West frame, i.e., (0.5 × (4.21 mm + 4.86 mm) + 4.36 mm =) 8.89 mm, say 8.9 mm.

3. **Compare with deflection limits specified in A23.3-14 Table 9.3:**

For "floor construction supporting non-structural elements likely to be damaged by large deflections" the limit is $\ell_n/480$.

- For the East-West Frame at Column Line 2 or 3, $\ell_n = 5150$ mm so the deflection limit is 5150/480 = 10.7 mm. The more severe deflection is the column strip deflection of 7.5 mm: the slab therefore **satisfies** this requirement.

- For the North-South Frame at Column Line A, $\ell_n = 4900$ mm so the deflection limit is 4900/480 = 10.2 mm. The more severe deflection is the column strip deflection of 4.2 mm: the slab therefore **satisfies** this requirement.

- Similarly for the North-South Frame at Column Line B, $\ell_n = 5200$ mm so the deflection limit is or 5200/480 = 10.8 mm. The more severe deflection is the column strip deflection of 4.9 mm: the slab therefore **satisfies** this requirement.

- Finally, the average clear diagonal length of the panel is
$$\sqrt{5050^2 + 5050^2} = 7140 \text{ mm}$$

so the deflection limit is or 7140/480 = 14.9 mm. The computed mid-panel deflection is 9.0 mm: the slab therefore **satisfies** this requirement.

For "floor construction supporting non-structural elements not likely to be damaged by large deflections" the limit is $\ell_n/240$. Clearly the slab also **satisfies** this requirement.

6

Deflections

6.5   References

American Concrete Institute Committee 435 (2000): *Control of Deflection of Concrete Structures (ACI 435R-95).* American Concrete Institute, Farmington Hills MI, 74 pp.

Bischoff, P.H., and Versey, S. (2011): "Minimum Thickness Requirements Needed to Satisfy Deflection Limits for One-Way Reinforced Concrete Construction (Paper GC 023)". *Proceedings, CSCE 2011 General Conference, Ottawa.* Canadian Society for Civil Engineering, Montreal, 10-page paper in electronic proceedings.

Bischoff, P.H. (2007): "Rational model for calculating deflection of reinforced concrete beams and slabs". *Canadian Journal of Civil Engineering,* **34**:992-1002.

Branson, D. E. (1963): "Instantaneous and Time-dependent Deflections of Simple and Continuous Reinforced Concrete Beams". *HPR Report № 7, Part 1,* Alabama Highway Department, Bureau of Public Roads, pp. 1-78 (published with Part 2 in 1965).

Cement Association of Canada (2006): *Concrete Design Handbook.* Cement Association of Canada, Ottawa, 994 pp.

Ghali, A. (1993): "Deflection of Reinforced Concrete Members: A Critical Review". *American Concrete Institute Structural Journal* **90** (4):364-373.

Grundy, P., and Kabaila, A. (1963): "Construction Loads on Slabs with Shored Formwork in Multistory Buildings". *American Concrete Institute Journal, Proceedings, 60* (12): 1729-1738. Reprinted in *Concrete International* in 2004, **26** (7): 99-112.

Monette, L., and Gardner, N. J. (2015): "Shored/Reshored Construction of Flat Plates". *Concrete International,* **37** (9): 25-32.

Scanlon, A., and Bischoff, P.H. (2008): "Shrinkage Restraint and Loading History Effects on Deflections of Flexural Members". *American Concrete Institute Structural Journal* **105** (4): 498-506.

Scanlon, A., and Suprenant, B. A. (2011): "Estimating Two-way Slab Deflections". *Concrete International* **33** (7): 29-34.

Zhou, W., and Kokai, T., (2010): "Deflection Calculation and Control for Reinforced Concrete Flexural Members". *Canadian Journal of Civil Engineering* **37**: 131-134.

6.6   Acknowledgements

The author gratefully acknowledges assistance received from Western Engineering students Li Hao Zhang and Caitlin Mancuso, from external reviewer M. J. D'Costa, and from members of the A23.3 Technical Committee, particularly J. G. Mutrie and D. M. Rogowsky. Any errors or omissions in this chapter are the fault of the author, however, not these individuals.

Short Columns

7.1   General Remarks

Columns must be proportioned to resist bending moment as well as axial load. The capacity of column cross sections is described using interaction diagrams (Tables 7.10 through 7.13). These tables are available for download from the CAC website at www.cement.ca.

Clause 10.15.2 of CSA A23.3* defines a limiting slenderness ratio $k\ell_u/r$ below which slenderness effects will be insignificant for non-sway frames. (See Table 8.1 for description of ℓ_u.)

The design of slender columns is covered in Chapter 8 of this handbook.

7.2   Maximum Axial Resistance under Small Moments

Values of the maximum axial load, $P_{r,\,max}$, for tied columns are shown in Tables 7.1.1 to 7.1.5 for common sizes of cross sections, concrete strengths of 25, 30, 35, 40 and 45 MPa and steel strengths of 400 MPa and 500 MPa. The material resistance factors $\phi_c = 0.65$ and $\phi_s = 0.85$ are incorporated into these graphs. Precast concrete columns for which $\phi_c = 0.70$ will have slightly higher capacities.

Column cross sections can resist more axial load when moments are small. Clause 10.10.4 of CSA A23.3 sets a maximum axial load resistance based on the assumption that some moment is inevitable. These graphs can be used as an estimating design aid as each displays the possible square column sizes appropriate for a specific axial load. They can also be used for rectangular and circular tied columns by choosing comparable areas. The diameter of a circular column is 1.128 times the size of a square column of the same area.

The capacity, $P_{r,\,max}$, of spiral columns will be 12.5% larger than tied columns because the upper limit is based on $0.90P_{ro}$ rather than $0.80P_{ro}$ (see Clause 10.10.4). This difference exists only for small eccentricities. (See Tables 7.13.1 to 7.13.16.) The remaining portions of the interaction curves are the same.

When ρ_t exceeds 4%, welded splices, mechanical connections, or end-bearing splices have to be staggered to satisfy Clause 12.17.2 of CSA A23.3. Columns with lapped splices can seldom have much more than 4% steel while, even with end-bearing splices, ρ_t will seldom exceed 6%.

Steeper lines correspond to ρ_t ratios between ½ and 1%. Columns with these low steel ratios may be useful in upper storeys to reduce the number of size changes in a column stack. The sharp change in capacity is based on the application of Clause 10.10.5.

7.3   Values of Gamma for Columns

Table 7.2 provides values of γ for common sizes of columns, with 40 mm and 50 mm cover to 10M ties or spirals. The value γ is the ratio of the centre-to-centre distance between the outermost reinforcing bars (measured perpendicular to the axis of bending) to the overall depth of the column, h. For other covers $\gamma = \gamma_{40} + 2(40 - c)/h$.

7.4   Minimum Column Sizes and Covers for Fire and Durability

Table 7.3 summarizes the requirements for minimum column size and cover for different fire ratings, column lengths, steel ratios, concrete type, and overdesign factor, P_r/P_f. Concrete types and requirements for fire resistance are discussed in Section 1 of this handbook.

---

* CSA Standard A23.3-14 "Design of Concrete Structures." From here on referred to as CSA A23.3.

Cover requirements for durability as specified in Clause 6.6.6.2 of CSA A23.1-14 "Concrete Materials and Methods of Concrete Construction", are also shown in this table.

Section 1 of this handbook provides information on construction intended for a de-icer salt environment. Bearing walls and columns that support slabs and ramps may be splashed with de-icers and are hence subject to corrosion. Such supporting elements should be constructed using at least the same quality of concrete and cover recommended for slabs and ramps.

7.5   Interaction Diagrams

Note: Interaction diagrams are no longer included in the print edition of the Concrete Design Handbook; however, they may be downloaded at www.cement.ca.

The strength of column cross sections can be determined using interaction diagrams with the factored axial resistance as the ordinate and the factored moment resistance as abscissa. To make the graphs applicable to all column sizes, P_r has been divided by A_g and M_r has been divided by $A_g h$. The material resistance factors $\phi_c = 0.65$ and $\phi_s = 0.85$ have been included in the calculation of the factored resistances so the charts give P_r/A_g, and $M_r/(A_g h)$ without modification. The charts are conservative for precast columns for which $\phi_c = 0.70$.

Four graphs with different values of γ are included for each concrete strength, column shape and reinforcing pattern. The interaction diagrams are plotted for 3 reinforcement patterns for rectangular cross sections and for circular sections with circular or helical ties, or spirals.

Tied rectangular column cross sections include those with equal amounts of reinforcement in each of the four faces (Tables 7.10.1 to 7.10.20); equal amounts of reinforcement in the two faces parallel to the axis of bending (Tables 7.11.1 to 7.11.20); and columns with equal amounts of reinforcement in the two side faces perpendicular to the axis of bending (Tables 7.12.1 to 7.12.20). Tables 7.11.1 to 7.11.20 should be used for columns with 4 bars since all 4 bars are located the same distance from the axis of the column.

The charts for circular columns have been plotted using P_r/h^2 and M_r/h^3. The capacities of circular tied and spiral columns differ only at small eccentricities when Clause 10.10.4 governs. The charts in Tables 7.13.1 to 7.13.16 can be used for both cases. A gray line shows the additional capacity of spiral columns.

Three radial lines in each diagram give the tensile stress ratio in the steel layer closest to the tensile face of the column. These are used to determine the type of column splices required. See Clause 12.17 of CSA A23.3

Some description of the assumptions incorporated into the calculation of these interaction curves may be of interest. Calculations have been based on a limiting strain of 0.0035 in the extreme compression fibre. The interaction curves have been based on an equivalent rectangular concrete stress block of depth $\beta_1 c$ with a uniform stress $\phi_c \alpha_1 f_c'$. The effect of the concrete displaced by the area of steel in regions of compressed concrete has been taken into account by deducting ϕ_c times the concrete stress from the stress in the compressed reinforcement. For this purpose the concrete stress was assumed to be εE_c at low compressive strains and $\alpha_1 f_c'$ at high strains.

In situations with a small moment with $c > h$, the graphs have been approximated by a straight line from P_{ro} to the P_r and M_r corresponding to $c = h$.

7

Short Columns

The interaction curves in Table 7.11.1 to 7.11.20 were developed for equal reinforcement in the two end faces. All of the other charts for rectangular columns have been based on 6 layers of steel. The curves for circular columns have been based on 4 equally spaced bars to either side of the axis of bending. These curves are reasonably conservative for any number of longitudinal bars ranging down to the minimum of 6 allowed for spirals.

Gamma, γ, is the ratio of the distance between the centres of the outermost reinforcing bars and the overall column depth, h. Gamma does not affect the column capacity $P_{r, max}$ with low moment. It has maximum effect at balanced conditions $(f_s / f_y = 1.0)$ and with higher values of ρ_t. It is conservative to use an interaction chart with γ smaller than the expected value. Only when γ approaches that of the next higher graph and $f_s / f_y > 0$ is it worthwhile to interpolate between graphs with different γ.

7.5.1. Column stiffness

As an aid in determining slenderness effects, the values of EI are given on each strength interaction graph.

Equation 10-20

If the effective stiffness of cross sections is determined without the influence of reinforcement,

$$EI_{20} = \frac{0.4E_c I_g}{1 + \beta_d} \text{ (Eq. 10-20 of CSA A23.3)}$$

The modulus of elasticity has been based on Eq. 8.2 of A23.3.

$$E_c = 4500\sqrt{f_c'}$$

For rectangular columns $I_g = bh^3/12$. The value of EI_{20} is given with each set of interaction graphs as a constant times bh^3.

For circular columns $I_g = \pi h^4/64$ so EI_{20} is shown as a constant times h^4.

Equation 10-19

The alternate equation for EI includes the influence of longitudinal reinforcement

$$EI_{19} = \frac{0.2E_c I_g + E_s I_{st}}{1 + \beta_d} \text{ (Eq. 10-19 of CSA A23.3)}$$

The values of I_{st} are different for each pattern of reinforcing.

Since both equation 10-19 and equation 10-20 are lower bound values, it follows that in each instance the larger value may be used.

Reinforcing on End Faces Only

For rectangular columns with the reinforcing on the two end faces that are parallel to the axis of bending, all of the reinforcing is centred a distance ½ γh from the column centreline

$$\therefore I_{st} = A_{st} \gamma^2 h^2/4 = \rho_t \gamma^2 bh^3/4$$

$$EI_{19} = (0.2\, E_c I_g + E_s \rho_t\, \gamma^2 bh^3/4)/(1 + \beta_d)$$

$$EI_{19} = \left(\frac{E_c}{60} + \frac{E_s\, \rho_t\, \gamma^2}{4} \right) bh^3\, /(1 + \beta_d) = kbh^3\, /(1 + \beta_d)$$

where $k = E_c/60 + E_s \rho_t\, \gamma^2/4$

The value of k has been shown for each value of ρ_t on each interaction chart.

Reinforcing on Side Faces

With reinforcing on the side faces that are perpendicular to the axis of bending, the value of I_{st} reduces as the number of bars/side is increased:

for 3 bars $I_{st} = \dfrac{2}{3} A_{st}\, \gamma^2\, h^2 \left(\dfrac{1}{4} \right) = \dfrac{\rho_t\, \gamma^2\, bh^3}{6}$

for 4 bars $I_{st} = \dfrac{2}{4} A_{st}\, \gamma^2\, h^2 \left(\dfrac{1}{4} + \dfrac{1}{36} \right) = \dfrac{\rho_t\, \gamma^2\, bh^3}{7.2}$

for 5 bars $I_{st} = \dfrac{2}{5} A_{st}\, \gamma^2\, h^2 \left(\dfrac{1}{4} + \dfrac{1}{16} \right) = \dfrac{\rho_t\, \gamma^2\, bh^3}{8}$

for 6 bars $I_{st} = \dfrac{2}{6} A_{st}\, \gamma^2\, h^2 \left(\dfrac{1}{4} + \dfrac{9}{100} + \dfrac{1}{100} \right) = \dfrac{\rho_t\, \gamma^2\, bh^3}{8.57}$

The chosen value of I_{st} of $\rho_t\, \gamma^2 bh^3/\, 8.57$ has been based on 6 bars/face, which will be conservative for columns with less than 6 bars/face;

Therefore $k = E_c/60 + E_s \rho_t\, \gamma^2/8.57$

Equal Reinforcement on all 4 Faces

When there are an equal number of bars on each face, the number of bars/face still affects I_{st}, but the variation is not as pronounced as for reinforcement only on the side faces.

for 3 bars $I_{st} = \dfrac{2}{8} A_{st}\, \gamma^2\, h^2 \left(\dfrac{3}{4} \right) = \dfrac{\rho_t\, \gamma^2\, bh^3}{5.33}$

for 4 bars $I_{st} = \dfrac{2}{12} A_{st}\, \gamma^2\, h^2 \left(\dfrac{4}{4} + \dfrac{2}{36} \right) = \dfrac{\rho_t\, \gamma^2\, bh^3}{5.68}$

for 5 bars $I_{st} = \dfrac{2}{16} A_{st}\, \gamma^2\, h^2 \left(\dfrac{5}{4} + \dfrac{2}{16} \right) = \dfrac{\rho_t\, \gamma^2\, bh^3}{5.82}$

for 6 bars $I_{st} = \dfrac{2}{20} A_{st}\, \gamma^2\, h^2 \left(\dfrac{6}{4} + \dfrac{2(9)}{100} + \dfrac{2}{100} \right) = \dfrac{\rho_t\, \gamma^2\, bh^3}{5.88}$

A moment of inertia based on 6 bars/side gives $k = E_c/60 + E_s \rho_t\, \gamma^2/5.88$

7

Short Columns

Circular Columns

For circular columns I_g is $\pi\, h^4/64$ and I_{st} varies depending upon both the number and orientation of the bars relative to the axis of bending. For 4, 8 or an infinite number of bars $I_{st} = A_s \gamma^2 h^2/8$. Using this value for I_{st}:

$$EI_{19} = kh^4/(1 + \beta_d)$$

$$\text{where } k = \frac{\pi}{4}(E_c/80 + E_s\, \rho_t\, \gamma^2/8)$$

7.5.2. Steel or concrete strengths which differ from charted values

The interaction curves have been based on 400 MPa reinforcement. In many regions of the interaction diagrams there will be little or no benefit from an increased steel strength because the stress in some or all of the reinforcement remains below yield.

For locations in the interaction diagrams where the strain in all of the compression reinforcement is higher than ε_y, the interaction curve can be used with ρ_t adjusted by multiplication by $400/f_y$. Interaction curve tables in this handbook are limited to concrete strengths of 25, 30, 35, 40 and 45 MPa and material resistance factors of $\phi_c = 0.65$ and ϕ_s of 0.85. The tables can be used with some simple adjustments for other values of these variables.

> $\phi_s > 0.85$.
> Multiply ρ_t by $(0.85/\phi_s)$
> i.e. for $\phi_s = 0.90$ and $\rho_t = 5\%$, use revised $\rho_t = 5(0.85/0.90) = 4.72\%$

> $\phi_c > 0.65$
> Reduce ρ_t by $(\Delta\phi_c)$
> i.e. for $\phi_c = 0.70$ and $\rho_t = 5\%$, use revised $\rho_t = 5\% - (0.70 - 0.65) = 4.5\%$

> $f'_c > 45$ MPa
> Reduce ρ_t by 0.12 (Δ)
> i.e. for $f'_c = 50$ MPa and $\rho_t = 5\%$, use revised $\rho_t = 5\% - 0.12(50 - 45) = 4.4\%$

Adjustment (a) applies to the entire interaction curve, while adjustments (b) and (c) apply only above the balance point.

7.5.3. Biaxial Bending

Rectangular cross sections subjected to biaxial bending and axial compression must be checked to ensure adequate strength under this combination of loads. A common way of estimating the column strength under biaxial bending is the reciprocal load method suggested by Bresler[*]:

$$\frac{1}{P_r/A_g} = \frac{1}{P_{rx}/A_g} + \frac{1}{P_{ry}/A_g} - \frac{1}{P_{ro}/A_g}$$

where:
> P_{rx} = factored axial load resistance if the load were applied at the eccentricity e_x with $e_y = 0$.
> P_{ry} = factored axial load resistance if the load were applied at the eccentricity e_y with $e_x = 0$.
> P_{ro} = factored axial load resistance if e_x and e_y were 0.
>   (P_{ro} is 1.25 times $P_{r,\,max}$ shown as a horizontal line on the interaction curves.)

---

* Bresler, Boris, "Design Criteria for Reinforced Columns under Axial Load and Biaxial Bending", ACI Journal, Proceedings V. 57, No. 11, Nov. 1960, pp. 481-490.

Design for biaxial bending can be started by augmenting the larger bending moment by about 10 percent. The cross section dimensions and reinforcement can be selected and then checked using the above equation.

Circular columns can be designed directly by computing $M_f = (M_{fx}^2 + M_{fy}^2)^{\frac{1}{2}}$. A column is then chosen which has $M_r \geq M_f$ and $P_r \geq P_f$.

7.6 Bars Required to Obtain Desired Steel Ratios

Construction costs can be minimized if column forms are reused as often as possible without readjustment during the construction of successive storeys. The ground floor columns of multi-storey frames should therefore normally be constructed with high strength concrete and proportioned for relatively high steel ratios. The reinforcement ratio can usually be increased to approximately 4 percent before the splicing of longitudinal steel creates clearance problems. After a high steel ratio has been used at the ground floor columns, the reduction of axial load at each higher floor permits the use of successively lower concrete strengths and steel ratios without changes in the column forms.

Tables 7.4 to 7.6 are provided to assist in the choice of column reinforcement. All bar combinations shown may be spliced with welded splices, mechanical connections or bearing type slices. If $\rho_t > 4\%$, splice locations must be staggered by at least 750 mm (see Clause 12.17.2).

The bar combinations above the solid zigzag line may be spliced using either tangential splices or radial splices.

When a reinforcing ratio, ρ_t, less than 0.01 is used as permitted by Clause 10.10.5, the column resistance shall be based on the factored resistance calculated for a steel ratio of ρ_t multiplied by the ratio $0.5(1+\rho_t/0.01)$.

Blank values in the tables correspond to ρ_t less than 0.5% or greater than 8% or to combinations of bars which would violate the minimum or maximum bar spacing requirements.

7.6.1. Reinforcement for Rectangular Columns

Tables 7.4 and 7.5 give the reinforcing ratios $\rho_t = A_{st}/(bh)$ for a wide range of b and h values for rectangular columns with various bar sizes and placement patterns.

7.6.2. Reinforcement for Circular Columns

Table 7.6 gives reinforcing ratios when various numbers of reinforcing bars are used in circular columns.

Table 7.7 indicates the maximum pitch, s, for 10M or 15M spirals with 25, 30, 35, 40, 45, or 50 MPa concrete. The table includes spirals made with 400 MPa and 500 MPa reinforcement. Clause 6.6.5.2 of CSA A23.1 limits the nominal maximum aggregate size to $(s - d_b)/1.4$. Spirals must have a clear spacing greater than 1.4 times the maximum nominal aggregate size but not less than 30 mm.

7.7 Compression Development and Lap Lengths

Table 7.8 is a tabulation of compression development lengths for deformed bars with $f_y = 400$ MPa. Table 7.9 is a tabulation of lap lengths for 400 MPa reinforcement in normal density concrete. Requirements for development length and splices are provided in Clause 12 of A23.3 and see additional information in Chapter 3 of this Handbook.

7

Short Columns

7.8   Notation

c = cover to surface of reinforcement
k = factor used in the calculation of flexural stiffness, see Section 7.5.1
P_{rx} = factored axial load resistance if the load were applied at eccentricity e_x with $e_y = 0$
P_{ry} = factored axial load resistance if the load were applied at eccentricity e_y with $e_x = 0$
R = required fire-resistance rating in hours
γ = ratio of centre to centre distance between the outermost reinforcing bars to the overall depth
ε = strain in concrete

7.9   Examples

Estimate of Column Loads for Examples

Given:

350 × 350 mm edge columns spaced at 7.5 m with a 200 mm two-way flat slab spanning 6.8 m to the interior columns.
350 mm wide edge beam projecting 300 mm below the slab.
Wall load averaging 2.35 kN/m².
Floor-to-floor height of 3.6 m.
Roof dead load of (0.2 m)(24 kN/m³) plus 2.2 kPa for roofing, insulation and an allowance for mechanical equipment.
Floor dead load of (0.2 m)(24 kN/m³) plus 1.2 kPa for flooring and partitions.
Tributary area: (6.8/2 + 0.175)(7.5) = 27 m²

Dead Load (Roof)

Roofing + slab	(7.0 kPa)(27 m²)	= 189
Edge Beam + column (18 kN + 10 kN)	28 kN	= 28
		217 kN

Dead Load (typical floor)

Floor load	(6.0 kPa)(27 m²)	= 162
Edge Beam + column (18 kN + 10 kN)	28 kN	= 28
Wall (2.35 kN/m²)	(2.35 kPa)(3.6 m)(7.5 m)	= 64
		254 kN

Snow Load on Roof

3.0 kPa for chosen location ($C_b = 0.8$)	0.8(3 kPa)(27 m²)	= 65 kN

Live Load on Floor

Office loading (2.4 kPa)	(2.4 kPa)(27 m²)	= 65 kN

Reduce live floor load by the tributary area reduction factor = $0.3 + (9.8/B)^{1/2}$ where B is the tributary area supported by the member (m²).

Shear walls provide lateral support so the columns can be designed as non-sway frames and wind loads don't need to be considered.

The factored axial load, P_f, is the largest of the loads obtained from the factored load combinations specified in NBCC 2015. (See Table C-1 in CSA A23.3)

Moment

Assume edge moment from 2-way flat floor slab with edge beams but no interior beams using direct design method, Clause 13.9 of A23.3-14:

$$M_f = 0.26(7.5)\left(\frac{1.25(6.0)+1.5(2.4)}{8}\right)6.8^2 = 0.125 \text{ MN·m} \qquad \text{CSA A23.3-14 Table 13.1}$$

The moment for equal size columns will be split evenly between the upper and lower column, therefore $M_f = 0.063$ MN·m

Level Supported	Snow (kN)	Cumulative Dead (kN)	Cumulative Live (kN)	Cumulative Area (m²)	Area Reduction Factor	Reduced Live (kN)	1.4D (MN)	1.25D +1.5L +1.0S (MN)	1.25D +1.5S +1.0L (MN)	P_f (MN)
								Factored Loads		
Roof	65	217					0.30	0.34	0.37	0.37
8		471	65	27	0.902	59	0.66	0.74	0.74	0.74
7		725	130	54	0.726	94	1.02	1.11	1.10	1.11
6		979	195	81	0.648	126	1.37	1.48	1.45	1.48
5		1233	260	108	0.601	156	1.73	1.84	1.80	1.84
4		1487	325	135	0.569	185	2.08	2.20	2.14	2.20
3		1741	390	162	0.546	213	2.44	2.56	2.49	2.56
2		1995	455	189	0.528	240	2.79	2.92	2.83	2.92

Example 7.1 Tied Column Design

Given:
f'_c = 40 MPa, f_y = 400 MPa.
All steel lap spliced (Clause 10.9.2) and bar size ≤ 35M (See Clause 12.14.2.1).
Storey height 3600 mm
Slab thickness 200 mm.
Three hour fire rating with Type S concrete and columns exposed to weather.

From Table 7.3 it can be seen that columns with their smaller dimension equal to at least 320 mm do not need to be overdesigned. They may have any reinforcement ratio. A minimum cover of 50 mm to the main steel is required for a 3 h fire rating (Table 7.3).

Minimum of 40 mm cover is required to ties and main steel 25M and smaller (Table 7.3) for columns exposed to weather.

A cover of 40 mm to 10M ties will satisfy both fire and durability requirements.

ℓ_u = 3600 − 200 = 3400 mm   (Clause 10.14.3.1)

Condition is elastic + at both the top and bottom of the column (Fig. N10.15.2 of the Explanatory Notes).
$k \approx 0.9$ $k\ell_u \approx 0.9(3400) = 3060$ mm
$r = 0.3h = 0.3(350) = 105$ mm (Clause 10.14.2) $k\,\ell_u/r = 3060/105 = 29.1$

Column Supporting 2nd Floor

P_f = 2.92 MN M_f = 0.063 MN·m

From Table 7.1.4 a 350 × 350 mm column with $\rho_t \approx 2.9\%$ will be adequate if the effects of moment are negligible.

Try 350 × 350 mm column, A_g = 0.1225 m²
Equation 10-16 indicates the limiting $k\ell_u/r$ that can be used in non-sway frames without considering slenderness. The column being designed may be considered fixed at the far ends under the given loads (Clause 9.3.2). The column moment at the far end will thus have the opposite sign to the column moment at the floor where the moment is applied. M_1/M_2 will be approximately 0.5. The maximum value of $k\ell_u/r$ that permits a column to be designed as a short column is therefore:

$$\frac{k\ell_u}{r} \leq \frac{25 - 10(-0.5)}{\sqrt{2.92/(40\,(0.1225))}} = 38.9$$

Slenderness may therefore be neglected.

From Table 7.4, 8 – 25M bars giving ρ_t = 3.27
     will be needed to get ρ_t > 2.9%.
From Table 7.2 γ = 0.64 for 25M bars.
P_f/A_g = 2.92/0.1225 = 23.8 MPa
$M_f/(A_g h)$ = 0.063/0.35³ = 1.47 MPa
From Table 7.10.13, $\rho_t \geq 2.9\%$
8 – 25M bars giving ρ_t = 3.27%   O.K.
From Table 7.10.13 f_s/f_y < 0.0 ∴ compression splice
From Clause 12.16.1, Table 3.10
     a splice length of 730 mm is required.

Column supporting 3rd floor

P_f = 2.56 MN, M_f = 0.063 MN·m

Try 350 × 350 mm column with ρ_t > 1.7% (Table 7.1.4)

Concentrate reinforcement on interior and
     exterior faces, 6 – 25M bars, ρ_t = 2.45%
     (Table 7.5)
P_f/A_g = 2.56/0.1225 = 20.9 MPa
$M_f/A_g h$ = 1.47 MPa
For γ = 0.60, required ρ_t = 1.7% (Table 7.11.14)
Use 6 – 25M bars giving ρ_t = 2.45%

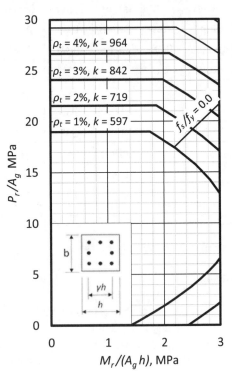

Table 7.10.13
Rectangular Columns with
Equal Numbers of Bars on all Faces
γ = 0.60, f'_c = 40 MPa

Capacity of Column with Minimum Reinforcing

Determine minimum and maximum axial loads P_r for a 350 × 350 mm column with M_f = 0.063 MN·m and ρ_t = 1%.

Use 4 – 20M bars ρ_t = 0.98% (Table 7.5), γ = 0.66 (Table 7.2)
For γ = 0.60, $M_f/(A_g h)$ = 1.47 MPa and ρ_t = 1%,
$P_r/A_g \leq 19.0$ MPa (Table 7.11.14)

$P_r \leq 19.0(0.1225) = 2.33$ MN

$M_r \leq 1.8 \times 0.35^3 = 0.077$ MN·m

A 350 × 350 mm column with 4 – 20M bars is adequate for supporting floors 4 through 8. (The concrete strength could be reduced at these upper levels)

Column Supporting Roof

The column supporting the roof is subjected to a low axial load and a moment roughly twice as high as for the floors. This is a situation where the lowest axial load is critical. (The critical section is now at the top of the column so the dead load should not include the weight of the column.)

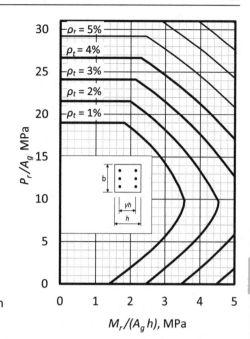

Table 7.11.14
Rectangular Columns
Bars on End Faces Only
$\gamma = 0.60$, $f'_c = 40$ MPa

$P_f = 0.36$ MN

$M_f = 0.26(7.5)\left(\dfrac{1.25(7.0) + 1.5(2.4)}{8}\right)6.8^2 = 0.139$ MN·m

Check Table 7.11.14 with 0.98% reinforcing as above.

$P_f / A_g = 0.36/0.1225 = 2.94$ MPa;

$M_f / h^3 = 0.139/0.35^3 = 3.24$ MPa

This point is below the balance point. The moment capacity reduces as the axial load is reduced. Four 20M bars are inadequate. This requires a ρ_t of approximately 2.1%. . Use a total of 6 – 25M bars with a ρ_t of 2.45% at the faces of the column supporting the roof.

Example 7.1(a) Tied Column with Uncharted Material Strengths

Assume $f'_c = 42$ MPa, $f_y = 500$ MPa, $P_f = 2.57$ MN, $M_f = 0.18$ MN·m

Try 350 × 350 mm column with $\gamma = 0.6$ with reinforcement on the column faces

    Use Table 7.11.14 for $f'_c = 40$ MPa, $f_y = 400$ MPa

    $P_f / A_g = 2.57/0.35^2 = 21$ MPa; $M_f / h^3 = 0.18/0.35^3 = 4.20$ MPa

    For $f'_c = 40$ MPa and $f_y = 400$ MPa the required $\rho_t = 4.15\%$

    Adjust values

Adjust for added concrete strength $\rho_t = 4.15 - 0.12(42 - 40) = 3.91\%$

At this location on the interaction curve with the reinforcement concentrated on the column faces the compression steel will yield. Therefore $\rho_t = 3.91(400/500) = 3\%$

Use 4 – 35M bars, $\rho_t = 3.27\%$ (Table 7.5); $\gamma = 0.61$ (Table 7.2)

Example 7.2(a) Circular Tied Column

Assume:

$P_f = 4.8$ MN	$M_f = 0.12$ MN·m	
$f'_c = 40$ MPa,	$f_y = 400$ MPa,	$\rho_t \approx 3.0\%$

From Table 7.1.4, A_g required $\approx$ 0.20 m²
$h \approx \left[(4/\pi) \, 0.20\right] \, \frac{1}{2} = 0.50$ m

Try h = 500 mm
  $P_f / h^2 = 4.8/0.5^2 = 19.2$ MPa;
  $M_f / h^3 = 0.12/0.5^3 = 0.96$ MPa
  $\rho_t = 3.1\%$ (Table 7.13.10)
  Use 9 – 30M, $\rho_t = 3.2\%$ (Table 7.6),
  $\gamma = 0.74$ (Table 7.2)

Determine maximum spacing using 10M ties
(Clause 7.12.5.2)
  $s \leq 16(30) = 480$ mm
  $s \leq 48(10) = 480$ mm $\leftarrow$ governs
  $s \leq 500$ mm
  Use 10M helical ties @ 480 mm pitch with 40 mm
  cover.
  Note: this is a tied column. The helical ties don't
  need to meet the steel volume requirements of
  Clause 10.9.4, or the spacing requirements of
  clause 7.12.4.

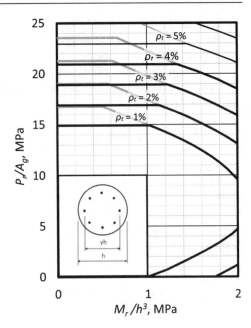

Table 7.13.10
Circular Tied or Spiral Columns
$\gamma = 0.70, f'_c = 40$ MPa

Example 7.2(b) Circular Spiral Column

Redesign the above circular column as a spiral column using upper gray lines in Table 7.13.10.
Need ρ_t of 2.8%. Use 8 – 30M with a ρ_t of 2.85% (Table 7.6)
Use 10M spiral (Clause 7.12.4), pitch = 60 mm (Clause 10.9.4, Table 7.7)

Example 7.3 Biaxial Bending of Rectangular Column

Assume the following loads:
P_f = 1.75 MN
M_{fy} = 0.10 MN·m and M_{fx} = 0.06 MN·m

Consider a 350 × 350 mm 40 MPa column with corner
reinforcing only (4 bars)   (Table 7.5)

$P_f / A_g = 1.75/0.1225 = 14.3$ MPa
$M_{fy} / (A_g h) = 0.10/0.35^3 = 2.33$ MPa
$M_{fx} / (A_g h) = 0.06/0.35^3 = 1.40$ MPa
Try 4 – 25M bars,
  $\rho_t = 1.63\%$ (Table 7.5)
  $\gamma = 0.63$ (Table 7.2)

Determine P_{ro}/A_g

$$\frac{P_{r}, \text{max}}{A_g} \approx 20.5 \text{ MPa} \qquad \text{(Table 7.11.14)}$$

$$P_{ro} / A_g = \frac{20.5}{0.8} \approx 25.6 \text{ MPa} \qquad \text{(Clause 10.10.4(b))}$$

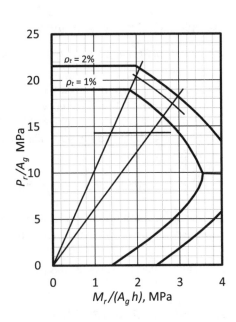

Table 7.11.14
Rectangular Columns
Bars on End Faces Only

P_{rx}/A_g and P_{ry}/A_g are obtained from Table 7.11.14.

Extend lines from the origin through points 1.4, 14.3 and 2.33, 14.3 until they cross the line for $\rho_t = 1.63\%$ at 20.5 MPa and 17.4 MPa.

These intersection points are P_{rx}/A_g and P_{ry}/A_g.

$$\frac{1}{P_r/A_g} = \frac{1}{P_{rx}/A_g} + \frac{1}{P_{ry}/A_g} - \frac{1}{P_{ro}/A_g}$$

$$\frac{1}{P_r/A_g} = \frac{1}{20.5} + \frac{1}{17.4} - \frac{1}{25.6}$$

$P_r/A_g = 14.9$ MPa $P_r/A_g > P_f/A_g$ therefore O.K.

(Capacity is actually slightly greater because $\gamma = 0.63$ which is greater than 0.60.)

Table 7.1.1 Axial Load Limit $P_{r,max}$ for Tied Columns, f'_c = 25 MPa

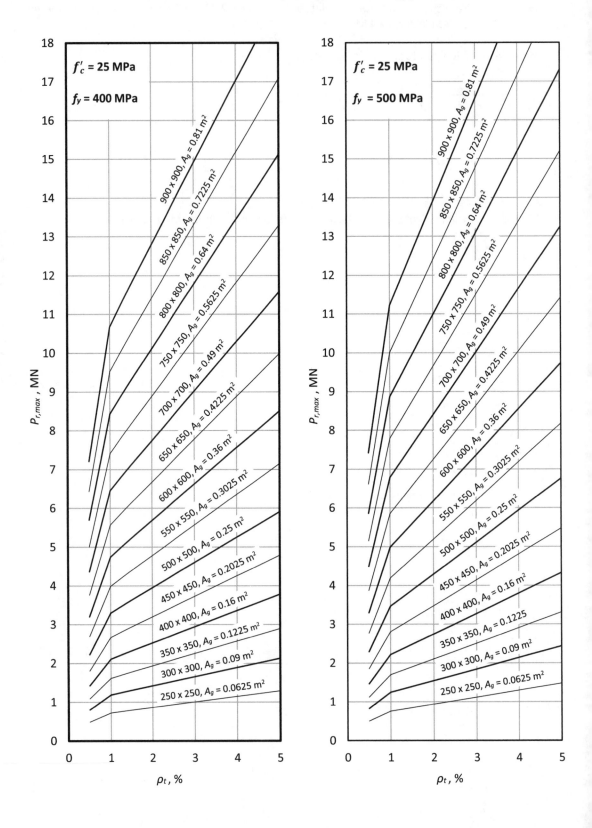

Table 7.1.2 Axial Load Limit $P_{r,max}$ for Tied Columns, f'_c = 30 MPa

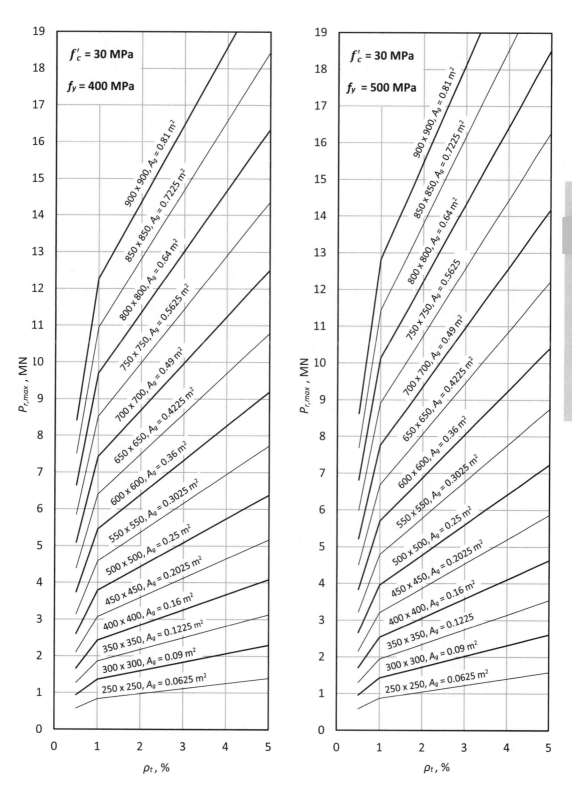

7

Short Columns

Table 7.1.3 Axial Load Limit $P_{r,max}$ for Tied Columns, f'_c = 35 MPa

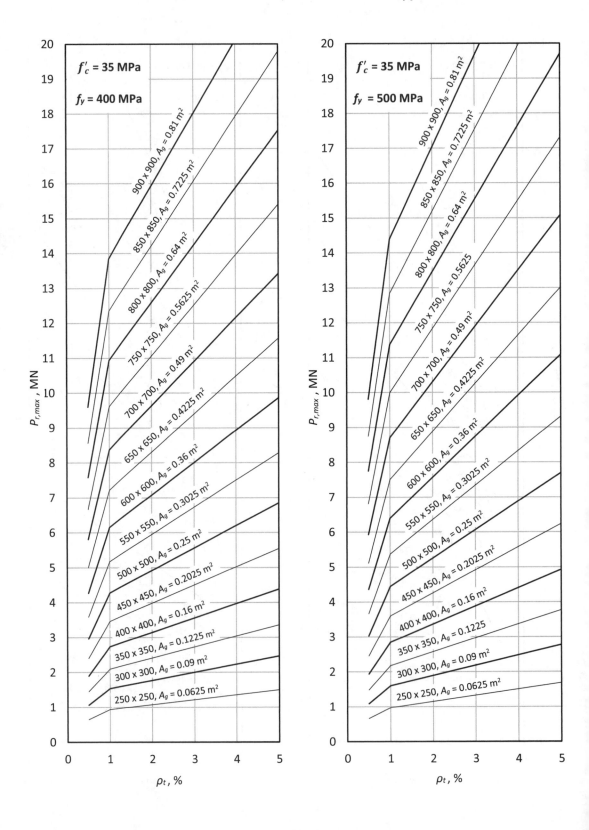

Table 7.1.4 Axial Load Limit $P_{r,max}$ for Tied Columns, f'_c = 40 MPa

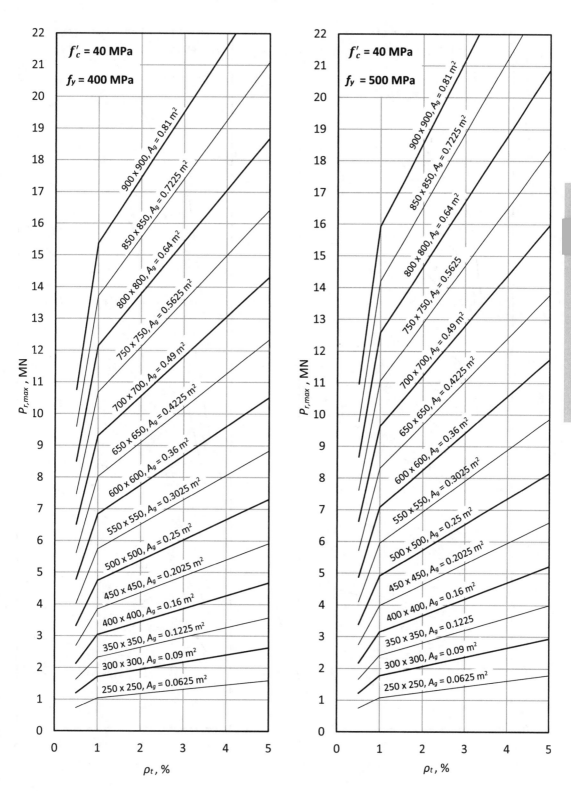

7

Short Columns

Table 7.1.5 Axial Load Limit $P_{r,max}$ for Tied Columns, f'_c = 45 MPa

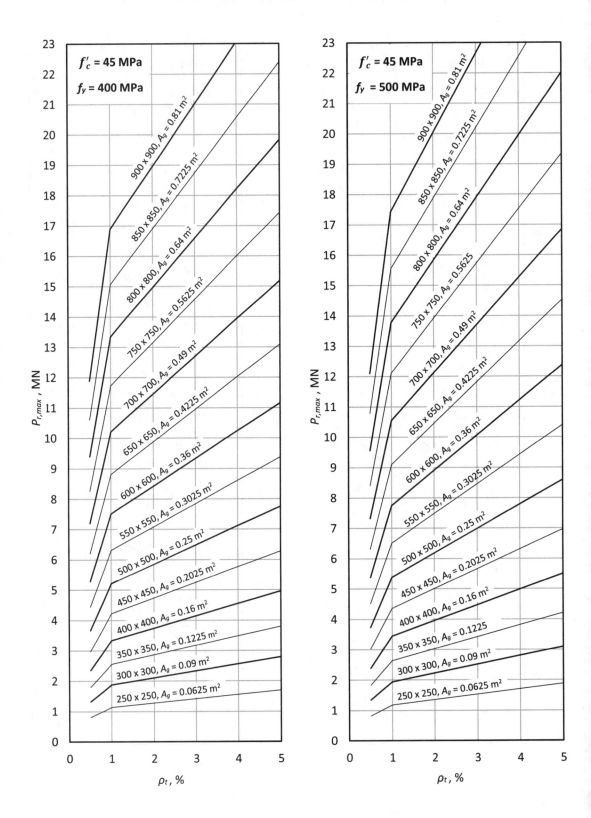

Table 7.2 Values of γ for Columns

h	Longitudinal Bar Size						
	15M	20M	25M	30M	35M	45M	55M
mm	40 mm cover to 10M ties						
250	0.54	0.52	0.50	0.48	0.46		
300	0.62	0.60	0.58	0.57	0.55	0.52	
350	0.67	0.66	0.64	0.63	0.61	0.59	
400	0.71	0.70	0.69	0.68	0.66	0.64	
450	0.74	0.73	0.72	0.71	0.70	0.68	
500	0.77	0.76	0.75	0.74	0.73	0.71	
550	0.79	0.78	0.77	0.76	0.75	0.74	
600	0.81	0.80	0.79	0.78	0.78	0.76	
650	0.82	0.82	0.81	0.80	0.79	0.78	
700	0.84	0.83	0.82	0.81	0.81	0.79	
750	0.85	0.84	0.83	0.83	0.82	0.81	
800	0.86	0.85	0.84	0.84	0.83	0.82	
850	0.86	0.86	0.85	0.85	0.84	0.83	
900	0.87	0.87	0.86	0.86	0.85	0.84	
950	0.88	0.87	0.87	0.86	0.86	0.85	
1000	0.89	0.88	0.88	0.87	0.87	0.86	
1100	0.90	0.89	0.89	0.88	0.88	0.87	
1200	0.90	0.90	0.90	0.89	0.89	0.88	
1300	0.91	0.91	0.90	0.90	0.90	0.89	
1400	0.92	0.91	0.91	0.91	0.90	0.90	
1500	0.92	0.92	0.92	0.91	0.91	0.90	
	50 mm cover to 10M ties						
300	0.55	0.53	0.52	0.50	0.48	0.45	
350	0.61	0.60	0.59	0.57	0.56	0.53	0.50
400	0.66	0.65	0.64	0.63	0.61	0.59	0.56
450	0.70	0.69	0.68	0.67	0.66	0.63	0.61
500	0.73	0.72	0.71	0.70	0.69	0.67	0.65
550	0.75	0.75	0.74	0.73	0.72	0.70	0.68
600	0.78	0.77	0.76	0.75	0.74	0.73	0.71
650	0.79	0.78	0.78	0.77	0.76	0.75	0.73
700	0.81	0.80	0.79	0.79	0.78	0.76	0.75
750	0.82	0.81	0.81	0.80	0.79	0.78	0.77
800	0.83	0.83	0.82	0.81	0.81	0.79	0.78
850	0.84	0.84	0.83	0.82	0.82	0.81	0.79
900	0.85	0.84	0.84	0.83	0.83	0.82	0.81
950	0.86	0.85	0.85	0.84	0.84	0.83	0.82
1000	0.87	0.86	0.86	0.85	0.85	0.84	0.83
1100	0.88	0.87	0.87	0.86	0.86	0.85	0.84
1200	0.89	0.88	0.88	0.88	0.87	0.86	0.85
1300	0.90	0.89	0.89	0.88	0.88	0.87	0.87
1400	0.90	0.90	0.90	0.89	0.89	0.88	0.88
1500	0.91	0.91	0.90	0.90	0.90	0.89	0.88
1600	0.92	0.91	0.91	0.91	0.90	0.90	0.89

Bars in shaded areas have covers adequate for Exposure Class **N** only.

Table 7.3 Minimum Column Dimensions and Cover for Rectangular or Circular* Columns

Condition	Concrete Type	Over-design Factor	Fire Rating, R Hours		
			1	2	3
$3.7 < k\ell_u \leq 7.3$ and $\rho_t \leq 3\%$	L or L40S	1	180	270	300
		1.25	165	248	300
		1.5	150	225	300
	S	1	240	300	320
		1.25	220	300	300
		1.5	200	300	300
	N	1	240	300	300
		1.25	220	300	300
		1.5	200	300	300
Other Conditions	L or L40S	1	150	225	300
		1.25	135	203	270
		1.5	125	187	249
	S	1	160	240	320
		1.25	144	216	288
		1.5	133	199	266
	N	1	140	220	300
		1.25	126	198	270
		1.5	116	183	249
Cover to Principal Reinforcement for fire			25	50	50

Cover Applicable to Both Principal and Confinement Reinforcement in Columns for Corrosion Protection based on CSA A23.1#

Not exposed to weather   (Class N)

   30M bars & smaller   30

   35M bars & larger $1.0\ d_b$

Exposed to weather

   25M bars & smaller   40

   30M bars & larger $1.5\ d_b$

Exposed to chlorides

   30M bars & smaller   60

   35M bars & larger $2.0\ d_b$

*Circular columns must have a diameter at least 1.2 times the size shown in the table.

The column sizes and cover requirements for fire are in accordance with Appendix D of supplement to National Building Code of Canada, 2015

#For parking structures, bridges, and offshore structures see CSA Standards S413, S6, and S474

7

Short Columns

Table 7.4 Reinforcement Ratios for Rectangular Columns Reinforced on Four Faces, 40 mm Cover to No. 10M Ties

Bars	Total	8	12	16	20	8	12	16	20	8	12	16	20	8	12	16	20	8	12	16	20
	Size	b or h	300				350				400				450				500		
b or h 300	15M	1.78	2.67			1.52	2.29			1.33	2.00			1.19	1.78			1.07	1.60		
	20M	2.67	4.00			2.29	3.43			2.00	3.00			1.78	2.67			1.60	2.40		
	25M	4.44				3.81				3.33				2.96				2.67			
	30M	6.22				5.33				4.67				4.15				3.73			
		350				400				450				500				550			
350	15M	1.31	1.96	2.61		1.14	1.71	2.29		1.02	1.52	2.03		0.91	1.37	1.83		0.83	1.25	1.66	
	20M	1.96	2.94	3.92		1.71	2.57	3.43		1.52	2.29	3.05		1.37	2.06	2.74		1.25	1.87	2.49	
	25M	3.27	4.90			2.86	4.29			2.54	3.81			2.29	3.43			2.08	3.12		
	30M	4.57				4.00				3.56				3.20				2.91			
	35M	6.53				5.71				5.08				4.57				4.16			
		400				450				500				550				600			
400	15M	1.00	1.50	2.00	2.50	0.89	1.33	1.78	2.22	0.80	1.20	1.60	2.00	0.73	1.09	1.45	1.82	0.67	1.00	1.33	1.67
	20M	1.50	2.25	3.00	3.75	1.33	2.00	2.67	3.33	1.20	1.80	2.40	3.00	1.09	1.64	2.18	2.73	1.00	1.50	2.00	2.50
	25M	2.50	3.75	5.00		2.22	3.33	4.44		2.00	3.00	4.00		1.82	2.73	3.64		1.67	2.50	3.33	
	30M	3.50	5.25			3.11	4.67			2.80	4.20			2.55	3.82			2.33	3.50		
	35M	5.00				4.44				4.00				3.64				3.33			
		450				500				550				600				650			
450	15M	0.79	1.19	1.58	1.98	0.71	1.07	1.42	1.78	0.65	0.97	1.29	1.62	0.59	0.89	1.19	1.48	0.55	0.82	1.09	1.37
	20M	1.19	1.78	2.37	2.96	1.07	1.60	2.13	2.67	0.97	1.45	1.94	2.42	0.89	1.33	1.78	2.22	0.82	1.23	1.64	2.05
	25M	1.98	2.96	3.95	4.94	1.78	2.67	3.56	4.44	1.62	2.42	3.23	4.04	1.48	2.22	2.96	3.70	1.37	2.05	2.74	3.42
	30M	2.77	4.15	5.53		2.49	3.73	4.98		2.26	3.39	4.53		2.07	3.11	4.15		1.91	2.87	3.83	
	35M	3.95	5.93			3.56	5.33			3.23	4.85			2.96	4.44			2.74	4.10		
		500				550				600				650				700			
500	20M	0.96	1.44	1.92	2.40	0.87	1.31	1.75	2.18	0.80	1.20	1.60	2.00	0.74	1.11	1.48	1.85	0.69	1.03	1.37	1.71
	25M	1.60	2.40	3.20	4.00	1.45	2.18	2.91	3.64	1.33	2.00	2.67	3.33	1.23	1.85	2.46	3.08	1.14	1.71	2.29	2.86
	30M	2.24	3.36	4.48	5.60	2.04	3.05	4.07	5.09	1.87	2.80	3.73	4.67	1.72	2.58	3.45	4.31	1.60	2.40	3.20	4.00
	35M	3.20	4.80	6.40		2.91	4.36	5.82		2.67	4.00	5.33		2.46	3.69	4.92		2.29	3.43	4.57	
		550				600				650				700				750			
550	20M	0.79	1.19	1.59	1.98	0.73	1.09	1.45	1.82	0.67	1.01	1.34	1.68	0.62	0.94	1.25	1.56	0.58	0.87	1.16	1.45
	25M	1.32	1.98	2.64	3.31	1.21	1.82	2.42	3.03	1.12	1.68	2.24	2.80	1.04	1.56	2.08	2.60	0.97	1.45	1.94	2.42
	30M	1.85	2.78	3.70	4.63	1.70	2.55	3.39	4.24	1.57	2.35	3.13	3.92	1.45	2.18	2.91	3.64	1.36	2.04	2.72	3.39
	35M	2.64	3.97	5.29		2.42	3.64	4.85		2.24	3.36	4.48		2.08	3.12	4.16		1.94	2.91	3.88	
		600				650				700				750				800			
600	20M	0.67	1.00	1.33	1.67	0.62	0.92	1.23	1.54	0.57	0.86	1.14	1.43	0.53	0.80	1.07	1.33	0.50	0.75	1.00	1.25
	25M	1.11	1.67	2.22	2.78	1.03	1.54	2.05	2.56	0.95	1.43	1.90	2.38	0.89	1.33	1.78	2.22	0.83	1.25	1.67	2.08
	30M	1.56	2.33	3.11	3.89	1.44	2.15	2.87	3.59	1.33	2.00	2.67	3.33	1.24	1.87	2.49	3.11	1.17	1.75	2.33	2.92
	35M	2.22	3.33	4.44	5.56	2.05	3.08	4.10	5.13	1.90	2.86	3.81	4.76	1.78	2.67	3.56	4.44	1.67	2.50	3.33	4.17
		650				700				750				800				850			
650	20M	0.57	0.85	1.14	1.42	0.53	0.79	1.05	1.32		0.74	0.98	1.23		0.69	0.92	1.15		0.65	0.87	1.09
	25M	0.95	1.42	1.89	2.37	0.88	1.32	1.76	2.20	0.82	1.23	1.64	2.05	0.77	1.15	1.54	1.92	0.72	1.09	1.45	1.81
	30M	1.33	1.99	2.65	3.31	1.23	1.85	2.46	3.08	1.15	1.72	2.30	2.87	1.08	1.62	2.15	2.69	1.01	1.52	2.03	2.53
	35M	1.89	2.84	3.79	4.73	1.76	2.64	3.52	4.40	1.64	2.46	3.28	4.10	1.54	2.31	3.08	3.85	1.45	2.17	2.90	3.62

All bar combinations shown may be spliced with bearing splices. Values above the line may be spliced with tangential or radial splices. If a reinforcement ratio greater than 4% is used, the splice location must be staggered by at least 750 mm.

Table 7.5 Reinforcement Ratios for Rectangular Columns Reinforced on two faces
40 mm Cover to 10M ties

Bars	Total	4	6	8	10	12	4	6	8	10	12	4	6	8	10	12	4	6	8	10	12
b=	Size	h= 250					300					350					400				
250	15M	1.28	1.92				1.07	1.60				0.91	1.37				0.80	1.20			
	20M	1.92	2.88				1.60	2.40				1.37	2.06				1.20	1.80			
300	15M	1.07	1.60	2.13			0.89	1.33	1.78			0.76	1.14	1.52			0.67	1.00	1.33		
	20M	1.60	2.40	3.20			1.33	2.00	2.67			1.14	1.71	2.29			1.00	1.50	2.00		
	25M	2.67	4.00				2.22	3.33				1.90	2.86				1.67	2.50			
	30M						3.11	4.67				2.67	4.00				2.33	3.50			
350	15M	0.91	1.37	1.83	2.29	2.74	0.76	1.14	1.52	1.90	2.29	0.65	0.98	1.31	1.63	1.96	0.57	0.86	1.14	1.43	1.71
	20M	1.37	2.06	2.74	3.43		1.14	1.71	2.29	2.86		0.98	1.47	1.96	2.45		0.86	1.29	1.71	2.14	
	25M	2.29	3.43	4.57			1.90	2.86	3.81			1.63	2.45	3.27			1.43	2.14	2.86		
	30M						2.67	4.00	5.33			2.29	3.43	4.57			2.00	3.00	4.00		
	35M						3.81	5.71				3.27	4.90				2.86	4.29			
400	15M	0.80	1.20	1.60	2.00	2.40	0.67	1.00	1.33	1.67	2.00	0.57	0.86	1.14	1.43	1.71	0.50	0.75	1.00	1.25	1.50
	20M	1.20	1.80	2.40	3.00	3.60	1.00	1.50	2.00	2.50	3.00	0.86	1.29	1.71	2.14	2.57	0.75	1.13	1.50	1.88	2.25
	25M	2.00	3.00	4.00	5.00		1.67	2.50	3.33	4.17		1.43	2.14	2.86	3.57		1.25	1.88	2.50	3.13	
	30M						2.33	3.50	4.67			2.00	3.00	4.00			1.75	2.63	3.50		
	35M						3.33	5.00	6.67			2.86	4.29	5.71			2.50	3.75	5.00		
450	15M	0.71	1.07	1.42	1.78	2.13	0.59	0.89	1.19	1.48	1.78	0.51	0.76	1.02	1.27	1.52		0.67	0.89	1.11	1.33
	20M	1.07	1.60	2.13	2.67	3.20	0.89	1.33	1.78	2.22	2.67	0.76	1.14	1.52	1.90	2.29	0.67	1.00	1.33	1.67	2.00
	25M	1.78	2.67	3.56	4.44	5.33	1.48	2.22	2.96	3.70	4.44	1.27	1.90	2.54	3.17	3.81	1.11	1.67	2.22	2.78	3.33
	30M						2.07	3.11	4.15	5.19		1.78	2.67	3.56	4.44		1.56	2.33	3.11	3.89	
	35M						2.96	4.44	5.93			2.54	3.81	5.08			2.22	3.33	4.44		
500	20M	0.96	1.44	1.92	2.40	2.88	0.80	1.20	1.60	2.00	2.40	0.69	1.03	1.37	1.71	2.06	0.60	0.90	1.20	1.50	1.80
	25M	1.60	2.40	3.20	4.00	4.80	1.33	2.00	2.67	3.33	4.00	1.14	1.71	2.29	2.86	3.43	1.00	1.50	2.00	2.50	3.00
	30M						1.87	2.80	3.73	4.67	5.60	1.60	2.40	3.20	4.00	4.80	1.40	2.10	2.80	3.50	4.20
	35M						2.67	4.00	5.33	6.67		2.29	3.43	4.57	5.71		2.00	3.00	4.00	5.00	
550	20M	0.87	1.31	1.75	2.18	2.62	0.73	1.09	1.45	1.82	2.18	0.62	0.94	1.25	1.56	1.87	0.55	0.82	1.09	1.36	1.64
	25M	1.45	2.18	2.91	3.64	4.36	1.21	1.82	2.42	3.03	3.64	1.04	1.56	2.08	2.60	3.12	0.91	1.36	1.82	2.27	2.73
	30M						1.70	2.55	3.39	4.24	5.09	1.45	2.18	2.91	3.64	4.36	1.27	1.91	2.55	3.18	3.82
	35M						2.42	3.64	4.85	6.06		2.08	3.12	4.16	5.19		1.82	2.73	3.64	4.55	
600	20M	0.80	1.20	1.60	2.00	2.40	0.67	1.00	1.33	1.67	2.00	0.57	0.86	1.14	1.43	1.71	0.50	0.75	1.00	1.25	1.50
	25M	1.33	2.00	2.67	3.33	4.00	1.11	1.67	2.22	2.78	3.33	0.95	1.43	1.90	2.38	2.86	0.83	1.25	1.67	2.08	2.50
	30M						1.56	2.33	3.11	3.89	4.67	1.33	2.00	2.67	3.33	4.00	1.17	1.75	2.33	2.92	3.50
	35M						2.22	3.33	4.44	5.56	6.67	1.90	2.86	3.81	4.76	5.71	1.67	2.50	3.33	4.17	5.00
650	20M		1.11	1.48	1.85	2.22		0.92	1.23	1.54	1.85		0.79	1.05	1.32	1.58		0.69	0.92	1.15	1.38
	25M	1.23	1.85	2.46	3.08	3.69	1.03	1.54	2.05	2.56	3.08	0.88	1.32	1.76	2.20	2.64	0.77	1.15	1.54	1.92	2.31
	30M						1.44	2.15	2.87	3.59	4.31	1.23	1.85	2.46	3.08	3.69	1.08	1.62	2.15	2.69	3.23
	35M						2.05	3.08	4.10	5.13	6.15	1.76	2.64	3.52	4.40	5.27	1.54	2.31	3.08	3.85	4.62
700	20M		1.03	1.37	1.71	2.06		0.86	1.14	1.43	1.71		0.73	0.98	1.22	1.47		0.64	0.86	1.07	1.29
	25M		1.71	2.29	2.86	3.43		1.43	1.90	2.38	2.86		1.22	1.63	2.04	2.45		1.07	1.43	1.79	2.14
	30M							2.00	2.67	3.33	4.00		1.71	2.29	2.86	3.43		1.50	2.00	2.50	3.00
	35M							2.86	3.81	4.76	5.71		2.45	3.27	4.08	4.90		2.14	2.86	3.57	4.29

All bar combinations shown may be spliced with bearing splices. Values above the line may be spliced with tangential or radial splices.

If a reinforcement ratio greater than 4% is used, the splice location must be staggered by at least 750 mm.

7

Short Columns

Table 7.6 Reinforcement Ratios (%) for Circular Columns, 40 mm Cover to 10M Ties or Spirals

Bars	Total Size	6	7	8	9	10	11	12	13	14	15	16	17	18	19	20	21	22	23
Column diameter 300	15M	1.70	1.98	2.26	2.55	2.83	3.11	3.40											
	20M	2.55	2.97	3.40	3.82	4.24	4.67												
	25M	4.24	4.95	5.66															
	30M	5.94	6.93																
350	15M	1.25	1.46	1.66	1.87	2.08	2.29	2.49	2.70	2.91	3.12	3.33							
	20M	1.87	2.18	2.49	2.81	3.12	3.43	3.74	4.05	4.37									
	25M	3.12	3.64	4.16	4.68	5.20	5.72												
	30M	4.37	5.09	5.82	6.55														
	35M	6.24	7.28																
400	15M	0.95	1.11	1.27	1.43	1.59	1.75	1.91	2.07	2.23	2.39	2.55	2.71	2.86	3.02				
	20M	1.43	1.67	1.91	2.15	2.39	2.63	2.86	3.10	3.34	3.58	3.82	4.06						
	25M	2.39	2.79	3.18	3.58	3.98	4.38	4.77	5.17	5.57									
	30M	3.34	3.90	4.46	5.01	5.57	6.13												
	35M	4.77	5.57	6.37	7.16														
450	15M	0.75	0.88	1.01	1.13	1.26	1.38	1.51	1.63	1.76	1.89	2.01	2.14	2.26	2.39	2.52	2.64	2.77	2.89
	20M	1.13	1.32	1.51	1.70	1.89	2.07	2.26	2.45	2.64	2.83	3.02	3.21	3.40	3.58	3.77			
	25M	1.89	2.20	2.52	2.83	3.14	3.46	3.77	4.09	4.40	4.72	5.03							
	30M	2.64	3.08	3.52	3.96	4.40	4.84	5.28	5.72										
	35M	3.77	4.40	5.03	5.66	6.29	6.92												
500	20M	0.92	1.07	1.22	1.38	1.53	1.68	1.83	1.99	2.14	2.29	2.44	2.60	2.75	2.90	3.06	3.21	3.36	3.51
	25M	1.53	1.78	2.04	2.29	2.55	2.80	3.06	3.31	3.57	3.82	4.07	4.33	4.58	4.84				
	30M	2.14	2.50	2.85	3.21	3.57	3.92	4.28	4.63	4.99	5.35	5.70							
	35M	3.06	3.57	4.07	4.58	5.09	5.60	6.11	6.62										
550	20M	0.76	0.88	1.01	1.14	1.26	1.39	1.52	1.64	1.77	1.89	2.02	2.15	2.27	2.40	2.53	2.65	2.78	2.90
	25M	1.26	1.47	1.68	1.89	2.10	2.31	2.53	2.74	2.95	3.16	3.37	3.58	3.79	4.00	4.21	4.42	4.63	
	30M	1.77	2.06	2.36	2.65	2.95	3.24	3.54	3.83	4.12	4.42	4.71	5.01	5.30					
	35M	2.53	2.95	3.37	3.79	4.21	4.63	5.05	5.47	5.89	6.31								
600	20M	0.64	0.74	0.85	0.95	1.06	1.17	1.27	1.38	1.49	1.59	1.70	1.80	1.91	2.02	2.12	2.23	2.33	2.44
	25M	1.06	1.24	1.41	1.59	1.77	1.95	2.12	2.30	2.48	2.65	2.83	3.01	3.18	3.36	3.54	3.71	3.89	4.07
	30M	1.49	1.73	1.98	2.23	2.48	2.72	2.97	3.22	3.47	3.71	3.96	4.21	4.46	4.70	4.95			
	35M	2.12	2.48	2.83	3.18	3.54	3.89	4.24	4.60	4.95	5.31	5.66	6.01						
650	20M	0.54	0.63	0.72	0.81	0.90	0.99	1.08	1.18	1.27	1.36	1.45	1.54	1.63	1.72	1.81	1.90	1.99	2.08
	25M	0.90	1.05	1.21	1.36	1.51	1.66	1.81	1.96	2.11	2.26	2.41	2.56	2.71	2.86	3.01	3.16	3.31	3.47
	30M	1.27	1.48	1.69	1.90	2.11	2.32	2.53	2.74	2.95	3.16	3.38	3.59	3.80	4.01	4.22	4.43	4.64	
	35M	1.81	2.11	2.41	2.71	3.01	3.31	3.62	3.92	4.22	4.52	4.82	5.12	5.42	5.73				
700	20M		0.55	0.62	0.70	0.78	0.86	0.94	1.01	1.09	1.17	1.25	1.33	1.40	1.48	1.56	1.64	1.71	1.79
	25M	0.78	0.91	1.04	1.17	1.30	1.43	1.56	1.69	1.82	1.95	2.08	2.21	2.34	2.47	2.60	2.73	2.86	2.99
	30M	1.09	1.27	1.46	1.64	1.82	2.00	2.18	2.36	2.55	2.73	2.91	3.09	3.27	3.46	3.64	3.82	4.00	4.18
	35M	1.56	1.82	2.08	2.34	2.60	2.86	3.12	3.38	3.64	3.90	4.16	4.42	4.68	4.94	5.20	5.46		

All bar combinations shown may be spliced with bearing splices; those above the line may be spliced with tangential or radial splices.

If a reinforcement ratio greater than 4% is used, the splice location must be staggered by at least 750 mm.

For a reinforcing ratio less than 1%, reduce the factored resistance as specified in Clause 10.10.5.

Table 7.7 Maximum Allowable Spiral Pitch for Circular Spiral Columns, 40 mm Cover to Spiral

	Column Diameter	Concrete Strength, MPa					
		25	30	35	40	45	50
10M Spiral **fy = 400 MPa**	300 mm	70	55	50	40		
	350	80	65	55	50	45	40
	400	85	70	60	55	45	40
	450	85	80	65	60	50	45
	500	85	85	70	60	55	50
	550	85	85	75	65	60	50
	600	85	85	80	70	60	55
	650	85	85	85	75	65	60
	700	85	85	85	75	70	60
	750	85	85	85	80	70	65
	800	85	85	85	80	75	65
	850	85	85	85	85	75	65
	900	85	85	85	85	75	70
	950	85	85	85	85	80	70
	1000 to 1100	85	85	85	85	80	75
	1150 to 1250	85	85	85	85	85	80
	1300 +	85	85	85	85	85	85
15M Spiral **fy = 400 MPa**	300 mm	90	90	90	85	75	70
	350	90	90	90	90	90	80
	400	90	90	90	90	90	85
	450 +	90	90	90	90	90	90
10M Spiral **fy = 500 MPa**	300 mm	85	70	60	55	45	40
	350	85	80	70	60	55	50
	400	85	85	75	65	60	55
	450	85	85	85	75	65	60
	500	85	85	85	80	70	60
	550	85	85	85	85	75	65
	600	85	85	85	85	80	70
	650	85	85	85	85	80	75
	700	85	85	85	85	85	75
	750	85	85	85	85	85	80
	800	85	85	85	85	85	80
	850 +	85	85	85	85	85	85
15M **fy = 500 MPa**	300 mm	90	90	90	90	90	85
	350 +	90	90	90	90	90	90

Table 7.8 Compression Development Lengths, ℓ_d, for Deformed Bars with f_y = 400 MPa[*]

f'_c MPa	Bar Size						
	15M	20M	25M	30M	35M	45M	55M
20	320	430	540	640	750	970	1180
25	290	380	480	580	670	860	1060
$f'_c \geq 30$	260	350	440	530	620	790	970

[*] For f_y of 500 MPa multiply lengths by 1.25
See Clause 12.4 for additional lengths for bundled bars
See Clause 12.3.3 for reduced lengths with additional transverse reinforcement

Table 7.9 Lap lengths for Uncoated[†] Reinforcement[‡] with f_y = 400 MPa in Normal Density Concrete[†]

Category	f'_c MPa	Bar size				
		15M	20M	25M	30M	35M
Compression only[*]		440	580	730	880	1020
Class A Tension Splice[#] $0<(f_s/f_y)_{max}<0.5$ With no more than 50% spliced within required lap length	20	480	640	1010	1210	1410
	25	430	580	900	1080	1260
	30	390	530	820	990	1150
	35	370	490	760	910	1060
	40	340	460	710	850	1000
	45	320	430	670	800	940
	50	310	410	640	760	890
Class B Tension Splice[#] for All other Situations	20	630	840	1310	1570	1830
	25	560	750	1170	1400	1640
	30	510	680	1070	1280	1500
	35	470	630	990	1190	1380
	40	440	590	920	1110	1290
	45	420	560	870	1050	1220
	50	400	530	830	990	1160

[*] For f_y of 500 MPa multiply compression lap by 1.46
[#] For f_y of 500 MPa multiply tension lap length by 1.25
[†] See Clause 12.2.4 for increased lengths for epoxy-coated reinforcement and for concrete with lower densities
[‡] See Clause 12.14.2.2 for increased lap lengths for bundled bars
See Clause 12.17.3 for reduced lap lengths with additional transverse reinforcement

7

Short Columns

8

By Murat Saatcioglu

Slender Columns

8.1   Introduction

The majority of reinforced concrete columns are subjected to primary stresses caused by flexure, axial force, and shear. Secondary stresses associated with deformations are usually very small in most columns used in practice. These columns are referred to as "short columns." Short columns are designed using the interaction diagrams presented in Chapter 7. The capacity of a short column is the same as the capacity of its section under primary stresses, irrespective of its length.

Long columns, columns with small cross-sectional dimensions, and columns with little end restraints may develop secondary stresses associated with column deformations, especially if they are not braced laterally. These columns are referred to as "slender columns". Fig. 8.1 illustrates secondary moments generated in a slender column by P-Δ effect. Consequently, slender columns resist lower axial loads than short columns with the same cross-section. This is illustrated in Fig. 8.1. Failure of a slender column is initiated either by the material failure of a section, or instability of the column as a member, depending on the level of slenderness. The latter is known as column buckling.

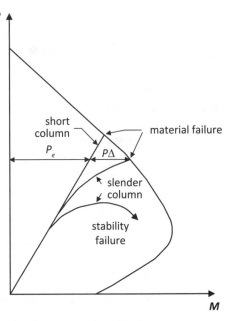

Fig. 8.1 Failure modes in short and slender columns

It is clear from the foregoing discussion that slender columns are subjected to higher bending moments than those computed by a first-order structural analysis that engineers conduct routinely for design purposes. This increase in moment due to secondary effects should be accounted for in design if the interaction diagrams given in Chapter 7 are to be used for design purposes.

8.2   Slenderness Ratio

The degree of slenderness in a column is expressed in terms of "slenderness ratio" as defined as $k\ell_u / r$; where, ℓ_u is unsupported column length; k is effective length factor reflecting the end restraint and lateral bracing conditions of a column; and r is the radius of gyration reflecting the size and shape of a column cross-section.

8.2.1.   Unsupported Length, ℓ_u

The unsupported length ℓ_u of a column is measured as the clear distance between the underside of the beam, slab, or column capital above, and the top of the beam or slab below. The unsupported length of a column may be different in two orthogonal directions depending on the supporting elements in respective directions. Table 8.1 provides examples of different support conditions and corresponding unsupported lengths (ℓ_u).

8.2.2.   Effective Length Factor, k

The effective length factor k reflects end restraint (support) and lateral bracing conditions of a column relative to a pin-ended and laterally braced "reference column." The reference column, shown in Fig. 8.2(a)(i), follows a half sine wave when it buckles, and is assigned a k factor of 1.0. Therefore, the effective length $k\ell_u$ for this column is equal to the unsupported column length ℓ_u. A column with fully restrained end conditions develops the deflected shape illustrated in Fig. 8.2(a)(ii). The portion of the column between the points of contraflexure follows a half sign wave, the same deflected shape as that of the reference column. This segment is equal to 50% of the unsupported column length ℓ_u. Therefore, the effective length factor k for this case is equal to 0.5. Effective length factors for columns with idealized supports can be determined from Fig. 8.2. It may be of interest to note that k varies between 0.5 and 1.0 for laterally braced columns, and 1.0 and ∞ for unbraced columns. A discussion of lateral bracing is provided in Sec. 8.3 to establish whether a given column can be considered to be as part of a sway or a non-sway frame.

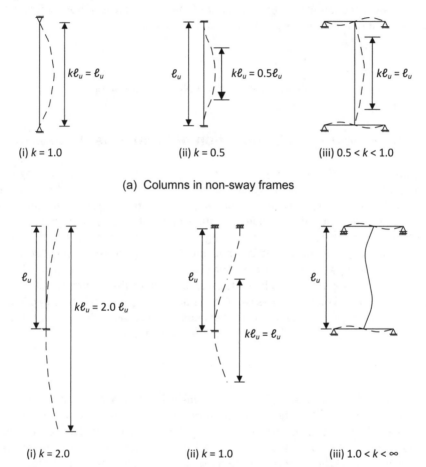

(i) k = 1.0   (ii) k = 0.5   (iii) 0.5 < k < 1.0

(a) Columns in non-sway frames

(i) k = 2.0   (ii) k = 1.0   (iii) 1.0 < k < ∞

(b) Columns in sway frames

Fig. 8.2 Effective length factor (k) for columns

Most columns have end restraints that are neither perfectly hinged nor fully fixed. The degree of end restraint depends on the stiffness of adjoining beams relative to that of the columns. Jackson and Moreland alignment charts, given in Fig. N10.15.1 of the Explanatory Notes can be used to determine the effective length factor k for different values of relative stiffnesses at column ends. The stiffness ratios ψ_A and ψ_B used in Fig. N10.15.1 of the Explanatory Notes should reflect concrete cracking and the effects of sustained loading, where:

$$\psi_i = \frac{\left(\sum EI/\ell_c\right)_{column}}{\left(\sum EI/\ell\right)_{beam}} \quad \text{at end } i \text{ of column}$$

Beams and slabs are flexure dominant members and may crack significantly more than columns under compression. The recommended reduced section properties are specified in CSA A23.3-14 Clause 10.14.1.2 and should be used in determining k. Alternatively, Fig. N10.15.2 of the Explanatory Notes may be used to establish conservative values of k for braced columns.

8.2.3. Radius of Gyration, r

The radius of gyration reflects the effect of cross-sectional size and shape on slenderness. For the same cross-sectional area, a section with higher moment of inertia produces a more stable column with a lower slenderness ratio. The radius of gyration r is defined below.

$$r = \sqrt{\frac{I}{A}} \tag{8.1}$$

It is permissible to use the approximations of $r = 0.3h$ for square and rectangular sections, and $r = 0.25d$ for circular sections.

8.3   Lateral Bracing and Designation of Frames as Non-sway

A frame is considered to be "non-sway" if it is sufficiently braced by lateral bracing elements like structural walls. Otherwise, it may be designated as a "sway" frame. Frames that provide resistance to lateral loads by columns only are considered to be sway frames. Structural walls that appear in the form of elevator shafts, stairwells, partial building enclosures or simply used as interior stiffening elements provide substantial drift control and lateral bracing. In most cases, even a few structural walls may be sufficient to brace a multi-storey multi-bay building. The designer can usually decide whether the frame is non-sway or sway by inspecting the floor plan. Frames with lateral bracing elements, where the total lateral stiffness of the bracing elements exceeds six times the summation of the stiffnesses of all the columns, may be classified as non-sway. A more accurate approach is specified in CSA A23.3-14 Clause 10.14.4 based on the stability index "Q" defined in Eq. 8.2. Accordingly, if $Q \leq 0.05$ the frame may be designated as non-sway and the columns of the frame as braced.

$$Q = \frac{\sum P_f \Delta_o}{V_f \ell_c} \tag{8.2}$$

where $\sum P_f$ is the total factored axial load acting on all the columns in a storey, V_f is the factored storey shear in the storey in question, Δ_o is the lateral storey drift (deflection of the top of the storey relative to the bottom of that storey) due to V_f. The storey drift Δ_0 should be computed using the reduced section properties specified in CSA A23.3-14 Clause 10.14.1.2 with β_d defined as the ratio of the maximum factored sustained shear within a storey to the maximum factored shear in that storey. If Q exceeds approximately 0.2, the structure may have to be stiffened laterally to provide overall structural stability.

8.4   Design of Slender Columns

Design of a slender column should be based on a second-order analysis which incorporates member curvature and lateral drift effects, as well as material non-linearity and sustained load effects. An alternative approach is specified in CSA A23.3-14 for columns with slenderness ratios not exceeding 100. This approach is commonly referred to as the "Moment Magnification Method," and is based on magnifying the end moments to account for secondary stresses. The application of this procedure is outlined in the following sections.

8.4.1.   Slender Columns in Non-Sway Frames

Slenderness effects may be ignored for columns in non-sway frames if the following inequality is satisfied:

$$\frac{k\ell_u}{r} \leq \frac{25 - 10(M_1/M_2)}{\sqrt{P_f/(f'A_g)}} \tag{8.3}$$

where M_1/M_2 is the ratio of smaller to larger end moments, with a negative value when the column is bent in double curvature, and a positive value when it is bent in single curvature. Fig. 8.3 illustrates columns in double and single curvatures. Columns are more stable and the secondary effects are smaller in double curvature than in single curvature. This is reflected in Eq. 8.3 through the sign of M_1/M_2 ratio. For negative values of this ratio, the limit of slenderness specified in Eq. 8.3 increases, allowing a wider range of columns to be treated as short columns. The M_1/M_2 ratio is not to be taken less than -0.5 when used in Eq. 8.3.

Slender columns in non-sway frames are designed for factored axial force P_f and amplified moment M_c. The amplified moment is obtained by magnifying the larger of the two end moments (M_2) to account for member curvature and resulting secondary moments between the supports, while the supports are braced against sidesway. If M_c computed for the curvature effect between the ends is smaller than the larger end moment M_2, the design is carried out for M_2.

$$M_c = \frac{C_m M_2}{1 - \dfrac{P_f}{\phi_m P_c}} \geq M_2 \tag{8.4}$$

where, $\phi_m = 0.75$, and the critical column load, P_c (Euler's buckling load) is:

$$P_c = \frac{\pi^2 EI}{(k\ell_u)^2} \tag{8.5}$$

8

Slender Columns

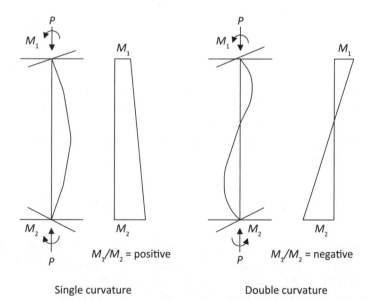

M$_1$/M$_2$ = positive   M$_1$/M$_2$ = negative

Single curvature   Double curvature

Fig. 8.3 Columns in single and double curvature

EI in Eq. 8.5 is computed either with due considerations given to the presence of reinforcement in the section, as specified in Eq. 8.6, or using Eq. 8.7.

$$EI = \frac{0.2E_c I_g + E_s I_{st}}{1 + \beta_d} \tag{8.6}$$

where β_d is the ratio of the maximum factored sustained axial load to the maximum factored axial load associated with the same load combination. The moment of inertia of reinforcement about the cross-sectional centroid (I_{st}) can be computed using Table 8.2.

$$EI = \frac{0.4E_c I_g}{1 + \beta_d} \tag{8.7}$$

Coefficient C_m is equal to 1.0 for members with transverse loads between the supports. For the more common case of columns without transverse loads between the supports;

$$C_m = 0.6 + 0.4\frac{M_1}{M_2} \geq 0.4 \tag{8.8}$$

Furthermore, the moment M_2 should not be less than the moment associated with minimum eccentricity about each axis separately, with $C_m = 1.0$.

$$M_2 \geq P_f (15 + 0.03h) \tag{8.9}$$

where h is the cross-sectional dimension in mm in the direction of eccentricity. Once the amplified moment M_c is obtained, the designer can use the appropriate interaction diagram from Chapter 7 to determine the required percentage of longitudinal reinforcement.

8.4.2. Slender Columns in Sway Frames

Columns in sway frames are designed for the factored axial load P_f and the combination of factored gravity load moments and magnified sway moments. This is specified below and illustrated in Fig. N10.16 of the Explanatory Notes.

$$M_1 = M_{1ns} + \delta_s M_{1s} \tag{8.10}$$

$$M_2 = M_{2ns} + \delta_s M_{2s} \tag{8.11}$$

where, M_{1ns} and M_{2ns} are end moments due to factored gravity loads; and M_{1s} and M_{2s} are sway moments normally caused by factored lateral loads. These moments can be obtained from a first-order elastic frame analysis. Magnified sway moments $\delta_s M_{1s}$ and $\delta_s M_{2s}$ are obtained either from a second order frame analysis, with member stiffnesses as specified in CSA A23.3-14 Clause 10.14.1.2, or by magnifying the end moments by sway magnification factor δ_s.

$$\delta_s = \frac{1}{1 - \dfrac{\sum P_f}{\phi_m \sum P_c}} \tag{8.12}$$

In a sway frame, all the columns of a given storey participate in sway mechanism and the stability of columns. Therefore, Eq. 8.12 includes $\sum P_f$ and $\sum P_c$ which give the summations of factored axial loads and critical axial loads for all the columns in the storey, respectively. The critical column axial load P_c can be computed using Eqs. 8.5 through 8.7 with the effective length factor k computed for unbraced columns (for sway frames), and β_d as the ratio of the maximum factored sustained shear within the storey to the maximum total factored shear in the storey.

Eq. 8.12 provides an average δ_s for all the columns in a storey. Therefore, it yields acceptable results if all the columns in a storey undergo the same storey drift. When significant torsion is anticipated under lateral loading, a second order analysis is recommended for finding the amplified sway moment, $\delta_s M_s$.

An alternative to Eq. 8.12 is given below for cases where Q computed from Eq. 8.2 is less than or equal to ⅓.

$$\delta_s = \frac{1}{1-1.2Q} \tag{8.13}$$

The sidesway magnification discussed above is intended to amplify the end moments associated with lateral drift. Although the amplified end moment is commonly the critical moment for most sway columns, additional magnification may become necessary due to the curvature of the column between the ends. This occurs if the slenderness ratio is high. The magnification of moment due to the curvature of column between the ends is similar to that discussed for braced columns in non-sway frames. This additional magnification is required for columns that satisfy the following condition:

$$\frac{\ell_u}{r} > \frac{35}{\sqrt{P_f/(f'_c A_g)}} \tag{8.14}$$

The larger of the end moments computed by Eqs. 8.10 and 8.11, for the load combination used in computing P_f, is then magnified using Eqs 8.4 through 8.8. As in the case of braced columns, the effective length factor k used in Eq. 8.5 is computed as if the column were a braced column, from Fig. N10.15.1(a) of the Explanatory Notes, and β_d used in Eq. 8.6 is taken as the ratio of the factored sustained axial load to the maximum factored axial load associated with the same load combination.

Sometimes columns of a sway frame may buckle under gravity loads alone, without the effects of lateral loading. In this case one of the gravity load combinations may govern the stability of the columns. The reduction of EI under sustained gravity loads may be another factor contributing to the stability of sway columns under gravity loads. Therefore, an additional provision is provided in CSA A23.3-14 Clause 10.16.5 to safeguard against column buckling in sway frames under gravity loads alone. Accordingly, the strength and stability of the structure is checked depending on the method of amplification used for sway moments. If a second order analysis was conducted to find $\delta_s M_{2s}$, two additional analyses are necessary using the reduced section properties specified in CSA A23.3-14 Clause 10.14.1.2 with β_d based on the sustained axial load. First, a second-order analysis is conducted under combined factored gravity loads and lateral loads equal to 0.5% of the gravity loads. Second, a first-order analysis is conducted under the same loading condition. The ratio of lateral drift obtained by the second-order analysis to that obtained by the first-order analysis is required to be limited to 2.5.

If the sway moment was amplified by computing the sway magnification factor (as opposed to conducting second order analysis), then δ_s computed by using factored gravity loads (ΣP_f and ΣP_c) is required to be positive and less than or equal to 2.5 to ensure the stability of the columns.

8.5 Design Examples

Example 8.1 – Design of an Interior Column Braced Against Sidesway

Consider a 10-storey office building, laterally braced against sidesway by an elevator shaft (Q is computed to be much less than 0.05). The building has an atrium opening at the second floor level with a two-storey high column in the middle of the opening to be designed. Design the column for the design forces given below, obtained from a first-order analysis. The framing beams are 400 mm wide and 500 mm deep with 7.0 m (center-to-centre) spans. The beam depth includes a slab thickness of 150 mm. The storey height is 4.3 m, and 40 MPa normal density concrete is used with mass density of 2400 kg/m³ in all beams and columns. f_y = 400 MPa. (See figure for Example 8.1). It is assumed that the bracing elements provide full resistance to lateral loads and the columns only resist gravity loads.

Unfactored loads	Dead load	Live load
Axial load (kN):	1776	1320
Top moment (kN·m):	-130	-79
Bottom moment (kN·m)	-15	-8

Note: Moments are positive if counterclockwise at column ends. The column is bent in double curvature.

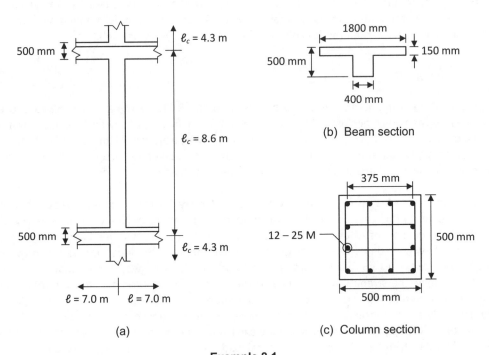

(a)

(b) Beam section

(c) Column section

Example 8.1

1. **Determine factored design forces:**

Note: M_1 is the lower, and M_2 is the higher end moment

i) $U = 1.4D$

$P_f = 1.4P_D = 1.4\,(1776) = 2486$ kN

$M_2 = 1.4M_{D2} = 1.4\,(130) = 182$ kN·m

$M_1 = 1.4M_{D1} = 1.4\,(15) = 21$ kN·m

ii) $U = 1.25D + 1.5\,L$

$P_f = 1.25P_D + 1.50P_L = 1.25\,(1776) + 1.50\,(1320) = 4200$ kN

$M_2 = 1.25M_{D2} + 1.50M_{L2} = 1.25\,(130) + 1.50\,(79) = 281$ kN·m

$M_1 = 1.25M_{D1} + 1.5M_{L1} = 1.25\,(15) + 1.50\,(8) = 31$ kN·m

Note: Load Combination (ii) governs the design

2. Estimate the column size:

For P_f = 4200 kN, select 500 × 500 mm from Table 7.1.4.

3. Calculate slenderness ratio $k\ell_u / r$:

The unsupported column length (Table 8.1); ℓ_u = 8600 – 250 – 250 = 8100 mm

The radius of gyration for a square column; r = 0.3 h = 0.3 (500) = 150 mm

Compute the effective length factor "k" from Fig. N10.15.1(a) in the Explanatory Notes.

First find stiffness ratios at the ends.

Beam moment of inertia (T-section): I_g = 7.7 × 10⁹ mm⁴

Column moment of inertia: $I_g = bh^3 / 12$ = (500) (500)³ / 12 = 5.2 × 10⁹ mm⁴

Using CSA A23.3-14 Eq. 8.1, E_c = 29 602 MPa

From CSA A23.3-14 Clause 10.14.1.2, $(EI)_{beam} = 0.35 E_c I_g$ = 0.35 (29 602) (7.7 × 10⁹) = 8.0 × 10¹³ N·mm²

From CSA A23.3-14 Clause 10.14.1.2, $(EI)_{col} = 0.7 E_c I_g$ = 0.7 (29 602) (5.2 × 10⁹) = 1.1 × 10¹⁴ N·mm²

$(EI / \ell)_{beam}$ = (8.0 × 10¹³) / (7000) = 1.1 × 10¹⁰ for both left and right beams

$(EI / \ell_c)_{col}$ = (1.1 × 10¹⁴) / (8600) = 1.3 × 10¹⁰ for the atrium column to be designed

$(EI / \ell_c)_{col}$ = (1.1 × 10¹⁴) / (4300) = 2.6 × 10¹⁰ for columns above and below

$\psi = (\Sigma EI / \ell_c)_{col} / (\Sigma EI / \ell)_{beam} = [(EI / \ell_c)_{col, above} + (EI / \ell_c)_{col, below}] / [(EI / \ell)_{beam, left} + (EI / \ell)_{beam, right}]$

ψ_A = (2.6 × 10¹⁰ + 1.3 × 10¹⁰) / (1.1 × 10¹⁰ + 1.1 × 10¹⁰) = 1.8

for $\psi_B = \psi_A$ = 1.8; select k = 0.84 from Fig. N10.15.1(a) of the Explanatory Notes

(Note that Fig. N10.15.2 of the Explanatory Notes gives a conservative value of k = 0.90)

$k\ell_u / r$ = 0.84 (8100) / 150 = 45.4

4. Check if slenderness can be neglected:

From Eq. 8.3; if $k\ell_u / r \leq [25 - 10(M_1 / M_2)]/\sqrt{P_f /(f'_c A_g)}$ then slenderness can be neglected.

Note: M_1 / M_2 can not be less than -0.5. In this problem M_1 / M_2 = -31 / 281 = -0.11

$[25 - 10(M_1 / M_2)]/\sqrt{P_f /(f'_c A_g)} = [25 - 10(-0.11)]/\sqrt{4200 \times 10^3 /(40 \times 500 \times 500)} = 40.3$

$k\ell_u / r$ = 45.4 > 40.3   Therefore, consider slenderness.

5. Compute critical load, P_c from Eq. 8.5 and associated EI from Eq. 8.6 or 8.7:

EI from Eq. 8.6 for assumed reinforcement ratio of ρ_t = 0.025, equally distributed on all faces with γ = 0.75; E_c = 29 602 MPa; E_s = 200 000 MPa; I_g = 5.2 × 10⁹ mm⁴

$I_{st} = 0.18 \rho_t bh^3 \gamma^2$ (from Table 8.2);

$I_{st} = 0.18 \, (0.025) \, (500) \, (500)^3 \, (0.75)^2 \ = 1.6 \times 10^8 \text{ mm}^4$

$1.25P_D = 1.25 \, (1776) = 2220 \text{ kN}$

$\beta_d = 2220 \, / \, 4200 = 0.53 \qquad\qquad EI = (0.2E_c \, I_g + E_s \, I_{st}) \, / \, (1 + \beta_d)$

$EI = [(0.2 \times 29\,602 \times 5.2 \times 10^9) + (200\,000 \times 1.6 \times 10^8)] \, / \, (1 + 0.53)$

$EI = 4.1 \times 10^{13} \text{ N·mm}^2$

Alternatively, EI from Eq 8.7 for $\beta_d = \ 0.53$;

$EI = 0.4E_c I_g \, / \, (1+ \beta_d) = [(0.4 \times 29\,602 \times 5.2 \times 10^9)/(1 + 0.53)] = 4.0 \times 10^{13} \text{ N·mm}^2$

Larger of the two values for EI is suggested by Sec. N10.15.3 of the Explanatory Notes as both EI equations are lower bounds.

From Eq. 8.5; $P_c = \pi^2 EI \, / \, (k\ell_u)^2$

$P_c = \pi^2 \times 4.1 \times 10^{13} \, / \, (0.84 \times 8100)^2 = 8741 \times 10^3 \text{ N}$

6.   Compute C_m from Eq. 8.8 :

$C_m = 0.6 + 0.4M_1 \, / \, M_2 \geq 0.4 \qquad C_m = 0.6 + 0.4 \, (\text{-}0.11) = 0.56$

7.   Compute magnified moment M_c from Eq. 8.4:

$M_c = C_m M_2 \, / \, [1 - P_f \, / \, (\phi_m \, P_c)] = 0.56 \, (281) \, / \, [1 - 4200 \, / \, (0.75 \times 8741)]$

$M_c = 1.56 \times 281 = 438 \text{ kN·m} \qquad \text{(magnified moment)}$

Check against minimum design moment as per Eq. 8.9;

$M_2 \geq P_f \, (15 + 0.03h) = 4200 \times 10^3 \, (15 + 0.03 \times 500) = 126 \times 10^6 \text{ N·mm}$ \hfill OK

8.   Select reinforcement ratio and design the column section:

Select the appropriate interaction diagram from Chapter 7. For $f_c' = 40$ MPa; $f_y = 400$ MPa, $\gamma = 0.75$ (assumed in step 5) and equal reinforcement on all four sides, select Tables 7.10.14 and 7.10.15, and interpolate between the two:

$P_f \, / \, A_g = 4200 \times 10^3 \, / \, (500)^2 = 16.8 \text{ MPa}$

$M_c \, / \, A_g \, h = 438 \times 10^6 \, / \, [(500)^2 \, (500)] = 3.5 \text{ MPa}$

From Table 7.10.14 for $\gamma = 0.7$; \qquad $\rho_t = 0.025$

From Table 7.10.15 for $\gamma = 0.8$; \qquad $\rho_t = 0.022$

Interpolating for $\gamma = 0.75$; \qquad $\rho_t = 0.0235$

$A_{st} = \rho_t \, A_g = 0.0235 \, (500)^2 = 5875 \text{ mm}^2 \qquad$ try 25 M bars ($A_{st} = 500 \text{ mm}^2$);

$5875 \, / \, 500 = 11.75$

Use 12 – 25 M longitudinal reinforcement, equally distributed on all sides.

Note: For further details of cross-sectional design refer to Chapter 7.

Example 8.2 – Design of an Exterior Column in a Sway Frame

A typical floor plan and a section through a four-storey apartment building is shown in the figure (See figure for Example 8.2). Design column 3-A at the ground level for combined gravity and east-west wind loading with $f_c' = 40$ MPa (normal density concrete) and $f_y = 400$ MPa.

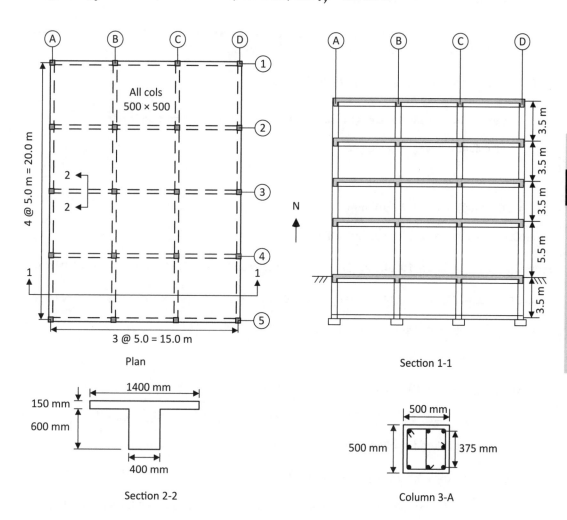

Plan

Section 1-1

Section 2-2

Column 3-A

Example 8.2

1.   Consider the applicable load combinations:

The structure is not braced against sidesway. Therefore, the column will be designed considering the loads that cause sidesway. Note that sidesway in this structure is caused by wind loading. No significant sidesway is anticipated due to the gravity loads since the structure is symmetric.

a) The load combinations that include wind loading;

Load Combination I: $U = 1.25D + 1.5L + 0.4W$

Load Combination II: $U = 1.25D + 0.5L + 1.4W$

b) The Load combinations for gravity loading;

Load Combination III: $U = 1.4D$

Load Combination IV: $U = 1.25D + 1.5L$

Note: The column may be critical under gravity loading only, even if it is part of a sway frame (CSA A23.3-14 Clause 10.16.5).

Conduct frame analyses to determine first-order design forces. Use the reduced section properties specified in CSA A23.3-14 Clause 10.14.1.2 for the analyses.

Try the preliminary column section given in the figure.

2.   Determine the effective length factor k for all columns at the ground level:

Note: All columns have the same geometry.

$I_{beam} = 2.3 \times 10^{10}$ mm⁴ (for T-section)

$I_{col} = (500)(500)^3 / 12 = 5.2 \times 10^9$ mm⁴

Using CSA A23.3-14 Eq. 8.1; $E_c = 29\ 602$ MPa

From CSA A23.3-14 Clause 10.14.1.2, $(EI)_{beam} = 0.35E_c I_g = 0.35\ (29\ 602)\ (2.3 \times 10^{10}) = 2.4 \times 10^{14}$ N·mm²

From CSA A23.3-14 Clause 10.14.1.2, $(EI)_{col} = 0.7E_c I_g = 0.7\ (29\ 602)\ (5.2 \times 10^9) = 1.1 \times 10^{14}$ N·mm²

$(EI / \ell)_{beam} = 2.4 \times 10^{14} / 5000 = 4.8 \times 10^{10}$ N·mm

$(EI / \ell_c)_{col,\ typical} = 1.1 \times 10^{14} / 3500 = 3.1 \times 10^{10}$ N·mm

$(EI / \ell_c)_{col,\ atrium} = 1.1 \times 10^{14} / 5500 = 2.0 \times 10^{10}$ N·mm

$\psi = (\Sigma EI / \ell_c)_{col} / (\Sigma EI / \ell)_{beam} = [(EI / \ell_c)_{col,\ above} + (EI / \ell_c)_{col,\ below}] / [(EI / \ell)_{beam,\ left} + (EI / \ell)_{beam,\ right}]$

i)   For exterior columns (columns on lines A and D):

$\psi_A = (3.1 \times 10^{10} + 2.0 \times 10^{10}) / 4.8 \times 10^{10} = 1.06$

$\psi_B = \psi_A = 1.06$; from Fig. N10.15.1(b) of the Explanatory Notes; $k = 1.35$ (for unbraced frame)

$k = 0.78$ from Fig. N10.15.1(a) of the Explanatory Notes for a braced column. This value is computed for further magnification of moments, if necessary, for column 3-A as per CSA A23.3-14 Clause 10.16.4.

ii)   For interior columns (columns on lines B and C):

$\psi_A = (3.1 \times 10^{10} + 2.0 \times 10^{10}) / (4.8 \times 10^{10} + 4.8 \times 10^{10}) = 0.53$

$\psi_B = \psi_A = 0.53$; from Fig. N10.15.1(b) of the Explanatory Notes, $k = 1.15$ (for unbraced frame)

3.   Compute critical load P_c from Eq. 8.5, and associated EI from Eq. 8.6 or 8.7:

Use Eq. 8.7 for simplicity, with $\beta_d = 0.0$ for sidesway effects (since the wind induced shear is not a sustained load) and an assumed value of $\beta_d = 0.6$ for braced frame effects.

From Eq. 8.7:

For sway frames: $EI = 0.4E_c I_g = 0.4 (29\ 602) (5.2 \times 10^9) = 6.2 \times 10^{13}$ N·mm²

For braced frames: $EI = 0.4E_c I_g / (1+ \beta_d) = 0.25 (29\ 602) (5.2 \times 10^9) = 3.8 \times 10^{13}$ N·mm²

$\ell_u = 5500 - 750 = 4750$ mm

i)   For exterior columns (columns on lines A and D):

$P_c = \pi^2 EI / (k\ell_u)^2 = \pi^2 (6.2 \times 10^{13}) / (1.35 \times 4750)^2 = 14\ 881 \times 10^3$ N   for a sway frame.

$P_c = \pi^2 EI / (k\ell_u)^2 = \pi^2 (3.8 \times 10^{13}) / (0.78 \times 4750)^2 = 27\ 322 \times 10^3$ N   for braced columns.

P_c for braced columns may be needed if further magnification of moments is required as per Clause 10.16.4 of CSA A23.3-14 for column 3-A.

ii)   For interior columns (columns on lines B and C):

$P_c = \pi^2 EI / (k\ell_u)^2 = \pi^2 (6.2 \times 10^{13}) / (1.15 \times 4750)^2 = 20\ 507 \times 10^3$ N   for a sway frame.

4.   Compute magnified sway moment $\delta_s M_s$:

i)   Load Combination I: $U = 1.25D + 1.5L + 0.4W$

Consider factored axial loads and bending moments obtained from first-order frame analysis conducted using the reduced section properties specified in CSA A23.3-14 Clause 10.14.1.2.

Load	1.25D + 1.5L	0.4W
P_f (kN) – Corner Column	2359	±18
P_f (kN) – Edge Column	3375	±26
P_f (kN) – Interior Column	5287	±6
$(M_f)_{top}$ kN·m – Column 3-A	-226	±43
$(M_f)_{bot}$ kN·m – Column 3-A	-239	±63

Note: Counterclockwise moment at column end is positive.

a) Sway magnification factor δ_s from Eq. 8.12.

$\Sigma P_f = 4 (2359 + 18) + 10 (3375 + 26) + 6 (5287 + 6) = 75\ 276$ kN

From Step 3; $\Sigma P_c = 10 (14\ 881) + 10 (20\ 507) = 353\ 880$ kN

$\delta_s = 1 / [1 - \Sigma P_f / (\phi_m \Sigma P_c)] = 1 / [1 - 75\ 276 / (0.75 \times 353\ 880)] = 1.40$

$\delta_s M_{1s} = 1.40 \times 43 = 60$ kN·m

$\delta_s M_{2s} = 1.40 \times 63 = 88$ kN·m

b) Compute design moments M_1 and M_2 from Eqs. 8.10 and 8.11, and Table 8.7.

$M_1 = M_{1ns} + \delta_s M_{1s} = 226 + 60 = 286$ kN·m

$M_2 = M_{2ns} + \delta_s M_{2s} = 239 + 88 = 327$ kN·m

8

Slender Columns

c) Check if further magnification of moments is required due to the curvature of the columns between the ends using Eq. 8.14.

$$\frac{\ell_u}{r} > \frac{35}{\sqrt{P_f / (f'_c A_g)}}$$

$P_f = 3375 + 26 = 3401$ kN

$\ell_u / r = 4750/(0.3 \times 500) = 31.7 < 35/\sqrt{3401 \times 10^3 /(40 \times (500)^2)} = 60.0$

Therefore, no further magnification is required.

ii) Load Combination II: $U = 1.25D + 0.5L + 1.4W$

Consider factored axial loads and bending moments obtained from first-order frame analysis conducted using the reduced section properties specified in CSA A23.3-14 Clause 10.14.1.2.

Load	1.25D + 0.5L	1.4W
P_f (kN) – Corner Column	1850	±64
P_f (kN) – Edge Column	2646	±91
P_f (kN) – Interior Column	4143	±21
$(M_f)_{top}$ kN·m – Column 3-A	-177	±152
$(M_f)_{bot}$ kN·m – Column 3-A	-188	±220

Note: Counterclockwise moment at column end is positive.

a) Sway magnification factor δ_s and magnified sway moments $\delta_s M_{1s}$ and $\delta_s M_{2s}$

$\sum P_f = 4 (1850 + 64) + 10 (2646 + 91) + 6 (4143 + 21) = 60\,010$ kN

From Step 3; $\sum P_c = 10 (14\,881) + 10 (20\,507) = 353\,880$ kN

$\delta_s = 1 / [1 - \sum P_f / (\phi_m \sum P_c)] = 1 / [1 - 60\,010 / (0.75 \times 353\,880)] = 1.29$

$\delta_s M_{1s} = 1.29 \times 152 = 196$ kN·m

$\delta_s M_{2s} = 1.29 \times 220 = 284$ kN·m

b) Compute design moments M_1 and M_2 from Eqs. 8.10 and 8.11, and Fig. N10.16 of the Explanatory Notes.

$M_1 = M_{1ns} + \delta_s M_{1s} = 177 + 196 = 373$ kN·m

$M_2 = M_{2ns} + \delta_s M_{2s} = 188 + 284 = 472$ kN·m

c) Check if further magnification of moments is required due to the curvature of the columns between the ends using Eq. 8.14.

$$\frac{\ell_u}{r} > \frac{35}{\sqrt{P_f / (f'_c A_g)}}$$

$P_f = 2646 + 91 = 2737$ kN

$$\ell_u / r = 4750/(0.3 \times 500) = 31.7 < 35/\sqrt{2737 \times 10^3 /(40 \times (500)^2)} = 66.9$$

Therefore, no further magnification is required.

5.   Check the stability of column under gravity loads only
(Load Combinations III and IV) as per CSA A23.3-14, Clause 10.16.5:

Consider factored axial loads and bending moments obtained from a first-order frame analysis, conducted using the reduced section properties specified in CSA A23.3-14 Clause 10.14.1.2.

i)   Load Combination III: $U = 1.4D$

Load	1.4D
P_f (kN) – Corner Column	1788
P_f (kN) – Edge Column	2555
P_f (kN) – Interior Column	4000
$(M_f)_{top}$ kN·m – Column 3-A	-171
$(M_f)_{bot}$ kN·m – Column 3-A	-183

Note: Counterclockwise moment at column end is positive.

Compute the sway magnification factor δ_s

ΣP_f = 4 (1788) + 10 (2555) + 6 (4000) = 56 702 kN

From Step 3; ΣP_c = 10 (14 881) + 10 (20 507) = 353 880 kN

$\delta_s = 1 / [1 - \Sigma P_f / (\phi_m \Sigma P_c)] = 1 / [1 - 56 702 / (0.75 \times 353 880)] = 1.27$

$\delta_s = 1.27 < 2.5$ OK

ii)   Load Combination IV: $U = 1.25D + 1.5L$

Load	1.25D + 1.5L
P_f (kN) – Corner Column	2359
P_f (kN) – Edge Column	3375
P_f (kN) – Interior Column	5287
$(M_f)_{top}$ kN·m – Column 3-A	-226
$(M_f)_{bot}$ kN·m – Column 3-A	-239

Note: Counterclockwise moment at column end is positive.

Compute the sway magnification factor δ_s

ΣP_f = 4 (2359) + 10 (3375) + 6 (5287) = 74 908 kN

8

Slender Columns

From Step 3;

$$\Sigma P_c = 10\,(14\,881) + 10\,(20\,507) = 353\,880 \text{ kN}$$

$$\delta_s = 1 / [1 - \Sigma P_f / (\phi_m \Sigma P_c)] = 1 / [1 - 74\,908 / (0.75 \times 353\,880)] = 1.39$$

$$\delta_s = 1.39 < 2.5 \qquad\qquad\qquad\qquad\qquad\qquad\qquad\qquad\qquad\qquad \text{OK}$$

6.   Design the column for the governing load combination:

Summary of Design Loads:

Load combinations	P_f (kN)	M_f (kN·m)
I − $U = 1.25D + 1.5L + 0.4W$	3401	327
II − $U = 1.25D + 0.5L + 1.4W$	2737	472
III − $U = 1.4D$	2555	183
IV − $U = 1.25D + 1.5L$	3375	239

Select the interaction diagrams given in Table 7.10.14 and 7.10.15 from Chapter 7 and interpolate for $\gamma = 375 / 500 = 0.75$.

For Load Combination II;

$$P_f / A_g = 2737 \times 10^3 / (500)^2 = 11.0 \text{ MPa}$$

$$M_f / A_g\, h = 472 \times 10^6 / (500)^3 = 3.8 \text{ MPa}$$

From Table 7.10.14 for $\gamma = 0.70$; select $\rho_t = 0.017$.

From Table 7.10.15 for $\gamma = 0.80$; select $\rho_t = 0.015$.

Interpolate for $\gamma = 0.75$; $\rho_t = 0.016$.

$A_{st} = 0.016\,(500)^2 = 4000 \text{ mm}^2$. Try 25 M bars ($A_{st} = 500 \text{ mm}^2$);

4000 / 500 = 8.0; Use 8 – 25 M bars equally distributed on all four faces.

Check the capacity for Load Combination I;

$$P_f / A_g = 3401 \times 10^3 / (500)^2 = 13.6 \text{ MPa}$$

$$M_f / A_g\, h = 327 \times 10^6 / (500)^3 = 2.6 \text{ MPa}$$

The point lies inside both interaction diagrams.   OK

Note: For further details of cross-sectional design refer to Chapter 7.

8.6   Design Aids

Table 8.1 provides examples of different support conditions and corresponding unsupported lengths (ℓ_u). Table 8.2 provides the moment of inertia of reinforcement about the cross-sectional centroid (I_{st}) for various column configurations.

Table 8.1 Unsupported column length, $\boldsymbol{\ell_u}$

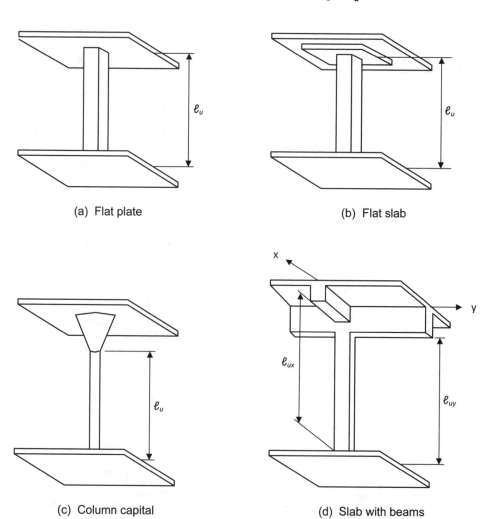

(a) Flat plate

(b) Flat slab

(c) Column capital

(d) Slab with beams

Table 8.2 Moment of inertia of reinforcement about sectional centroid

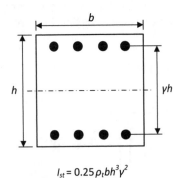

$$I_{st} = 0.25\,\rho_t bh^3\gamma^2$$

(a) Bars in two end faces

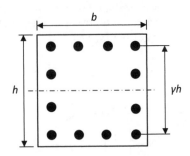

$$I_{st} = 0.187\,\rho_t bh^3\gamma^2 \quad \text{8 bars (3 per face)}$$
$$I_{st} = 0.176\,\rho_t bh^3\gamma^2 \quad \text{12 bars (4 per face)}$$
$$I_{st} = 0.172\,\rho_t bh^3\gamma^2 \quad \text{16 bars (5 per face)}$$

(b) Equal reinforcement on four sides

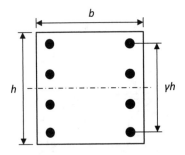

$$I_{st} = 0.167\,\rho_t bh^3\gamma^2 \;\text{(3 bars per face)}$$
$$I_{st} = 0.117\,\rho_t bh^3\gamma^2 \;\text{(6 bars per face)}$$

(c) Bars in two side faces

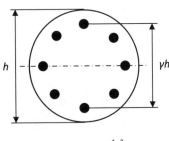

$$I_{st} = 0.098\,\rho_t h^4\gamma^2$$

(d) Uniformly distributed reinforcement

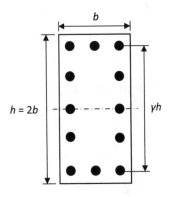

$$I_{st} = 0.128\,\rho_t bh^3\gamma^2 \;\text{(for 16 bars as shown)}$$

(e) Bars uniformly spaced on all sides

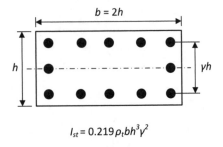

$$I_{st} = 0.219\,\rho_t bh^3\gamma^2$$

(f) Bars uniformly spaced on all sides

Note: This table is based on Table 12-1 of Wight, J.K. and MacGregor, J.G., Reinforced Concrete: Mechanics and Design, Sixth Edition, Pearson Education, Upper Saddle River, New Jersey, 2012

9

By Tibor Kokai

Foundations

9

Foundations

9.1   Introduction

In this edition of the handbook, design examples are presented for shallow and deep foundation systems and pile caps.

Changes in Cl.11, Cl.13 and Cl.21 affect the design process and required footing dimensions and reinforcement configuration; the relevant clauses include: Cl.11.3.2, Cl.11.3.6.2.b), Cl.13.3.4.4. and Cl.21.10.

Design tables are not provided in this edition of the Handbook but the relevant calculations are described in the following sections.

9.2   Special Loading Conditions

The sample calculations presented focus on the shear and flexural design of critical sections within foundation elements. To reduce the complexity of the design examples and to demonstrate the design procedure, only the effects of the gravity loading are considered for most examples, but consideration of lateral loading effects is also demonstrated in this handbook.

Design of foundation elements by practitioners must also consider special loading cases including differential settlements or unbalanced soil pressures acting on the structure, as specified in the National Building Code of Canada (NBCC 2010). Unbalanced soil pressures (in the case of a sloping grade, or an excavation near an existing building) often result in higher shear forces and overturning moments on the foundations than those calculated from wind or earthquake actions.

9.3   Selecting the Foundation Type

The foundation type used (e.g., spread footings vs. deep foundations) depends largely on the soil parameters/conditions, such as: bearing capacity, elevation of the bearing strata, water table level, and limitations on settlements. It is always prudent to consult the geotechnical engineer and cost consultant when deciding on the foundation type to be used.

9.4   Spread Footings

Spread footings are shallow structural elements that transfer loads from the superstructure to the bearing strata – see definition in CSA A23.3-14 Clause 3.1.

9.4.1.   Design Procedure

The design procedure can be broken into two general steps: 1. defining the shape and type of the spread footings; and 2. design of cross sections to meet the structural performance requirements.

1.   Shape and type of spread footings: There are four basic types of spread footings: individual spread footings, wall (or strip) footings, continuous footings and mats (or combined footings). The type of spread footings to be used is a function of the supported structure and its geometry (column and wall layout, load intensity, etc.).

2.   In the case of continuous footings that support multiple columns along a single line/grid or mats that support multiple columns and walls along several lines/grids, special care is needed when assessing the soil-footing structure interaction. The soil spring constant is load dependent, thus non-linear analysis is required or an iterative linear analysis can be used to converge to an acceptable stress/deflection equilibrium state.

Design of cross sections: The main design steps are as follows:

a)   Select the plan area of the footing and the thickness.

b)   Calculate or obtain settlements from the geotechnical consultant and assess the effects of settlements on the structure.

c)   Calculate required flexural and if necessary shear reinforcement. Check constructability of the selected flexural and shear reinforcement density.

d)   Check development of flexural and shear reinforcement.

e)   Check bearing stresses at the column-footing interface.

9.4.2.   Footing Area

The minimum footing area can be established from the ULS and SLS soil bearing resistances and the corresponding load combinations. The larger footing area from the ULS and SLS criteria will govern and can be used with the corresponding factored soil stresses for the cross sectional design of the footing.

The factored loads acting on a spread footing are depicted in Figure 9.1. A similar approach is used for service loads. Note that in Figure 9.1 and the following equations the moment at the column base is taken as $M_f = 0$ kN·m such that the soil reaction pressure can be taken as uniform. For simplicity in this discussion, potential buoyancy due to the water table is not considered.

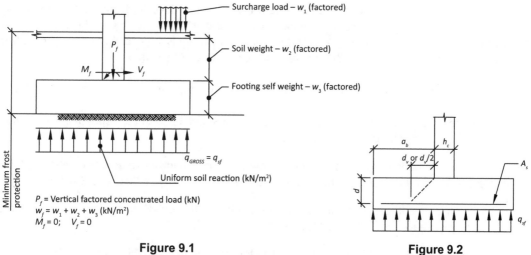

Figure 9.1   **Figure 9.2**

The total factored soil pressure (q_{sf}), also referred to as factored "gross soil pressure" (q_{GROSS}), must be less than or equal to the factored soil bearing resistance (q_{sr}):

$$q_{sf} = P_f / A_f + w_f \le q_{sr} \tag{9.1.a}$$

$$A_f \ge P_f / (q_{sf} - w_f) \tag{9.1.b}$$

The minimum required footing area is therefore calculated from the factored gross soil pressure (total factored load) acting on the subgrade. A similar procedure is followed for service loads, thus:

$$A_s \ge P_s / (q_s - w_s) \tag{9.1.c}$$

where q_s is the maximum bearing pressure for SLS criteria. There are no deformations or internal stresses in the footing from the load w_f or w_s. Only the P_f / A_f component, the factored "net soil pressure", causes internal forces in the footing. Thus the footing depth and reinforcement is established based on the factored net soil pressure using the larger of the two footing areas calculated.

9.4.3. Shear – Minimum Footing Thickness

It is common practice to design spread footings without shear reinforcement. Therefore the minimum thickness is usually governed by the one-way or two-way shear capacity, or the strut-and-tie design parameters for the case of short, thick footings. To allow shallower spread footings, shear reinforcement may be provided as defined in Clauses 11 and 13.

Note that the minimum depth of footings above the flexural reinforcement is specified at 150 mm – see Clause 15.7. In some cases, the minimum footing thickness can also be governed by the required compression or tension development length of the reinforcement from the supported structure.

The minimum thickness defined in 9.4.3.1 and 9.4.3.2 is based on the assumption that the soil pressure is uniform and thus only vertical load is acting on the footing.

9.4.3.1. One-way Shear

The minimum thickness of continuous strip/wall footings and some rectangular footings is typically governed by one-way (or beam) shear as defined in Clause 11.3. Since these shallow structural elements are usually constructed without shear reinforcement, the factored shear resistance is defined by Clause 11.3.4. The minimum effective shear depth, d_v, is determined from the shear demand (V_f) and shear capacity (V_r) at the critical section located at d_v or $d_v/2$ from the face of the support – see Clauses 11.3.2.1 and 11.3.2.2 and Figure 9.2. The shear capacity, V_r, is a function of both d_v and β (the factor accounting for shear resistance of cracked concrete in Clause 11.3.6).

When deriving the minimum required d_v one has to consider the following:

- Parameter β is defined in Clauses 11.3.6.2, 11.3.6.3 and 11.3.6.4 corresponding to different levels of approximation or geometric constraints.

- The β value defined in Clause 11.3.6.2 is always larger than the value from Clause 11.3.6.3 (simplified method), and can be used at critical sections satisfying Clause 11.3.6.2(b).

- Assuming the critical section at $d_v/2$ as opposed to d_v is the logical start as it is unlikely that the footing will have $a_b/d_v > 5$ (see Clauses 11.3.2.1(c) and 11.3.2.2).

- Additional sections may need to be checked for footings with variable thickness

Based on the above discussion and using consistent units for a 1 m wide strip, the minimum thickness of a footing using a critical section at $d_v/2$ from the face of the support can be solved as:

$$d_v = \left(q_{sf}a_b\right)/\left(\left(0.5q_{sf}\right)+\phi_c\lambda\beta\sqrt{f_c'}\right) \tag{9.2}$$

using $\beta = 0.21$ from Clause 11.3.6.2, q_{sf} (MPa), f_c' (MPa), a_b (m) and d_v (m).

If the geometric and other requirements of Clause 11.3.6.2 are not met, β as a function of d_v is normally solved according to Clause 11.3.6.3. Alternatively, β as a function of d_v and the reinforcement configuration can be solved according to Clause 11.3.6.4. In both cases, an iterative solution can be used to solve β and the corresponding minimum value of d_v.

The above discussion uses the sectional shear design provisions in Clause 11.3.6.3 and can be readily adapted for the case where shear reinforcement is used to reduce the overall height.

For cases where a_b/d_v is less than about 2, the strut-and-tie method in Clause 11.4 can give higher strengths, thereby also allowing for shallower footings. However, design by Clause 11.4 can result in increased reinforcement quantities with additional constraints on the reinforcement details.

9.4.3.2. Two-way Shear

The minimum effective thickness of square or almost square isolated footings is usually governed by the two-way (or punching) shear capacity, as specified in Clause 15.5.1 and Clause 13.3.4. The critical section for two-way shear is taken at $d/2$ away from the face of the support as per Clause 15.5.2 and Clause 13.3.3. The minimum footing depth is established by comparing the shear demand, v_f, to the shear capacity, v_r, on this section.

The shear capacity is determined from the geometric criteria described in Clause 13.3.4.1 to Clause 13.3.4.4. When the footing extends equally on all sides of the column, the condition is similar to an "interior" column. Therefore, for all cases having a column aspect ratio of $\beta_c \leq 2.0$, v_c is governed by Equation (13-7) in Clause 13.3.4.1(c) with further modifications to account for an effective depth greater than 300 mm in Clause 13.3.4.4. For square columns, $h_e = \sqrt{A_c}$.

If $d < 300$ mm, equating the maximum shear stress in the critical section v_f with the maximum factored shear resistance v_r, one obtains the following equation:

$$v_c = 0.38\lambda\phi_c\sqrt{f_c'} = (A_f q_{sf} - q_{sf}h_e^2 - 2q_{sf}h_e d - q_{sf}d^2)/(4h_e d + 4d^2) \tag{9.3}$$

where: q_{sf} (MPa), v_c (MPa), h_e (m), A_f (m^2) and d (mm).

Rearranging the above equation one gets a quadratic equation for d:

$$d^2(4v_c + q_{sf}) + d\,(4h_e v_c + 2q_{sf}h_e) - q_{sf}(A_f - h_e^2) = 0 \tag{9.4}$$

When $d > 300$ mm, Clause 13.3.4.3 reduces the value of v_c if $a_b > 2_d$ according to Clause 13.3.4.4. Equating the maximum shear stress to the shear resistance similar to Equation 9.4 results in a cubic equation:

$$(1.3/(1+d))0.38\lambda\phi_c\sqrt{f_c'} = (A_f q_{sf} - q_{sf}h_e^2 - 2q_{sf}h_e d - q_{sf}d^2)/(4h_e d + 4d^2) \tag{9.5}$$

9.4.3.3. Footings supporting Vertical Loads, Moments and Shear Forces

When the moment acting at the base of the column is not negligible, the footing design must account for this condition.

Unless a more accurate soil-structure interaction is considered, a linear variation in soil bearing pressure can be assumed. The footing size can then be chosen to ensure that the maximum factored soil stress does not exceed the factored soil bearing capacity. For bending about one axis:

$$q_{sf} = (P_f / A_f) + (M_f / S) \leq q_{sr} \tag{9.6}$$

Variations on this approach are needed for the case where a portion of the footing can uplift.

The calculated soil bearing pressure distribution can be used to determine the cross sectional shear forces at the critical sections for one-way and two-way shear.

One-way shear capacity is checked by considering cross-sections taken across the full width of the footing. When bending occurs about both column axes, this check is usually easiest by considering a 1 m wide cross-section that is under the highest shear force.

Two-way shear must be checked by considering the direct shear from the column axial force in combination with the shear stresses resulting from the unbalanced moment, as defined in Clause 13.3.5. Obviously, the required shear depth will be increased by the presence of moment. (See reference 2).

Overturning and sliding resistance must also be checked in accordance with the NBCC. (Reference 1).

9.4.4. Flexure

Minimum reinforcement in a spread footing is governed by Clause 10.5.1.2, which refers to Clause 7.8. As specified in Clause 7.8, this minimum reinforcement must be provided in each direction of the reinforced spread footings.

The flexural reinforcement requirements are based on the soil pressure distribution solved earlier and the critical sections defined in Clause 15.4. Reinforcement is designed in accordance with Clauses 10 and 11.4 where applicable (see Clause 10.7).

9.4.4.1. Development of Tension Reinforcement

When the clear cover to the reinforcement is greater than d_b, where d_b is the nominal bar diameter in mm, and when the clear spacing between bars is greater than 1.4 d_b, then the development length specified by Clause 12.2.3 may be used. Assuming that only straight bars will be used ending 75 mm from the edge of the footing, the maximum bar diameter, for a given a_b, can be found from

$$\max d_b = \sqrt{f_c'}\,(a_b - 0.075)1000/(0.45k_1k_2k_3k_4f_y) \tag{9.7}$$

where a_b (m), d_b (mm) and parameters k_1, k_2, k_3 and k_4 are as specified by Clause 12.2.4. For uncoated bars, normal density concrete, and distance between the reinforcement and base of the footing less than 300 mm, $k_1 = k_2 = k_3 = 1.0$. For 20 M and smaller bars, $k_4 = 0.8$, otherwise $k_4 = 1.0$.

9.4.4.2. Distribution of Flexural Reinforcement

According to Clause 15.4.4, a certain percentage of the total reinforcement in the short direction of rectangular spread footings must be in a concentrated strip at the column. The width of the strip is equal to greater of (1) the length of the short side of the footing, or (2) the length of the supported wall or column. This percentage to be concentrated is $100 \times 2/(\beta + 1)$ where β is the ratio of the long to short side of the footing. The remainder of the reinforcement is to be placed uniformly outside of this strip.

When it is desirable to space the bars in the short direction uniformly to expedite fieldwork and minimize the possibility of error, increase the amount of reinforcement accordingly.

9.4.4.3. Development of Shear Reinforcement

Transverse/Shear reinforcement shall be anchored as defined in Clause 12.13.2 and Clause 7.1.2. Thus at least one end of a stirrup/crosstie must have a 135 degree hook (typically at the top of the footing).

Care should be taken that the shear reinforcement legs are well distributed over the footing cross-section such that the shear resistance is consistent with model used for the flexural capacity distribution.

9.4.5. Strut-and-Tie Model – Deep Flexural Members

Flexural members with clear span to overall depth ratios less than 2 are designed as deep flexural members – see Clause 10.7. In lieu of more accurate procedures a strut-and-tie model may be used as defined in Clause 11.4. Refer to Chapter 4 of this Design Handbook for an explanation of the strut-and-tie method.

Alternatively, for flexural analysis of deep beams, (see reference 3) the reduced level arm method can be used, such that the lever arm z equals to:

$$z = 0.4 \, (d + M_f / V_f) \qquad \text{for } dV_f / M_f \geq 1.0 \tag{9.8a}$$

$$z = 1.2 \, M_f / V_f \qquad \text{for } dV_f / M_f = 2d / a_b \geq 2.0 \tag{9.8b}$$

where M_f and V_f are the moment and shear acting at the face of the column. The required steel area is then obtained from

$$A_s = M_f / (\phi_s f_y z) \tag{9.9}$$

In the case of deep beam action, additional anchorage requirements apply since the arching action results in steel stresses significantly higher than predicted by the flexural model. In lieu of a detailed analysis accounting for the reduction in steel stress along the development length, it is recommended that standard hooks be provided at the outside edge of the footing whenever the spread footing acts as a deep beam. If standard hooks are not practical, welded plates can be used to anchor the reinforcement (see Chapter 4 Shear and Torsion of this Design Handbook).

9.4.6. Plain Concrete Spread Footings

In plain (unreinforced) concrete footings the flexural stresses are limited by Clause 22.6.5 and the shear stresses by Clause 22.6.6. The total thickness of footing is calculated by adding 50 mm to the minimum depth required by the flexural and shear criteria. Clause 22.6.2 specifies the minimum footing depth as 200 mm.

9.4.7. Spread Footings with Caps or Pedestals

Spread footings with caps: Caps are used with spread footings to reduce the effective cantilever (a_b) of the footing – see Fig 9.3.a. By using a cap of sufficient size and thickness, the critical sections are relocated to the thinner portion of the footing beyond the cap. Thus, the factored shear force and bending moments at the critical sections are smaller and the total volume of concrete and reinforcement can be reduced. Caps are also justified and practical to use when bearing elevations vary. While there is a saving on the materials used, constructing a footing with a cap is more complex than constructing a spread footing without one.

The transfer of the column forces by bearing and the minimum column reinforcement (Clause 15.9) must be checked at sections 1 and 2 – see Figure 9.3.a. Reinforcement for compression must be developed below section 1, while tension reinforcement shall be developed below section 2.

9

Foundations

Caps typically have a 1:1 to 1:2 overhang to depth ratio. Taller caps are considered pedestals. See Figure 9.3.b and c for cap reinforcement as a function of arrangement of the column verticals and dowels.

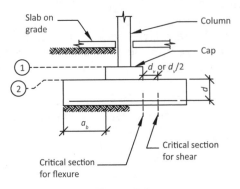

Figure 9.3a

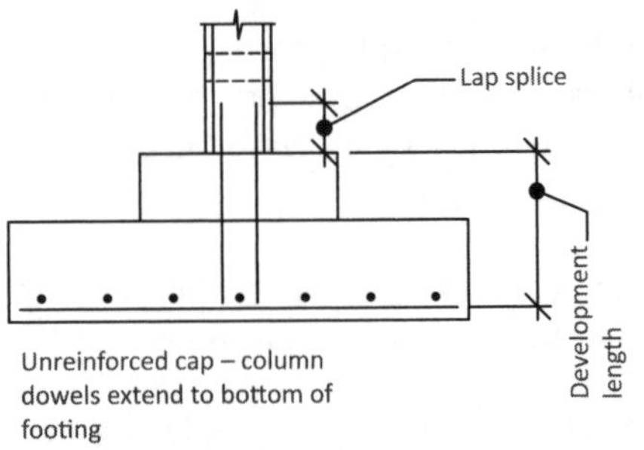

Figure 9.3b

Spread footings with pedestals: Pedestals are used when the bearing stratum is deep below the slab-on-grade and the superstructure (column) is not extended to the top of the footing – see Figure 9.3.d.

The pedestal is designed and detailed as a column, while checking bearing and minimum reinforcement requirements (Clause 15.9) at sections 1 and 2 – see Figure 9.3.d. Lateral support of the pedestal is usually provided by the slab-on-grade and the surrounding soil.

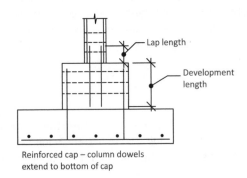

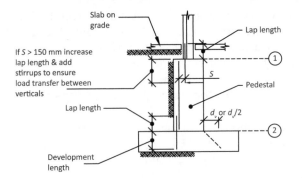

Figure 9.3c

Figure 9.3d

9.4.8. Combined Footings and Mats

Combined footings: Combined footings support more than one column located along a single grid line – see Figure 9.4.

For approximate analysis, it may be assumed that the footing is infinitely rigid thus resulting in a uniform soil stress distribution. The resultant of the subgrade reaction and the resultant of the acting loads must be in equilibrium with each other. This can be achieved by selecting an appropriate footing geometry – see references 2 and 4.

The assumption of an infinitely rigid footing (uniform soil stress distribution) is acceptable for combined footings where the column spacing to footing shear depth ratio does not exceed approximately 4:1.

For combined footings where the infinitely rigid footing assumption is not valid, the above-described approximate analysis is not acceptable. To establish a more accurate stress distribution and cross sectional forces, the theory of beams on elastic foundations should be applied as described by the following differential equation:

$$EI\frac{d^4y(x)}{dx^4} + ky = q(x)$$

(9.10)

where: EI stiffness of the combined footing (beam element)

        $y(x)$ deflection of the beam/footing element

        k Winkler coefficient (spring constant/modulus or subgrade reaction) – (units kN/m or MN/m) defined by the geotechnical consultant

        $q(x)$ loading (kN/m)

A closed form solution of the above differential equation exists for only a few load cases, however, it is relatively easy to solve any particular problem by using the finite element method (FEM).

The above Winkler solution can be further refined by assuming that the supporting springs do not deform independently of each other (see references 4 and 5).

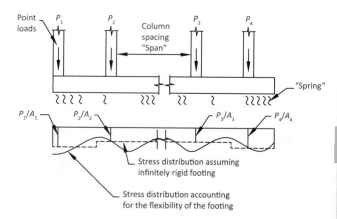

Figure 9.4

Mat foundations: Mat foundations are large reinforced concrete slabs supporting columns and/or walls located along several grid lines. It becomes a matter of definition as to when a spread or combined footing becomes a mat. A mat foundation is typically considered as a foundation concept when piles are not economical to use or when individual spread footings are too large.

The design of mats is based on the theory of slabs supported on an elastic foundation. There is a strong resemblance between the methods for the design of flat slabs and mats. Using FEM, the designer can assess the soil-stress distribution and the cross sectional forces in the mat slab. It is very important to consider that the modulus of subgrade reaction is not a linear function of the soil deformation. If a linear spring constant is used, several iterations may be required to arrive at an acceptable soil-stress distribution. For more complex analysis methods, see references 4, 5 and 6.

The following issues need to be considered during design and construction of mats:

- Constructability: Simplicity of the top and bottom reinforcement arrangement is important since mats can be quite thick. The stability of the reinforcing cage during concreting needs to be ensured.

- Shear reinforcement: Stirrups or headed studs may be used if necessary. Spacing of stirrups shall consider constructability.

- Concrete temperature control: In placement of mass concrete, the heat of hydration, which continues to build for several days, is a major cause for concern. As the concrete surface cools, a thermal gradient is formed across the concrete section, which can cause the concrete to crack. Controlling the initial and maximum concrete temperatures and the temperature

9

Foundations

gradient, is key to avoiding excessive thermal stresses – for available techniques and required parameters, see CSA A23.1.

9.5   Deep Foundations

Deep foundations are elongated structural elements that transfer loads from the superstructure to the bearing strata, by utilizing end bearing, friction, or both.

There are a great variety of deep foundation types in use that vary based on the materials (timber, structural steel, reinforced, unreinforced and pre stressed concrete and combinations of these) and the construction methods (drilled or driven piles, excavated systems, etc.) used.

This edition of the Design Handbook addresses driven or drilled piles.

9.5.1.   Piles

For definition of piles see Clause 3.1 of CSA A23.3-14. Piles are usually used for the following purposes:

1.   To carry axial compression forces.

2.   To carry tension, uplift forces by utilizing side friction or rock/soil anchors.

3.   To carry horizontal shear forces. All piles have some lateral load carrying capacity, but when piles are driven at an angle to the vertical (batter piles) they can carry significant horizontal loads. Usual slopes for batter piles vary from 1H:12V to 5H:12V.

4.   To control deflections and improve the capacity of a mat foundation. Sometimes it is necessary to augment the mat with piles to create a combined system which is superior to the mat foundation alone.

9.5.1.1. Pile Type Selection Criteria

The decision on the type of piles to be used and the method of construction to be utilized is based on local economic and geotechnical (site-specific) considerations. It is always prudent to consult the geotechnical engineer and the pile contractor for the methods of construction and the desired types of piles.

See reference 4 for the variety of piles in use and the associated details.

9.5.1.2. Pile Design Criteria

The design of piles consists of two steps:
    1.   determination of the cross sectional forces in individual piles; and
    2.   design of pile cross sections.

9.5.1.2.1.   Determination of the Cross Sectional Forces in Individual Piles

CSA A23.3 defines several design criteria that can influence the cross-sectional forces:

1.   Clause 15.2.3 requires that the forces account for the construction tolerance. A specified placement tolerance in any direction, that is not less than 50 mm, shall be considered when designing the pile, pile caps and other foundation elements. The impact of this tolerance can be especially critical grade beams or multiple piles within groups may not be present to resolve the moments generated

by eccentricity in the alignment of components after this tolerance is considered.

2. For plain concrete piles, Clause 22.8.1 sets the minimum eccentricity criterion at $0.1\,d_p$.

3. For vertical loads, Clause 15.2.2 provides requirements for linear or non-linear soil-structure interaction. However, under shear and moment induced by lateral force demands such as wind or earthquake, Clause 15.8.1 indicates that the pile-soil interaction and the non-linear soil behavior must be considered for determining the cross sectional forces. In references 4 and 7, numerous methods are presented for determining the pile-soil interaction. The most common approach is to use finite element analysis software to model the pile as a beam on elastic foundation. This approach can easily consider the changes in soil constants along the height of the pile. The subgrade response characteristics (spring constants) are normally established by the geotechnical engineer. See Figure 9.5.

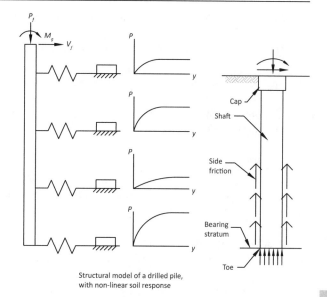

Structural model of a drilled pile, with non-linear soil response

Figure 9.5

If linear spring constants are used, the process becomes iterative, since the spring constant is a function of the soil stresses.

4. Clauses 15.8.2.2 and 22.8.2 require that the outer 25 mm of uncased drilled piles be ignored when establishing end bearing and side friction. This reduction in diameter must also be considered when the pile-soil interaction is assessed. Thus, when determining the cross sectional forces, the moment of inertia and cross-sectional area of the pile are determined from the reduced diameter.

This requirement is based on past visual inspections of exposed uncased drilled piles. It accounts for the fact that the concrete quality is questionable near the pile surface due to the interaction of the wet concrete with the soil during concreting.

9.5.1.2.2. Design of Pile Cross Sections

The following criteria for design of cast-in-place piles is set by CSA A23.3:

1. Clauses 15.8.2.2 and 22.8.2 require that the outer 25 mm of uncased drilled piles be ignored. Thus the factored resistance of the cross sections is based on the reduced cross section.

2. Clause 15.8.2.3 specifies an additional reduction factor of 0.9 applied to the factored resistances specified in Clauses 10 and 11for uncased drilled piles. This factor was introduced to account for construction techniques used and the fact that the concrete in the drilled pile is usually not vibrated.

3. Clause 22.8.3 for plain concrete uncased drilled piles specifies the use of an additional reduction factor of 0.8 applied to the maximum factored stresses specified in Clause 22.8.5.

4.   Clause 22.1.1 specifies a minimum concrete strength of 15 MPa for plain concrete.

5.   Clause 22.1.2 prohibits the use of plain concrete piles where ductility is required.

6.   Additional relevant pile design issues are addressed in Clause 15.8.2 and Clause 22.

7.   Assessment of the lateral support conditions for piles must be done in accordance with Clause 15.8.2.1.

9.5.2.   Pile Caps

Pile caps transfer loads from the superstructure to piles or a group of piles – see pile cap definition in Clause 3.1.

Single drilled piles may support walls or columns without a pile cap provided that the bearing stresses and the interface reinforcement/connection meet the code criteria.

The use of pile caps is warranted by the fact that the construction tolerance for piles is larger than the construction tolerance for the superstructure; hence it plays a role as a "transitional element" between the less and more accurately located/constructed structural elements. For example, accurately placing column dowels into the top of a drilled pile is much harder than into a pile cap. Use of pile caps with multiple piles or with grade beams to interconnect pile caps can also be important to resolve force eccentricities that result from pile placement tolerances or other unbalanced load cases.

9.5.2.1. Selection of Pile Cap Types

The pile cap type is usually determined by the number of piles used and a variety of geometrical constraints such as site issues, interference with other pile caps, and pile spacing limits. Provide a sufficient number of piles to support the loads and to ensure that the pile-cap and cap-superstructure system is structurally stable – see Figure 9.6 (reference 15). In the case of a two-pile system, a column load may be eccentric perpendicular to the line connecting the two piles, resulting in an unstable system unless the piles (or other structural elements) are designed to resist the corresponding moment. Thus a three-pile system can be more appropriate for supporting a single column in some cases. A two-pile system, however, can easily support a wall since the eccentricity (in any direction) does not induce extra moments into the piles.

9.5.2.2. Main Design Issues

Pile caps are usually thick structural concrete elements with small span to depth ratios where beam theory (plane sections assumption) is not applicable. For such members, Clause 10.7.1 recommends the use of the strut-and-tie method (STM) described in Clause 11.4. While the STM can be used to approximate the resistance of the discontinuous/disturbed regions (D-regions), the provisions in Clause 11.4 were developed for planar (two-dimensional) elements. (See reference 9). For example, Clause 11.4.5 describes use of minimum distributed reinforcement on each face, which may not be appropriate for large, three-dimensional structural elements such as pile caps. Nevertheless, when defining the nodal stress limits, Clause 11.4.4.1 allows for the beneficial effects of three-dimensional confinement if substantiated by test results.

The modified STM, as proposed by Adebar et al (see references 10, 11, 12 and 17) accounts for the beneficial effects of the three-dimensional confinement, while not requiring the use of minimum distributed reinforcement. This can improve the constructability of simple, statically determinate pile caps where the strut-and-tie model is selected to be similar to the stress trajectories in the elastic uncracked state and where significant deformation capacity to allow force redistribution is not required.

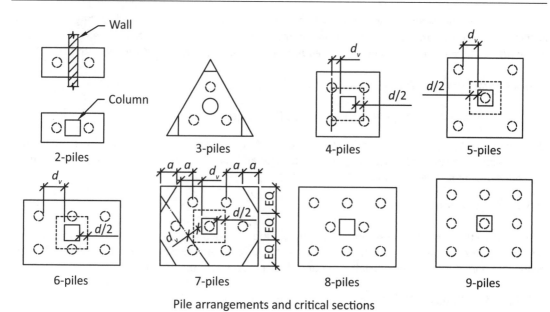

Pile arrangements and critical sections

Figure 9.6

On the other hand, if the pile cap is part of a statically indeterminate system where deformation capacity is required, the provisions for distributed crack control reinforcement are critical. Examples can include pile caps with openings, those subjected to load reversals or to unbalanced loading from differential settlements. Detailing of the crack control reinforcement (at the bottom of the cap) from Clause 11.4.5 should ensure that it is well distributed in all directions.

Pile caps, which do not qualify as deep pile caps, may be designed based on the STM provisions in Clause 11.4 or the sectional design methods in Clauses 10, 11 and 13 of CSA A23.3.

When the strut-and-tie method is used, the shear depth can be less than required by the sectional method for members with shear span to depth ratio less than approximately 2.5.

While it is not a common practice, pile caps may be reinforced for shear utilizing stirrups or other shear reinforcement.

Finally, it is important to recognize that, unlike typical beams, the width of a pile cap is often much larger than the supports (piles) or the columns above. Therefore, regardless of whether sectional or strut-and-tie design methods are used, the designer must be aware of the resulting load path between the elements of varying width. This may require the use of an effective design width smaller than the actual width, or detailing of reinforcement to resist the spreading action of the load path. The overall reinforcement detailing must be consistent with the structural model.

9.5.2.3. Description of the Design Procedure

The depths of simple pile caps are normally selected to satisfy both the traditional sectional shear limits for V_r (ignoring any concentrated loads between the critical section and the pile) and the nodal/bearing stress limits for STM (as specified in the modified strut-and-tie method). That is, the nodal stress limits replace the shear design for deep pile caps where a large portion of the pile loads do not intercept the critical shear sections at d_v or $d/2$ from the column face.

Since no shear reinforcement is provided in simple pile caps (similar to spread footings), pile caps usually contain only bottom tension reinforcement. Only those pile caps which utilize a bottom mat for tension/flexural reinforcement and do not require shear reinforcement are addressed in this Handbook.

The design steps are as follows:

1. Establish the pile cap depth based on the sectional method – see 9.5.2.3.1.

2. For deep pile caps, use the depth established in step 1 to check the compressive struts and bearing stresses in accordance with the modified strut-and-tie method and determine the required reinforcement – see 9.5.2.3.2.

9.5.2.3.1. Sectional Method

While the sectional method does not accurately describe the behavior of a typical "deep" pile cap, it is still appropriate for designing "shallow" pile caps. It is also an effective method for design of pile caps below shear walls that support axial, shear and in-plane overturning moments.

9.5.2.3.1.1. Shallow Pile Caps

The behavior of shallow pile caps is very similar to the behavior of spread footings, thus the sectional method can be applied, using Clauses 10, 11 and 13. Figure 9.7 shows the definition of shallow pile caps based on Clause 11.3.6.2 (b).

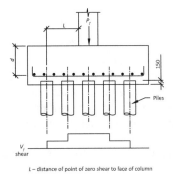

Sectional design of shallow pile caps involves the following steps:

1. Determine the required effective shear depth 'd_v' based on one-way shear criteria using Clauses 11.3.4 and 11.3.6 at the critical section defined by Clauses 11.3.2, 15.2.3 and 15.5.3. See Figure 9.6.

Figure 9.7

2. Determine the minimum depth "d" based on two-way shear criteria from Clause 13.3.4 at the critical section defined by Clauses 13.3.3, 15.2.3 and 15.5. See Figure 9.6.

3. Perform corner pile shear checks for shallow caps only as per Clause 13.3.6.2. Corner column shear checks need not be performed for deep pile caps since the corner pile in a deep pile cap behaves very differently from a corner column supporting a slab. This check is only necessary if the corner pile (in case of a three-pile cap) is enclosed by a pile cap corner that is less than 90 degrees.

4. Use the larger pile cap depth from steps 1 to 3.

5. Determine flexural reinforcement for the critical sections based on Clauses 10 and 15 and the reinforcement anchorage based on Clause 12.

6. Check the bearing stresses for the superstructure columns and the piles – Clause 10.8.

   Note: See bearing details in 9.5.2.4.

9.5.2.3.1.2. Pile Caps Supporting Shear Walls

Pile reactions are established based on Clause 15.2.2 and the pile cap is generally designed based on the steps described for "shallow" pile caps (see 9.5.2.3.1.1). Note that shear walls used as part of the seismic force resisting system may have additional load and resistance criteria per Clause 21 and are beyond the scope of this Section.

The strut-and-tie method for pile caps was developed for simple geometries and for concentric loads only, inducing compression into piles. For more complex geometries and loads, which include moments and shears, the strut-and-tie method can become too complex for practical engineering use. Hence the design of pile caps supporting shear walls or columns with significant moments/shears should be based on the sectional method.

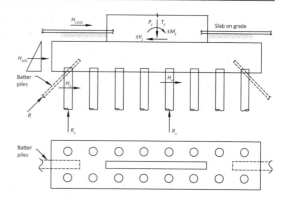

Figure 9.8

The design steps are listed below (see Figure 9.8):

1. Determine the pile reactions assuming rigid body behavior of the wall and footing system by using the formula: $R = P/A + M/S$, where A is the total area of piles, S is the sectional moment of all piles about the neutral axis of the pile group, and P and M are the loads acting at the centroid of the pile group. Other method to establish the pile reactions may be used if they consider the relative stiffness of the interconnected elements (shear wall, pile cap and piles).

2. Assess the minimum pile cap depth as described in 9.5.2.3.1.1.

3. Determine the required flexural reinforcement in both directions. Since the sectional method underestimates the pile cap flexural reinforcement (see 9.5.2.3.3), the calculated reinforcement needs to be adjusted accordingly.

4. Assess the load path for the horizontal shear. The horizontal shear may be resisted by the sum of the shear resistances of: individual piles, batter piles, slab-on-grade reaction and passive soil resistance against the pile caps and grade beams (if approved by the geotechnical engineer). Not all of the above act simultaneously as each potential force transfer system will have a different stiffness. In the case of shear walls that are part of the seismic force resisting system, refer to Clause 21 for additional criteria.

5. In case of uplift, care should be taken about the proper anchorage of the piles into the pile cap and special reinforcement details including top reinforcement will be required.

9.5.2.3.2. Strut-and-Tie Method for Deep Pile Caps

9.5.2.3.2.1. Experimental Results

Considerable research has examined deep beams that support one or more concentrated loads on a system of two or more supports, similar to isolated, deep pile caps. For these members, it was observed (see references 10, 11 and 12) that:

1. Even with a symmetrical pile layout, the pile reactions could deviate significantly.

2. "Banded" bottom tie reinforcement at the piles resulted in 20% or higher failure load compared to the same reinforcement with a uniform spacing. The uniformly spaced reinforcement from the sectional method does not follow the internal flow of forces appropriately – see 9.5.2.3.3. However, pile caps with only banded reinforcement had poor crack control.

3. Pile compressive struts did not fail by crushing but by splitting longitudinally. Longitudinal splits occurred due to transverse spreading of the compression stresses – (Figure 9.9).

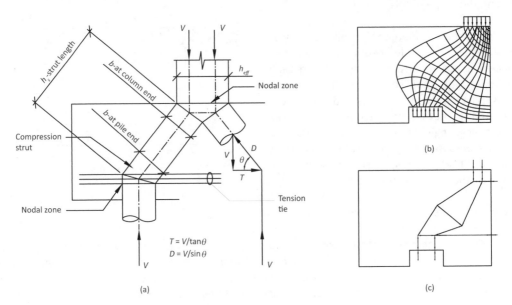

Strut-and-tie model for a deep beam or pile cap:
(a) idealized load-resisting truss;
(b) linear elastic stress trajectories with transverse tension due to spreading of compression;
(c) refined truss model with concrete tension tie to resist transverse tension

Figure 9.9

9.5.2.3.2.2. Bearing Stress Limits

Based on the above and other experiments, the strut forces must be limited to avoid diagonal tensional failure. Rather than employing a refined strut-and-tie model (Figure 9.9.a and c) a simplistic truss model was proposed to depict the force flow but with modified bearing stress limits to ensure that diagonal splitting would not occur (see Figures 9.11 and 9.7.7.4). Note that Adebar's method uses a modified STM where the compressive struts are defined by the pile top-pile cap and column bottom-pile cap planes (see Figure 9.11), as opposed to the strut-and-tie model described in Clause 11.4 and shown in Figures 9.9.a and c.

The shear check for deep piles is therefore replaced with a bearing stress check at the two ends of each compressive strut.

Adebar et al. suggested that in D-regions, without minimum reinforcement (for crack control) in two directions, the bearing stresses should be limited to:

$$f_b = 0.6\phi_c f'_c + 6\alpha\,\beta\,\phi_c\sqrt{f'_c}\ \text{[MPa]} \tag{9.11}$$

Where: accounts for confinement:

$$\alpha = \frac{1}{3}\left(\sqrt{\frac{A_2}{A_1}} - 1\right) \le 1; \quad \text{thus there is a reduction when } \sqrt{\frac{A_2}{A_1}} \le 4 \tag{9.11a}$$

where: A_1 and A_2 are defined similarly to Clause 10.8.1 and β accounts for the aspect ratio of the strut (see examples 9.7.7 and 9.7.8).

$$0.0 \leq \beta = 0.33 \, (h_s / b_s - 1) \leq 1.0 \tag{9.11b}$$

h_s / b_s is the aspect ratio of the strut, which can be approximated at the column as $h_s / b_s \cong 2d/h_{eff}$ and at piles, where only one compressive strut acts, as $h_s / b_s \cong d/d_p$. See Figure 9.9 for definitions of dimensions.

For the purpose of the bearing stress check, circular, polygonal or rectangular sections can be transformed into a square pile of equal area, $h_{eff} = \sqrt{A_{pile}}$.

For the purpose of the STM, the bearing area of an H–pile is defined by the depth of the section and the width of the flange.

9.5.2.3.2.3. Strut-and-Tie Method Design Steps

The following main steps are necessary to complete the strut-and-tie design of a deep pile cap:

1. Establish the pile layout – see Figure 9.10.

2. Establish the pile cap depth by the sectional method – see 9.5.2.3.1.

3. Define the strut-and-tie geometry and calculate the tie forces – see Figure 9.7.7.4.

4. Check strut bearing stresses – see 9.5.2.3.2.2 and 9.5.2.4.

5. Calculate minimum tie reinforcement, minimum pile cap reinforcement and minimum reinforcement required for interfaces – Clause 15.9.2. Confirm that all reinforcement is suitably anchored per the criteria in Clause 11.4

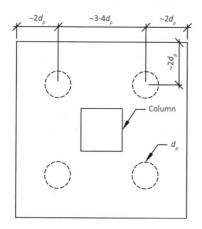

- Pile spacing to be confirmed by geotechnical consultant. Usually ~3d_p is used.
- Edge distance of 2d_p required for confinement.
- Embed piles minimum 150 mm into pile caps.

Figure 9.10

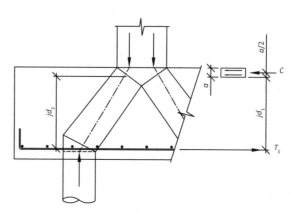

- $jd_1 > jd_2$
- jd_1 – internal lever arm for sectional method
- jd_2 – internal lever arm for S & T method

Figure 9.11

9.5.2.3.3. Comparison of the Sectional and Strut-and-Tie Methods

Figure 9.11 shows the internal lever arms' relationship for the STM and the sectional methods. Since the sectional method utilizes the full width of the pile cap, usually the compression block depth 'a' is very shallow resulting in a relatively large jd_1, as opposed to a smaller jd_2 for the STM. This explains why the sectional method can underestimate the required tension reinforcement, thus resulting in an unsafe design. See example 9.7.7.

9.5.2.4. Bearing Details

Bearing stresses must be checked at the interfaces of the pile cap and the superstructure and the pile cap and the piles as described previously.

In construction practice the following typical cases/details occur:

1. Bearing on cast-in-place, precast or concrete filled steel pipe piles:

   For these pile types the bearing surface is easily definable and meeting Clause 15.9.2 is easily done. In the case of net uplift, proper anchorage and detail of reinforcement must be provided.

2. Bearing on H-piles:

   For H-piles the bearing stresses can be significant, especially if the pile load induces a typical stress level of about $0.3 f_y$. At these pile stress levels the concrete stresses are in the range of $6 f_c'$. (Similar concrete stresses occur under the heads of headed studs). These stress levels are acceptable if the H-pile is well confined (see Figure 9.10 – edge distance) and embedded at least 150 mm into the pile cap. Based on reference 16, a cap plate is not required in these cases.

   Mitigating the above stress concentrations is a good practice, but installing cap plates on H piles is very costly. Other methods of concrete confinement could include:

   a) spiral reinforcement over the H-piles;

   b) shear studs welded to the H-piles;

   c) horizontal bottom steel placed over the H-piles or through them. H-piles in net tension must have adequate tension anchorage in accordance with the Standard.

9.6   Acknowledgements

Sincere thanks for the advice and great help of the CSA A23.3 Technical Committee, the CAC (Helene Dutrisac and Richard McGrath) and my colleagues from RJC (Grant Newfield MSc, Adam Lubell PhD and Adamou Saidou MSc).

9.7   Design Examples

Example 9.7.1   Wall Footing

Determine footing depth and reinforcement for the wall footing shown. Also compute the required depth for a plain footing. Use a factored soil reaction of $q_{sr} = 290$ kPa,

$f_c' = 25$ MPa,   and $f_y = 400$ MPa.

Calculations and Discussions:

1. Reinforced one-way footing

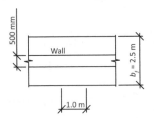

Figure 9.7.1-1

1.1 Determine minimum effective shear depth, d_v, required by one-way shear a_b=1000 mm.

For footings it is unlikely that the shear increase within d_v from the face be less than 20% (cl. 11.3.2.1.c). Thus the critical shear section is assumed to be located $0.5d_v$ from the face of the wall (cl. 11.3.2.2).

$$V_f = 0.001 \times q_{sr} \times (a_b - 0.5d_v) \text{kN/m}$$

The shear resistance of the section is $V_c = \phi_c \lambda \beta \sqrt{f_c'} d_v$ kN/m as per cl. 11.3.4

Assuming the point of zero shear is more than $2d_v$ (Clause 11.3.6.2.b) from the face of the wall and the maximum aggregate size is not less than 20mm, β is (see Clause 11.3.6.3.b);

$$\beta = \frac{230}{1000 + d_v} \qquad V_c = V_f \quad \text{gives } d_v = 436 \text{ mm}$$

Check cl. 11.3.6.2: a_b = 1000 mm ≥ 2 × d_v = 2 × 436 = 872 mm. The point of zero shear is more than $2d_v$ from the face of the wall, therefore our assumptions were correct.

1.2 Determine required flexural reinforcement:

Check deep beam action in accordance with Clause 10.7.1. $\quad d = d_v/0.9 = 484$ mm

a_b/d = 1000/484 = 2.07 > 2.0, therefore no deep beam action.

$$M_f = q_{sr} \frac{a_b^2}{2} = 145 \text{kNm/m}; \qquad K_r = \frac{M_f \times 10^6}{bd^2} = 0.62$$

K_r = 0.62 yields to ρ = 0.186. $A_s = \rho b d$ = 0.186 × 1000 × 484 = 900 mm²

Minimum reinforcement based on Clauses 10.5.1.2 (a) and 7.8, assuming total depth of footing as t_f = 484 + 15 (half bar diameter) + 75 (cover) = 574 mm and using t_f = 575 mm, is: $A_{s, min}$ = 1150 mm²/m, which is more than the calculated A_s. ($A_{s, min}$ must be provided in both directions.)

1.3 Find maximum bar size that can be developed in distance a_b − 0.075 = 0.925 m.

From cl. 12.2.3, max d_b = 25 M (l_d = 900 mm)

1.4 Reinforcement summary:

Short direction:	20 M bars @ 260 mm c/c BLL (bottom lower layer)
Long direction:	20 M @ 260 mm c/c BUL (bottom upper layer).

1.5 Total footing depth:

t_f = 484 + 10 (half bar diameter) + 75 (cover) = 569 mm. Round up this value to the next 25 mm and use a total footing depth of t_f = 575 mm – as assumed in 1.2.

Transfer of wall forces at wall base and development of wall reinforcement into the footing is not checked in this example – see Clause 15.9.

2. Unreinforced one-way footing

2.1 Minimum depth required for flexure (Clause 22.6.5):

$M_f = q_{sf} a_b^2/2$ = 145 kN·m/m, maximum stress in tension (cl. 22.6.5):

$$f_t = 0.37 \lambda \phi_c \sqrt{f_c'} = 1.20 \text{MPa}$$

From $f_t = M/S$; $d = \sqrt{6M_f /(f_t b)} = 851$mm , where $b = 1000$ mm.

Total footing depth: $h = 851 + 50 = 901$ mm.   Use 925 mm

Clause 22.6.3 requires the addition of 50 mm because of the irregular soil surface.

2.2 Check one-way shear (Clause 22.6.6.1):

The critical section is 'h' away from the face of the wall. V_r is calculated according to cl. 22.6.6.1.

$$V_f = q_{sr}(a_b - h) = 21.8\,\text{kN}$$

$$V_r = \frac{2}{3}\left(0.18\lambda\phi_c\sqrt{f_c'}\,b(h - 50\text{mm})\right) = 341.3\,\text{kN} \geq V_f$$

Example 9.7.2   Wall Footing

Determine footing width, depth and reinforcement for the wall shown in Figure 9.7.2-1. Use factored rock resistance of q_{sr} = 2000 kPa, service bearing capacity of q_{ss} = 1600 kPa, f_c' = 35 MPa, and f_y = 400 MPa.

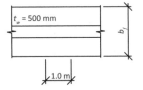

Factored wall load P_f = 4500 kN/m

Service wall load P_s = 3300 kN/m

Figure 9.7.2-1

Calculations and Discussions:

1.   Required footing width: Assuming w_f is negligible

    ULS condition: b_f = 4500/2000 = 2.25 m;

    SLS condition: b_f = 3300/1600 = 2.06 m   thus ULS condition governs the required footing width.

2.   Calculation of effective shear depth: a_b = (2.25 – 0.5)/ 2 = 0.875 m

    Assuming that $a_b < 2d_v$, (Clause 11.3.6.2 (b)) β =0.21. The concrete shear resistance is $v_r = \phi_c\lambda\beta\sqrt{f_c'}$,   thus v_r = 0.81 MPa.

    At maximum bearing capacity ($q_{sf} = q_{sr}$), the factored shear at the critical section: $V_f = q_{sf}(a_b - 0.5d_v)$

    Minimum shear depth from the maximum shear stress condition at the critical section is:

    $v_f = V_f/(1.0d_v) = (q_{sf}a_b - 0.5q_{sf}d_v)/(1.0d_v)$;   thus the effective shear depth is

    $d_v = (q_{sf} a_b)/(v_f + 0.5q_{sf}) = 0.968$ m – thus the assumption of $a_b < 2d_v$ was correct.

    Therefore $d = d_v /0.9 = 1.08$ m   use d = 1.1 m.

3.   Flexural design: Check for deep beam action – Clause 10.7.

    $a_b /d = 0.875/1.1 = 0.80 < 2.0$ thus deep beam action needs to be considered.

    The deep beam action will be assessed by two methods: The reduced lever arm method and the Strut-and-Tie method.

3.1 Reduced lever arm method

Lever arm:

$$dV_f / M_f = 2d/a_b = 2 (1.1)/0.875 = 2.5 > 2, \quad \text{thus } z = 1.2 M_f/V_f = 1.2 a_b/2 = 0.525 \text{ m}$$

(Note that V_f in the above equation refers to the shear at the face of the wall)

Required reinforcement:

$$A_s = M_f/(\phi_s f_y z) = (0.5 (0.875^2) (2000 \times 10^3)/(0.85 (400) (0.525)) = 4289 \text{ mm}^2/\text{m}$$

Minimum reinforcement:

Based on Clauses 10.5.1.2 (a) and 7.8, and assuming the total depth of footing as $t_f = 1100 + 75$ (cover) $+ 15$ (assumed half bar diameter) $= 1190$ mm, thus use $t_f = 1200$, the required minimum reinforcement is: $A_{s,min} = 2400 \text{ mm}^2/\text{m}$, which is less than the calculated A_s.

Maximum rebar size that can be developed into $a_b - 0.075 = 0.8$ m from cl. 12.2.3 is max $d_b = 25$ M.

Reinforcement:

Use:

25 M @ 115 mm c/c BLL – HH (bottom lower layer, hooked-hooked) – short direction

25 M @ 200 mm c/c BUL (bottom upper layer) – long direction

Transfer of wall forces at wall base and development of wall reinforcement into the footing has not been checked in this example – see Clause 15.9.

3.2 Design flexural steel based on strut-and-tie method

Based on $d = 1.1$ m, the total depth of $t_f = 1100 + 75 + 15$ (half bar diameter) $\cong 1200$ mm from steps 1 and 2 will be used for further design.

Based on the force diagram in Figure 9.7.2-2b, the compressive force in the strut MN is given by $C_{MN} = 0.5 P_f (0.25 b_f - 0.25 h_c)/(d - 0.5 d_c)$. Limiting the compressive stress in the strut to $0.85 \phi_c f_c$ requires a compression depth $d_c = 47$mm. The maximum Tie force T_f is thus $T_f = C_{MN} = 915$ kN

Required tension reinforcement:

$$A_s = T_f/(\phi_s f_y) = 0.915 \times 10^6/(0.85 (400)) = 2691 \text{ mm}^2/\text{m}$$

This is 63% of the reinforcement by Park and Paulay's reduced lever arm method.

Reinforcement:

Based on the reinforcement development considerations in item 3.1, use:

25 M @ 180 mm c/c BLL – HH (bottom lower layer, hooked-hooked) – short direction

25 M @ 200 mm c/c BUL (bottom upper layer) – long direction

9

Foundations

Check capacity of struts:

Strut A-M

$\alpha_A = 49.9;$ $h_A = 188 \sin(49.9) = 143$ mm; $C_A = 490$ kN; $T_A = 316$ kN

Strain along the tension reinforcement in point A: See Figure 9.7.2-4

$\varepsilon_x = T_A/(EA_s) = 0.316/(200\ 000\ (500 \times 10^{-6})/0.18) = 0.569 \times 10^{-3}$

Principal tensile strain in the strut – Clause 11.4.2.3:

$\varepsilon_1 = \varepsilon_x + (\varepsilon_x + 0.002) \cot^2\alpha_s = 0.569 \times 10^{-3} + (0.569 \times 10^{-3} + 0.002) \cot^2 49.9 = 2.39 \times 10^{-3}$

Limiting compressive stress in the strut – Clause 11.4.2.3:

$f_{cu} = f_c' /(0.8 + 170\ \varepsilon_1) \leq 0.85\ f_c'$
$f_{cu} = 35/(0.8 + 170\ (2.39 \times 10^{-3})) = 29.0$ MPa < 29.8 MPa

Strut resistance:

$P_r = \phi_c A_c f_{cu} = 0.65\ (1)\ (0.143)\ (29.0) = 2.70$ MN > 0.49 MN,   thus strut capacity is adequate.

The other struts can be checked in a similar way; however strut A-M governs for f_{cu} limit.

Check nodal stresses:

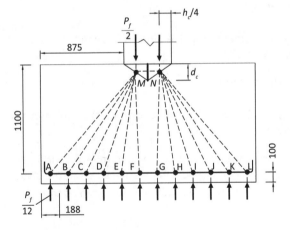

Figure 9.7.2-2a

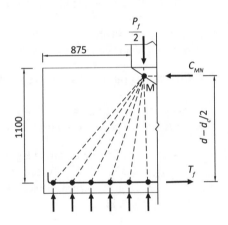

Figure 9.7.2-2b

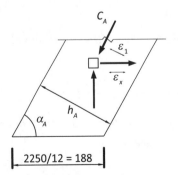

Figure 9.7.2-3

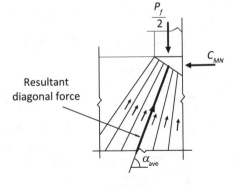

Figure 9.7.2-4

Wall bearing stress based on Clause 10.8.1:

P_f = 4500 kN; A_c = 1 (0.500) = 0.500 m²   thus concrete stress is f_c = 4.5/0.5 = 9.0 MPa.

Limiting stress based on Clause 11.4.4.1 is $0.85m\ \phi_c f_c'$ = 19.3 MPa > f_c.   OK

Concrete area (A_c) was taken at the wall and footing interface. The confinement factor m is 1.0 (cl. 10.8.1).

Check nodes M and N:

At the top of the diagonal struts, the stress is calculated based on Clause 11.4.2.2, Figure 11.5 c. using average angle (α_{ave} = 67.9, Figure 9.7.2-3).The resultant of the diagonal strut forces on the node M is $0.5P_f / \sin\alpha_{ave}$ = 2.43 MN. The stress on the node is thus:

$$f_c = \frac{2.43\times10^6}{1000\times(250\sin67.9+47\cos67.9)} = 9.75\,\text{MPa}$$

Limiting stress based on Clause 11.4.4.1 is $0.85\ m\ \phi_c f_c'$ = 19.3 MPa > f_c.   OK

Ultimately Clause 10.8 may be used for checking the stresses at the wall-footing interface.

Transfer of wall forces at wall base and development of wall reinforcement into the footing is not checked in this example.

Example 9.7.3   Square Footing

For the square footing and square column with factored load as indicated, select the total required thickness for footing size of 2.5 × 2.5 m.

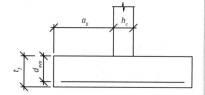

P_f = 1875 kN	f_c' = 30 MPa	w_f is negligible
h_c = 500 mm	f_y = 400 MPa	

Calculations and Discussions:

Figure 9.7.3-1

1. Compute factored reaction:

    q_{sf} = 1875/2.5² = 300 kPa

2. Minimum effective shear depth – one-way shear:

    a_b = (2500 – 500) (½) = 1000 mm

The shear force 0.5 d_v from the face of the column is:

$V_f = q_{sf} \times b_f (a_b - 0.5d_v)$ = 0.750 $(a_b - 0.5d_v)$ kN; the shear resistance is

$V_c = \phi_c \lambda\beta\sqrt{f_c'}b_f d_v = 8.90\beta d_v$ kN

Assuming the point of zero shear is more than $2d_v$ from the face of the wall and the maximum aggregate size is not less than 20 mm, β is 230 /(1000 + d_v)   (cl. 11.3.6.3).
$V_c = V_f$ gives: d_v = 411 mm; $d = d_v$ / 0.9 = 457 mm.

3. Minimum depth – two-way shear:

    The critical shear section is located at $0.5d$ from the face of the column (cl. 13.3.3.1). The punching shear stress is:

    $$v_f = \frac{q_{sf}}{b_0 d}\left[b_f^2 - (h_c + d)^2\right] \times 10^{-3} \text{ MPa} ; \quad b_0 \text{ is the punching perimeter given by } 4\,(h_c + d).$$

    Assume cl. 13.3.4.1 c) governs the two-way shear resistance thus $v_r = 0.38\lambda\phi_c\sqrt{f_c'}$. If the distance for the point of zero shear to the face of the column is more than $2d$, v_r shall be multiplied by $1300\,/(1000 + d)$ (cl. 13.3.4.3), thus :

    $$\frac{1300}{1000 + d} v_r = \frac{1300 \times 0.38\lambda\phi_c\sqrt{f_c'}}{1000 + d} = \frac{1759}{1000 + d} \text{ MPa}$$

    Solving $\dfrac{1300}{1000 + d} V_r = V_f$ yields to $d = 369$ mm.

    Check that cl. 13.3.4.1.c gives the lowest shear resistance:

    $$v_r = \left(1 + \frac{2}{\beta_c}\right)0.19\lambda\phi_c\sqrt{f_c'} = 2.03\,\text{MPa} \quad (\text{cl.}\,13.3.4.1\text{-a})$$

    $$v_r = \left(\frac{\alpha_s d}{b_0} + 0.19\right)\lambda\phi_c\sqrt{f_c'} = 2.19\,\text{MPa} \quad (\text{cl.}\,13.3.4.1\text{-b})$$

    $$v_r = 0.38\lambda\phi_c\sqrt{f_c'} = 1.35\,\text{MPa} \quad\quad\quad (\text{cl.}\,13.3.4.1\text{-c})$$

    a_b = 1000 mm ≥ $2d$ = 2 × 369 = 738 mm. The point of zero shear is more than $2d$ from the face of the column as assumed.

    Thus one-way shear governs, $d = 457$mm.

4. Total footing depth assuming 20 M bars in both directions: t_f = 457 + 75 + 20 = 552 mm.

    Use t_f = 575 mm (rounding it up to the next 25 mm).

    Note that the d_{ave} will be used for calculating the flexural reinforcement in both directions.

5. Flexural reinforcement:

    Check deep beam action in accordance with Clause 10.7.1.

    a_b/d = 1000/(575 – 75 – 20) = 1000/480 = 2.08 > 2.0, therefore no deep beam action.

    $M_f = q_{sr}b_f\dfrac{a_b^2}{2} = 375$kNm $K_r = 0.651$ which gives $\rho = 0.195$

    $A_s = \rho\, b\, d = 2340$ mm^2

    $A_{s,\,min}$ = 0.002 (2500) (575) = 2875 mm^2 > A_s,   thus the minimum reinforcing governs.

6. The maximum bar size that can be developed in distance $a_b - 0.075 = 0.925$ m is 25 M (cl. 12.2.3)

    Number of bars = 2875 / 500 = 5.75 – 25 M bars, thus   Use: 6 – 25 M bars BEW
                                                                (bottom each way).

Example 9.7.4   Square Footing

Determine the minimum footing thickness and required reinforcement for a concentrically loaded square spread footing. Assume that w_f is negligible.

Service loads:

Dead load D_s = 3648 kN h_c = 500 mm

Live load L_s = 600 kN f_c' = 30 MPa

Snow load S_s = 380 kN f_y = 400 MPa q_{sr} = 625 kPa q_{ss} = 480 kPa

Calculations and Discussions:

1. Column design loads:

   ULS: P_f = 1.25 (3648) + 1.5 (600) + 1.0 (380) = 5840 kN

   SLS: P_f = 1.00 (3648) + 1.00 (600) = 4248 kN

2. Required footing area:

   ULS: A_f = 5840/625 = 9.34 m², b_f = 3.06 m

   SLS: A_f = 4248/480 = 8.85 m², b_f = 2.98 m

   ULS condition governs, use b_f = 3.1 m square footing for further calculations.

3. Minimum footing thickness:

   3.1 One-way shear: a_b = (3100 – 500)/2 = 1300 mm, q_{sf} = 5840/3.1² = 608 kPa

   $$V_f = q_{sf} \times b_f (a_b - 0.5d_v) = 1.885 (a_b - 0.5d_v) \text{ kN}$$

   Assume Clause 11.3.6.2-b and Clause 11.3.2.2 applies thus β = 0.21 and $V_c = \phi_c \lambda \beta \sqrt{f_c'} b_f d_v = 2.318 d_v$ kN . Setting $V_c = V_f$ gives d_v = 751 mm. Therefore minimum depth from one-way shear stress condition is $d = d_v /0.9 = 835$ mm.

   $2d_v$ = 1502 mm > a_b thus cl. 11.3.6.2(b) applies as assumed.

   3.2 Two-way shear:

   The critical shear section is located at 0.5d from the face of the column (cl. 13.3.3.1). The punching shear stress is:

   $$v_f = \frac{q_{sf}}{b_0 d}\left[b_f^2 - (h_c + d)^2\right] \times 10^{-3} \text{ MPa} ; \qquad b_0 \text{ is the punching perimeter given by } 4(h_c + d)$$

   Assume cl. 13.3.4.1(c) governs the two-way shear resistance thus $v_r = 0.38 \lambda \phi_c \sqrt{f_c'}$. Assuming the distance for the point of zero shear to the face of the column is less than 2d (ie cl. 13.3.4.4 applies), the shear resistance is $v_r = 0.38 \lambda \phi_c \sqrt{f_c'} = 1.35$ MPa . Setting $v_c = v_f$ gives $d = 736$ mm a_b = 1300 mm < 2d = 2 × 736 = 1472 mm   The point of zero shear is less than 2d from the face of the column thus cl. 13.3.4.4 applies.

Check that cl. 13.3.4.1 c) give the lowest shear resistance:

$$v_r = \left(1 + \frac{2}{\beta_c}\right) 0.19 \lambda \phi_c \sqrt{f_c'} = 2.03\,\text{MPa} \quad \text{(cl. 13.3.4.1-a)}$$

$$v_r = \left(\frac{\alpha_s d}{b_0} + 0.19\right) \lambda \phi_c \sqrt{f_c'} = 2.80\,\text{MPa} \quad \text{(cl. 13.3.4.1-b)}$$

$$v_r = 0.38 \lambda \phi_c \sqrt{f_c'} = 1.35\,\text{MPa} \qquad \text{(cl. 13.3.4.1-c)}$$

Conclusion: The one-way shear stress condition governs, and our assumption of the critical section was correct thus use d_{ave} = 850 mm (by rounding up to the next 25 mm).

3.3 Assuming no net tension in the column, the maximum reinforcement diameter in a column supported by a footing with d = 850 mm is 45 M (cl. 12.3.2).

4. Flexural design:

Check for deep beam action in accordance with Clause 10.7.1:

a_b/d = 1300/850 = 1.53 < 2, therefore deep beam action needs to be considered.

4.1 Reduced lever arm method:

Lever arm: dV_f/M_f = 2d/a_b = 2 (850 / 1300) = 1.31   1 < 1.31 < 2
thus z = 0.4 ($d + M_f/V_f$) = 0.4 ($d + a_b/2$) = 600 mm

Required reinforcement:

$A_s = M_f/(\phi_s f_y z)$ = (608 (1.3^2) (0.5) (3.1)) × 10^3/(0.85 (400) (0.600)) = 7807 mm^2

Minimum reinforcement:

Based on Clause 10.5.1.2 (a) and Clause 7.8, and the total depth of footing of

t_f = 850 + 75 + 25 = 950 mm.   Use t_f = 950 mm

$A_{s,\,min}$ = 5890 mm^2 < 7807 mm^2

Reinforcement:

Use: 16 – 25 M BEW HH (bottom each way, hooked-hooked)

4.2 Design flexural steel based on strut-and-tie method:

Based on the d = 850 m the total depth of
t_f = 850 + 75 + 25 = 950 mm will be used for further design.

Using the same process as in Example 9.7.2, the factored compressive force in the strut MN is given by
C_{MN} = 325 P_f/jd (figure 9.7.4-2). The strut section area is

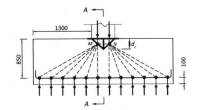

Figure 9.7.4-1

$$A_{MN} = \left(h_c + \frac{a_b}{d} d_c\right) d_c = (500 + 1.529 d_c) d_c$$

Limiting the stress in the strut to 0.85 $\phi_c f_c'$
requires a minimum compression depth d_c = 199 mm which yields to $C_{MN} = T_f$ = 2653 kN. A conservative value of 0.67 is used for α in figure 9.7.4-3 for defining the location of the compressive force C_{MN}.

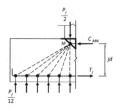

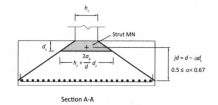

Section A-A

Figure 9.7.4-2   **Figure 9.7.4-3**

Required tension reinforcement:

$A_s = T_f /(\phi_s f_y) = 2653 \times 10^3/(0.85\,(400)) = 7803$ mm²

Note: This is the same reinforcement as calculated with the reduced lever arm method.

Reinforcement to be developed in $a_b - 0.075 = 1.225$ m:

The maximum bar size that can be developed is 35 M.

Reinforcement:

Use: 16 – 25 M BEW HH (bottom each way, hooked-hooked).

Check capacity of struts at the tension reinforcement level (bottom): See Figure 9.7.2-3

$\alpha_A = 29°$ $h_A = 258 \sin 29 = 125$ mm $C_A = 1005$ kN; $T_A = 880$ kN

Strain along the tension reinforcement in point A:

$\varepsilon_x = T_A/(E A_s) = 0.880 /(200\,000\,(16)\,(500 \times 10^{-6})) = 0.550 \times 10^{-3}$

Principal tensile strain in the strut – Clause 11.4.2.3:

$\varepsilon_1 = \varepsilon_x + (\varepsilon_x + 0.002)\cot^2\alpha_s = 0.550 \times 10^{-3} + (0.550 \times 10^{-3} + 0.002)\cot^2 29 = 8.85 \times 10^{-3}$

Limiting compressive stress in the strut – Clause 11.4.2.3:

$f_{cu} = f_c' /(0.8 + 170\varepsilon_1) \le 0.85 f_c'$

$f_{cu} = 30/(0.8 + 170\,(8.85 \times 10^{-3})) = 13.02$ MPa $< 0.85\,f_c' = 25.5$ MPa – acceptable stress level.

Strut resistance:

$P_r = \phi_c A_c f_{cu} = 0.65\,(3.1)\,(0.125)\,(13.02) = 3.28$ MN >1.01 MN, thus strut capacity adequate.

(The other struts can be checked in the similar way; however strut A-M governs for f_{cu} limit.)

Check nodal stresses: See Figure 9.7.2-3

Column Bearing stress (cl. 10.8.1)

Limiting stress based on Clause 11.4.4.1 is $0.85\,m\,\phi_c f_c'$. The confinement factor *m* is $\sqrt{A_f / A_c} \le 2 = 2$. The maximum admissible stress is thus 33.15 MPa. The stress at the base of the column is $P_f / A_c = 5840 \times 10^3/500^2 = 23.36$ MPa   OK

9

Foundations

Nodes M and N

At the top of the diagonal struts, the stress is calculated based on Clause 11.4.2.2, Figure 11.5 c. using average angle (α_{ave} = 47.8). The resultant of the diagonal strut forces on the node M is $0.5P_f / \sin(\alpha_{ave})$ = 3.94 MN. The average width of the node is 804 mm. The stress on the node is thus:

$$f_c = \frac{3.94 \times 10^6}{804 \times (250\sin 47.8 + 199\cos 47.8)} = 15.37\,\text{MPa}$$

Limiting stress based on Clause 11.4.4.1 is $0.85\,m\,\phi_c f_c'$ = 33.15 MPa $> f_c$.   OK

Ultimately Clause 10.8 may be used for checking the stresses at the column-footing interface.

Example 9.7.5   Rectangular Footing

Determine the required thickness and reinforcement for the column and footing shown.

Footing:	4.6 × 3.0 m	f_c' = 20 MPa
Column:	1000 × 600 mm	q_{sr} = 300 kPa
	f_y = 400 MPa	w_f is negligible

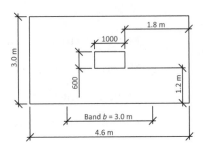

Figure 9.7.5-1

Calculations and Discussions:

1. Minimum effective shear depth – one-way shear:

   Long direction:

   a_b = 1800 mm, q_{sf} = 300 kPa.

   $V_f = q_{sr} \times b_f\,(a_b - 0.5\,d_v) = 0.9\,(a_b - 0.5\,d_v)$ kN

   $V_r = V_c = \phi_c \lambda \beta \sqrt{f_c'}\,b_f d_v = 9.011\beta d_v$ kN

   Assuming the point of zero shear is more than $2d_v$ from the face of the column
   (ie β = 230 /(1000 + d_v)) and solving for d_v yields to a value of d_v > 900 meaning a_b < 2d and clause 11.3.6.2-b applies (β = 0.21). With d_v = 0.5, a_b = 900 mm, V_c = 1648 kN ≥ V_f = 1215 kN

   Check short direction:

   $$V_f = q_{sr} \times 4.6\left(\frac{3-0.6}{2} - 0.5 \times 0.9\right) = 1035\,\text{kN}$$

   $$V_c = \phi_c \lambda \beta \sqrt{f_c'}\,b_f d_v = 0.65 \times 1 \times 0.21 \times \sqrt{20} \times 4600 \times 900 \times 0.001 = 2527\,\text{kN} > V_f$$

2. Minimum depth – two-way shear:

   Using the same process as in example 9.7.3 yields to a required effective depth d of 689 mm.

   Since the one-way shear governs use d = 900/0.9=1000 mm. Assuming 25 M bars the total depth is then: t_f = 1000 + 25 + 75 = 1100 mm.

3. Compute A_s required in the long direction:

   Check deep beam action: a_b/d = 1800/1000 = 1.8 < 2 – thus deep beam action needs to be considered.

Using the reduced lever arm method:

$d\, V_f/M_f$ = 1000 (2)/1800 = 1.11 > 1   thus, z = 0.4 $(d + M_f/V_f)$ = 0.4 $(d + a_b/2)$ = 760 mm

$A_s = M_f/(\phi_s f_y z)$ = (300 (1.8²) (0.5) (3.0)) × 10³/(0.85 (400) (0.76)) = 5642 mm²

$A_{s,\,min}$ = 0.002 (3000) (1100) = 6600 mm² > 5642 mm²

From Equation (9.7) of this Design Handbook the maximum diameter bar to be developed is max d_b = 42.8 mm, thus   Use 14 – 25 M BLL.

4. Compute A_s required in the short direction:

Check deep beam action: a_b/d = 1200/1000 = 1.2 < 2 thus deep beam action needs to be considered.

Using reduced lever arm method:

$d\, V_f/M_f$ = 1000(2)/1200 = 1.67 > 1   thus, z = 0.4 $(d + M_f/V_f)$ = 0.4 $(d + a_b/2)$ = 640 mm

$A_s = M_f/(\phi_s f_y z)$ = (300 (1.2²) (0.5) (4.6)) × 10³/(0.85 (400) (0.51)) = 4566 mm²

$A_{s,\,min}$ = 10 120 mm² > 4566 mm²

From Equation (9.7) of this Design Handbook the maximum diameter bar to be developed is max d_b = 28 mm, thus   Use 21 – 25 M BUL HH.

Check bar distribution – Clause 15.4.4.1 (b).

β = 4.6/3 = 1.53;   Reinforcing in band/Total reinforcing = 2/(β + 1) = 0.79

Reinforcing required in band: A_{sb} = 0.79 (4566) = 3607 mm²

In the bandwidth of 3.0 m, the reinforcement is

10 500 (3.0 / 4.6) = 6850 mm² > 3607 mm², thus   OK

Reinforcement summary:

Long way: 14 – 25 M BLL HH (bars hooked since the other direction is a deep beam).

Short way: use 21 – 25 M BUL HH.

Example 9.7.6   Footings Supporting Shear Walls

The following example illustrates the shear design requirements for a footing supporting a shearwall. The footing is to be designed for both gravity loads due to Dead and Live loads and overturning   moments due to wind and seismic. The footing is first to be sized and then checked for shear for all load combinations due to D, L, W, and E. The seismic forces were determined based on $R_d R_o$ = 2 × 1.4 = 2.8. The ULS bearing capacity is 500 kPa. The seismic design of the footing follows the General Method as outlined in clause 21.10.3. The shear design requirements are based on chapter 15 and 11.

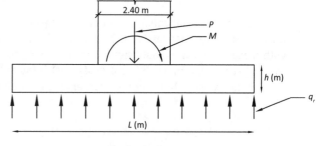

Footing loads

9

Foundations

Assume the footing is subject to the following unfactored loads:

Unfactored Load Case	Load
P_D (Dead Load)	1000 kN
P_L (Live Load)	400 kN
M_w (Wind Overturning Moment)	3214 kN·m
M_E (Seismic Overturning Moment)	4300 kN·m

The footing has to be initially sized for overturning based on both wind and seismic requirements. In order to size the footing, the load combination per NBCC with Dead Load only is considered, as this will generally allow the designer to establish a minimum size of footing required to resist overturning. Based on preliminary calculations, a depth of 900 mm and width of 3400 mm was selected. Combinations for both wind and seismic have to be considered in sizing the footing.

Wind Overturning combined with Dead Load

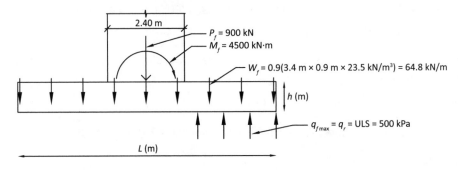

Footing loads – $0.9D + 1.4W$

- Unfactored Loads

  $P_D = 1000$ kN + footing selfweight

  $M_W = 3214$ kN·m

- Factored Loads

  $P_f = 0.9P_D = 900$ kN + 0.9 × footing selfweight

  $M_f = 1.4 \times 3214 = 4500$ kN·m

Seismic Overturning combined with Dead Load
Clause 21.10.3.2.3 – Capacity Protected

For seismic, using the general method, clause 21.10.3.2.1 (a) requires that overturning of the footing must satisfy one of clauses 21.10.3.2.2 to 21.10.3.2.4. Since the wall was designed as moderately ductile with reasonably low over-strength, it makes sense to utilize clause 21.10.3.2.3 (capacity protected) as this will result in a more efficient design. Otherwise, simply using clause 21.10.3.2.2 ($R_dR_0 = 1.0$) or 21.10.3.2.4 (NCP) would result in a larger footing than required.

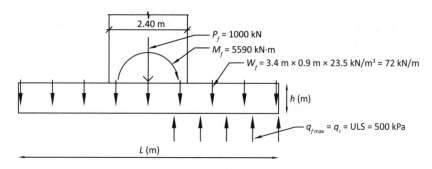

Footing loads – DL + E

- Based on the seismic design of the shearwall, for this example assume the nominal over-strength γ_w = 1.3 and probable over-strength γ_{pr} = 1.7. For this clause, the bearing resistance = ULS = 500 kPa. First check whether nominal or probable moments have to be used.

- $R_d R_o / \gamma_w$ = 2.8 /1.3 = 2.15 < 2.5   therefore nominal moment can be used.

- Unfactored Loads P_D = 1000 kN + footing

  M_E = 4300 kN·m

  γ_w = 1.3

- Factored Loads P_f = 1.0 P_D = 1000 kN + 1.0 × footing selfweight

  M_f = 4300 × 1.3 = 5590 kN·m

The minimum footing size must satisfy overturning both the Case 1 (wind) and Case 2 (seismic) conditions. For each factored load case, assuming a uniform rectangular stress block for the soil bearing, the eccentricity between center of bearing pressure and center of gravity loads is equal to the total moment divided by the total gravity loads. The bearing length can be considered to be 2 × ($L/2 – e$). By solving a quadratic equation, the minimum length of footing can be determined for each load case. The following table summarizes the two load cases. Based on Load Cases 1 and 2, the following table indicates that clause 21.10.3.2.3 (Case 2) for seismic governs the minimum size of the footing.

Footing Sizer

Footing Size – Based on Wind (Case 1)		Footing Size Based on 21.10.3.2.3 (Case 2) General Method – Capacity Protected Foundation	
B (footing width in m)	3.4	B (footing width in m)	3.4
ULS (ultimate bearing kPa)	500	ULS (ultimate bearing kPa)*	500
h (height of footing)	0.9	h (height of footing)	0.9
0.9 × P_{DL} (Dead Load in kN)	900	P_{DL} (Dead Load in kN)	1000
P_L (Live Load in kN)	0	P_L (Live Load in kN)	0
M_f (Factered Wind Moment)	4500	$M_{ot\,res}$ (Overturing Moment Resistance)	5590
0.9 × w (footing wt in kN/m)	64.84018	w (footing wt in kN/m)	72.04464
L (Length footing in m)	7.3482	L (Length footing in m)	8.015271
w (bearing width in m)	0.809682	w (bearing width in m)	0.927916

* For some cases in 21.10.3 q_r is a function of the ULS × a factor

The following figure shows the required footing. For the footing design, a lever arm between the compression and tension zones of the wall of 1.8 m is assumed for the design example. This would have to be confirmed in detailed design.

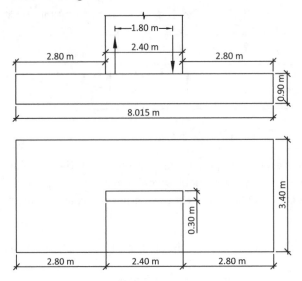

Footing elevation and plan

The factored footing loads must now be determined for both gravity, wind and seismic load combinations per the NBCC. Although not shown here, sliding would also need to be checked.

For the purpose of the example, for both the wind and seismic we have assumed a lever arm of 1.8 m between the compression and tension zone for determining the shear and bending moment diagrams. For the seismic load case, footing forces per clause 21.10.3.2.1 (b) for ULS combinations can be developed based on the Required Overturning Resistance M_r = 5590, and ULS = 500 kPa for bearing.

Furthermore, based on the following figure, all footing forces can be determined and are as shown in the following table where the Tension and Compression forces are calculated for each load case based on the following equations:

- $T_f = M_f / 1.8 \text{ m} - P_f / 2$

- $C_f = M_f / 1.8 \text{ m} + P_f / 2$

- Where P_f is the factored load in the wall (not including the footing weight)

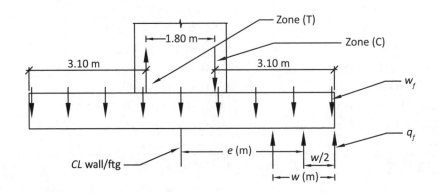

Zone Forces and Bearing Pressures for Various Load Combinations

Load Cases		Load Combinations	P_f (kN)	P_f (no ftg) (kN)	M_f (kN·m)	M_e (kN·m)	Zone (T) (kN)	Zone (C) (kN)	e (m)	w (m)	q_f (kPa)
D	1000 kN	1.4D	2208	1400	0		-700	700	0	8.015	81
L	400 kN	1.25D + 1.5L	2572	1850	0		-925	925	0	8.015	94
M_w	3214 kN·m	0.9D + 1.4W	1420	900	4500		2050	2950	3.170	1.676	249
$M_{E\,(noninal)}$	5590 kN·m	1.25D + 0.5L + 1.4W	2172	1450	4500		1775	3225	2.072	3.871	165
ULS	500 kPa	1.25D + 1.5L + 1.4W	2572	1850	1286		-211	1639	0.500	7.015	108
L ftg	8.015 m	1D + E	1577	1000		5590	2606	3606	3.544	0.928	500
h ftg	0.9 m	1D + 0.5L + E	1777	1200		5590	2506	3706	3.145	1.725	303
b ftg	3.4 m										
lever arm	1.8 m										

For each load combination, the resulting shear force and bending moments in the footing needs to be checked. To illustrate the shear design requirements we will consider load case 4 (1.25DL + 0.5L + 1.4W) and case 6 (1D + E). However, all load cases would need to be checked:

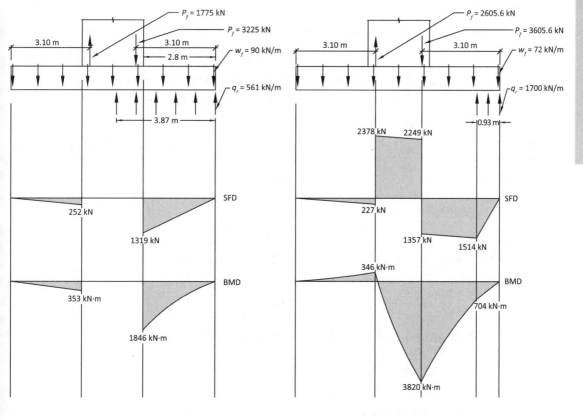

Load Case 4 (1.25D + 0.5L + 1.4W)   Load Case 6 (1D + 1E)

Shear Design of Footing (Using Simplified method)

For wind design in this example we can assume that the shear forces and bending forces in the footing only need be considered at the critical sections between the toe and face of wall and the forces in the footing below the wall need not be considered. However, for seismic, since the wall is moderatly ductile and a hinge at the base of the wall is assumed, we will assume the footing needs to be designed for the forces determined assuming the wall does not support (is not connected to) the footing between the zones.

Footing Parameters

$f_c' = 35$ MPa

β based on Clause 11.3.6.2 (Special Members) – does not apply since we do not satisfy

a)   as overall thickness is > 350 mm nor

b)   as the distance from zero shear to face of wall is $> 2 \times d_v$. Therefore, consider 11.3.6.3.

β based on Clause 11.3.6.3 (Simplified Method) – since we do not satisfy 11.3.6.2 (b) and assuming we do not provide minimum stirrups (per clause a), use clause b where:

$\beta = 230/(1000 + d_v)$ assuming minimum size of coarse aggregate 20 mm

$b = 3400$ mm

$h = 900$ mm   where: Bottom Cover   = 75 mm + 15 mm +30 mm/2 = 105 mm

                                         (15 M stirrups with 30 m Bottom Steel)

                      Top Cover   = 50 mm + 15 mm + 20 mm/2 = 75 mm

                                         (15 M stirrups with 20 m Top Steel)

$d = 900 - 105 = 795$ mm

d_v = the greater of 0.9d (715 mm) or 0.72h (648 mm)   Use 715 mm (Clause 3.2)

Calculation of V_c per Clause 11.3.4

- V_c (unreinforced) $= \phi_c \lambda \beta \sqrt{f_c'} b_w d_v$ where:

  $\phi_c = 0.65$ $\lambda = 1$

  $\beta = 230 /(1000 + d_v) = 0.134$ (Clause 11.3.6.3 (b))

  $f_c' = 35$ MPa $b = 3400$ $d_v = 715$

- $V_c = 0.65 \times 1 \times 0.134 \times \sqrt{35} \times 3400 \times 715 = 1252$ kN

Minimum Shear Stirrups if Required   per clause 11.2.8.1 where

a) $V_f > V_c$

b)   Beams deeper than 750mm

c)   Flexural members where $T_f > 0.25 T_{cr}$

Note: Footings exempt only where strut and tie per clause 11.4 is used.

Per clause 11.2.8.1, where not using strut and tie, minimum stirrups are required for footings per clause (a) where $V_f > V_c$

Minimum Shear Stirrups and Maximum Spacing per clause 11.2.8.1 and 11.3.8.1

- Maximum spacing not to exceed – $0.7d_v$ (500 mm) or 600 (Clause 11.3.8.1)

- Use 500 mm

- $A_v > 0.06\sqrt{f_c'}\,b_w s / f_y$ (Clause 11.2.8.1)

  $f_c' = 35$ MPa $\qquad b_w = 3400 \qquad s = 500$ mm $\qquad f_y = 400$ MPa

- $A_v \geq 0.06 \times \sqrt{35} \times 3400 \times 500 / 400 = 1508\,\text{mm}^2$

**Use 8 legs 15 M stirrups at 500 mm
o.c. throughout for minimum stirrups
Check $V_r > V_f$**

Shear Design for Wind in flexural regions per clause 11.3.2

Shear in Toe

- Per load combination 4, $V_f = 1319$ kN at face of wall.

- Per clause 11.3.2.1, considering $d_v = 715$ mm, check clause (a) to (c) to confirm using critical section at d_v from face of support

  a) Reaction forces in direction of applied shear does introduce compression into the member.

  b) There is no concentrated load causing a shear force $> 0.3\lambda\phi_c\sqrt{f_c'}\,b_w\,d_v$ within d_v from support.

  c) However, the load within d_v from face of support does increase the magnitude of shear at the face by > 20%, therefore check clause 11.3.2.2

- Per clause 11.3.2.2, since (a) and (b) of 11.3.2.1 were satisfied, use shear at $0.5\,d_v$ for critical section

  V_f @ $0.5\,d_v = 1325$ kN – 0.715 m / 2 × (563 – 90) = 1156 kN

  Since $V_f = 1156$ kN < $V_c = 1252$ kN no shear reinforcing is required for wind load case 4.

Shear Design for Seismic in flexural regions per clause 11.3.2

Shear in Toe

- Per load combination 6, $V_f = 1357$ kN at face of wall and increased to 1514 kN 1.89 m from face of wall then decreases to 0 at the toe.

- Per clause 11.3.2.1, considering $d_v = 715$ mm, there is no sense in reinforcing the footing based on shear at d_v. Since $V_f > V_c$ for most of the toe, provide minimum shear reinforcing per clause 11.2.8.1 a)

- Therefore V_c (reinforced) $= \phi_c \lambda \beta \sqrt{f_c'}\,b_w d_v$ (clause 11.3.4)

  where:

  $\phi_c = 0.65 \qquad\qquad \lambda = 1$

  $\beta = 0.18$ (Clause 11.3.6.3 (a))

$f_c' = 35$ MPa $b = 3400$ $d_v = 715$

- $V_c = 0.65 \times 1 \times 0.18 \times \sqrt{35} \times 3400 \times 715 = 1682$ kN   (clause 11.3.4)

- $V_r = \phi_s A_v f_y d_v \cot\theta / s$ (clause 11.3.5)

  where:

  $\phi_s = 0.85$ $A_v = 1600$ $f_y = 400$ $d_v = 715$

  $\cot\theta = 1.42$ where $\theta = 35°$ (clause 11.3.6.3)

- $V_s = 0.85 \times 1600 \times 400 \times 715 \times 1.42 / 500 = 1104$ kN

- $V_r = V_c + V_s = 1682 + 1104 = 2786$ kN $> V_f$ at all locations. Therefore, reinforce toe with minimums stirrups

Use 8 legs 15 M stirrups at 500 mm o.c. throughout toe each end footing

Shear Under Wall

- Since a possible hinge above the footing may occur, review the footing shear assuming the wall does not provide support to the footing in the zone under the wall.

- Per load case 6, $V_f = 2249$ kN to 2379 kN $> V_c$, use minimum stirrups throughout under the wall with $V_r = 2786$ kN

- Therefore, use 8 legs 15 M stirrups throughout.

Use 8 legs 15 M stirrups at 500 mm o.c. throughout under wall

Footing Design for both Wind and Earthquake

- Reinforce complete footing with 8 legs 15 M stirrups at 500 mm o.c. throughout the footing.

Example 9.7.7   Square Pile Cap Design

Determine the pile cap dimensions and reinforcement for the given column load and piles.

Factored column load: $P_f = 4800$ kN (No moment acts at the base of column).

Column size: 500×500 mm; $f_c' = 35$ MPa.

Factored pipe pile capacity (by the geotechnical consultant) is $P_r = 1300$ kN.

Pipe pile: DN300;   Ø323, 9×9.52, spaced at 4 pile diameters.

Pile cap concrete strength at 28 days: $f_c' = 30$ MPa.

Pile location tolerance is 50 mm in any direction.

1. Number of piles required: $n = 4800/1300 = 3.7$ thus use 4 piles.

    Maximum factored pile reaction is: $R_f = 4800/4 = 1200$ kN.

2. Preliminary depth based on sectional method

Since the pile cap will be ultimately designed by the S & T method, Clauses 11.3.2.1 b) and c) can be ignored. For pile cap designs where the S & T method is not used, the above clause needs to be considered. The plan geometry is shown in 9.7.7-1.a.

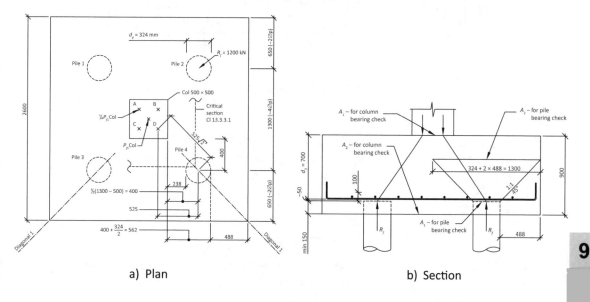

a) Plan   b) Section

Figure 9.7.7-1

9

Foundations

2.1 One-way shear

Calculation of V_f is described on Figure 9.7.7-2.a. Stress limits are set by Clause 11.3.6.2 and Equation (11-6) from Clause 11.3.4.

Equating $(0.65)(1)(0.21)\sqrt{30}(2.6)d_v = 2(1.2)\dfrac{0.288 + 0.324 - d_v}{0.324}$

where: b_w = 2.6 m;

                 β = 0.21

                 ϕ_c = 0.65

                 R_f = 1.2 MN

        c = 562 – 324 + 50 (construction tolerance) = 288 mm.

Thus, d_v = 0.48 m and d = 0.53 m. See Figure 9.7.7-3.a for the variation of V_f as a function of d_v. V_f = 0 at the outer edge of the pile at: 562 + 50 (tolerance) = 612 mm.

Note: Considering Clauses 11.3.2.1 b) and c), the shear would be taken at $d_v/2$ and the required d_v will be 0.8 m. These clauses can be ignored because the S & T method is being used for the design.

In the above equation $0 \leq V_f \leq 2400$ kN.

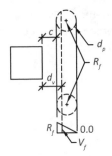

c – includes for construction tolerance

R_f – sum of pile reactions to be considered

V_f – factored shear in the critical section

$$\frac{R_f}{d_p} = \frac{V_f}{c+d_p-d_v}; \quad V_f = \frac{c+d_p-d_v}{d_p} \cdot R_f = r \cdot R_f$$

a) One-way shear

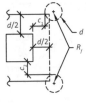

c_1 and c_2 – include for construction tolerance

V_f – $R_f - R_f(1-r_1)(1-r_2)$, shear proportional to the partial area beyond the critical section

V_f – $R_f(1-(1-r_1)(1-r_2))$

$$r_1 = \frac{c_1+d_p-\dfrac{d}{2}}{d_p}; \quad r_2 = \frac{c_2+d_p-\dfrac{d}{2}}{d_p}$$

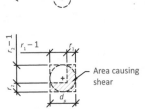

Note: The above linear approximation actually uses $A\, d_p \times d_p$ "square pile", as per Cl. 15.5.3.

b) Two-way shear

Figure 9.7.7-2

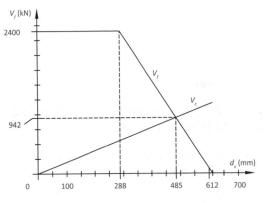

a) One-way shear   b) Two-way shear

Figure 9.7.7-3

2.2 Two-way shear

Determination of V_f is described in Figure 9.7.7-2.b. Stress limits are set by Clause 13.3.4.1.c.

Equating $0.38(1)(0.65)\sqrt{30}(4)(0.5+d)d = 4(1.2)\left\{1-\left(1-\dfrac{0.288+0.324-d/2}{0.324}\right)^2\right\}$

where the area of critical section $b_o d = 4(0.5+d)d$; $\phi_c = 0.65$ and $R_f = 4(1.2) = 4.8$ MN;

Calculation of c_1, with 50 mm tolerance considered: $c_1 = 400 - \dfrac{324}{2} + 50 = 288$ mm

From the $V_r = V_f$ equation $d = 0.705$ m ~ 0.7 m.

Note: Clause 13.3.4.4 is therefore not applicable.

See Figure 9.7.7-3.b for variation of V_f as a function of d. $V_f = 0$ at outer edge of pile (see Figure 9.7.7-2.b and c), which is 612 mm from the face of column.

In the above equation $0 \le V_f \le 4800$ kN.

For the S & T method $d = 700$ mm will be used; thus the total depth of the pile cap is $h = 700 + 30$ (assumed rebar diameter) $+ 150 \cong 900$ mm. Based on Clause 11.3.6.2 (b) this is a deep pile cap.

3. Strut-and-tie method

Bearing resistance, based on Equation (9.11) above is:

$f_b = 0.6\phi_c(30) + 6\alpha\beta\phi_c\sqrt{30} = 11.7 + 21.4\alpha\beta$ (MPa)

At column: A_2 – pile cap area, A_1 – column area

$\sqrt{\dfrac{A_2}{A_1}} = \sqrt{\dfrac{2.6^2}{0.5^2}} = 5.2 > 4$ thus $\alpha = 1.0$; $\beta = 0.33\left(\dfrac{2(0.7)}{0.5}-1\right) = 0.6$

thus $f_b = 11.7 + 21.4(1.0)(0.6) = 24.5$ MPa – bearing resistance

Factored bearing stress under the column is: $f_{bf} = P_f/A_c = 4.8/0.5^2 = 19.2$ MPa < 24.5 MPa.

At pile: $\sqrt{\dfrac{A_2}{A_1}} = \sqrt{\dfrac{650^2\pi}{162^2\pi}} = 4.01 > 4$ thus $\alpha = 1.0$; $\beta = 0.33\left(\dfrac{700}{324}-1\right) = 0.38$

$f_b = 11.7 + 21.4(1.0)(0.38) = 19.8$ MPa

Factored bearing stress is: $f_{bf} = R_f/A_p = 1.2/(0.162^2\,\pi) = 14.6$ MPa < 19.8 MPa.

4. Internal forces and reinforcement

See Figure 9.7.7-5 for arrangement of reinforcement.

4.1 Tie force and tie reinforcement (see Figure 9.7.7-4):

$T_{diag} = R_f/\tan\theta = 1200/\tan 43.3 = 1273$ kN $T_f = T_{diag}/\sqrt{2} = 900$ kN – factored tension.

$A_{s,required} = 1000\,T_f/(0.85\,f_y) = 2648$ mm^2 per tie.

9

Foundations

4.2 Minimum reinforcement:

$A_{s,min} = 0.002\,A_g = 0.002\,(1000)\,(900) = 1800\ mm^2/m$, thus a total of $A_{s,min} = 4680\ mm^2$ is required in each direction. Since the total tension tie reinforcement (in each direction) is

$2 \times 2648 = 5296\ mm^2$ is almost equal to $A_{s,min}$, distribute all reinforcement uniformly, thus use 11 – 25 M BEW. In case of significant difference between the tension tie and the minimum reinforcement, place the minimum reinforcement uniformly and concentrate the difference in the ties over the piles.

4.3 Dowels from piles into the pile cap:

Add dowels from piles into pile cap as per Clause 15.9.2.1.

$$A_{dowel} = 0.005\,(324/2)^2\,\pi = 412\ mm^2$$

It is a good practice to provide a minimum of 4 vertical dowels, tied.

Thus use: 4 – 15 M verticals with 15 M @240 mm ties, extend dowels into cap and pile for the tension development length. (Piles are filled with 25 MPa concrete.)

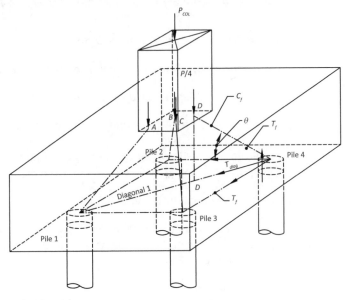

a) 3D-force diagram

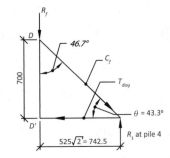

b) Along diagonal "1"

Figure 9.7.7-4

5. Comparing the Strut-and-Tie method with the sectional method

Bottom reinforcement by sectional method:

Factored moment at the face of the column:

$M_f = 2R_f\,(0.4) = 960\ kN \cdot m$.

$d = 900 - 150 - 30 = 720\ mm$ depth of compression stress block $a = 33\ mm$ tension reinforcement required based on the sectional method is thus: 4014 mm^2.

This reinforcement is significantly less than calculated by the S & T method.

The magnitude of under reinforcement is ~ 25%, see explanation under 9.5.2.3.3.

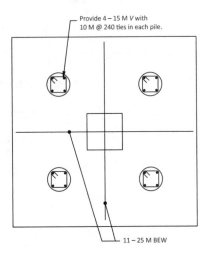

Figure 9.7.7-5 Reinforcement

Example 9.7.8   Rectangular Pile Cap Design

Determine pile cap dimensions and reinforcement for the given column load and piles. Due to construction and geometrical constraints the pile cap has to be rectangular.

Factored column load: P_f = 4400 kN (No moment acts at the base of column).

Column size: 400 × 500 mm; f_c' = 35 MPa. Factored pipe pile capacity (by the geotechnical consultant) is P_r = 600 kN. Pipe pile suggested by the geotechnical consultant is: DN200; Ø219.1 × 8.18, spaced at 4 pile diameters. Pile cap concrete strength at 28 days: f_c' = 30 MPa.

Pile location tolerance is 50 mm in any direction.

1. Number of piles required: n = 4400/600 = 7.33 thus use 8 piles

    Factored pile reaction is: R_f = 4400/8 = 550 kN

2. Preliminary depth is based on sectional method as discussed in Example 9.7.7.

    See Figure 9.7.8-1 for plan geometry.

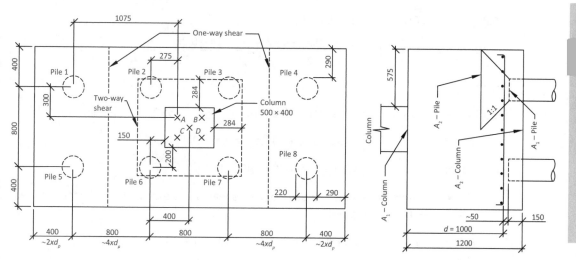

a) Pile cap plan and elevation

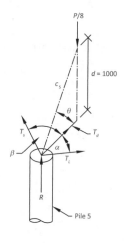

d = 1200 − 150 − a/2 = 1050 − (~30) = 1020 thus use 1000 mm

c_5 − compressive strut for pile 5

T_d − diagonal tension

T_s − tension in short direction

T_L − tension in long direction

$T_d = R / \tan\theta$

$T_L = T_d \cos\alpha$

$T_s = T_d \cos\beta$

$\beta = 90 = \alpha$

b) Strut-and-tie firces

Figure 9.7.8-1

2.1 One-way shear

Based on Figure 9.7.7-2.a, and assuming that the critical section is between the inner piles (2, 3, 6 and 7) and outer piles (1, 4, 5 and 8), and equating $V_c = V_f$ by using Clauses 11.3.4 and 11.3.6.2:

$$0.65(1)(0.21)\sqrt{30}(1.6)d_v = 2(0.55)$$

Solving for d_v, yields $d_v = 0.92$ m.

The critical section (at $920/2 = 460$ mm from the face of the column) is between the inner and outer piles as assumed.

2.2 Two-way shear

The location of indicated section (at $d/2$) is based on the assumption that piles 1, 4, 5 and 8 are fully outside of the critical section and that a portion of pile reactions of piles 2, 3, 6 and 7 will contribute to the factored shear. Equating V_c with V_f (Clause 13.3.4.1.c and using Figure 9.7.7-2.b):

$$0.38(1)(0.65)\sqrt{30}(2)((0.4+d)+(0.5+d))d =$$

$$= 4(0.55) + 4(0.55)\left\{1 - \left(1 - \frac{0.09 + 0.22 - d/2}{0.22}\right)\left(1 - \frac{0.14 + 0.22 - d/2}{0.22}\right)\right\}$$

Where:

$2((0.4 + d) + (0.5 + d))\, d$ is the shear surface area $\qquad$ 0.55 MN – pile reaction

$c_1 = 0.09$ m; $\qquad c_1 = 150 - 110 + 50 \text{ (tolerance)} = 90$ mm

$c_2 = 0.14$ m; $\qquad c_2 = 200 - 110 + 50 = 140$ mm

In the above equation we assume the point of zero shear is less than $2d$ from the face of the column (ie Clause 13.3.4.4 applies).

The solution yields $d = 568$ mm with $V_f = 3.13$ MN $< 8(0.55) = 4.4$ MN

Note: Clause 13.3.4.4 applies as assumed.

Based on one and two-way shear checks the largest value $d_v = 0.92$ m, thus $d = 1.02$ m ≈ 1.0 m will be used for the strut-and-tie check.

Pile cap total depth is $h = 1000 + 30$ (bar diameter) $+ 150 \approx 1200$ mm. This pile cap is classified as a deep pile cap based on Clause 11.3.6.2 (b).

3. Strut-and-tie method

The bearing resistance, based on previous example is: $\qquad f_b = 11.7 + 21.36\, \alpha\beta$

At column: $\qquad \sqrt{\dfrac{A_2}{A_1}} = \sqrt{\dfrac{1.6(3.2)}{0.4(0.5)}} = 5.06 > 4 \qquad$ thus $\alpha = 0.33\,(4.0 - 1) = 1.0$

$$h_{eff} = \sqrt{0.4(0.5)} \cong 0.5\,\text{m} \qquad \beta = 0.33\left(\frac{2(1.0)}{0.5} - 1\right) = 1.0$$

$f_b = 11.7 + 21.36\,(1)\,(1.0) = 33.1$ MPa

Factored bearing stress under the column: $f_{bf} = 4.4/(0.4\,(0.5)) = 22$ MPa < 33.1 MPa $\qquad$ OK

At pile: $\sqrt{\dfrac{A_2}{A_1}} = \sqrt{\dfrac{0.4^2}{0.11^2}} = 3.63$ thus $\alpha = 0.33(3.63 - 1) = 0.87$

$\beta = 0.33\left(\dfrac{1.0}{0.22} - 1\right) = 1.17 > 1$ thus $\beta = 1.0$

f_b = 11.7 + 21.36 (0.87) (1.0) = 30.3 MPa

Factored bearing stress over the pile top: $f_{bf} = \dfrac{0.55}{0.11^2\, \pi} = 14.5\,\text{MPa} < 30.3\,\text{MPa}$ OK

4.   Internal forces and reinforcement

See Figure 9.7.8.2 for arrangement of reinforcement.

4.1 Tie forces and reinforcement: See Figure 9.7.8-1b:

Pile No.	θ	α	β	T_d kN	T_s kN	T_L kN
1, 5, 4, 8	41.9	15.6	74.4	613	165	590
2, 3, 6, 7	67.9	47.5	42.5	224	165	151

Ties	Factored tension kN	$A_{s,\,required}$ mm²	$A_{s,\,provided}$ mm²
1-5; 4-8	165	485	1 – 25 M
2-6; 3-7	165	485	1 – 25 M
1-2; 5-6; 3-4; 7-8	590	1735	4 – 25 M
2-3; 6-7	590 +151 = 741	2179	5 – 25 M

4.2 Minimum reinforcement

$A_{s,min}$ = 0.002 A_g = 0.002 (1200) (1000) = 2400 mm²/m.

In short direction, $A_{s,min}$ = 3.2 (2400) = 7680 mm², which is more than the total tie reinforcement of 4 (500) = 2000 mm²; thus use 16 – 25 M BUL uniformly spaced.

In long direction,
$A_{s,min}$ = 1.6 (2400) = 3840 mm²,
which is less than the
total reinforcement of
2 (5) (500) = 5000 mm².

Since the difference between the minimum and the required tension tie reinforcement is relatively small use 10 – 25 M BLL uniformly spaced.

4.3 Dowels from Piles into the Pile cap: **Figure 9.7.8-2**

See explanation in example 9.7.7.

A_{dowel} = 0.005 (220/2)² π = 190 mm²

Since the area is very small use 2 – 15 M vertical for each pile without ties.

Example 9.7.9   Design of a Drilled Pile

Determine the reinforcement required for the uncased drilled pile with the following parameters:

    Pile shaft diameter: 1219 mm (auger size)

    Pile length: 12 m

    Concrete: $f_c' = 30$ MPa

Factored loads calculated at the top of the drilled pile:

    $P_f = 9800$ kN compression $V_f = 700$ kN shear

    Construction tolerance: $e = 75$ mm

Geotechnical parameters: Rock end bearing: $q_{sf} = 9.0$ MPa

                         Side friction: $v_s = 0.4$ MPa, in the lower 2 metres.

                         Linear spring constant in upper 10 m: $k_1 = 20$ MN/m³

                         Linear spring constant in lower 2 m: $k_2 = 750$ MN/m³

1. Establish structural model – see Figure 9.7.9-1a-b:

    Use reduced pile shaft diameter based on Clause 15.8.2.2, thus $d_p = 1169$ mm. Use this diameter for establishing all geometrical properties, bearing and side friction capacities and shaft resistance.

    Spring constants: Spring support spacing of 1.0 m c/c was used. The spacing is arbitrary, but a closer spacing will provide better results. In general terms the spring constant can be established as

    K_1 (MN/m) = k_1 (MN/m³) A (m²);

    where $A = 1.0$ (spring spacing) × reduced d_p (pile diameter), represents the shaft's bearing area concentric to the selected spring support. Thus:

    $K_1 = 20$ (1.169) (1.0) = 23.4 MN/m,

    $K_2 = 750$ (1.169) (1.0) = 876.7 MN/m – see Figure 9.7.9-1.a and b.

    The spring support reactions must be checked against the soil bearing capacity (not checked in this example) to ensure that the soil is capable of supporting the horizontal loads. In case the soil bearing capacity is exceeded, the geotechnical consultant may adjust the spring constants or a different pile diameter or length used to converge to equilibrium.

2. Bearing capacity check:

    Pile area: $A = 1.07$ m²   Pile perimeter: $C = 3.67$ m

    Bearing capacity check (compression): $B_r = 9$ (1.07) + 2 (3.67) (0.4) = 12.6 MN > 9.8 MN thus the size of the drilled pile is acceptable.

3. Cross sectional forces

    See Figure 9.7.9-1.c – f for the cross sectional forces. The cross sectional forces were established using SAP 2000 software.

4. Design of cross section:

    Based on Clause 15.8.2.3 an additional 0.9 reduction factor must be applied to the factored resistances defined in Clauses 10 and 11.

Shear design:

V_c: Based on Clause 11.3.4, Clause 11.2.10.3 ($b_w = d$), Clause 11.3.6.3 (a) ($\beta = 0.18$) and Clause 15.8.2.3: $d = 1169 - 75 - 15 - 35/2 = 1062$ mm; where 15 M ties, 75 mm cover and 35 M verticals are assumed. $d_v = 0.9d = 955$ mm,

$$V_c = 0.9(0.65)(1)(0.18)\sqrt{30}(1.062)(0.955) = 0.58 \text{ MN} < V_f = 0.7 \text{ MN}$$

Required V_s: $V_s = V_f - V_c$,   thus $V_{s,min} = 0.7 - 0.58 = 0.12$ MN.

Minimum area of shear reinforcement based on Equation (11-1) and 350 mm tie spacing:

$$A_{s,min} = 0.06\sqrt{30}\frac{1.062(0.35)}{400}10^6 = 305 \text{ mm}^2 / 350 \text{ mm}$$

Note: 15 M @ 350 mm stirrup spacing was used to increase the cage stiffness.

Calculating V_s: Using $\theta = 35°$ (Clause 11.3.6.3) and Clause 11.3.5.1

using 15 M @ 350 stirrups.

$$V_s = 0.9\phi_s A_v f_y d_v \cot\theta / s = 0.9 (0.85) 400 \times 10^{-6} (400) (0.955 \cot 35)/0.35 = 0.48 \text{ MN}$$

Calculation of V_r: $V_r = V_c + V_s = 0.58 + 0.48 = 1.06$ MN $> V_f = 0.7$ MN   Use 15 M @ 350 ties

Flexure: Use 12 – 30 M V

Note: In this example the interface between the pile cap and the pile shaft has not been addressed.

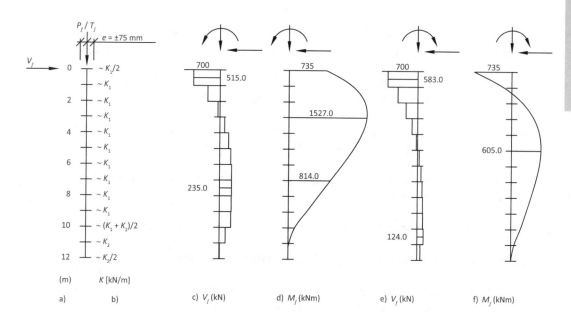

(m)   K [kN/m]

a)   b)   c) V_f (kN)   d) M_f (kNm)   e) V_f (kN)   f) M_f (kNm)

Figure 9.7.9-1

9.8 References

(1) National Building Code of Canada, 2015, National Research Council.

(2) James G. MacGregor and F. Michael Bartlett, Reinforced Concrete Mechanics and Design, Prentice Hall Canada Inc., 2000.

(3) Park R. and Paulay T.: Reinforced Concrete Structures, Wiley-Interscience Publication, John Wiley and Sons, Toronto, 1975.

(4) Joseph E. Bowles, Foundation Analysis and Design, 5th Edition, The McGraw-Hill Companies Inc., 1997.

(5) Edward J. Ulrich, Design and Performance of Mat Foundations – State of the Art Review, ACI-SP152, 1995.

(6) Suggested Analysis and Design Procedures for Combined Footings and Mats, ACI Manual of Concrete Practice 2003, ACI 336.2R-88 (Reapproved 2002).

(7) Design and Construction of Drilled Piles, ACI Manual of Concrete Practice 2003, ACI 336.3R-93 (Reapproved 1998).

(8) Canadian Foundation Engineering Manual

(9) Michael P. Collins and Denis Mitchell: Prestressed Concrete Structures, Response Publications, Canada, 1997.

(10) Adebar, P., Kuchma, D., and Collins, M.P., "Strut-and-Tie Models for the Design of Pile Caps: An Experimental Study," *ACI Structural Journal*, Vol. 87, No. 1, Jan.-Feb. 1990, pp. 81–92.

(11) Adebar, P., and Zhou, Z., "Bearing Strength of Compressive Struts Confined by Plain Concrete," *ACI Structural Journal*, Vol. 90, No. 5, Sept.-Oct. 1993, pp. 534–541.

(12) Adebar, P., and Zhou, Z, Design of Deep Pile Caps by Strut-and-Tie Models *ACI Structural Journal*, Vol. 93, No. 4, July-Aug. 1996, pp. 437–448.

(13) Adebar, P., "One-way shear strength of large footings," *Canadian Journal of Civil Engineering*, 27(3), June 2000, pp. 553–562.

(14) Concrete Design Handbook, Footings, Canadian Portland Cement Association, 1995.

(15) Concrete Reinforcing Steel Institute (CRSI), Design Handbook, 1996

(16) State of Ohio Department of Highways: Investigation of the strength of the connection between a concrete cap and the embedment end of a steel H-pile, 1947.

(17) Adebar, P., An evaluation of pile cap design methods in accordance with the Canadian design standard," *Canadian Journal of Civil Engineering*, Vol. 31, pp. 1123–1126.

(18) Design of Concrete Structures, CSA A23.3-14.

10

By Wayne Kassian

Prestressed Concrete

10.1 Notation

a = depth of equivalent rectangular compression block

A = area of that part of cross section between flexural tension face and centroid of gross section

A_c = area of concrete cross section

A_{cr} = area of cracked section

A_g = gross area of section

A_s = area of tension reinforcement

A_{sb} = minimum area of bottom reinforcement crossing one face of the periphery of a column and connecting the slab to the column or support to provide structural integrity

A_s' = area of compression reinforcement

A_p = area of prestressing tendons in tension zone

A_{tr} = area of uncracked transformed section

A_v = area of shear reinforcement perpendicular to the axis of the member

b = width of compression face member

b_o = perimeter of critical section for slabs

b_v = effective web width

b_w = width of web

c = neutral axis depth

C_r = factored axial load capacity of concrete stress block

C_t = creep coefficient

c_y = neutral axis depth assuming $f_{pr} = f_{py}$

d = effective depth (see Eq. 10.5.13)

d_p = effective depth for prestressing steel

d_s = effective depth for reinforcing steel

d = distance to centroid of compression steel from extreme compression fibre

d_v = effective shear depth

e = eccentricity of tendon

e_{cr} = eccentricity of tendons in cracked transformed section

e_{tr} = eccentricity of tendons in uncracked transformed section

E_c = modulus of elasticity of concrete

E_p = modulus of elasticity of prestressing tendons

E_s = modulus of elasticity of reinforcement

f_c = concrete stress at level considered

f_c' = specified concrete cylinder strength

f_{ce} = compression stress in the concrete due to effective prestress only (after allowance for all prestress losses) at the extreme fibre of a section where tensile stresses are caused by applied loads

f_{ci}' = concrete strength at prestress transfer

f_{cp} = effective prestress at the centroid of the section (see notation in Clause 2.3 of CSA A23.3)

f_{ns} = steel stress in non-prestressed reinforcement as defined in Eq. 10.5.18

f_{pe} = effective stress in prestressing tendons (after losses)

f_{po} = stress in prestressing tendons when the stress in the surrounding concrete is zero

f_{pr} = stress in prestressing tendons at factored resistance

f_{pi} = initial stress in tendon after stressing

f_{pu} = tensile strength of prestressing tendon

f_{py} = yield strength of prestressing tendon

f_{re} = intrinsic relaxation loss in prestressing tendons

f_r = modulus of rupture

f_s = difference in steel stress in the non-prestressed reinforcement as defined by Eq. 10.5.1 or Eq. 10.5.4 or stress in the non-prestressed tension reinforcement at factored resistance

10

Prestressed Concrete

f'_s = stress in compression reinforcement at factored resistance
f_y = specified yield strength of tension reinforcement
f'_y = specified yield strength of compression reinforcement
h = overall depth of member
h_f = depth of compression flange
I_c = moment of inertia of concrete section
I_{cr} = moment of inertia of the cracked section
I_e = effective moment of inertia
I_g = moment of inertia of gross concrete section
I_{tr} = moment of inertia of uncracked transformed section
J = property of the critical shear section analogous to the polar moment of inertia
k = c/d
k_p = factor for type of prestressing steel
k_1 = coefficient (Eq. 10.4.6)
k_y = coefficient for distance of centroid from compression fibre
K_u = coefficient = $M_r / f'_c bd_p^2$
ℓ = length of span
ℓ_d = development length
ℓ_o = effective length of tendon as described in Section 10.6.6
ℓ_n = length of clear span (two-way slabs)
ℓ_1 = length of span in the direction that moments are being determined, measured centre-to-centre of supports
ℓ_2 = length of span transverse to ℓ_n or transverse to ℓ_1
M_{cr} = cracking moment
M_D = moment due to specified dead load
M_{dc} = decompression moment
M_f = moment due to factored loads
M_g = moment due to girder weight
M_L = moment due to specified live load
M_{net} = moment due to net load
M_p = total moment due to prestressing
M'_p = primary moment due to prestressing
M''_p = secondary moment due to prestressing
M_r = factored moment resistance
M_s = moment due to specified loads
M_{sust} = sustained load moment
n = modular ratio
n_p = E_p/E_c
n_s = E_s/E_c
N = total number of post-tensioning tendons
p = coefficient (Eq. 10.5.14)
P = decompression force
$P_{(i)}$ = prestressing force before transfer
P_i = prestressing force after transfer
P_o = jacking force
P_r = axial load resistance
P_x = prestress force at distance × from jacking end
P_e = effective prestress force after all losses
P_s = force in non-prestressed reinforcement due to time-dependent effects
P_{ro} = factored axial load resistance of column with zero eccentricity
P_{rmax} = maximum factored load resistance (= 0.8 P_{ro})
r = radius of gyration

s	= sag of prestressing tendons or, spacing of shear reinforcement
s_1	= length of critical section (Eq. 10.8.6)
S	= section modulus for tension fibre
T	= factored tensile force in a group of bars
t	= time since prestressing (Eq. 10.4.6)
v_c	= shear stress resisted by concrete
v_f	= factored shear stress
v_r	= shear stress resistance
V_c	= shear force resisted by concrete
V_{cr}	= cracking shear resistance
V_f	= factored shear force
V_p	= shear resisted by prestressing
V_r	= factored shear resistance
V_{se}	= shear due to specified loads
w_{bal}	= portion of load balanced by prestressing
w_{net}	= portion of specified load not balanced by prestressing
w_s	= specified load
x	= distance from jacking end (m)
x_a	= length of cable affected by anchorage slip
y_{cr}	= distance to tension fibre being considered from centroid of cracked section
y_{tr}	= distance to extreme tension fibre from centroid of uncracked transformed section
z	= quantity limiting distribution of flexural tension reinforcement
α	= M_s/bd^2 (see Eq. 10.5.17) or, angular change of prestressing tendon between jacking end and point × (radians)
α_b	= b_w/b
α_c	= creep reduction coefficient determined from Fig.10.4
α_D	= load factor on dead load
α_f	= h_f/d
α_L	= load factor on live load
α_p	= load factor on prestressing force
α_r	= relaxation reduction coefficient from Fig. 10.3
α_1	= ratio of average stress in rectangular compression block to the specified concrete strength
β	= f_{pi}/f_{pu}, or factor accounting for shear resistance of cracked concrete
β_1	= ratio of depth of equivalent rectangular compression block to depth to neutral axis = a/c
Δf_c	= change in concrete stress
Δf_p	= change in prestress due to creep, shrinkage and relaxation
Δf_s	= change in stress in reinforcement due to creep and shrinkage
Δ_i	= initial deflection
ΔL	= anchor set
Δ_t	= time-dependent deflection
Δ_i^{su}	= initial deflection due to sustained load
Δ_t^{su}	= time dependent deflection due to sustained load
Δ_i^p	= initial deflection due to prestressing
Δ_t^p	= time dependent deflection due to prestressing
ΔP	= change in prestressing force (loss)
ΔP_{el}	= change in prestressing force due to elastic loss
ΔP_{elt}	= total change in prestressing force due to elastic loss in a post-tensioned member
ΔP_p	= force in prestressed reinforcement corresponding to f_c due to dead load and effective prestress
ΔP_s	= force in non-prestressed reinforcement corresponding to f_c due to dead load and effective prestress
ε_{ce}	= strain in concrete corresponding to a stress of f_{pe} in the steel and zero applied load

10

Prestressed Concrete

ε_p	= strain at level of prestressed reinforcement
ε_s	= strain in non-prestressed tension reinforcement
ε_{pe}	= strain in prestressing steel corresponding to f_{pe}
ε_{sh}	= shrinkage strain
ε_{total}	= total strain
ε_s'	= strain in compression reinforcement
ε_x	= longitudinal strain at mid-depth of the member due to factored loads
ε_y'	= yield strain of compression reinforcement
θ	= angle of inclination of diagonal compressive stresses to the longitudinal axis of member
μ	= coefficient of curvature friction
κ	= wobble friction coefficient
λ	= factor to account for low density concrete
ρ	= reinforcement area ratio
ρ_p	$= A_p / A_c$
ρ_s	$= A_s / A_c$
ϕ_c	= resistance factor for concrete
ϕ_s	= resistance factor for reinforcing bars
ϕ_p	= resistance factor for prestressing tendons
ω_{pu}	= reinforcement index
Ω	$= \Delta f_s / f_{pi}$

10.2   Introduction

This Chapter of the Handbook provides a summary of the procedures for the design of fully and partially prestressed concrete members in accordance with CSA Standard A23.3, Clause 18.

The design examples that are presented have been selected to provide a broad spectrum of practical cases. Due to the general nature of the examples, it is anticipated that the designer will find them to be useful when clarification of the text is required.

A list of useful references can be found at the conclusion of this chapter. Further information may be obtained from the current edition of the Design Manual for Precast and Prestressed Concrete published by the Canadian Precast Prestressed Concrete Institute, Ottawa, Canada.

Sign Convention

Throughout this Chapter a positive stress in concrete is tensile and a negative stress is compressive.

10.3   Permissible Concrete Stresses in Flexural members

10.3.1. General

The limits on permissible stresses in concrete given in Clause 18.3 provide for adequate serviceability but do not ensure adequate strength. Stresses are calculated using specified (unfactored) loads and compared with the given limits.

10.3.2. Permissible Concrete Stresses at Transfer

Clause 18.3.1 provides the limits of tensile and compressive concrete stresses immediately after transfer of the prestress force.

Whereas the tensile stresses may be exceeded, provided bonded reinforcement is added to resist the total tensile force (and developed in accordance with Clause 12), the extreme fibre stress in compression should not exceed $0.6 f'_{ci}$ unless tests or analyses show that performance will not be impaired. Beyond this limit creep increases non-linearly and the camber becomes unpredictable. In computing the prestress force immediately after transfer allowance should be made for losses due elastic shortening, shrinkage, relaxation of the tendons, temperature change and the anchorage seating. If the member is post-tensioned additional losses due to friction should be included.

10.3.3. Permissible Concrete Stresses due to Prestress and Specified Loads

Clause 18.3.2 provides the limits for tensile and compressive concrete stresses due to prestress and specified loads when cracking in the precompressed tensile zone is to be avoided. When cracking of the precompressed tensile zone is acceptable, the stress limit given in 18.3.2(c) can be exceeded, resulting in a partially prestressed member, that is subject to the additional requirements of Clause 18.3.3. The permissible extreme fibre stress in compression due to total load is $0.6 f'_c$ while that due to sustained loads is $0.45 f'_c$. Exceeding the permissible stresses due to sustained loads will cause excessive creep of the concrete and result in undesirably high deflections.

The prestress force should be reduced from the initial force, to allow for all prestress losses, when computing concrete stresses due to prestress and specified loads. Losses from the time of transfer are influenced by relaxation, creep, shrinkage, non-prestressed reinforcement, composite action and sustained loads, and may be calculated as discussed in Section 10.4. The calculation of permissible stresses is illustrated in Example 10.5.

10.3.4. Section Properties

The section properties (area, moment of inertia, section moduli and location of the section centroid) are calculated using traditional formulae. In addition, consideration must be given to the effect of openings at a particular cross section.

In general, the section properties should be calculated by taking into account the effects of the prestressed and non-prestressed reinforcement. However, in most practical cases the effects of reinforcement are small enough to be negligible. If a substantial quantity of non-prestressed reinforcement is required for a partially prestressed member, all reinforcement should be included when calculating the section properties.

For partially prestressed members (that are assumed to be cracked under application of specified loads), it is recommended that the designer use bilinear moment-deflection relationships to investigate instantaneous deflections. Alternatively, the effective moment of inertia can be calculated in accordance with Clause 9.8.2.3 and the deflection can then be calculated by substituting I_e for I_g in the deflection calculation.

10.3.5. Critical Section for Pretensioned Members

For concrete stresses immediately after transfer, the critical section is usually near the end of the element, although in elements with depressed or draped tendons, the stresses at mid-span or at the depressed points may also be critical and should be checked. The critical end stress in pretensioned elements occurs at the point where the prestressing force has been completely transferred to the concrete, usually assumed to be about 50 strand diameters from the end. For convenience, it is normal practice to calculate the stress at the end assuming full transfer and, only if necessary, check the stress at the transfer point.

10

Prestressed Concrete

Under uniform specified loads, the critical section in flexure is at mid-span for elements with straight tendons and near 40% of the span for elements with tendons depressed at the mid-point. For other combinations of specified load and tendon profile, the critical section can be found by analysis.

10.4   Prestress Losses and Deflection

10.4.1. General

The loss of prestress is defined as the difference between the initial prestress and the effective prestress. While the loss of prestress does not significantly affect the strength of a member it affects the serviceability, namely camber and deflection, the magnitude of the concrete stresses, and the extent of cracking in partially prestressed members. The prestress losses may be divided into instantaneous losses, that occur at the time of application of the prestressing force, and time-dependent losses, that develop after the prestressing force has been applied. In post-tensioned structures the instantaneous losses occur during the post-tensioning operation, as a result of curvature friction and wobble friction, anchor set, and elastic losses caused by sequential stressing of the tendons. In pretensioned members the instantaneous losses are due to the elastic shortening of the concrete only. The loss of prestress due to relaxation of the prestressing steel occurring before prestress transfer needs to be considered when calculating the prestress force being transferred to the concrete.

The time-dependent losses in post-tensioned and pretensioned concrete are due to creep and shrinkage of the concrete, and relaxation of the prestressing steel.

10.4.2. Instantaneous Losses

Elastic losses

In pretensioned members the elastic loss corresponds to the elastic strain at the level of the tendon due to the combined effects of prestressing force and the girder weight applied at transfer.

The change of force ΔP_{el} in the prestressing steel is accurately determined by the

Relation

$$\Delta P_{e\ell} = \left[\frac{P_{(i)}}{A_{tr}} + \frac{\left(P_{(i)}e_{tr} + M_g\right)}{I_{tr}} e_{tr} \right] \frac{E_p}{E_c} A_p \qquad (10.4.1)$$

where

$P_{(i)}$	= prestressing force before transfer (after deducting relaxation losses occurring prior to transfer)
A_{tr}	= area of uncracked transformed section (including transformed areas of prestressed and non-prestressed reinforcement)
I_{tr}	= moment of inertia of uncracked transformed section
e_{tr}	= eccentricity of tendons in uncracked transformed section
M_g	= moment due to girder weight
E_p	= modulus of elasticity of prestressing tendons
E_c	= modulus of elasticity of concrete
A_p	= area of prestressing tendons in tension zone

It should be noted that the prestressing force acting on the concrete is compressive and therefore is assumed to be negative in Eq. 10.4.1. In addition, eccentricities below the centroid of the section are taken as positive.

In post-tensioned members the overall elastic loss, $\Delta P_{e\ell t}$ is due to sequential stressing of the tendons and is given by

$$\Delta P_{e\ell t} = \frac{N-1}{2N} \Delta P_{e\ell}$$

(10.4.2)

where N is the total number of post-tensioning tendons.

Friction losses

The friction loss depends on the type of tendon and the type of duct used for a particular post-tensioning system.

Values of curvature friction μ, associated with the intentional curvature of a tendon, and of wobble friction, κ, associated with unintentional curvature of the duct, should be obtained from the manufacturers of the tendons. The range of values given in the table below serve as a guide to values that might be expected.

Type of tendon and sheath	Wobble Coefficient, κ per metre length x10⁻³	Curvature Coefficient, μ
Tendons in flexible metal sheathing		
Wire tendons	3.3 – 5.0	0.15 – 0.25
7 wire strand	1.6 – 6.5	0.15 – 0.25
high strength bars	0.3 – 2.0	0.08 – 0.30
Tendons in rigid metal sheath		
7 wire strand	0.70	0.15 – 0.25
Pre-greased tendons		
Wire tendons and 7 wire strand	1.0 – 6.5	0.05 – 0.15
Mastic coated tendons		
Wire tendons and 7 wire strand	3.3 – 6.6	0.05 – 0.15

10

Prestressed Concrete

The curvature friction coefficient is a proper friction coefficient, that is a dimensionless quantity, while the wobble friction coefficient is given per metre length.

The force at distance x from the jacking end of the tendon is

$$P_x = P_o e^{-(\mu\alpha + \kappa x)}$$

(10.4.3)

where

P_x = prestress force at distance x from jacking end

P_o = jacking force

μ = coefficient of curvature friction

α = total change in angle between jacking end and point x (in radians)

κ = wobble friction coefficient (m¹)

x = distance from jacking end to point where loss is desired (in metres).

Anchor set

Anchor set develops at the anchorage when the prestressing force is transferred to the anchorage due to the slip necessary to set the anchor. This results in a decrease of prestress over a certain distance from the anchor. Average values for the anchor set are 8 mm to 12 mm slip for 13 mm diameter and 15 mm diameter strands, respectively. The value of the anchor set for a particular prestressing system can be provided by the post-tensioning contractor.

The length, x_a, over which the stress in the tendon is affected is

$$x_a = \left[\frac{E_p A_p x_1}{\Delta P_{x_1}} \Delta L \right]^{1/2} \tag{10.4.4}$$

and the reduction in prestress at the anchor is

$$\Delta P = 2\,\Delta P_{x_1} \frac{x_a}{x_1} \tag{10.4.5}$$

In Eqns. 10.4.4 and 10.4.5:

ΔP_{x_1} = prestress loss at distance x_1 from jacking end

x_1 = arbitrary distance from jacking end; for best results x_1 should be about equal to x_a

ΔL = anchor set

Care should be taken to ensure that compatible units are used in these equations.

10.4.3. Time-dependent Losses

The time-dependent loss of prestress depends on the magnitude of creep and shrinkage of the concrete, the intrinsic relaxation of the prestressing steel, the concrete stress at the level of the tendon and the section parameters. The intrinsic relaxation is the relaxation obtained from tests under constant strain.

The creep and shrinkage can be predicted with the information provided in Chapter 1, Section 1.2.3 and Table 1.2.

In lieu of detailed information from the manufacturer the intrinsic relaxation of prestressing tendons may be predicted as

$$f_{re}(t) = \frac{\log t}{k_1} \left(\frac{f_{pi}}{f_{py}} - 0.55 \right) f_{pi} \tag{10.4.6}$$

In this equation

$f_{re}(t)$ = intrinsic relaxation at time t (under constant strain)

f_{pi} = initial stress in tendon after stressing

f_{py} = 0.85 f_{pu} for stress relieved wires and strands

= 0.90 f_{pu} for low relaxation strands

f_{pu} = tensile strength of prestressing tendon

t = time since prestressing (hours)

k_1 = 10 to 12 for stress relieved steel

= 45 for low relaxation steel

Assuming 50 years as the lifetime of the structure the final value for the intrinsic relaxation of stress-relieved steel (with $k_1 = 12$) is:

$$f_{re} = 0{,}470 \left(\frac{f_{pi}}{f_{py}} - 0.55 \right) f_{pi} \tag{10.4.7}$$

and for low relaxation steel (with $k_1 = 45$)

$$f_{re} = 0.125 \left(\frac{f_{pi}}{f_{py}} - 0.55 \right) f_{pi} \tag{10.4.8}$$

These equations are valid for temperatures up to 20°C. At higher temperatures the relaxation increases (see Fig. 10.2).

The loss of prestress, Δf_p, for a member with one layer of tendons and non-prestressed steel at about the same level can be estimated from the relation (Ref. 10.1)

$$\Delta f_p = \frac{n f_c C_t + \varepsilon_{sh} n E_c + f_{re}}{1 + n(\rho_p + \rho_s)(1 + e^2/r^2)(1 + 0.8 C_t)} \tag{10.4.9}$$

where

n = average modular ratio

f_c = concrete stress at level of tendon due to sustained load and initial prestressing force P_i

C_t = creep coefficient

ε_{sh} = shrinkage strain

ρ_p = A_p / A_c

ρ_s = A_s / A_c

A_c = area of concrete cross section

e = eccentricity of tendon

r^2 = I_c / A_c

I_c = moment of inertia of concrete section

The factor 0.8 in the denominator is the value of the so-called aging coefficient (Ref. 10.2 and 10.3) assumed for practical creep calculations. Since the relaxation loss is considerably reduced by the creep and shrinkage of the concrete, the intrinsic loss f_{re} may be replaced by a reduced value $\alpha_r f_{re}$. The coefficient α_r is determined from Fig. 10.3 using the parameters $\beta = f_{pi}/f_{pu}$ and $\Omega = \Delta f_s/f_{pi}$. The stress f_{pi} is the initial stress applied to the tendon, f_{pu} is the tensile strength of the tendon, and Δf_s is the loss of prestress due to creep and shrinkage only.

$$\Delta f_s = \frac{n f_c C_t + \varepsilon_{sh} n E_c}{1 + n(\rho_p + \rho_s)(1 + \frac{e^2}{r^2})(1 + 0.8 C_t)} \tag{10.4.10}$$

The value Δf_s is also the time-dependent stress in the non-prestressed steel, the centroid of which is assumed to coincide with that of the prestressing steel. The total reduction in the compression acting on the concrete is

$$\Delta P = \Delta f_p A_p + \Delta f_s A_s \tag{10.4.11}$$

Since the stress at the level of the tendon, f_c, is normally compressive, and ε_{sh} and Δf_{re} are always negative, both Δf_p and Δf_s are always negative, resulting in a reduction of the tension in the tendon and an increased compression in the non-prestressed steel (see Examples 10.5 and 10.6.).

10

Prestressed Concrete

If the non-prestressed steel is uniformly distributed throughout the section the term ρ_s in the denominator of eq. 10.4.9 is omitted, and the creep and shrinkage coefficients are multiplied by the creep reduction coefficient α_c depicted in Fig. 10.4 as a function of ρn and the creep coefficient C_t. Thus:

$$\Delta f_p = \frac{n f_c \alpha_c C_t + \varepsilon_{sh} \alpha_c n E_c + f_{re}}{1 + n \rho_p (1 + e^2/r^2)(1 + 0.8 \alpha_c C_t)} \tag{10.4.12}$$

For detailed treatment of the general case with multiple layers of steel see References 10.1 and 10.2.

10.4.4. Deflections

Two different cases are encountered when computing the deflection of prestressed concrete members namely, uncracked and cracked members. These two cases will be discussed separately.

Uncracked members

The elastic deflections at the time of prestressing are calculated by conventional methods of analysis. The downward deflection due to gravity load is reduced by the upward deflection (camber) due to prestressing. Expressions for computing the camber for the most common tendon profiles are given in Fig. 10.5. Expressions for deflections due to other types of loading are given in Table 1.14.

The initial deflection due to prestressing force is calculated using the initial prestressing force, P_i.

The time-dependent deflections Δ_t^{su} due to sustained loads are obtained by multiplying the initial deflections Δ_i^{su} by the creep coefficient C_t giving

$$\Delta_t^{su} = \Delta_i^{su} C_t \tag{10.4.13}$$

The time-dependent deflections due to prestressing are obtained from the following equation

$$\Delta_t^p = \Delta_i^p [C_t - \frac{\Delta P}{P_i}(1 + 0.8 C_t)] \tag{10.4.14}$$

The term $\Delta_i^p C_t$ is the time-dependent deflection assuming that the prestressing force is constant and equal to P_i. The second term in the square bracket is due to the prestress loss ΔP as defined by Eq. 10.4.11. Equation 10.4.14 includes the effect of shrinkage on deflection. The general case with multiple layers of steel is discussed in References 10.1 and 10 2.

The calculation of the deflection due to prestress by using the effective prestress leads to less accurate results, which may, however, still be acceptable considering the uncertainty of the values of creep and shrinkage.

Cracked members

Partially prestressed members are designed so that cracking may be expected under full specified loads. The deflection may be calculated using an effective moment of inertia of the cracked section or a bilinear moment curvature diagram. Such a diagram may be established using the information given in Section 10.5, using Fig. 10.7 for rectangular sections and using Figs. 10.8.1 to 10.8.16 for T-beams, or in Table 10.2.

The effective moment of inertia for a cracked prestressed concrete beam is expressed by the relation:

$$I_e = I_{cr} + (I_{tr} - I_{cr})(\frac{M_{cr}}{M_s - M_{dc}})^3 \le I_g \tag{10.4.15}$$

where

$$M_{cr} = f_r I_{tr}/y_{cr} \qquad (10.4.16)$$

$$M_{dc} = f_{pd} I_{tr}/y_{tr} \qquad (10.4.17)$$

In these equations

I_{cr} = moment of inertia of cracked section

I_{tr} = moment of inertia of the uncracked transformed section, or less accurately of the gross section

y_{tr} = distance to extreme tension fibre from centroid of uncracked transformed section

f_{pd} = concrete stress due to effective prestress at the extreme fibre where tensile stresses are caused by applied loads (negative value)

M_s = maximum moment due to specified loads

In continuous structures the average value of I_e has to be established. This is discussed in Chapter 6.

Further details about the calculation of deflections of partially prestressed members are found in Ref. 10.4.

10.5   Partially Prestressed Members

In many prestressed concrete structures it is not likely that the full specified load will be applied during the lifetime of the structure. It is therefore possible to design the structural members so that some cracking will occur under full specified load if it should be applied. Under the dead load, however, cracking should normally not occur.

The advantages of partial prestressing are:

- a reduction of camber

- a reduction in prestress force that may allow an increase of the tendon eccentricity

- reduction of cracking in the end zones of post-tensioned structures

- a reduction in relaxation loss where partial prestressing is achieved by a lower stress in the tendon

Partial prestressing may be achieved in different ways:

(1) By providing non-prestressed steel in addition to the prestressing tendons. This would normally occur in post-tensioned construction

(2) By reducing the effective prestress below the maximum allowable stress and relying on the increase in tendon stress after decompression and cracking to resist the increase in moment. This is a useful option in pretensioned construction because of difficulties in placing non-prestressed steel.

In order to assure that the cracks developing in a partially prestressed member are within acceptable limits, crack width criteria similar to those for reinforced concrete have to be satisfied.

For the calculation of the quantity z the same equation (Eq. 10-6 in the Code) as for reinforced concrete members has been adopted. In this equation, the steel stress f_s is the increase in stress in the reinforcing or (bonded) prestressing steel beyond the state of decompression.

The steel stress increase f_s may be calculated as the stress corresponding to the difference between the moment due to specified loads M_s and the decompression moment M_{dc} according to:

$$f_s = \frac{M_s - M_{dc}}{(A_p + A_s)d} \qquad (10.5.1)$$

The decompression moment M_{dc} is the moment that reduces the compressive stress on the tensile face of a prestressed member to zero. It should be emphasized that the decompression moment does not correspond to the state of decompression of the whole section. Complete decompression requires the removal of the bending moment due to applied loads and the application of the fictitious decompression force, P, as discussed below.

Equation 10.5.1 gives reasonable results for most members, but for members with a small value of ρ it is normally conservative. For this reason a more detailed method of calculating f_s is presented here (see Ref 10.5).

The rigorous calculation of f_s for a given moment M_s is complicated since it is undertaken for a cracked section subjected to an axial force and a bending moment, and because creep and shrinkage of the concrete put the non-prestressed steel in compression and thus reduce the compression in the precompressed tension fibres. The reference point for the determination of f_s is zero stress in the concrete section. The following fictitious decompression force would create zero stress throughout the concrete section:

$$P = P_e + \Delta P_p + P_s + \Delta P_s \qquad (10.5.2)$$

where

P_e = effective prestress (after all losses)

$\Delta P_p = \dfrac{-f_c}{E_c} E_p A_p$

= force in tendons corresponding to the concrete stress f_c at the level of the tendon under dead load and effective prestress

P_s = force in the non-prestressed steel due to time-dependent strain in the non-prestressed steel

$\Delta P_s = \dfrac{-f_c}{E_c} E_s A_s$

= force in non-prestressed steel corresponding to the concrete stress f_c at the level of the non-prestressed steel under dead load and effective prestress.

The concrete stress f_c is negative when compressive, and the forces ΔP_p and ΔP_s are normally small and may be neglected.

The effective prestress $P_e = A_p(f_{pi} - \Delta f_p)$ where f_{pi} is the initial prestress and Δf_p is calculated according to Eq.10.4.9.

The time-dependent force in the non-prestressed steel

$$P_s = A_s \Delta f_s \qquad (10.5.3)$$

where Δf_s is defined by Eq. 10.4.10.

With the decompression force P, known, the steel stress under specified load is equal to n times the concrete stress at the level of the steel:

$$f_s = (\frac{P}{A_{cr}} + \frac{P\,e_{cr} + M_s}{I_{cr}} y_{cr}) n \qquad (10.5.4)$$

In this equation the terms with subscript "cr" refer to the cracked sections. The parameter y_{cr} is the distance of the steel considered from the centroid of the cracked section, and n is the modular ratio for the steel considered (i.e. n_s or n_p).

Cracked section properties

The cracked section properties for a given section are dependent on the decompression force P and the moment M_s due to specified loads.

The calculation of the cracked section properties involves the determination of the neutral axis depth, c, the centroidal depth of the section, y_{cr}, the area, A_{cr}, and the moment of inertia, I_{cr}. With the notation and the forces of Fig. 10.6 we have to solve the following cubic equation in c for the general case of T-section (Ref. 10.5)

$$\frac{1}{3}Pc^3 - \frac{1}{2}[M_s - P(d_p - c)]bc^2 + \left[\begin{array}{c} n_sA_s(d_s - c)^2 \\ + n_pA_p(d_p - c)^2 \end{array}\right]P + [n_sA_s(d_s - c) + n_pA_p(d_p - c)] \qquad (10.5.5)$$

$$x[M_s - P(d_p - c)] - \frac{1}{3}P(b - b_w)(c - h_f)^3 + \frac{1}{2}(b - b_w)(c - h_f)^2[M_s - P(d_p - c)] = 0$$

The centroidal depth, area and the moment of inertia of the cracked section are, respectively:

$$y_{cr} = \frac{\frac{1}{2}(b - b_w)h_f^2 + \frac{1}{2}b_wc^2 + n_sA_sd_s + n_pA_pd_p}{(b - b_w)h_f + b_wc + n_sA_s + n_pA_p} \qquad (10.5.6)$$

$$A_{cr} = b_wc + (b - b_w)h_f + n_sA_s + n_pA_p \qquad (10.5.7)$$

$$I_{cr} = \frac{1}{12}[h_f^3(b - b_w) + b_wc^3] + \left[(y_{cr} - \frac{h_f}{2})^2(b - b_w)h_f\right] + (y_{cr} - \frac{c}{2})^2 b_wc \qquad (10.5.8)$$

$$+ (d_s - y_{cr})^2 n_sA_s + (d_p - y_{cr})^2 n_pA_p$$

For rectangular sections $b = b_w$, so that Eqns. 10.5.5 to 10 5.8 simplify to:

$$\frac{1}{3}Pc^3 - \frac{1}{2}[M_s - P(d_p - c)]bc^2 + [n_sA_s(d_s - c)^2 + n_pA_p(d_p - c)^2]P \qquad (10.5.9)$$

$$+ [n_sA_s(d_s - c) + n_pA_p(d_p - c)][M_s - P(d_p - c)] = 0$$

$$y_{cr} = \frac{\frac{1}{2}bc^2 + n_sA_sd_s + n_pA_pd_p}{bc + n_sA_s + n_pA_p} \qquad (10.5.10)$$

$$A_{cr} = bc + n_sA_s + n_pA_p \qquad (10.5.11)$$

$$I_{cr} = \frac{1}{12}bc^3 + (y_{cr} - \frac{c}{2})^2 bc + (d_s - y_{cr})^2 n_sA_s + (d_p - y_{cr})^2 n_pA_p \qquad (10.5.12)$$

Assuming $(A_s + A_p)$ to be located at

$$d = \frac{A_sE_sd_s + A_pE_pd_p}{A_sE_s + A_pE_p} \qquad (10.5.13)$$

and introducing the parameters $\quad k = c/d \quad \alpha_b = b_w/b \quad p = Pd_p/M_s \quad \alpha_f = h_f/d \quad$ and

$$np\,\frac{A_sE_s + A_pE_p}{E_c\,bd} \qquad (10.5.14)$$

the neutral axis depth coefficients for T-Sections and rectangular sections, respectively, can be expressed by

$$k^3p - 3k^2(p-1) - 6n\rho(1-k) - (1-\alpha_b)(k-\alpha_f)^2(kp + 2p\alpha_f - 3p + 3) = 0 \qquad (10.5.15)$$

$$k^3p - 3k^2(p-1) - 6n\rho(1-k) = 0 \qquad (10.5.16)$$

Knowing k, the section properties can be determined and the steel stress f_s, calculated using Eq. 10.5.4. To facilitate determination of f_s, Figs. 10.7 and 10.8.1 to 10.8.15 have been established expressing f_s in the non-dimensional form $f_s/(n\alpha)$ as a function of $n\rho$ for different values of p. The term n is the modular ratio and

$$\alpha = \frac{M_s}{bd^2} \qquad (10.5.17)$$

If the two steels are not located at the same level, the stress in the non-prestressed steel is:

$$f_{ns} = f_s \frac{d_s - kd}{d(1-k)} \qquad (10.5.18)$$

The use of the design charts is demonstrated in Examples 10.6 and 10.9.

10.6   Factored Flexural Resistance

10.6.1. Introduction

The factored flexural resistance of an element must be greater than the moment due to factored load.

$$M_r \geq M_f$$

The factored flexural resistance can be determined for any section using procedures that take into account equilibrium and strain compatibility. For many sections a satisfactory approximate solution can be obtained using the Equations (18-1) and (18-2) to determine the stress in the tendons at factored resistance. Equation (18-2) differs slightly from the previous CSA Standard A23.3-M 94.

Figure 10.1 provides typical stress-strain curves for 1860 MPa strand commonly used in Canada. Grade 1720 MPa strand is not commonly used and is provided for historical reference only. Tables 1.3 and 1.4 provide sizes and properties for strand, wire and deformed prestressing bars.

Typical concrete strengths for prestressed concrete members range from 30 to 50 MPa. Release strengths f'_{ci} will generally be in the range from 20 to 30 MPa.

10.6.2. Analysis of Section Reinforced with Bonded Tendons and Non-prestressed Steel

Provided $f_{pe} > 0.6 f_{py}$ and c/d_p is not greater than 0.5, the stress in the prestressing tendons at factored resistance, f_{pr}, may be found from the approximate equation given in Clause 18.6 :

$$f_{pr} = f_{pu}[1 - k_p(c/d_p)] \qquad (18-1)$$

where $k_p = 2(1.04 - f_{py}/f_{pu})$

The term k_p accounts for the different shapes of the stress-strain curves for the different types of prestressing steel and values of f_{py}/f_{pu} for typical prestressing steels are given in Clause 18.4 of A23.3. The term c/d in Eq. 18-1 may be found from a consideration of the conditions in a section at factored resistance. Fig. 10.6.2 shows the strain distribution and related stress block for a T-section containing prestressed and non-prestressed tensile reinforcement, as well as non-prestressed compression reinforcement. Equilibrium of forces in the section requires

$$\phi_s A'_s f'_s + \alpha_1 \phi_c f'_c h_f (b - b_w) + \alpha_1 \phi_c f'_c a b_w = \phi_p A_p f_{pr} + \phi_s A_s f_s$$

Substituting for f_{pr} from Eq. 18-1, setting $a = \beta_1 c$ and rearranging gives

$$\frac{c}{d} = \frac{\phi_p A_p f_{pu} + \phi_s A_s f_s - \phi_s A'_s f'_s - \alpha_1 \phi_c f'_c h_f (b - b_w)}{\alpha_1 \phi_c f'_c \beta_1 b_w d_p + \phi_p k_p A_p f_{pu}}$$

The depth of the equivalent rectangular stress block may be found from the figure below in a similar manner and is given by:

$$a = \frac{\phi_p A_p f_{pr} + \phi_s A_s f_s - \phi_s A'_s f'_s - \alpha_1 \phi_c f'_c h_f (b - b_w)}{\alpha_1 \phi_c f'_c b_w}$$

and the factored resistance is

$$M_r = \phi_p A_p f_{pr}(d_p - a/2) + \phi_s A_s f_s(d_s - a/2) - \phi_s A'_s f'_s (d' - a/2)$$

$$\alpha_1 \phi_c f'_c h_f (b - b_w)\left(\frac{h_f}{2} - \frac{a}{2}\right)$$

The stresses f_s and f'_s will generally be equal to f_y and f'_y respectively. If the strain at the level of the reinforcing steel is less than the yield strain a strain compatibility analysis will be needed to establish these stresses.

The above is the most general formulation. All of the simpler cases can be determined by eliminating the redundant terms. If $a < h_f$ the section should be treated as a rectangular section with $b_w = b$.

A step-by-step analysis of a section using both the code equation and strain compatibility to determine f_{pr} is illustrated in Example 10.1. In this example the stress-strain curve for Grade 1860 low-relaxation strand of Fig 10.1 is used.

10

Prestressed Concrete

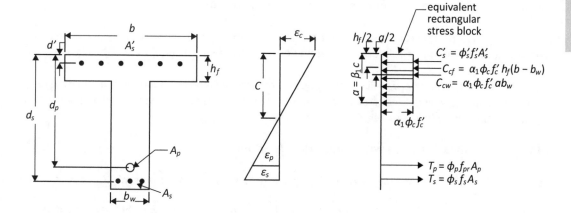

Figure 10.6.2

10.6.3. Minimum Factored Flexural Resistance

Based on Clause 18.7 flexural members (except 2-way slabs) must be designed so that

$$M_r > 1.2M_{cr} \quad \text{unless} \quad M_r > 1.33M_f$$

The cracking moment M_{cr} is given by: $M_{cr} = -P_e(e + S/A_c) + f_r S$

where

P_e	=	effective prestress force after losses
e	=	eccentricity of tendon
A_c	=	area of concrete cross section
f_r	=	modulus of rupture = $0.6\lambda \sqrt{f_c'}$ MPa
S	=	section modulus for tension fibre

It should be noted that P_e is a compressive force on the concrete and should be taken as negative in calculating M_{cr}

10.6.4. Design Tables

Tables 10.1(a) and (b) provide a simple way of quickly estimating the capacity of a given section or establishing the required size of a design section. The tables include the values of k_p for common prestressing steels, as well as α_1 and β_1 for concrete strengths ranging from 30 to 80 MPa.

It should be noted that $\phi_c = 0.65$ has been assumed in Table 10.1 (a). However, Clause 16.1.3 permits a value of $\phi_c = 0.70$ to be used for precast elements manufactured in certified plants, so $\phi_c = 0.70$ has been assumed in Table 10.1 (b)

The use of Table 10.1.(b) is illustrated in Example 10.4.

10.6.5. Over-Reinforced Sections with Bonded Tendons

It is generally not economical to design over-reinforced beams. These will occur only in rare instances when for some reason more reinforcement than desired must be used.

In over-reinforced sections c/d_p will generally be greater than 0.5 and the approximate equation for f_{pr} cannot be used. However, the approximate equation can still be used to provide a starting point for an iterative strain-compatibility and equilibrium analysis.

10.6.6. Analysis of Section with Unbonded Tendons

Equation (18-2) differs from that used in CSA Standard A23.3-94 in that the term $\sum_n (d_p - c_y)$ now clarifies how to apply this equation to continuous beams where d_p may vary between positive and negative moment regions.

The approximate equation prescribed by Clause 18.6.2(b) of the standard is the following:

$$f_{pr} = f_{pe} + \frac{8000}{\ell_0} \sum_n (d_p - c_y) \leq f_{py} \qquad (18\text{-}2)$$

where $\displaystyle\sum_{n} \left(d_p - c_y\right)$ is the sum of the distance $(d_p - c_y)$ for each of the plastic hinges in the span under consideration.

$$c_y = \frac{\phi_p A_p f_{py} + \phi_s A_s f_s - \phi_s A_s' f_s' \alpha_1 \phi_c f_c' h_f (b - b_w)}{\alpha_1 \phi_c \beta_1 f_c' b}$$

and ℓ_0 = overall length of tendon between anchors.

This equation emphasizes the importance of making a realistic assessment of the number of plastic hinges that would have to develop before the particular span under consideration would collapse. The analysis of a section with unbonded tendons is illustrated in Example 10.2 and 10.9.

10.6.7. Prestressed Members Subjected to Flexure and Axial Loads

The design of these members is usually carried out by choosing a section and the reinforcing, and then calculating a sufficient number of points on an interaction diagram to establish whether the design is adequate.

The procedure can most easily be illustrated by a sample Calculation as indicated in Example 10.3. The easiest approach is to assume a series of neutral axis locations with the strain of 0.0035 at the extreme compression fibre and to then determine the corresponding values of P_r and M_r.

10.7 Factored Shear Resistance

As discussed in Chapter 4, the shear resistance attributed to the concrete is calculated using Eq. (11-6). The value of β can be determined using the simplified method, the general method, or taken as 0.21 for special member types in accordance with Clause 11.3.6.2. When using the simplified method, the maximum yield strength limit of 400 MPa in Clause 11.3.6.3 is intended for non-prestressed reinforcement only. For prestressed members, this yield strength limitation does not apply.

The application of the methods for shear design of reinforced concrete members is explained in detail in Chapter 4. For this reason only the differences between non-prestressed and prestressed concrete members with regard to shear design are discussed here.

First, the shear force due to prestressing, V_p, may be included in the shear resisted by concrete, Eq. (11-4). Second, due to prestressing the longitudinal strain, ε_x at mid-depth of the member is affected by the prestressing force $A_p f_{po}$ in the numerator of Eq. (11-13) and by the term $E_p A_p$ in the same equation. The stress f_{po} represents the stress in the prestressing tendons at decompression, that is defined as the tendon stress when the strain in the surrounding concrete is zero. In lieu of detailed calculations, f_{po} may be taken as $0.7 f_{pu}$ for bonded tendons outside the transfer length and f_{pe} for unbonded tendons.

As for reinforced concrete the longitudinal strain at mid-depth ε_x shall not be taken greater than 0.003 (Clause 11.3.6.4 (f)) and if ε_x is negative, it shall not be taken less than -0.0002, (Clause 11.3.6.4 (c)).

10.8 Prestressed Concrete Slabs

10.8.1. General

In Chapter 5 the analysis and design of reinforced concrete slabs is discussed in detail. In this section only those aspects of the design of prestressed slabs that are different from reinforced slabs will be discussed. Only unbonded slabs are considered here.

10

Prestressed Concrete

While the design of reinforced concrete slabs is done only for factored loads, prestressed slabs, as all other prestressed members, also have to satisfy the permissible stress criteria of Clause 18.3.2 or in the case of partially prestressed members have to satisfy crack control criteria under specified loads (Clause 18.3.3).

10.8.2. One-Way Slabs

The design of one-way prestressed slabs is essentially a wide beam design. The only difference is the amount of transverse non-prestressed steel required that is normally governed by the minimum requirements of Clause 7.8. The thickness of continuous one-way slabs prestressed slabs may be taken as $\ell/40$ to $\ell/50$.

The analysis of one-way slabs subjected to uniform loading is efficiently done by the load balancing method whereby a certain fraction of the dead load is balanced by the upward load caused by prestressing. For normal live loads about 75 to 85 percent of the dead load needs to be balanced if no cracks are allowed (i.e. satisfying Clause 18.3.2c). For partially prestressed slabs only about 60 percent of the dead load needs to be balanced.

For a parabolic tendon profile, the load balanced by the effective prestress

$$w_{bal} = \frac{8 P_e s}{\ell^2}$$ (10.8.1)

where

P_e = effective prestress after all losses (normally per metre width)

s = sag of tendon

ℓ = length of span measured centre-to-centre of supports

The balanced load and prestressing result in zero flexural stress so that only an axial stress P_e/A_c, is present, where A_c is the cross sectional area of the slab per metre width. Bending moments are caused only by the net load

$$w_{net} = w_s - w_{bal}$$ (10.8.2)

where w_s = specified load (dead load plus live load).

The moments due to w_{net} are determined by established methods of structural analysis.

If the flexural tensile stresses exceed the value permitted in Clause 18.3.2(c), the criteria of Clause 18.3.3 have to be satisfied. The moment due to factored loads is calculated in accordance with Eq. 10.8.3.

10.8.3. Two-Way Slabs

Slab Thickness

Prestressed slabs can be considerably more slender than non-prestressed slabs. The thickness h may range between $\ell/40$ to $\ell/50$ with $\ell/45$ being a frequently used value. Because of the smaller thickness, punching shear becomes more critical, particularly at exterior columns. Drop panels or shear reinforcement may be provided to increase the shear resistance locally if it is not desirable to increase the overall slab thickness or to provide an edge beam.

Analysis

One of the major differences between the design of reinforced and prestressed two-way slabs is that only the procedures of Clause 13.8, or more detailed methods of analysis, can be used for the design. The approach outlined in Clause 13.8.2 was formally called "Equivalent Frame Method" and involves non-prismatic modelling of member stiffnesses. The Prismatic Modelling Method described in Clause 13.8.3 is simpler as it uses a simple equation for the reduced column stiffness. Examples 10.9 and 10.10, respectively, illustrate the design of a fully prestressed slab and a partially prestressed slab. The load balancing concept, together with the Prismatic Modelling Method is used to analyze two-way prestressed slabs. For slabs without stiff beams, 75 to 90 percent of the dead load is balanced by the effective prestress (in each direction). These percentages apply to slabs in which no cracks are expected to develop under full specified load. For partially prestressed slabs it is normally adequate to balance 60 to 70 percent of the slab dead load.

Calculation of Flexural Stress

The flexural stresses are calculated for the moments due to the net (unbalanced) loads. The positive and negative moments determined according to the methods of Clause 13.8 for the full width of the slab strip (width ℓ_2) shall be assigned to column strip according to Clause 18.12.2.1. This clause specifies that 75% of the interior negative moment, 100% of the exterior negative moment and 60% of the positive moment shall be taken by the column strip, unless a more detailed analysis is made. This requirement will assure that the moments due to the load not balanced by prestressing are assessed realistically and that the calculated flexural stresses are realistic values.

The axial stress, however, is more or less uniformly distributed across the width of the panel, particularly at the interior supports (see Clause 18.12.2.2).

If the flexural stress exceeds the value permitted in Clause 18.3.2(c), cracking is expected to occur and the crack control criteria of Clause 18.8.3 have to be satisfied.

Factored Moment

In continuous structural systems prestressing introduces secondary moments. These secondary moments are added to the moments due to factored loads such that

$$M_f = \alpha_D M_D + \alpha_L M_L + \alpha_p M''_p \tag{10.8.3}$$

In this equation: α_D and α_L are the load factors for dead load and live load respectively, M_D and M_L are the moments due to specified dead and live loads, M''_p is the secondary moment due to prestressing and α_p is the load factor for moments due to reactions introduced by prestressing (secondary moments). According to Clause 18.10, $\alpha_p = 1.0$.

The moments due to factored loads may be determined at the face of the column. The flexural resistance of the cross section is calculated according to Clause 18.6.

Minimum Reinforcement

In prestressed two-way slabs, minimum bonded reinforcement has to be provided in accordance with Clause 18.12.5 and Table 18-1.

10

Prestressed Concrete

Shear

The shear strength of reinforced concrete slabs is discussed in detail in Chapter 5. In prestressed concrete the beneficial effect of the axial stress $f_{cp} = P_e/A_c$ and the vertical component of the prestressing force at the critical section, V_p, increase the shear resistance of the concrete, V_c, considerably. According to Clause 18.12.3.3 the factored shear stress resistance of the concrete is given by Eq. 18-5 as:

$$v_c = \beta_p \lambda \phi_c \sqrt{f_c'} \sqrt{1 + \frac{\phi_p f_{cp}}{0.33 \lambda \phi_c \sqrt{f_c'}}} + \frac{V_p}{b_o d} \tag{10.8.4}$$

where

β_p = the smaller of 0.33 or $(\alpha_s d/b_o + 0.15)$

α_s = 4 for interior columns, 3 for edge columns and 2 for corner columns

b_o = perimeter of the critical section specified in Clause 13.3.3

f_{cp} = the average value of f_{cp} in the two directions not to exceed 3.5 MPa

V_f = factored vertical component of all prestressing forces crossing the critical section

However, the beneficial effect of prestressing can only be counted on if

(a)   no portion of the column cross section is closer to a discontinuous edge than 4 times the slab thickness, h_s,

(b)   the strength of the slab concrete is not taken greater than 35 MPa and

(c) f_{cp} in Eq.10.8.4 shall not exceed 3.5 MPa.

Shear reinforcement consisting of stirrups or headed shear reinforcement may be used to increase the shear resistance. The design of shear reinforcement consisting of headed studs with anchor plates, referred to in Clause 13.3.8 is discussed in some detail in the following section. The design of this reinforcement is described in detail in References 10.6 and 10.7. The design of stirrup reinforcement is specified in Clause 13.3.9.

Headed Shear Reinforcement

When headed shear reinforcement is used as shear reinforcement anchor plates having an area of at least 10 times the cross sectional area of the rods have to be provided.

The design of the headed shear reinforcement (studs) is based on the assumption that the factored shear resisted by concrete is (Clause 13.3.8.3)

$$v_c = 0.28 \, \lambda \, \phi_c \sqrt{f_c'} \tag{10.8.5}$$

The required area of headed shear reinforcement of one headed vertical bar along the critical section

$$A_v = \frac{(v_f - v_c) \, s_1 s}{\phi_s f_{yv}} \tag{10.8.6}$$

where

s = spacing between rows of rods measured perpendicular to the column face.

s_1 = length of critical section considered divided by rows of headed bars.

The shear reinforcement shall extend to a distance away from the column face so that the shear stress v_f at a distance $d/2$ from the outermost row of shear reinforcement does not exceed v_c of Eq. 10.8.7.

The spacing requirements for the headed shear reinforcement are specified in Clause 13.3.8.6. The upper limit on the shear stress resistance of slabs with headed studs is $0.75\lambda\phi_c\sqrt{f_c'}$, (Clause 13.3.8.2).

Normal closed stirrups are only allowed if the slab thickness is at least 300 mm (Clause 13.3.9.1) and the design of the shear reinforcement is based on a shear stress resistance of the concrete of (Clause 13.3.9.3):

$$v_c = 0.19\lambda\phi_c\sqrt{f_c'} \qquad (10.8.7)$$

The design equation for A_v is given by Eq. 10.8.6 and the extension of the shear reinforcement is the same as for headed shear reinforcement. The upper limit for the shear stress resistance of slabs with stirrups is $v_c = 0.55\lambda\phi_c\sqrt{f_c'}$, (Clause 13.3.9.2).

Structural Integrity

Progressive collapse may develop as a result of a local slab failure caused by punching if there is no mechanism provided to suspend the slab at the point of punching failure. According to Ref. 10.8 an effective mechanism to prevent progressive collapse is the membrane type action provided by draped tendons passing through the columns or reaction areas. In general two tendons in each direction over the column will be sufficient to satisfy the provisions of CSA Standard A23.3 (Clauses 18.12.6.3 and 13.10.6). These requirements are expressed by the following equation (c.f. Eq. 13-26 of the Standard).

$$\Sigma A_{sb} \geq \frac{2V_{se}}{f_{py}} \qquad (10.8.8)$$

where

A_{sb} = area of prestressing steel and non-prestressed reinforcement crossing through one face of the periphery of a column

V_{se} = shear force transmitted to column or column capital, defined by Eq.10.8.9

f_{py} = yield strength of tendon (see Table N 18-4) and

V_{se} = $w_s[\ell_{1a}\ell_{2a} - c_1c_2]$ (10.8.9)

In Eq. 10.8.9

w_s = total specified load but not less than twice the self-weight of the slab

ℓ_{1a} = average length for spans adjacent to a column

ℓ_{2a} = length of span transverse to ℓ_1

c_1 = size of rectangular or equivalent rectangular, support area of slab

c_2 = size of rectangular or equivalent rectangular support area transverse to c_1

Partial Prestressing

For partially prestressed beams, one-way slabs and two-way slabs on stiff supports, the determination of the parameters needed for the calculation of the stress f_s in Eq. 10-6 of CSA Standard A23.3 is straightforward. For flat slabs, these parameters need some discussion.

To determine the necessary parameters it is best to consider a one metre wide strip of the column strip. For this strip the following terms are defined:

M_s: the moment due to specified load is 75% of the total negative moment, at the face of the column, divided by the width of the column strip.

P_e :   the effective prestressing force is the total force in the panel (in one direction) divided by the width of the panel, ℓ_2.

A_s: total area of the non-prestressed steel (in one direction) divided by the width of the column strip.

A_p: total area of the prestressing steel divided by the width of the panel, ℓ_2. If the tendons are unbonded, A_p should not be considered in Eqs. 10.5.13 and 10.5.14.

For flat slabs with unbonded tendons, Eq. 10.5.1 simplifies to

$$f_s = \frac{M_{net} - P_e(h_s/6 + e)}{A_s d} \qquad\qquad (10.8.10)$$

where

M_{net} = 75% of the total panel moment due to net load, at face of support, divided by the width of the column strip.

P_e, A_s = as defined above

h_s = slab thickness

d = effective slab depth.

e = tendon eccentricity

See Example 10.10. Note: M_{net}, P_e and e are positive in Eq. 10.8.10.

10.9   Composite Flexural Members

The general requirements for composite flexural members are provided in Clause 17 and it is implicit in this clause that both the strength and serviceability limit states have to be satisfied.

It is generally considered more economical to place the topping without additional shoring. Hence, the mass of the cast-in-place concrete must be carried by the precast member alone and the strength of the system must be evaluated for both the non-composite and composite sections.

Besides an analysis of the deflections at the various loading stages, serviceability checks should also be carried out considering the time-dependent prestress losses (relaxation, creep and shrinkage) from the time of transfer. As previously discussed, the losses will not significantly affect strength but should be investigated to obtain an assessment of immediate and long-term camber or deflection.

10.10 References

10.1   Neville, A M., Dilger, W.H. and Brooks, J.J., "Creep of Plain and Structural Concrete", *Longman* 1983, 392 pp.

10.2   Dilger, W.H., "Creep Analysis of Prestressed Concrete Members Using Creep-Transformed Section Properties", *PCI Journal*, Vol. 27, No. 1, Jan.Feb.1982, pp. 98 - 118.

10.3   Bazant, Z., "Prediction of Concrete Creep Using Age-Adjusted Effective Modulus Method", *ACI Journal* 69, 1972, pp. 212-17.

10.4   Branson, D.E. and Trost, H., "Application of the Effective Method in Calculating Deflections of Partially Prestressed Members", *PCI Journal*, Vol. 27, No.5, Sept.-Oct., 1982, pp. 62 77.

10.5 Dilger, W.H. and Suri, K.M., "Steel stresses in Partially Prestressed Concrete Flexural Members", *PCI Journal*, Vol. 31, No. 3, May-June 1986, pp. 88 113.

10.6 Dilger, W.H. and Ghali, A., "Shear Reinforcement for Concrete Slabs", *ASCE Journal,* Vol. 107, No. ST12, Dec. 1981, pp. 2903 2920.

10.7 Ghali, A. and Elgabry, A., M.K., "Design of Stud-Shear Reinforcement for Slabs", *ACI Structural Journal*, Vol. 87, No. 3, May-June 1990.

10.8 Mitchell, D. and Cook, W.D., "Preventing Progressive Collapse of Slab Structures", *ASCE Journal*, Vol. 110, No. 7, July 1984, pp. 1513 1532.

EXAMPLE 10.1

Flexural Resistance with Bonded Prestressed Steel

Concrete: f'_c = 40 MPa, E_c = 4500 $\sqrt{40}$ = 28 460 MPa

Steel: See sketch below

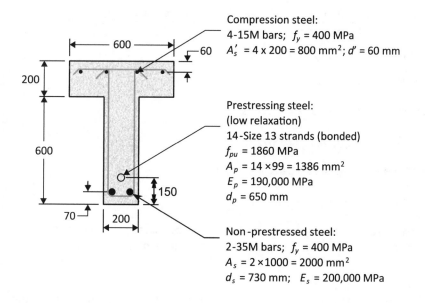

Compression steel:
4-15M bars; f_y = 400 MPa
A'_s = 4 x 200 = 800 mm²; d' = 60 mm

Prestressing steel:
(low relaxation)
14-Size 13 strands (bonded)
f_{pu} = 1860 MPa
A_p = 14 ×99 = 1386 mm²
E_p = 190,000 MPa
d_p = 650 mm

Non-prestressed steel:
2-35M bars; f_y = 400 MPa
A_s = 2 ×1000 = 2000 mm²
d_s = 730 mm; E_s = 200,000 MPa

10

Prestressed Concrete

Fig. 10.1.1

Section Properties:

A_c = 0.2 (0.6) + 0.6 (0.2) = 0.240 m²

$$y_b = \frac{0.12 \cdot 0.3 + 0.12 \cdot 0.7}{0.24} = 0.500 \text{ m}$$

e = 0.350 m

$$I_c = \frac{0.20 (0.60)^3}{12} + \frac{(0.20)^3 0.60}{12} + 0.12 (0.20)^2 + 0.12 (0.20)^2 = 0.0136 \text{ m}^4$$

β_1 = 0.97 − 0.0025 f'_c= 0.87 > 0.67 α_1 = 0.85 − 0.0015 (40) = 0.79 > 0.67

k_p = 2 (1.04 − 0.90) = 0.28

$\alpha_1 \phi_c f'_c = 0.79\,(0.65)\,40 = 20.54$ MPa

$\phi_p A_p f_{pu} = 0.9\,(1386)\,1860\,(10^{-6}) = 2.320$ MN

$\phi_s A_s f_y = 0.85\,(2000)\,400\,(10^{-6}) = 0.68$ MN

$\phi_s A'_s f'_y = 0.85\,(800)\,400\,(10^{-6}) = 0.272$ MN

$\alpha_1 \phi_c f'_c h_f\,(b - b_w) = 20.54\,(0.20)\,0.40 = 1.643$ MN

$c/d_p = \dfrac{2.320 + 0.680 - 0.272 - 1.643}{20.54\,(0.87)\,0.2\,(0.65) + 0.28\,(2.320)} = 0.365$

as $c/d_p \le 0.50$ Eq. (18-1) may be used giving $f_{pr} = f_{pu}\,(1 - k_p\,c/d_p) = 1860\,[1 - 0.28\,(0.365)] = 1670$ MPa

Although the code equation may be used in this case to compute f_{pr}, the strain compatibility approach in computing f_{pr} is presented for completeness.

Use code equation for the first iteration

$\phi_p A_p f_{pr} = 0.9 \cdot 1386(10^{-6})1670 = 2.083$ MN

$c = \dfrac{\phi_p A_p f_{pr} + \phi_s A_s f_s - \phi_s A'_s\,f'_s - \alpha_1 \phi_c f'_c\,h_f(b - b_w)}{\alpha_1 \phi_c f'_c\,\beta_1 b_w} = \dfrac{2.083 - 1.235}{3.574} = 0.237\text{m}$

$\varepsilon'_s = -0.0035\,(-237 + 60)/(-237) = -0.00261$

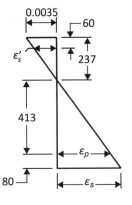

$\varepsilon'_y = -400/200\,000 = -0.00200$

compression steel yields since strain exceeds yield strain.

$\varepsilon_s = -0.0035\,(730 - 237)/(-237) = 0.00728$

tension steel yields since strain exceeds yield strain.

$\varepsilon_p = -0.0035\,(650 - 237)/(-237) = 0.00610$

The prestressing steel has an additional prestrain corresponding to the elastic strain in the steel when the concrete stress is zero at the level of the tendon.

Fig. 10.1.2

Assume $f_{pe} = 0.6f_{pu} = 1116$ MPa

$f_{ce} = P_e\left[\dfrac{1}{A_c} + \dfrac{e^2}{I_c}\right] + \dfrac{M_D}{I_c}e = -1386(10^{-6})1116\left[\dfrac{1}{0.240} + \dfrac{0.350^2}{0.0136}\right] + \dfrac{500(10^{-3})0.350}{0.0136} = -7.5$ MPa

Note that a dead load moment of 500 kN·m has been assumed in computing f_{ce}

$\varepsilon_{ce} = -7.5/28\,460 = -0.00026$

$\varepsilon_{pe} = \dfrac{f_{pe}}{E_p} - \varepsilon_{ce} = \dfrac{1116}{190\,000} - (-0.00026) = 0.00613$

Total strain in prestressing steel = 0.00613 + 0.00610 = 0.01223

From the stress-strain curve in Fig. 10.1 $f_{pr} = 1760$ MPa

This is higher than the initial estimate of 1670 MPa. The correct value of f_{pr} is bracketed by these values i.e $1670 < f_{pr} < 1760$ MPa

Try f_{pr} = (1670 + 1760)/2 = 1715 MPa

$$c = \frac{2.083(1715/1670) - 1.235}{3.574} = 0.253 \text{ m}$$

ε_p = -0.0035 (650 – 253)/(-253) = 0.00549

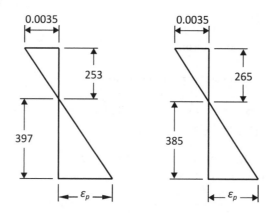

Fig. 10.1.3

Total strain = 0.00613 + 0.00549 = 0.0116 and from Fig. 10.1 f_{pr} = 1750 MPa

Try f_{pr} =1750 MPa

$$c = \frac{2.083(1750/1670) - 1.235}{3.574} = 0.265 \text{ m}$$

Total strain = 0.00613 + 0.00508 = 0.0112 and from Fig. 10.1 f_{pr} = 1750 MPa (approx).

This matches the trial value so that this is the correct solution. Note that the strain compatibility approach gives a higher value of f_{pr} than the code equation.

By inspection it is clear that the strains in the non-prestressed tension and compression steels exceed the yield strains

$$M_r = \phi_p A_p f_{pr}(d_p - \frac{a}{2}) + \phi_s A_s f_y(d - \frac{a}{2}) - \phi_s A'_s f'_y(d' - \frac{a}{2}) - \alpha_1 \phi_c f'_c h_f(b - b_w)(\frac{h_f}{2} - \frac{a}{2})$$

$a = \beta_1 c = 0.87$ (265) = 230 mm, a/2 = 115 mm

$\phi_p A_p f_{pr} = 0.9$ (1386 × 10⁻⁶) 1750 = 2.183 MN

M_r = 2.183 (650 – 115) + 0.68 (730 – 115) – 0.272 (60 – 115) – 1.643 (100 – 115) = 1626 kN·m

EXAMPLE 10.2

Flexural Resistance with Unbonded Prestressed Steel

Assume: 10 m span with 400 mm overhangs on each end

f'_c = 40 MPa, α_1 = 0.79, β_1 = 0.87

4 – Size 13 low-relaxation strands:

$A_p = 396$ mm², $f_{pu} = 1860$ MPa $d_p = 700$ mm

Assume $f_{pe} = 1100$ MPa

$f_{py} = 0.9\,(1860) = 1674$ MPa

The centroid of the section is 500 mm from bottom.

The concrete area below the centroid: $A = 100\,000$ mm².

The minimum area of bonded reinforcing (Clause 18.8.1) is $0.004A = 400$ mm². Use 2 – 15M bars.

Assuming that the depth of the stress block is less than 200 mm and that the non-prestressed reinforcement is Grade 400.

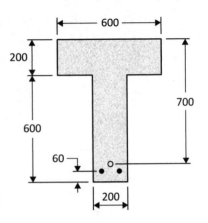

Fig. 10.2.1

$$c_y = \frac{\phi_p A_p f_{py} + \phi_s A_s f_y}{\alpha_1 \phi_c f'_c \beta_1 b} = \frac{0.9 \cdot 396 \cdot 1674 + 0.85 \cdot 400 \cdot 400}{0.79 \cdot 0.65 \cdot 40 \cdot 0.87 \cdot 600} = 68 \text{ mm}$$

For one plastic hinge and anchors each end of the beam $\ell_o = 10\,800$ mm

Eq. (18-2):

$$f_{pr} = f_{pe} + \frac{8000}{10800}(700 - 68) = 1100 + 468 = 1568 \text{ MPa}$$

$$M_r = \phi_p A_p f_{pr}(d_p - a/2) + \phi_s A_s f_y (d - a/2)$$

$$a = \frac{\phi_p A_p f_{pr} + \phi_s A_s f_y}{\alpha_1 \phi_c f'_c b} = \frac{0.9 \cdot 396 \cdot 1568 + 0.85 \cdot 400 \cdot 400}{0.79 \cdot 0.65 \cdot 40 \cdot 600} = 56 \text{ mm} < 200 \text{ mm}$$

$$M_r = 0.559\,(700 - 56/2) + 0.136\,(740 - 56/2) = 376 + 97 = 473 \text{ kN·m}$$

EXAMPLE 10.3

Analysis of Pretensioned Short Column

$f'_c = 50$ MPa, $\gamma_c = 2400$ kg/m³

$$E_c = (3300 \sqrt{f'_c} + 6900)\left(\frac{\gamma_c}{2300}\right)^{1.5} = 32\,230 \text{ MPa}$$

$\alpha_1 = 0.775$, $\beta_1 = 0.845$, $\alpha_{1\phi c} f'_c = 25.19$ MPa

$A_p = 99$ mm² /strand $E_p = 190\,000$ MPa, $f_{pe} = 1100$ MPa

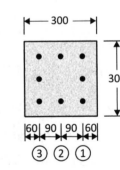

Fig. 10.3.1

Determine prestrain with zero concrete stress

$\varepsilon_{pe} = 1100/190\,000 = 0.00579$

$$f_c = P/A = \frac{1100\,(99)8}{300^2} = 9.68 \text{ MPa}$$

$\varepsilon_{ce} = -9.68/32\,230 = -0.00030$

$\varepsilon_{pe} - \varepsilon_{ce} = 0.00579 - (-0.00030) = 0.00609$

Axial load with zero eccentricity

$\varepsilon_c = -0.0035$

$\varepsilon_{total} = 0.00609 - 0.0035 = 0.00259$

$f_{pr} = 0.00259 \cdot 190\,000 = 492$ MPa   tension

$C_r = \alpha_1 \phi_c f'_c\, bc = 25.19\,(0.3)^2 = 2.267$ MN   compression

$T_1 + T_2 + T_3 = \phi_p A_p f_{pr} = 0.9 \cdot 8 \cdot 99\,(10^{-6})\,492 = 0.351$ MN
tension

$P_{ro} = 2.267 - 0.351 = 1.916$ MN   compression

$P_{max} = 0.8 \times 1.916 = 1.533$ MN   compression
(see Clause 10.10.4)

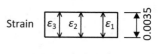

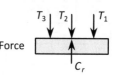

Fig. 10.3.2

Consider $c = 300$ mm, $a = 253$ mm (Fig. 10.3.3)							
Section	Area mm²	ε_p	ε_{total}	f_{pr} MPa	P_r MN	Moment Arm, mm	M_r kN·m
Concrete					+1.915	+23.25	+44.4
1	297	-0.00280	0.00329	625	-0.167	+90	-15.0
2	198	-0.00175	0.00434	825	-0.147	0	0
3	297	-0.00070	0.00539	1024	-0.274	-90	+24.7
					1.327		54.1

$P_r = 1.327$ MN compression

$M_r = 54.1$ kN·m

Note: $\varepsilon_{total} = 0.00609 + \varepsilon_p$

$P_r = \alpha_1 \phi_c f'_c\, ba - \sum (\phi_p A_p f_{pr})$

$M_r = \alpha_1 \phi_c f'_c\, ba\,(h/2 - a/2) - \sum (\phi_p A_p f_{pr}\, y)$

where   y = distance from plastic centroid to the force.

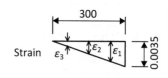

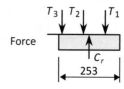

Fig. 10.3.3

10

Prestressed Concrete

Consider c = 250 mm, a = 211mm (Fig. 10.3.4)							
Section	Area	ε_p	ε_{total}	f_{pr}	P_r	Moment arm	M_r
Concrete	63 375				+1.596	+44.37	+70.84
1	297	-0.00266	0.00343	652	-0.174	+90	-15.68
2	198	-0.00140	0.00469	891	-0.159	0	0
3	297	-0.00014	0.00595	1130	-0.302	-90	+27.20
					0.961		82.36
P_r = 0.961 MN, M_r = 82.36 kN·m							

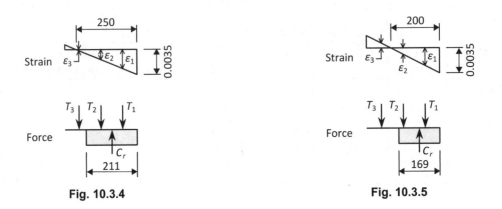

Fig. 10.3.4   Fig. 10.3.5

Consider c = 200 mm, a = 169 mm (Fig. 10.3.5)							
Section	Area	ε_p	ε_{total}	f_{pr}	P_r	Moment arm	M_r
Concrete	50 700				+1.277	+65.5	+83.64
1	297	-0.00245	0.00364	692	-0.185	+90	-16.64
2	198	-0.00087	0.00522	991	-0.177	0	0
3	297	0.00070	0.00679	1290	-0.345	-90	+31.03
					0.570		98.03
P_r = 0.570 MN, M_r = 98.03 kN·m							

Consider c = 160 mm, a = 135 mm (Fig. 10.3.6)							
Section	Area	ε_p	ε_{total}	f_{pr}	P_r	Moment arm	M_r
Concrete	40 560				+1.022	+82.4	+84.18
1	297	-0.00219	+0.00390	741	-0.198	+90	-17.84
2	198	-0.00022	+0.00587	1115	-0.199	0	0
3	297	+0.00175	+0.00784	1490	-0.398	-90	35.84
					0.227		102.18
P_r = 0.227 MN, M_r = 102.2 kN·m							

Fig. 10.3.6   Fig. 10.3.7

Consider c = 144 mm, a = 122 mm (Fig. 10.3.7)							
Section	Area	ε_p	ε_{total}	f_{pr}	P_r	Moment arm	M_r
Concrete	36 504				+0.920	+89.1	+81.98
1	297	-0.00204	0.00405	769	-0.206	+90	-18.50
2	198	0.00015	0.00624	1185	-0.211	0	0
3	297	+0.00233	0.00842	1600	-0.428	-90	+38.50
					+0.075		101.98
P_r = 0.075 MN, M_r = 102.0 kN·m							

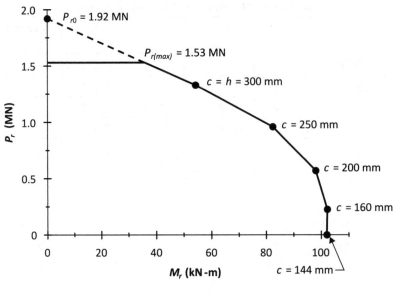

Fig. 10.3.8

EXAMPLE 10.4

Calculation of A_p and A_s to Resist Factored Loads

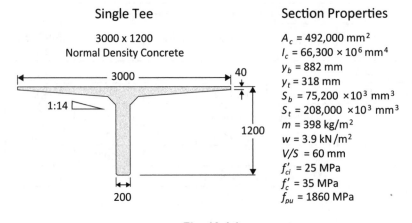

Fig. 10.4.1

Given:

Prestressed reinforcement:

All strands to be Grade 1860 low-relaxation and bonded. A_p = 99 mm² /strand (Size 13 strand)

d_p = 1050 mm

e_c = 1050 – 318 = 732 mm

Non-prestressed reinforcement: f_y = 400 MPa

A_s = 500 mm² /bar (25M)

$$d_s = 1100 \text{ mm}$$

Specified loads: Dead load $= 3.9$ kN/m²

Superimposed dead load $= 1.5$ kN/m²

Live load $= 2.0$ kN/m²

Span $= 27\,000$ mm

Solution:

$w_f = 3.0\,[1.25\,(3.9) + 1.25\,(1.5) + 1.5\,(2.0)] = 29.25$ kN·m

$$M_f = \frac{w_f l^2}{8} = \frac{29.25(27.0)^2}{8} = 2665 \text{ kN·m}$$

$f_{pr} = f_{pu}(1 - k_p c\,/d_p)$ where $k_p = 2\,(1.04 - f_{py}/f_{pu}) = 0.28$

Assume $a < h_f$ and treat as a rectangular section with A_s and A_p giving

$$c/d_p = \frac{\phi_p A_p f_{pu} + \phi_s A_s f_y}{\alpha_1 \phi_c \beta_1 f_c' \, b\, d_p + \phi_p k_p A_p f_{pu}}$$

$$a = \frac{\phi_p A_p f_{pr} + \phi_s A_s f_y}{\alpha_1 \phi_c f_c' b} \quad \text{and} \quad M_r = \phi_p A_p f_{pr}(d_p - a/2) + \phi_s A_s f_y (d - a/2)$$

The above equations are valid provided: $c\,/d_p \le 0.5$ $f_{pe} \ge 0.6\,f_{py}$

Now select values of A_s and A_p, and compute f_{pr} and M_r using $\alpha_1 = 0.797$ and $\beta_1 = 0.882$.

The following results were obtained assuming $\phi = 0.70$ according to Clause 16.1.3 for elements produced in a certified precast manufacturing plant.

A_s mm²	No. of strands	A_p mm²	c/d_p	f_{pr} MPa	a mm	M_r kN·m	$1.2\,M_{cr}$ kN·m
0	16	1584	0.0482	1835	45	2688	2197
0	18	1782	0.0541	1832	50	3011	2432
1000	14	1386	0.0484	1835	45	2718	1963
1000	16	1584	0.0543	1832	50	3042	2197
2000	12	1188	0.0486	1835	45	2748	1728
2000	14	1386	0.0546	1832	51	3072	1963
3000	12	1188	0.0548	1831	51	3102	1728

Although the effective depth of the compression block, a, is greater than the thickness of the flange at the tip, the precise calculation causes insignificant adjustments to the results.

The results satisfy the basic equations and are all valid solutions with respect to factored flexural resistance since $M_r > M_f$ in each case.

Clause 18.7 requires that $M_r \ge 1.2\,M_{cr}$, where M_{cr} is the cracking moment based on the modulus of rupture, f_r. At this stage of the design, it is sufficient to make a realistic assessment of the final prestress force, after all losses have occurred. In this example it is assumed that the initial stress in the tendons is $0.75\,f_{pu}$ with losses of 20%.

10

Prestressed Concrete

$\therefore f_{pe} = 0.8 (0.75) 1860 = 1116$ MPa

and M_{cr} can be calculated from, $M_{cr} = (-\dfrac{P}{A} - \dfrac{P \cdot e}{S_b} + f_r) S_b$

where $f_r = 0.6\lambda \sqrt{f_c'}$ Eq. (8-3)

Note that P is a compressive force on concrete and should be taken as negative.

Although this design example is concerned with the factored flexural strength of the member, it is customary to design partially prestressed members such that the moment due to sustained loads does not exceed the cracking moment.

The maximum specified moment due to dead load plus superimposed dead load is 1476 kN·m which is less than M_{cr} for all combinations of A_p and A_s except for the two cases where $A_p = 1188$ mm^2 for which $M_{cr} = 1440$ kN·m.

Table 10.1(b) can also be used to determine A_p for a precast member with bonded prestressed reinforcement only.

With $K_u = \dfrac{M_f}{f_c' bd_p^2} = \dfrac{2665(10^6)}{35(3000)1050^2} = 0.0230$ from Table 10.1(b) with $k_p = 0.28$ and $f_c' = 35$ MPa

$\omega_{pu} = 0.0264$

$A_p = \omega_{pu} f_c' bd_p/f_{pu} = 0.0264 \cdot 35 \cdot 3000 \cdot 1050/1860 = 1565$ mm^2

Provide 16 – Size 13 strands, $A_p = 1584$ mm^2

Examples 10.5 and 10.6 investigate the permissible stress requirements of Clauses 18.3.1 and 18.3.2

EXAMPLE 10.5

Calculation of Critical Concrete Stresses to Comply with Clauses 18.3.1 and 18.3.2 (fully prestressed member)

Given:

The data and notation from Example 10.4 $E_c = 26\ 600$ MPa

Solution:

For an initial estimate of A_p, find A_p required at mid-span due to action of all specified loads and assume 20% prestress losses.

Moment due to specified loads

$M_s = 3.0 (3.9 + 1.5 + 2.0) 27^2 /8 = 2023$ kN·m

In accordance with Clause 18.3.2.(c), maximum permissible extreme fibre stress in tension in the precompressed tensile zone (for fully-prestressed member) is $0.5\lambda \sqrt{f_c'}$ which is 2.96 MPa.

$\therefore \dfrac{-P_e}{A_c} + \dfrac{-P_e e}{S_b} + \dfrac{M_s}{S_b} \leq 2.96$ MPa

where $A_c = 492\ 000$ mm^2, $e = e_c = 732$ mm and $S_b = 75\ 200\ (10^3)$ mm^3 from which, the minimum final prestress force, $P_e = 2055$ kN

∴ Initial prestress force, $P_i = 2055/0.8 = 2569$ kN

Initial prestress force/strand $= 0.75\,(1860)\,99\,(10^{-3}) = 138.1$ kN

∴ Minimum number of Size 13 strands required to satisfy Clause 18.3.2(c) is:

$2569/138.1 = 18.6$ strands

Hence, initial estimate of minimum number of strands for symmetrical pattern is 20, giving $A_p = 1980$ mm².

Instantaneous prestress losses:

$$\Delta P_{e\ell} = \left[\frac{P_{(i)}}{A_{tr}} + \frac{\left(P_{(i)}e_{tr} + M_g\right)}{I_{tr}}e_{tr}\right]\frac{E_p}{E_c}A_p \qquad \text{(Eq. 10.4.1)}$$

In this example, using low-relaxation steel, $P_i \approx P_o$ and, because ρ_p is small, the properties of the gross concrete section can be used $P_o = 0.75 \cdot 20 \cdot 99 \cdot 1860\,(10^{-3}) = 2762$ kN

$$\Delta P_{e\ell} = \left[\frac{2762 \cdot 10^3}{492\,000} + \frac{(-2762 \cdot 10^3 \cdot 732 + 1066 \cdot 10^6)\,732}{66\,300 \cdot 10^6}\right]\frac{190{,}000}{26\,600}\cdot 1980\left(10^{-3}\right)$$

$$= -228 \text{ kN} \qquad (=8\% \text{ of } P_o)$$

Time-dependent prestress losses:

According to Eqns. (1.9) and (1.10), respectively:

Creep Coefficient $\quad C_t = \dfrac{t^{0.6}}{10 + t^{0.6}}C_u Q_{cr}\quad$ Shrinkage $\quad \varepsilon_{sh} = \dfrac{t}{C_s + t}\varepsilon_{shu}P_{sh}$

According to Table 1.2: $\quad Q_{cr} = Q_a\,Q_h\,Q_f\,Q_r\,Q_s\,Q_v\quad$ and $\quad P_{sh} = P_c\,P_h\,P_f\,P_r\,P_s\,P_v$

The coefficients Q and I are determined for the following assumptions:

	Q	P
Age at loading – 1 day, steam cured	1.00	–
Cement content – 300 kg/m³	–	0.93
Relative Humidity – 60%	0.87	0.80
Ratio of fine to total aggregate – 0.40	0.98	0.86
Volume to surface ratio – 60 mm	0.89	0.89
Slump – 50 mm	0.95	0.97
Air content – 7%	1.09	1.00

With $C_u = 2.35$ and $\varepsilon_{shu} = 780\,(10^{-6})$, (see Section 1.2.3) we get at time t_∞:

$C_\infty = 2.35 \times 1.00 \times 0.87 \times 0.98 \times 0.89 \times 0.95 \times 1.09 = 1.84$

$\varepsilon_{sh\infty} = 780 \times 10^{-6} \times 0.93 \times 0.80 \times 0.86 \times 0.89 \times 0.97 \times 1.00 = 430 \times 10^{-6}$

Intrinsic relaxation at 20°C after 50 years (Eq. 10.4.7), $f_{re} = 50$ MPa.

Concrete stress at level of tendons due to sustained load and initial prestress

$P_i = 2762 - 228 = 2534$ kN

10

Prestressed Concrete

$$f_c = \frac{P_i}{A_c} + \frac{(M_{sust} + P_i e)e}{I_c}$$

$$f_c = \frac{-2534 \cdot 10^3}{492,000} + \frac{((1066 + 410)10^6 - 2534 \cdot 10^3 \cdot 732)\,732}{66\,300 \cdot 10^6} = -9.33 \text{ MPa}$$

We first determine the loss of prestress due to creep and shrinkage alone to be able to determine the relaxation reduction coefficient α_r according to Fig. 10.3.

$$\rho_p = A_p/A_c = 1980/(492\,000) = 0.00402$$

$$n_p = 190\,000/26\,600 = 7.14$$

$$r = (I/A)^{1/2} = [66.3 \cdot 10^9/492\,000]^{1/2} = 367 \text{ mm}$$

From Eq. (10.4.10)

$$\Delta f_s = \frac{7.14\,(-9.33)1.84 - 430\,(10^{-6})190\,000}{1 + 7.14 \cdot 0.00402\left\{\left[1 + \left(\frac{732}{367}\right)^2\right][1 + 0.8(1.84)]\right\}} = -\frac{204.3}{1.35} = -151\,\text{MPa}$$

$$\beta = \frac{f_{pi}}{f_{pu}} = 0.75$$

$$\Omega = \frac{\Delta_{fs}}{\Delta_{pi}} = \frac{151}{0.75 \cdot 1860} = 0.11, \text{ and from Fig. 10.3 } \alpha_r = 0.72$$

Prestress loss, including reduced relaxation,

$$\Delta f_{pr} = -151 - \frac{50 \cdot 0.72}{1.35} = -178 \text{ MPa}$$

This corresponds to a 13 percent loss of the initial prestress.

Hence, total prestress loss = 8% + 13% = 21%.

Prestress Force: $P_i = 0.92 \cdot 2762 = 2541 \text{ kN}$

$$P_e = 0.79 \cdot 2762 = 2182 \text{ kN}$$

Check if deflected strands are required at transfer by determining the maximum eccentricity of prestress force at ends of member, e_e, assuming no additional top reinforcement.

For top tension

$$\max e_e = (0.5\sqrt{f'_{ci}} + \frac{P_i}{A_c})\frac{S_t}{P_i} = (2.50 + 5.16)\frac{208 \cdot 10^6}{2541 \cdot 10^3} = 627 \text{ mm}$$

For bottom compression

$$\max e_e = \left(0.6\, f'_{ci} - \frac{P_i}{A_c}\right)\frac{S_b}{P_i} = (15.00 - 5.16)\frac{75.2 \cdot 10^6}{2541 \cdot 10^3} = 291 \text{ mm (governs)}$$

Stresses at transfer and at final condition for various sections are given in the following table,

where, f_b = concrete stress in bottom fibre and f_t = concrete stress in top fibre

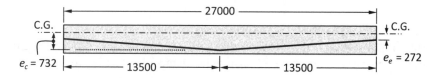

Centroid of Prestressing Force

Fig. 10.5.1

Load	End at Transfer Prestress = P_i		Mid-span at Transfer Prestress = P_i		0.4 ℓ at Final Condition Prestress = P_e	
	f_b	f_t	f_b	f_t	f_b	f_t
P_i/A_c or P_e/A_c	-5.16	-5.16	-5.16	-5.16	-4.53	-4.53
$P_i e/S$ or $P_e e/S$ M_g/S M_{sd}/S M_ℓ/S	-9.19	+3.32	-24.73 +14.18	+8.94 -5.13	-18.57 +13.62 +5.24 (+6.98)	+6.71 -4.92 -1.89 (-2.52)
Stresses	-14.35	-1.84	-15.71	-1.35	-4.24 (+2.74)	-4.63 (-7.15)
Allowable	-0.67 f'_{ci}	-0.6 f'_{ci}	-0.6 f'_{ci}	-0.6 f'_{ci}	+0.5 $\sqrt{f'_{ci}}$	-0.45 f'_c (-0.6 f'_c)
	-16.75	-15.00	-15.00	-15.00	+2.96	-15.75 (-21.00)
	OK	OK	NG	OK	OK	OK

Note: Msd denotes Moment due to superimposed dead load

e_e = 272 mm e_c = 732 mm $e_{(0.4\,\ell)}$ = 640 mm

Note that Clause 18.3.2 specifies a permissible compressive stress of 0.45 f'_c under sustained loads and 0.6f'_c under total load. In the above table stress under total load is shown in parenthesis.

Therefore, to satisfy the requirements of Clauses 18.3.1 and 18.3.2, provide 20-Size 13 strands with profile shown, but increase f'_{ci} to 27 MPa in order to accommodate the compressive stress of 15.71 MPa that occurs in the bottom at the mid-span of the member at transfer.

Referring to the results of Example 10.4, the value of A_p to satisfy permissible stresses is greater than that required for factored flexural resistance. This is often the case with prestressed members designed in accordance with Clause 18.3.2(c).

EXAMPLE 10.6

Calculation of Critical Stresses and Crack Widths to Comply with Clause 18.3.3 (partially prestressed member)

Given: The data from Example 10.4 with $A_p = 1188$ mm²

$A_s = 2000$ mm²

Solution:

From the results of Example 10.5, it is apparent that if A_p is reduced from 1980 mm² to 1188 mm², the member does not comply with Clause 18.3.2(c) and the member is partially prestressed.

Transformed Section Properties:

$$A_{tr} = (492,000 - 1188 - 2000) + \left(1188 \cdot \frac{190,000}{26,600}\right) + 2000 \cdot \frac{200,000}{26,600} = 512\,300 \text{ mm}^2$$

$$y_{tr} = \frac{(492\,000 \cdot 882) + (13\,026 \cdot 100) + (7290 \cdot 150)}{512\,300} = 852 \text{ mm}$$

$e_{tr} = 852 - (1200 - 1050) = 702$ mm

$I_{tr} = 77.7 \cdot 10^9$ mm⁴

Instantaneous prestress losses:

$$\Delta P_{e\ell} = \left[\frac{P_{(i)}}{A_{tr}} + \frac{(P_{(i)} e_{tr} + M_g) e_{tr}}{I_{tr}}\right] \frac{E_p}{E_c} A_p$$

$P_{(i)} = 0.75 \cdot 1188 \cdot 1860 \times 10^{-3} = 1657$ kN

$$\Delta P_{e\ell} = \left[\frac{-1657 \times 10^3}{512,300} + \frac{(-1657 \times 10^3 \cdot 702 + 1066 \times 10^6)\,702}{77.7 \times 10^9}\right] \frac{190,000}{26,620} \cdot 1188 \times 10^{-3}$$

$$= -34.8 \text{ kN } (2\%)$$

Time-dependent losses:

The following data were established in Example 10.5 for the time-dependent material properties:

Creep Coefficient $C_\infty = 1.84$

Shrinkage $\varepsilon_{sh\infty} = 430 \times 10^{-6}$

Intrinsic Relaxation $f_{re} = 50$ MPa

Concrete stress at the tendon level under sustained load (= dead load)

$$f_c = \frac{-1657 \times 10^3}{512\,300} + \left[\frac{(1066 + 410) - 1657 \cdot 0.732}{77.7 \times 10^9}\right] 732 \times 10^6 = -3.23 + 2.48 = -0.75 \text{ MPa}$$

Since both layers of steel have a common centroid the loss of prestress without relaxation is equal to the compressive stress in the non-prestressed steel.

With

$$\rho_p n_p = \frac{1188}{492,000} \times \frac{190,000}{26,600} = 0.0172 \text{ and}$$

$$\rho_s n_s = \frac{2000}{492,000} \times \frac{200,000}{26,600} = 0.0305$$

$$\Delta f_s = \frac{7.3\,(-0.75)1.84 \;-\; (430 \times 10^{-6} \cdot 190,000)}{1+(0.0172 +0.0305)\left[\left(1+\left(\dfrac{732}{367}\right)^2\right)(1+0.8 \cdot 1.84)\right]} = \frac{-91.8}{1.587} = -57.8 \text{ MPa}$$

Relaxation reduction coefficient:

With $\beta = 0.75$, $\Omega = \dfrac{57.8}{0.75 \cdot 1860} = 0.041$ we obtain from Fig. 10.3: $\alpha_r = 0.95$ so that the loss, including

relaxation is:

$$\Delta f_{pr} = -57.8 - \frac{50 \cdot 0.95}{1.587} = -87.7 \text{ MPa} \ \ (5\%)$$

The total reduction of the compression on the concrete is

$$\Delta P = (87.8 \cdot 1188 + 57.8 \cdot 2000)\,10^{-3} = 219 \text{ kN}$$

This corresponds to a reduction in compressive stress at the bottom fibre of:

$$\Delta f_c = \frac{219\,(10^3)}{492\,(10^3)} + \frac{219\,(10^3)\,732}{66.3\,(10^9)} \cdot 882 = 2.58 \text{ MPa}$$

Total prestress loss = 2% + 5% = 7%

Prestress force: $\quad P_i = 0.98\,(1657) = 1624$ kN

$\qquad\qquad\qquad P_e = 0.93\,(1657) = 1541$ kN

With deflected strands such that $e_e = 540$ mm and $e_c = 705$ mm, the following concrete stresses are calculated at transfer.

Load	End at Transfer		Mid-span at Transfer	
	f_b	f_t	f_b	f_t
$P_{(i)}/A_{tr}$	-3.17	-3.17	-3.17	-3.17
$P_{(i)}\,e_{tr}/S_{tr}$	-9.08	+3.71	-12.02	+4.91
M_g/S_{tr}			+11.69	-4.77
Stresses	-12.26	+0.54	-3.50	-3.03
Allowable	$-0.67\,f'_{ci}$	$+0.5\,\sqrt{f'_{ci}}$	$-0.6\,f'_{ci}$	$-0.6\,f'_{ci}$
	-16.75	+2.50	-15.00	-15.00
	OK	OK	OK	OK

In this table f_b and f_t are concrete stresses in bottom and top fibre, respectively.

Hence, concrete stresses at transfer are within permissible limits of Clause 18.3.1.

10

Prestressed Concrete

Crack Control:

Components of the decompression force P are:

$P_e = 1541$ kN

$P_s = \Delta f_s A_s = -57.8 \cdot 2000 \times 10^{-3} = -116$ kN

$\Delta P_p = \dfrac{-f_c}{E_c} E_p A_p = \dfrac{0.75}{26\,600} \, 190 \times 10^3 \cdot 1188 \times 10^{-3} = 6.4$ kN

$\Delta P_s = \dfrac{-f_c}{E_c} E_s A_s = \dfrac{0.75}{26\,600} \, 200 \times 10^3 \cdot 2000 \times 10^{-3} = 11.3$ kN

It is obvious that the terms ΔP_p and ΔP_s are small and could be neglected.

The following parameters are needed to determine $f_s/(n\alpha)$ from Figures 10.8.1 to 10.8.15:

$d = \dfrac{A_s E_s d_s + A_p E_p d_p}{A_s E_s + A_p E_p} = \dfrac{2000 \cdot 200 \cdot 1100 + 1188 \cdot 190 \cdot 1050}{2000 \cdot 200 + 1188 \cdot 190} \times \dfrac{10^3}{10^3} = 1082$ mm

$n\rho = \dfrac{A_p E_p + A_s E_s}{E_c bd} = \dfrac{(1188 \cdot 190 + 2000 \cdot 200)10^3}{26\,600 \cdot 3000 \cdot 1082} = 0.00725$

$p = \dfrac{P d_p}{M_s} = \dfrac{1408 \cdot 1050 \, (10^3)}{(1066 + 410 + 547)10^6} = 0.731$

$\alpha_b = \dfrac{b_w}{b} = \dfrac{200}{3000} = 0.0667$

$\alpha_f = \dfrac{h_f}{d} = \dfrac{90}{1082} = 0.0832$

With these values were find by interpolation $f_s/n\alpha = 43$

Steel stress at the level of the centroid of the steel:

$f_s = 43 \dfrac{nM_s}{bd^2} = 43 \left[\dfrac{7.5 \, (2023)10^6}{3000 \, (1082)^2} \right] = 186$ MPa

Disregarding the bundled prestressing steel for the calculation of A, we find

$A = \dfrac{200(2)100}{4} = 10\,000$ mm^2

Thus

$z = f_s \sqrt[3]{d_c A} = 186 (50 \cdot 10\,000)^{1/3} (10^{-3}) = 14.8$

For interior exposure (assumed), $z \le 20$ (Clause 18.8.3)

Hence, 12-Size 13 strands plus 4 – 25M bars satisfy concrete stresses at transfer and crack control under specified loads.

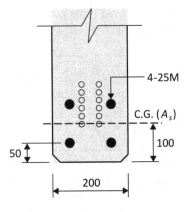

Midspan Detail

Fig. 10.6.1

EXAMPLE 10.7

Shear Design of a Prestressed Concrete Member – Simplified Method

When using the Simplified Method, the maximum yield strength limit of 400 MPa in Clause 11.3.6 is intended for non-prestressed reinforcement only. For prestressed members, this yield strength limit does not apply.

The beam of Example 10.4 is designed for shear.

Data given: h = 1200 mm b_w = 200 mm A_p = 1980 mm²

            a_g = 20 mm w_f = 29.25 kN/m f_{pu} = 1860 MPa

            f'_c = 35 MPa f_y = 400 MPa for A_v

The member has been produced in a manufacturing plant certified in accordance with Clause 16.1.3 so $\phi_c = 0.70$

Effective prestress P_e = 2210 kN (assuming initial prestress of 75% f_{pu} and 20% losses)

Slope of the tendons (732 − 272)/13 500 = 0.03407

V_p = 0.9 (2210) 0.03407 = 68 kN

Shear force at distance d_v = 0.72h = 0.72(1200) = 864 mm from face of support:

V_f = 29.25 [27/2 − (0.10 + 0.864)] = 367 kN

Since h = 1200 mm > 750 mm, Clause 11.2.8.1(b) specifies that minimum shear reinforcement be provided over the full length of the beam.

Minimum shear reinforcement (Clause 11.2.8.2):

$(\dfrac{A_v}{s})min = 0.06\sqrt{f'_c}\dfrac{b_w}{f_y} = 0.06\sqrt{35}(\dfrac{200}{400}) = 0.177\,mm^2/mm$

For 10M stirrups the spacing is s = 2(100)/ 0.177 = 1130 mm

The maximum spacing of transverse reinforcement is limited to 0.7d_v or 600 mm (Clause 11.3.8.1):

0.7d_v = 0.7 (864) = 605 mm.

Hence for minimum shear reinforcement, provide 10M stirrups at 600 mm.

Using the Simplified Method Clause 11.3.6.3 with θ = 35° the shear resistance provided by these stirrups:

$V_s = \dfrac{\phi_s\,A_v f_y d_v \cot\theta}{s} = 0.85(2 \cdot 100) \cdot 400 \cdot \dfrac{864}{600} \cdot \cot(35)10^{-3} = 140\,kN$ Eq. (11-7)

Calculation of V_c :

$V_c = \phi_c\,\lambda\beta\sqrt{f'_c}b_w d_v$ Eq. (11-6)

If a section contains at least the minimum transverse reinforcement, β = 0.18, thus:

V_c = 0.7(1.0) 0.18 $\sqrt{35}$ (200) 864(10^{-3}) = 129 kN

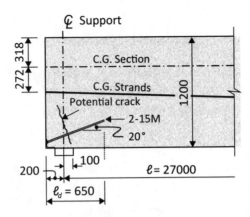

Fig. 10.7.1 Beam end zone

Transfer length = 50 (13) = 650 mm (Clause 11.2.11)

The solution to this example will be determined by constructing the V_c and V_f diagrams.

The shear force due to prestressing, V_p, is zero at the end of the member and increases linearly to reach its maximum value at 650 mm from the end. At the face of the support, 300 mm from the beam end:

$$V_r = V_c + V_s + V_p = 129 + 140 + 68 \,(300) \,/ \,650 = 300 \text{ kN}$$

In the end region V_f = 367 kN. At the face of the support V_f exceeds 300 kN so additional shear reinforcement will be required, see shaded area in Fig. 10.7.2. With V_c = 129kN, V_p = 31 kN and using 10M stirrups:

$$s = \frac{\phi_s \, A_v f_y d_v \cot\theta}{V_f \quad V_c \quad V_p} = 0.85(400)2(100) \, \frac{864}{367 - 129 - 31} \cdot \cot(35)10^{-3} = 405 \text{ mm}$$

The shear resistance diagram of Fig. 10.7.2 indicates that the point where the factored shear force V_f exceeds $V_r = V_c + V_{smin} + V_p$ =129 + 140 + 68 = 337 kN is 1.88 m from the face of the support. Provide 10M at 405 mm over this length.

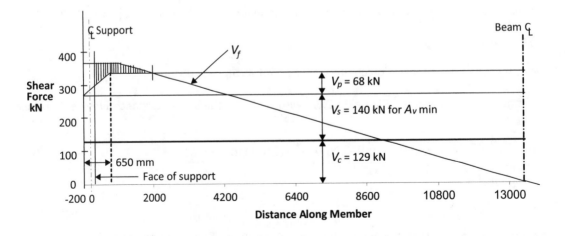

Fig. 10.7.2 Shear design diagram

In order to complete the shear design of Example 10.7, the additional tension and anchorage requirements of longitudinal reinforcement, (Clauses 11.3.9.1 and 11.3.9.5) and the capacity of the inclined shear friction plane must be examined. This is illustrated in Example 10.8 (5) and 10.8 (6) respectively.

EXAMPLE 10.8

Shear Design of Prestressed Concrete Member – General Method

The beam of Example 10.4 is designed for shear.

Data given: h = 1200 mm b_w = 200 mm A_p = 1980 mm²

a_g = 20 mm w_f = 29.25 kN/m f_{pu} = 1860 MPa

f_c' = 35 MPa f_y = 400 MPa

The member has been produced in a manufacturing plant certified in accordance with CSA A23.4 so ϕ_c = 0.70

Effective prestress P_e = 2210 kN (assuming initial prestress of 75% f_{pu} and 20% losses)

Slope of the tendons (732 − 272)/13 500 = 0.03407

V_p = 0.9 (2210) 0.03407 = 68 kN

1. Factored Shear Force and Moment:

According to Clause 11.3.2, the critical section may be taken at a distance d_v from the face of the support where d_v is the larger of 0.9d or 0.72h (Clause 3.2). Due to the draped strand, d_v = 0.72 (1200) = 864 mm (= 0.864 m). Shear force and moment due to factored load at (864 + 100) = 964 mm (= 0.964 m) from the centreline of the support are (see Fig. 10.7.1):

V_f = 29.25 (13.50 − 0.964) = 367 kN.

M_f = 0.5 (29.25) 0.964 (27.00 − 0.964) = 367 k·Nm

and check Clause 11.3.6.4(a) that M_f is not less than $(V_f − V_p)d_v$ = (367 − 67.8) 0.864 = 258 kN·m.

2. Determination of ε_x

According to Eq. 11-13 with N_f = 0, A_s = 0, f_{po} = 0.7f_{pu} and $A_p f_{po}$ = 2578 kN

$$\varepsilon_x = \frac{367/0.864 + 367 - 67.8 - 2578}{2(190\,000)1980(10^{-3})} = -0.002464$$

Since the value of ε_x is negative, it shall be taken either as zero, or the value shall be calculated with the denominator of Eq. (11-13) replaced by 2 $(E_s A_s + E_p A_p + E_c A_{ct})$, Clause 11.3.6.4(c). In example 10.8 ε_x is assumed to be zero.

10

Prestressed Concrete

3. Determination of β

Assuming no transverse reinforcement, Eq. (11-10) applies. The prestressing strands are fanned out at the member end. With 20 strands in two rows, the average spacing would be approximately $(1200 - 2(50)/9 = 122$ mm, say 125 mm. The exact spacing would have to be established according the end block geometry at the manufacturing plant. With $s_z = 125$ mm:

$$s_{ze} = \frac{35 s_z}{(15 + a_g)} = \frac{35(125)}{(15 + 20)} = 125 \geq 0.85 s_z = 0.85(125) = 106 \text{ mm}$$

using $\varepsilon_x = 0$ and $s_{ze} = 125$ in.   Eq. (11-11):

$$\beta = \frac{0.4}{1 + 1500(0)} \cdot \frac{1300}{(1000 + 125)} = 0.462$$

$$V_c = 0.7(1.0)0.462 \sqrt{35} (200)0.864 = 330 \text{ kN}$$ Eq.(11-6)

$$V_c = V_p = 330 + 68 = 398 \text{ kN}$$

Since V_f is less than 398 kN, stirrups are not required.

4. Determination of θ

$$\theta = 29 + 7000 \, \varepsilon_x = 29°$$ Eq. (11-12)

5. Check of tension reinforcement near support, (Clauses 11.3.9.1 and 11.3.9.5)

At the inside edge of the bearing area,

$$V_f = 29.25(13.5 - 0.1) = 392 \text{ kN}, \; M_f = 0.5(29.25)0.1(27.0 - 0.1) = 39.3 \text{ kN·m} \qquad \text{and}$$

$$V_p = 68(300/650) = 31.3 \text{ kN}.$$

In addition, a horizontal force, H_f, has to be considered at the support. This force depends on the friction developed at the interface between the bearing and the girder. For a sliding bearing (e.g. teflon), friction is very small so that the horizontal force may be neglected. On the other hand, the friction coefficient between concrete surfaces may be as high as 0.8. Assume (arbitrarily) a friction coefficient of 0.3. Thus, the reaction due to factored load, $R_f = (29.25) 27.0/2 = 395$ kN, produces $H_f = 0.3 (395) = 118$ kN

Transposing this horizontal force (that is applied at the bottom of the member) to the mid-height of the beam yields a normal force $N_f = H_f$ and a moment $M_f = N_f(h/2) = 118 (1.20)/2 = 70.8$ kN·m, that is to be added to the above moment; thus: $M_f = 39.3 + 70.8 = 110$ kN·m. According to Eq. (11-14) with $V_s = 0$:

$$F_{lt} = \frac{M_f}{d_v} + 0.5 N_f + (V_f - V_p) \cot \theta = 110/0.864 + 0.5(118) + (392 - 31.3) \cot (29°) = 837 \text{ kN}$$

According to Clause 11.3.9.5 this tension force shall be developed at the point, where a line inclined at angle θ to the longitudinal axis and extending from the inside edge of the bearing area intersects the reinforcement. As shown in Fig. 10.8.1, only the two (straight) bottom strands do not develop the full prestressing force as they cross the inclined plane at angle θ. The full effective prestressing force $P_e = 2210$ kN far exceeds the force F_{lt} so that there is no need to calculate the exact value of the force in the bottom strands at the inclined crack.

6. Shear friction

In addition to the above check, the interface shear between a wedge sheared off at an angle from the inside edge of the bearing to the end face of the beam (see Fig. 10.8.1) needs to be investigated.

For the shear stress resistance the following code equation is used.

$$v_r = \lambda \phi_c k \sqrt{\sigma f_c'} + \phi_s \rho_v f_y \cos \alpha_f$$

Eq. (11-26)

For monolithically placed concrete $k = 0.6$. σ and ρ_v are defined in the Standard as:

$$\sigma = \rho_v f_y \sin \alpha_f + N / A_g$$

Eq. (11-27)

$$\rho_v = A_{vf} / A_{cv}$$

Eq. (11-28)

N is the unfactored permanent (dead) load perpendicular to the shear plane.

With $w_D = 3 (3.9 + 1.5) = 16.2$ kN/m, $R_D = 16.2 (27.0/2) = 219$ kN. The corresponding unfactored horizontal force $H_D = 0.3(219) = 65.6$ kN. The resulting force acting perpendicular to the shear plane is N.

Assuming that the strands contribute to the shear stress resistance at the inclined shear friction plane, the most critical conditions exist at the steepest plane that is intersected only by the pair of straight strands at the bottom of the beam, see Fig. 10.8.1. For the geometry shown in the figure, $\alpha_f = 37.8°$. The area of the inclined shear friction plane $A_{cv} = 75\,970$ mm² and $\rho_v = 2 (99)/75\,970 = 0.00261$. The embedment length of the two strands beyond the shear friction plane is 236 mm yielding an effective stress at shear plane 1116 (236/650) = 404 MPa. The normal stress due to unfactored normal force $N = 219$ kN and concurrent horizontal force $H = 65.6$ kN, $\sigma = 1.75$ MPa and $\lambda = 1.0$, $\phi_c = 0.70$, $f_c' = 35$ MPa, the shear stress resistance according to Clause 11.5.3 is

$$v_r = 1.0 (0.7) 0.6 \sqrt{35 [(404) 0.00261 (\sin 38°) + 1.75]} + 0.9 (404) 0.00261 (\cos 38°) = 4.59 \text{ MPa}$$

$$> v_f = 4.41 \text{ MPa} \qquad \text{OK}$$

No additional steel required.

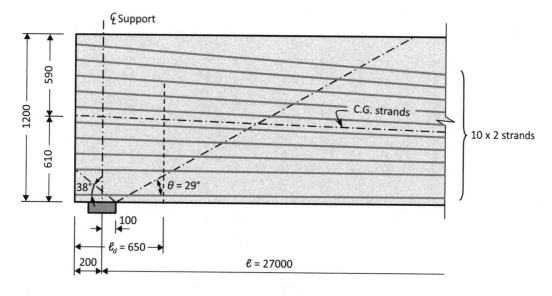

Fig. 10.8.1

10

Prestressed Concrete

EXAMPLE 10.9

Design of Fully Prestressed Concrete Slab

1. **Geometry**   (See Fig. 10.9.1)

2. **Materials**

Concrete Strength:

Slab: $f'_c = 30$ MPa, $f'_{ci} = 25$ MPa, $\alpha_1 = 0.805$, $\beta_1 = 0.895$

Column: $f'_c = 40$ MPa

Prestressing Steel:

Low-relaxation strand, 15 mm diameter $f_{pu} = 1860$ MPa,

                                                     $f'_{py} = 1670$ MPa,

                                                     $A_p = 140$ mm^2

Non-prestressed Steel: $f_y = 400$ MPa

3. **Slab Thickness**

   $h = \ell/45 = 7500/45 = 167$ mm, select 170 mm

4. **Loads**

Specified Loads

Dead Load: 170 mm slab (170/1000) 2.4 (9.81)   = 4.00 kN/m^2

Partitions: = 1.30 kN/m^2

---

                                             w_D = 5.30 kN/m^2

Live Load: w_L = 2.40 kN/m^2

                              $w_s = w_D + w_L$ = 7.70 kN/m^2

$w_L < (3/4)\, w_D$ – Use full live loads on all spans (Clause 13.8.4.2)

Factored Loads:

$w_{Df} = 1.25\,(5.30)$ = 6.63 kN/m^2

$w_{Lf} = 1.50\,(2.40)$ = 3.60 kN/m^2

---

                                    w_f = 10.23 kN/m^2

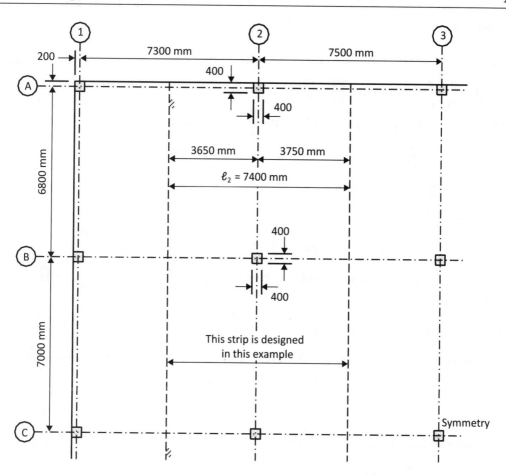

Fig. 10.9.1 Slab geometry

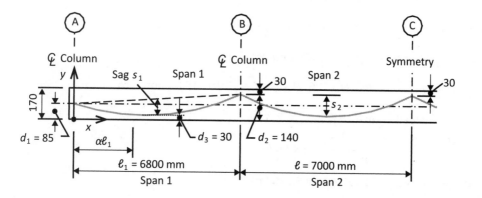

Fig. 10.9.5 Tendon profile

5. Cable Profile

Point of maximum eccentricity in span 1 is at $x = \alpha \ell_1$ (see Fig. 10.9.5):

$$\alpha = 1/[1+(\frac{d_2-d_3}{d_1-d_3})^{1/2}] = 1/[1+(\frac{140-30}{85-30})^{1/2}] = 0.4142$$

Equation of parabola of span 1 (y from bottom of slab in mm, x in m)

$$y = \frac{d_1-d_3}{(\alpha\ell_1)^2}x^2 + 2\frac{d_1-d_3}{\alpha\ell_1}x + d_1 \qquad y = 6.93 \cdot 10^{-6}x^2 - 0.03905\,x + 85$$

At $x = \ell_1/2 = 3400$ mm: $y = 32$ mm

Sag in span 1:

$$s_1 = 85 - 32 + \frac{1}{2}(85-30) = 80 \text{ mm} = 0.080 \text{ m}$$

An approximate value of $s_1 = 82$ mm is obtained by assuming that the maximum eccentricity occurs at mid span.

6. Load Balancing

Assume that approximately 80 percent of the dead load is balanced by the effective prestressing force

$$w_{bal} = 0.80 \times 5.30 = 4.24 \text{ kN/m}^2$$

Span 1

Required effective prestressing force (per metre)

$$P_e = \frac{w_{bal}\ell_1^2}{8s_1} = \frac{4.24 \times 6.80^2}{8 \times 0.080} = 306 \text{ kN}$$

For full width of panel $P_e = 306\,(7.40) = 2267$ kN

Assuming the effective prestress to be $0.6f_{pu}$, we have per tendon

$$P_e = 0.60f_{pu}A_p = 0.6\,(1860)\,140\,(10^{-3}) = 156 \text{ kN}$$

Number of tendons required $N = 2267/156 = 14.5$. Select 15 tendons providing $15\,(156) = 2340$ kN.

Actual balanced load in span 1:

$$w_{bal} = \frac{8P_e s_1}{\ell_1^2} = \frac{8 \cdot 2340 \cdot 0.080}{6.80^2} = 32.4 \text{ kN/m}$$

Per metre width $w_{bal} = 32.4/7.40 = 4.38$ kN/m^2

Unbalanced Load $w_{net} = w_s - w_{bal} = 7.70 - 4.38 = 3.32$ kN/m^2

Span 2

Utilizing the maximum possible cable sag $s_2 = 140 - 30 = 110$ mm results in a balanced load (neglecting friction), per meter width

$$w_{bal} = \frac{8P_e s_2}{\ell_2\ell_1^2} = \frac{8 \cdot 2340 \cdot 0.110}{7.40 \cdot 7.00^2} = 5.68 \text{ kN/m}$$

This is too high since it exceeds the dead load. A balanced load $w_{bal} = 4.70$ kN/m² is chosen. The sag corresponding to this balanced load is

$$S_2 = \frac{4.70 \cdot 7.4 \cdot 7.00^2}{8 \cdot 2340} = 0.091 \text{ m } (91 \text{ mm})$$

Unbalanced load in span 2

$$w_{net} = 7.70 - 4.70 = 3.00 \text{ kN/m}^2$$

7. Analysis according to Clause 13.8.3 – Prismatic modelling of members

7.1 Section Properties

Slab – Beam:

$$I_s = (1/12) \, \ell_2 \, h_s^3 = (1/12) \, 7400 \, (170)^3 = 3.03 \times 10^9 \text{ mm}^4$$

Column:

$$I_c = (1/12) \, 400 \, (400)^3 = 2.13 \times 10^9 \text{ mm}^4$$

Effective moment of inertia of column (Clause 13.8.3.3)

$$I_{ec} = \psi \, I_c$$

From Eq. (13-22) for $\ell_2/\ell_1 > 1.0$:

$$\psi = 0.6 \, (\ell_2/\ell_1 - 0.5) + (1.3 - 0.6\ell_2/\ell_1) \, \alpha_1 \ell_2 /\ell_1$$

For both spans $\alpha_1 \ell_2 /\ell_1 = 0$.

Column A: $\ell_2/\ell_1 = 7400/6800 = 1.088$
$\psi = 0.6 \, (1.088 - 0.5) = 0.353$

Column B: $\ell_2/\ell_1 = 7400/6900 = 1.072;$
$\psi = 0.6 \, (1.072 - 0.5) = 0.343$

Column C: $\ell_2/\ell_1 = 7400/7000 = 1.057$
$\psi = 0.6 \, (1.057 - 0.5) = 0.334$

Thus: $I_{ec1} = 0.353 \, (2.13) \, 10^9 = 0.752 \, (10^9) \text{ mm}^4$
$I_{ec2} = 0.343 \, (2.13) \, 10^9 = 0.731 \, (10^9) \text{ mm}^4$
$I_{ec3} = 0.334 \, (2.13) \, 10^9 = 0.711 \, (10^9) \text{ mm}^4$

10

Prestressed Concrete

7.2 Frame Geometry

The dimensions and the moment of inertia used in the frame analysis are shown in Fig. 10.9.7.2.

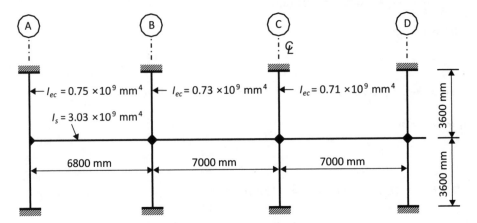

Fig. 10.9.7.2 Frame Geometry

7.3 Results of Frame Analysis

The results for the unbalanced (net) loads are shown in Fig. 10.9.7.3 (1).

7.4 Check of Flexural Stresses

Maximum Stress at Face of Column B

Moment at face of column (calculated for slab width ℓ_2 = 7.4 m) due to unbalanced loads is 92.0 kN·m. (See Fig. 10.9.7.3(1)) In the column strip 75 percent of the total moment is resisted (Clause. 18.12.2.1). The moment per metre in the column strip at the face of the column is obtained with a width of the column strip 0.5 (7.00 + 6.80)/2 = 3.45 m:

$$M_B = -\frac{90.0\,(0.75)}{3.45} = -20.0 \text{ kN·m}$$

Fig. 10.9.7.3 Moment and shear force diagrams

Concrete stress in top fibre

$$f_c = \frac{P_e}{A_c} - \frac{M}{S} = \frac{-2340 \times 10^3}{7400 \times 170} - \frac{(-20.0)10^6}{170^2 \times 1000/6} = -1.86 + 4.16 = 2.30 \text{ MPa}$$

Permissible $f_c = 0.50\sqrt{30} = 2.74$ MPa   OK

Note: The axial stress is calculated as the average stress over the full width of the slab (Clause. 18.12.2.2).

Concrete stress in bottom fibre

$$f_c = -1.86 - 4.16 = -6.02 \text{ MPa} < \textit{Permissible } f_c = 0.60f'_c = 18.0 \text{ MPa (Compression)} \qquad \text{OK}$$

(1) Moments due to specified loads and prestressing (= unbalanced loads)

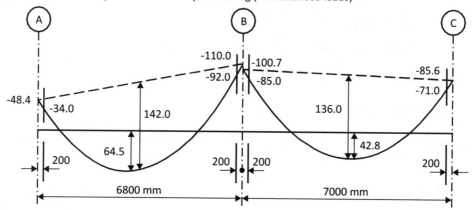

(2) Moments due to factored loads (with and without secondary moments)

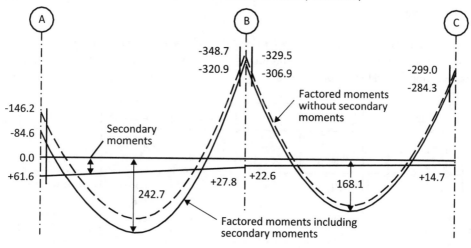

(3) Shear force due to factored loads and secondary moments

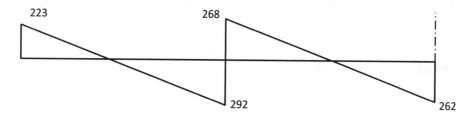

Fig. 10.9.7.3 Moment and shear force diagrams

Mid Span

Maximum moment in Span 1 from Fig. 10.9.7.3(1). The positive moment in the column strip is equal to 60% of the total positive moment. Moment per metre (width 3.45 m)

$$M_1 = \frac{64.5 \cdot 0.60}{3.45} = 11.2 \text{ kN·m/m}$$

Bottom fibre stress

$$f_c = -1.86 + \frac{11.2 \cdot 10^6}{170^2 \cdot 1000/6} = -1.86 + 2.33 = 0.47 \text{ MPa}$$

$$< \text{permissible } f_c = 0.50\sqrt{30} = 2.74 \text{ MPa}$$

Non-prestressed steel not required because $f_c \leq 0.2\sqrt{f'_c} = 1.09$ MPa, (Table 18-1).

8. Factored Flexural Resistance

The factored flexural resistance, M_f, must be at least equal to the bending moment due to factored load, plus the secondary moment due to prestressing:

$$M_f = \alpha_D M_D + \alpha_L M_L + \alpha_p M''_p$$

According to CSA Standard A 23.3 Clause 18.10 $\alpha_p = 1.0$ and Annex C, Table C1: $\alpha_D = 1.25$, $\alpha_L = 1.50$.

8.1 Factored Moments

The factored moments due to $w_f = 10.23$ kN/m² = 75.7 kN/m are plotted in Fig. 10.9.7.3(2), together with the secondary moments, M''_p, and the moments at the column faces, and in the spans. These moments are summarized in the following table:

Support		A	B_{left}	B_{right}	C
$\alpha_D M_D + \alpha_L M_L$	kN·m	-146.2	-348.7	-329.5	-299.0
$\alpha_p M''_p$ [1]	kN·m	+61.6	+27.8	+22.6	+14.7
M_f	kN·m	-84.6	-320.9	-306.9	-284.3
V_f	kN	222.6	292.2	268.2	261.7
M_f at column face[2]	kN·m	-41.6	-264.0	-254.0	-233.5
M_f – span	kN·m	242.0		168.0	

[1] The secondary moments are obtained from where $M''_p = M_{unbal} - M_s - M'_p$ where $M'_p = P_e e$

[2] At column face $M_f = -84.6 + 222.6 \times 0.20 - \frac{1}{2}(0.2)^2 \, 75.7 = -41.6$ kN·m

8.2 Factored Flexural Resistance

8.2.1 At interior columns

According to Clause 18.8.1 (Table 18-1):

$$\min A_s = 0.0006 \, h_s l_n = 0.0006 \cdot 170 \cdot 6600 = 673 \text{ mm}^2$$

Provide 7 – 10M bars = 700 mm². These bars shall be placed within a zone $c_2 + 3h = 400 + 3 \times 170 = 910$ mm at the column (Clause. 18.12.5.2).

Stress in unbonded tendon at flexural failure (Eq. 18-2)

$$f_{pr} = f_{pe} + \frac{8000}{l_o} \sum_n (d_p - c_y) \le f_{py}$$

Total length of tendon between anchors: $\ell_o = 2\,(200 + 6800 + 7000) = 28\,000$ mm.

Three hinges are necessary to form a mechanism in this frame. In negative moment zones: $d_p = 140$ mm,

$A_p = 15\,(140) = 2100$ mm²,

$f_{py} = 1670$ MPa,

$f_y = 400$ MPa

$$c_y = \frac{0.9\,(2100)1670 + 0.85\,(700)400}{0.805\,(0.895)0.65\,(30)7400} = 33 \text{ mm}$$

In positive moment zone no non-prestressed reinforcement is provided, thus:

$$c_y = \frac{0.9\,(2100)1670}{0.805\,(0.895)0.65\,(30)7400} = 30 \text{ mm}$$

$$f_{pr} = 0.6\,(1860) + \frac{8000}{28\,000}\left[(85 - 33) + (140 - 33) + (140 - 30)\right] = 1193 \text{ MPa} < 1670 \text{ MPa}$$

$$a = \frac{\phi_p A_p f_{pr} + \phi_s A_s f_y}{\alpha_1 \phi_c f'_c l_2} = \frac{0.9\,(2100)1193 + 0.85\,(700)400}{0.805\,(0.65)30\,(7400)} = 22 \text{ mm}$$

$M_f = 0.9 \cdot 2100 \cdot 1193\,(140 - 11) + 0.85 \cdot 700 \cdot 400\,(140 - 11) = 322 \cdot 10^6$ Nmm $= 322$ kN·m > 268 kN·m

9. Shear Design

9.1 At Exterior Column

9.1.1 Shear Force

Shear due to factored loads on slab and M''_p :		= 222.6 kN
Facade: Brick + glass, 2.4 kN/m:	1.25 (2.4) 7.4	= 22.2 kN
	Total Shear: V_f	= 244.8 kN

The beneficial effect of prestressing on shear resistance cannot be considered (Clause. 18.12.3.3). At exterior columns a portion of the unbalanced moment is transferred to the column by eccentricity of shear.

10

Prestressed Concrete

9.1.2 Section Properties of Critical Section

With $d = 130$ mm, $d/2 = 65$ mm (see Fig. 10.9.9.1.2)

$A_1 = d(2b_1 + b_2) = 130 (2 \times 465 + 530) = 190 \times 10^3$ mm^2

$e_1 = \dfrac{b_1^2}{2b_1 + b_2} = \dfrac{465^2}{2 \cdot 465 + 530} = 148$ mm

$e_3 = b_1 - e_1 - 200 = 465 - 148 - 200 = 117$ mm

$J = \dfrac{1}{6}(b_1 d^3 + b_1^3 d) + b_2 d e_1^2 + 2 d b_1 (\dfrac{1}{2}b_1 - e_1)^2$

$= \dfrac{1}{6}(465 \cdot 130^3 + 465^3 \cdot 130) + 530 \cdot 130 \cdot 148^2 +$

$2 \cdot 130 \cdot 465(\dfrac{1}{2} 465 - 148)^2 = 4.72 \cdot 10^9$ mm^4

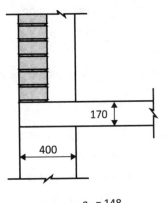

9.1.3 Moment Transfer by Eccentricity of Shear

The moment to be transferred from the slab to the column, M_f, is the unbalanced moment due to factored load to be taken at the centroid of the critical section, i.e., the moment obtained at the column axis, minus the shear times the eccentricity e_3.

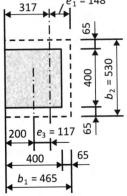

$M_f = -84.6 + 222.6 \times 0.117 = -58.6$ kN·m

$\gamma_v = 1 - \dfrac{1}{1 + \dfrac{2}{3}\left(\dfrac{b_1}{b_2}\right)^{1/2}} = 1 - \dfrac{1}{1 + \dfrac{2}{3}\left(\dfrac{465}{530}\right)^{1/2}} = 0.384$,   (Clause. 13.3.5.3)

Fig. 10.9.9.1.2

Maximum shear stress under factored loads:

$v_f = \dfrac{V_f}{A} + \dfrac{\gamma_v M_f e_1}{J} = \dfrac{244.8 \cdot 10^3}{190 \cdot 10^3} + \dfrac{0.384 \cdot 58.7 \cdot 10^6 \cdot 148}{4.72 \cdot 10^9} = 1.29 + 0.70 = 1.99$ MPa

The shear stress resistance of concrete (Clause 13.3.4) is controlled by Eq.13-7.

$v_r = v_c = 0.38 \lambda \phi_c \sqrt{f_c'} = 0.38 \cdot 1.0 \cdot 0.65 \sqrt{30} = 1.35$ MPa < 1.99 MPa

Shear reinforcement is required.

9.1.4 Design of Shear Reinforcement

The shear stress $v_f = 1.99$ MPa is at the upper limit of the allowable value for stirrups $v_c = 0.55 \lambda \phi_c \sqrt{f_c'} = 1.96$ MPa (c.f. Clause 13.3.9.2), but less than the maximum allowable value for headed shear reinforcement $v_c = 0.75 \lambda \phi_c \sqrt{f_c'} = 2.67$ MPa (Clause 13.3.8.2). However normal stirrups are not allowed for this slab since $h < 300$ mm (Clause 13.3.9.1).

Headed Shear Reinforcement

Using shear reinforcement ($f_{vy} = 400$ MPa), which is mechanically anchored at top and bottom (Clause. 13.3 8) the shear stress resistance of concrete

$v_c = 0.28 \lambda \phi_c \sqrt{f_c'} = 0.28 \cdot 1.0 \cdot 0.65 \sqrt{30} = 1.00$ MPa

Using two rows of headed bars along the strip of width $b_2 = 530$ mm, the area of shear reinforcement per unit length of each row is:

$$\frac{A_v}{s} = \frac{(v_f - v_c)b_2/2}{\phi_s f_{vy}} = \frac{(1.99 - 1.00)\,530/2}{0.85 \cdot 400} = 0.78\ \frac{\text{mm}^2}{\text{mm}}$$

Selecting 9.5 mm diameter headed stirrups ($A_v = 71$ mm²) requires

$$s \le \frac{71}{0.78} = 91\ \text{mm}$$

According to Clause 13.3.8.6, max $s = 0.75d = 0.75\,(130) = 98$ mm for a shear stress $v_f \le 0.56\lambda\phi_c\sqrt{f_c'} = 2.00$ MPa. Select $s = 90$ mm. The first stirrup is to be located at $0.4d = 52$ mm, say 50 mm, from column face.

The selected bars with area $A_v = 71$ mm² must have an anchor plate area of at least $10 \times 71 = 710$ mm², corresponding to a head diameter of 30 mm.

The headed shear reinforcement has to extend to a zone where $v_f = v_c = 0.19\lambda\phi_c\sqrt{f_c'} = 0.68$ MPa.

The arrangement of the headed shear reinforcement is shown on Fig. 10.9.9.1.4.

At distance 565 mm from the faces of the column (see Fig. 10.9.9.1.4)

$$A = (3 \cdot 400 + 2 \cdot 565\sqrt{2})130 = 364 \cdot 10^3\text{mm}^2$$

$$e_1 = \frac{2 \cdot 400(565 + 400/2) + 2\sqrt{2} \cdot 565\,(565/2)}{3 \cdot 400 + 2 \cdot 565\sqrt{2}} = 380\ \text{mm}$$

$$e_3 = 965 - 380 - 400/2 = 385\ \text{mm}$$

$$J = d\sum \frac{\ell_i}{3}(y_i^2 + y_i y_j + y_j^2)$$

where y_i and y_j are the coordinates of the end points of the strait segments of length l_i along the critical section with respect to its centroidal axis.

$$J = \frac{130}{3}\left\{\begin{matrix}400\left[(-585)^2 + (-585)(-185) + (-185)^2\right]2 + \\ 799\left[(-185)^2 + (-185)380 + 380^2\right]2 + 400(3)380^2\end{matrix}\right\} = 31.8\,(10^9)\text{mm}^4$$

Factored moment at $e_3 = 0.385$ m from center line of column

$$M_f = -84.6 + 222.6 \cdot 0.385 - 10.23 \cdot 7.40(0.385)^2\,/2 = -4.5\ \text{kN·m}$$

$$V_f = 244.8 - (1.530 \cdot 0.965 - 0.565^2)\,10.23 = 233\ \text{kN}$$

For the critical section outside the shear reinforced zone $b_1 = 965$ mm, $b_2 = 1530$ mm, thus

$$\gamma_v = 1 - \frac{1}{1 + \dfrac{2}{3}\left(\dfrac{965}{1530}\right)^{1/2}} = 0.346$$

$$v_f = \frac{233 \cdot 10^3}{364 \cdot 10^3} + \frac{0.346 \cdot 4.5 \cdot 10^6}{31.8 \cdot 10^9}(380) = 0.64 + 0.02 = 0.66\ \text{MPa} < v_c = 0.69\ \text{MPa} \qquad \text{OK}$$

10

Prestressed Concrete

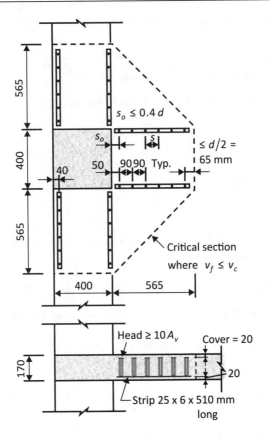

Fig. 10.9.9.1.4 Arrangement of headed reinforcement

9.2 At Interior Column B

Shear force (see table in Section 8.1) $V_f = 292.2 + 268.2 - 10.23\,(0.53^2) = 557$ kN

Unbalanced moment $M_f = 320.9 - 306.9 = 14.0$ kN·m

Properties of the critical section (see Fig. 10.9.9.2)

$A = 4\,(130)\,530 = 275\,(10^3)$ mm^2

$J = \dfrac{1}{6}[530(130^3)+130(530^3)] + \dfrac{1}{2}130\,(530^3) = 13.10\,(10^9)\,\text{mm}^4$

$\gamma_v = 1 - \dfrac{1}{1+\dfrac{2}{3}\left(\dfrac{530}{530}\right)^{0.5}} = 0.40$

$v_f = \dfrac{557\,(10^3)}{275\,(10^3)} + \dfrac{0.40\,(14.0)10^6(530/2)}{13.10\,(10^9)} = 2.02 + 0.12 = 2.14$ MPa

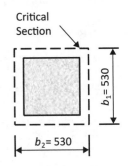

Fig. 10.9.9.2

Assuming that 2 tendons cross the critical section in one direction and 4 (bundled) tendons in the other direction, the vertical component of the prestressing force is: $V_p = 2(2 + 4)\, P_e \sin\beta$
where P_e = effective prestressing force per strand and β = slope of strand at the critical section. It is assumed that the cable profile over the columns is a cubic parabola over length $\alpha\ell$.

Equation of the cubic parabola for $0 \le x \le \alpha\ell$

$$e(x) = -\frac{s}{\alpha^2\ell^3}(4-\delta)x^3 - \frac{2}{\alpha\ell^2}[4\alpha - 2(4-\delta)]x^2 + e_A$$

where s = sag

$$\delta = \frac{e_A - e_B}{s}$$

The other symbols are defined in Fig. 10.9.9.2.b.

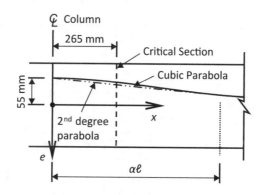

Fig. 10.9.9.1.b

Considering Span 2, $e_A = e_B = $ -55 mm, $s = 91$ mm, $\delta = 0$, and assuming $\alpha\ell = 700$ mm, i.e., $\alpha = 0.1$;

$$e(x) = -\frac{91}{0.1^2 \cdot 7000^3}(4-0)x^3 - \frac{91}{0.1 \cdot 7000^2}[4 \cdot 0.1 - 2(4-0)]x^2 - 55$$

$$= -0.106 \cdot 10^{-6}x^3 + 141 \cdot 10^{-6}x^2 - 55$$

Slope $\beta = de(x)/dx$: $\beta(x) = $ -0.318 $(10^{-6})\, x^2 + 282\,(10^{-6})\, x$

At critical section ($x = 265$ mm) $\beta = 0.0524$

Assuming the same slope to apply for all cables we find with $P_e = 156$ kN per strand:

$$V_p = 2\,(2+4)\,156 \times 0.0524 = 98\ \text{kN}$$

Shear resisted by concrete (CSA Standard A23.3 Eq.18-5): With $f_{cp} = 1.86$ MPa

$$v_c = 0.33 \cdot 1.0 \cdot 0.65\sqrt{30}\left[1 + \frac{0.9 \cdot 1.86}{0.33 \cdot 1.0 \cdot 0.65\sqrt{30}}\right]^{0.5} + 0.9\,\frac{98 \cdot 10^3}{275 \cdot 10^3} = 2.15\ \text{MPa}$$

$$\approx v_f = 2.14\ \text{MPa} \hspace{4cm} \text{OK}$$

The limitations for applications of Eq. 18-5 are satisfied (Clause 18.12.3.3).

10

Prestressed Concrete

10. Structural Integrity

CSA Standard A 23.3, Eq. (13-26) has to be satisfied (Clause 13.10.6)

$$\sum A_{sb} = \frac{2V_{se}}{f_y} = \frac{2(2)4.00\,(10^{-3})7400\,(6900)}{0.9\,(1860)} = 488 \text{ mm}^2 < 8\,(140) = 1120 \text{ mm}^2$$

(2 strands in each direction).

11. Cable Layout

The cable layout is shown in Fig. 10.9.11.

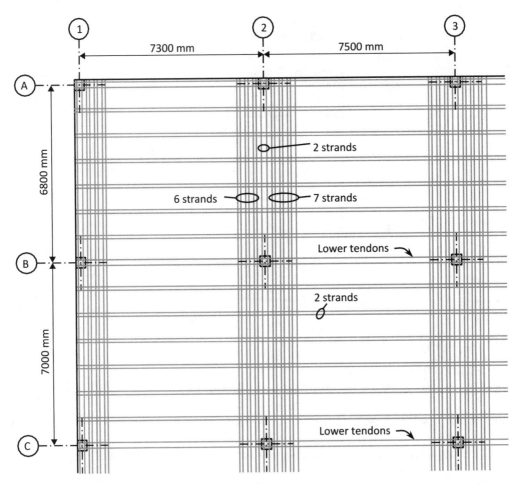

Strand layout: the strands are banded in one direction and in the other direction
they are placed in pairs at equal spacing.

Fig. 10.9.11 Cable layout

EXAMPLE 10.10

Design of Partially Prestressed Concrete Slab

Example 10.9 is redesigned as a partially prestressed slab

1. Load Balancing

Assuming that about 60% of the dead load is balanced by prestressing

$w_{bal} = 0.6 \times 5.30 = 3.18$ kN/m²

Span 1:

$$P_e = \frac{3.18 \times 6.80^2}{8 \times 0.080} = 230 \text{ kN/m}$$

For full width of panel $\qquad P_e = 230 \times 7.40 = 1702$ kN

Number of tendons $N = 1702/156 = 10.9$. Select 11 tendons. Load balanced by 11 tendons with $P_e = 11 (156) = 1716$ kN:

$w_{bal} = 8 \times 1716 \times 0.080/(6.80^2) = 23.7$ kN/m

Per m width: $w_{bal} = 23.7/7.40 = 3.20$ kN/m²

Net Load: $w_{net} = 7.70 - 3.20 = 4.50$ kN/m²

Span 2:

Making use of maximum possible sag $s = 170 - 2 (30) = 110$ mm.

$w_{bal} = 8 \times 1716 \times 0.11/(7.00)^2 = 30.8$ kN/m

Per m width: $w_{bal} = 30.8/7.40 = 4.16$ kN/m²

Net Load: $w_{net} = 7.70 - 4.16 = 3.54$ kN/m²

2. Moments and Stresses

From frame analysis (see Fig. 10.9.7.2) $M_{AB} = -66.3$ kN·m

$M_{BA} = -144.4$ kN·m

$M_{BD} = -126.2$ kN·m

$M_{DB} = -97.3$ kN·m

$M_1 = 89.1$ kN·m

$M_2 = 49.0$ kN·m

Moment at face of column B: $M_{BA} = -120.2$ kN·m

10

Prestressed Concrete

Column Strip:

Negative moment per metre width (Clause 18.12.2.1)

$$M = \frac{-120.2 \times 0.75}{3.45} = -26.1 \text{ kNm}$$

$$f_c = \frac{(-1716)10^3}{170(7400)} + \frac{26.1(10^6)}{170^2(1000)/6} = -1.36 + 5.42 = +4.06 \text{ MPa} > 0.5\sqrt{f_c'} = 2.73 \text{ MPa}$$

Slab will crack in the vicinity of the column under full service load.

The average compressive stress criterion of Clause 18.12.2.3 is satisfied, i.e.

f_{cp} = 1.36 MPa > 0.8 MPa

Minimum non-prestressed steel required (Table 18-1)

A_s = 0.00075 × 170 × 6600 = 842 mm²

It is anticipated that more non-prestressed steel will be required to provide the necessary factored flexural resistance (see 10.4).

Positive moment per meter width of column strip

M = 89.4 × 0.6 / 3.45 = 15.5 kN·m/m

Stress in bottom fibre:

$$f_c = -1.36 + \frac{15.5 \times 10^6}{170^2 \times 1000/6} = -1.36 + 3.22 = 1.86 \text{ MPa} < 2.73 \text{ MPa} > 0.2\sqrt{f_c'} = 1.10 \text{ MPa}$$

Slab will not crack in positive moments zone of the column strip.

For steel provided see strength requirements

Middle Strip:

Moment per metre width in middle strip at face of column

$$M = \frac{-120.2(0.25)}{7.40 - 3.45} = -7.60 \text{ kNm/m}$$

Top fibre stress

$$f_c = -1.36 - \frac{-7.60(10^6)}{170^2(1000)/6} = 0.22 \text{ MPa} < 2.73 \text{ MPa} \qquad \text{OK}$$

Positive moment per metre width of middle strip

M = 89.1 (0.40) / 3.95 = 9.02 kN·m/m

Bottom fibre stress

$$f_c = -1.36 + \frac{9.02 \times 10^6}{170^2 \times 1000/6} = 0.52 \text{ MPa} < 1.10 \text{ MPa} \qquad \text{OK}$$

No additional steel required.

3. Moments due to Factored Loads

The moments due to the factored load w_f = 10.23 kN/m^2 are the same as for example 10.9 but the secondary moments, M''_p are different. The values are listed below:

Support			A	B_{left}	B_{right}	C
$\alpha_D M_D + \alpha_L M_L$		kN·m	-144.8	-349.1	-329.8	-298.7
$\alpha_p M''_p$		kN·m	+ 42.1	+24.0	+27.6	+33.2
M_f		kN·m	-101.7	-325.1	-302.2	-265.5
V_f		kN	224.6	290.2	262.6	252.1
M_f at column face		kN·m	-58.6	-268.6	-251.2	-216.6
M_f – span		kN·m	231.0		153.3	

4. Factored Flexural Resistance

4.1 At Edge Column

Factored moments at face of column M_f = -58.6 kN·m

Assuming 4 tendons to be anchored within a width $b_b = (c_2 + 3h_s)$ = 910 mm   (Clause 13.10.2)

A_p = 4 × 140 = 560 mm^2

f_{pr} = 1193 MPa   see Example 10.9.

Non-prestressed steel: Table 18-1.

A_s = 0.00075 × 170 (6800 – 400) = 816 mm^2

Provide: 3 – 15M + 4 – 10M bars with A_s = 1000 mm^2

$$a = \frac{0.9\,(1193)560 + 0.85\,(400)1000}{0.805\,(0.65)30(910)} = 66 \text{ mm}$$

M_r = 0.9 (1193) 560 (85 – 66/2)+ 0.85 (1000) 400 (140 – 66/2) = 67.6 × 10^6 Nmm

$\qquad\qquad$ = 67.6 kN·m > 58.6 kN·m   OK

Note: The 3 – 15M bars are bent into column.

4.2 At Interior Column

Factored moment at face of column: M_f = -268.6 kN·m

Factored moment resistance provided by 11 – 15mm strands (A_p = 1540 mm^2) assuming f_{pr} = 1200 MPa:

M_{pr} = 0.9 (1200) 1540 (140 – 10) = 216 (10^6) N·mm = 216 kN·m

Estimate of the non-prestressed steel required:

$$A_s = \frac{M_f - M_{pr}}{\phi_s f_y(d - a/2)} = \frac{(268.6 - 216.0)10^6}{0.85\,(400)(140 - 10)} = 1190 \text{ mm}^2$$

Provide 12 – 10M bars with A_s = 1200 mm^2.

Check:

In negative moment region:

$$c_y = \frac{0.9\,(1670)1540 + 0.85\,(400)1200}{0.805\,(0.895)0.65\,(30)7400} = 26 \text{ mm}$$

In positive moment region:

$$c_y = \frac{0.9\,(1670)1540}{0.805\,(0.895)0.65\,(30)7400} = 22 \text{ mm}$$

$$f_{pr} = 0.6\,(1860) + \frac{8000}{28000}[(85 - 26) + (140 - 22) + (140 - 26)] = 1200 \text{ MPa}$$

$$a = \frac{0.9\,(1200)1540 + 0.85\,(400)1200}{0.805\,(0.65)30\,(7400)} = 18 \text{ mm}$$

$$M_r = [0.9\,(1200)\,1540\,(140 - 18/2) + 0.85\,(400)\,1200\,(140 - 18/2)]\,10^{-6}$$

$$= 271.3 \text{ kNm} > 268.6 \text{ kNm} \qquad\qquad\qquad \text{OK}$$

Provide 12 – 10M bars @ 300 mm in column strip.

4.3 Span 1

Positive moment due to factored loads for full width of panel M_f = 231 kN·m. Factored moment resistance provided by tendons M_{pr} = 217.9 kN·m Non-prestressed steel required for strength:

$$A_s = \frac{(231 - 217.9)10^6}{(0.85)400\,(140 - 9)} = 294 \text{ mm}^2 \qquad \text{Provide 4 – 10M bars in column strip.}$$

5.   Crack Control

According to Eq. 10.8.10 with 10M bars @ 300 mm at face of column B and a prestressing force P_e =1716 / 7.40 = 232 kN/m:

$$f_s = \frac{M_{net} - P_e(h/6 + e)}{A_s d} = \frac{26.1(10^6) - 232(10^3)(170/6 + 55)}{(100/0.30)140} = 145 \text{ MPa}$$

$z = f_s(d_c\,A)^{1/3}$ = 145 [(30) 2 (30) 300]$^{1/3}$ = 11 800 N/mm = 11.8 kN/mm < 20 kN/mm .

$\qquad\qquad\qquad\qquad\qquad\qquad\qquad\qquad\qquad\qquad$ OK   (Clause. 18.8.3).

Table 10.1a Flexural Resistance Coefficients, k_u, for Rectangular Elements with Bonded Prestressing Steel Only

(Assuming $\phi_c = 0.65$ and $\phi_p = 0.90$)

	$k_p = 0.28$						$k_p = 0.38$						$k_p = 0.48$					
f'_c	30	40	50	60	70	80	30	40	50	60	70	80	30	40	50	60	70	80
α_1	0.805	0.790	0.775	0.760	0.745	0.730	0.805	0.790	0.775	0.760	0.745	0.730	0.805	0.790	0.775	0.760	0.745	0.730
β_1	0.895	0.870	0.845	0.820	0.795	0.770	0.895	0.870	0.845	0.820	0.795	0.770	0.895	0.870	0.845	0.820	0.795	0.770
w_{pu}	k_u						k_u						k_u					
0.005	0.0045	0.0045	0.0045	0.0045	0.0045	0.0045	0.0045	0.0045	0.0045	0.0045	0.0045	0.0045	0.0045	0.0045	0.0045	0.0045	0.0045	0.0045
0.010	0.0089	0.0089	0.0089	0.0089	0.0089	0.0089	0.0089	0.0089	0.0088	0.0088	0.0088	0.0088	0.0088	0.0088	0.0088	0.0088	0.0088	0.0088
0.015	0.0132	0.0132	0.0132	0.0132	0.0132	0.0132	0.0132	0.0132	0.0132	0.0132	0.0131	0.0131	0.0131	0.0131	0.0131	0.0131	0.0131	0.0131
0.020	0.0175	0.0175	0.0175	0.0175	0.0174	0.0174	0.0174	0.0174	0.0174	0.0174	0.0174	0.0173	0.0174	0.0174	0.0173	0.0173	0.0173	0.0173
0.025	0.0217	0.0217	0.0217	0.0217	0.0216	0.0216	0.0216	0.0216	0.0216	0.0215	0.0215	0.0215	0.0215	0.0215	0.0215	0.0214	0.0214	0.0214
0.030	0.0259	0.0259	0.0258	0.0258	0.0258	0.0257	0.0258	0.0257	0.0257	0.0256	0.0256	0.0255	0.0256	0.0256	0.0255	0.0255	0.0254	0.0254
0.035	0.0300	0.0300	0.0299	0.0299	0.0298	0.0298	0.0298	0.0298	0.0297	0.0296	0.0296	0.0295	0.0296	0.0296	0.0295	0.0294	0.0294	0.0293
0.040	0.0341	0.0340	0.0339	0.0339	0.0338	0.0337	0.0338	0.0337	0.0337	0.0336	0.0335	0.0334	0.0336	0.0335	0.0334	0.0333	0.0332	0.0331
0.045	0.0380	0.0380	0.0379	0.0378	0.0377	0.0377	0.0377	0.0377	0.0376	0.0375	0.0374	0.0373	0.0374	0.0373	0.0372	0.0371	0.0370	0.0369
0.050	0.0420	0.0419	0.0418	0.0417	0.0416	0.0415	0.0416	0.0415	0.0414	0.0413	0.0412	0.0410	0.0412	0.0411	0.0410	0.0409	0.0407	0.0406
0.055	0.0459	0.0458	0.0457	0.0455	0.0454	0.0453	0.0454	0.0453	0.0452	0.0450	0.0449	0.0447	0.0450	0.0448	0.0447	0.0445	0.0444	0.0442
0.060	0.0497	0.0496	0.0494	0.0493	0.0492	0.0490	0.0492	0.0490	0.0489	0.0487	0.0486	0.0484	0.0487	0.0485	0.0483	0.0481	0.0480	0.0477
0.065	0.0535	0.0533	0.0532	0.0530	0.0529	0.0527	0.0529	0.0527	0.0525	0.0523	0.0521	0.0519	0.0523	0.0521	0.0519	0.0517	0.0515	0.0512
0.070	0.0572	0.0570	0.0569	0.0567	0.0565	0.0563	0.0565	0.0563	0.0561	0.0559	0.0557	0.0554	0.0558	0.0556	0.0554	0.0551	0.0549	0.0546
0.075	0.0609	0.0607	0.0605	0.0603	0.0601	0.0598	0.0601	0.0599	0.0596	0.0594	0.0591	0.0589	0.0593	0.0591	0.0588	0.0585	0.0583	0.0580
0.080	0.0645	0.0643	0.0641	0.0638	0.0636	0.0633	0.0636	0.0634	0.0631	0.0628	0.0626	0.0623	0.0628	0.0625	0.0622	0.0619	0.0616	0.0612
0.085	0.0680	0.0678	0.0676	0.0673	0.0670	0.0668	0.0671	0.0668	0.0665	0.0662	0.0659	0.0656	0.0661	0.0658	0.0655	0.0652	0.0648	0.0644
0.090	0.0716	0.0713	0.0710	0.0708	0.0705	0.0701	0.0705	0.0702	0.0699	0.0695	0.0692	0.0688	0.0694	0.0691	0.0688	0.0684	0.0680	0.0676
0.095	0.0750	0.0747	0.0744	0.0741	0.0738	0.0735	0.0738	0.0735	0.0732	0.0728	0.0724	0.0720	0.0727	0.0723	0.0719	0.0715	0.0711	0.0706
0.100	0.0784	0.0781	0.0778	0.0775	0.0771	0.0767	0.0772	0.0768	0.0764	0.0760	0.0756	0.0752	0.0759	0.0755	0.0751	0.0746	0.0742	0.0737
0.105	0.0818	0.0815	0.0811	0.0807	0.0803	0.0799	0.0804	0.0800	0.0796	0.0792	0.0787	0.0782	0.0791	0.0786	0.0782	0.0777	0.0772	0.0766
0.110	0.0851	0.0848	0.0844	0.0840	0.0835	0.0831	0.0836	0.0832	0.0827	0.0823	0.0818	0.0813	0.0822	0.0817	0.0812	0.0807	0.0801	0.0795
0.115	0.0884	0.0880	0.0876	0.0871	0.0867	0.0862	0.0868	0.0863	0.0858	0.0853	0.0848	0.0842	0.0852	0.0847	0.0842	0.0836	0.0830	0.0824
0.120	0.0916	0.0912	0.0907	0.0903	0.0898	0.0893	0.0899	0.0894	0.0889	0.0883	0.0878	0.0872	0.0882	0.0877	0.0871	0.0865	0.0858	0.0852
0.125	0.0948	0.0943	0.0939	0.0934	0.0928	0.0923	0.0929	0.0924	0.0919	0.0913	0.0907	0.0900	0.0911	0.0906	0.0899	0.0893	0.0886	0.0879
0.130	0.0979	0.0974	0.0969	0.0964	0.0958	0.0952	0.0959	0.0954	0.0948	0.0942	0.0935	0.0928	0.0940	0.0934	0.0928	0.0921	0.0913	0.0906
0.135	0.1010	0.1005	0.0999	0.0994	0.0988	0.0981	0.0989	0.0983	0.0977	0.0970	0.0963	0.0956	0.0969	0.0962	0.0955	0.0948	0.0940	0.0932
0.140	0.1041	0.1035	0.1029	0.1023	0.1017	0.1010	0.1018	0.1012	0.1005	0.0998	0.0991	0.0983	0.0997	0.0990	0.0982	0.0975	0.0966	0.0958
0.145	0.1071	0.1065	0.1058	0.1052	0.1045	0.1038	0.1047	0.1040	0.1033	0.1026	0.1018	0.1010	0.1024	0.1017	0.1009	0.1001	0.0992	0.0983
0.150	0.1100	0.1094	0.1087	0.1080	0.1073	0.1066	0.1075	0.1068	0.1061	0.1053	0.1045	0.1036	0.1052	0.1044	0.1035	0.1027	0.1018	0.1008
0.155	0.1129	0.1123	0.1116	0.1108	0.1101	0.1093	0.1103	0.1096	0.1088	0.1080	0.1071	0.1062	0.1078	0.1070	0.1061	0.1052	0.1043	0.1032
0.160	0.1158	0.1151	0.1144	0.1136	0.1128	0.1120	0.1130	0.1123	0.1114	0.1106	0.1097	0.1087	0.1104	0.1096	0.1087	0.1077	0.1067	0.1056
0.165	0.1186	0.1179	0.1171	0.1163	0.1155	0.1146	0.1157	0.1149	0.1141	0.1131	0.1122	0.1112	0.1130	0.1121	0.1111	0.1101	0.1091	0.1080
0.170	0.1214	0.1206	0.1198	0.1190	0.1181	0.1172	0.1184	0.1175	0.1166	0.1157	0.1147	0.1136	0.1155	0.1146	0.1136	0.1125	0.1114	0.1103
0.175	0.1241	0.1233	0.1225	0.1216	0.1207	0.1197	0.1210	0.1201	0.1192	0.1182	0.1171	0.1160	0.1180	0.1170	0.1160	0.1149	0.1138	0.1126
0.180	0.1269	0.1260	0.1251	0.1242	0.1232	0.1222	0.1236	0.1226	0.1216	0.1206	0.1195	0.1184	0.1205	0.1194	0.1184	0.1172	0.1160	0.1148
0.185	0.1295	0.1286	0.1277	0.1267	0.1257	0.1247	0.1261	0.1251	0.1241	0.1230	0.1219	0.1207	0.1229	0.1218	0.1207	0.1195	0.1182	0.1169
0.190	0.1321	0.1312	0.1303	0.1293	0.1282	0.1271	0.1286	0.1276	0.1265	0.1254	0.1242	0.1230	0.1253	0.1241	0.1230	0.1217	0.1204	0.1191
0.195	0.1347	0.1338	0.1328	0.1317	0.1306	0.1295	0.1311	0.1300	0.1289	0.1277	0.1265	0.1252	0.1276	0.1264	0.1252	0.1239	0.1226	0.1212
0.200	0.1373	0.1363	0.1352	0.1341	0.1330	0.1318	0.1335	0.1324	0.1312	0.1300	0.1287	0.1274	0.1299	0.1287	0.1274	0.1261	0.1247	0.1232

10

Prestressed Concrete

$$K_u = \frac{M_f}{f'_c b d_p^2}$$

$$A_p = \frac{w_{pu} f'_c b d_p}{f_{pu}}$$

Table 10.1b Flexural Resistance Coefficients, k_u, for Rectangular Elements with Bonded Prestressing Steel Only

(Assuming $\phi_c = 0.70$ and $\phi_p = 0.90$)

	$k_p = 0.28$						$k_p = 0.38$						$k_p = 0.48$					
f_c'	30	40	50	60	70	80	30	40	50	60	70	80	30	40	50	60	70	80
α_1	0.805	0.790	0.775	0.760	0.745	0.730	0.805	0.790	0.775	0.760	0.745	0.730	0.805	0.790	0.775	0.760	0.745	0.730
β_1	0.895	0.870	0.845	0.820	0.795	0.770	0.895	0.870	0.845	0.820	0.795	0.770	0.895	0.870	0.845	0.820	0.795	0.770
w_{pu}	k_u						k_u						k_u					
0.005	0.0045	0.0045	0.0045	0.0045	0.0045	0.0045	0.0045	0.0045	0.0045	0.0045	0.0045	0.0045	0.0045	0.0045	0.0045	0.0045	0.0045	0.0045
0.010	0.0089	0.0089	0.0089	0.0089	0.0089	0.0089	0.0089	0.0089	0.0089	0.0089	0.0088	0.0088	0.0089	0.0088	0.0088	0.0088	0.0088	0.0088
0.015	0.0132	0.0132	0.0132	0.0132	0.0132	0.0132	0.0132	0.0132	0.0132	0.0132	0.0132	0.0132	0.0132	0.0132	0.0131	0.0131	0.0131	0.0131
0.020	0.0175	0.0175	0.0175	0.0175	0.0175	0.0175	0.0175	0.0175	0.0174	0.0174	0.0174	0.0174	0.0174	0.0174	0.0174	0.0174	0.0173	0.0173
0.025	0.0218	0.0218	0.0217	0.0217	0.0217	0.0217	0.0217	0.0217	0.0216	0.0216	0.0216	0.0215	0.0216	0.0216	0.0215	0.0215	0.0215	0.0214
0.030	0.0260	0.0259	0.0259	0.0259	0.0258	0.0258	0.0258	0.0258	0.0258	0.0257	0.0257	0.0256	0.0257	0.0257	0.0256	0.0256	0.0255	0.0255
0.035	0.0301	0.0301	0.0300	0.0300	0.0299	0.0299	0.0299	0.0299	0.0298	0.0298	0.0297	0.0297	0.0298	0.0297	0.0296	0.0296	0.0295	0.0294
0.040	0.0342	0.0341	0.0341	0.0340	0.0340	0.0339	0.0340	0.0339	0.0338	0.0338	0.0337	0.0336	0.0337	0.0337	0.0336	0.0335	0.0334	0.0333
0.045	0.0382	0.0382	0.0381	0.0380	0.0379	0.0378	0.0379	0.0379	0.0378	0.0377	0.0376	0.0375	0.0376	0.0376	0.0375	0.0374	0.0373	0.0371
0.050	0.0422	0.0421	0.0420	0.0419	0.0418	0.0417	0.0418	0.0417	0.0416	0.0415	0.0414	0.0413	0.0415	0.0414	0.0413	0.0411	0.0410	0.0409
0.055	0.0461	0.0460	0.0459	0.0458	0.0457	0.0456	0.0457	0.0456	0.0455	0.0453	0.0452	0.0451	0.0453	0.0452	0.0450	0.0449	0.0447	0.0445
0.060	0.0500	0.0499	0.0498	0.0496	0.0495	0.0494	0.0495	0.0494	0.0492	0.0491	0.0489	0.0487	0.0490	0.0489	0.0487	0.0485	0.0483	0.0482
0.065	0.0538	0.0537	0.0535	0.0534	0.0532	0.0531	0.0532	0.0531	0.0529	0.0528	0.0526	0.0524	0.0527	0.0525	0.0523	0.0521	0.0519	0.0517
0.070	0.0576	0.0574	0.0573	0.0571	0.0569	0.0567	0.0569	0.0568	0.0566	0.0564	0.0562	0.0559	0.0563	0.0561	0.0559	0.0557	0.0554	0.0552
0.075	0.0613	0.0611	0.0610	0.0608	0.0606	0.0603	0.0606	0.0604	0.0602	0.0599	0.0597	0.0594	0.0599	0.0596	0.0594	0.0591	0.0588	0.0586
0.080	0.0650	0.0648	0.0646	0.0644	0.0641	0.0639	0.0642	0.0639	0.0637	0.0634	0.0632	0.0629	0.0634	0.0631	0.0628	0.0625	0.0622	0.0619
0.085	0.0686	0.0684	0.0682	0.0679	0.0677	0.0674	0.0677	0.0674	0.0672	0.0669	0.0666	0.0663	0.0668	0.0665	0.0662	0.0659	0.0655	0.0652
0.090	0.0722	0.0719	0.0717	0.0714	0.0711	0.0708	0.0712	0.0709	0.0706	0.0703	0.0700	0.0696	0.0702	0.0699	0.0695	0.0692	0.0688	0.0684
0.095	0.0757	0.0754	0.0752	0.0749	0.0746	0.0742	0.0746	0.0743	0.0740	0.0736	0.0733	0.0729	0.0735	0.0732	0.0728	0.0724	0.0720	0.0716
0.100	0.0792	0.0789	0.0786	0.0783	0.0779	0.0776	0.0780	0.0776	0.0773	0.0769	0.0765	0.0761	0.0768	0.0764	0.0760	0.0756	0.0751	0.0747
0.105	0.0826	0.0823	0.0820	0.0816	0.0813	0.0809	0.0813	0.0809	0.0806	0.0801	0.0797	0.0793	0.0800	0.0796	0.0792	0.0787	0.0782	0.0777
0.110	0.0860	0.0857	0.0853	0.0849	0.0845	0.0841	0.0846	0.0842	0.0838	0.0833	0.0829	0.0824	0.0832	0.0828	0.0823	0.0818	0.0813	0.0807
0.115	0.0894	0.0890	0.0886	0.0882	0.0878	0.0873	0.0878	0.0874	0.0869	0.0865	0.0860	0.0854	0.0863	0.0859	0.0853	0.0848	0.0842	0.0836
0.120	0.0927	0.0923	0.0919	0.0914	0.0909	0.0905	0.0910	0.0906	0.0901	0.0896	0.0890	0.0884	0.0894	0.0889	0.0884	0.0878	0.0872	0.0865
0.125	0.0959	0.0955	0.0951	0.0946	0.0941	0.0935	0.0942	0.0937	0.0931	0.0926	0.0920	0.0914	0.0925	0.0919	0.0913	0.0907	0.0900	0.0893
0.130	0.0992	0.0987	0.0982	0.0977	0.0972	0.0966	0.0973	0.0967	0.0962	0.0956	0.0950	0.0943	0.0954	0.0948	0.0942	0.0936	0.0929	0.0921
0.135	0.1023	0.1018	0.1013	0.1008	0.1002	0.0996	0.1003	0.0997	0.0992	0.0985	0.0979	0.0972	0.0984	0.0977	0.0971	0.0964	0.0956	0.0949
0.140	0.1055	0.1049	0.1044	0.1038	0.1032	0.1025	0.1033	0.1027	0.1021	0.1014	0.1007	0.1000	0.1013	0.1006	0.0999	0.0991	0.0984	0.0975
0.145	0.1085	0.1080	0.1074	0.1068	0.1061	0.1055	0.1063	0.1057	0.1050	0.1043	0.1035	0.1028	0.1041	0.1034	0.1027	0.1019	0.1010	0.1002
0.150	0.1116	0.1110	0.1104	0.1097	0.1090	0.1083	0.1092	0.1085	0.1078	0.1071	0.1063	0.1055	0.1069	0.1062	0.1054	0.1046	0.1037	0.1028
0.155	0.1146	0.1140	0.1133	0.1126	0.1119	0.1111	0.1121	0.1114	0.1106	0.1098	0.1090	0.1081	0.1097	0.1089	0.1081	0.1072	0.1063	0.1053
0.160	0.1176	0.1169	0.1162	0.1155	0.1147	0.1139	0.1149	0.1142	0.1134	0.1126	0.1117	0.1108	0.1124	0.1116	0.1107	0.1098	0.1088	0.1078
0.165	0.1205	0.1198	0.1191	0.1183	0.1175	0.1167	0.1177	0.1169	0.1161	0.1152	0.1143	0.1134	0.1151	0.1142	0.1133	0.1123	0.1113	0.1103
0.170	0.1234	0.1226	0.1219	0.1211	0.1202	0.1193	0.1205	0.1197	0.1188	0.1179	0.1169	0.1159	0.1177	0.1168	0.1158	0.1148	0.1138	0.1127
0.175	0.1262	0.1255	0.1247	0.1238	0.1229	0.1220	0.1232	0.1223	0.1214	0.1205	0.1195	0.1184	0.1203	0.1194	0.1184	0.1173	0.1162	0.1150
0.180	0.1290	0.1282	0.1274	0.1265	0.1256	0.1246	0.1259	0.1250	0.1240	0.1230	0.1220	0.1209	0.1229	0.1219	0.1208	0.1197	0.1186	0.1174
0.185	0.1318	0.1310	0.1301	0.1292	0.1282	0.1272	0.1285	0.1276	0.1266	0.1255	0.1244	0.1233	0.1254	0.1243	0.1233	0.1221	0.1209	0.1197
0.190	0.1345	0.1337	0.1327	0.1318	0.1308	0.1297	0.1311	0.1301	0.1291	0.1280	0.1269	0.1257	0.1279	0.1268	0.1256	0.1245	0.1232	0.1219
0.195	0.1372	0.1363	0.1354	0.1343	0.1333	0.1322	0.1337	0.1327	0.1316	0.1304	0.1293	0.1280	0.1303	0.1292	0.1280	0.1268	0.1255	0.1241
0.200	0.1399	0.1389	0.1379	0.1369	0.1358	0.1346	0.1362	0.1351	0.1340	0.1328	0.1316	0.1303	0.1327	0.1315	0.1303	0.1290	0.1277	0.1263

$$K_u = \frac{M_f}{f_c' b d_p^2}$$

$$A_p = \frac{w_{pu} f_c' b d_p}{f_{pu}}$$

Table 10.2   Moment of Inertia of Rectangular Transformed Section

ρ_p	$I_{cr}/bd^3 = k^3/3 + n\rho_p(1-k)^2$						
	$k = \sqrt{(n\rho_p)^2 + 2(n\rho_p)} - n\rho_p$						
	$\rho_p = A_p/bd \quad n = E_s/E_c$						
	20	30	40	50	60	70	80
Normal Density Concrete (2400kg/m³) 0.0005	0.0038	0.0033	0.0030	0.0028	0.0026	0.0025	0.0023
0.001	0.0073	0.0064	0.0058	0.0054	0.0050	0.0047	0.0045
0.0015	0.0105	0.0092	0.0084	0.0078	0.0073	0.0069	0.0066
0.002	0.0136	0.0120	0.0109	0.0101	0.0095	0.0090	0.0085
0.0025	0.0165	0.0146	0.0133	0.0123	0.0116	0.0109	0.0104
0.003	0.0193	0.0171	0.0156	0.0145	0.0136	0.0129	0.0123
0.0035	0.0220	0.0195	0.0178	0.0165	0.0155	0.0147	0.0141
0.004	0.0246	0.0218	0.0200	0.0186	0.0175	0.0166	0.0158
0.0045	0.0271	0.0241	0.0220	0.0205	0.0193	0.0183	0.0175
0.005	0.0296	0.0263	0.0241	0.0224	0.0211	0.0201	0.0192
0.0055	0.0319	0.0285	0.0261	0.0243	0.0229	0.0217	0.0208
0.006	0.0343	0.0305	0.0280	0.0261	0.0246	0.0234	0.0224
0.0065	0.0365	0.0326	0.0299	0.0279	0.0263	0.0250	0.0239
0.007	0.0387	0.0346	0.0318	0.0296	0.0280	0.0266	0.0254
0.0075	0.0408	0.0365	0.0336	0.0313	0.0296	0.0281	0.0269
0.008	0.0429	0.0384	0.0353	0.0330	0.0312	0.0297	0.0284
0.0085	0.0450	0.0403	0.0371	0.0347	0.0327	0.0312	0.0298
0.009	0.0470	0.0421	0.0388	0.0363	0.0343	0.0326	0.0313
0.0095	0.0489	0.0439	0.0405	0.0378	0.0358	0.0341	0.0326
0.01	0.0508	0.0457	0.0421	0.0394	0.0373	0.0355	0.0340
Semi-Low Density Concrete (2000kg/m³) 0.0005	0.0049	0.0043	0.0039	0.0036	0.0034	0.0032	0.0030
0.001	0.0093	0.0082	0.0075	0.0069	0.0065	0.0061	0.0058
0.0015	0.0134	0.0118	0.0108	0.0100	0.0093	0.0088	0.0084
0.002	0.0172	0.0152	0.0139	0.0129	0.0121	0.0114	0.0109
0.0025	0.0209	0.0185	0.0169	0.0157	0.0147	0.0139	0.0133
0.003	0.0243	0.0216	0.0197	0.0183	0.0172	0.0164	0.0156
0.0035	0.0276	0.0245	0.0225	0.0209	0.0197	0.0187	0.0178
0.004	0.0308	0.0274	0.0251	0.0234	0.0220	0.0209	0.0200
0.0045	0.0339	0.0302	0.0277	0.0258	0.0243	0.0231	0.0221
0.005	0.0368	0.0329	0.0302	0.0282	0.0266	0.0252	0.0241
0.0055	0.0397	0.0355	0.0326	0.0304	0.0287	0.0273	0.0261
0.006	0.0425	0.0380	0.0349	0.0326	0.0308	0.0293	0.0281
0.0065	0.0451	0.0405	0.0372	0.0348	0.0329	0.0313	0.0300
0.007	0.0478	0.0428	0.0395	0.0369	0.0349	0.0332	0.0318
0.0075	0.0503	0.0452	0.0416	0.0390	0.0368	0.0351	0.0336
0.008	0.0528	0.0474	0.0438	0.0410	0.0388	0.0369	0.0354
0.0085	0.0552	0.0497	0.0458	0.0429	0.0406	0.0388	0.0371
0.009	0.0575	0.0518	0.0479	0.0449	0.0425	0.0405	0.0389
0.0095	0.0598	0.0539	0.0498	0.0468	0.0443	0.0423	0.0405
0.01	0.0621	0.0560	0.0518	0.0486	0.0461	0.0440	0.0422

10

Prestressed Concrete

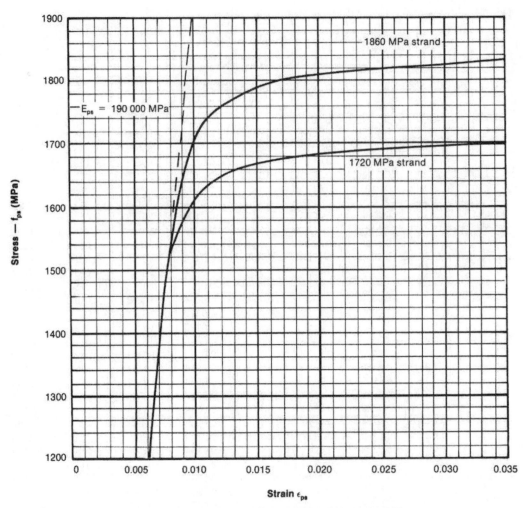

These curves are based on the following equations

For $\epsilon_{ps} \leq 0.008$, $f_{ps} = 190\,000\,\epsilon_{ps}$ (MPa)

Grade 1720 — For $\epsilon_{ps} > 0.008$, $f_{ps} = 1710 - \dfrac{0.400}{\epsilon_{ps} - 0.006} < 0.98\,f_{pu}$ (MPa)

Grade 1860 — For $\epsilon_{ps} > 0.008$, $f_{ps} = 1848 - \dfrac{0.517}{\epsilon_{ps} - 0.0065} < 0.98\,f_{pu}$ (MPa)

7-wire stress-relieved and low-relaxation strand shall comply with
ASTM A416/416M. The designer should check that the properties of the steel used correspond to the assumed values.

Fig. 10.1   Typical stress-strain curve, 7-wire stress-relieved and low-relaxation prestressing strand

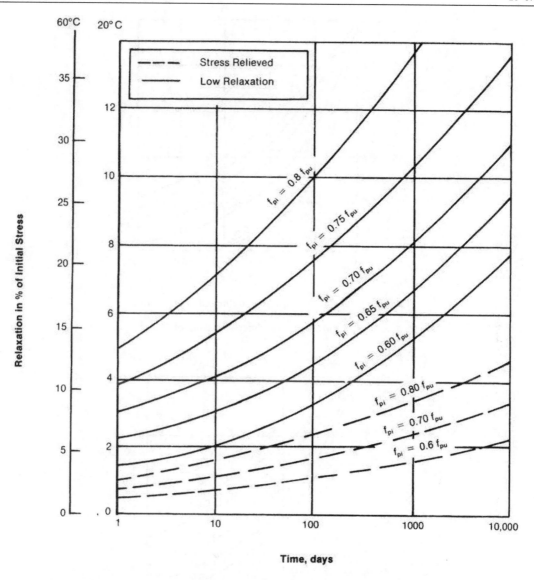

Fig. 10.2   Intrinsic relaxation of stress relieved and low relaxation strand for different levels of initial stress f_{psi} at 20° C and 60° C.

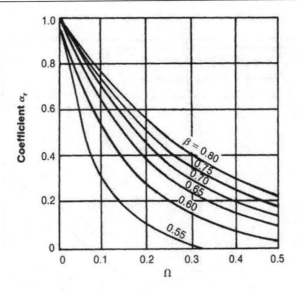

Fig. 10.3   Relaxation reduction coefficient α_r as a function

of $\Omega = \dfrac{\Delta f_s}{f_{pi}}$ for different values of $\beta = \dfrac{f_{pi}}{f_{pu}}$

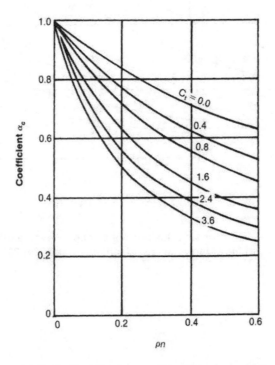

Fig. 10.4   Coefficient α_c as a function of ρn and C_t

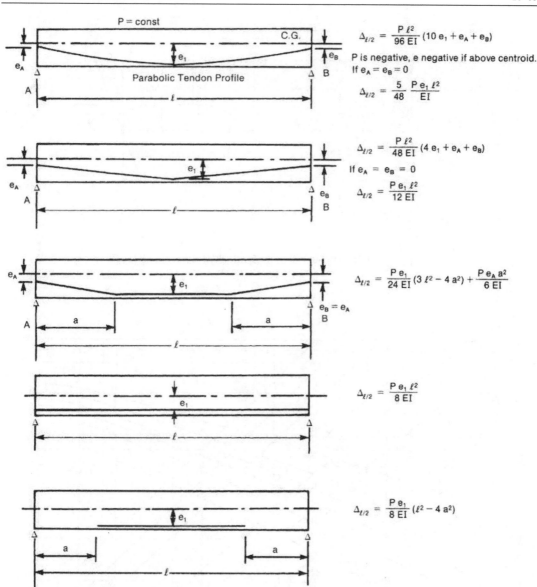

$$\Delta_{\ell/2} = \frac{P\,\ell^2}{96\,EI}\,(10\,e_1 + e_A + e_B)$$

P is negative, e negative if above centroid.
If $e_A = e_B = 0$

$$\Delta_{\ell/2} = \frac{5}{48}\,\frac{P\,e_1\,\ell^2}{EI}$$

$$\Delta_{\ell/2} = \frac{P\,\ell^2}{48\,EI}\,(4\,e_1 + e_A + e_B)$$

If $e_A = e_B = 0$

$$\Delta_{\ell/2} = \frac{P\,e_1\,\ell^2}{12\,EI}$$

$$\Delta_{\ell/2} = \frac{P\,e_1}{24\,EI}\,(3\,\ell^2 - 4\,a^2) + \frac{P\,e_A\,a^2}{6\,EI}$$

$$\Delta_{\ell/2} = \frac{P\,e_1\,\ell^2}{8\,EI}$$

$$\Delta_{\ell/2} = \frac{P\,e_1}{8\,EI}\,(\ell^2 - 4\,a^2)$$

Fig. 10.5   Deflection formulas for prestressed concrete beams with different tendon profiles.

10

Prestressed Concrete

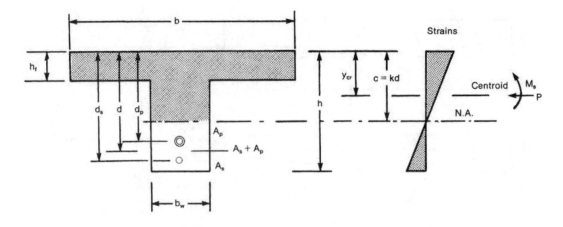

Fig. 10.6   T-Section subjected to M_s and decompression force P

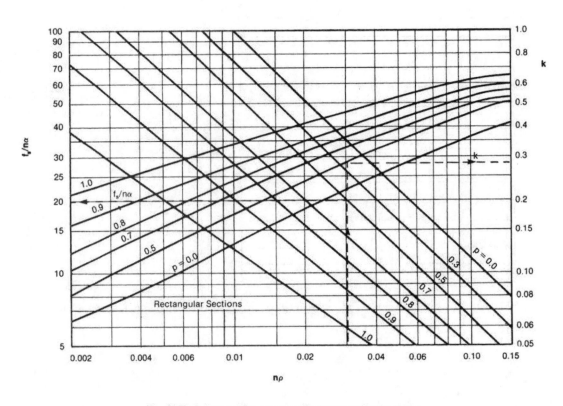

Fig. 10.7 $f_s/n\alpha$ and k versus $n\rho$ for rectangular sections.

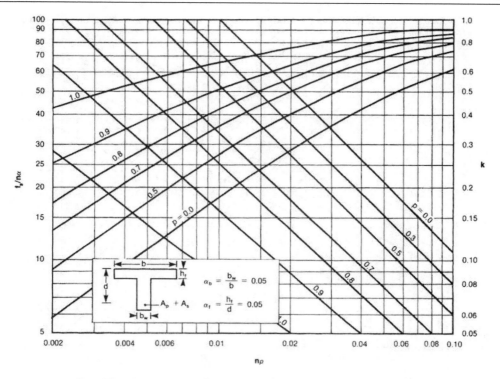

Fig. 10.8.1 $f_s/n\alpha$ and k versus $n\rho$ for T-beams with $\alpha_b = 0.05$ and $\alpha_f = 0.05$.

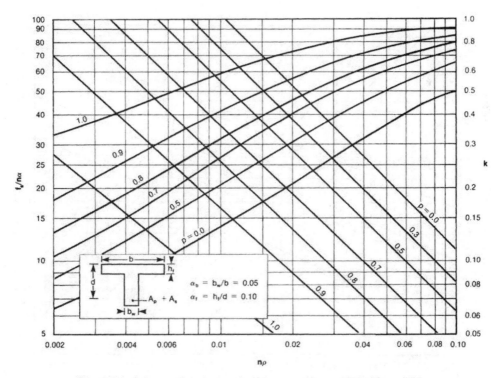

Fig. 10.8.2 $f_s/n\alpha$ and k versus $n\rho$ for T-beams with $\alpha_b = 0.05$ and $\alpha_f = 0.10$.

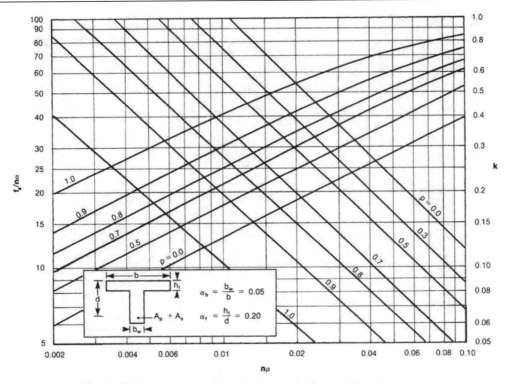

Fig. 10.8.3 $f_s/n\alpha$ and k versus nρ for T-beams with $\alpha_b = 0.05$ and $\alpha_f = 0.20$.

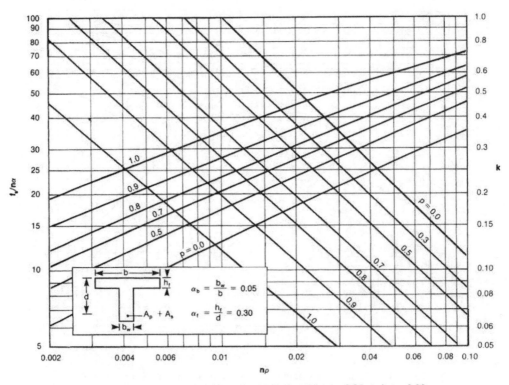

Fig. 10.8.4 $f_s/n\alpha$ and k versus nρ for T-beams with $\alpha_b = 0.05$ and $\alpha_f = 0.30$.

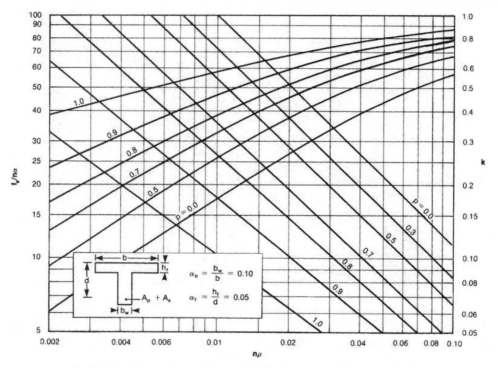

Fig. 10.8.5 $f_s/n\alpha$ and k versus nρ for T-beams with $\alpha_b = 0.10$ and $\alpha_f = 0.05$.

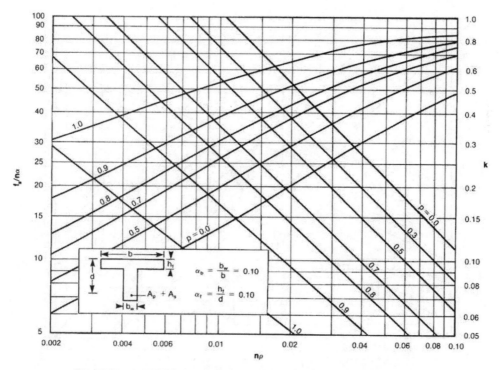

Fig. 10.8.6 $f_s/n\alpha$ and k versus nρ for T-beams with $\alpha_b = 0.10$ and $\alpha_f = 0.10$.

10

Prestressed Concrete

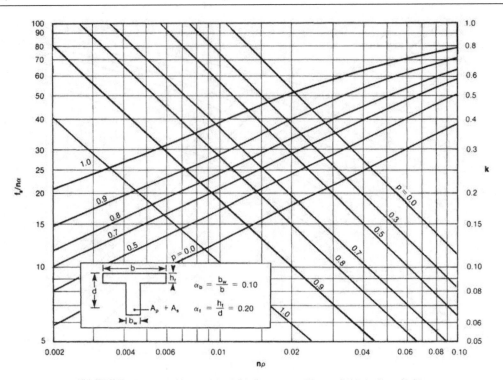

Fig. 10.8.7 $f_s/n\alpha$ and k versus nρ for T-beams with $\alpha_b = 0.10$ and $\alpha_f = 0.20$.

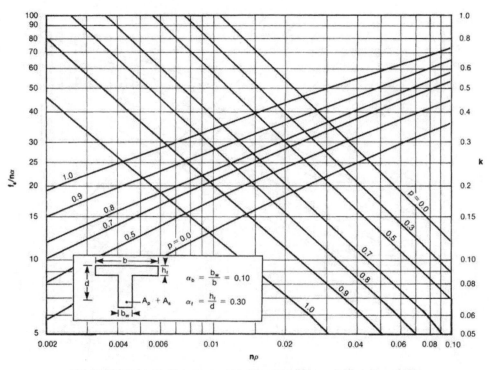

Fig. 10.8.8 $f_s/n\alpha$ and k versus nρ for T-beams with $\alpha_b = 0.10$ and $\alpha_f = 0.30$.

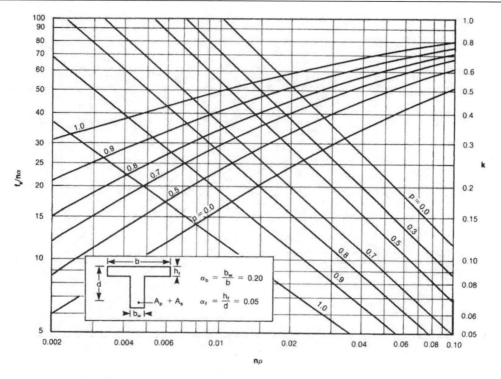

Fig. 10.8.9 $f_s/n\alpha$ and k versus $n\rho$ for T-beams with $\alpha_b = 0.20$ and $\alpha_f = 0.05$.

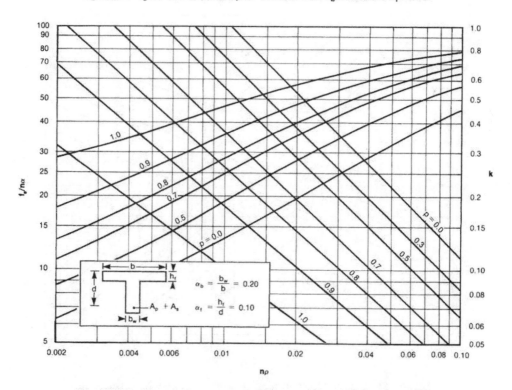

Fig. 10.8.10 $f_s/n\alpha$ and k versus $n\rho$ for T-beams with $\alpha_b = 0.20$ and $\alpha_f = 0.10$.

10

Prestressed Concrete

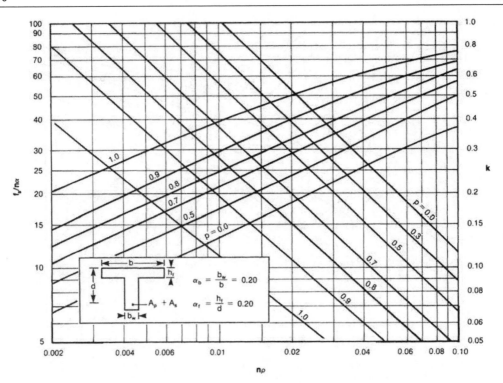

Fig. 10.8.11 $f_s/n\alpha$ and k versus $n\rho$ for T-beams with $\alpha_b = 0.20$ and $\alpha_f = 0.20$.

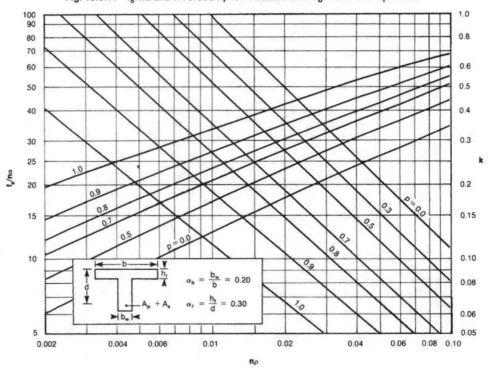

Fig. 10.8.12 $f_s/n\alpha$ and k versus $n\rho$ for T-beams with $\alpha_b = 0.20$ and $\alpha_f = 0.30$.

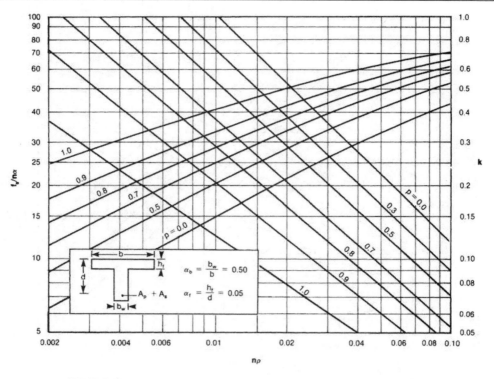

Fig. 10.8.13 $f_s/n\alpha$ and k versus nρ for T-beams with α_b = 0.50 and α_f = 0.05.

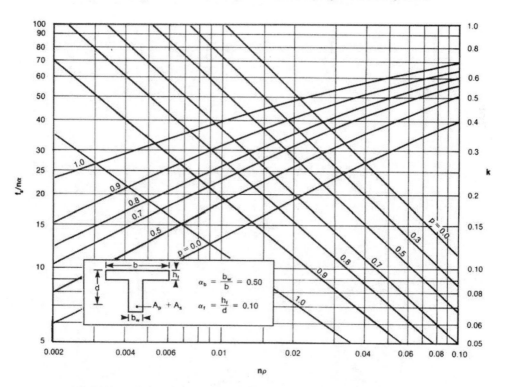

Fig. 10.8.14 $f_s/n\alpha$ and k versus nρ for T-beams with α_b = 0.50 and α_f = 0.10.

10

Prestressed Concrete

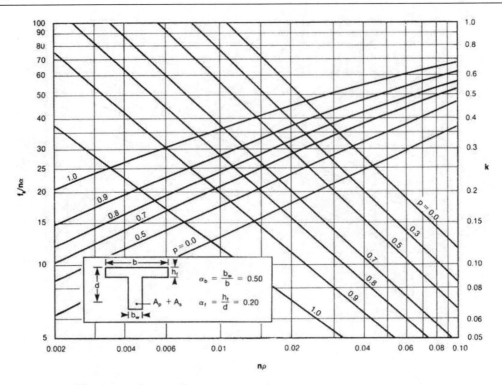

Fig. 10.8.15 $f_s/n\alpha$ and k versus nρ for T-beams with $\alpha_b = 0.50$ and $\alpha_f = 0.20$.

Denis Mitchell
Patrick Paultre
Perry Adebar

Seismic Design

11.1 Introduction

The 2015 National Building Code of Canada (NBCC) gives the minimum lateral earthquake force, V, for the equivalent static force procedure as:

$$V = \frac{S(T_a)M_v I_E W}{R_d R_o}$$

except that:

a) For walls, coupled walls and wall-frame systems, V shall not be less than
$$S(4.0)M_v I_E W / (R_d R_o)$$

b) For moment-resisting frames, braced frames and other systems, V shall not be less than
$$S(2.0)M_v I_E W / (R_d R_o), \text{ and}$$

c) For buildings located on a site other than Class F and having an SFRS with an R_d equal to or greater than 1.5, V need not be greater than the larger of
$$\frac{2}{3}S(0.2)I_E W / (R_d R_o) \text{ and}$$
$$S(0.5)I_E W / (R_d R_o)$$

where:

$S(T_a) =$ design spectral response acceleration, expressed as a ratio to gravitational acceleration for a period of T_a

$M_v \ =$ factor to account for higher mode effect on base shear

$I_E \ =$ earthquake importance factor of the structure

$T_a \ =$ fundamental lateral period of vibration of the building in seconds in the direction under consideration

$W \ =$ dead load, plus 25% of the design snow load, plus 60% of storage load and the full contents of any tanks. Minimum partition load need not exceed 0.5 kPa

$R_d \ =$ ductility-related force modification factor that reflects the capability of a structure to dissipate energy through inelastic behaviour

$R_o \ =$ overstrength-related force modification factor accounting for the dependable portion of reserve strength in a structure.

The designer chooses the type of SFRS, with the corresponding force modification factors, R_d and R_o. The values of R_d and R_o are a function of the type of lateral load resisting system and the manner in which the structural members are designed and detailed. Table 11.1 provides a guide for the required design and detailing provisions of CSA Standard A23.3 associated with the corresponding factors, R_d and R_o.

Table 11.1
Design and Detailing Provisions Required for Different Reinforced Concrete Structural Systems and Corresponding R_d and R_o Factors

Type of SFRS	R_d	R_o	Summary of design and detailing requirements in CSA A23.3-14
Ductile moment resisting frames	4.0	1.7	Beams capable of flexural hinging with shear failure and bar buckling avoided. Beams and columns must satisfy ductile detailing requirements. Columns properly confined and stronger than beams. Joints properly confined and stronger than beams.
Moderately ductile moment resisting frames	2.5	1.4	Beams and columns must satisfy detailing requirements for moderate ductility. Beams and columns to have minimum shear strengths. Joints must satisfy moderate ductility detailing requirements and must be capable of transmitting shears from beam hinging.
Ductile coupled walls	4.0	1.7	At least 66% of base overturning moment resisted by wall system must be carried by axial tension and compression in coupled walls. Coupling beams to have ductile detailing and be capable of flexural hinging or resist loads with diagonal reinforcement (shear failure and bar buckling avoided). Walls must have minimum resistance to permit attainment of nominal strength in coupling beams and minimum ductility level.
Moderately ductile coupled walls	2.5	1.4	At least 66% of base overturning moment resisted by wall system must be carried by axial tension and compression in coupled walls. Coupling beams to have moderately ductile detailing and be capable of flexural hinging or resist loads with diagonal reinforcement (shear failure and bar buckling avoided). Walls must have minimum resistance to permit attainment of factored strength in coupling beams and minimum ductility level.
Ductile partially coupled walls	3.5	1.7	Coupling beams to have ductile detailing and be capable of flexural hinging or resist loads with diagonal reinforcement (shear failure and bar buckling avoided). Walls must have minimum resistance to permit attainment of nominal strength in coupling beams and minimum ductility level.
Moderately ductile partially coupled walls	2.0	1.4	Coupling beams to have moderately ductile detailing and be capable of flexural hinging or resist loads with diagonal reinforcement (shear failure and bar buckling avoided). Walls must have minimum resistance to permit attainment of factored strength in coupling beams and minimum ductility level.
Ductile shear walls	3.5	1.6	Walls must be capable of flexural yielding without local instability, shear failure or bar buckling. Walls must satisfy ductile detailing and ductility requirements.
Moderately ductile shear walls	2.0	1.4	Walls must satisfy detailing and ductility requirements for moderate ductility. Walls must have minimum shear strength.
Conventional construction: Moment resisting frames	1.5	1.3	Beams and columns must have factored resistances greater than or equal to factored loads. Columns and beams must satisfy minimum detailing requirements for conventional construction. Closely spaced hoops required in columns unless factored resistance of columns greater than factored resistance of beams or if $R_d R_o = 1.3$.

11

Seismic Design

Table 11.1 (Continued)

Type of SFRS	R_d	R_o	Summary of design and detailing requirements in CSA A23.3-14
Conventional construction: Shear walls	1.5	1.3	Walls must have factored resistances greater than or equal to factored loads. Factored shear resistance must exceed shear corresponding to factored flexural resistance or shear corresponding to $R_dR_o = 1.3$. Walls must satisfy minimum detailing requirements for conventional construction and minimum ductility requirements.
Conventional construction: Two-way slabs without beams	1.3	1.3	Top reinforcement within column strip to resist required factored moment with 50% of top reinforcement concentrated in immediate column vicinity and with 100% concentrated in immediate column vicinity at edge slab-column connections. Minimum detailing requirements must be satisfied and two-way shear stress limited under gravity load effects.
Other SFRS(s)	1.0	1.0	

Note: Tilt-up construction force modification factors and design and detailing requirements not shown.

11.2   Seismic Design Considerations

Seismic design is concerned not only with providing the required strength but also with providing minimum levels of ductility and choosing appropriate structural systems. These goals may be achieved by:

i.   choosing structural systems which are as symmetrical as possible in plan and as uniform as possible in elevation (minimizing structural irregularities);

ii. designing the primary lateral load resisting structural components so that desirable energy dissipating systems will form (e.g., "weak-beam strong-column");

iii. detailing the energy dissipating regions of the primary lateral load resisting components to ensure that substantial inelastic deformations can be achieved without significant loss of strength, and

iv. ensuring that secondary members which are not part of the lateral load resisting system can maintain their gravity load carrying capacity as they undergo the required lateral deformations.

In the design of ductile and moderately ductile members it is necessary to determine the hierarchy of strengths of different members. To ensure that certain hierarchy of strengths are achieved the CSA Standard defines "probable", "nominal" and "factored" resistances. Table 11.2 summarizes the various types of flexural resistances used in the CSA Standard and suggests approximate relationships between these resistances.

Table 11.2
Factored, Nominal and Probable Moment Resistances

Type of flexural resistance	Calculated using	Where used	Approximate relationships for flexure
M_r = factored resistance	$\phi_c = 0.65$ $\phi_s = 0.85$	All members must satisfy $M_r \geq M_f$	
M_n = nominal resistance	$\phi_c = 1.0$ $\phi_s = 1.0$	To ensure columns stronger than beams	$M_n \approx 1.2 M_r$
M_p = probable resistance	$\phi_c = 1.0$ $\phi_s = 1.0$ $f_s = 1.25 f_y$		$M_p \approx 1.47 M_r$

Note: The relationship between M_n and M_r for the case of flexure and axial load depends on the level of axial load

11.3   Loading Cases

For loading combinations including earthquake, the factored load combinations shall include:

Principal loads: $1.0D + 1.0E$
and either of the following combinations of principal and companion loads:

1) For storage occupancies, equipment areas and service rooms:
    $1.0D + 1.0E + 1.0L + 0.25S$

2) For other occupancies:
    $1.0D + 1.0E + 0.5L + 0.25S$

11.4   Design of a 12-Storey Office Building in Montreal

11.4.1.   Description of Building and Loads

The twelve-storey reinforced concrete building shown in Fig. 11.1 is located in Montreal and is founded on stiff soil. It has a centrally located elevator core. Each floor consists of a 200 mm thick flat plate with 6 m interior spans and 5.5 m end spans. The columns are all 550 × 550 mm and the thickness of the core wall components 400 mm. The wall thickness of 400 mm initially chosen such that it exceeds $\ell_u/14 = 4650/14 = 332$ mm (Clause 21.5.3). This value is checked in Section 11.4.6.5. The core wall measures 6.4 m by 8.4 m, outside to outside of the walls. Two 400 mm wide × 1000 mm deep coupling beams connect the two C-shaped walls at the ceiling level of each floor. The core walls extend one storey above the roof at the 12th floor level forming an elevator penthouse at the 13th floor level. The slab has a 100 mm overhang.

11

Seismic Design

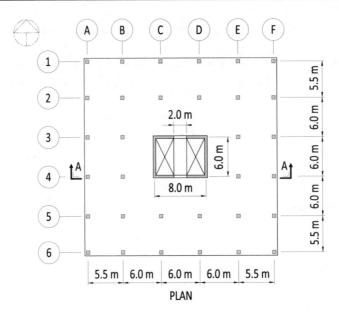

PLAN

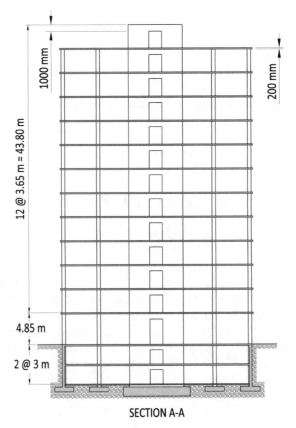

SECTION A-A

Fig. 11.1 Plan and elevation of twelve-storey office building

Material Properties

Concrete: normal density concrete with f'_c = 30 MPa

Reinforcement: f_y = 400 MPa

Gravity and Wind Loadings

Floor live load: 2.4 kN/m² on typical office floors

4.8 kN/m² on 12 m by 12 m corridor area around core

Roof load: 2.5 kN/m² full snow load

1.6 kN/m² mechanical services loading in 6 m wide strip over corridor bay

Dead loads: self-weight of members calculated at 24 kN/m³

1.0 kN/m² partition loading on all floors

0.5 kN/m² ceiling and mechanical services loading on all floors

0.5 kN/m² roofing

Wind loading: varies from 0.7 to 1.0 kN/m² net lateral pressure over the height of the building, obtained from the dynamic procedure as required by NBCC because the fundamental frequency of the building is below 1Hz (i.e., larger than 1 s fundamental lateral period)

The building is to be designed with a fire-resistance rating of 2 hours.

Note: The calculations shown have numbers that have been rounded. More significant figures in a spreadsheet have been used.

11.4.2. Analysis Assumptions

To determine the forces in the walls and the coupling beams and the periods of vibration, the three-dimensional core wall system was analyzed using ETABS. To make allowances for cracking, member stiffnesses were based on effective properties equal to $0.25I_g$ for the moment of inertia and $0.45A_g$ for the shear area for all diagonally reinforced coupling beams as required by Clause 21.2.5.2. The walls were modeled with an effective flexural stiffness of $0.5EI_g$ and an effective axial stiffness of $0.5EA_g$, determined as a function of R_d, R_o and γ_w (see Clause 21.2.5.2). Because the value of γ_w is not known at this initial stage it was assumed to be equal to R_o and the lower of the two wall stiffness reduction factors was conservatively used to determine the effective stiffness of the core wall system.

11.4.3. Seismic Loading

For the force modification factors, R_d and R_o, we will assume that the core-wall system will take 100% of the lateral loads as allowed by the NBCC. In the N-S direction we will design and detail the walls as ductile shear walls and hence R_d = 3.5 and R_o = 1.6. In the E-W direction we will design and detail the coupling beams and walls as a ductile coupled walls system and hence R_d = 4.0 and R_o = 1.7. In order for the E-W direction to qualify as a ductile coupled wall system we must check the degree of coupling as determined by analysis of the structure.

11.4.3.1.   Minimum Lateral Earthquake Force

The structure is located in Montreal and is founded on stiff soil. Therefore the site classification is "D". Since $S_a(0.2)/PGA = 1.57 \leq 2.0$ then $PGA_{ref} = 0.8 \times PGA$. With $PGA_{ref} = 0.8 \times 0.379 = 0.303$, the site coefficients are: $F(0.2) = 0.998$, $F(0.5) = 1.198$, $F(1.0) = 1.308$, $F(2.0) = 1.358$ and $F(5.0) = 1.409$.. The design spectral response acceleration, $S(T)$, is dependent on the period, T. The 5% damped spectral response accelerations, $S_a(T)$, for Montreal are given in Table 11.3. Table 11.3 also gives the design spectral response accelerations, $S(T)$, obtained from the product of the site coefficients and S_a as shown in Fig. 11.2.

Table 11.3
Spectral response accelerations and design spectral response accelerations

	$T \leq 0.2$	$T = 0.5$	$T = 1.0$	$T = 2.0$	$T = 5.0$
$S_a(T)$	0.595	0.310	0.148	0.068	0.018
$S(T)$	0.594	0.373	0.194	0.092	0.025

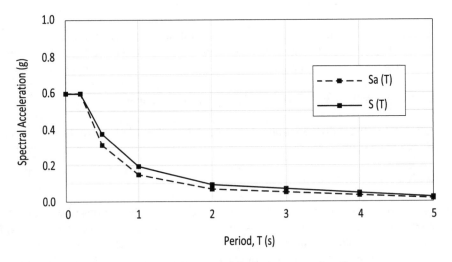

Figure 11.2 Design spectral response acceleration

The empirical fundamental lateral period, T_a, for this shear wall structure in the N-S and E-W directions, is given by:

$T_a = 0.05h_n^{3/4} = 0.05 \times 45.0^{3/4} = 0.869$ s

N-S Direction

The calculated period for the core wall only (SFRS) in the N-S direction, using the computer program ETABS, is 2.17 s. Note that a 3-D model including the walls, the slabs and the columns was also analysed and resulted in a period of 2.00 s. Because this period is within 15% of the periods of the walls alone, then a period of 2.17 s was used.

The value of the fundamental lateral period cannot be taken greater than $2 \times 0.869 = 1.74$ s and hence use $T_a = 1.74$s. From linear interpolation, $S(T_a) = 0.119$ (see Fig. 11.22).

The values of M_v and J depend on the type of SFRS, the ratio of $S(0.2)/S(5.0) = 0.594/0.025 = 23.8$ and the value of T_a. It is necessary to interpolate the values of M_v between $S(0.2)/S(5.0)$ values of 20 and 40, and to interpolate the value of $S(T_a)M_v$ between periods of 1.0 and 2.0 s. The value of J must be interpolated between $S(0.2)/S(5.0)$ values of 20 and 40 and periods of 1.0 and 2.0 s. These interpolation results in $M_v = 1.18$ and $J = 0.62$.

This office building has an earthquake importance factor, $I_E = 1.0$. For this ductile shear wall $R_d = 3.5$ and $R_o = 1.6$.

Hence the seismic base shear, V, is:

$$V = \frac{S(T_a)M_v I_E W}{R_d R_o} = \frac{0.119 \times 1.18 \times 1.0 \times W}{3.5 \times 1.6} = 0.0251W$$

$$V_{min} = \frac{S(4.0)M_v I_E W}{R_d R_o} = \frac{0.0473 \times 1.74 \times 1.0 \times W}{3.5 \times 1.6} = 0.01471W$$

$$V_{max} = max\left(\frac{2}{3}\frac{S(0.2)I_E W}{R_d R_o}, \frac{S(0.5)I_E W}{R_d R_o}\right) = 0.0707W$$

For this structure, $W = 90975$ kN. Hence $V = 0.0251W = 0.0251 \times 90975 = 2287$ kN.

The portion of V concentrated at the top of the building is $F_t = 0.07T_a V = 0.07 \times 1.74 \times 2287 = 278$ kN, but need not be taken greater than $0.25V = 0.25 \times 2287 = 572$ kN.

The calculations of the seismic lateral forces at each floor level are summarized in Table 11.9.

E-W Direction

The calculated period for this structure in the E-W direction, using the computer program ETABS is 1.94 s. It is noted that this period may be used because the period for the full 3-D structure (1.75 s) (walls, slabs and columns) is within 15% of this value. The value of the fundamental lateral period cannot be taken greater than $2 \times 0.869 = 1.74$ and hence use $T_a = 1.74$ s. From linear interpolation, $S(T_a) = 0.119$ (see Fig. 11.22).

It is necessary to interpolate the values of M_v between $S(0.2)/S(5.0)$ values of 20 and 40, and to interpolate the value of $S(T_a)M_v$ between periods of 1.0 and 2.0 s. The value of J must be interpolated between $S(0.2)/S(5.0)$ values of 20 and 40 and periods of 1.0 and 2.0 s. These interpolation results in $M_v = 1.00$ and $J = 0.86$.

For the ductile coupled wall system in the E-W direction $R_d = 4.0$ and $R_o = 1.7$.

Hence the seismic base shear, V, is:

$$V = \frac{S(T_a)M_v I_E W}{R_d R_o} = \frac{0.119 \times 1.00 \times 1.0 \times W}{4.0 \times 1.7} = 0.0175W$$

$$V_{min} = \frac{S(4.0)M_v I_E W}{R_d R_o} = \frac{0.047 \times 1.04 \times 1.0 \times W}{4.0 \times 1.7} = 0.0073W$$

$$V_{max} = max\left(\frac{2}{3}\frac{S(0.2)I_E W}{R_d R_o}, \frac{S(0.5)I_E W}{R_d R_o}\right) = 0.0582W$$

11

Seismic Design

For this structure W = 90975 kN.

Hence V = 0.0175W = 0.0175 × 90975 = 1591 kN.

The portion of V concentrated at the top of the building is F_t = 0.07$T_a V$ = 0.07 × 1.74 × 1591 = 194 kN, but need not be taken greater than 0.25V = 0.25 × 1591 = 398 kN.

The calculations of the seismic lateral forces at each floor level using the equivalent static force procedure are summarized in Table 11.4. The weight of the penthouse has been included at the roof level.

Table 11.4
Lateral Load Calculations for Each Floor Level

Floor	h_i (m)	W_i (kN)	$h_i W_i$ (kN·m)	N-S		E-W	
				F_x	T_x	F_x	T_x
12	45.00	8264	371863	606.3	1803.9	421.9	1255.1
11	41.35	7489	309690	273.3	813.1	190.2	565.7
10	37.70	7489	282353	249.2	741.3	173.4	515.8
9	34.05	7489	255017	225.1	669.5	156.6	465.8
8	30.40	7489	227680	200.9	597.8	139.8	415.9
7	26.75	7489	200344	176.8	526.0	123.0	366.0
6	23.10	7489	173007	152.7	454.2	106.2	316.0
5	19.45	7489	145670	128.6	382.5	89.4	266.1
4	15.80	7489	118334	104.4	310.7	72.7	216.2
3	12.15	7489	90997	80.3	238.9	55.9	166.2
2	8.50	7489	63661	56.2	167.1	39.1	116.3
1	4.85	7817	37912	33.5	99.5	23.3	69.3
0							
Total		90975	2276527	2287	6805	1591	4734

11.4.3.2. Accidental Torsion

The 3-D model shown in Fig. 11.3 was used to calculate accidental torsional effects by applying the lateral forces F_x (see Table 11.4) at an accidental eccentricity of ±0.1D_{nx}, where D_{nx} is the plan dimension of the building at level x, perpendicular to the direction of seismic loading. This gives an accidental torsional eccentricity of 2.975 m, from the centre of mass (same as centre of rigidity) for loading in the N-S and E-W directions. The values of T_x are given in Table 11.4.

The structure was analysed with a 3-D model of the core-wall structure for both wind and seismic loading, with and without eccentricity. In these analyses the participation of the flat plate and columns was neglected.

Figure 11.3 3D Model used for dynamic analysis

11.4.3.3. Degree of Coupling

In the calculations of the base shear it was assumed that there was sufficient coupling of the walls in the E-W direction to qualify this wall system as a ductile coupled wall system rather than a partially coupled wall system. To check the degree of coupling by the wall system in the E-W direction, the base overturning moment resisted by axial tension and compression forces in the walls (resulting from shear in the coupling beams), divided by the total base overturning moment is determined. Although the design forces were obtained from dynamic analysis, it is not appropriate to use these values to determine the degree of coupling because the values obtained from modal combination (e.g., SRSS or CQC) does not satisfy static equilibrium. The degree of coupling was determined using static analysis with the F_x forces from the equivalent static force procedure, giving:

$$\frac{T\ell}{M_1+M_2+T\ell}=\frac{1056\times6.5}{2\times1090+1065\times6.5}=0.76$$

where

T = axial tension and compression acting at centroid of coupled walls

ℓ = distance between centroids of coupled walls, equal to 6.5 m for this example

The degree of coupling is 76%, which is exceeds the minimum limit for ductile coupled walls of 66%. Hence R_d = 4.0 and R_o = 1.7, as assumed above.

11.4.3.4. Check on Structural Irregularity

To determine if the structure is sensitive to torsion, the values of B need to be determined at all levels from the maximum and average displacements of the structure at in the E-W and N-S directions. The maximum value, B (determined at the extreme points of the structure), in the N-S direction occurs in the first storey, with a displacement due to accidental torsion of 6.0 mm and a displacement due to F_x of 5.8 mm. Hence:

$$B=\frac{\delta_{max}}{\delta_{ave}}=\frac{5.8+6.0}{5.8}=2.0$$

Because B is greater than 1.7, the structure is sensitive to torsion and hence is designated as irregular. The maximum value of B in the E-W direction occurs in the first storey and is 1.8.

Note that a 3-D analysis of the structure, including the columns and slabs as well as the actual mass distributions indicates that the first and fourth modes of vibration are torsional with periods of 3.25 and 0.99 s, respectively. This confirms that the structure is indeed torsionally sensitive.

This design example illustrates the steps necessary to design this common type of structure, that is torsionally sensitive.

11.4.3.5. Dynamic Analysis

The NBCC requires that the Dynamic Analysis Procedure be used except that the Equivalent Static Force Procedure may be used for structures that meet any one of the three conditions in parts (a), (b) and (c) of Clause 4.1.8.7. For this building, the term $I_E F_a S_a(0.2)$ is greater than 0.35 and hence the condition in part (a) is not satisfied. The presence of the structural irregularity due to torsion sensitivity means that the Equivalent Static Force Procedure cannot be used (part (b) of 4.1.8.7). Part (c) of 4.1.8.7 is also not satisfied. Accordingly, the Equivalent Static Force Procedure is not permitted as an alternative to the

Dynamic Analysis Procedure for this example building. The first step is to determine V_e from a linear dynamic analysis. The design base shear V_d is obtained from:

$$V_d = \frac{V_e}{R_d R_o} I_E$$

Because this is an irregular structure, that requires dynamic analysis (NBCC 4.1.8.7), V_d shall not be taken less than $1.0V$ rather than $0.8V$, permitted for a regular structure.

All forces and deflections obtained from the linear dynamic analysis are scaled by the factor V_d/V_e to obtain the design values. However, in order to obtain realistic values of anticipated deflections and drifts, the design values need to be multiplied by $R_d R_o/I_E$.

Fig. 11.3 shows the 3-D ETABS model that considers only the core wall system (SFRS) and is used for the dynamic analysis. The second model used is the entire structure including the frame members not considered part of the SFRS (columns and the slabs) to check the ductility and strength of these members subjected to seismically induced deformations. The total mass for each floor was concentrated at the centre of mass (same as centre of rigidity for this example) and rigid diaphragms were assumed at each floor level. Sway effects (P-Delta) were included using the ETABS program option. For this analysis, compressive loads on the walls were obtained from the consistent loading case of $1.0D + 0.5L + 0.25S$, with live load reduction factors.

The first three lateral modes in the N-S and E-W directions are shown in Fig. 11.4, together with the associated periods of vibration and the modal participating mass ratios. Note that the sum of these ratios is 96.0% and 94.0% of the total mass in the N-S and E-W directions, respectively. These ratios exceed the minimum required ratio of 90% of the total mass (NBCC). Spectral modal superposition, using SRSS for the first three modes in the both directions was used to determine all forces and deformations.

The base shear in the N-S direction determined by dynamic analysis is $V_{ed} = 10840$ kN. Therefore:

$$V_d = 10810 \times \frac{1.0}{3.5 \times 1.6} = 1936 \text{ kN}$$

However for this irregular building V_d shall not be taken less than $V = 2287$ kN. Hence, all forces obtained from the dynamic analysis shall be multiplied by $V_d/V_e = 2287/10840 = 0.211$ in the N-S direction.

The base shear in the E-W direction determined by dynamic analysis is $V_{ed} = 9279$ kN. Therefore:

$$V_d = 9279 \times \frac{1.0}{4.0 \times 1.7} = 1365 \text{ kN}$$

However for this irregular building V_d shall not be taken less than $V = 1591$ kN. Hence, all forces obtained from the dynamic analysis shall be multiplied by $V_d/V_e = 1591/9279 = 0.172$ in the E-W direction.

11

Seismic Design

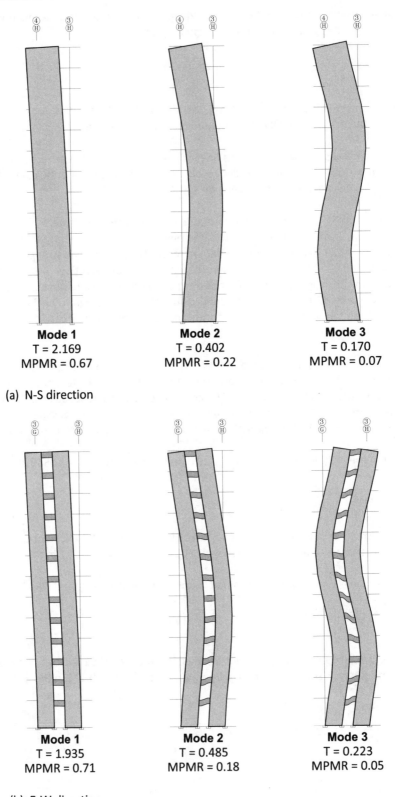

(a) N-S direction

(b) E-W direction

Figure 11.4 Mode shapes, corresponding lateral periods of vibration and modal participation mass ratios in the N-S and E-W directions

11.4.3.6. Deflections and Drift Ratios

The deflections obtained from the dynamic analysis are multiplied by the factor 0.211 in the N-S direction and 0.172 in the E-W direction. To account for the total anticipated displacements, including the inelastic effects it is necessary to multiply these deflections by the factor $R_d R_o / I_E$ to obtain the design values. The deflections obtained from dynamic analysis include P-Delta effects. The deflections arising from accidental torsional eccentricity are added to the deflections from the dynamic analysis.

The maximum total interstorey drift in the N-S direction occurs in the eighth storey in the N-S direction and in the sixth storey in the E-W direction. From the dynamic analysis the interstorey drift in this storey is 0.00092 and the interstorey drift from accidental torsion at this level is 0.00024, for a maximum interstorey drift of 0.00120. Therefore the anticipated interstorey drift, including inelastic effects, is 0.00120 × 3.5 × 1.6/1.0 = 0.0067. Similarly the maximum anticipated interstorey drift in the E-W direction is 0.0054. These anticipated maximum interstorey drift ratios are less than the NBCC limit of 0.025.

11.4.4. Design Forces

The results from the 3-D analyses for both seismic and wind loading are summarized in Tables 11.6, 11.7, 11.8 and 11.9. It is noted that for wind loading, the case with eccentric wind loading does not govern. Table 11.10 gives the forces from seismic loading analysis in the N-S direction, without and with accidental torsion effects. Table 11.11 gives the forces from seismic loading analysis in the E-W direction, without accidental torsion effects.

Table 11.12 gives the forces from accidental torsion due to seismic loading analysis in the E-W direction. It is noted that accidental torsion is resisted by shear flow around the components of the C-shaped walls and by shear in the coupling beams. The accidental torsion does not create any global moments, axial loads or shears in the C-shaped walls, but results in local moments, axial loads and shears in the component parts, AB, BC and CD (see Fig. 11.8).

11

Seismic Design

Table 11.5

Storey	P_D (kN)	P_L (kN)	P_{snow} (kN)
13	945	207	179
12	1682	391	179
11	2420	511	179
10	3158	621	179
9	3895	725	179
8	4633	826	179
7	5371	924	179
6	6108	1020	179
5	6846	1115	179
4	7584	1209	179
3	8322	1302	179
2	9059	1394	179
1	9595	1394	179

Table 11.6
Results of Seismic Loading Analysis (1.0E) in N-S direction for one wall, including accidental torsion

Storey	Wall moment without torsion (kNm)	Wall moment with torsion (kNm)	Wall shear without torsion (kN)	Wall shear with torsion (kN)
13 top	0	218	0	48
13 bot	0	394	0	48
12 top	0	671	331	372
12 bot	1208	1729	331	372
11 top	1208	2063	495	572
11 bot	3011	3586	495	572
10 top	3011	3984	542	638
10 bot	4954	5575	542	638
9 top	4954	6043	521	648
9 bot	6719	7343	521	648
8 top	6719	7888	501	672
8 bot	8171	8718	501	672
7 top	8171	9342	527	745
7 bot	9339	9716	527	745
6 top	9339	10412	593	861
6 bot	10356	10452	593	861
5 top	10356	11204	689	1012
5 bot	11403	11735	689	1012
4 top	11403	11852	813	1200
4 bot	12706	13671	813	1200
3 top	12706	12905	952	1407
3 bot	14502	16363	952	1407
2 top	14502	15678	1073	1603
2 bot	16927	20039	1073	1603
1 top	16927	19512	1145	1706
1 bot	21008	26314	1145	1706

Table 11.7
Results of Seismic Loading Analyses (1.0E) in E-W direction (Coupled Wall) for one wall

Storey	Wall moment (kN·m)	Wall axial load (kN)	Wall shear (kN)	Coupling beam shear without torsion (kN)	Coupling beam shear with torsion (kN)	Redistributed coupling beam shear (kN)
13 top	367	113	0	57	83	165
13 bot	367	113	0		′	
12 top	929	286	227	86	120	165
12 bot	223	286	227			
11 top	980	542	356	128	168	165
11 bot	507	542	356			
10 top	890	863	415	162	210	165
10 bot	932	863	415			
9 top	911	1220	433	183	240	250
9 bot	1242	1220	433			
8 top	1061	1589	447	198	264	250
8 bot	1429	1589	447			
7 top	1217	1960	474	211	286	250
7 bot	1555	1960	474			
6 top	1337	2332	510	227	310	250
6 bot	1673	2332	510			
5 top	1428	2713	553	246	335	370
5 bot	1795	2713	553			
4 top	1454	3107	614	265	357	370
4 bot	1964	3107	614			
3 top	1337	3515	690	278	368	370
3 bot	2329	3515	690			
2 top	1180	3917	759	272	352	370
2 bot	3084	3917	759			
1 top	1765	4253	796	224	285	370
1 bot	5330	4253	796			

11

Seismic Design

Table 11.8
Local forces due to accidental torsion (1.0E) in E-W direction (Coupled Wall Direction) in different components of C-shaped wall

Storey	Wall component AB or CD (±) 3.2 m long segments			Wall component BC (±) 6.4 m long segment		
	Moment (kN·m)	Axial load (kN)	Shear, (kN)	Moment, (kN·m)	Axial load, (kN)	Shear, (kN)
13 top	53.9	-34.3	-22.4	-46.6	0.0	34.8
13 bot	-27.9	-34.3	-22.4	80.5	0.0	34.8
12 top	69.0	-59.0	-33.3	134.3	0.0	-27.7
12 bot	-52.5	-59.0	-33.3	33.2	0.0	-27.7
11 top	91.0	-70.5	-45.0	205.8	0.0	-56.2
11 bot	-73.4	-70.5	-45.0	0.8	0.0	-56.2
10 top	108.8	-77.3	-54.5	249.7	0.0	-74.2
10 bot	-90.1	-77.3	-54.5	-21.1	0.0	-74.2
9 top	130.4	-81.2	-65.9	296.0	0.0	-97.0
9 bot	-110.2	-81.2	-65.9	-57.9	0.0	-97.0
8 top	154.8	-79.6	-79.2	346.6	0.0	-126.5
8 bot	-134.4	-79.6	-79.2	-115.1	0.0	-126.5
7 top	177.9	-70.2	-92.4	389.5	0.0	-157.9
7 bot	-159.4	-70.2	-92.4	-187.0	0.0	-157.9
6 top	198.2	-51.8	-104.5	419.5	0.0	-190.0
6 bot	-183.4	-51.8	-104.5	-274.1	0.0	-190.0
5 top	216.1	-21.5	-116.0	439.5	0.0	-226.9
5 bot	-207.1	-21.5	-116.0	-388.7	0.0	-226.9
4 top	230.0	26.1	-126.2	446.2	0.0	-271.0
4 bot	-230.6	26.1	-126.2	-542.9	0.0	-271.0
3 top	234.4	97.9	-132.9	423.6	0.0	-318.1
3 bot	-250.7	97.9	-132.9	-737.5	0.0	-318.1
2 top	219.0	198.9	-128.2	345.5	0.0	-368.9
2 bot	-249.1	198.9	-128.2	-1000.9	0.0	-368.9
1 top	261.0	377.1	-131.8	430.3	0.0	-387.7
1 bot	-378.5	377.1	-131.8	-1450.2	0.0	-387.7

Table 11.9
Results of Wind Loading Analyses (1.4W)

Storey	N-S Direction	E-W Direction (Coupled Wall Direction)		
	Wall moment (kN·m)	Wall moment (kN·m)	Wall axial load (kN)	Coupling beam shear (kN)
13 top	0	186	57	29
13 bot	0	186	57	
12 top	0	472	145	44
12 bot	204	200	145	
11 top	204	657	286	70
11 bot	610	100	286	
10 top	610	766	491	103
10 bot	1212	-66	491	
9 top	1212	823	765	137
9 bot	2004	-276	765	
8 top	2004	836	1107	171
8 bot	2978	-520	1107	
7 top	2978	809	1516	204
7 bot	4128	-794	1516	
6 top	4128	735	1986	235
6 bot	5444	-1102	1986	
5 top	5444	602	2511	262
5 bot	6920	-1458	2511	
4 top	6920	379	3076	283
4 bot	8545	-1892	3076	
3 top	8545	4	3659	292
3 bot	10310	-2465	3659	
2 top	10310	-651	4217	279
2 bot	12216	-3318	4217	
1 top	12216	-1835	4674	228
1 bot	14967	-5684	4674	

The design forces for both seismic and wind loading are given in Fig. 11.5 and 11.6. The distribution of wall moments for wind loading is typical for a coupled wall system. The distribution of wall moments for seismic loading was obtained from modal combinations (SRSS) and therefore the moments obtained are absolute values.

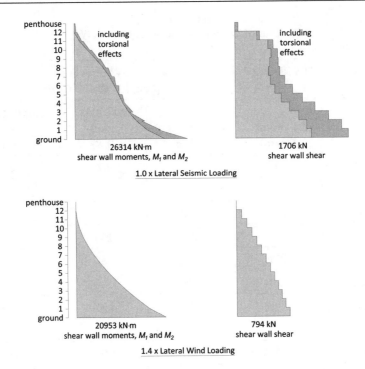

Figure 11.5 Seismic and wind loading forces in the N-S direction

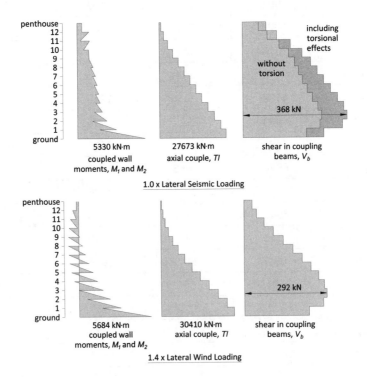

Figure 11.6 Seismic and wind loading forces in the E-W direction

11.4.5. Design of Coupling Beams

11.4.5.1. Design Forces for Coupling Beams

The maximum coupling beam shear due to factored wind loading is 292 kN and due to earthquake effects (including accidental torsion) is 368 kN. Hence the seismic loading case governs the design of the coupling beams. These maximum shears occur in the coupling beams in the third storey (see Tables 11.7 and 11.9).

In designing the coupling beams we can account for redistribution of moments among the beams. Table 11.7 presents the redistributed shear forces in the coupling beams that will be used for design. The sum of the coupling beam shears is equal to 3510 kN and is larger than the calculated total shear force of 3379 kN.

The coupling beams have a depth of 1000 mm and a clear span of 2000 mm and hence satisfy the dimensional limitation that the depth must not be greater than twice the clear span (Clause 21.5.8.2.1). The ductile coupling beams must be designed with diagonal reinforcement, rather than longitudinal bars and vertical hoops, because the clear span of each beam is not equal to or greater than four times the effective depth (see Clauses 21.5.8.1.2 and 21.3.1).

Since the design torsions arise only from accidental torsional eccentricity, which can act in either direction, the same coupling design forces and beam details will be used on the north and south sides of the core wall.

11.4.5.2. Design and Detailing of Coupling Beams

Fig. 11.7 shows the details of the diagonal reinforcement in a coupling beam. From the geometry of the reinforcement, the angle α between the centroidal axis of one set of diagonal bars and the horizontal is 18.0°.

If 4-25M bars are provided in each set of diagonal bars then the factored shear resistance is:

$V_r = 2\phi_s A_s f_y \sin \alpha = 2 \times 0.85 \times 4 \times 500 \times 400 \times \sin 18.0 = 420$ kN.

This reinforcement provides a factored shear resistance of 420 kN which is larger than the required 370 kN in the lower five coupling beams.

The diagonal reinforcement must have closely spaced hoops as required in Clause 21.5.8.2.4 with a maximum spacing given by the smaller of:

   a) $6d_{b\ell} = 6 \times 25 = 150$ mm

   b) $24d_{bh} = 24 \times 10 = 240$ mm

   c)   100 mm (controls the spacing)

Hence use 10M hoops spaced at 100 mm in the lowest five coupling beams.

If the reinforcement in the coupling beams is reduced to 4-20M starting at the 6th floor level for 4 storeys, then the factored resistance per beam is:

$V_r = 2\phi_s A_s f_y \sin\alpha = 2 \times 0.85 \times 4 \times 300 \times 400 \times \sin 18.0 = 252$ kN.

10M hoops spaced at 100 mm controls the spacing in the coupling beams from the 6th floor to the 9th floor. The top four coupling beams will contain 4-15M bars, giving $V_r = 168$ kN per beam. The beams with 4-15M bars would require a hoop spacing of 90 mm.

This arrangement gives a total shear capacity for the 13 beams of:

$\sum V_r = 5 \times 420 + 4 \times 252 + 4 \times 168 = 3780$ kN.

This shear resistance of the thirteen coupling beams exceeds the required total coupling beam shear resistance of 3379 kN.

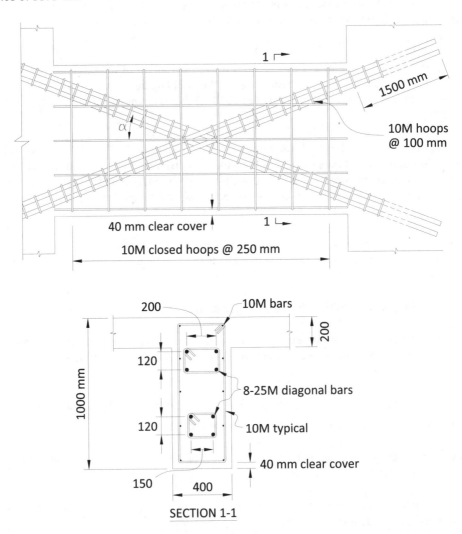

SECTION 1-1

Figure 11.7 Coupling beam reinforcing details for the first 5 storeys.

The diagonal reinforcement must extend into the wall at each end a minimum distance of $1.5\ell_d$, resulting in embedment lengths of 1250, 800 and 600 mm for the 25M, 20M and 15M bars, respectively. In addition to the diagonal reinforcement, provide minimum hoop reinforcement in the vertical direction and longitudinal reinforcement, but only in the clear span of the beam, as shown in Fig. 11.7.

11.4.5.3. Ductility of Coupling Beams

The inelastic rotational capacity of the coupling beams must be greater than the rotational demand. The rotational demand is given by (Clause 21.5.8.4.4).

$$\theta_{id} = \left(\frac{\Delta_f R_d R_o}{h_w}\right) \frac{\ell_{cg}}{\ell_u} = \left(\frac{0.0307 \times 4.0 \times 1.7}{45.0}\right) \frac{6.5}{2.0} = 0.015$$

The rotational capacity of diagonally reinforced coupling beams (Clause 21.5.8.4.5) is 0.04. Hence the coupling beams have sufficient ductility.

11.4.6. Design of Ductile Walls

11.4.6.1. Design Forces in N-S and E-W Direction

The resistance of a wall depends on the level of axial load in the wall. For the case of the uncoupled walls in the N-S direction the compressive axial load at the base of the wall depends only on the gravity loads because the seismic forces do not cause axial forces the wall. The forces associated with the two loading cases are:

a) $1.0D : P_s = 9595$ kN

b) $1.0D + 0.5L + 0.25S : P_s = 10336$ kN

For the case of the coupled walls in the E-W direction, the axial load in the walls is caused by gravity loads and by the shears in the coupling beams due to the seismic loading. In accordance with the requirements in Clauses 21.5.8.3.2 and 21.8.5.3.4 the axial load, P_n, must be determined. At a given floor level, this force corresponds to the development of the nominal capacities of the coupling beams above this floor level. The nominal shear resistance, V_n, for the coupling beam containing 4-25M diagonal reinforcing bars is:

$$V_n = 2\phi_s A_s f_y \sin\alpha = 2 \times 1.0 \times 4 \times 500 \times 400 \times \sin 18.0 = 495 \text{ kN.}$$

Similarly the nominal resistance for the beams from the 6th to the 9th floor containing 4-20M bars is 297 kN and 198 kN for the top four beams containing the 4-15M.

In order to satisfy the capacity design requirement, the factored wall moments will be increased at each level x by the factor γ_{bx}, determined as:

$$\gamma_{bx} = \frac{\Sigma V_n}{\Sigma V_f}$$

where:

$\Sigma V_n =$ sum of the shears corresponding to the nominal flexural resistance of coupling beams above level x

$\Sigma V_f =$ sum of factored shears above level x

The beam overstrength factors, cumulative dead and live loads and the factored axial loads and factored moments in each wall multiplied by γ_{bx} are shown on Table 11.10. The values of ΣV_f are taken as the wall axial loads given in Table 11.10, since the axial load in the wall is the sum of the shears in the pairs of coupling beams above the level being considered.

Table 11.10
Coupling Beam Overstrength Factors and Dead and Live Loads per Wall

Storey	V_n (kN)	V_f (kN)	γ_{bx}	P_f (kN)	P_n (kN)
13 top	198	57	3.50	113	± 396
13 bot				113	± 396
12 top	198	86	2.77	286	± 791
12 bot				286	± 791
11 top	198	128	2.19	542	± 1187
11 bot				542	± 1187
10 top	198	162	1.83	863	± 1578
10 bot				863	± 1578
9 top	297	183	1.77	1220	± 2155
9 bot				1220	± 2155
8 top	297	198	1.70	1589	± 2706
8 bot				1589	± 2706
7 top	297	211	1.64	1960	± 3217
7 bot				1960	± 3217
6 top	297	227	1.58	2332	± 3686
6 bot				2332	± 3686
5 top	495	246	1.65	2713	± 4479
5 bot				2713	± 4479
4 top	495	265	1.68	3107	± 5231
4 bot				3107	± 5231
3 top	495	278	1.70	3515	± 5963
3 bot				3515	± 5963
2 top	495	272	1.71	3917	± 6700
2 bot				3917	± 6700
1 top	495	224	1.75	4253	± 7462
1 bot				4253	± 7462

From Table 11.10, the axial load, P_n, at the base of the wall is 7462 kN. This axial load can be either in compression (negative) or in tension (positive). For the applicable loading cases from the NBCC, the axial load at the base of the wall is:

a) $1.0D + 1.0E$: $P_f = P_s + P_n = -17057$ kN

b) $1.0D - 1.0E$: $P_f = P_s - P_n = -2133$ kN

c) $1.0D + 1.0E + 0.5L + 0.25S$: $P_f = P_s + P_n = -17798$ kN

d) $1.0D - 1.0E + 0.5L + 0.25S$: $P_f = P_s - P_n = -2874$ kN

The required moment capacity at the base of each wall, given in Table 11.7, is 5330 kN·m for seismic loading without accidental torsion. It is noted that the required moment at the base of each wall due to wind (see Table 11.9) is 5684 kN·m.

To account for the local forces (see Table 11.8) from accidental torsion a simplified approach will be taken. Although the axial loads and moments on parts AB and CD have opposite signs it will be assumed that the C-shaped wall is subjected to an additional axial load of twice the axial tension or compression acting on segments AB or CD and an additional moment of twice the moment acting in these segments. For example, at the base of the structure the additional axial load for design is 2 × ±377 = ±754 kN and the additional moment is 2 × 379 = ±758 kN·m. Hence, the required moment capacity at the base of each wall including local effects due to accidental torsion is 5330 + 758 = 6088 kN·m. Hence the seismic capacity design requirements control the design.

11.4.6.2. Design Forces in N-S Direction

From Tables 11.6 and 11.9, the base moment in each wall due to lateral seismic loading is 26314 kN·m (including accidental torsion) and the base moment due to factored wind loading is 14967 kN·m. Hence, for flexural design in the N-S direction, the earthquake loading controls. The corresponding axial load for one wall is -10336 kN (see Section 11.4.6.1).

11.4.6.3. Design of Base of Wall for Flexure and Axial Load

Preliminary choice of vertical reinforcement

(a) **Minimum area of concentrated reinforcement (Clause 21.5.6.2)**

In the 3.2 m long walls in the E-W direction:

$A_s = 0.0015 b_w \ell_w = 0.0015 \times 400 \times 3200 = 1920$ mm²

In the 6.4 m long wall (segment BC) in the N-S direction

$A_s = 0.0015 b_w \ell_w = 0.0015 \times 400 \times 6400 = 3840$ mm²

Therefore try 4–25M bars (A_s = 2000 mm²) as concentrated reinforcement at the extremities and corners of the C-shaped walls. Outside the plastic hinge regions, only two-thirds of this area of the concentrated reinforcement is required (Clause 21.5.6.1).

Provide a clear cover for the hoops of 40 mm, resulting in a minimum clear cover of 50 mm for the vertical and horizontal reinforcement in the wall, as required for a two-hour fire-resistance rating.

It has been decided that the horizontal wall reinforcement will be anchored within the region of concentrated reinforcement to develop $1.25 f_y$ (Clause 21.5.5.3). The development length required for the 10M bars, using the simplified equation in Clause 12.2.3 is:

$$\ell_d = 0.45 \, k_1 k_2 k_3 k_4 \frac{1.25 \times f_y}{\sqrt{f'_c}} d_b = 0.45 \times 1 \times 1 \times 1 \times 0.8 \frac{500}{\sqrt{30}} \times 10 = 329 \text{ mm}$$

The length provided in the region of concentrated reinforcement (see Fig. 11.8) is 320 mm. With the significant cover provided on the bars and the additional confinement provided in this region of concentrated reinforcement, the development length can be shown to be less than 320 mm using Eq. 12-1 in Clause 12.2.2. Hence, the hoop configuration shown in Fig. 11.8 is adequate.

11

Seismic Design

(b) Maximum area of concentrated reinforcement (Clause 21.5.4.3)

Clause 21.5.4.3 limits the reinforcement ratio, including regions with lap splices, to 0.06. With the layout of the 4-25M bars at the ends of the flanges and at the web-flange junctions, as shown in Fig. 11.8, the percentage of steel equals (4 × 500)/(400 × 400) = 0.0125. This arrangement allows for lap splicing of the reinforcement without exceeding the limit of 0.06.

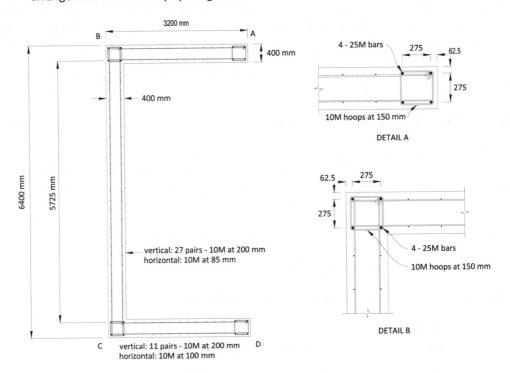

Fig. 11.8 Details of reinforcement in walls.

At the base of the walls the spacing of the horizontal distributed reinforcement must be decreased to 85 mm in component BC and to 100 mm in components AB and CD (see shear design in Section 11.4.6.7).

(c) Maximum diameter for distributed reinforcement (Clause 14.1.8.2)

In the 400 mm thick walls, the maximum diameter of distributed reinforcement is 400/10 = 40 mm.

(d) Distributed reinforcement (Clauses 21.5.5)

In the plastic hinge region, the spacing of the distributed reinforcement must not exceed 300 mm in each direction (Clause 21.5.5.2). Outside of this region, the maximum spacing is 500 mm (Clause 14.1.8.4). The distributed reinforcement ratio must be greater than or equal to 0.0025 in each direction (Clause 21.5.5.1).

Because the wall thickness exceeds 210 mm, two curtains of reinforcement must be provided (Clause 14.1.8.3). In the 400 mm thick wall elements, the maximum spacing, assuming two curtains of 10M vertical reinforcing bars is (2 × 100)/(0.0025 × 400) = 200 mm. Hence, at the base of the walls, use 2 curtains of 10M bars at 200 mm spacing in the vertical direction.

Calculation of M_r at base of walls

The required moment capacity in the E-W direction from analysis is 5330 kN·m per wall. As can be seen from Table 11.11, the "tension" wall has a minimum factored moment resistance of 13892 kN·m, while the compression wall has a minimum factored moment resistance of 21677 kN·m. Hence the factored flexural resistances exceed the required factored moments. Figure 11.9 illustrates the moment resistances for the walls in the E-W direction.

It is noted that the total minimum forces in the E-W "tension" wall, including global (Table 11.7) and local (Table 11.8) forces at its base is:

N_f = -2133 + 2 × 377 = -1379 kN and M_f = 5330 + 2 × 379 = 6088 kN·m.

The total maximum forces in the E-W "compression" wall, including global (Table 11.6) and local (Table 11.7) forces at its base is:

N_f = -17798 − 2 × 377 = -18552 kN and M_f = 5330 + 2 × 379 = 6088 kN·m.

Table 11.11 shows the factored forces due to the combined effects of global forces due to earthquake and local forces due to torsion in the E-W direction. Table 11.11 also gives the factored axial load and moment for the design of the N-S wall, including the effects of torsion.

The factored moment resistances for different loading cases were determined using the stress block factors of Clause 10.1.7, strain compatibility and a maximum concrete compressive strain of 0.0035.

As can be seen from Table 11.11, the factored moment resistances exceed the required factored moments for all cases.

Table 11.11
Predicted Factored Moment Resistances and Depths of Compression per Wall at the base
(Global wall forces)

	Load Case	N_f* (kN)	M_f (kN·m)	M_r (kN·m)	c mm
E-W (1 "C-shaped" wall)					
"tension" wall	1.0D - 1.0E	-1379	6088	13892	446
	1.0D + 0.5L + 0.25S - 1.0E	-2120	6088	15246	501
"compression" wall	1.0D + 1.0E	-17811	6088	21677	226
	1.0D + 0.5L + 0.25S + 1.0E	-18552	6088	22216	233
N-S (per wall)					
	1.0D + 1.0E	-9595	26314	48056	285
	1.0D + 0.5L + 0.25S + 1.0E	-10336	26314	50226	299

*Compression is negative

In the N-S direction, the factored moment resistance for both load cases significantly exceeds the required moment (see Table 11.11 and Fig. 11.10).

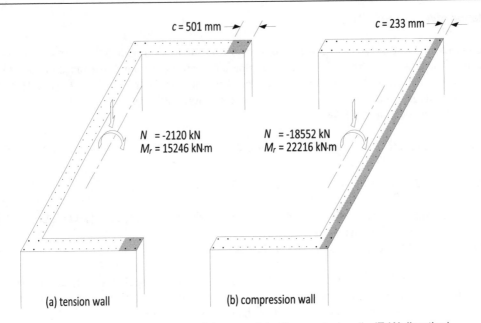

Fig. 11.9 Factored moment resistances of ductile coupled walls (E-W direction)

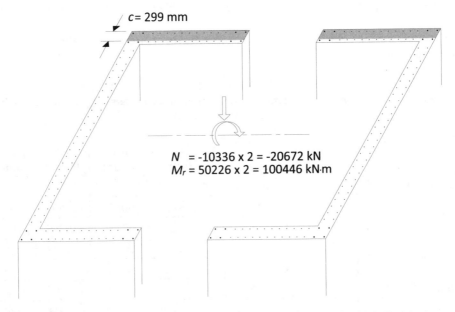

Fig. 11.10 Factored moment resistance of ductile shear walls (N-S direction)

11.4.6.4. Ductility of Walls

E-W Direction – Ductile Coupled Walls (Clause 21.5.8.4.2)

For ductile coupled walls, the inelastic rotational demand θ_{id} is taken as:

$$\theta_{id} = \frac{\Delta_f R_o R_d}{h_w} = \frac{0.0307 \times 1.7 \times 4.0}{45.0} = 0.0046$$

Not to be taken less than 0.004.

The inelastic rotational capacity θ_{ic}, taking ℓ_w as the length of the coupled wall system (Clause 21.5.7.3) and assuming $\varepsilon_{cu} = 0.0035$ is:

$$\theta_{ic} = \left(\frac{\varepsilon_{cu}\,\ell_w}{2c} - 0.002 \right) = \left(\frac{0.0035 \times 8.4}{2 \times 0.501} - 0.002 \right) = 0.027$$

Not to be taken greater than 0.025.

Because the rotational capacity of 0.025 exceeds the rotational demand of 0.0046, sufficient ductility is provided.

N-S Direction – Ductile Shear Walls (Clause 21.5.7.2)

For ductile shear walls, the ratio of the probable flexural resistance to the factored flexural resistance, M_f, at the base is 2.18 and hence the inelastic rotational demand θ_{id} is taken as:

$$\theta_{id} = \frac{\left(\Delta_f R_o R_d - \Delta_f \gamma_w \right)}{\left(h_w - \frac{\ell_w}{2} \right)} = \frac{\left(0.0434 \times 1.6 \times 3.5 - 0.0434 \times 2.18 \right)}{\left(45.0 - \frac{6.4}{2} \right)} = 0.0035$$

Not to be taken less than 0.004.

The inelastic rotational capacity θ_{ic}, assuming $\varepsilon_{cu} = 0.0035$ is:

$$\theta_{ic} = \left(\frac{\varepsilon_{cu}\,\ell_w}{2c} - 0.002 \right) = \left(\frac{0.0035 \times 6.4}{2 \times 0.299} - 0.002 \right) = 0.035$$

Not to be taken greater than 0.025.

Because the rotational capacity of 0.025 exceeds the rotational demand of 0.004, sufficient ductility is provided.

Confinement of concentrated reinforcement (Clause 21.5.7.5)

Because the inelastic rotational capacities of the walls in the E-W and N-S directions were determined using $\varepsilon_{cu} = 0.0035$, it is not necessary to check the confinement requirements of Clause 21.5.7.5 for the concentrated reinforcement in the walls.

11.4.6.5.   Checking Wall Thickness for Stability (Clause 21.5.3)

Clause 21.5.3 requires a wall thickness of $\ell_u/10$ in those parts of a wall that, under factored vertical and lateral loads, are more than half way from the neutral axis to the compression face of the wall section.

The 3200 mm long portions of the E-W "tension wall" may be considered as simple rectangular wall elements as shown in Fig. 11.9 with a neutral axis depth of 501 mm. Since the neutral axis depth is less than $4b_w = 4 \times 400 = 1600$ mm and is less than $0.3\ell_w = 0.3 \times 3200 = 960$ mm, the $\ell_u/10$ limit need not apply (see Clause 21.5.3.3). According to Clause 21.5.3.1 the wall thickness in the plastic hinge region must not be less than $\ell_u/14 = 4650/14 = 332$ mm. Hence the wall thickness of 400 mm is adequate.

For the 6400 mm long portion of the E-W "compression wall", it is noted that $c/2 = 233/2 = 116$ mm, which is less than the wall thickness, and furthermore, the wall is laterally supported at its ends by

11

Seismic Design

the 3200 mm wall portions. Hence, this portion of the wall need not have a thickness of $\ell_u/10$ (see Clause 21.5.3.3).

For stability considerations for the wall loaded in the N-S direction, the value of $c/2 = 299/2 = 150$ mm is smaller than the 400 mm thickness of the flanges. Therefore the 400 mm wall dimension is adequate and the width of the flange of 3200 mm, greatly exceeds $\ell_u/5$ (see Clause 21.5.3.3).

Therefore all of the stability requirements are satisfied.

11.4.6.6. "Buckling Prevention" Ties for Concentrated Reinforcement (Clause 21.5.6.4)

The concentrated reinforcement should have buckling prevention ties in accordance with Clause 7.6.5 and the ties must be detailed as hoops (Clause 21.6.6.9). In plastic hinge regions, the hoop spacing shall not exceed (Clause 21.2.8.1):

a) $6d_{b\ell} = 6 \times 25 = 150$ mm

b) $24d_{bh} = 24 \times 10 = 240$ mm

c) One-half the wall thickness $= 400/2 = 200$ mm

Hence provide 10M hoops at a spacing of 150 mm as shown in Fig. 11.8.

11.4.6.7. Design for Shear at Base of Walls (Clause 21.6.9)

The walls must be designed to resist the shear corresponding to the formation of plastic hinges at their bases (Clause 21.5.2.2.5).

Determine probable moment resistances of walls

In order to determine the probable moment resistances of the walls, axial load-moment calculations were carried out with $\phi_c = \phi_s = 1.0$ and using an equivalent "yield" strength of steel of $1.25f_y$. In the E-W direction, we only need to determine the probable moment resistance of the "compression wall" subjected to an axial load corresponding to $P_s + 1.25P_n$, since it results in the larger resistance. From calculations, the probable moment resistance of the wall, M_{pw}, is 26971 kN·m in the EW direction and 59601 kN·m per wall in the NS direction.

It is assumed that earthquake loading causes plastic hinging at the base of the walls. Assuming that the ratio of the shear to moment at the base of a wall remains constant as the moment increases to the probable resistance, the shear at the base as the wall develops a plastic hinge will be:

$$V = \frac{M_{pw}}{M_f} \times V_f$$

N-S direction:

$$V = \frac{M_{pw}}{M_f} \times V_f = \frac{59601}{26314} \times 1706 = 3864 \text{ kN}$$

This value must be amplified to account for the inelastic effects of higher modes (Clause 21.5.2.2.7). The values of T_L and T_U are 0.5s and 1.0s, respectively. The resulting amplification factor is 1.39 and hence:

$V = 1.39 \times 3864 = 5371$ kN

In calculating the shear capacity of the wall, the effective shear depth d_v need not be taken less than $0.8\ell_w = 0.8 \times 6400 = 5120$ mm (Clause 21.5.9.2).

In the region of expected plastic hinging, at the base of the wall, the inelastic rotational demand θ_{id} is less than 0.005 and hence the factored shear demand cannot exceed (Clause 21.5.9.5.2):

$0.15\phi_c f_c' b_w d_v = 0.15 \times 0.65 \times 30 \times 400 \times 5120 = 5990$ kN

The factored shear demand of 5371 kN is less than this upper limit.

Because the inelastic rotational demand θ_{id} is less than 0.005, the factored shear resistance is calculated using $\beta = 0.18$ (Clause 21.5.9.5.2). The axial load on the "tension" wall is -10336 kN (compression). This axial load is less than: $0.1 f_c' A_g = 0.1 \times 30 \times (3200 \times 2 \times 400 + 5600 \times 400) = 14400$ kN. Hence θ is taken as 45° (Clause 21.5.9.5.2). The factored shear resistance (Clauses 11.3.4 and 11.3.5), assuming pairs of 10M bars at 85 mm spacing is:

$$V_r = \phi_c \beta \sqrt{f_c'} b_w d_v + \frac{\phi_s A_v f_y d_v \cot\theta}{s}$$

$$= 0.65 \times 0.18 \sqrt{30} \times 400 \times 5120 + \frac{0.85 \times 200 \times 400 \times 5120 \times \cot 45°}{85}$$

$$= 1312 + 4096 = 5408 \text{ kN}$$

Hence the shear resistance is adequate with pairs of 10M horizontal bars spaced at 85 mm.

It is noted that the accidental torsion causes shear in segments AB and CD. This shear, due to accidental torsion, must be considered in design, accounting for the fact that the critical flange will be in tension and have large flexural cracks due to the attainment of plastic hinging for loading in the N-S direction. A method to check the shear resistance of these segments, accounting for large cracks and possible redistribution of shear resisting torsion, is described in the calculations below for loading in the E-W direction.

E-W direction:

The design shear for segment AB, including torsional effects is:

$$V = \frac{M_{pw}}{M_f} \times V_f = \frac{26971}{5330 + 756} \times 530 = 2348 \text{ kN}$$

For segment CD, the shear from accidental torsion acts in the opposite direction from that in segment AB. Hence the total shear for segment CD is 398 – 132 = 266 kN. This results in a design shear for this segment of:

$$V = \frac{M_{pw}}{M_f} \times V_f = \frac{26971}{5330 + 756} \times 266 = 1178 \text{ kN}$$

Segments AB and CD must both be designed for the larger shear of 2348 kN because the accidental torsion can reverse.

In calculating the shear capacity of the wall, in accordance with Clause 21.5.9.2, we will assume an effective shear depth, $d_v = 0.8\ell_w = 0.8 \times 3200 = 2560$ mm.

11

Seismic Design

In the region of expected plastic hinging, at the base of the wall, the inelastic rotational demand θ_{id} is less than 0.005 and hence the factored shear demand in one segment cannot exceed:

$0.15\phi_c f'_c b_w d_v = 0.15 \times 0.65 \times 30 \times 400 \times 2560 = 2995$ kN

The factored shear demand of 2274 kN is less than this upper limit.

Because the inelastic rotational demand θ_{id} is less than 0.005, the factored shear resistance is calculated using $\beta = 0.18$. The axial load on the tension wall is -1379 kN. This axial load is less than:
$0.1f'_c A_g = 0.1 \times 30 \times (3200 \times 800 + 5600 \times 400) = 14400$ kN.

Hence θ is taken as 45° (Clause 21.5.9.5.2). The factored shear resistance (Clauses 11.3.4 and 11.3.5) for wall segment AB at the base with pairs of 10M bars at a spacing of 100 mm is:

$$V_r = \phi_c \beta \sqrt{f'_c} b_w d_v + \frac{\phi_s A_v f_y d_v \cot\theta}{s}$$

$$= 0.65 \times 0.18 \sqrt{30} \times 400 \times 2560 + \frac{0.85 \times 200 \times 400 \times 2560 \times \cot45°}{100}$$

$$= 656 + 1741 = 2397 \text{ kN}$$

Hence the shear strength in the E-W direction is adequate with 2 horizontal 10M bars at 100 mm spacing.

Extend the 10M horizontal reinforcement into the confined core of the region of concentrated reinforcement as close to the outside surface of the walls as cover will permit (see Fig 11.8 and Section 11.4.6.3).

11.4.6.8.   Checking Sliding Shear Resistance at Construction Joints (Clause 14.1.6)

In accordance with Clause 14.1.6, we must check the sliding shear resistance of the construction joints. Since the vertical uniformly distributed reinforcement is constant over the height of the walls, the most critical situation is at the base of the walls. It is assumed that construction joints are intentionally roughened.

N-S direction:

In the N-S direction, the required shear strength is 5371 kN per wall. If the 8-25M bars at the ends of BC together with the 27 pairs of 10M bars are accounted for, the factored shear stress resistance from Clauses 11.5.1 and 11.5.2 is:

$$v_r = \phi_c \left(c + \mu \left(\rho_v f_y + \frac{N}{A_g} \right) \right)$$

$$= 0.65 \left(0.50 + 1.0 \left(0.0037 \times 400 + \frac{9595 \times 1000}{800 \times 3200 + 400 \times 5600} \right) \right)$$

$$= 2.586 \text{ MPa}$$

Hence, the sliding shear resistance is: $2.586 \times A_{cv} = 2.586 \times 400 \times 6400 = 6620$ kN.

Since the sliding shear resistance exceeds the shear corresponding to plastic hinging, sliding shear will be prevented.

E-W direction:

In the E-W direction, the required shear strength of segment AB is 2348 kN. It will be assumed that the net compressive axial load is acting on the segments AB and CD. If the 16-25M bars at the ends of AB and CD together with the 44-10M bars are accounted for, the factored shear stress resistance from Clause 11.5 is:

$$v_r = \phi_c \left(c + \mu \left(\rho_v\, f_y + \frac{N}{A_g} \right) \right)$$

$$= 0.65 \left(0.50 + 1.0 \left(0.0048 \times 400 + \frac{1379 \times 1000}{800 \times 3200} \right) \right)$$

$$= 1.923 \quad \text{MPa}$$

Hence, the sliding shear resistance of segment AB is: $1.923 \times A_{cv} = 1.923 \times 400 \times 3200 = 2461$ kN.

The sliding shear resistance is adequate.

11.4.6.9. Determination of Plastic Hinge Region (Clause 21.5.2.1.2)

As the wall cross sectional dimensions remain constant over the 48.65 m height of the wall and provided that the main flexural reinforcement is appropriately curtailed, only one plastic hinge region will form, near the base of the walls. The plastic hinge length is a function of the height of the wall and the length of the longest shear wall or the overall length of the coupled shear wall.

The plastic hinge length extends above the base a distance equal to
$0.5\ell_w + 0.1h_w = 0.5 \times 8.4 + 0.1 \times 48.65 = 9.07$ m (Clause 21.5.2.1.2). Therefore detail the first three storeys as plastic hinge regions.

11.4.6.10. Design Bending Moment and Shear Envelopes (Clauses 21.5.2.2.3 and 21.5.2.2.8)

To determine the horizontal and vertical reinforcement over the height of the walls, bending moment and shear envelopes need to be determined. To this end, bending moment and shear diagrams need to be amplified by the ratio of M_r/M_f, with both values of moments calculated at the top of the plastic hinge zone.

11.4.6.11. Changes in Horizontal Distributed Reinforcement Over the Height of the Walls (Clauses 21.5.5.1 and 21.5.5.2)

The maximum spacing of the 2-10M horizontal bars, outside of the plastic hinge region is 200 mm, since the minimum reinforcement ratio of 0.0025 must be satisfied. Therefore use 2-10M bars at 200 mm spacing above the plastic hinge region.

11.4.6.12. Changes in Vertical Distributed Reinforcement Over the Height of the Walls (Clauses 21.5.5.1 and 21.5.5.2)

The minimum reinforcement ratio of 0.0025 governs the selection of vertical distributed reinforcement. Hence use 2-10M bars at 200 mm spacing over the entire height of the wall.

11.4.6.13. Changes in Concentrated Vertical Reinforcement Over the Height of the Walls (Clause 21.5.6.1)

The minimum area of concentrated reinforcement which can be used outside the plastic hinge region is $0.001b_w\ell_w$ (Clause 21.5.6.1). At one end of the 3200 mm long wall, the minimum amount of concentrated reinforcement is $0.001 \times 400 \times 3200 = 1280$ mm². Similarly, the minimum amount of concentrated reinforcement required at the intersection of the wall components is $2560 - 1280 = 1280$ mm² (Clause 21.5.6.3). Hence use 4-25M concentrated reinforcement over the full height of the walls.

Note that if changes to the vertical reinforcement are possible, then the requirements of clause 21.5.2.2.3 must be satisfied.

Table 11.12
Verification of the local capacity of the walls

Storey	Position	Beam V_n (kN·m)	"Tension" wall M_f (kN·m)	M_{loc} (kN·m)	$P_D + P_n$ (kN)	M_r (kN·m)
Penthouse	Top	198	367	1259	-549	12341
	Bottom		367	367	-549	12341
12	Top	198	929	1820	-891	12984
	Bottom		223	223	-891	12984
11	Top	198	980	1871	-1233	13622
	Bottom		507	507	-1233	13622
10	Top	198	890	1782	-1579	14260
	Bottom		932	932	-1579	14260
9	Top	297	911	2248	-1740	14556
	Bottom		1242	1242	-1740	14556
8	Top	297	1061	2399	-1927	14897
	Bottom		1429	1429	-1927	14897
7	Top	297	1217	2554	-2154	15308
	Bottom		1555	1555	-2154	15308
6	Top	297	1337	2674	-2423	15788
	Bottom		1673	1673	-2423	15788
5	Top	495	1428	3657	-2368	15691
	Bottom		1795	1795	-2368	15691
4	Top	495	1454	3682	-2353	15664
	Bottom		1964	1964	-2353	15664
3	Top	495	1337	3566	-2359	15675
	Bottom		2329	2329	-2359	15675
2	Top	495	1180	3409	-2359	15675
	Bottom		3084	3084	-2359	15675
1	Top	495	1765	3994	-2133	15270
	Bottom		5330	5330	-2133	15270

11.4.6.14. Bending Resistance of Wall Piers (Clause 21.5.8.3.2)

It is necessary that the factored resisting moment of the coupled walls at the ends of the coupling beams be large enough to allow the hinges to form in the coupling beams and not in the walls. The critical loading condition is $1.0D + 1.0E$ giving rise to the axial load $P_s \pm P_n$. For this loading case, the required local bending moment evaluated at the center of gravity of the C-shaped wall is $M_{loc} = M_f + 2V_n \times (\ell_{cg} - \ell_u)/2$. Table 11.12 presents the calculation over the height of the walls.

As can be seen from Table 11.12 on the preceding page, the local bending capacity of the wall, M_{loc}, is considerably less than the factored moment resistance of the C-shaped wall.

11.4.7. Frame Members Not Considered Part of the SFRS, Foundation Movements and Design Below Grade

This example illustrates the design of the SFRS above grade and does not consider:

a) the response of frame members not considered part of the SFRS (e.g., columns and slab-column connections),

b) the influence of foundation movements, and

c) the design of the structure below grade (e.g., shear wall, diaphragms, and foundation).

The next design example illustrates these additional features.

11.4.8. Comparisons with the Design Using the 2004 CSA Standard

The structure designed in this chapter is similar to the structure designed in accordance with the provisions of the 2004 CSA A23.3 Standard (Reference 1), except that 1000 mm deep diagonally reinforced coupling beams were used instead of 900 mm deep coupling beams. It is noted that, one important change in the 2014 CSA standard was the introduction of a shear magnification factor to account for inelastic effects of higher modes.

11.5   Design of a 30-Storey Residential Building in Vancouver

A 30-storey residential building is to be built on a site in Vancouver, BC. Such buildings invariably have a ductile core with ductile (cantilever) shear walls in one direction and ductile coupled walls in the perpendicular direction.

11.5.1.   Description of Site

The soil on the site was classified as very dense glacial till based on test-hole information. The factored bearing capacity for transient earthquake loads is 1200 kPa and Poisson's ratio of soil is 0.2. Shear wave velocities were measured at 1 m increments to a depth of 39 m. The average shear wave velocity V_s = 500 m/s. Thus the Site Class is C. Using a mass density of soil γ_s = 2000 kg/m³, the initial shear modulus of the soil $G_0 = \gamma_s \cdot V_s^2 / 1000 = 500\ 000$ kPa. This information will be needed to determine foundation movements.

11

Seismic Design

11.5.2. Preliminary Design of Building

The following summarizes the preliminary design of the building, which is the information that will be used to conduct the seismic analysis. Number of stories at or above grade = 30; number of stories below grade = 5. Height of shear walls from top of base slab (top of foundation) to top of penthouse = 106.4 m (349.3 ft), while to the top of the roof slab = 101.6 m (333.3 ft). Height of building from grade level to top of penthouse = 90.0 m (295.2 ft), while to the top of roof slab = 85.1 m (279.1 ft). Overall dimensions of above-grade floor plates: 25.9 m × 25.9 m = 671 m² (85 ft × 85 ft = 7 200 ft²). Overall dimensions of building below grade (lot size): 45.7 m × 45.7 m = 2 088 m² (150 ft × 150 ft = 22 500 ft²). Clear story heights (top of slab below to underside of slab above): second floor and above = 2.59 m (8.5 ft); mechanical penthouse level = 4.88 m (16 ft); first floor above grade and first floor below grade = 4.27 m (14 ft); other floors below grade = 2.74 m (9 ft). Floor slab (flat plate) thicknesses: floors above grade = 190 mm; floors at grade and below grade = 250 mm. Thickness of perimeter basement walls = 300 mm.

Fig. 11.11 summarizes the initial design of the core, which contains a three-elevator shaft and a stair shaft. The core consists of three C-shaped cantilever shear walls with an overall length of 8.94 m (29 ft. – 4 in.). The three cantilever walls, labelled W1, W2, W3 from left to right in Fig. 11.11 have "web" thicknesses of 405 mm (16 in.), 305 mm (12 in.) and 355 mm (14 in.), respectively. The "flanges" of the walls are all 710 mm (28 in.) thick to accommodate the diagonal reinforcement in the coupling beams over the door openings. The overall length of the core in the coupled-wall direction is 7.72 m (25 ft. – 4 in.).

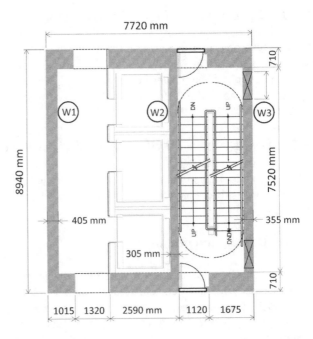

Fig. 11.11 Preliminary design of building: ETABS model of full building (left); plan view of core (right)

The door openings between walls W1 and W2 (into the elevator lobby) are 1320 mm (52 in.) wide and are 2185 mm (7 ft. – 2 in.) high, while the two openings between walls W2 and W3 (into the stairway) are 1120 mm (44 in.) wide and 2085 mm (6 ft. – 10 in.) high. The resulting coupling beam depths over the different levels of the building are summarized in Table 11.13.

Table 11.13 Summary of coupling beam depths.

Level	Thick. of slab above	Storey height (mm)	Coupling beam depths (mm)	
			CB1-2 (dr. ht.=2185)	CB2-3 (dr. ht.=2085)
Penthouse	190	4880	2640*	2240*
L2 – L30	190	2590	595	695
P1 – L1	250	4270	2335	2435
P5 – P2	250	2750	815	915

* Opening height increased to satisfy maximum coupling beam depth.

The gravity-load frame in the building consists of 190 mm thick flat plate floor slabs supported on 12 gravity-load columns spaced evenly around the perimeter of the building (four per side). The columns are set back from the edge of the slab (i.e., the slab overhangs the end of the columns) as shown in Fig. 11.11 (left). As the design of the gravity-load frame cannot be finalized until considering how the geometry of the columns influences the seismic deformation demands on the frame (see Section 11.5.11), preliminary sizes and locations of the columns were used to conduct the seismic analysis of the building.

11.5.2.1. Material Properties for Concrete Walls

All reinforcement in the building is grade 400 MPa, while the reinforcement used to construct the ductile core walls is also weldable grade (Clause 21.2.7). All concrete is normal density. The following specified compression strengths are assumed for the preliminary design of the core walls (and will be increased if needed): above Level 20, f'_c = 30 MPa; levels 11 to 20, f'_c = 35 MPa; below Level 11, f'_c = 45 MPa.

11.5.3. Seismic Analysis

11.5.3.1. Gravity Loads for Seismic Design and Seismic Mass

Dead loads due to self-weight of members calculated using 24 kN/m³. Dead loads superimposed on floors (from finishes and partitions indicated on the structural drawings): 0.72 kN/m² (15 psf). Dead load due to cladding around perimeter of building: 1.9 kN/m. Live load superimposed on floors (not included in calculation of mass): 1.9 kN/m².

The seismic mass was calculated to be 505 000 kg per typical floor with about 70% of the mass coming from the slabs and superimposed dead loads (finishes and partitions), 21% from the core, 5% from the columns, and 4% from the cladding. The mass of the top floor with elevator penthouse and the mass of the first floor are somewhat larger. The total seismic mass for the building levels above grade is 15.5×10^6 kg.

11.5.3.2. Modelling of Building in ETABS

A three dimensional model of the building, including the five levels below grade, was developed in ETABS 2015. The walls were modelled using thin shell elements which utilize automated rectangular meshing, while the columns and coupling beams were modelled using frame elements. Note that frame elements were chosen for the coupling beams to ensure the flexibility of these members was correctly modeled. All columns had moment releases at each end to ensure the gravity-load frame

11

Seismic Design

(columns and slabs) did not contribute to the lateral resistance of the building. A second model of the building without the moment releases in the columns indicated that the reduction in the period of the building (used to determine forces) due to the gravity-load frame was small because of the flexibility of the cracked flat plate slabs. The deformation of the soil below the foundation, which is five levels below grade, was neglected; however an additional model of only the levels below grade was used to determine the influence of soil deformation (and cracking of the below-grade concrete structure) on the force distribution below grade and the resulting deformation of the structure above grade (see Section 11.5.10). The soil above the foundations on the outside of the basement walls was not included in the model. The earthquake motions were input at the foundation level, five floors below grade.

The slabs were modelled as shells with automatic meshing. For the wind and seismic cases, the slabs above grade were modelled as rigid diaphragms and used to calculate mass, while the slabs below grade were modelled as semi-rigid diaphragms.

Reduced section properties were used to account for cracking of concrete in accordance with Clause 21.2.5.2. As the coupling beams in ductile coupled walls are designed according to Clause 21.5.8.2 (with diagonal reinforcement), $A_{ve} = 1.2 \times 0.45 A_g$ and $I_e = 0.25 I_g$. Note the 1.2 factor is to correct for the fact that ETABS uses a shear area of $A_{ve} = 5/6 \, A_g$. The reduction factor α_w to be applied to the wall rigidities depends on the nominal flexural overstrength of the walls γ_w, which is not known until the wall reinforcement has been determined; thus γ_w was initially assumed to equal R_o in Equation 21.2 (Clause 21.2.5.2) and $\alpha_w = 0.5$. $A_e = 0.5 \, A_g$ is the rigidity that most influences the flexural stiffness of the coupled walls, while $I_e = 0.5 I_g$ controls the flexural stiffness in the cantilever wall direction. As it was subsequently determined that there is significant flexural overstrength of the walls, additional analysis of the building was done with refined rigidities to make a refined estimate of the displacement demands (see Section 11.5.8).

Table 11.14 summarizes the first three modes of the building. The lateral mode in the coupled wall direction has a period of 6.2 s, while the lateral mode in the cantilever direction has a period of 4.7 s. The third mode is torsion with a period of 2.4 s. The analysis of the building included P-Δ (non-iterative based on mass), which increases the apparent flexibility of the building. Note that the lateral periods of the building were calculated to be 5.9 (rather than 6.2) and 4.6 (rather than 4.7) when P-Δ was not included. 12 modes of the building were included in the analysis resulting in between 95% to 98% of the mass participating in each of the three directions.

Table 11.14 First three building modes of vibration.

Mode	Period (s)	Mass Participation (%)		
		x-dir. (coupled)	y-dir. (cantilever)	z-dir. (torsion)
1	6.24	70	0	0
2	4.72	0	69	0
3	2.37	0	0	80

11.5.3.3. Seismic Demands According to 2015 NBCC

As the Site Class is C, the site coefficient for spectral acceleration F(T) are conveniently all equal to 1.0, and the design spectral response accelerations, S(T), to be used to analyze the building on this particular site are equal to the 5% damped spectral response accelerations, $S_a(T)$, for Vancouver given in 2015 NBCC and summarized in Table 11.15.

Table 11.15 Design spectral response accelerations for Vancouver Site Class C.

T (s)	≤ 0.2	0.5	1.0	2.0	5.0	10.0
$S_a(T) = S(T)$	0.848	0.751	0.425	0.257	0.080	0.029

Table 11.16 summarizes the seismic demands on the building according to 2015 NBCC. Analysis according to 4.1.8.11.(10) for the torsional sensitivity of the building resulted in $B_x = 1.2$ in the coupled-wall direction and $B_x = 1.3$ in the cantilever-wall direction. As both are less than 1.7, the building is not torsionally sensitive. The effects of accidental torsional moments acting concurrently with the lateral earthquake forces that cause them were accounted for using a three-dimensional analysis with the centres of mass shifted by a distance of +/- 5% of the plan dimension of the building.

The fundamental lateral period of vibration of the building, T_a, used to calculate the minimum lateral earthquake force according to NBCC is a function of the height of the building, h_n, from the *base* to the top level (level n), where the *base* of the structure is the level at which horizontal earthquake motions are considered to be imparted to the structure. In the ETABS analysis of the building, the earthquake motions were imparted at the level of the foundation. Considering that the building has a significant mechanical penthouse, one interpretation of the NBCC requirements is that $h_n = 106.4$ m and thus $2 \times T_a = 3.3$ s, which is significantly shorter than the fundamental lateral periods of vibration determined by the ETABS model of the building. Owing to the stiff structure below grade and the surrounding soil, which was not included in the ETABS model, the earthquake is likely to be imparted to the real building at some point between the foundation level and the grade level. In the current example, the following numbers were used to determine the minimum lateral earthquake force: $h_n = 90$ m and $2 \times T_a = 2.9$ s. Further discussion of this topic is given in Ref. 2.

NBCC 4.1.8.12.(10) states that all storey shears, storey forces and member forces shall be scaled by the same scaling factor V_d/V_e; however a different scaling factor is permitted for deflections. For the purpose of calculating deflections, it is permitted to use a value for the minimum lateral earthquake force V based on the value for T_a determined from an appropriate structural model, except that T_a shall not exceed 4.0 s (4.1.8.12.(11)). The scaling factors for forces (relative to the design base shear V_d) are 1.585 (coupled) and 1.380 (cantilever), while the scaling factors for deflections are 1.090 (coupled) and 1.00 (cantilever) based on the initially assumed effective stiffness values (see Table 11.16). The scaling factors for displacement were updated when the refined estimates of building displacement were made in Section 11.5.8.

11

Seismic Design

Table 11.16 Summary of Seismic Demands According to 2015 NBCC

NBCC Reference	Parameter	Coupled wall	Cantilever wall
	(a) Seismic weight, W =	152 300 kN	152 300 kN
	(b) Fundamental period from ETABS, T =	6.24 s	4.72 s
4.1.8.12.(5) & 4.1.8.12.(6)	(c) Design elastic base shear, V_{ed} = Elastic base shear, V_e =	15 629 kN	20 332 kN
4.1.8.5.(1); 4.1.8.9	(d) I_E = 1.0; $R_d R_o$ =	4.0 × 1.7 = 6.8	3.5 × 1.6 = 5.6
4.1.8.12.(7)	(e) Design base shear, $V_d = V_{ed} I_E / R_d R_o$ =	2298 kN	3631 kN
4.1.8.11.(3).(c) & 4.1.8.11.(3).(d).(iii)	(f) Empirical period $T_a = 2 \times 0.05 h_n^{0.75}$ = 2×1.463 =	2.93 s	2.93 s
4.1.8.4.(9)	(g) S (2.93) =	0.203	0.203
4.1.8.11.(6)	(h) M_v =	1.004	1.137
4.1.8.11.(2)	(i) Min. lateral earthquake force, V (T_a = 2.93 s) =	4553 kN	6261 kN
4.1.8.12.(8)	(j) Scaled design base shear (regular structure) $V_d = 0.8V$ =	**3642 kN**	**5009 kN**
	(k) Scaling factor* for forces (j)/(e) =	1.585	1.380
4.1.8.11.(2)	(l) Min. lateral earthquake force (for deflection) V (T_a = 4.0 s) =	3131 kN	4309 kN
4.1.8.12.(11)	(m) Scaled design base shear V_d = $0.8V$ (for deflect.) =	2505 kN	3447 kN
	(n) Scaling factor* for deflections (m)/(e) =	1.090	1.000
4.1.8.13.(2)	(o) Total multiplier* for deflections (n) × $R_d R_o / I_E$ =	7.41	5.60

* Reference forces or displacements are those corresponding to design base shear given in (e).

11.5.4. Wind Analysis

For a 30-story building in Vancouver, the factored wind forces are often larger than the factored seismic forces. Thus a wind analysis was done as part of this example; however as the purpose is to demonstrate the seismic design requirements, the wind forces were not determined in a rigorous way.

The natural frequencies of the building were determined using the same ETABS model that was used for seismic analysis (see Section 11.5.3.2) except that different effective stiffness properties were used. For simplicity, average effective stiffness properties were used over the height of the building as was done for seismic analysis. The selection of the effective stiffnesses was also not rigorously done. A 30% reduction in stiffness was used to account for horizontal cracking of the concrete walls, i.e., $A_e = 0.7 A_g$ and $I_e = 0.7 I_g$. The following reduced section properties were used for the coupling beams: $A_{ve} = 1.2 \times 0.30 A_g$ and $I_e = 0.30 I_g$; however in retrospect, using a lower A_{ve} for the wind analysis than was used for the seismic analysis is nonsensical as a higher level of damage is expected in the coupling beams due to the design earthquake. Revised calculations were not done.

The natural periods of vibration of the building model used for wind analysis in the coupled and cantilever direction were determined to be 5.33s and 4.04s, respectively. According to NBCC Clause 4.1.7, the Wind Tunnel Procedure shall be used to determine the specified wind loads in very dynamically sensitive buildings defined as the lowest natural frequency less than 0.25hz (period greater than 4.0 s); however this was not possible for the current example. Thus the Dynamic Procedure was used to determine the wind loads. The windward and leeward pressures were applied to the building envelope in the ETABS model. The full wind pressures were applied in each direction. The following assumptions were used to determine the windward and leeward pressures: Importance factor I_w = 1.0; 1 in 50 year hourly wind pressure in Vancouver q_{50} = 0.45 kPa; exposure factor based on rough terrain; damping ratio β = 0.02.

11.5.5. Design Forces

The factored design forces at grade level are summarized in Table 11.17. The total forces applied to the core, as well as the maximum forces applied to each of the individual wall piers, W1, W2, W3, as defined in Fig. 11.11, are provided. In the case of the axial loads (dead and live), the axial forces in the individual wall piers sum to the total axial load applied on the core. However, the maximum shear forces and maximum bending moments applied onto the individual wall piers in the cantilever direction do not sum up to equal the total shear force and bending moment applied to the core as the maximum pier forces include the demand from accidental torsion. The accidental torsion does not influence the maximum shear forces and bending moments in the coupled wall direction because the shear flow around the closed tube causes equal and opposite forces on the two "flanges" of the wall piers.

Table 11.17 Summary of factored forces at grade level; both total forces applied to core, as well as maximum forces applied to individual wall piers.

Axial load (kN) due to gravity loads

Dead load, 1.0D

Core	W1	W2	W3
75 482	22 721	28 850	23 911
100%	30.1%	38.2%	31.7%

Live load, 0.5L

Core	W1	W2	W3
3 124	965	1 185	974
100%	30.9%	37.9%	31.2%

Shear force (kN) – Cantilever Wall Direction

Earthquake, 1.0E

Core	W1	W2	W3
5 009	2 638	1 578	2 212
100%	53%	32%	44%

Wind, 1.4W

Core	W1	W2	W3
4 395	1 862	904	1 630
100%	42%	21%	37%

Shear force (kN) – Coupled Wall Direction

Earthquake, 1.0E

Core	W1	W2	W3
3 642	461	2 286	895
100%	13%	62%	24%

Wind, 1.4W

Core	W1	W2	W3
5 013	532	3 226	1 256
100%	11%	64%	25%

11

Seismic Design

Bending moment (kNm) – Cantilever Wall Direction

Earthquake, 1.0*E*   Wind, 1.4*W*

Core	W1	W2	W3
166 970	46 357	70 423	56 666
100%	28%	42%	34%

Core	W1	W2	W3
215 222	57 299	88 739	69 184
100%	27%	41%	32%

Bending moment (kNm) – Coupled Wall Direction

Earthquake, 1.0*E*

Core	W1	W2	W3
117 157	1 389	12 227	4 002
100%	1%	10%	3%

	W1	W2	W3
P_E (kN)	14 558	242	14 672
x (m)	3.708	0.061	3.223
BM (kNm)	53 976	14.7	47 295
	45%	0%	40%

Wind, 1.4*W*

Core	W1	W2	W3
246 194	2 092	23 318	7 435
100%	1%	9%	3%

	W1	W2	W3
P_W (kN)	29 861	154	30 913
x (m)	3.708	0.061	3.223
BM (kNm)	110 709	9	99 651
	46%	0%	41%

The bending moments applied to the three wall piers in the coupled wall direction sum up to 14% of the total overturning moment applied to the core. The remainder of the overturning moment due to earthquake is resisted by axial forces P_E in the wall piers. The horizontal distance between the centroid of the core and the centroid of the individual wall piers are labelled x and the calculations summarized at the bottom right of Table 11.17 confirms that the axial loads in the wall piers due to the coupling beam forces resist the remaining 86% of the total overturning moment, making the core fully coupled.

The maximum bending moment due to earthquake at grade level in the coupled-wall direction is 117 157 kNm, while the maximum shear force due to earthquake at grade level in the coupled-wall direction is 3642 kN. The ratio of maximum bending moment to maximum shear force is 117 157 kNm/3642 kN = 32.2 m, which is 38% of the building height to the top of the roof slab. In the cantilever-wall direction, the maximum bending moment due to earthquake at grade level is 166 970 kNm, while the maximum shear force is 5009 kN, and the ratio of maximum bending moment to maximum shear force is 33.3 m, 39% of the building height. Note that the ratios of maximum bending moment to maximum shear force remain constant because the same scaling factor is used for both bending moment and shear force.

Figure 11.12 presents the total factored shear forces and total factored bending moments applied to the core over the height. The factored bending moment due to wind forces is considerably larger than the factored bending moment due to earthquake forces in the coupled wall direction. The difference is larger than was expected. The uplift forces in the outside wall piers due to the wind forces is what ends up controlling the design of the vertical reinforcement in these two wall piers, therefore a refined wind analysis, for example using the Wind Tunnel Procedure, would influence the final design of the building. The factored shear force due to wind is also somewhat larger than the factored shear force due to earthquake in the coupled-wall direction; however the earthquake capacity design requirement that ensures a flexural yielding mechanism in the walls is what controls the shear design of the walls in both directions by a considerable margin.

The analysis of the building including the levels below grade clearly indicate the maximum shear forces occur below the grade level and are much higher than the base shear (by about a factor of 2.0 in Fig. 11.12). These large shear forces are caused by the prying action of the wall between the stiff diaphragms below grade. Clearly these very large shear forces must be considered in the design of the walls and are discussed in Section 11.5.10.

11.5.6. Design of Coupling Beams

Before designing the vertical reinforcement in the walls, the coupling beams need to be designed over the full height of the building as the actual (nominal) strengths are needed in order to determine the maximum uplift force from the coupling beam shear forces that the wall piers must be designed for (as per Clause 21.5.8.3.4). Fig. 11.13 summarizes the factored shear forces in the coupling beams between wall piers $W2$ and $W3$ due to wind $(1.4W)$ and due to earthquake $(1.0E)$ with accidental torsion (T) and without accidental torsion (no T). In this building, the increase in coupling beam shear forces due to the accidental torsion is small because the building is not torsionally sensitive and the accidental torsion was created by only a 5% shift in the centre of mass. In many buildings, the difference is significantly larger.

The design of the coupling beams between wall piers $W2$ and $W3$ is briefly described below. The door opening (coupling beam length) is 1120 mm and from level 2 to level 30, the coupling beam depth is 695 mm. These coupling beam dimensions result in the diagonal reinforcement being placed at an angle $\alpha = 25.3$ deg. (see Section 11.4.5.2 for the design procedure). The number of diagonal reinforcing bars was selected at each level to result in a factored shear resistance V_r greater than the factored shear force demand V_f from the wind $(1.4W)$ at each level. As damage is expected (even desirable) in the coupling beams at the design level earthquake, it is not necessary to maintain $V_r \geq V_f$ (seismic) at every level. It is important, however, to satisfy $\Sigma V_r \geq \Sigma V_f$ over an appropriate portion of the building height. In the current example, the provided factored resistance of the coupling beams are less than the factored demand from earthquake (including accidental torsion) over about a 15 m height starting at 60 m above grade level; however additional shear resistance is provided over the top 15 m of the building height so that the sum of the shear resistance is greater than the sum of the factored shear forces over the top 30 m of height (about one-third of the building height). It is important to minimize the accumulative overstrength of the coupling beams as once the dead load in the wall piers is overcome by the uplift force from the coupling beams, additional overstrength in the coupling beams requires additional vertical reinforcement in the wall piers.

11

Seismic Design

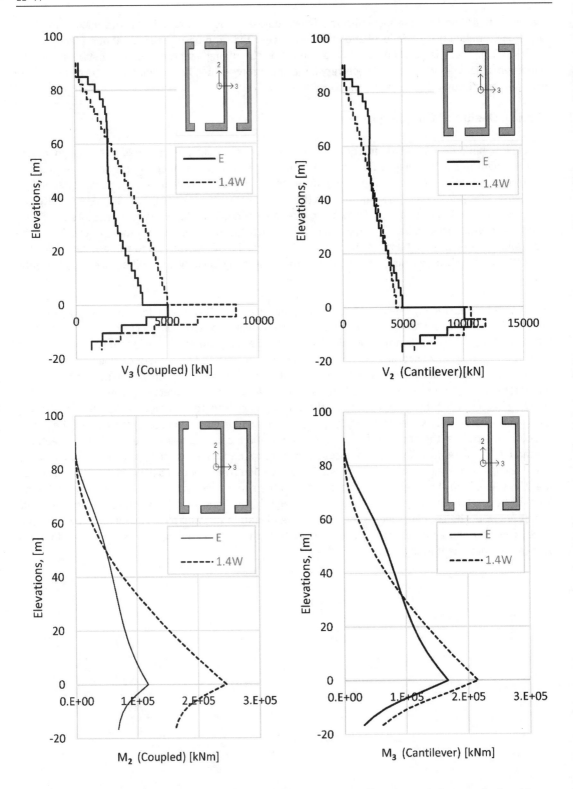

Fig. 11.12 Factored shear force diagram (top) and factored bending moment diagram (bottom) for coupled wall direction (left) and cantilever wall direction (right)

The diagonal reinforcement provided in each direction of the coupling beams are as follows (from the top): 4 – 15M (2 levels), 6 – 15M (9 levels), 8 –15M (2 levels), 6 – 20M (3 levels), 8 – 20M (5 levels), 6 – 25M (8 levels), 8 – 20M (1 level). At the first level, the coupling beam is 2435 mm deep. The 8 – 15M at Level 1 are to be placed at an angle α = 68.3 deg.

As per Clause 21.5.8.3.4, ductile coupled walls must be designed with the axial forces in the wall piers due to the coupling beam forces (P_E given in Table 11.17) increased at each level by the following ratio: sum of coupling beam nominal resistances above the level under consideration – to – sum of factored forces in coupling beams without accidental torsion above the level under consideration. At grade level, this ratio was determined to be 1.83 between wall piers $W2$ and $W3$. Coincidentally, this ratio was very similar (1.82) at grade between wall piers $W1$ and $W2$, although the coupling beam designs, and the factored demands are very different.

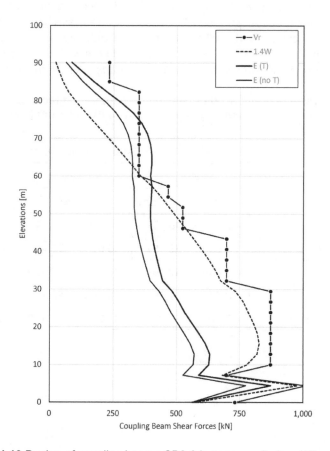

Fig. 11.13 Design of coupling beams CB2-3 between wall piers $W2$ and $W3$.

11.5.7. Design of Ductile Walls

The example in Section 11.4 demonstrates the design of ductile walls at grade level and above grade level, while the current example demonstrates the design at grade level and below grade level.

11.5.7.1. Design of Vertical Reinforcement in Walls

Table 11.18 summarizes the combinations of factored axial load P_f and factored bending moment M_f that the three wall piers must be designed for. In the cantilever-wall direction there are two load cases with earthquake loads and three load cases with wind loads. In the coupled-wall direction, the two load

11

Seismic Design

cases with earthquake loads must be repeated with the axial force due to earthquake increased by a factor of about 1.8 to account for the nominal strength of the coupling beams as per Clause 21.5.8.3.4. This load case is labelled as $1.0E^*$. In addition, because the wall piers are not symmetrical in the coupled-wall directions, the seven load cases (two E load cases, two E^* load cases and three W load cases) must all be repeated in the two directions resulting in 14 load cases in the coupled wall directions.

The approach taken to design the vertical reinforcement in the walls was to begin with all the required minimum reinforcement – minimum distributed reinforcement as per Clause 21.5.5 and minimum concentrated reinforcement as per Clause 21.5.6. With minimum reinforcement, the three wall piers have sufficient capacity to resist the five load cases in the cantilever-wall direction, and $W2$ has sufficient capacity to resist the 14 load cases in the coupled-wall direction. Additional vertical reinforcement was required in wall piers $W1$ and $W2$ to resist the combined axial load and bending moment in the coupled-wall direction. Figure 11.14 compares the factored axial load – bending moment interaction diagrams after the final reinforcement design with the 14 load cases for weak axis bending of wall piers $W1$ and $W2$. The critical loading case for both wall piers is the case with large uplift due to the overturning from wind forces combined with reduced axial compression in the walls due dead load ($1.4W + 0.9D$). Figure 11.15 summarizes the final design for the vertical reinforcement in the three walls.

Table 11.18 Summary of factored axial forces and corresponding factored bending moments applied to the wall piers at grade level due to the different load cases

| | Cantilever-wall Direction | | | | | |
| | W1 | | W2 | | W3 | |
	P_f (kN)	M_f (kNm)	P_f (kN)	M_f (kNm)	P_f (kN)	M_f (kNm)
$1.0E + 1.0D$	-22 721	46 357	-28 850	70 423	-23 911	56 666
$1.0E + 1.0D + 0.5L + 0.25S$	-23 686	46 357	-30 035	70 423	-24 885	56 666
$1.4W + 0.9D$	-20 449	57 299	-25 965	88 739	-21 520	69 184
$1.4W + 1.25D$	-28 401	57 299	-36 063	88 739	-29 889	69 184
$1.4W + 1.25D + 0.5L + 0.25S$	-29 366	57 299	-37 247	88 739	-30 863	69 184

	Coupled-wall Direction					
	W1		W2		W3	
	P_f (kN)	M_f (kNm)	P_f (kN)	M_f (kNm)	P_f (kN)	M_f (kNm)
$1.0E + 1.0D$	-8 163	1 389	-28 609	12 227	-38 583	4 002
$1.0E + 1.0D + 0.5L + 0.25S$	-9 128	1 389	-29 793	12 227	-39 557	4 002
$1.0E^* + 1.0D$	4 212	1 389	-28 403	12 227	-51 054	4 002
$1.0E^* + 1.0D + 0.5L + 0.25S$	2 519	1 389	-29 600	12 227	-51 295	4 002
$1.0E + 1.0D$	-37 279	-1 389	-29 092	-12 227	-9 239	-4 002
$1.0E + 1.0D + 0.5L + 0.25S$	-38 244	-1 389	-30 276	-12 227	-10 213	-4 002
$1.0E^* + 1.0D$	-49 654	-1 389	-29 297	-12 227	3 232	-4 002
$1.0E^* + 1.0D + 0.5L + 0.25S$	-49 891	-1 389	-30 469	-12 227	1 525	-4 002
$1.4W + 0.9D$	9 411	2 091	-25 810	23 318	-52 434	7 436
$1.4W + 1.25D$	1 459	2 091	-35 908	23 318	-60 803	7 436
$1.4W + 1.25D + 0.5L + 0.25S$	494	2 091	-37 092	23 318	-61 777	7 436
$1.4W + 0.9D$	-50 309	-2 091	-26 120	-23 318	9 394	-7 436
$1.4W + 1.25D$	-58 261	-2 091	-36 217	-23 318	1 025	-7 436
$1.4W + 1.25D + 0.5L + 0.25S$	-59 227	-2 091	-37 402	-23 318	51	-7 436

E^* = axial force increased to account for nominal strength of coupling beams as per Clause 21.5.8.3.4.

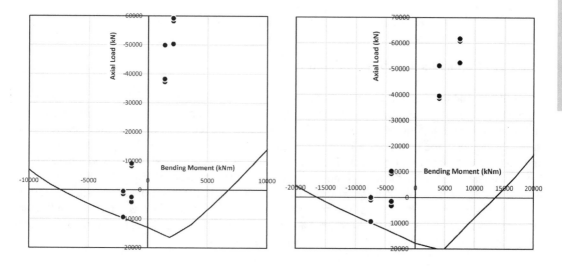

Fig. 11.14 Axial force – bending moment interaction diagrams for weak-axis bending of wall pier W1 (left) and wall pier W3 (right); dots represent load cases given in Table 11.18, while the lines are the calculated factored capacity.

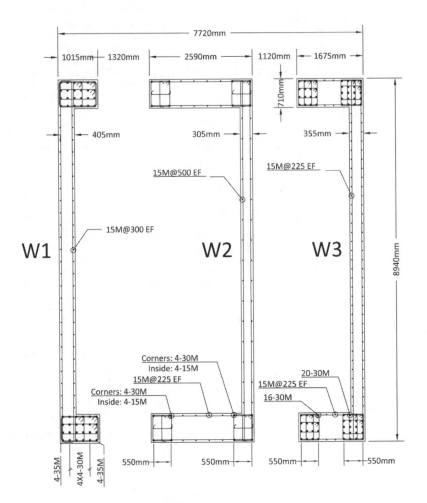

Fig. 11.15 Summary of vertical reinforcement design at grade level.

11.5.7.2. Nominal and Probable Flexural Resistance of Walls

The wall nominal flexural resistance is needed to make a refined estimate of the effective stiffness of the walls, to check the ductility of the cantilever walls and for the analysis of the structure below-grade structure. The probable flexural resistance of the walls is needed to determine the shear demands in the wall (above and below grade). As lower-bound estimate of nominal flexural resistance is safe, an upper-bound estimate of probable flexural resistance is safe, and axial compression increases the flexural resistance of walls, the axial compression due to 1.0D should be used to determine the nominal flexural resistance, and the axial compression due to 1.0D + 0.5L + 0.25S should be used to determine the probable flexural resistance. For the current building, the additional axial compression in the walls at grade level due to 0.5L + 0.25S is only a 4% increase over 1.0D. Thus the axial compression due to 1.0D was used to determine all flexural resistances for simplicity.

Cantilever-wall direction

The factored, nominal and probable flexural resistances in the cantilever wall piers can be determined very easily from the same sectional analysis by adjusting the material resistance factors and yield strength of the reinforcement as described in Table 11.2. Table 11.19 summarizes the results for the three wall piers.

Table 11.19 Factored, nominal and probable flexural resistances of the cantilever walls

	Total	W1	W2	W3
M_r (kNm)	513 583	159 506	166 902	187 175
M_n (kNm)	560 085	176 688	177 852	205 545
M_p (kNm)	615 555	195 679	189 898	229 978

A large portion of the flexural resistance of the walls is due to the applied axial load, which is equal to about $0.1f_c'A_g$ in all three wall piers. Note that $M_n = 1.09M_r$, $M_p = 1.10M_n$ and $M_p = 1.20\ M_r$. It is interesting to compare these number, which are typical for high-rise cantilever shear walls, with the approximate relationships given in Table 11.2 for other types of members.

Coupled-wall direction

As described in Section 11.5.5, the overturning resistance of the core in the coupled-wall direction is primarily due to the axial forces in the two exterior wall piers. The flexural resistance of the individual wall piers generally provide a small contribution towards the flexural resistance of the entire core. The flexural overstrength of the core in a highly coupled wall is a system property and cannot be determined by looking at individual wall piers as can be done in the cantilever direction or a lightly coupled wall system. Fig. 11.16 summarizes the forces involved in the problem for a three wall-pier system. P_1, P_2, P_3 are the axial loads due to gravity (1.0D), equal to 22 721 kN, 28 850 kN and 23 911 kN, respectively.

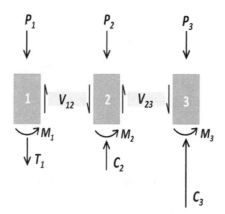

Fig. 11.16 Freebody to determine overstrength of coupled wall system with three wall piers for the case of lateral load acting to the right.

Nominal flexural resistance

Referring to Fig. 11.16, $V_{12} = P_E(W1) \times 1.83 = 14\ 558$ kN $\times 1.83 = 26\ 641$ kN, where: $P_E(W1)$ is maximum axial force in wall determined from linear dynamic analysis (see Table 11.17); 1.83 is the ratio of the sum of coupling beam nominal shear resistances over full height – to – sum of factored shear forces in coupling beams without accidental torsion (Section 11.5.6.). Thus T_1 required for equilibrium is 26 641 – 22 721 = 3 920 kN (tension). The total cross sectional area of the vertical reinforcement in wall pier $W1$ is 48 400 mm². The maximum vertical tension force that can be resisted by the nominal strength of this reinforcement is: $A_s \times 1.0f_y = 48\ 400$ mm² $\times 400$ MPa $/ 1000 = 19\ 360$ kN. Thus T_1 is defined by the capacity of the coupling beams, not by yielding of vertical reinforcement. M_1 is determined by doing a sectional analysis of wall pier $W1$ using the nominal reinforcement strength and an applied tension force of 3 920 kN. $V_{23} = P_E$ (W3) × 1.82 = 14 672 kN × 1.82 = 26 703 kN. $C_2 = P_2 + V_{12} - V_{23} = 28\,850 + 26\,641 - 26\,703 = 28\,788$ kN (comp). M_2 is determined from a sectional analysis of wall pier W2 using the nominal reinforcement strength and an applied compression force of 28 788 kN. $C_3 = P_3 + V_{23} = 23\,911 + 26\,703 = 50\,614$ kN (comp), and M_3 is determined from a sectional analysis of wall pier W3 with 50 614 kN axial compression.

As the three wall piers are interconnected by rigid floor slabs, they must have compatible curvatures. It is not appropriate to calculate the bending moment capacities of the wall piers using the maximum compression strain of 0.0035 and very different compression strain depths as the bending moments would not be compatible (would occur at very different curvatures). Thus the complete moment-curvature responses of the three wall piers were developed and these are compared in Fig. 11.17. The nominal resistance of the three walls were taken at a curvature of 10 rad/km (see Fig. 11.17 left) and are as follows: $M_1 = 9\,036$ kNm, $M_2 = 32\,851$ kNm, and $M_3 = 34\,891$ kNm. Note that in this case, the curvature capacities of the three wall piers are similar.

The applied vertical loads due to dead load P_1, P_2, P_3 have a resultant acting at the centroid of the core and thus do not cause an overturning moment on the core. Similarly, the axial force C_2 on wall pier W2 is located essentially at the centroid of the core. Thus the total nominal flexural resistance of the coupled wall is given by $M_n = C_3 \times 3.223$ m $+ T_1 \times 3.708$ m $+ M_1 + M_2 + M_3 = 163\,129 + 14\,535 + 9\,036 + 32\,851 + 34\,891 = 254\,441$ kNm.

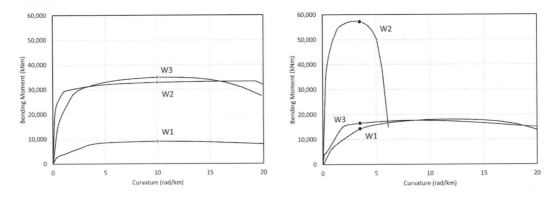

Fig. 11.17 Bending moment – curvature relationships for weak-axis bending of the three wall piers: (left) W1 in tension and W3 in compression; (right) W1 in compression and W3 in tension

The entire analysis was repeated in the opposite direction (W1 in compression and W3 in tension). In this direction, W2 has a much reduced curvature capacity due to the narrow width of the compression stress block. The contributions from bending of the individual wall piers was determined at a curvature of only 3.5 rad/km in this case (see Fig. 11.17 right) as follows: $M_1 = 14\,262$ kNm, $M_2 = 57\,185$ kNm, and $M_3 = 16\,500$ kNm. The total nominal flexural resistance of the coupled wall in this direction is given by $M_n = C_1 \times 3.708$ m $+ T_3 \times 3.223$ m $+ M_1 + M_2 + M_3 = 183\,034 + 8\,999 + 14\,262 + 57\,185 + 16\,500 = 279\,980$ kNm.

As the nominal resistance is different in the two directions, and a lower-bound value is more conservative, all calculations with nominal flexural resistance will be done with the smaller value, namely $M_n = 254\,441$ kNm.

Probable flexural resistance

All the calculations described above were repeated to determine the probable flexural resistance of the coupled wall system. The probable flexural resistance is needed to determine the shear demands in the wall system. The procedure is identical except that the coupling beam strengths are increased by a factor of 1.25 and the strength of the vertical reinforcement is increased to $1.25f_y$. In the direction when $W1$ is in tension and $W3$ is in compression, the result is: $M_p = C_3 \times 3.223$ m $+ T_1 \times 3.708$ m $+ M_1 + M_2 + M_3$ $= 184\ 646 + 39\ 231 + 5\ 168 + 35\ 236 + 40\ 017 = 304\ 297$ kNm. In the opposite direction ($W1$ in compression and $W3$ in tension) $M_p = C_1 \times 3.708$ m $+ T_3 \times 3.223$ m $+ M_1 + M_2 + M_3 = 207\ 730 + 30\ 515$ $+14\ 691 + 60\ 663 + 15\ 485 = 329\ 084$ kNm.

As the probable resistance is different in the two directions, and an upper-bound value is more conservative, all calculations with probable flexural resistance will be done with the larger value, namely $M_p = 329\ 084$ kNm.

Wall overstrength factor γ_w

The wall overstrength factor γ_w is defined as the ratio of the load corresponding to nominal moment resistance of the wall system to the factored load on the wall system, but need not be taken as less than 1.3. The nominal moment resistance is well defined (see above); however the bending moment associated with the appropriate "factored load on the wall system" requires some careful consideration.

When the wall overstrength factor is used to calculate the effective flexural stiffnesses of the wall (accounting for inelastic response) or the inelastic rotational demands on cantilever walls, the factored loads that should be used are the ones that have been scaled for the calculation of deflection (see Section 11.5.3.3). On the other hand, when the wall overstrength factor is used to determine the amplification of the shear force to account for inelastic effects of higher modes (Clause 21.5.2.2.7), the wall overstrength factor should be calculated using the factored loads on the wall system prior to scaling to meet the minimum lateral earthquake force based on the empirical period, i.e., $V_{ed}\ I_E / R_d R_o$. See the explanatory notes to Clause 21.5.2.2.7 for a further discussion.

Cantilever-wall direction: the design base shear $V_d = V_{ed}\ I_E / R_d R_o$ in the cantilever direction is 3631 kN (Table 11.16), and the corresponding total bending moment applied to the core is 121 036 kNm. Thus $\gamma_w = 560\ 085/121\ 036 = 4.63$ for the calculation of increased shear force due to inelastic effects of higher modes. As the scaled design base shear for deflections is 3447 kN, which is smaller than 3631 kN, the scaling factor for deflections is 1.0 and the wall overstrength factor for deflections is also $\gamma_w = 4.63$. Note that when the effective stiffness values for the walls are adjusted in Section 11.5.8, the wall overstrength factor is adjusted accordingly.

Coupled-wall direction: the lower of the two values of nominal moment resistance of the wall system M_n (254 441 kNm) is used to calculate the wall overstrength factor γ_w. In this case, the wall overstrength factor is used only to estimate the effective stiffness of the wall. The design base shear in the coupled-wall direction is 2298 kN (Table 11.16), and the corresponding total bending moment applied to the core is 73 923 kNm. Thus $\gamma_w = 254\ 441/73\ 923 = 3.44$. When the effective stiffness values for the walls are adjusted in Section 11.5.8, the wall overstrength factor is adjusted accordingly.

11.5.7.3.   Design of Walls for Shear at Grade

Cantilever-wall direction

The factored shear force at grade must be increased by the ratio of the probable bending moment resistance to the factored bending moment, both calculated at grade (Clause 21.5.2.2.6): $V_d \times M_p / M_f = 5009$ kN $\times 615\ 555/166\ 970 = 5009$ kN $\times 3.69 = 18\ 466$ kN.

The factored shear force must be further increased to account for inelastic effects of higher modes (Clause 21.5.2.2.7): $1.0 + 0.25\ (R_d R_0 / \gamma_w - 1) = 1.0 + 0.25\ (5.6 / 4.63 - 1) = 1.052$. Because of the large overstrength, the shear force has to be increased by only 5.2% to account for the inelastic effects of higher modes: 18 466 kN $\times 1.052 = 19\ 426$ kN.

The factored shear force need not be taken larger than the shear force resulting from design load combinations that include earthquake, with load effects calculated using $R_d R_o$ equal to 1.3 (Clause 21.5.2.2.5): $V_e/1.3 = 20\,332$ kN/ $1.3 = 15\,640$ kN. Thus the building must be designed for a shear force of 15 640 kN in the cantilever-wall direction.

Based on the geometry of the wall, an appropriate shear depth $d_v = 8940$ mm $- 710$ mm $= 8230$ mm; however d_v need not be taken less than $0.8l_w = 0.8 \times 8940$ mm $= 7152$ mm. Thus take $d_v = 8230$ mm.

Assume uniform shear stress in the three walls. The total shear area $= \sum b_w \cdot d_v = (405 + 305 + 355) \times 8230 = 8.76 \times 10^6$ mm^2. Thus the shear stress $= 15\,640 \times 1000$ N $/ 8.76 \times 10^6$ mm$^2 = 1.79$ MPa, and the shear stress ratio $= v / \phi_c f_c' = 1.79$ MPa $/ (0.65 \times 45$ MPa$) = 0.061$. The inelastic rotational demand on the wall $= 0.0023$ (See Section 11.5.9). When $\theta_{id} \le 0.005$, the shear stress ratio must be less than or equal to 0.15. Thus the shear stress on the wall above grade is acceptable ($V_f \le V_{r,max}$).

When $\theta_{id} \le 0.005$, $\beta = 0.018$; $v_c = \beta \phi_c \sqrt{f_c'} = 0.18 \times 0.65 \times \sqrt{45} = 0.785$ MPa. The required shear stress to be resisted by distributed horizontal reinforcement in the wall: $v_s = 1.79 - 0.785 = 1.01$ MPa. As the axial load on the wall P is approximately $0.1f_c'A_g$, take $\theta = 45$ deg. and $\cot\theta = 1.0$. The required amount of horizontal distributed reinforcement for shear: $\rho_v = 1.01$ MPa$/(0.85 \times 400$ MPa$) = 0.00296$, which is only slightly more than minimum (0.0025). The following reinforcement provides a uniform percentage of distributed horizontal reinforcement in the three walls: 15M@330 mm E.F. in W1, 15M@440 mm E.F. in W2, and 15M@380 mm E.F. in W3. Provide 15M@300 mm to meet the maximum spacing limit in Clause 21.5.5.2. In the plastic hinge region this reinforcement must be anchored with straight bar embedment (or a hook) to develop $1.25f_y$ within the region of tied concentrated vertical reinforcement (Clause 21.5.5.3).

In Vancouver, two additional 1016 mm openings are required in wall pier W3 at the ground-floor level for exiting requirements (these are indicated in Fig. 11.11). The additional design requirements to ensure the shear force can be transmitted around these openings is presented in Reference 2.

Table 11.20 Summary of shear force demands and resistances in the cantilever-wall direction.

	Core	W1	W2	W3	$\sum W_i$
Factored shear force, including accid. torsion (kN)	5 009	2 638	1 578	2 212	6 428
Portion of scaled base shear (5 009 kN)	100%	53%	32%	44%	128%
Portion of total shear resistance (6 428 kN)	78%	41%	25%	34%	100%
Thickness of wall (mm)	-	405	305	355	-
Provided shear resistance (kN)*	15 640	5 966	4 493	5 230	15 689
Portion of total shear resistance	100%	38%	29%	33%	100%

* Prior to reducing spacing of horizontal reinforcement to 300 mm.

Coupled-wall direction

The factored shear force at grade must be increased by the ratio of the probable bending moment resistance to the factored bending moment, both calculated at grade (Clause 21.5.2.2.6). When the lateral load is to the right ($W1$ in tension) $V_d \times M_p / M_f$ = 3 642 kN × 304 297/117 157 = 3 642 kN × 2.60 = 9 460 kN. When the lateral load is to the left ($W1$ in compression) $V_d \times M_p / M_f$ = 3 642 kN × 329 084/117 157 = 3 642 kN × 2.81 = 10 230 kN. If a refined shear analysis is done, the resistance of the wall system will also be different in the two directions as a wall with a large compression flange will have a higher shear resistance than a wall with a large tension flange (see Reference 2). When the lateral load is acting to the left ($W1$ in compression), both $W2$ and $W3$ have tension flanges and are weaker in shear. Thus the larger shear demand occurs in the same direction as the lower shear resistance. In a simplified shear analysis were the influence of the compression flanges are ignored (as presented here), the larger shear force demand is critical. In this case, the webs of the three wall piers will be designed to resist a shear force of 10 230 kN in either direction. Note that the shear force demand on coupled walls does not need to be increased to account for the inelastic effects of higher modes in the coupled-wall direction.

Assume the shear is resisted only by the (two) 710 mm wide "webs" of each coupled wall pier – ignore contributions from "flanges." Assume further that the shear stress in these webs are uniform. The shear depth d_v for each wall pier is equal to $0.8 \times l_w$. Thus the total shear area $= 0.8 \times \Sigma l_w \times 710$ mm × 2 $= 6.0 \times 10^6$ mm^2, and the shear stress $= 10\,230 \times 1000$ N $/ 6.0 \times 10^6$ mm^2 = 1.71 MPa. The shear stress ratio $= v / \phi_c f'_c$ = 1.71 MPa $/ (0.65 \times 45$ MPa) = 0.058.

The inelastic rotational demand on the wall θ_{id} = 0.0099 (See Section 11.5.9), and at that level of inelastic rotation, the shear stress ratio must be less than or equal to 0.125 (Clause 21.5.9.5.2). Thus the maximum possible shear resistance $V_{r,max}$ is greater than the applied shear force on the walls V_f.

When θ_{id} = 0.0099, β = 0.092 (Clause 21.5.9.5.2), and $v_c = \beta \phi_c \sqrt{f'_c}$ = 0.92 × 0.65 × $\sqrt{45}$ = 0.40 MPa. The shear stress that must be resisted by distributed horizontal reinforcement in the wall is v_s = 1.71 − 0.40 = 1.31 MPa. As the axial load on the wall P is approximately $0.1 f'_c A_g$, take θ = 45 deg. (Clause 21.5.9.5.2) and $\cot\theta$ = 1.0. The required amount of horizontal distributed reinforcement for shear: ρ_v = 1.31 MPa/(0.85 × 400 MPa) = 0.0039.

Provide 20M@215 mm E.F. distributed horizontal reinforcement in all 710 mm thick walls with a hook at each in order to develop $1.25 f_y$ within the region of tied concentrated vertical reinforcement.

11.5.8.   Refined Estimates of Wall Deflections

Refined spectrum

Figure 11.18 presents the 2015 NBCC design spectral response values expressed in terms of displacement. The discrete acceleration values given in Table 11.15 at T = 0.2, 0.5, 1, 2, 5 and 10s were converted to displacement (mm) using the relationship S_d = 9.81 · S_a · $(T/2\pi)^2$ · 1000 = $250 S_a T^2$. NBCC states that intermediate values of design spectral acceleration (between the points defined by NBCC) shall be determined by linear interpolation. As the ratio of spectral displacement to spectral acceleration is proportional to T^2, the linear variation of acceleration between the defined points results in parabolic variations of displacement as shown Fig. 11.18. The large period range between defined points in the 2015 spectrum – between 2 and 5s and between 5 and 10s – results in unacceptably large 'bulges' in the spectral displacements. Note that if the period is reduced from 5s to 4.2s, the spectral displacement increases from 503 mm to 561 mm. The 2014 edition of CSA S6, which includes displacement-based design requirements, specifies that design spectral displacement values shall be determined using linear interpolation between the defined points at T = 0.2, 0.5, 1, 2, 5 and 10s. This displacement spectrum is also shown in Fig. 11.18. Note that using linear interpolation, the spectral displacement at T = 4.2s is 437 mm, rather than 561 mm, which means that the error due to the NBCC 'bulge' is 28% at that particular period.

In order to make realistic estimates of building displacements, a modified acceleration response spectrum was input into ETABS. The linear variation of spectral displacements shown in Fig. 11.18 were used to calculate the appropriate acceleration response spectrum using the inverse of the equation given above $S_a = S_d / (250 \cdot T^2)$.

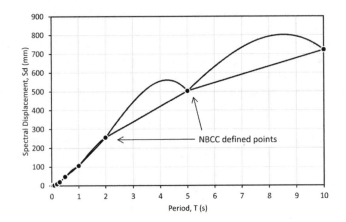

Fig. 11.18 Spectral displacements as defined by NBCC at specific points and the variation between these points.

Refined estimates of effective stiffness

The effective stiffness values used to model cracking of the walls ($I_e = 0.5I_g$ and $A_{xe} = 0.5A_g$) were based on the assumption of minimum wall overstrength $\gamma_w = 1.3$. The calculations above indicate the walls have much larger overstrengths; 4.63 in the cantilever wall direction and 3.44 in the coupled wall direction. Thus refined estimates of effective stiffness could be made in order to make more accurate estimates of the building deflections. Note however that lower estimates of effective stiffness result in larger (safe) estimates of building deflections, and therefore it is not necessary to make refined estimates of (higher) effective stiffness. The refined estimates of effective stiffness will not influence the design forces if the refined estimate of period remains larger than two times the empirical period defined in NBCC, which will generally be the case in tall shear wall buildings.

If the effective stiffness values are increased, the corresponding maximum elastic bending moments applied to the core will increase, and the corresponding overstrength values will reduce. Thus some iteration is required to determine the exact effective stiffness; however the effort involved is reduced by the fact the relationships involved are smooth functions (so long as the NBCC spectrum is modified as described above).

For any assumed value of effective stiffness, the factored bending moment on the core is given by $M_f = M_e I_E / R_d R_o$ where M_e is the maximum bending moment determined in the ETABS analysis without accidental torsion. The wall overstrength factor can then be calculated as described in Section 11.5.7.2, and Eq. 21.2 in Clause 21.2.5.2 can be used to determine the appropriate effective stiffness for the particular wall overstrength factor. If the calculated effective stiffness does not equal the assumed value, a new estimate can be made. Note that if the assumed effective stiffness is less than the calculated effective stiffness from Eq. 21.2 it will give safe estimates of displacements and therefore a more refined estimate is not necessary. For the current example, a number of iterations were used to determine the "exact" section properties, and the results are summarized below. It is not necessary to iterate to the exact solution. As long as the assumed effective stiffness is lower than the calculated effective stiffness based on the overstrength, the assumed effective stiffness will give safe estimates of displacement. The smaller the difference between assumed effective stiffness and calculated effective stiffness, the more accurate the estimate of effective stiffness.

Cantilever-wall direction

Using the revised section property $I_e = 0.85I_g$, the fundamental period $T_1 = 3.71s$ (previously 4.72s). Using the acceleration spectrum that gives a linear variation of spectral displacements between the NBCC defined points (Fig. 11.18), the maximum displacement of the walls at the roof level (with accidental torsion) were found to be Δ_e = 608 mm (W1), 594 mm (W2), 597 mm (W3). The spectral displacement S_d (at T = 3.7s) = 396 mm. Note that 608/396 = 1.5. Note that a simple relationship exists between the building displacements and the spectral displacement at the fundamental period because the first mode displacements generally control the maximum displacements.

Using the revised period, the design elastic base shear V_{ed} = elastic base shear V_e = 23 764 kN (previously 20 332 kN, line (c) in Table 11.16) and the design base shear, $V_d = V_{ed} I_E / R_d R_o$ = 4244 kN (previously 3631 kN, line (e) in Table 11.16). As 4244 kN is less than 0.8V = 5009 kN (line (j) in Table 11.16), the strength design requirements do not change. The revised wall overstrength factor γ_w = 3631/4244 × 4.63 = 3.9. The revised scaling factor for deflections = 3447/4244 ≤ 1.00 use 1.00 (previously 1.00). Thus the design displacements $\Delta_f R_d R_o$ = 608 mm (W1), 594 mm (W2), 597 mm (W3).

Coupled-wall direction

11

Using the revised section properties $I_e = 0.65I_g$ and $A_{xe} = 0.65A_g$, the revised fundamental period T = 5.52 s (previously 6.24 s). Using the acceleration spectrum that gives a linear variation of spectral displacements between the NBCC defined points (Fig. 11.18), the maximum displacement of the walls at the roof level (with accidental torsion) = Δ_e = 788 mm. Note that the spectral displacement S_d (at T = 5.5s) = 525 mm, and 788/525 = 1.5.

The design elastic base shear, V_{ed} = elastic base shear, V_e = 15 888 kN (previously 15 629 kN, line (c) in Table 11.16) and the design base shear, $V_d = V_{ed} I_E / R_d R_o$ = 2336 kN (previously 2298 kN, line (e) in Table 11.16). As 2336 kN is less than 0.8V = 3642 kN (line (j) in Table 11.16), the strength design requirements do not change. The revised wall overstrength factor γ_w = 2298/2336 × 3.44 = 3.4. The revised scaling factor for deflections = 2505/2336 = 1.072 (previously 1.090). Thus the design displacement of the walls at roof level = 1.072 × $\Delta_f R_d R_o$ = 1.072 × Δ_e = 845 mm.

The analysis also provided displacements at other points in the building, which are needed for the analysis of the gravity-load resisting frame; however the rotation of the wall at grade needs to be corrected to account for cracking of the below-grade structure in order to determine the total building displacements. This is discussed further in Section 11.5.10. The rigid body rotation of the wall affects the demands on the gravity-load resisting frame but does not influence the deformation demands of the walls themselves, which is discussed in the next section.

11.5.9. Wall Ductility

Cantilever-wall direction

Maximum displacement = $\Delta_f R_d R_o$ = 608 mm, γ_w = 3.9, $R_d R_o$ = 5.6, Δ_f = 608/5.6 = 108.6 mm.
$\theta_{id} = (\Delta_f R_d R_o - \Delta_f \gamma_w)/(h_w - l_w/2) = (608 - 108.6 \times 3.9)/(85\,100 - 8940/2) = 0.0023$.
As the actual inelastic rotational demand of the wall is less than 0.004, the inelastic rotational capacity must be greater than the minimum value 0.004.

The bending moment – curvature response of the three wall piers indicates that W1 has the minimum curvature capacity. This is consistent with that wall pier being subjected to a similar level of axial compression as the other three wall piers; but having a much smaller width of "flange" (1015 mm versus 1675 mm for W3 and 2590 mm for W2). Sectional analysis of the wall pier W1 subjected to an axial compression force of 23 686 kN and bending about the strong axis results in a compression strain depth c = 1758 mm. Thus the curvature capacity of the wall pier is $\phi_u = \varepsilon_{cu}/c$ = 0.0035/1758 mm = 1.99 × 10⁻⁶ rad/mm.

The inelastic rotational capacity can be determined from Eq. 21.12 (Clause 21.5.7.3)
$\theta_{ic} = (\varepsilon_{cu}/c - 0.004/l_w) \cdot l_w/2 = (1.99 \times 10^{-6}$ rad/mm $- 0.004/8940$ mm$) \times 8940$ mm$/2 = 0.0069$.
As 0.0069 > 0.0040, the wall has sufficient ductility.

Coupled-wall direction

$\Delta_f R_d R_o$ = 845 mm, $\theta_{id} = \Delta_f R_d R_o/h_w$ = 845/85 100 = 0.0099. From Fig. 11.17, W2 is the critical wall pier in the coupled-wall system due to the narrow width of the compression stress block when the lateral loads are acting to the left (W1 is in axial compression, W3 is in axial tension). A sectional analysis of W2 subjected to an axial compression force of 30 469 kN ($P_2 + V_{23} - V_{12}$ from Section 11.5.7.2) and using the factored material strengths results in c = 970 mm. Thus the curvature capacity of the wall pier (when the maximum compression strain reaches 0.0035) is equal to $\phi_u = \varepsilon_{cu}/c$ = 0.0035/970 mm = 3.61 × 10⁻⁶ rad/mm. The inelastic rotational capacity of the wall pier can be determined from Eq. 21.12 (Clause 21.5.7.3): $\theta_{ic} = (\varepsilon_{cu}/c - 0.004/l_w) \cdot l_w/2 = (3.61 \times 10^{-6}$ rad/mm $- 0.004/7720$ mm$) \times 7720$ mm$/2 = 0.0119$. As 0.0119 > 0.0099, the wall has sufficient ductility.

Coupling beams

$\theta_{id} = (\Delta_f R_d R_o/h_w) \cdot (l_{cg}/l_u) = 0.0099 \cdot (l_{cg}/l_u)$
W1 – W2: l_{cg}/l_u = 3708 mm/1320 mm = 2.809
W1 – W2: l_{cg}/l_u = 3284 mm/1120 mm = 2.932

Thus the maximum demands are in the coupling beams between W2 and W3 and the inelastic rotational demand is: θ_{id} = 0.0099 × 2.932 = 0.029. As this is less than 0.04 (the limit for coupling beams with diagonal reinforcement), the wall meets the ductility requirements.

11.5.10. Analysis of Structure Below Grade

In all of the building analyses presented above, the structure below grade was modelled using uncracked section properties. In reality, the structure will be subjected to forces larger than that causing cracking and thus the structure will soften. It is difficult to determine exactly what the appropriate effective stiffness values are. Thus Clause 21.5.2.2.9 requires that the factored shear force and corresponding factored bending moment applied to the shear wall below grade (below the plastic hinge) be determined using an analysis that considers the lower-bound or upper-bound value of effective stiffnesses of the members as appropriate to determine a safe estimate of the factored shear force. A simplified analysis considering only the structure below the plastic hinge was done. The results from the analysis in the cantilever-wall direction are presented below, while the results for the coupled wall direction are presented in Reference 2.

Four separate analyses were done and the effective stiffness assumptions used for these analyses are summarized in Table 11.21 Case 1 gives the design bending moments in the tower walls and the overturning moment that foundation must be designed for. Case 2A gives the maximum shear force in tower walls. It is identical to Case 2B, which gives the design forces in diaphragms and perimeter walls, except no horizontal force is applied in Case 2A, while the maximum base shear associated with the probable overturning capacity M_p is applied in Case 2B. Case 3 is used to make a best estimate of the rotation of the walls at grade (top of structure restraining foundation). Further information about how the effective stiffness values were determined is given in Reference 2.

Table 11.21 Summary of force and stiffness assumptions used in the four analysis cases for the structure below grade.

Cases:	1	2 A/B	3
Applied overturning moment	M_n	M_p	M_n
Applied horizontal force	$V@M_n$	$0 / V@M_p$	$V@M_n$
Flexural stiffness of core walls	$1.0E_c I_g$ [1]	[3]	[3]
Footing and supporting soil/rock below core walls	Rigid	[4]	[4]
Shear stiffness of core walls	$1.0G_c A_v$	$0.5G_c A_v$	$0.2G_c A_v$
Shear stiffness of diaphragms	$0.05G_c A_v$ [2]	$0.5G_c A_v$	$0.1G_c A_v$
Shear stiffness of perimeter walls	$0.1G_c A_v$	$0.5G_c A_v$	$0.2G_c A_v$
Flexural stiffnesses of diaphragms and perimeter walls	$0.2E_c I_g$	$0.5E_c I_g$	$0.2E_c I_g$

[1] Reduced to $0.8E_c I_g$ due to large bending moments in core walls
[2] Increased to $0.10G_c A_v$ due to large diaphragm shear forces requiring significant reinforcement
[3] Effective stiffness adjusted based on calculated bending moment
[4] Footing rotation included in analysis

Figure 11.19 summarizes the results of the analysis for Case 1. In the first analysis (Case 1(a)) using the effective stiffnesses given in Table 11.21, the bending moment in the wall increased below grade. Therefore the effective flexural rigidity of the tower wall was reduced to $0.8E_c I_g$ as the wall will be significantly cracked over the full height below grade. Also, Case 2A analysis (results presented later) indicated that significant shear forces will develop in the diaphragm requiring the diaphragm to be designed for significant shear force. Thus the lower-bound shear rigidity of the diaphragms (with good crack control reinforcement) was increased to $0.10G_c A_v$. The results of the revised analysis is labelled Case 1(b) in Fig. 11.19. This analysis demonstrated that the vertical reinforcement in the tower walls (increased 20% from the reinforcement shown in Fig. 11.15 as per Clause 21.5.2.2.4) must be essentially constant over the height of the wall below grade.

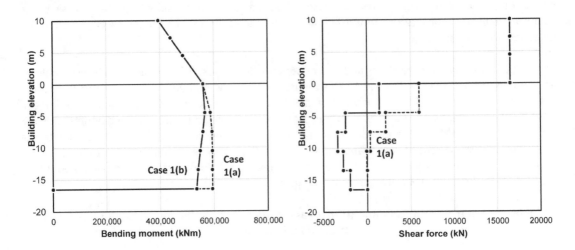

Fig. 11.19 Summary of results of Case 1 analysis used to determine bending moment demands on tower wall and foundation (left) and corresponding shear forces (right)

The analysis also indicates the foundation must be designed for an overturning moment of 535 000 kNm, which is slightly less than the nominal bending moment M_n = 560 085 kNm applied at grade level in Case 1. The foundation was designed for a vertical load due to gravity equal to 102 400 kN plus the self-weight of the footing. The details of the footing design are given in Reference 2. The final footing size is 16.0 m long (parallel to cantilever wall direction), 14.75 m wide (parallel to coupled-wall direction) and 2.6 m deep.

The bending moment – rotation relationship for the footing was developed using two methods – the procedure described in Clause 21.10.3.3.2, and a refined procedure described in the Explanatory Notes section N21.10.3.3.2. Figure 11.20 summarizes the bending moment – rotation relationships. The refined procedure indicates that up to a bending moment of about 350 000 kNm, the moment – rotation relationship is approximately linear, and the rotational stiffness of the footing is 587.1×10^6 kNm/rad. A linear rotational spring with this stiffness was included in the Case 2 and Case 3 analyses.

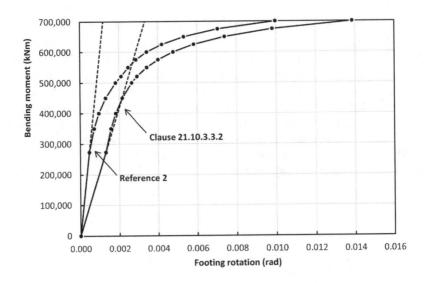

Fig. 11.20 Bending moment – rotation relationship for the footing

The flexural rigidity of the core walls has a significant influence on the amount of overturning moment that is transmitted to the footing versus transferred to the perimeter foundation walls by the floor diaphragms. Thus a refined analysis was done to determine the flexural rigidity of the core walls. The nonlinear bending moment – curvature relationship for the core walls was developed and the results are shown in Fig. 11.21. This relationship indicates the wall is essentially uncracked when the applied bending moment is less than 300 000 kNm. Thus a flexural rigidity of $1.0E_c I_g$ was used when the bending moment is less than 300 000 kNm. As the bending moment increases above 300 000 kNm, the flexural rigidity must be reduced. Table 11.22 summarizes the appropriate values for the flexural rigidity based on the bending moment curvature relationship shown in Fig. 11.21. The short dashed lines in Fig. 11.21 indicate the assumed response using the reduced flexural rigidities given in Table 11.22.

Table 11.22 Effective flexural rigidity of tower wall below grade based on moment – curvature relationship in Fig. 11.21

M (kNm)	$E_c I_e / E_c I_g$
> 500 000	0.3
> 400 000; ≤ 500 000	0.4
> 300 000; ≤ 400 000	0.7
≤ 300 000	1.0

Figure 11.22 summarizes the results from Case 2A and 2B. In this case the probable bending moment resistance M_p = 615 555 kNm was applied at grade level. Also, the shear rigidities of the core walls, diaphragms and perimeter walls and the flexural rigidities of the diaphragms and perimeter walls were increased to an upper-bound values as summarized in Table 11.21. Due to the reduction in flexural rigidity of the core walls, the additional flexibility provided by the footing spring and the increase in the stiffness of the base structure, the bending moment in the core walls now decreased to about 200 000 kNm at the footing. This confirms that the linear footing spring stiffness (valid up to 350 000 kNm) is appropriate.

11

Seismic Design

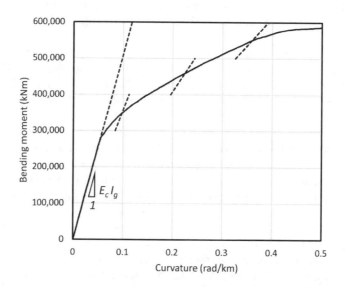

Fig. 11.21 Bending moment – curvature relationship for the combined three cantilever core walls below grade showing the equivalent linear stiffness to be used over different bending moment ranges.

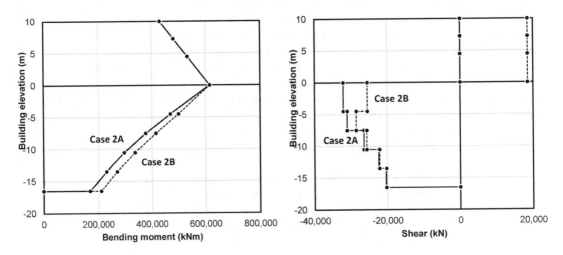

Fig. 11.22 Summary of results of Case 2A and 2B: total bending moment in core walls (left) and corresponding shear force (right).

The maximum shear force applied to the core walls is 32 142 kN determined from Case 2A. Note that this shear force is 74% larger than the maximum shear force associated with the probable bending resistance, which is 18 466 kN. Note also that it is not appropriate to limit the design shear force for the walls below grade to the limit on the base shear, i.e., shear force resulting from design load combinations that include earthquake with load effects calculated using $R_d R_o$ equal to 1.3 (15 640 kN), because the prying action of the diaphragms magnifies the base shear.

The shear force of 32 142 kN results in a shear stress = 32 142 × 1000 N / 8.76 × 10^6 mm^2 = 3.67 MPa. The shear stress ratio = $v/\phi_c f'_c$ = 3.67 MPa / (0.65 × 45 MPa) = 0.125, which is less than the limit for shear walls in the plastic hinge length (0.15). As additional vertical reinforcement is provided to prevent yielding of the vertical reinforcement below grade, it is appropriate to design the shear walls below grade using Clause 11, similar to what is done above the plastic hinge zone.

The maximum diaphragm forces result from Case 2B. The diaphragm at grade level (elevation 0) is subjected to a total horizontal load of 18 466 kN (shear in wall above grade) + 25 486 kN (reverse shear in wall below grade) = 43 952 kN. Thus the diaphragm must be designed for a shear force of 43 952 kN/ 2 = 21 976 kN. The most suitable provisions to design the diaphragm is Clause 21.6.3.3 for conventional construction squat shear walls.

Using 80% of the diaphragm dimension (45.7 m) as the shear depth, the shear stress in the 250 mm thick floor slab v = 21 976 × 1000 N / (250 mm × 0.8 × 45 700 mm) = 2.40 MPa. Assuming f'_c = 30 MPa in the floor slab, the shear stress ratio = $v/\phi_c f'_c$ = 2.40 MPa / (0.65 × 30 MPa) = 0.123. As this is less than the limit of 0.20 (Clause 21.6.3.3 a), the applied shear force does not exceed the maximum shear resistance.

As it is desirable to provide equal distributed reinforcement in the two directions of the diaphragm, choose θ = 45 deg. to determine the required amount of reinforcement. Thus $\rho = v/\phi_s f_y$ = 2.40 MPa/340 MPa = 0.00706. Provide 15M @ 225 mm at the top and bottom of the slab and in both directions. Note that the reinforcement required in the slab to resist the bending moments due to the slab self-weight and the superimposed loads (1.0D + 0.5L) must be added to the reinforcement required to resist in-plane shear due to 1.0E.

Case 3 analysis was done to determine the rotation of the core walls at grade level. From the equal and opposite vertical displacements of the two ends of the shear wall, the rotation of the walls at grade level was determined to be 0.00505 when the base structure was subject to a bending moment equal to the nominal flexural resistance of the core in the cantilever-wall direction.

A similar analysis as summarized above must be done for the building in the coupled-wall direction. This is presented in Reference 2.

11.5.11. Members Not Considered Part of the SFRS

11.5.11.1. Definition of gravity-load frames

Fig. 11.23 shows a plan view of the building at a typical floor level above grade. In each of the two directions of the building (cantilever-wall direction and coupled-wall direction), there are six different gravity-load frames. Fig. 11.23 identifies the six frames in the cantilever-wall direction.

Assuming that the architecture of the building is simple and that the plan is doubly symmetric, the number of gravity-load frames that must be analyzed is greatly reduced. Assuming further that there are only two types of columns, the corner columns C1, C4, C9 and C12, and all the other columns, the problem simplifies to only two different gravity-load frames that need to be analyzed in the cantilever-wall direction of the building. Gravity-load frame GF1 is made up of four columns C1, C2, C3 and C4 interconnected by the floor slab, while gravity-load frame GF2 is made up of one column C5 attached to cantilever wall W1 by the slab. Gravity-load frame GF6 is identical to GF1, while GF3, GF4, and GF5 are identical to GF2.

11

Seismic Design

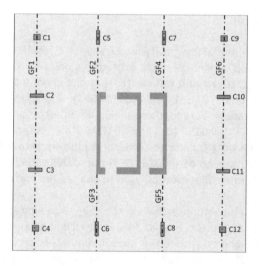

Fig. 11.23 Typical floor plan above grade showing the different gravity-load frames (GF) in the cantilever-wall direction.

11.5.11.2. Deformation demands on gravity-load resisting frame

The displacement of the gravity-load frames are needed at the roof level in order to utilize the simplified procedure for shear walls given in Clause 21.11.2.2. The roof displacement for gravity-load frame GF2 is identical to the roof displacement of wall pier W1. As described in Section 11.5.8, the maximum design displacements of the walls at the roof level (with different levels of accidental torsion) were found to be $\Delta_f R_d R_o$ = 608 mm (W1), 594 mm (W2), 597 mm (W3). These displacements were calculated using the refined section property $I_e = 0.85I_g$, and the refined acceleration spectrum with linear variation of spectral displacements between the NBCC defined points (see Fig. 11.18). Note that GF2 was selected for analysis over GF4 because wall W1 has a larger roof displacement than wall W3.

The results from the same ETABS analysis (with refined stiffness and refined spectrum) were also used to determine the maximum displacements along the different gravity-load frames. Comparing the maximum roof displacements along gravity-load frames GF1 and GF6, the maximum roof displacement occurs at GF1 when the building is subjected to accidental torsion. The roof displacement is equal to 675 mm.

In all of the ETABS analysis described above, the structure below grade was included in the model; but the section properties that were used are the uncracked section properties and the soil below the foundation was assumed to be rigid. In these analyses, the maximum rotation of the cantilever core walls at grade level varied from 0.0020 to 0.0021 for the three different walls and for the different load cases (different levels of accidental torsion).

Section 11.5.10 presents the results of an analysis (Case 3) that was done to determine the rotation of the core walls at grade level accounting for cracking of the structure below grade and deformation of the soil below the foundation. The rotation of the shear walls at grade was determined to be 0.00505 when the base structure was subject to a bending moment equal to the nominal flexural resistance of the core in the cantilever-wall direction. Thus an additional interstorey drift ratio equal to 0.00505 − 0.0020 = 0.00305 must be added to the envelope of interstorey drifts over the building height (from Fig. 21.1 in CSA A23.3) determined from the results of the ETABS analysis in which the structure below grade was modelled as an uncracked structure and the flexibility of the footing was ignored. This additional interstorey drift ratio accounts for the increased displacements due to foundation movements as required by Clause 21.11.2.1 (d).

The roof displacement of 675 mm along gravity-load frame GF1 results in a global drift ratio Δ/h_w = 675 mm/85,100 mm = 0.00793, while the global drift ratio along GF2 is 0.00714. As per Fig. 21.1 in CSA A23.3, the maximum interstorey drift ratio at the top of a shear wall building (in the cantilever-wall direction) is 1.6 × Δ/h_w = 0.0127 (GF1) and 0.0114 (GF2). Adding the additional interstorey drift ratio due to the increased rotation at grade, these maximum interstorey drift ratios over the top 25% of the building height increase to 0.0157 (GF1) and 0.0145 (GF2). At grade level of the building, the gravity-load frame must be designed for an interstorey drift ratio equal to 0.7 × Δ/h_w plus the additional rotation (0.00305). These turn out to be 0.0086 (GF1) and 0.0081 (GF2). Fig. 11.24 summarizes the envelopes of interstorey drift ratios that must be used to analyze the two gravity-load frames.

NBCC requires that the largest interstorey drift ratio at any level be limited to 0.025. The results of the ETABS analysis in which the structure below grade was modelled as an uncracked structure and the flexibility of the footing was ignored resulted in a maximum interstorey drift ratio (when accidental torsion was included) of 0.0091. Accounting for the increased displacements of the structure resulting from foundation movement (as required by 2015 NBCC Clause 4.1.8.16.1) and cracking of the structure below grade, and accounting for the increased drift ratios due to the inelastic rotation of shear walls (as required by 2014 CSA Clause 21.11.2.1), the maximum interstorey drift ratio increases to 0.0157. For the current building with five levels below grade, this is a 73% increase in the maximum interstorey drift ratio. For the current building, about half the increase comes from accounting for the nonlinear variation of interstorey drifts due to the formation of a plastic hinge in the shear walls at grade, and the other half comes from the flexibility of the below-grade structure and foundation. For other buildings, particularly buildings with fewer levels below grade, the increase in maximum interstorey drift levels may be significantly more. As 0.016 is less than 0.025, the building meets the NBCC drift limit.

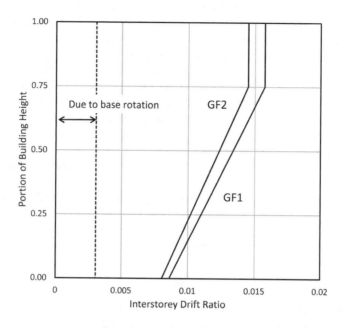

Fig. 11.24 Summary of interstorey drift ratios that the two gravity-load frames GF1 and GF2 must be designed for over the height of the building.

11.5.11.3. Design of slabs for deformation demands

The slab-column connections must be designed for the seismic drift demands in accordance with Clause 21.11.4. The reduction factor R_E on the punching shear resistance of slabs must be calculated in the gravity-load frames GF1 and GF2 using the interstorey drift ratios given in Fig. 11.24. Over the top 25% of the building height, the interstorey drift ratio in GF1 is 0.0157. Thus the reduction factor R_E = $(0.005/0.0157)^{0.85}$ = 0.378 in that portion of the building. At the first floor above grade level of the building, the interstorey drift ratio is 0.0086 and the reduction factor R_E = $(0.005/0.0086)^{0.85}$ = 0.631. The interstorey drift ratio varies linearly over the height of the building; but the reduction factor various nonlinearly. Assuming a linear variation of R_E between grade level and 75% of the building height is unsafe (the actual reduction factor is smaller). Example calculations of applying the reduction factor to the shear resistance of slabs is given in Reference 1.

11.5.11.4. Design of columns for deformation demands

Two separate checks must be made on the deformation demands on gravity-load columns. Over the height of the plastic hinge region in the shear walls, the maximum column (or bearing wall) dimension or the axial compression applied to the column (or bearing wall), must be limited so that the compression strain depth is less than the limit given in Clause 21.11.3.3.2: $c \le 0.0035/(2\theta_{id} + 0.004)~l_w$. In the cantilever-wall direction, $\theta_{id} = 0.0023$ (see Section 11.5.9), therefore the minimum value of $\theta_{id} = 0.004$ must be used (Clause 21.5.7). The length of the wall l_w = 8940 mm. Thus the compression strain depth c must be less than $0.0035/0.012 \times 8940$ mm = 2600 mm. Due to the low inelastic rotation demands in the wall, this large limit on the compression strain depth will not influence the axial load capacity of any gravity-load columns in this particular building based on the preliminary sizes of the columns (the limit on c is much larger than the maximum dimensions of the columns). If it is proposed to transition the columns into long, narrow columns ("wallumns"), this limit will start to restrict the axial compression that can be resisted by these members. Some example calculations and further information is given in Reference 2.

The second type of analysis that must be done is to determine the drift that is induced into the gravity-load columns, i.e., the column drift, due to the building interstorey drift. In this case, the primary issue is the relative flexibility of the floor system and the columns. When a floor system is very flexible relative to the column, the column drift will be very small even if the building drift is large. This can be seen at the right-hand side of Fig. N21.11.2.2(b) in the explanatory notes. On the other hand, when the floor system is very stiff, for example when there is a large transfer girder framing into the shear walls, the column drift may be up to 50% larger than the building interstorey drift. This can be seen at the left-hand side of Fig. N21.11.2.2(b). The columns supporting the transfer girder will normally not be able to tolerate this very large column drift demand, and a solution will need to be found to reduce the stiffness of the floor system. One solution that can be used is to provide a flexural hinge between the transfer girder and the shear wall. Some example calculations and further information is given in Reference 2.

For the current building, which has flexible floor systems (flat plate slabs) and where the column cross-sections are relatively square, the Clause 21.11 requirements for gravity-load columns does not influence the design of columns. The Clause 21.11 requirements become significant when transfer girders are included in the floor system or when bearing walls or elongated columns ("wallumns") are used.

11.6   References

(1) Mitchell, D. and Paultre, P., "Chapter 11 – Seismic Design", Concrete Design Handbook, Third Edition, Cement Association of Canada, Ottawa, 2006, pp. 11-1 – 11-60.

(2) Adebar, P., "Design and Evaluation of Concrete Shear Wall Buildings in Canada," https://www.civil.ubc.ca/adebar/concrete-wall-buildings

(3) Benz, E.C., Response-2000 Computer Program, http://www.ecf.utoronto.ca/~bentz/r2k.htm

12

By Richard J. McGrath

Anchorage

12

Anchorage

12.1   Introduction

CSA A23.3-14[12-1] Annex "D" is included as an "informatory", (non-mandatory) part of the A23.3 Standard, and provides design requirements for anchorage to concrete. Anchorage design requirements were first introduced in the 1984 A23.3 Standard as Appendix "H", and were later carried forward unchanged as Appendix "D" in the 1994 edition. Those anchorage requirements were based on the 45° cone model which was developed in the mid 1970's and documented by researchers such as Cannon, Godfrey, and Moreadith[12-2]. The requirements were only applicable for cast-in-place headed anchors.

Following the development of the 45° cone model, a comprehensive series of anchorage tests were performed at the University of Stuttgart in the 1980's. A variety of anchor types were tested with various embedment depths, edge distances, and group configurations in both cracked and uncracked concrete. The Kappa (K) method[12-3, 12-4] that emerged from the work at Stuttgart, was further refined in the 1990's at the University of Texas in Austin. The design procedures resulting from the work in Texas comprise what is now known as the Concrete Capacity Design (CCD) method[12-5, 12-6]. The CCD method for anchorage design was first introduced in Annex D of the 2004 edition of the CSA A23.3 Standard.

The 2014 anchorage specifications are again contained in a non-mandatory Annex "D" of the A23.3 Standard. These requirements are similar to those found in the ACI 318-14 Code[12-7] with the exception that they have been adapted for use with the Limit States Design provisions of the CSA A23.3-14 Standard and the load factors required by the 2015 National Building Code of Canada (NBCC) [12-8]. The resistance levels provided by CSA A23.3 Annex "D" have been calibrated to support the same service load levels as provided by the ACI 318-14 Code. New anchorage specifications in the 2014 edition include:

1)   New provisions for seismic loading of anchors

2)   The inclusion of adhesive anchors

3)   Provisions for anchor reinforcement for tension loads

4)   New lightweight concrete factor λ_a

5)   New requirements for anchor installation and inspection

A number of design aids are provided at the end of this chapter. Additional related anchor design aids, previously contained at the end of Chapter 12, are now available as a free download from the CAC website at www.cement.ca.

12.2   General Principles

When designing anchors, consideration must be given to the capacity of both the steel anchor and the embedded portion of the anchor.

The Concrete Capacity Design (CCD) method for the design of anchors considers fracture mechanics (size effect) in utilizing a 35° projected failure surface for the embedded portion of the anchor. This results in expressions with the embedment depth raised to the power of 1.5, *($h_{ef}^{1.5}$) as opposed to the earlier 45° method which used h_{ef}^2*. In the CCD method, the capacity expressions have been calibrated to the extensive database of experimental tests that have been conducted over the last 30 years. The equation coefficients have been selected to predict the 5% fractile failure level from these tests. This implies, with a 90% confidence level, that 95 times out of 100 the actual strength of the anchor will exceed the nominal strength. Addressing a greater variety of anchor types, and design conditions, the CCD method provides a more consistent level of safety for a wider variety of anchorage failure modes in both cracked and uncracked concrete and represents a significant advancement in anchorage design.

12.3 Design Provisions

12.3.1. General Requirements

Section D.4 of Annex "D" refers the designer to Clause 8 of the Standard for the applicable load factors and load combinations to be use in the design of anchors.

12.3.2. Plastic vs Elastic Analysis

The analysis method used to distribute forces to individual anchors in a group anchor arrangement will depend on a number of variables, including the rigidity of the attached base plate, the embedment of the anchors and the nature of the loading.

Sufficiently stiff base plates may be capable of distributing a concentric tension load equally to all anchors in a group, simplifying the design. A more flexible base plate on the other hand may yield, allowing prying action to take place in some of the anchors in the group and thus necessitating a more detailed analysis of the resulting forces on individual anchors in the group.[12-9, 12-10]

Unless sufficient ductility is provided by the anchors to allow for a redistribution of the forces to the individual anchors in a group, an elastic analysis approach should be used. Where sufficient ductility exists, a plastic design approach may be more appropriate. The plastic approach will assume that the resulting tension force is equally distributed to all tension anchors in the group. The plastic design approach requires that the anchors be provided with sufficient embedment to preclude a brittle concrete breakout failure prior to a ductile steel failure. For group anchors resisting moment, the plastic analysis is similar to the case of multiple layers of reinforcement in a concrete beam. Anchors at a sufficient distance from the neutral axis are considered to have yielded. In group anchors where concrete breakout is the critical failure mode, little if any redistribution of forces will take place between individual anchors and an elastic analysis approach is required.

The exact location of the compressive resultant in a group anchor subjected to moment cannot currently be established regardless of the analysis method used. Since plane sections do not remain plane, traditional beam theory will not provide a definitive solution to this problem. At present, this aspect of the anchorage design is an evolving science, and the following conservative approach to this problem as illustrated in Figure 12.1 is suggested. To conservatively estimate the load on the anchors, locate the compressive resultant at the leading edge of the compression element of the attached member. This will ensure that the minimum lever arm is assumed in the moment of resistance provided by the anchor group. To conservatively design the base plate stiffness, take the compression resultant as acting at the leading edge of the base plate. A more detailed discussion on this topic can be found in references 12.9 and 12.10.

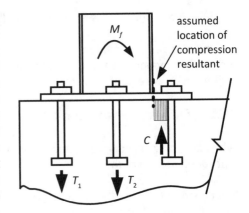

Figure 12.1 Location of compression resultant

12.3.3. Seismic Design Considerations

Design provisions for anchors resisting seismic loads are contained in Clause D.4.3 and have been revised in the 2014 Standard. All post installed anchors used to resist seismic loads must be qualified in accordance with ACI 355.2 or ACI 355.4 as applicable. Annex "D" prohibits the location of anchors in plastic hinge zones of concrete structures as the degree of cracking in these regions is expected to exceed the conditions on which the anchor specifications are based.

The seismic design provisions for anchors are required when the following two criteria are met.

1) The load combinations include seismic effects under the condition $I_E F_a S_a(0.2) \geq 0.35$, and

2) *When the tensile or shear seismic load component is greater than 20% of the total factored load resulting from the load combination that includes seismic loads.*

12.3.3.1. Seismic Tension Loads

Clause D.4.3.5.3 provides design requirements when seismically induced tension loads meet the criteria noted above. In such cases four design options are presented and are briefly outlined below. Note that in each case, the requirements of Clause D.4.3.5.4 must be met.

1) Restrict failure to the ductile steel component of the anchor by providing a nominal concrete breakout capacity greater than the probable capacity of the steel anchor[12-22] which is taken as 1.2 times the nominal strength of the anchor. In addition, the factored concrete based tensile resistance, calculated in accordance with D.4.3.5.4, must exceed the factored tensile resistance of the anchor, N_{sar}.

2) Provide a breakout capacity, in accordance with D.4.3.5.4, greater than the maximum tension force produced by yielding of the attachment or,

3) Provide a breakout capacity, in accordance with D.4.3.5.4, greater than the maximum tension force produced by a non-yielding attachment or,

4) Provide a breakout capacity, in accordance with D.4.3.5.4, equal to the maximum tension load produced by the attachment when seismic loads are calculated using $R_d R_0 = 1.3$ in accordance with the 2015 NBCC.

12.3.3.2. Seismic Shear Loads

Options 2 to 4 noted above for tension loads are provided as well for the design of seismic shear loads in Clause D.4.3.6. Option 1 is not permitted for seismic shear loads as a satisfactory level of ductility cannot be achieved in the shear failure of a steel anchor component. The concrete breakout capacity reduction factors contained in Clause D.4.3.5.4 are not applicable to seismic shear loading. In the case of near edge anchor applications the use of "anchor reinforcement" in accordance with Clause D.7.2.9 may be required to provide the necessary shear capacity.

12.3.4. Concrete Density and Strength

All concrete capacity expressions contained in Annex "D" assume normal density concrete. As specified in D.4.4 when low-density concrete is used all values of $\sqrt{f_c'}$ should be multiplied by λ_a as defined in Clause D.4.6 of CSA A23.3-14. For calculation purposes, the value of f_c' is limited to 70 MPa for cast-in anchors and 55 MPa for post-installed anchors. These limits represent the scope of the database of

12

Anchorage

tests on which the CCD method is based. Designers are required to verify by tests the capacity of post-installed anchors in concrete stronger than 55 MPa.

12.4   General Requirements for Resistance of Structural Anchors

The resistance of an anchor is determined on the basis of seven possible failure modes as described in D.5.1.1 and Table D.1.

Tension capacity is taken as the lesser of:

$N_r \leq$ Steel strength of anchor in tension N_{sar}, or

Concrete breakout resistance in tension N_{cbr}, or

Pullout resistance of anchor in tension N_{pr}, or

Concrete side face blowout resistance in tension N_{sbr}

Shear capacity is taken as the lesser of:

$V_r \leq$ Steel strength of anchor in shear V_{sar}, or

Concrete breakout resistance of anchor in shear V_{cbr}, or

Concrete pryout resistance of anchor in shear N_{cpr}

The critical values of N_r and V_r determined from the failure modes listed above are then taken as the factored resistance of the anchor in tension and shear.

In all instances the factored resistance is required to equal or exceed the factored load effect:

$N_r \geq N_f$

$V_r \geq V_f$

Where seismic loads are included, Clause D.4.3, requires that the factored resistance values listed above for concrete be reduced by an additional 25%. See section 12.3.3. Clause D.5.1.3 of the A23.3 Standard provides additional capacity reductions for adhesive anchors subjected to sustained tension loads. See section 12.5.7.2.

Clause D.5.2.1 of Annex "D" provides the designer with the option of using alternative design procedures provided they result in predicted capacities in agreement with the results of tests. The nominal resistance must be based on the 5% fractile of the basic individual anchor resistance.

The provisions of Annex "D" are based on tests conducted on anchors ≤ 100 mm in diameter.

The force modification factor "R" defined in clause D.5.3 is applied to the tension and shear capacity expressions in Annex "D" to ensure proper calibration of the Limit States Design (LSD) resistance levels in A23.3-14 with the ultimate strength design (USD) provisions of the ACI 318-14 Code.

In Clause D.5.3(c) R factors are listed for concrete related shear and tension failures associated with two conditions, A and B. Condition A applies where supplemental reinforcement[12.11, 12.12] is provided to restrain the concrete failure prism. Further information on supplemental reinforcement is given if Sections 5.5 for restraint of tension breakout sections and Section 6.3 for shear breakout sections. Condition "B" applies where such reinforcement is not present.

Condition "A" should not be assumed in cases of pullout or pryout failure as the effective anchorage of the breakout section is not considered possible in these cases. Likewise in the case of post-installed anchors it would be difficult to ensure that the required reinforcement was located so as to effectively restrain the breakout section. As a result Condition "B" should always be assumed for post-installed anchors. Reference 12-13 provides a more detailed discussion on the detailing of supplemental reinforcement to prevent breakout failure.

Tables 12.5 and 12.6 provide anchor tension and shear capacities for a variety of anchor sizes, embedment depths and concrete strengths. Condition "B" is assumed for all concrete breakout capacity calculations. The anchor bolt data used to generate Tables 12.5 and 12.6 is given in Table 12.4. The $A_{se,N}$ values used in Table 12.5 are calculated values based on the assumptions listed in Section 12.5.1. Tension and shear capacity tables for 20 MPa concrete and a limited number of anchor diameters are included at the end of this chapter. A complete set of these anchor tension and shear tables covering additional anchor diameters and concrete strengths can be downloaded from the CAC website at www. cement.ca

12.5 Design Requirements for Tensile Loading

12.5.1. Steel Anchor Tensile Resistance

The capacity of the steel anchor is determined using the effective cross sectional area of the anchor and the specified tensile strength of the steel f_{uta}. Typical embedment steels exhibit significant variation in actual yield strength above specified minimums, and have widely differing ratios of yield to tensile strength. Therefore in keeping with the LSD approach of the A23.3-14 Standard, $\phi_s f_{uta}$ rather than $\phi_s f_{ya}$ is used. Clause D.6.1.2 limits f_{uta} of the steel anchor to $1.9 f_{ya}$ to ensure that the anchor does not yield under service loads. This limit is derived by dividing the average load factor using a live to dead load ratio of 1.0, by the product of the steel material resistance factor f_s and the largest R value applicable to ductile steel anchors in tension. The R values listed in Clause D.5.3 are rounded down from the exact calibrated values. The upper limit on f_{uta} of 860 MPa represents the scope of the tests used in developing the requirements of the CCD method. This limit will probably be approached only with stainless steel anchors.

The term $A_{se,N}$ in Clause D.6.1.2 is to be taken as the net tensile area of a steel anchor. If welded steel studs are used, $A_{se,N}$ would be the gross area A_g of the stud, Where threaded rods are used, $A_{se,N}$ would be taken as the net tensile area in the threaded region of the anchor. In lieu of more detailed calculations the following expressions can be used to calculate the net area of threaded bolts for tension only.

$$A_{se} = \frac{\pi}{4}(d - 0.938P)^2 \quad \text{for metric rods, where } P = \text{the pitch of the thread, or}$$

$$A_{se} = \frac{\pi}{4}\left(d - \frac{0.974}{n}\right)^2 \quad \text{for imperial rods, where } n = \text{the number of threads per inch.}$$

In Canada, anchor rod material for most applications is produced to CSA G40.21 Grade 300 W (f_y = 300 MPa) or ASTM A36 with f_y = 248 MPa. However, the ASTM A36 round stock is more readily available. Anchor rods may be threaded at one or both ends to receive a washer and nut, or may be bent at the other end to form a hook. For applications where high strength rods are required typically ASTM A193 B7 rods are used. For applications where rods are required to have corrosion protection AISI 304 or 316 stainless steels meeting the requirements of ASTM F593 are typically used. The term "anchor rod" is used to differentiate it from the ASTM A325 and A490 bolt material specifications. The term "standard anchor bolt" when used in this Chapter means a bolt with dimensions conforming to those for Square and Hex Headed Bolts listed in ASME Standard B18.2.1-2012 or ASTM A307 Bolts. Table 12.1 in Section 12 presents a list of ASTM steel types for cast-in-place headed anchor bolts. ASTM bolt and nut dimensions (in inches) are listed in Table 12.2 in Section 12. Table 12.3 lists the bearing area A_{brg} for ASTM square and hexagonal nuts. More detailed information on anchor bolts and anchor rods can be found in the details of the applicable ASME or ASTM standards

12.5.2. Concrete Breakout for Tensile Resistance

The concrete breakout cone depicted in Figure D.4(c) and D.6(a) of Annex "D" is assumed in the derivation of equations (D-3) and (D-4) for single and group anchors as shown below.

$$N_{cbr} = \frac{A_{Nc}}{A_{Nco}} \Psi_{ed,N}\, \Psi_{c,N}\, \Psi_{cp,N}\, N_{br} \tag{D-3}$$

$$N_{cbgr} = \frac{A_{Nc}}{A_{Nco}} \Psi_{ec,N}\, \Psi_{ed,N}\, \Psi_{c,N}\, \Psi_{cp,N}\, N_{br} \tag{D-4}$$

The individual terms are reviewed below. N_{cbr} capacity values are listed in Table 12.5.

N_{br} is the factored concrete breakout resistance of a single anchor in tension in cracked concrete unaffected by free edges or overlapping stress cones, and is derived as follows:

$$N_{br} = k_1\sqrt{f_c'} \cdot k_2 h_{ef}^{\;2} \cdot k_3 h_{ef}^{\;-0.5}$$

where k_1, k_2, k_3 are calibration factors. The product of these calibration factors is the resulting k_c coefficient that appears in the concrete breakout capacity expressions in Annex "D".

$$k_c = k_1\, k_2\, k_3$$

The $h_{ef}^{1.5}$ term accounts for a size effect. The consideration of fracture mechanics accounts for the higher tensile stresses that exist at the embedded head of the anchor as illustrated in Figure 12.2 below.

The resulting nominal capacity expression for N_{br} is given by:

$$N_{br} = k_c\sqrt{f_c'}\, h_{ef}^{1.5}$$

In Annex "D" the LSD concrete material resistance factor ϕ_c is applied along with the resistance modification factor "R" to yield the expression:

$$N_{br} = k\phi_c\lambda_a\sqrt{f_c'}\, h_{ef}^{\;1.5}R \tag{D.6.2.2}$$

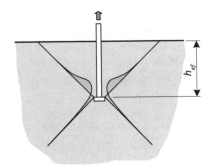

The constant k_c is calibrated to the 5% fractile of test results on headed anchors in concrete with crack widths up to 0.3 mm. Where crack widths are expected to exceed this value, crack control reinforcement should be provided to ensure this limit is not exceeded. The term λ_a is now contained directly in the tension capacity equations in the 2014 edition and is given in Clause D.4.6. The term λ_a presents additional lightweight concrete strength reductions for certain anchor types and for the bond resistance of adhesive anchors.

Figure 12.2 Stress distribution around an anchort

When calculating the concrete breakout capacity, Clause D.6.2.8 allows the designer to modify the effective depth of embedment through the use of a washer or plate at the head of the anchor. The failure surface is then calculated as projecting outward from the effective perimeter of the plate or washer, providing the modified effective depth h_{ef} as illustrated in Figure 12.3.

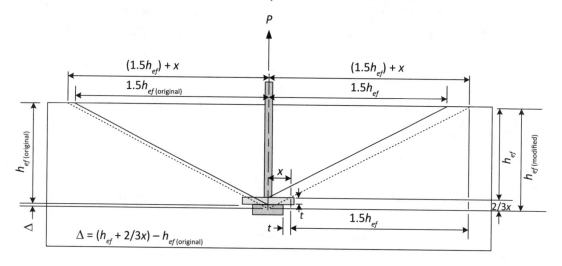

Figure 12.3 Increasing h_{ef} using a washer or plate

The term A_{Nc}/A_{Nco} accounts for the presence of adjacent anchors and or free edges. A_{Nco} is the projected area of a 35° failure plane of a single anchor measured relative to the surface of the concrete as depicted in Annex "D" Figure D.6. A_{Nc} is a similarly projected area limited by edges and adjacent anchors. For single anchors located distant from free edges the A_{Nc}/A_{Nco} term equals 1.0.

Clause D.6.2.3 requires that the designer use a modified h_{ef} value in calculating the breakout capacity when three or more edges are within $1.5h_{ef}$ of the anchor. This determination of this modified effective embedment depth h_{ef}' is illustrated in Figure D.8 of Annex D.

The term ψ_{ec} is used to reflect the reduced capacity of group anchors loaded eccentrically and is calculated using equation D-8 as shown below:

$$\psi_{ec,N} = \frac{1}{\left(1 + \dfrac{2e'_N}{3h_{ef}}\right)} \quad \text{where } e'_N \le \frac{s}{2} \tag{D-8}$$

The expression for $\psi_{ec,N}$ is based on the punching shear analysis of eccentrically loaded flat slabs[12-14]. These tests indicate that the chosen expression represents a conservative estimate of the effects of eccentricity on anchor groups. Figure D.9 in Annex "D" illustrates the determination of e_N' used in the calculation of $\psi_{ec,N}$ above. The dimension e_N' is measured from the point of load application to the centre of gravity of the anchors resisting the tensile force. When an anchor group is loaded in such a way that only some of the anchors are in tension, only those anchors in tension are used in determining e_N'. The dimension "s" is used here to define the limit of application of equation D-9, can be taken as the center to center spacing of the outermost anchors in tension as illustrated in Figure 12.4.

12

Anchorage

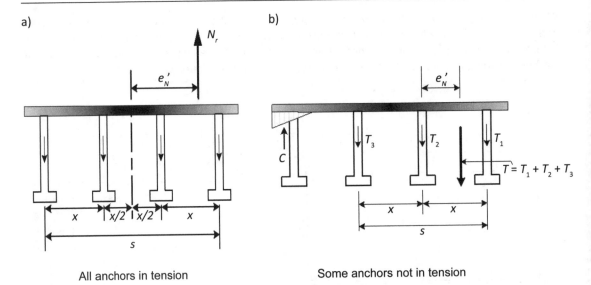

Figure 12.4 Determination of e_N'

The term $\psi_{ed,N}$ is a modification factor for edge effects. Free edges influence the capacity of cast in place headed anchors where the edge distance is $< 1.5h_{ef}$. This dimension can be greater for post-installed anchors. The presence of a free edge distorts the distribution of concrete stresses around an anchor similar to the presence of cracks in the concrete, reducing the capacity of the embedment. In such cases $\psi_{ed,N}$ is used to capture this effect by further reducing the calculated capacity of the embedment beyond that provided by A_{Nc}/A_{Nco} ; $\psi_{ed,N}$ is given by equations D-10 and D-11 in Annex "D" as shown below:

$$\psi_{ed,N} = 1.0 \qquad\qquad \text{if } c_{a,min} \geq 1.5h_{ef}$$

$$\psi_{ed,N} = 0.7 + 0.3\frac{c_{a,min}}{1.5h_{ef}} \qquad \text{if } c_{a,min} < 1.5h_{ef}$$

(D.6.2.5)

The distortion in the anchor stress distribution due to edge effects is similar to that caused by the presence of cracks at an anchor location. Tests indicate that the concrete breakout loads in cracked concrete is approximately 70% of the values obtained in uncracked concrete. As a result, a lower limit of $\psi_{ed,N} = 0.7$ has been established for the limiting case of edge distance $c_{a1} = 0.0$, where the maximum disruption of the symmetric stress distribution occurs[12-14].

$\psi_{c,N}$ accounts for the influence of cracks on the anchor capacity. When cracks are present $\psi_{c,N}$ is taken as 1.0 for both cast-in headed anchors and post installed anchors. All post-installed anchors used in cracked concrete must be qualified by ACI 355.2 for use in cracked concrete. Where cracking is not present a 25% increase is applied to cast-in headed anchor capacities and a 40% premium is applied to post-installed anchor designs.

$\psi_{cp,N}$ is an additional factor applicable to post-installed anchors used in uncracked concrete without supplemental reinforcement to control cracking. Clause D.6 assumes that anchors will develop their basic breakout strength if the shortest edge distance is at least $1.5h_{ef}$. While this is true for cast-in headed anchors, it is not necessarily true for post-installed anchors. Expansion or torque controlled post-installed anchors, and some undercut anchors, impose tensile stresses on the surrounding concrete during installation. These stresses are additive to the tensile stresses that are imposed on the concrete when the anchor is loaded. The result is that the required minimum edge distance required to achieve the basic breakout section may well exceed $1.5h_{ef}$. In such cases Annex "D" provides the additional reduction factor $\psi_{cp,N}$ which in turn is dependent on the critical edge distance c_{ac}, for that particular type of anchor being used. $\psi_{cp,N}$ is calculated as follows:

$$\psi_{cp,N} = 1.0 \qquad \text{if } c_{a,min} \geq c_{ac}$$

$$= \frac{c_{a,min}}{c_{ac}} \geq \frac{1.5h_{ef}}{c_{ac}} \qquad \text{if } c_{a,min} < c_{ac} \tag{D.6.2.7}$$

In calculating $\psi_{cp,N}$ the critical edge distance c_{ac} is obtained from Clause D.9.7 or alternatively from tests in accordance with ACI 355.2/355.2R.

12.5.3. Pullout

The pullout provisions of Annex "D" apply to cast-in headed and hooked bolts only.[12-5, 12-6] Equations D-15 to D-17 are used to determine cast-in anchor pullout capacity. The effective bearing area "A_{brg}" of a bolt head is the gross area of the bolt head minus the area of the anchor shaft. Pullout capacity can be increased by using washers or plates to increase the bearing area A_{brg}. When this is done the perimeter limits defined in Clause D.6.2.8 should be observed. Equation D-16 predicts the onset of local crushing at the anchor head and not the actual pullout of the anchor[12-5]. Pullout tests using very lightweight concrete with weak aggregates have demonstrated a significantly reduced pullout capacity as a result of local crushing at the bearing surface of the anchor head. This reduction in strength may not be adequately captured by the application of the lightweight concrete factor λ_a to the design expression.

Hooked bolts will fail through bearing at the inside of the hook[12-9]. The minimum hook length e_h for L and J bolts is measured from the inner surface of the anchor shaft to the outside tip of the L or J bolt as illustrated in Figure 12.5.

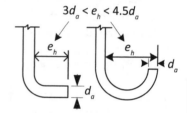

Figure 12.5 Dimension e_h for L and J bolts

Through the use of the $\psi_{c,P}$ factor in Equation D-15, Annex "D" allows a 40% increase in the pullout capacity of a cast-in anchor in uncracked concrete over that provided in cracked concrete. The Resistance Modification Factor "R" in equations D-16 and D-17 will always be 1.0 as the application of Condition "A" to the pullout failure mode is not permitted by Annex "D".

The additional variables associated with post-installed anchors make it impossible to predict the pullout capacity of these anchors with a general expression. As a result, Annex "D" requires that the pullout capacity of post-installed anchors be verified by tests in conformance with ACI 355.2.

Pullout capacity values are listed in Table 12.5

12.5.4. Side Face Blowout

Side face blowout occurs when the lateral pressure which develops at the embedded head of cast-in anchors under load exceeds the confining strength of the surrounding concrete. Equations D-18 and D-19 in Annex "D" predict side face blowout capacities for single and group anchors within a distance $0.4h_{ef}$ of a free edge. Edge distances greater than this preclude blowout failures for cast-in-headed anchors. These equations are not applicable to J or L bolt anchors for which there are currently no side face blowout expressions. L bolts located in close proximity to a free edge with the hook oriented parallel to the free edge will exhibit a blowout type failure. With no expression provided for this L bolt failure, designers are encouraged to use headed anchors in close proximity to free edges. Side face blowout capacities are listed in Table 12.5.

Where a second orthogonal free edge c_{a2} is within $3c_{a1}$ of the anchor, (a corner for example), Clause D.6.4 further reduces the side face blowout strength by up to 50% as dimension c_{a2} reduces from a value of $3c_{a1}$ to c_{a1}. This reduction factor is given by the expression $(1 + c_{a2} / c_{a1}) / 4$ where $1 \le (c_{a2} / c_{a1}) \le 3$.

The provisions of Clause D.6.4 are based on reference[12-15]. The equations are calibrated for use with cast-in headed anchors and are not meant to be used with L or J bolts. Post-installed anchors in proximity to a free edge tend to develop splitting failures that are not characteristic of the side-face blowout failures covered by Clause D.6.4. As a result these provisions are not applicable to post-installed anchors. The splitting failure of post-installed anchors is evaluated by tests in accordance with ACI 355.2[12-16].

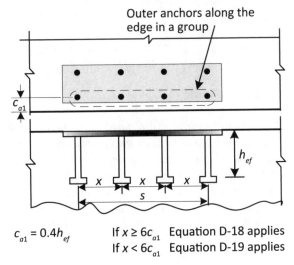

$c_{a1} = 0.4h_{ef}$

If $x \ge 6c_{a1}$ Equation D-18 applies
If $x < 6c_{a1}$ Equation D-19 applies

While the term "s" in the notation section of Annex D is defined as the distance between individual anchors, for the purpose of Equation D-19, the term "s" is taken as the spacing between the outer anchors parallel to a free edge as illustrated in Figure 12.6.

Figure 12.6 Dimension s for use in Clause D.6.4.2.

12.5.5. Supplemental Reinforcement for Tension

Clause D.5.3(c) permits a 15% increase in capacity for tension embedment sections that are restrained from breakout by supplemental reinforcement. To utilize this 15% increase in capacity however the designer must ensure that the supplemental reinforcement is designed to restrain the full breakout force required for the anchor. In looking at the concrete tensile stress distribution around an embedded anchor in Figure 12.7, it is obvious that the reinforcement will be most effective when placed in the region of greatest tensile stress, i.e. close to the anchor. Tests have shown that only reinforcement running parallel to the applied load and in close proximity to the anchor is effective in restraining the concrete breakout section[12-11, 12-12]. This is often achieved using hairpin reinforcement or hooked bars. The basic concept is illustrated in Fig 12.7.

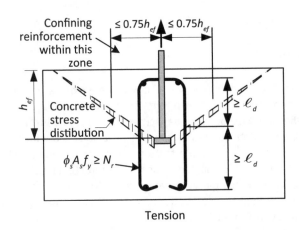

Tension

Figure 12.7 Supplemental reinforcement restraining tension breakout

When detailing supplemental reinforcement it should be oriented in the same direction as the applied load and it should not be placed any farther than $0.75h_{ef}$ from the anchor. Reinforcement more distant from the anchor than this will not be able to restrain the large tensile stresses that surround the immediate area around the anchor. Reinforcement placed perpendicular to the anchor and close to the surface of the concrete will have virtually no effect on restraining the concrete breakout section. The reinforcement must also be properly detailed to develop its yield strength across the failure plane of the concrete as illustrated in figure 12.7. Usually this can only be achieve with the use of hairpin reinforcing bars and well anchored bars with hooks. The hook should engage a horizontal bar to improve the anchorage.

12.5.6. Tension Anchor Reinforcement

In cases where sufficient concrete breakout capacity cannot be utilised to develop the required tensile capacity of the anchor, clause D.6.2.9 permits the use of anchor reinforcement in place of the concrete breakout capacity. The location and detailing of the anchor reinforcement is critical to its ability to provide the required resistance. Tension anchor reinforcement detailing is illustrated in Figure D.10. The anchor reinforcement must be sufficiently developed in accordance with CSA A23.3 Clause 12 on both sides of the concrete failure surface.

12.5.7. Adhesive Anchors

Annex D Clause 6.5 now contains provisions for adhesive anchors with embedment depths ranging from 4 to 20 anchor diameters. All adhesive anchors for both seismic and non-seismic applications are required to be qualified to the ACI 355.4 test standard.

12.5.7.1.   Tension Capacity of Adhesive Anchors

12

Anchorage

The expression for the factored resistance in tension of adhesive anchors takes the same form as that for cast-in-place and mechanical post installed anchors and is given below for single and group adhesive anchors.

$$N_{ar} = \frac{A_{Na}}{A_{Nao}}\psi_{ed,Na}\,\psi_{cp,Na}\,N_{bar} \qquad\qquad \text{Eq. D.20}$$

$$N_{agr} = \frac{A_{Na}}{A_{Nao}}\psi_{ec,N}\,\psi_{ed,Na}\,\psi_{cp,Na}\,N_{bar} \qquad\qquad \text{Eq. D.21}$$

In the expressions above the term N_{bar} represents the bond capacity of a single adhesive anchor unaffected by cracking or edge effects. The term $\psi_{c,N}$ does not appear in Eqs. D.20 and D.21 as the recognition of cracking in the concrete is included directly in the bond stress value τ_{cr}. Unlike headed bolts and post installed mechanical anchors, adhesive anchors exhibit a different breakout area defined by equations D.22 and D.23 in Annex D and illustrated in Figure D.12a and D.12b. See section 12.5.7.3 for additional concrete breakout considerations when designing adhesive anchors.

$$A_{Noa} = (2c_{Nao})^2 \qquad\qquad \text{Eq. D.22}$$

N_{bar} is given by the expression

$$c_{Na} = 10d_a\sqrt{\frac{\tau_{uncr}}{7.60}} \qquad\qquad \text{Eq. D.23}$$

The bond strength of a single adhesive anchor in tension is given by Eq. D.24.

The value τ_{cr} is determined from testing in accordance with ACI355.4.

If the characteristic τ_{cr} values are not know at the time of design then the lower bound values presented in Table D.2 of Annex D can be used if the requirements of Clause D.6.5.2 are met. R is taken from Clause D.5.3.

$$N_{bar} = \lambda_a \phi_c \tau_{cr} \pi d_a h_{ef} R$$ Eq. D.24

Note that τ_{uncr} is used in Equation D.23 to determine c_{Na} and τ_{cr} is used in Equation D.24 to determine N_{bar}.

The consideration of the effects of eccentricity, edge effects and splitting are calculated in a manner similar to that for mechanical post installed mechanical anchors. The related ψ factors for adhesive anchors are listed below:

Eccentricity: $\psi_{ec,Na} = \dfrac{1}{\left(1 + \dfrac{2e'_N}{c_{Na}}\right)}$ but $\psi_{ec,N} \leq 1.0$ D.6.5.3

Edge Effects:

$$\psi_{ed,Na} = 1.0 \qquad\qquad \text{if } c_{a,min} \geq c_{Na}$$

$$\psi_{ed,Na} = 0.7 + 0.3\left(\dfrac{c_{a.min}}{c_{Na}}\right) \qquad \text{if } c_{a,min} < c_{Na}$$ D.6.5.4

Splitting:

$$\psi_{cp,Na} = 1.0 \qquad\qquad \text{if } c_{a,min} \geq c_{ac}$$

$$\psi_{cp,Na} = \dfrac{c_{a,min}}{c_{ac}} \geq \dfrac{c_{Na}}{c_{ac}} \qquad \text{if } c_{a,min} < c_{ac}$$ (D.6.5.5)

The critical edge distance "c_{ac}" is taken from Clause D.9.7.

12.5.7.2.　　　Sustained Tension Loads

Clause D.5.1.3 requires an additional 45% reduction in the calculated capacity of adhesive anchors when subjected to sustained tension loads. This capacity reduction was calibrated from testing done in accordance with ACI 355.4 and is intended to account for creep in adhesive anchors under sustained loading over time.

12.5.7.3.　　　Additional Concrete Breakout Resistance Check

In addition to the bond resistance calculations noted in Section 12.5.7.1, adhesive anchors must also be checked for concrete breakout in a manner similar to post-installed mechanical anchors, (see Section 12.5.2), to ensure that concrete breakout does not control the design of the anchor.

12.6　Design Requirements for Shear Loading

In the design for shear, the designer must check three possible failure modes:

a) shear failure of the steel anchor,

b) concrete breakout of the embedment, and

c) concrete pryout failure.

12.6.1. Steel Anchor Shear Resistance

As in the case of tension capacity, Clause D.7.1.2 limits f_{uta} of the steel anchor to $1.9f_{ya}$ to ensure that the anchor does not yield under service loads. The derivation of this limit is discussed in Section 5.1. The f_{uta} strength of steel is used instead of the yield strength because anchor materials do not exhibit a well-defined yield point. The upper limit on f_{uta} of 860 MPa represents the scope of the tests used in developing the requirements of Annex "D".

The shear resistance of the cast-in headed stud anchors is given by equation D-30.

$$V_{sar} = A_{se,V}\phi_s f_{uta}R$$

Eq.(D-30)

Tests[12-17] show that cast-in headed stud anchors welded to a base plate do not exhibit the 40% reduction in shear strength characteristic of headed and hooked bolts. As a result, the 0.6 reduction is not applied to these anchors in shear.

$A_{se,V}$ in equations D-20 and D-21 represents the net cross-sectional area of a single steel anchor or of all anchors in shear in a group. While not explicitly stated in Clause D.7.1.2, if threads in the steel anchor intercept the shear plane the effective area of the anchor should be taken as being $0.70A_g$. For shear calculations, CSA Standard S16-14 Limit States Design of Steel Structures requires that 70% of the gross area be taken as the effective net area A_{se} for threaded bolts. V_{sar} capacity values for threaded anchor bolts are given in Table 12.6.

Many post-installed anchors with expansion mechanisms have reduced cross-sectional areas. In such cases the manufacturer should always supply the effective cross-sectional area data for the anchors being used.

In some cases with post-installed anchors, the sleeve may act independently from the shaft of the anchor in resisting shear. In recognition of this, the area of the sleeve is excluded from equation D-31. However, Clause D.7.1.2(c) has been included to recognize the beneficial effect that anchor sleeves may have on the shear resistance of the steel anchor when supported by tests conducted in accordance with ACI 355.2.

The 20% reduction in shear capacity required by Clause D.7.1.3 reflects the effect of flexural stresses that develop in the anchor if the supporting grout pad fractures under the application of the shear load.

12.6.2. Concrete Breakout

Equations D-32 and D-33 give the shear breakout capacity for single and group anchors respectively when loaded in shear perpendicular to a free edge.

In cases where shear acts parallel to a free edge, Clause D.7.2.1(c) limits the shear force to no greater than twice the capacity determined for shear forces acting perpendicular to the edge. This is illustrated in Figure D-14(a) in Annex "D".

When an anchor is located near a corner, the designer is required to evaluate the shear capacity in both orthogonal directions and limit the shear load to the lesser of the two.

The determination of shear concrete breakout resistance is given by Equation D-33 of Annex "D" shown below:

$$V_{cbgr} = \frac{A_{Vc}}{A_{Vco}} \psi_{ec,V}\,\psi_{ed,V}\,\psi_{c,V}\psi_{h,V}\,V_{br}$$

(D-33)

12

Anchorage

As in the case for tension, a 35° breakout prism angle is assumed. The shear breakout capacity is determined by first evaluating the basic concrete breakout resistance for an anchor in shear V_{br}, and then by applying the additional factors accounting for group effects, eccentricity of loading, edge conditions, and cracking in the concrete. These contributing factors are discussed below.

A_{Vc}/A_{Vco} represents the ratio of the shear breakout area of a group anchor arrangement "A_{Vc}" vs the full shear breakout area of a single anchor "A_{Vco}" unaffected by edge distance, spacing or section depth. Figure D.12 in Annex "D" illustrates the area A_{Vco} while Figure D.10(a), (b) and (c) illustrate the area A_{Vc} applicable for conditions involving limited section depth, edge constraints and anchor spacing.

For anchor groups loaded in shear towards a free edge the two conditions illustrated in Figure D.13(d) case 1 and case 2 should be investigated. If the anchors are spaced sufficiently far enough apart such that their failure surfaces do not intersect, $\geq 1.5c_{a1}$, then two possible failure conditions should be investigated. If the two anchors are not rigidly connected then the front anchor, which possesses a smaller failure surface, would present the critical design condition. Where the two anchors are rigidly connected, the shear capacity will be determined by the back anchor[12-12]. In this case when the front anchor begins to break out, the entire shear load is transferred to the back anchor. The lone back anchor will then carry the entire load and the break out section associated with that anchor will become the critical failure surface.

The factored concrete breakout resistance of an anchor is affected by the anchor stiffness and diameter[12-4, 12-5, 12-18] and is given by equation D-35 in Annex "D" as shown below.

$$V_{br} = 0.58 \left(\frac{\ell_e}{d_a}\right)^{0.2} \sqrt{d_o} \, \phi_c \, \lambda_a \sqrt{f'_c} \, c_{a1}^{1.5} R \tag{D-35}$$

For anchors welded to a steel attachment in accordance with Clause D.7.2.3, equation D-37 shown below is used to calculate the shear capacity.

$$V_{br} = 0.66 \left(\frac{\ell_e}{d_a}\right)^{0.2} \sqrt{d_o} \, \phi_c \, \lambda_a \sqrt{f'_c} \, c_{a1}^{1.5} R \tag{D-37}$$

The term λ_a is now contained directly in the shear capacity equations in the 2014 edition and is given in Clause D.4.6. The term λ_a presents additional lightweight concrete strength reductions for certain anchor types and for the bond resistance of adhesive anchors.

Anchors with a larger shear stiffness ratio ℓ_e/d_a are able to transfer the shear load over a greater depth in the concrete and thus provide greater shear resistance than more flexible anchors. The ℓ_e/d_a ratio is limited to 8.0 when used in equations D-35 and D-37 of Annex "D". The constants in these equations were calibrated from test results[12-5, 12-19]. They represent the 5% fractile values calibrated for cracked concrete.

Clause D.7.2.3(c) requires the use of supplemental reinforcement. More information on the use of supplemental reinforcement is given in references 12-18, 12-13, and 12-20.

Clause D.7.2.4 requires that where shear anchors are located in narrow or thin sections, and the anchor is influenced by three or more edges, the value of c_{a1} used in the shear capacity equations in Annex "D" should be modified as illustrated in Figure D.15 and Fig. 12.8. As can be seen in Fig. 12.8, if more than one c_{a2} edge distance is less than c_{a1}, then the larger c_{a2} value should be used to calculate the modified c_{a1} value. This modified c_{a1} value should be used in calculating the factors $\psi_{ed,V}$ and $\psi_{h,V}$ noted below.

The factor $\psi_{ec,V}$ accounts for eccentric shear load application on an anchor group. The shear load is assumed oriented towards a free edge. The determination of e'_V is illustrated in Figure D.16 in Annex "D".

The dimension s is determined on the basis of the distance between the outermost anchors loaded in shear in the same direction as the applied shear. This is illustrated in Figure D-16 of Annex "D".

Where edge distances limit the breakout area of the anchor in shear, additional reductions in the breakout resistance of the concrete, beyond that predicted by the reduced breakout area, must be accounted for. This is done using the factor $\psi_{ed,V}$ which is calculated as follows:

$$\psi_{ed,V} = 1.0 \qquad\qquad \text{if } c_{a2} \geq 1.5c_{a1}$$

$$\psi_{ed,V} = 0.7 + 0.3\left(\frac{c_{a2}}{1.5c_{a1}}\right) \quad \text{if } c_{a2} < 1.5c_{a1}$$

Clause D.7.2.7 requires that $\psi_{c,V}$ be taken as 1.0 if a cracking analysis has not been conducted and no supplemental reinforcement has been provided to control cracking. Where it has been determined that the concrete will remain uncracked at service load levels, then a 40% increase in the shear capacity of the anchor is permitted. However, In order to take advantage of this increased capacity, the analysis must include temperature and shrinkage effects in addition to structural load effects. Values for $\psi_{c,V}$ vary from 1.0 and 1.4 provided reinforcement in accordance with Clause D.7.2.7 is provided. These requirements are based on a limited number of anchor tests which may not represent the behaviour of all anchor types and sizes. These provisions should not be used with anchors in excess of 25 mm in diameter. A maximum crack width of 0.3 mm is assumed with $\psi_{c,V} = 1.0$. If higher values of $\psi_{c,V}$ are used, designers are encouraged to evaluate the anchorage case in question utilizing the reinforcement provided to ensure that the crack widths will be less than 0.3 mm. More information on supplemental reinforcement can be found in references 12-11, 12-12, and 12-21.

The term $\psi_{h,V}$ recognises that the reduction in shear strength for sections of limited depth is not directly proportional to the reduction in shear breakout area of the concrete. This term is always greater than or equal to 1.0.

$$\psi_{h,V} = \sqrt{\frac{1.5 \times c_{a1}}{h_a}}$$

Table 12.6 lists V_{cbr} values for a variety of anchor sizes and embedment conditions.

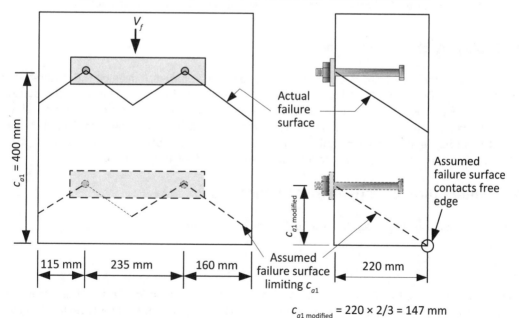

$$c_{a1 \text{ modified}} = 220 \times 2/3 = 147 \text{ mm}$$

Figure 12.8 Modified free edge distance c_{a1} in shallow members

12.6.3. Concrete Pryout Resistance

The pryout resistance of cast-in anchors has been found to be equal to the tensile concrete breakout capacity for embedment depths less than 65 mm and twice that value for embedment depths greater than 65 mm[12-5]. Pryout resistance values are listed in Table 12.6.

12.6.4. Supplemental Reinforcement for Shear

Supplemental reinforcement restraining a shear breakout section is depicted in Figure 12.9 below. As in the case of tension breakout the reinforcement should be aligned with the force on the anchor and be located in close proximity to the anchor. The hairpin reinforcement shown in Fig. 12.9 has proven in tests to be very efficient in restraining the anchor but will not prevent the concrete section from breaking out. Hairpin reinforcement will prove more efficient when placed in direct contact with the anchor and angled down from the surface of the concrete as shown. Reference 12.3 provides more detailed information on supplemental reinforcement.

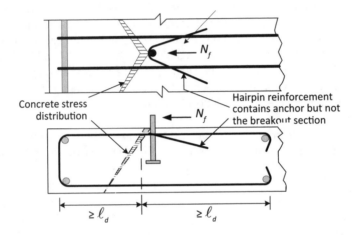

Figure 12.9 Supplemental reinforcement restraining shear breakout

12.6.5. Shear Anchor Reinforcement

In cases where sufficient concrete breakout capacity cannot be utilised to develop the required shear capacity of the anchor, clause D.7.2.9 permits the use of anchor reinforcement in place of the concrete breakout capacity. The location and detailing of the anchor reinforcement is critical to its ability to provide the required resistance. Shear anchor reinforcement detailing is illustrated in Figure D.17a and D.17b. The anchor reinforcement must be sufficiently developed on both sides of the concrete failure surface or engage the anchor and be properly anchored beyond the breakout section.

12.7   Interaction of Tensile and Shear Forces

The trilinear provision of Clause D.8 is a simplification of the expression:

$$\left(\frac{N_r}{N_f}\right)^{\zeta} + \left(\frac{V_r}{V_f}\right)^{\zeta} \leq 1.0$$

where ζ varies from 1.0 to 2.0. The provisions of Clause D.8, assume $\zeta = 5/3$. Tests indicate that a 20% tolerance can be accommodated before interaction effects need be considered for cases involving both tension and shear effects. Clause D.5.1.4 allows alternative interaction expressions provided they agree with test results.

12.8 Edge Distances, Spacing, and Thickness to Preclude Splitting Failure

Splitting failures, as illustrated in Figure D.4(A)(e), occur where anchors are

a) located in close proximity to an edge,

b) spaced too closely together, or

c) anchored in a thin section of concrete.

Splitting failure is dictated to a large extent by the type of anchor being used. Anchors which do not exert additional lateral stress on the concrete can tolerate shorter edge distances and closer spacing than anchors that rely on lateral pressure to develop their resistance. As a result, anchors that will be torqued prior to the application of load are more sensitive to splitting failure and require larger edge distances.

Post-installed anchors are required to have a minimum spacing of $6d_a$ vs $4d_a$ for untorqued cast-in anchors. Minimum edge distances for post-installed anchors range from $6d_a$ to $10d_a$, while the minimum edge distance for untorqued cast-in anchors is governed only by the minimum cover requirements of Clause 7.9.

Tests have indicated that assumed concrete breakout capacities are not met when $c_{a,min} = 1.5h_{ef}$ for many post-installed anchors. This effect is recognized with the application of $\psi_{cp,N}$ in equations D-3 and D-4. Clause D.9.7 provides default values for the critical edge distance c_{ac} to be used in the determination of $\psi_{cp,N}$ in Clause D.6.2.7. These values are applicable to post-installed anchors only. Alternatively the designer may use values for c_{ac} based on ACI 355.2 qualification reports for the particular post-installed anchor being used.

12.9 Installation

Certain types of post-installed anchors can be sensitive to installation variables such as hole-diameter and condition, angle of inclination, cracking, degree of installation torque, etc. Post-installed anchors should always be installed in accordance with the Manufacturer's Printed Installation Instructions (MPII), as these specifications are the basis for the ACI 355.2 product evaluation testing. During the evaluation, post-installed anchors are classified into one of three categories depending on their degree of sensitivity to the installation variables. Different values of the Resistance Modification Factor "R" are applied to the three different category classifications.

Adhesive anchor capacity can be strongly affected by the quality of the installation. As a result, Annex D requires that when adhesive anchors are installed in a horizontal or upwardly inclined orientation, the installer is certified to the ACI/CRSI Adhesive Anchor Installer Certification program, or equivalent. Where required by contract documents, proof testing is conducted in accordance with the ACI 355.4 test standard. Additional inspection procedures may also be required when adhesive anchors are used.

12.10 References

12-1) "CSA A23.3-14 Design of Concrete Structures," Canadian Standards Association. Rexdale Ontario, Canada.

12-2) Cannon, R.W., Godfrey D.A., and Moreadith, F.L., "Guide to the Design of Anchor Bolts and Other Steel Embedments," Concrete International, V. 3, No. 7, July 1981, pp. 28-41.

12

Anchorage

12-3) Eligehausen, R., Fuchs, W., and Mayer, B., "Load Bearing Behavior of Anchor Fastenings in Tension," Betonwerk und Fertigteil-technik, 12/1987. pp. 29-35.

12-4) Eligehausen, R., Fuchs, W., "Loadbearing Behavior of Anchor Fastenings Under Shear, Combined Tension and Shear or Flexural Loadings," Betonwerk und Fertigteil-technik, No. 2, 1988, pp. 48-56.

12-5) Fuchs, W., Eligehausen, R., and Breen J.E., "Concrete Capacity Design (CCD) Approach for Fastening to Concrete," ACI Structural Journal, V. 92, No. 1, January-February, 1995, pp. 73-94.

12-6) Eligehausen, R., and Balogh, T., "Behavior of Fasteners Loaded in Tension in Cracked Reinforced Concrete," ACI Structural Journal, V. 92, No. 3, May-June 1995, pp. 365-379.

12-7) "Building Code Requirements for Structural Concrete (ACI 318-14) and Commentary (ACI 318-14)," American Concrete Institute, Farmington Hills, MI.

12-8) "National Building Code of Canada 2015," National Research Council of Canada, Ottawa, Ontario, Canada.

12-9) Cook, R.A. and Klingner, R.E., "Ductile Multiple-Anchor Steel-to-Concrete Connections," Journal of Structural Engineering, ASCE, V.118, No. 6, June 1992, pp. 1645-1665.

12-10) Lotze, D. and Klingner, R.E., "Behavior of Multiple-Anchor Connections to Concrete from the Perspective of Plastic Theory," Report PMFSEL 96-4, Ferguson Structural Engineering Laboratory, The University of Texas at Austin, March 1997.

12-11) Rodriguez, M., Lotze, D., Gross, J.H., Zhang, Y., Klingner, R.E. and Graves, III, H. L., "Dynamic Behavior of Tensile Anchors to Concrete," Structures Journal, American Concrete Institute, Farmington Hills, Michigan, V. 98, No. 4, July-August 2001, pp. 511-524.

12-12) Gross, J.H., Klingner, R.E., and Graves, III, H. L., "Dynamic Behavior of Single and Double Near-Edge Anchors Loaded in Shear," Structures Journal, American Concrete Institute, Farmington Hills, Michigan, V. 98, No. 5, September-October 2001, pp. 665-676.

12-13) "Design of Fastenings in Concrete – Design Guide," Comité Euro-International du Béton (CEB) Thomas Telford Services Ltd., London, Jan 1997.

12-14) Eligehausen, R., Mallée, R., and Silva, J. F., "Anchorage in Concrete and Masonry Construction," Whiley-VCH, Berlin, 2005.

12-15) Furche, J. and Eligehausen, R., "Lateral Blow-out Failure of Headed Studs near a Free Edge," Anchors in Concrete-Design and Behavior, SP130, ACI Detroit, 1991, pp. 235-252.

12-16) "Qualification of Post-Installed Mechanical Anchors in Concrete (ACI 355.2-04) and Commentary (ACI 355.2R-04)," American Concrete Institute.

12-17) Anderson, N.S. and Meinheit, D. F., "Design Criteria for Headed Stud Groups in Shear: Part 1 – Steel Capacity and Back Edge Effects," PCI Journal, V. 45, No. 5, September/October 2000, pp. 46-75.

12-18) "Fastenings to Concrete and Masonry Structures, State of the Art Report," Comité Euro-International du Béton, (CEB), Bulletin No. 216, Thomas Telford Services Ltd., London, 1994.

12-19) Shaikh, A. F., and Yi, W., "In-Place Strength of Welded Headed Studs," PCI Journal, V. 30, No.2, March/April 1985, pp. 56- 81.

12-20) Klingner, R.E., Mendonca, J.A., and Malik, J.B., "Effect of Reinforcing Details on the Shear Resistance of Anchor Bolts under Reversed Cyclic Loading," ACI Journal Proceedings V. 79, No. 1, January-February 1982, pp. 3-12.

12-21) Zhang, Y.-G., Klingner, R. E. and Graves, III, H. L., "Seismic Response of Multiple-Anchor Connections to Concrete," Structures Journal, American Concrete Institute, Farmington Hills, Michigan, V. 98, No. 6, November-December 2001, pp. 811-822.

12-22) Hoehler, M., and Eligehausen, R., 2008, "Behavior and Testing of Anchors in Simulated Seismic Cracks," *ACI Structural Journal,* V. 105, No.3, May-June, pp. 348-357.

12-23) Vintzileou, E., and Eligehausen, R., 1992, "Behavior of Fasteners under Monotonic or Cyclic Shear Displacements," *Anchors in Concrete: Design and Behavior,* SP-130, American Concrete Institute, Farmington Hills, MI, pp. 181-203.

12.11 Design Examples

Example 12.1 Tension capacity with no edge effects

What is the maximum factored tensile capacity of the single AWS D1.1 welded stud anchor shown? Assume the stud is distant from any edges, the normal density concrete is cracked at service loads, and no supplemental reinforcement is used.

Welded Stud:

  shank diameter d_a = 15.7 mm,

  head diameter d_{head} = 25.4 mm,

  f_{ya} = 344 MPa, f_{uta} = 414 MPa.

Assume ductile steel.

  f_c' = 30 MPa ϕ_c = 0.65 ϕ_s = 0.85 h_{ef} = 125 mm

Determine the tensile capacity of the steel stud

  ($A_{se,N} = A_g$ for an unthreaded steel stud)

  f_{uta} / f_{ya} = 414 / 344 = 1.2 < 1.9 (D.6.1.2)

  $A_{se,N} = \dfrac{\pi d^2}{4} = \dfrac{\pi\, 15.7^2}{4} = 193\,\text{mm}^2$

  $N_{sar} = A_{se,N}\phi_s f_{uta} R$ Eq.(D-2)

  R = 0.8 (ductile steel loaded in tension) (D.5.3(a))

  N_{sar} = 193 × 0.85 × 414 × 0.8 = 54 333 N

  N_{sar} = 54.3 kN

Determine the tensile concrete breakout capacity

$$N_{br} = k_c \lambda_a \phi_c \sqrt{f_c'} h_{ef}^{1.5} R \qquad \text{Eq.(D-7)}$$

$\lambda_a = 1.0$

$R = 1.0$ \hfill (D.5.3(c))

(condition "B" tension load with no supplementary reinforcement)

$$N_{br} = 10 \times 1.0 \times 0.65 \times 1.0 \times \sqrt{30} \times 125^{1.5} \times 1.0 = 49{,}755 \,\text{N}$$

$N_{br} = 49.7$ kN

$$N_{cbr} = \frac{A_{Nc}}{A_{Nco}} \psi_{ed,N} \ \psi_{c,N} \ \psi_{cp,N} \ N_{br} \qquad \text{Eq. (D-3)}$$

$$A_{Nco} = 9h_{ef}^2 \qquad \text{Eq. (D-5)}$$

$A_{Nc} = A_{Nco}$ (the anchor is distant from all edges)

$\psi_{ed,N} = 1.0$ (anchor is distant from all edges) \hfill (D.6.2.5)

$\psi_{c,N} = 1.0$ (cracked concrete) \hfill (D.6.2.6)

$\psi_{cp,N}$ is applicable to post-installed anchors only. Taken as 1.0 for cast-in anchors \hfill (D.6.2.7)

$N_{cbr} = 1.0 \times (1.0 \times 1.0 \times 1.0) \times 49.7 = 49.7$ kN

Check pullout capacity

$$N_{pr} = 8A_{brg}\phi_c f_c' R \qquad \text{(D.6.3.4)}$$

The bearing area A_{brg} of the head of the steel stud =

$$A_{brg} = \frac{\pi(d_{head}^2 - d_a^2)}{4} = \frac{\pi(25.4^2 - 15.7^2)}{4} = 313 \text{ mm}^2$$

$R = 1.0$ (condition "B" always assumed for pullout failure) \hfill (D.5.3(c) Note)

$N_{pr} = 8 \times 313 \times 0.65 \times 30 \times 1.0 = 48\ 843$ N \qquad $= 48.8$ kN

$N_{cpr} = \psi_{c,P} N_{pr}$

For cracked concrete $\psi_{c,P} = 1.0$

$N_{cpr} = 1.0 \times 48.8 = 48.8$ kN

Side Face Blowout – not applicable as edge distance $> 0.4h_{ef}$ \hfill (D.6.4.1)

Summary:

$N_{sar} = 54.3$ kN

$N_{cbr} = 49.7$ kN

$N_{cpr} = 48.8$ kN \qquad $\rightarrow$ \qquad Governs

The tensile strength of the anchor is governed by the anchor pullout capacity.

N_r = 48.8 kN

Example 12.2 Shear capacity with no edge effects

Determine the factored shear capacity of the 19 mm (3/4") threaded Grade A ASTM A307 anchor shown. Assume uncracked 30 MPa concrete, f_{ya} = 250 MPa, f_{uta} = 414 MPa. Regular weight concrete.

f_{uta} / f_{ya} = 1.65 < 1.9   OK   (D.7.1.2)

Calculate the Shear Capacity of the A307 Bolt.

$V_{sr} = A_{se,V} \, \phi_s \, 0.6 f_{uta} \, R$ Eq.(D-21)

($A_{se,V}$ can be assumed to be $0.70 A_g$ for a threaded anchor bolt as specified for shear)   (D.6.1.2)

Calculate $A_{se,V}$ of the 19 mm anchor.

$A_{se,V} = 0.7 \dfrac{\pi d_a^2}{4} = 0.7 \dfrac{\pi 19^2}{4} = 198 \, \text{mm}^2$

R = 0.75 (ductile steel anchor loaded in shear)   (D.5.3(a))

V_{sar} = 0.85 × 198 × 0.6 × 414 × 0.75 = 31 354 N

V_{sar} = 31.3 kN

(Table 12.6 gives a value of 33.0 kN for this bolt but uses the effective area values listed in Table 12.4 rather than the approximate value above)

Determine the shear concrete breakout capacity

$V_{cbr} = \dfrac{A_{Vc}}{A_{Vco}} \Psi_{ed,V} \, \Psi_{c,V} \, \Psi_{h,V} \, V_{br}$ (D.7.2.1)

$A_{Vco} = 4.5 c_{a1}^2$ Eq.(D-34)

$A_{Vc} = A_{Vco}$ (no edge or thickness constraints)

$\Psi_{ed,V}$ = 1.0 (no edge effects considered)

$\Psi_{c,V}$ = 1.4 (assume concrete uncracked at service loads)   (D.7.2.7)

$\Psi_{h,V} = \sqrt{\dfrac{1.5 c_{a1}}{h_a}} = \sqrt{\dfrac{1.5 \times 125}{200}} = 0.98$ but $\Psi_{h,V} \geq 1.0$ use 1.0   (D.7.2.8)

$V_{br} = 0.58 \left(\dfrac{\ell_e}{d_a} \right)^{0.2} \sqrt{d_a} \, \phi_c \, \lambda_a \sqrt{f_c'} \, c_{a1}^{1.5} R$ Eq.(D-35)

λ_a = 1.0 (cast-in-place anchor in normal density concrete)   (D.4.6)

R = 1.0 (condition "B", shear load without supplementary reinforcement)   (D.5.3(c))

$\dfrac{\ell_e}{d_a} = \dfrac{150}{19} = 7.89 < 8$ therefore use 7.89

12

Anchorage

$$V_{br} = 0.58(7.89)^{0.2}\sqrt{19} \times 0.65 \times 1.0 \times \sqrt{30} \times 125^{1.5} \times 1.0 = 19{,}012\,N$$

V_{br} = 19.0 kN

V_{cbr} = 1.0 × 1.0 × 1.4 × 1.0 × 19.0 = 26.6 kN

Check the pryout capacity

$$V_{cpr} = k_{cp}\,N_{cbr} \qquad\qquad (D.7.3)$$

k_{cp} = 2.0 Pryout capacity taken as twice the tensile breakout capacity for $h_{ef} \geq$ 65 mm

Calculate N_{cbr} to complete the pryout capacity determination.

$$N_{cbr} = \frac{A_{Nc}}{A_{Nco}}\psi_{ed,N}\,\psi_{c,N}\,\psi_{cp,N}\,N_{br} \qquad\qquad (D.6.2.1)$$

A_{Nc} = (125 + 1.5h_{ef}) × 3h_{ef}

A_{Nc} = (125 + (1.5 × 150)) × 3 × 150 = 157 500 mm²

A_{Nco} = 9h_{ef}^2 = 9 × 150² = 202 500 mm²

$$\psi_{ed,N} = 0.7 + 0.3\frac{c_{a,min}}{1.5h_{ef}} \qquad \text{if } c_{a,min} < 1.5h_{ef} \qquad (D.6.2.5)$$

$$\psi_{ed,N} = 0.7 + 0.3\frac{125}{1.5(150)} = 0.867$$

$\psi_{c,N}$ = 1.25 (assume uncracked concrete)   (D.6.2.6)

$\psi_{cp,N}$ = 1.0 (cast-in-place anchor)

Calculate N_{br}

$$N_{br} = k_c\phi_c\lambda_a\sqrt{f_c'}\,h_{ef}^{1.5}R \qquad\qquad \text{Eq. (D.6)}$$

where R = 1.0 for condition "B" without supplementary reinforcement   (D.5.3)

$$N_{br} = 10 \times 0.65 \times 1.0 \times \sqrt{30} \times 150^{1.5} \times 1.0 = 65{,}404\,N$$

N_{br} = 65.4 kN

$$N_{cbr} = \frac{157{,}500}{202{,}500}(0.867 \times 1.25 \times 1.0) \times 65.4 = 55.1\,kN \qquad \text{Eq. (D.3)}$$

$$V_{cpr} = k_{cp}\,N_{cbr} = 2.0\,N_{cbr} \qquad\qquad (D.7.3)$$

V_{cpr} = 2.0 × 55.1 = 110.2 kN

Summary

V_{sar} = 31.3 kN

V_{cbr} = 26.6 kN   →   Governs

V_{cpr} = 110.2 kN

The maximum factored shear capacity of the anchor

$V_r = 26.6$ kN

Example 12.3 Shear with the influence of thin section and edge effects

Determine the concrete breakout capacity in shear for the 13 mm diameter threaded anchor embedded in the 200 mm deep uncracked concrete section shown.

Assume uncracked normal density concrete with $f_c' = 40$ MPa, $f_c = 0.65$,

$d_a = 13$ mm, $h_{ef} = 130$ mm,

$c_{a1} = 150$ mm, $c_{a2,min} = 120$ mm, $h = 200$ mm

Calculate breakout capacity in Shear V_{cbr}

$$V_{cbr} = \frac{A_V}{A_{Vo}} \psi_{ed,V}\ \psi_{c,V}\ \psi_{h,V}\ V_{br} \qquad \text{Eq.(D-32)}$$

$$\psi_{ed,V} = 0.7 + 0.3\frac{120}{1.5(150)} = 0.86 \qquad \text{Eq.(D-41)}$$

$\psi_{c,V} = 1.4$ (assume uncracked concrete) $\qquad$ (D.7.2.7)

$$\psi_{h,V} = \sqrt{\frac{1.5c_{a1}}{h_a}} = \sqrt{\frac{1.5\times150}{200}} = 1.06 \qquad \text{Eq.(D.42)}$$

$A_{Vco} = 4.5c_{a1}{}^2 = 4.5 \times 150^2 = 101\ 250$ mm²

Determine A_{Vc}. The thin section will not allow the full depth of the concrete breakout section to develop. Calculate A_{Vc} accordingly.

$1.5 \times c_{a1} = 225 > 200$ mm $\qquad\qquad \therefore$ use 200 mm in calculating A_{Vc} below.

$A_{Vc} = (120 + 1.5c_{a1}) \times 200$

$A_{Vc} = (120 + (1.5 \times 150)) \times 200$

$A_{Vc} = 69\ 000$ mm²

Now calculate V_{br}

$$V_{br} = 0.58\left(\frac{\ell_e}{d_a}\right)^{0.2}\sqrt{d_a}\ \phi_c\lambda_a\sqrt{f_c'}\ c_1^{1.5}R \qquad \text{Eq.(D-25)}$$

use $\lambda_a = 1.0$ (cast-in-place anchor in normal density concrete) $\qquad$ (D.4.6)

$R = 1.0$, shear without supplementary reinforcement (Condition "B") $\qquad$ (D.5.3(c))

$\ell_e / d_a = 130 / 13 = 10.0 > 8.0$ therefore use 8.0 $\qquad$ (D.3)

$V_{br} = 0.58(8)^{0.2}\sqrt{13}\times0.65\ x1.0\times\sqrt{40}\times150^{1.5}\times1.0 = 23{,}938\,$N

12

Anchorage

$V_{br} = 23.9$ kN

$$V_{cbr} = \frac{69,000}{101,250}(0.86 \times 1.4 \times 1.06)23.9 = 20.7\,\text{kN}$$

The concrete breakout capacity V_{cbr} for the anchor assembly in the direction of the applied load is 20.7 kN.

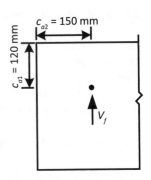

Clause D.7.2.1 requires that breakout capacity of anchors near a corner be evaluated in both orthogonal directions towards the free edges, see Fig. D.11 in Annex "D". The breakout strength of the single anchor shown in Example 12.3 would have to be evaluated again taking $c_{a1} = 120$ mm and an edge distance of 150 mm as shown. The lesser of these two capacities would then be taken as the critical breakout capacity of the embedment in shear.

Example 12.4 Group of headed studs in tension near an edge

This example problem has been adapted from Example problems 34.2 and 34.3 of the "Notes on ACI 318-05", published by the Portland Cement Association. Normal density concrete assumed.

Design a group of four AWS D1.1 Type B welded headed studs spaced 150 mm c/c each way and eccentrically loaded with a factored load, $N_f = 45$ kN.

Assume: $f_c' = 30$ MPa $\phi_c = 0.65$ $\phi_s = 0.85$ ductile Steel: $f_{uta} = 414$ MPa, $f_{uta}/f_{ya} < 1.9$,

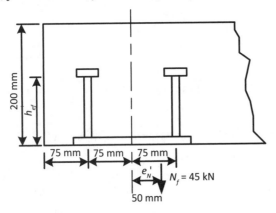

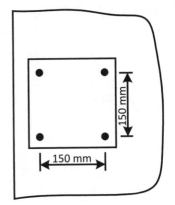

Calculate the required anchor diameter

Due to the eccentric application of the load, the two interior studs will receive a load of

45 kN × (75 + 50) / (75 + 75) = 37.5 kN

Each of the two interior studs will support 37.5 / 2 = 18.7 kN.

Calculate the required area of steel for the studs

$$N_{sar} = A_{se,N}\,\phi_s f_{uta}\,R$$ Eq.(D-2)

where R for steel tension = 0.8 for a ductile element   (D.5.4)

Rearranging gives $A_{se,N} = \dfrac{N_{sar}}{\phi_s f_{uta} R} = \dfrac{18,700}{0.85 \times 414 \times 0.8} = 66.4\,\text{mm}^2$

From Table 12.3 select a ½" diameter stud which will provide $A_{se,N}$ = 127 mm² (0.196 in²) OK

The anchor should be selected with consideration given to the pullout resistance as well. The selected anchor has a head diameter of 25.4 mm.

N_{sar} provided = 4 × 127 × 0.85 × 414 × 0.8 = 143 012 N = 143.0 kN > N_f = 45 kN OK

Determine the required h_{ef} based on the concrete breakout capacity in tension

Assume Condition "B" applies (no supplementary reinforcement)

$$N_{cbgr} = \frac{A_{Nc}}{A_{Nco}} \psi_{ec,N}\, \psi_{ed,N}\, \psi_{c,N}\, \psi_{cp,N}\, N_{br}$$ Eq.(D-3)

Welded studs are manufactured in discrete lengths. The ½" diameter anchor selected is 102 mm long and will provide 115 mm of embedment depth when welded to a 13 mm thick base plate.

Evaluate the terms in Equation (D-3) using h_{ef} = 115 mm.

$A_{Nc} = (75 + 150 + 1.5h_{ef}) \times (1.5h_{ef} + 150 + 1.5h_{ef})$

$A_{Nc} = (75 + 150 + 172) \times (172 + 150 + 172) = 196\ 118$ mm²

$A_{Nco} = 9h_{ef}^2 = 9(115)^2 = 119\ 205$ mm² (failure surface without edge effects) (D.6.2.1)

Check for Group Effect $A_{Nc} < A_{Nco}$ (D.6.2.1)

196 118 mm² < 4 × (119 205) = 476 820 mm² OK (group effect)

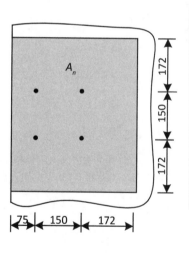

Calculate eccentricity coefficient $\psi_{ec,N}$ with the applied load acting at a distance of 50 mm from the centroid of the anchors

s = 150 mm e'_N = 50 mm < s / 2 = 75 mm OK

$$\psi_{ec,N} = \frac{1}{\left(1 + \dfrac{2e'_N}{3h_{ef}}\right)} = \frac{1}{\left(1 + \dfrac{2(50)}{3(115)}\right)} = 0.775$$

Calculate edge effect coefficient $\psi_{ed,N}$

$$\psi_{ed,N} = 0.7 + 0.3\frac{c_{min}}{1.5(h_{ef})}$$ (D.6.2.5)

$$\psi_{ed,N} = 0.7 + 0.3\frac{75}{1.5(115)} = 0.83$$

$\psi_{c,N}$ = 1.0 (cracked concrete) (D.6.2.6)

$\psi_{cp,N}$ = 1.0 (for cast-in anchors) (D.6.2.7)

Determine N_{br} for a single stud unaffected by edges

$$N_{br} = k_c \phi_c \lambda_a \sqrt{f'_c} h_{ef}^{1.5} R$$ Eq.(D-7)

where R = 1.0 for Condition "B" (no supplementary reinforcement) (D.5.3(c))

λ_a = 1.0 (cast-in-place anchor and normal density concrete)

12

Anchorage

$$N_{br} = 10 \times 0.65 \times 1.0 \times \sqrt{30} \times 115^{1.5} \times 1.0 = 43.9 \, kN$$

Now calculate N_{cbgr} as

$$N_{cbgr} = \frac{A_N}{A_{No}} \psi_{ec,N} \, \psi_{ed,N} \, \psi_{c,N} \, \psi_{cp,N} \, N_{br}$$

$$N_{cbgr} = \frac{196,118}{119,205} \left(0.775 \times 0.83 \times 1.0 \times 1.0\right) 43.9 = 46.4 \, kN > N_f = 45 \, kN \qquad OK$$

Check the pullout capacity N_{pr} for the two most heavily loaded studs.

The ½" diameter studs are manufactured with a 1" diameter head. The provided bearing area A_{brg} = 380 mm².

$$N_{pr} = 8 A_{brg} \, \phi_c f_c' \, R \qquad\qquad (D.6.3.4)$$

N_{pr} = 8 × 380 × 0.65 × 30 × 1.0 = 59 280 N

N_{pr} = 59.3 kN > 18.7 kN (the maximum load on each interior anchor)   OK

Check minimum edge distance requirements.

Welded headed anchor studs are not torqued so the minimum cover requirements of Annex "A" of CSA A23.3 apply. The required cover for reinforcement with exposure class N concrete is 30 mm. The provided cover of 75 – (25.4 / 2) = 62.3 mm > 30 mm.   OK

Summary

N_f = 45.0 kN

N_{sar} = 143.0 kN

N_{cbgr} = 46.4 kN   →   Governs

N_{pr} = 59.3 kN

The four ½" diameter studs selected with f_{uta} = 414 in the arrangement illustrated will provide sufficient anchorage for the eccentric factored load of 45 kN.

12.12 Design Aids

TABLE 12.1
Mechanical properties of ASTM Fastening materials
Source: Strength design of anchors, by R. Cook,
Portland Cement Association, publication code EB080.01

Material specification[1]	Grade or type	Diameter (in)	Tensile strength min (MPa)	Yield strength, min		Elongation min		Reduction of area min, (%)
				MPa	method	%	length	
AWS D.1.1[1]	B	¼ – 1	449	344	0.2%	20	2"	50
ASTM A307[2]	A	≤ 4	414	...	...	18	2"	...
ASTM A354[3]	BC	≤ 4	860	751	0.2%	16	2"	50
	BD	≤ 4	1034	896	0.2%	14	2"	40
ASTM A449[4]	1	≤ 1	828	634	0.2%	14	4D	35
		1 – 1 ½	724	558	0.2%	14	4D	35
		> 1 ½	620	400	0.2%	14	4D	35
ASTM A687[5]		⅝ – 3	...	724	...	15	2"	45
ASTM F1554[6]	36	≤ 2	400 – 551	248	0.2%	23	2"	40
	55	≤ 2	517 – 655	379	0.2%	21	2"	30
	105	≤ 2	860 – 1034	724	0.2%	15	2"	45

[1] *Structural Welding Code* – Steel – This specification covers welded headed studs or welded hooked studs (unthreaded).

[2] *Standard Specification for Carbon Steel Bolts and Studs*, 414 MPa Tensile Strength – This material is commonly used for concrete fastening applications. Grade C is equivalent to ASTM A36 steel.

[3] *Standard Specification for Quenched and Tempered Alloy Steel Bolts*, Studs and Other Externally threaded Fasteners – The strength of Grade BD is equivalent to ASTM A490.

[4] *Standard Specification for Quenched and Tempered Steel Bolts and Studs* – This specification is referenced by ASTM A325 for "equivalent" anchor bolts.

[5] *Standard Specification for Anchor Bolts* – This specification covers high-strength fasteners for anchorage application with enhanced Charpy V-notch properties. The material does not have a minimum specified tensile strength (maximum is given as 1034 MPa).

[6] *Standard Specification for Anchor Bolts* – This specification covers straight and bent, headed and headless, anchor bolts in three strength grades. Anchors are available in diameters ≤ 100 mm but reduction in area requirements vary for anchors < 50 mm.

12

Anchorage

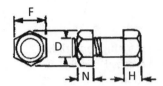
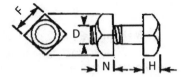

Table 12.2
ASTM Bolt and nut dimensions in inches

Nominal diameter of bolt	Square bolts		Hex bolts		Minimum thread lengths		Square nuts		Hex nuts	
	Width across flats basic F	Head height basic H	Width across flats basic F	Head height basic H	Length under head		Width across flats basic F	Thickness basic H	Width across flats basic F	Thickness basic H
					6 inches and under	over 6 inches				
Inches	Inches	Inches	Inches	Inches	Inches	Inches	Inches	Inches	Inches	Inches
$1/4$	$3/8$	$11/64$	$7/16$	$5/32$	$3/4$	1	$7/16$	$7/32$	$7/16$	$7/32$
$3/8$	$9/16$	$1/4$	$9/16$	$15/64$	1	$1\,1/4$	$5/8$	$21/64$	$9/16$	$21/64$
$1/2$	$3/4$	$21/64$	$3/4$	$5/16$	$1\,1/4$	$1\,1/2$	$13/16$	$7/16$	$3/4$	$7/16$
$5/8$	$15/16$	$27/64$	$15/16$	$25/64$	$1\,1/2$	$1\,3/4$	1	$35/64$	$15/16$	$35/64$
$3/4$	$1\,1/8$	$1/2$	$1\,1/8$	$15/32$	$1\,3/4$	2	$1\,1/8$	$21/32$	$1\,1/8$	$41/64$
$7/8$	$1\,5/16$	$19/32$	$1\,5/16$	$35/64$	2	$2\,1/4$	$1\,5/16$	$49/64$	$1\,5/16$	$3/4$
1	$1\,1/2$	$21/32$	$1\,1/2$	$39/64$	$2\,1/4$	$2\,1/2$	$1\,1/2$	$7/8$	$1\,1/2$	$55/64$
$1\,1/8$	$1\,11/16$	$3/4$	$1\,1/16$	$11/16$	$2\,1/2$	$2\,3/4$	$1\,11/16$	1	$1\,11/16$	$31/32$
$1\,1/4$	$1\,7/8$	$27/32$	$1\,7/8$	$25/32$	$2\,3/4$	3	$1\,7/8$	$1\,3/32$	$1\,7/8$	$1\,1/16$

Table 12.3
Bearing areas A_{brg} for square and hexagonal nuts
Source: Notes on ACI 318-11, published by the Portland Cement Association

Anchor diameter d_a mm (in)	Anchor diameter d_a mm	Gross area of anchor A_g mm²	Effective area of anchor $A_{se,N}$ mm²	Bearing area of heads and nuts A_{brg} mm²			
				Square	Heavy square	Hex	Heavy hex
0.250	6.350	32	21	92	130	75	108
0.375	9.525	71	50	181	234	106	193
0.500	12.700	127	92	299	367	188	301
0.625	15.875	198	146	412	530	293	433
0.750	19.050	285	215	532	723	422	588
0.875	22.225	388	298	723	945	575	766
1.000	25.400	507	391	945	1196	750	968
1.125	28.575	641	492	1196	1478	950	1194
1.250	31.750	792	625	1476	1789	1172	1443
1.375	34.935	959	748	1785	2129	1219	1715
1.500	38.100	1140	910	2126	2499	1688	2012
1.750	44.450	1552	1226	–	–	–	2674
2.000	50.800	2027	1613	–	–	–	3430

Table 12.4
ASTM Anchor data used in developing Tables 12.5 and 12.6

Anchor diameter d_a	Gross area of anchor	Effective area of anchor $A_{se,N}$	Bearing area A_{brg} of hex nut
in	in²	in²	in²
0.250	0.049	0.032	0.117
0.375	0.110	0.078	0.164
0.500	0.196	0.142	0.291
0.625	0.307	0.226	0.454
0.750	0.442	0.334	0.654
0.875	0.601	0.462	0.891
1.000	0.785	0.606	1.163
1.125	0.994	0.763	1.472
1.250	1.227	0.969	1.817
1.375	1.485	1.160	2.199
1.500	1.767	1.410	2.617
1.750	2.405	1.900	4.144
2.000	3.142	2.500	5.316

12

Anchorage

13

By Gerry Weiler
Kevin Lemieux

Tilt-up Concrete Wall Panels

13

Tilt-up

13.1   Introduction

Tilt-up concrete buildings have been constructed in Canada for over 50 years and have developed into a popular material of choice for commercial and industrial structures in many areas. The Canadian codes first addressed tilt-up concrete wall panels in CSA A23.3–94 Design of Concrete Structures. The latest edition, CSA A23.3–14, includes minor modifications to the provisions for tilt-up in Chapter 23, and has added a new clause with specific seismic design requirements for tilt-up construction in Chapter 21.

Changes in NBCC 2015, Part 4 will have an effect on the seismic design of low rise buildings, including those using tilt-up panels, particularly for buildings in high-risk seismic areas where the seismic design loads will increase. Also, Seismic Force Modification Factors, R_d and R_o, specific for Tilt-up Construction have been added to the systems table in Part 4.

This guide provides comprehensive design recommendations for tilt-up panels with vertical loading, transverse out-of-plane loading and in-plane shear. It also provides recommendations for panel connections, construction details and tolerances. Further development of this design standard is required in areas including:

- Analysis and design of moderately ductile walls and frames with R_d = 2.0.

13.2   Concrete Wall Panel Analysis Method

Tilt-up concrete wall panels are most often used as load bearing wall elements spanning vertically from the floor slab to the roof. Bending moments induced by out-of-plane transverse loads (wind or seismic) may be significantly greater than those caused by eccentric axial loads. The P–Δ effects due to axial loads will increase these moments. Limit states failure of a slender wall panel is defined as the point where the maximum factored bending moment at or near mid height exceeds the resisting moment of the concrete section.

The maximum bending moment can be separated into two components:
- Primary moment due to applied loadings.
- Secondary moment due to P–Δ deflections.

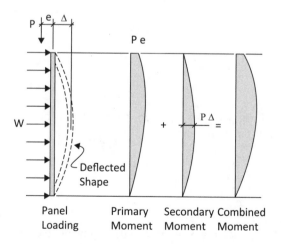

Primary moments are determined from a conventional static analysis. In most cases, it is the moment at mid height that is of concern since this is where maximum bending moment and P–Δ deflections and eventual failure will normally occur.

13

Tilt-up

Secondary moments are the result of an axial load, P, acting on a deflected shape; hence the term P–Δ moments. The deflection of a wall panel is dependent on its bending stiffness. For reinforced concrete, this bending stiffness can be difficult to evaluate since it varies with a number of parameters, including:

- Wall thickness
- Concrete compressive strength
- Concrete tensile strength
- Reinforcing steel quantities
- Location of reinforcing steel in the wall section
- Applied axial load
- Bending curvature

The bending properties of a concrete section behave in an elasto-plastic manner. Both strength and stiffness will vary with changes in axial compression and bending curvature. In most cases, however, the main concern is the failure condition due to factored loads, where the resisting moment and bending stiffness can be determined with reasonable accuracy by simple calculations.

13.2.1. Moment Magnifier for P–Δ Analysis

CSA A23.3, Chapter 23 has adopted the moment magnifier method of analysis for evaluation of the P–Δ effects in slender concrete walls subjected to the combined effects of axial and out-of-plane lateral loads. This method is poorly understood by most designers, primarily because of the complex way it has been employed in various codes for the design of slender columns in concrete, steel and wood. The following is a brief summary of the derivation for the moment magnifier equation.

Maximum bending moment at panel mid-height is given by:

$$M_{max} = M_0 + P \Delta_{max}$$

where

M_{max} = maximum moment including P–Δ effects
M_0 = maximum moment not including P–Δ effects
P = applied axial load
Δ_{max} = maximum panel deflection at mid height

The relation between maximum bending moment and deflection is:

$$\Delta_{max} = \frac{5}{48} \frac{\ell^2 \, M_{max}}{EI} = \frac{M_{max}}{K_b}$$

where

K_b = Bending stiffness, expressed as a bending moment per unit of deflection
ℓ = clear vertical span of the member
K_b = $\dfrac{M_{max}}{\Delta_{max}} = \dfrac{48 \, EI}{5\ell^2}$
E = Elastic Modulus
I = Moment of inertia

The maximum moment, M_{max}, can now be written in the following form:

$$M_{max} = M_0 + \frac{P \, M_{max}}{K_b}$$

Rearranging the parameters:

$$M_{max} = M_0 \left(\frac{1}{1 - P / K_b} \right) = M_0 \, \delta$$

Where

$$\delta = \left(\frac{1}{1 - P / K_b} \right) = \text{moment magnification factor}$$

Alternately, the maximum bending moment including P–Δ effects may be obtained by iteration of deflection calculations with applied axial and lateral loadings. The results obtained by either the iterative method or moment magnifier method will be identical as long as the loading conditions, panel geometry and assumptions for material properties are consistent.

13.2.2. Panel Bending Stiffness

The parameter K_b is used to define bending stiffness of the wall panel:

$$K_b = \frac{48 \, EI}{5\ell^2} \quad \text{(kN-m/m)}$$

Bending stiffness represents the maximum bending moment in the panel divided by the maximum deflection:

$$K_b = \frac{M_{max}}{\Delta_{max}}$$

Where the member is simply supported, the maximum moment will occur at or near mid-span. It is worthwhile to note that K_b is approximately equivalent to the more familiar Euler critical buckling load:

$$P_{cr} = \frac{\pi^2 \, EI}{\ell^2}$$

Critical buckling capacity is a by-product of the P–Δ analysis and represents the maximum axial load that can be sustained by a pin ended slender column (or wall) in the absence of any other applied loadings. The factor $\pi^2 = 9.87$ defines a sinusoidal single curvature deflected shape due to an axial load applied with a small initiating eccentricity. The deflected shape for a beam subjected to a uniformly distributed transverse load would be parabolic and the appropriate factor would be 48/5 = 9.6. This is considered to be more representative for tilt-up panels. P_{cr} is expressed as a force (kN), and K_b is expressed as a bending moment per unit deflection (kN–m/m).

This method of analysis assumes that the bending properties of the cross section are elastic. However, reinforced concrete sections do not behave elastically throughout the full range of flexural bending. Testing (ref 2) has shown that the calculated properties of the cracked concrete section at failure load levels provide accurate but somewhat conservative results for design of slender concrete walls such as employed in tilt-up construction. This was originally adopted by the Uniform Building Code in the 1990's, and is now the basis for design of tilt-up wall panels in ACI 318 and CSA A23.3. The main limitation to this method is that it is only applicable where axial compression loads are relatively small or less than about 0.1 $A_g \, f_c'$. Typically, the axial loads on wall panels for most tilt-up buildings are below this threshold.

13

Tilt-up

13.2.3.   CSA A23.3 Chapter 23 Requirements

The basic design equations given in Chapter 23 are:

$$M_f = M_b \delta_b \tag{23.2}$$
$$\text{and } M_r \geq M_f \tag{23.3}$$

where

M_f	=	factored moment including P–Δ effects
M_b	=	factored moment not including P–Δ effects
M_r	=	factored resisting moment
δ_b	=	moment magnification factor

When combined axial and transverse loadings are applied to a wall panel, the maximum moment can be calculated as follows:

$$M_f = \text{Primary Moment} + \text{Secondary Moment}$$
$$= M_b + P_f \Delta$$

$$M_b = \frac{w_f \ell^2}{8} + P_{tf} \frac{e}{2} + (P_{wf} + P_{tf}) \Delta_0$$

P_f	=	$P_{wf} + P_{tf}$ = factored axial load at mid height
P_{wf}	=	factored panel weight above mid height
P_{tf}	=	factored axial load at the top of panel
e	=	axial load eccentricity at the top of the panel
w_f	=	factored lateral load
Δ_0	=	initial deflection at panel mid height
Δ	=	maximum total deflection at mid height = M_f / K_b

When there are other forces contributing to the primary moment such as transverse point loads, these should also be included when computing M_b.

Clause 23.3.1.2 specifies an upper limit for axial load on the mid-height cross section:

$$\frac{P_{wf} + P_{tf}}{A_g} < 0.09 \, \phi_c \, f'_c \tag{23.1}$$

The factored moment M_f can now be written in the following form:

$$M_f = M_b + \frac{P_f M_f}{K_{bf}} = M_b \left\{ \frac{1}{1 - P_f / K_{bf}} \right\} = M_b \delta_b$$

$$\delta_b = \frac{1}{1 - P_f / K_{bf}} = \text{moment magnification factor} \geq 1.0$$

Bending stiffness, K_{bf} is given by:

$$K_{bf} = \frac{48 \, E_c I_{cr}}{5\ell^2} \quad (\text{kN-m/m})$$

where

ℓ	=	unsupported vertical span of wall panel (m)
E_c	=	$4500 \sqrt{f'_c}$ (MPa	$\tag{8.2}$

I_{cr} = cracked section moment of inertia (mm⁴)

$$I_{cr} = \frac{bc^3}{3} + \frac{E_s}{E_c} A_{s,eff} (d - c)^2$$

$A_{s,eff}$ = effective area of reinforcement (mm²)
E_s = 200,000 (MPa)
d = reinforcement depth (mm)
b = width of section (mm)

$$a = \frac{A_{s,eff} \, \phi_s \, f_y}{\alpha_1 \, \phi_c \, f_c' \, b} \quad \text{and} \quad c = \frac{a}{\beta_1} \quad \text{(mm)}$$

α_1	=	$0.85 - 0.0015 f_c' \geq 0.67$	(10.1)
	=	0.805 for 30 MPa concrete	

β_1	=	$0.97 - 0.0025 f_c' \geq 0.67$	(10.2)
	=	0.895 for 30 MPa concrete	

ϕ_c = 0.65   and ϕ_s = 0.85,   See Clauses 8.4.2 and 8.4.3.

For design of panels in buildings, it is necessary to apply strength resistance factors to account for material variations and workmanship. The factors ϕ_c and ϕ_s are used to modify the calculated strength of concrete and the steel reinforcement in accordance with Chapter 10 provisions.

In addition, the bending stiffness must also be modified using the member resistance factor ϕ_m, as required by Clause 10.15.3.1. This effectively increases P–Δ magnification:

$$\delta_b = \frac{1}{1 - \dfrac{P_f}{\phi_m K_{bf}}}$$

where

ϕ_m = 0.75

The primary reason for applying this factor is to take into account the effect of construction tolerance variations on the bending stiffness. For example, a 140 mm panel would have a cracked section moment of inertia, I_{cr} as follows:

Assume:

f_c' = 30 MPa f_y = 400 MPa E_c = 24,650 MPa E_s = 200,000 MPa
b = 300 mm h = 140 mm d = 70 mm $A_{s,eff}$ = 200 mm²

$$a = \frac{200 \times 0.85 \times 400}{0.805 \times 0.65 \times 30 \times 300} = 14.44 \text{ mm}$$

$$c = \frac{14.44}{0.895} = 16.1 \text{ mm}$$

$$I_{cr} = \frac{300 \times 16.1^3}{3} + \frac{200,000}{24,650} \times 200 (70 - 16.1)^2$$

$$= (0.42 + 4.71) \times 10^6 = 5.13 \times 10^6 \text{ mm}^4$$

A reduction in d from 70mm to 60mm would result in a decrease in I_{cr}

13

Tilt-up

$$I_{cr} \quad = \quad 3.54 \times 10^6 \quad mm^4$$

$$\text{Reduction} = \frac{3.54}{5.13} = 0.69 \ (31\%)$$

The resisting moment M_r is calculated by conventional methods defined in Chapter 10.

$$M_r \quad = \quad \phi_s A_{s,eff} f_y (d - a/2) \ \geq \ M_f \tag{23.3}$$

A modification in the area of reinforcement is used to partially account for the increased bending moment resistance due to applied axial loads:

$$A_{s,eff} \quad = \quad A_s + \frac{P_f}{\phi_s f_y} \left(\frac{h}{2d} \right) \tag{23.4}$$

The axial load at the critical section or panel mid height is used.

It is noted that axial loads on the concrete section will also increase the bending stiffness, resulting in a subsequent reduction in mid-height deflection. The Uniform Building Code (UBC 97) and ACI 318 code has recognized this for design of tilt-up panels where the modified area of reinforcement is used in the evaluation of bending stiffness. However, CSA A23.3 does not specifically permit this modification.

Clause 10.5.2 provides limits for tension reinforcement in flexural members:

$$\frac{c}{d} \leq \frac{700}{700 + f_y} \tag{10.5}$$

or

$$\frac{A_s}{bd} \leq \frac{\alpha_1 \beta_1 \phi_c f'_c}{\phi_s f_y} \left(\frac{700}{700 + f_y} \right)$$

This should be routinely checked, particularly for panels with large openings and narrow legs.

13.2.4.   Panel Height to Thickness Limits

Clause 23.2.3 provides a limitation to the maximum height to thickness ratios of tilt-up panels, depending on the reinforcement configuration used in the cross section:

	Maximum ℓ/t
• Single mat of reinforcement (centered in the panel cross section)	50
• 2 mats of reinforcement (25mm clear of each face)	65

The strength design provisions in Chapter 23 are self-limiting, and arbitrary limits on panel structural thickness or maximum deflections due to factored loads are not necessarily required. These requirements do, however, serve as practical limits for slender concrete walls since reinforcement quantities become excessive beyond this, and thicker concrete sections will often be more economical. Panel height to thickness ratios may also be controlled by limitations on service load deflections. The limits indicated above should be divided by 2 for cantilever panels on a fixed base.

13.3   Deflection Limitations Due to Service Loads

Limitations on out-of-plane or lateral deflections for slender walls have long been a concern of building officials and code committees, not only because of the increased bending moments due to P–Δ effects, but also the potential for longterm warping of these elements. Experience with actual buildings, however, suggests that long-term deflections are not a serious problem. This is partially due to the fact that the lateral forces causing bending in panels are largely transient in nature, and the concrete section at service load conditions is much stiffer than at factored loads.

NBCC 2015 provides a reduction in service loads by the application of the Serviceability Limit State (SLS) Importance Factor Is = 0.9 for snow loads and Iw = 0.75 for wind loads. Some guidance is provided in the NBCC Structural Commentaries for the effect of companion loads when checking serviceability requirements. This can be important for lateral deflections on tilt-up panels where eccentric axial loads occur in combination with transverse loading due to wind, but the maximum effect of each will rarely coincide. It is left to the designer to make a judgement as to whether reductions in service companion loads are appropriate.

13.3.1.   CSA A23.3 Requirements for Deflection Limitation

Clause 23.3.2 of CSA A23.3 provides a limit of $\ell/100$ for non-seismic transverse deflections of walls for service loads. The method for calculating the deflection Δ_s is as follows:

$$\Delta_s \;=\; \frac{5}{48}\,\frac{M_s\,\ell^2}{E_c\,I_e} = \frac{M_s}{K_{bs}} \tag{23.5}$$

$$M_s \;=\; M_{bs}\,\delta_{bs}$$

$$M_{bs} \;=\; \frac{w_s\,\ell^2}{8} + P_{ts}\,\frac{e}{2} + (P_{ws} + P_{ts})\,\Delta_0$$

$$\delta_{bs} \;=\; \frac{1}{1 - \dfrac{P_s}{K_{bs}}} \geq 1.0$$

$$P_s \;=\; P_{ws} + P_{ts}$$

$$K_{bs} \;=\; \frac{48\,E_c\,I_e}{5\,\ell^2} \quad (kN\text{-}m/m)$$

I_e is the effective moment of inertia as defined in Clause 9.8.2.3:

$$I_e \;=\; I_{cr} + (\,I_g - I_{cr})\left(\frac{M_{cr}}{M_a}\right)^3 \leq I_g \tag{9.1}$$

and

$$M_{cr} \;=\; \frac{f_r\,I_g}{Y_t} \tag{9.2}$$

where f_r shall be taken as half the value given in Equation 8.3.

$$f_r \;=\; \frac{1}{2}\,(0.6\,\lambda\,\sqrt{f_c'}\,)\ (MPa)$$

13

Tilt-up

I_{cr} should be based on a triangular stress distribution as follows:

$$I_{cr} = \frac{b\,(kd)^3}{3} + \frac{E_s\,A_s\,(d-kd)^2}{E_c}$$

where $kd = \dfrac{-n\,A_s + \sqrt{(n\,A_s)^2 + 2\,b\,n\,A_s\,d}}{b}$; $n = \dfrac{E_s}{E_c}$

Alternatively, a rectangular stress distribution can be used, giving slightly less conservative results.

The prescribed deflection limit of ℓ/100 will sometimes control the design of panels with large openings, or with reinforcement in the middle of the concrete cross-section. A thicker cross section may be necessary to meet the requirements. See Design Examples for deflection calculations.

The method of analysis adopted by CSA A23.3 for service load deflections of concrete members due to flexure has reduced the value of f_r to half of the value in Equation 8.3 to give better results with thinner concrete sections, such as tilt-up wall panels.

13.3.2.   Creep and Initial Deflections

Permanent out-of-plane panel deflections can occur as a result of initial deflections in combination with the effects of long-term creep in concrete under sustained loading. Initial out-of-straightness or warping of tilt-up panels may be the result of uneven casting beds, excessive bending caused by the tilting process, thermal gradients, or shrinkage rate variations. The advent of laser screeds for casting floor slabs on which panels are poured has lessened the problem in recent years. Clause 23.3.1.4 prescribes an initial deflection $\Delta_0 = \ell / 400$ at mid height of the panel. This has generally been adequate for most applications.

Long-term creep deflections may be imparted due to sustained axial loading, particularly if these loads are applied with significant eccentricities relative to the centerline axis of the panel. These can be accounted for in design by increasing the initial deflection of the panel. Fortunately, this has not been a significant problem historically for tilt-up panels, since applied axial loads are often relatively small.

13.4   Loading Conditions

13.4.1.   Load Combinations

NBCC 2015 uses load factors and load combinations that includes the concept of "Companion Loads". This method is much more rational for design load evaluation and is particularly suited to tilt-up panels. The following load combinations should be considered:

Principal Loads	Companion Loads
1) 1.4D	—
2) (1.25D or 0.9D) + 1.5L	1.0S or 0.4W
3) (1.25D or 0.9D) + 1.5S	1.0L or 0.4W
4) (1.25D or 0.9D) + 1.4W	0.5L or 0.5S
5) 1.0D + 1.0E	0.5L + 0.25S

A reduced load factor is used for companion loads when used in combination with the principal loads. Additionally, load combinations with companion load factors of zero must also be considered. Load combinations that include crane loads can also be found in NBCC 2015. For 2015, the NBCC has increased the companion load factor in combinations (2) and (3) for snow or live load to 1.0 from 0.5

as the previous factor could have resulted in some non-conservative load combinations. Where the companion live load is for storage areas, equipment areas and service rooms, the load factor must be increased by 0.5. A load factor of 1.0 is used for seismic loads since they are already considered to be ultimate loads.

Combinations (1) through (3) seldom apply to tilt-up design except for shorter panels with large axial loads. In most cases, combination (4) or (5) will control the design for out-of-plane bending. For the common load case of large bending moments due to lateral forces combined with small axial loads, the critical section for bending will occur near panel mid height. As axial load and top end eccentricity increase, this point will shift upwards.

Combinations (4) and (5) apply to in-plane shear forces on tilt-up panels causing overturning, uplift or sliding. NBCC does not specifically permit live loads or snow loads to be used to increase the resistance. This will affect calculations for sliding resistance and panel overturning.

13.4.2.   Lateral Wind Loads on Panel Elements

Wind pressures are applied to the wall panel as uniformly distributed lateral loads. For exterior walls, lateral load effects will often be the dominant factor in the design. NBCC 2015 Clause 4.1.7.3 specifies the static procedure for wind pressure as the algebraic difference between external and internal pressure or suction:

p = $I_w \, q \, C_t \, (C_e \, C_p \, C_g + C_{ei} \, C_{pi} \, C_{gi})$

I_w = Importance factor. For normal importance buildings, this will be 1.0 for strength calculations (ULS) and 0.75 for serviceability (SLS).

q = 1 in 50 year reference velocity pressure.

C_e = External exposure factor. Depends on nature of surrounding terrain and building height. A value between 0.7 and 1.0 is applicable for most single storey buildings.

C_t = Topographic factor to account for buildings on hills or escarpments. 1.0 for most cases on level terrain.

$C_p \, C_g$ = Combined exterior pressure/gust coefficient. Values in the order of +1.3 or −1.5 are often used for individual tilt-up wall panels per Figure 4.1.7.6-B.

C_{ei} = Internal exposure factor. Typically calculated using one half the building height.

C_{pi} = Interior pressure coefficient. Values of +0.3 or −0.45 will be applicable for buildings with only a few small openings and ± 0.7 for a significant number of large openings.

C_{gi} = Interior gust effect factor = 2.0 (a calculation is also permitted for large structures).

Typical lateral wind load on a 10m high x 7m wide panel for a single storey warehouse in an urban environment:

Assume q = 0.5 kPa;   Panel area = 7 x 10 = 70 m²

Exposure factor $C_e = 0.7 \left(\dfrac{h}{12} \right)^{0.3} \geq 0.7$

External C_e = $0.7 \left(\dfrac{10}{12} \right)^{0.3} = 0.66 \rightarrow 0.7$ min

Internal C_{ei} = $0.7 \left(\dfrac{5}{12} \right)^{0.3} = 0.54 \rightarrow 0.7$ min

Topographic factor $C_t = 1.0$

13

Tilt-up

Pressure coefficients:

External $C_pC_g = +1.3$ and -1.5 (from Figure 4.1.7.6-B)

Internal $C_{pi} = -0.45$ and $+0.30$; $C_{gi} = 2.0$
(positive denotes forces toward the surface and negative denotes away from the surface)

Importance factor: ULS $I_w = 1.0$ for normal importance;   SLS $I_w = 0.75$ for all categories

Strength (ULS):
Inward pressure $p = 1.0 \times 0.5 \times 1.0 \times (0.7 \times 1.3 + 0.7 \times 0.45 \times 2.0) = 0.77$ kPa
Outward pressure $p = 1.0 \times 0.5 \times 1.0 \times [0.7 \times (-1.5) + 0.7 \times (-0.30) \times 2.0] = -0.735$ kPa

Deflection (SLS):
Inward pressure $p = 0.75 \times 0.77 = 0.58$ kPa
Outward pressure $p = 0.75 \times (-0.735) = -0.55$ kPa

13.4.3.   Lateral Seismic Loads on Panel Elements

Seismic forces for the design of individual wall panels are obtained from NBCC 2015 Clause 4.1.8.18 for Elements of Structures. The basic relation is:

V_p = $0.3\, F_a\, S_a(0.2)\, I_E\, S_p\, W_p$
F_a = $F(0.2)$ as defined in Table 4.1.8.4-B, site coefficient for spectral acceleration that is dependent on Site Class and PGA_{ref}.
$S_a(0.2)$= 5% damped spectral response acceleration at 0.2 seconds. The value of this coefficient will depend on the building site location and is obtained from the published climatic data.

S_p = $\dfrac{C_p\, A_r\, A_x}{R_p}$ where $0.7 \leq S_p \leq 4.0$

A_x = Height Factor $= 1 + 2\,\dfrac{h_x}{h_n}$

h_x, h_n = height above the base level. For out-of-plane forces, h_x can be taken as the center of mass of the panel at each storey.
I_E = Importance Factor for Earthquakes = 1.0 for Normal Importance Buildings
W_p = Weight of component or element

Category 1 of NBCC Table 4.1.8.18 will typically apply to the design of tilt-up panel elements for out-of-plane bending:

C_p = Element or component factor. Usually taken as 1.0.
A_r = Element or component force amplification factor. For short period buildings with flexible walls, this is equal to 1.0.
R_p = Element or component response modification factor associated with the ductility of the component.
      = 2.5 for most reinforced tilt-up wall panels.

Typical lateral seismic design forces for tilt-up wall panels in a single storey building in Vancouver with stiff soil conditions would be:

$$PGA = 0.369$$
$$S_a(0.2) = 0.848$$
$$S_a(0.2)/PGA = 2.3 > 2.0 \rightarrow PGA_{ref} = PGA = 0.369$$
$$F_a = F(0.2) = 0.96 \quad \text{(interpolated from Table 4.1.8.4-B, Site Class D)}$$
$$h_x = 0.5\,h_n$$
$$A_x = 1 + 2 \times \frac{0.5\,h_n}{1.0\,h_n} = 2.0$$
$$S_p = \frac{1.0 \times 1.0 \times 2.0}{2.5} = 0.8$$
$$I_E = 1.0$$
$$V_p = 0.3 \times 0.96 \times 0.848 \times 1.0 \times 0.8\,W_p = 0.20\,W_p$$

This is a slight reduction from NBCC 2010 due to changes for $S_a(0.2)$ and F_a at this location. For cantilever walls and large parapets, A_r should be increased to 2.5 for Category 2.

Lateral seismic forces will sometimes exceed wind pressure, particularly for thicker panels in high seismic zones.

13.4.4.   Axial Loads

Vertical loads from roof or floor joists can often be considered as uniformly distributed line loads for the purposes of wall panel design. These loads should be applied at an eccentricity to the centerline axis of the panel either intentionally or due to accidental bearing irregularities. A *minimum eccentricity* of one half the panel thickness is recommended, and should be in addition to the effect of lateral pressures.

Axial load eccentricities should not be used to reduce the bending moment caused by wind or seismic lateral loads. In addition, wind uplift on roof members should not be used to reduced axial load.

Where large concentrated loads are supported directly on the panel, the effective width b_d of the design cross-section should be limited as indicated in the figure below. Additional reinforcement, where required, should be located in this area of the panel. The maximum factored axial stress on the design width, b_d, is limited to $0.09\,\phi_c\,f'_c$ for the purposes of using the methods in Chapter 23.

13

Tilt-up

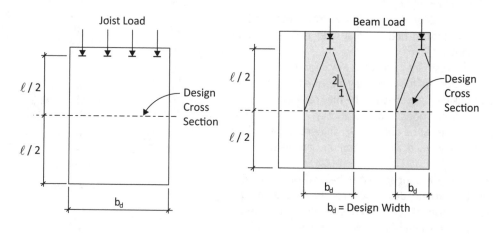

13.4.5.   Panel Self Weight

The effect of panel self-weight must be considered since it represents a significant contribution to P–Δ moments in slender walls. It is usually sufficient to assume that the weight of panel above the mid-height section acts as an additional concentrated axial load applied at the top with no eccentricity. This is illustrated by the following derivation:

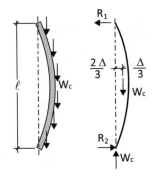

$$R_1 \quad = \quad R_2 = \frac{2\,W_c\,\Delta}{3\,\ell}$$

The mid-height moment is:

$$M \quad = \quad \frac{R_1\,\ell}{2} + \frac{W_c}{2}\,\frac{\Delta}{3} = \frac{W_c\,\Delta}{2}$$

$$W_c \quad = \quad \text{self weight of concrete wall panel}$$

Displacements at the top of the panel due to roof diaphragm flexibility have little or no effect on a pinned base panel. This is because full lateral support from the roof or floor assembly can almost always be assumed. The additional P–Δ effects due to the component of self-weight resulting from a 10 m high panel that is leaning 50 mm is negligible.

13.5   Continuity and End Fixity

Most tilt-up panels are designed as simply supported vertical slabs spanning between the footings and the roof structure. Where a panel is rigidly connected to the floor slab or the footing, some degree of end fixity can be considered. In other cases, a panel may be laterally supported by an intermediate floor, resulting in negative bending at the point of support and a reduction of positive bending between supports. It is difficult to analyze this condition and at best only approximate methods are practical.

Some of the analysis problems and limitations include the following:

- The bending moments are affected by lateral deflection at supports, particularly at flexible roof diaphragms.
- Effects of loading due to soil pressure below the floor slab may be significant.
- Lateral wind or seismic forces from intermediate floor or roof structures may add to the bending moments.
- Lateral restraint provided by footings or the connection to footings may be questionable such that full end fixity may not be fully realized.
- P–Δ calculations for statically indeterminate elements must be obtained by an iterative technique that is only practical with computer analysis.

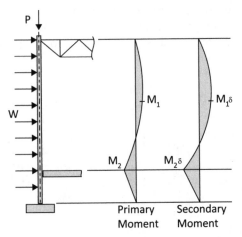

Because of these concerns, it is best to be somewhat conservative in the design approach. One technique involves the use of a reduced effective panel height coefficient, k. A value of k = 0.8 is suitable for an elastic column fixed at one end and pinned at the other. Since concrete stiffness is not uniform and the ends are seldom completely fixed, k should not be taken as less than 0.9.

An alternative method of analysis is based on the assumption that the initial positive mid-height moment and negative support moment of the panel will increase proportionally by approximately the same amount when considering P–Δ magnifications. The primary moments are first calculated by conventional elastic methods. Both the positive and negative moments are then increased proportionally by the P–Δ moment magnifier.

Sometimes, designers try to reduce the effective panel height by connecting bottom chord extensions from the roof joists to the panel. In addition, they may assume that this also provides end fixity, thereby reducing the effective height even more. This technique could be dangerous since it could actually increase the panel bending moment due to joist rotation at the end support, and impart loads on the joist and connections that may not be fully accounted for by the joist designer. In general, it is not recommended for most applications.

The designer should also be aware that there might be a temporary condition during construction where lateral support at the intermediate floor slab is not present. This will increase the unsupported height of the panel and could become the controlling design condition. It is not sufficient to assume that this will be addressed by those responsible for tilt-up panel lifting and bracing.

13.6   Openings in Panels

The effect of openings for out-of-plane bending in tilt-up panels can be approximated by a simple one dimensional strip analysis that gives sufficient accuracy and economy for most designs.

Where openings occur, the entire lateral and axial load (including self weight) is distributed to supporting legs or design strips each side of the opening. The effective width of the strip should be limited to about 12 times the panel thickness in order to protect against localized stress concentrations at the edge of the opening. This limitation is intended primarily as a practical guideline. The tributary width for design can usually be taken as the leg width plus one half the width of adjacent openings.

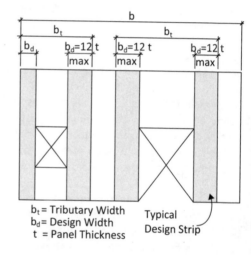

b_t = Tributary Width
b_d = Design Width
t = Panel Thickness
Typical Design Strip

13

Tilt-up

For very wide openings, it may be necessary to provide an edge thickening or pilaster to carry the loads at each supporting leg. In addition, a horizontal header beam may also be required.

13.7   Isolated Footings and Pier Foundations

In many areas of Canada, soil conditions or frost depth requirements dictate the use of pier foundations. For convenience and economy, these piers are often located at the panel joints only. This has the effect of concentrating the vertical stresses at the edges of the panel.

Vertical support should effectively be grouped at either end as indicated in the following figure. Where the clear panel height is greater than approximately 1½ times the clear distance between footings, the effect of isolated footings can usually be ignored.

Depending on the width of pier cap and effective bearing area at the bottom of the panel, additional hooked reinforcing or confining ties may be required to prevent localized shear or bearing failure. In many cases, there is continuous horizontal support provided at the top by the roof deck and at the bottom by ties to the floor slab. Where this occurs, lateral loads can be uniformly distributed across the width of panel.

Where panels contain multiple openings across the width, the exterior legs that are supported on the isolated footings should be designed to resist the axial load plus the tributary lateral load attributed to that portion of the panel. The intermediate legs may be designed to resist their tributary lateral loads only.

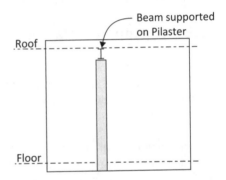

13.8 Stiffening Pilasters

Extra panel thickenings or pilasters are sometimes necessary to support heavy vertical loads. They may also be required at the edge of large openings as suggested in Section 13.6 of this Guide.

Some designers specify ties around all vertical reinforcing bars in a pilaster for the full height of the panel in accordance with the requirements in CSA A23.3 Chapter 10, for compression members. The axial stresses from roof or floor beams are usually concentrated at the point of bearing and quickly dissipate into the panel. The panel design is often controlled by flexural tension of the vertical reinforcement and confining ties may not necessarily be required by code.

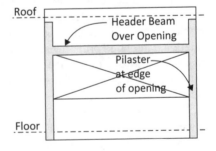

CSA A23.3 is unclear as to when a pilaster member is to be considered a column and subject to the requirements for ties. The definition for non-bearing walls in Chapter 3 is based on a factored vertical axial stress of less than $0.04\ f_c'$. Provisions in Clause 21.7 imply that a compression stress of $0.09\ \phi_c\ f_c'$ in a member can be used as the threshold below which it need not be considered as a column requiring confinement ties. As a minimum, ties should be specified in the vicinity of the point of bearing to ensure that the axial load is adequately distributed into the panel and that local bearing failure does not occur.

13.9 Concentrated Lateral Loads

Concentrated lateral loads can occur as a result of the following:
a) Suspended elements such as canopies
b) End reactions from header beams over wide panel openings
c) Lateral wind or seismic forces from intermediate floor or roof structures
d) Lateral loads from cranes or other equipment

The effect of these loads can be included in the analysis by adding the localized bending moment directly to the other primary bending moments. This is a somewhat simplistic approach, and the results obtained should be applied with some discretion.

The following illustrates the additional horizontal (and vertical) loads resulting from an attached canopy:

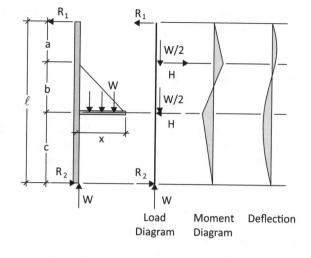

W = Weight of Canopy

R_1 = End reaction = $\dfrac{W\,x}{2\,\ell}$ = R_2

H = horiz. line load = $\dfrac{W\,x}{2b}$

Load Diagram   Moment Diagram   Deflection

Where the horizontal reaction is a point load, the effective panel design width should be limited to about 12 times the panel thickness at the point of application. The load should be distributed evenly across this design width. Additional reinforcement may be required in this localized area.

13.10 Cantilever Panels

Tilt-up panels are sometimes required to function as vertical cantilevers. Typical examples include free-standing signs and screen walls, or parapets above the roof of a building. If the cantilever is high, P–Δ effects will increase the bending moments on the panel. A simple but conservative way to analyze a fixed end cantilever panel is to assume a simply supported panel with a height 2 times the cantilever height. The more correct method of analysis is the following:

M_b = $\dfrac{w_f\,\ell_c^2}{2}$; ℓ_c = cantilever height

w_f = factored lateral load on cantilever (kPa)

M_f = $M_b + \dfrac{W_c\,\Delta}{3} = M_b + \dfrac{W_c}{3}\dfrac{M_f\,\ell_c^2}{4\,E\,I}$

W_c = factored weight of concrete panel above the base

Δ = $\dfrac{M_f\,\ell_c^2}{4\,E\,I} = \dfrac{M_f}{K_b}$; $K_{bc} = \dfrac{4\,E\,I}{\ell_c^2}$

M_f = $M_b\,\delta_c$ where $\delta_c = \dfrac{1}{1 - \dfrac{W_c}{3\,\phi_m\,K_{bc}}}$

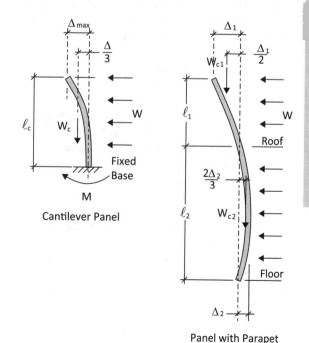

Cantilever Panel

Panel with Parapet

The dynamic effects of wind buffeting or seismic accelerations may temporarily increase the cantilever deflection since there may be very little structural damping. This should be taken into account when selecting design forces.

13

Tilt-up

Where the cantilever is a high parapet, a more detailed analysis may be required. As can be seen by the adjacent diagram, rotation of the panel section at the roof connection can significantly increase the deflection and the associated P–Δ effects.

13.11 In–Plane Shear

Design procedures for in-plane shear forces are distinctly different from the methods used in design for out-of-plane bending. Forces from the roof or floor diaphragms acting parallel to the plane of the wall induce shears stresses and overturning moments in the panels. In seismic areas, the in-plane shear requirements may control the panel thickness and reinforcing design.

The following are design considerations for tilt-up panels subjected to in-plane forces:
- Resistance to sliding
- Resistance to panel overturning
- Concrete shear resistance
- Increased localized axial forces and out-of-plane P–Δ effects
- Load distribution to foundations
- Frame action in panels with openings
- Seismic ductility

13.11.1.   Resistance to Panel Overturning

When roof and floor diaphragm forces are applied parallel to the plane of the wall panels, overturning moments and in-plane shears are induced. The overturning moments are usually taken about an outside corner of panel. Resistance to overturning is obtained from a combination of panel weight, tributary roof or floor loads, panel edge connectors and tie down anchors to the foundations. The actual point of rotation will be close to the corner of the panel, at the center of the bearing area between the footing and the soil. In most cases, it is sufficient to assume that the width of bearing is zero and does not contribute to the overturning moment. This should be checked when R is large and soil bearing capacity is small. For large R values, spalling of the concrete may occur which will reduce the effective length and should be accounted for.

Factored Overturning Moment
$M_{of} \leq$ Resisting Moment M_r

M_{of} = $V_{roof} \times \ell_{roof} + V_{floor} \times \ell_{floor} + V_{panel} \times \ell_{panel}$
V_{roof} = roof diaphragm shear force
ℓ_{roof} = distance from roof diaphragm to bottom of panel
V_{floor} = floor diaphragm shear force
ℓ_{floor} = distance from floor diaphragm to bottom of panel
V_{panel} = panel self-weight shear force (seismic only)
ℓ_{panel} = distance from panel center of gravity to bottom of panel

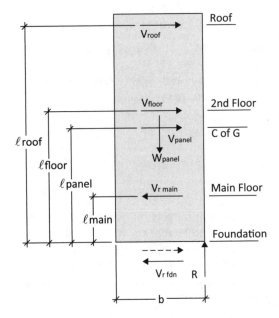

Panel Overturning Resistance

The resisting moment is given by:

$$M_r = (W_{roof} + W_{floor} + W_{panel})\frac{b}{2} + V_{r\,main}\,\ell_{main}$$

W_{roof} = weight of tributary roof structure
W_{floor} = weight of tributary floor structure
W_{panel} = weight of panel
$V_{r\,main}$ = resisting shear force at main floor
ℓ_{main} = distance from main floor to bottom of panel
b   = width of panel

In addition:

$V_{r\,fdn}$ = resisting shear force at the foundation of panel. This could be a negative number depending on the wall geometry and number of panel edge connectors used.
R   = vertical reaction at footing

All applied shear forces contributing to overturning are factored. Forces and weights that resist overturning must be reduced in accordance with the load combination factors given in NBCC 4.1.3.2 and as outlined previously in Section 13.4.1 of this Design Guide. No additional safety factor need be applied. The unsupported edge of the panel must be checked to ensure that out-of-plane instability does not occur as a result of increased compression forces due to overturning. If this becomes a problem, additional reinforcement or edge thickenings can be used. Within some limits, all the panels can be connected together such that a panel edge in compression is stabilized by the adjacent panel edge in tension.

Where the overturning capacity is insufficient, edge connections to an adjacent panel or tie down anchors to the foundation can be added until the overturning equation is satisfied:

Additional M_r = b x connector capacity

Capacity design principles may require the connections to be designed for the full weight of the adjacent panels including the applied loads. This additional uplift resistance may be limited to the weight of connected foundations or adjacent panel(s). Foundations must also be checked to ensure that the structural capacity of the footing or the soil resisting pressure is not exceeded. The soil resisting pressure is a factored or ultimate limit states value (ULS), and may be 1.5 to 2 times greater than the normal allowable or serviceability soil bearing pressure (SLS). The geotechnical engineer should be consulted for assistance.

13.11.2. Resistance to Sliding

Resistance to sliding forces can be obtained by a combination of friction to the footing and connections to the floor slab or foundation. The coefficient of friction for factored sliding resistance between the bottom of the panel and the footing can usually be taken as approximately 0.5. For seismic design, Clause 21.7.3.3 defines the sliding shear friction resistance as being calculated in accordance with Clause 11.5.1 using c = 0, μ = 0.75 and ϕ_c = 0.65. In some cases, friction may be all that is required but shear connectors at the base are still required for structural integrity. When friction resistance is insufficient, it can be supplemented by mechanical connections between the panel and footing or floor slab. A minimum of 2 connections per panel are recommended for all panels, but particularly when resisting seismic forces. These may be cast-in-place reinforcement dowels or welded embedded metal connections. Friction between the soil and footing or floor slab, or passive soil resistance must also be checked. The geotechnical engineer should be consulted for assistance.

13

Tilt-up

13.11.3. Concrete Shear Resistance for In-Plane Forces

Requirements for concrete shear resistance for non-seismic conditions are covered in CSA A23.3 Chapter 11. Clause 11.3 requires:

$$V_r \geq V_f \tag{11.3}$$

$$\text{and } V_r = V_c + V_s \, (+ V_p) \tag{11.4}$$

Concrete shear resistance is given by:

$$V_c = \phi_c \lambda \beta \sqrt{f_c'} \, b_w \, d_v \tag{11.6}$$

λ = 1.0 for normal weight concrete

ϕ_c = 0.65

β = 0.18 where minimum transverse reinforcement is used

b_w = thickness of concrete section = panel thickness t

d_v = effective shear depth = 0.9d or 0.72h   (See Clause 3.2, Symbols)

For the case of walls, Clause 3.2 allows the effective shear depth to be taken as not less than:

$$d_v = 0.8 \, \ell_w$$

where:

ℓ_w = length of wall = panel width b

In using this reduction, it is assumed that the requirements of Clause 11.2.5 for anchorage of small diameter shear reinforcement are satisfied without the need for end hooks.

For 30 MPa concrete,

$$V_c = 0.65 \times 0.18 \sqrt{f_c'} \, 0.8bt = 0.51bt \text{ or } 0.51A_g$$

The shear resistance of the transverse reinforcement is:

$$V_s = \frac{\phi_s \, A_v \, f_y \, d_v \, \cot \theta}{s} \tag{11.7}$$

For ϕ_s = 0.85, θ = 35⁰ and f_y = 400 MPa

$$V_s = \frac{0.486 \, A_v \, d_v}{s}$$

The minimum area of shear reinforcement is:

$$A_v = 0.06 \sqrt{f_c'} \, \frac{b_w \, s}{f_y} \tag{11.1}$$

where

s = spacing of transverse reinforcement

≤ 0.7 d_v ≤ 600 mm   (See 11.3.8.1)

For f_c' = 30 MPa

$$A_v = 0.06\sqrt{30} \, \frac{ts}{400} = 0.00082 \, A_g$$

t = thickness of wall

The minimum areas for distributed reinforcement specified for walls in Clauses14.1.8.5 and 14.1.8.6 will generally be greater than this:

Minimum vertical reinforcement   0.0015 A_g

Minimum horizontal reinforcement   0.0020 A_g

The upper limit for shear resistance is given by:

$$V_{r,max} \leq 0.25\, \phi_c\, f'_c\, b_w\, d_v \qquad (11.5)$$

For 30 MPa concrete and $t = b_w$, $d_v = 0.8b$

$$V_{r,max} \leq 0.25 \times 0.65 \times 30 \times t \times 0.8b = 3.90bt \text{ or } 3.90A_g$$

Clause 14.1.8.4 limits the spacing of distributed reinforcement to 3 times the wall thickness or 500mm, whichever is less. Where the principal (vertical) reinforcement is placed in two layers, the horizontal distributed reinforcement can be placed on alternating faces with the spacing measured between alternate bars. See Section 13.13.3 of this Design Guide. The provisions of Chapter 21 for seismic design provide further requirements for shear resistance. This is discussed in the next sections.

13.11.4. Seismic Requirements for In-Plane Shear Forces

Tilt-up construction is now recognized in NBCC 2015 as a defined seismic force resisting system (SFRS) with conventional, limited ductility, or moderately ductile walls and frames. Chapter 21 of CSA A23.3-14 has introduced Clause 21.7 for the seismic design of tilt-up buildings with limited ductility ($R_d = 1.5$) or that are moderately ductile ($R_d = 2.0$). Conventional walls and frames ($R_d = 1.3$) are not covered in Clause 21.7 as they are not permitted in moderate to high seismic areas. For low seismic areas, typical construction and design practices for tilt up construction were considered sufficient and no special requirements are necessary for $R_d = 1.3$.

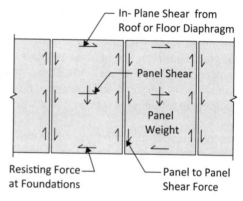

In-Plane Shear Forces

The focus on seismic design for tilt-up construction is that the governing ultimate limit state for the walls is ductile and non-ductile limit states shall be prevented. Limited ductility walls and frames use a force-based approach while moderately ductile walls and frames use a displacement based approach.

A large number of tilt-up buildings are one or two storey structures with structural steel roof and floor framing systems. These buildings often rely on perimeter concrete walls to resist the seismic forces. The typical seismic force resisting system (SFRS) may be a complex mixture of load paths and components with widely varying properties. It is common to have a combination of flexible steel deck roof diaphragms, rigid concrete topped steel deck floor diaphragms, and stiff tilt-up panel shear walls. Many commercial and industrial structures will also employ supplementary steel bracing or moment frames as part of the SFRS. The tilt-up wall lines can be made up of a variety of panel shapes and sizes that are difficult to analyze with any degree of accuracy. It is not unusual to expect some portions of the building to behave differently compared to others. These factors will provide designers with a significant challenge.

The traditional methods for designing concrete tilt-up panel shear walls have focused on attaining sufficient strength to meet the prescribed seismic forces. Typically, one ensured that there was adequate overturning resistance and shear strength on the basis that ductility was automatically taken care of by the selection of the appropriate R-value. When there was any uncertainty, additional panel reinforcement or edge connectors would be added, on the assumption that more was better. There has been a general awareness on the need for continuity of the load path, capacity design of the components within the load path, and ensuring that the overall structure has been adequately tied together. Many designers have assumed that seismic ductility would be achieved through panel rocking, yielding of the

13

Tilt-up

panel edge connections and, to some extent, deformation of the roof diaphragm. In most cases, the specified concrete shear stresses were relatively small and the risk of shear failure was low. Achieving ductility and energy dissipation within a solid concrete tilt-up panel was not usually a consideration. This traditional philosophy forms the basis of limited ductility design with an $R_d = 1.5$.

One of the desirable features of using tilt-up panels in the SFRS is their ability to re-distribute seismic shear forces within a line of panel components. All panels can contribute to the seismic resistance, but some more than others. If the overturning resistance of a narrow panel is exceeded, the excess forces can be transferred to the wider panels by means of the connecting drag struts (steel edge angles). Similarly, excess shear force on panel edge connections do not necessarily mean that total failure will occur at this point. Deflection compatibility within the panel line ensures that the forces are re-distributed to the other panels. If the connections have reasonable ductility, it is possible to have most or all of the panels working together.

As mentioned, there is now a specific reference to tilt-up design in Chapter 21 of CSA A23.3–14, Clause 21.7, Tilt-up construction ($R_d = 1.5$ and $R_d = 2.0$). This clause is based on some of the traditional design procedures used in the industry as well as recent academic research. It takes some specific requirements for walls and frames from other sections of Chapter 21 but adjusted for tilt-up construction. General requirements are included for shear design, connection forces, overturning, sliding resistance, compression members, solid panels and frames. These requirements are the basis for the design and detailing of tilt-up walls with limited ductility ($R_d = 1.5$).

For tilt-up walls designed as moderately ductile ($R_d = 2.0$) there are additional requirements to account for inelastic displacement demand. These include requirements for ductile roof diaphragms, displacement demands on solid panel connections, and rotational demands on panel frames. NBCC 2005 introduced the concept of ductile flexible diaphragms which could be designed for $R_d R_o = 2.0$. NBCC 2015 has now introduced formulas for the fundamental lateral period of buildings with flexible diaphragms. When used, this period could result in lower seismic design forces when compared to other period formulas that assume rigid diaphragms. Tilt-up buildings that use this period calculation must be designed as moderately ductile.

The most likely option for most designers in high seismic areas is to consider the tilt-up walls as limited ductility members with $R_d = 1.5$ and $R_o = 1.3$. This would result in the least change based on current design philosophies. The use of moderately ductile design ($R_d = 2.0$, $R_o = 1.3$) could increase with the addition of the diaphragm in building period calculations, which may result in lower seismic design forces. However, this is more likely in areas of moderate seismicity where the design forces on the diaphragm are lower and the diaphragm can be much larger. In areas of high seismicity, the design forces are much larger and the size of the diaphragm and distance between shear walls is limited by the capacity of the diaphragm. The distance between shear walls has a direct correlation with the period of the diaphragm. More detailed design examples and familiarity with inelastic displacement demand will also increase the use of moderately ductile design. It is important to note that NBCC Clause 4.1.8.10(2)(c) requires an SFRS with an R_d of 2.0 or greater for post-disaster buildings.

Wall lines in tilt-up buildings do not always consist of a series of solid panel elements. Below is an illustration of a typical wall line for a single storey tilt-up building. The shear forces from the roof will largely be resisted by the few solid panels. The narrow legs on the remaining panels will be very flexible compared to the solid panels, but will assist in the distribution of the base shear forces into the foundations and contribute to the overturning resistance of the system through panel edge connectors.

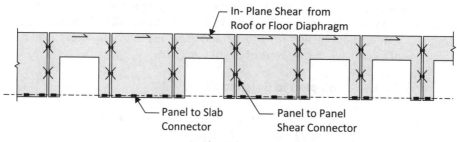

In-Plane Shear Forces

The connections between the panels would ideally have sufficient ductility to allow for re-distribution of forces through the various panel components, but strong enough to limit and control the overturning forces in the panels. For R_d = 2.0 design, the inelastic displacement demand for solid panels is usually concentrated in the panel edge connectors or panel base connectors. Some standard connectors currently used are considered to be ductile but may not have sufficient displacement capacity to meet the inelastic demand. Further research in this area is needed.

13.11.5. Seismic Shear Walls Consisting of Solid Panels

Where the wall line consists of a series of panels that are mostly solid, the in-plane seismic resistance can be achieved by ensuring that panel overturning and concrete shear failure does not occur when the specified seismic forces are applied. The following design procedures are proposed for limited ductility R_d = 1.5:

- Design solid tilt-up concrete panel shear walls elements for limited ductility requirements in accordance with Clause 21.7, *Tilt-up construction*, for seismic force levels based on R_d = 1.5 and R_o = 1.3.
- Design the concrete cross section for a minimum shear resistance based on the shear force corresponding to the factored overturning moment capacity of the individual wall panel or wall panel group. The shear force need not exceed the design load combinations calculated using $R_d R_o$ = 1.3 as per Clause 21.7.2.1.2. Use the procedures in Chapter 11 as previously outlined in Section 13.11.3 of this Guide.
- Provide a minimum shear reinforcement ratio of 0.0015 in the vertical direction and 0.002 in the horizontal direction in accordance with the recommendations of Chapter 14. If the shear stress exceeds $0.1 \, \phi_c \sqrt{f_c'}$ the vertical steel reinforcement ratio is to be increased to 0.002 and additional requirements of Clause 21.6.3.3 are to be followed.
- Compute panel overturning moments based on R_d = 1.5 and R_o = 1.3 forces. Where required, provide ductile edge connectors such as the EM5 to achieve the required overturning resistance. See Section 13.12 of this Guide. Check the compression edge of unconnected panels for out-of-plane stability as discussed in Section 13.11.1 of this Design Guide and Clause 21.7.3.5. If required, provide ties in accordance with 21.7.3.6.
- Compute sliding forces for R_d = 1.5 and R_o = 1.3. These can be resisted by the connections in combination with friction between the panels and the foundations. Ductile connections, such as the EM5 or cast-in dowels can be used. Where non-ductile connections are employed, such as weld plates with studs, the design forces should be based on $R_d R_o$ = 1.3. Sometimes, the floor slab is poured through the openings at the base of a panel, effectively "locking in" the panel. This can increase the resistance to sliding with concrete bearing and decrease the number of mechanical connections. A minimum of 2 mechanical connections per panel is recommended.

13

Tilt-up

There may be situations where the shear forces become so large that the overturning capacity in the panel line will be insufficient. Tie down anchorage to the foundations will then be required. Increased foundation sizes, both for uplift resistance and for additional compression forces may be required. Further discussion of this is beyond the scope of the Design Guide.

13.11.6. Frame Panels Subjected to Seismic Shear

Panels with large openings that rely on frame action to resist in-plane seismic shear forces can be designed in accordance with Clause 21.7.4 with additional requirements for $R_d = 2.0$ in Clause 21.7.5. Plastic hinging may occur in some of the panel joints and adequate resistance must be provided to ensure that concrete shear failure does not occur. Clause 21.7.4.4 requires that the shear resistance should be greater than the sum of the shear required to develop the factored or nominal moment at the joint plus the effect of gravity loads, but need not exceed the shear force obtained using earthquake loads based on $R_d R_o = 1.3$.

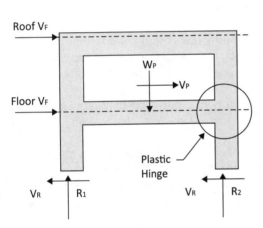

Portal Frame Panel

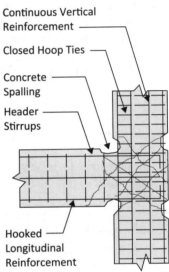

Plastic Hinge Region

There may be several joints within a tilt-up panel frame, but often the flexural yielding occurs in only one or two of them. The design of the plastic hinge region for columns and beams is defined in 21.7.4.3. For columns expected to develop plastic hinges, the minimum column dimension perpendicular to the axis of bending shall be not less than 600 mm. The plastic hinge length from the face of the joint should be no less than 1.5 times the largest column dimension. For beams, the plastic hinge length from the face of the joint shall be not less than twice the beam depth.

Outside the plastic hinge region and where the applied compression stresses in the tilt-up panel components are less than $0.09 \, \phi_c \, f'_c$, reinforcement can be detailed in accordance with Clause 10, 11, and 23 as walls or beams rather than columns. Single ties or stirrups should be provided throughout the member for added confinement and integrity unless the member is very deep and shear reinforcement is not required. The thickness of the panel cross section should not be less than 190mm where ties are used. Where the compression stress exceeds $0.09 \, \phi_c \, f'_c$ ties shall be provided in accordance with 21.7.3.6:

a) Ties shall be arranged such that every corner and alternate longitudinal bar shall have lateral support.
b) Crossties or legs of overlapping ties shall have centre-to-centre spacings not exceeding 350mm.
c) The tie shall consist of a 10M bar or larger.

d)   The maximum spacing of the ties shall not exceed the smallest of 16 times the diameter of the smallest enclosed longitudinal bar, 300mm, or the thickness of the panel.

e)   For R_d = 2.0, all ties shall be detailed as hoops or seismic crossties and the spacing of the ties shall not exceed 12 times the diameter of the small enclosed longitudinal bar.

For columns in the plastic hinge region, and over the beam-column joint, the spacing of the ties shall not exceed 12 times the diameter of the smallest enclosed longitudinal bar for R_d = 1.5 and 8 times for R_d = 2.0. Additionally, for R_d = 2.0, ties shall be detailed as hoops or seismic crossties.

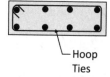

Hoop
Ties

For beams in the plastic hinge region, the beam shall contain 10M or larger stirrups spaced at the smallest of:

a)   d/4

b)   12 times the diameter of the smallest longitudinal bar in the top or bottom layer of reinforcement, and

c)   300 mm.

Cross
Ties

For R_d = 2.0, the stirrups shall be detailed as hoops.

Hoop
Ties

Joints shall be designed to satisfy Clauses 21.4.6.1 to 21.4.6.3. Longitudinal bars should be continuous through the joints in tilt-up frame panels. Vertical bars are typically detailed to run the full height of the panel. It is sometimes attractive to use larger size bars to avoid the tight spacing requirements in the plastic hinge region. However, the diameter of straight beam and column reinforcing bars pass through the joint shall not be larger than one-eighth the panel thickness for R_d = 1.5 and one-tenth the panel thickness for R_d = 2.0.

Clause 21.7.5 provides additional requirements for R_d = 2.0 tilt-up frames to account for displacements. If the rotational demand exceeds 0.02 radians, the frame shall also satisfy the requirements of 21.4, Moderately ductile moment-resisting frames. An upper limit of 0.04 radians is also given. This requires a displacement analysis of the building structure, and is beyond the scope of this Guide.

To determine where a plastic hinge may form, there should be a lower bound where the detailing rules for 21.7.4.3 are not required. A realistic approach would be to perform an elastic analysis of the panel frame, based on R_dR_o = 1.0, to determine where flexural yielding might be expected to occur, and to design only those portions to meet the requirements of Clause 21.7.4.3.

The initial analysis should be carried out based on the prescribed seismic loads for Limited Ductility with R_d = 1.5 and R_o = 1.3. The forces obtained would then be increased by 1.5 x 1.3 = 1.95 (this is not always the same as starting with forces based on R_dR_o = 1.0). If the stresses in the longitudinal reinforcement under this magnitude of loading were less than the yield stress of the reinforcement ($\phi_s f_y$), then the requirements for plastic hinging may not be necessary. The tendency in some design offices has been to take a somewhat conservative approach, where the ties are specified in all cases when it is *possible* to have compression yielding of the longitudinal reinforcement.

Tilt-up wall panel frames will often have deep header sections such that the flexural yielding or plastic hinging would likely occur only in the vertical legs. Where the longitudinal reinforcement in the header is not expected to yield for seismic forces obtained as described in the previous paragraph, the stirrup spacing limitations of Clause 21.7.4.3.2 would not apply.

The panel legs should also be checked to ensure that there will be sufficient post-seismic capacity to support the gravity loads imposed by the floor and roof structures. Where plastic hinging occurs

13

Tilt-up

in a joint, it is reasonable to expect that some of the concrete cross section will be damaged. The outer edge longitudinal bars and the surrounding concrete in a panel leg may no longer be effective for supporting gravity loads and out-of-plane wind loads. Where the leg cross section is sufficiently wide, the undamaged inner portions will be called upon to carry the loads. A minimum leg width to thickness ratio of 4.0 is therefore recommended, in order to help ensure that complete failure will not occur. A panel with a thickness of 190mm should therefore have a minimum leg width of 760mm. Narrower panel legs as small as 600mm can be used but they may be insufficient to develop the necessary flexural and shear resistance, while keeping reinforcement spacing reasonable.

13.12 Connections for Tilt-up Panels

Design requirements for connections to tilt-up panels generally follow traditional methods. Connections must be designed to resist forces equal to or greater than the maximum load imposed on the panel component. Ideally, connections in panels designed for seismic conditions should typically be stronger and more ductile than those for non-seismic forces.

The three main categories of connections for tilt-up panels are:
- Cast-in place concrete in-fill sections
- Welded embedded metal
- Drilled-in anchors

13.12.1. Cast-In-Place Concrete In-fill Sections

This type of connection involves casting concrete around reinforcing bars projecting from the panel in order to tie into another building component.

These connections are often very strong and can be used to distribute loads over a greater length. Good ductility can be achieved if the overlapping bars are confined by closed ties. Cast-in-place connections are used infrequently because they are considerably more expensive than other types of connections. They may also cause problems such as panel cracking resulting from concrete shrinkage and excessive restraint.

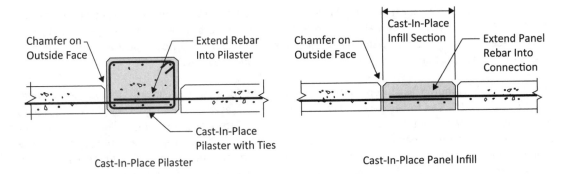

Cast-In-Place Pilaster   Cast-In-Place Panel Infill

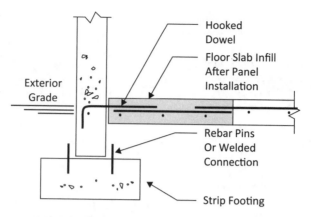

Panel On Strip Footing

13.12.2. Welded Embedded Metal

Welded embedded metal is the type of connection preferred by most designers and builders due to its relative cost advantage and construction flexibility in various applications. Strength and ductility can vary considerably, depending on the length of embedment and configuration of the anchor.

Steel plates with studs are suitable for shear and tension forces as long as they are located well away from the panel edges (300 mm or more).

The lack of sufficient embedment makes these connectors non-ductile. Steel angles or plates with short studs located at the edge of the panel should be avoided entirely. Often concrete shrinkage in the panels after welding causes stress build-up that may result in premature failure.

Where possible, embedded metal connections should have deformed bar anchors extending into the concrete panel. These are more expensive to fabricate and install but provide superior strength and performance, particularly for seismic loadings. In general, this type of connector can provide reasonable seismic ductility. For example, the EM5 connector deformed approximately 40mm prior to failure during cyclic testing.

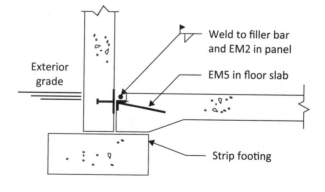

Panel on Strip Footing

13

Tilt-up

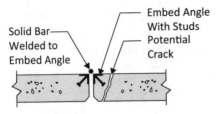

Panel Edge Connector
(not recommended)

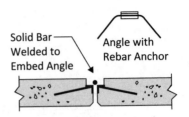

Panel Edge Connector
(for seismic shear transfer)

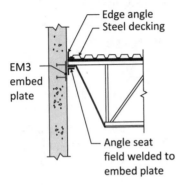

Steel Joist on Angle Seat

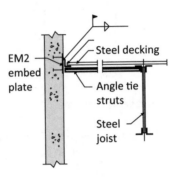

Edge Angle Connection

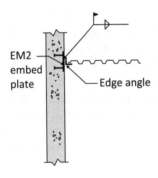

Shear Plate Connection

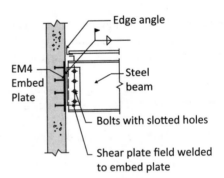

Steel Beam Connection

The following figure contains five standard connection types that have been used in tilt-up panels. These have been tested in static and cyclic loading (ref 6). Recommended factored load capacities are also indicated.

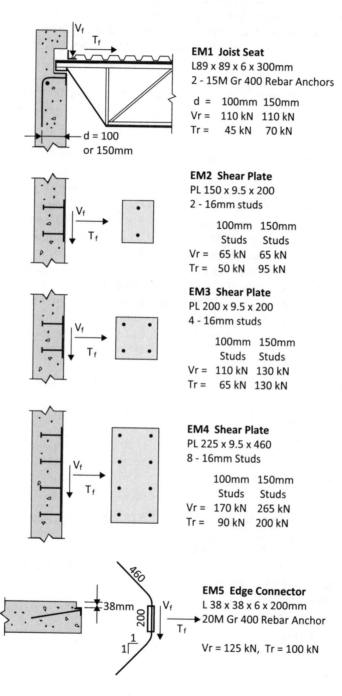

EM1 Joist Seat
L89 x 89 x 6 x 300mm
2 - 15M Gr 400 Rebar Anchors

d =   100mm 150mm
Vr =   110 kN   110 kN
Tr =   45 kN   70 kN

EM2 Shear Plate
PL 150 x 9.5 x 200
2 - 16mm studs

	100mm Studs	150mm Studs
Vr =	65 kN	65 kN
Tr =	50 kN	95 kN

EM3 Shear Plate
PL 200 x 9.5 x 200
4 - 16mm studs

	100mm Studs	150mm Studs
Vr =	110 kN	130 kN
Tr =	65 kN	130 kN

EM4 Shear Plate
PL 225 x 9.5 x 460
8 - 16mm Studs

	100mm Studs	150mm Studs
Vr =	170 kN	265 kN
Tr =	90 kN	200 kN

EM5 Edge Connector
L 38 x 38 x 6 x 200mm
20M Gr 400 Rebar Anchor

Vr = 125 kN, Tr = 100 kN

Standard Tilt-up Connectors

13.12.3. Drilled-In Anchors

Expansion bolts and adhesive anchors are used extensively in tilt-up construction. Their application should be restricted to supporting light loads or for repairs. They have very little ductility when compared to cast-in-place or welded deformed bar anchors making them unsuitable where seismic forces or differential foundation movement is expected. Expansion anchors can also cause problems in thin panel sections particularly where edge distance is inadequate.

Power driven fasteners or drive pins may be used for light architectural components or light gauge steel stud framing. Design loads should be restricted due to the limited reliability of these fasteners in concrete.

13.12.4. Connections for Seismic Forces

Tilt-up panel connections for seismic applications must be capable of resisting forces equal to or greater than that specified by the NBCC for the overall structural system. Ideally, the connection type would be assigned values of R_d and R_o based on testing. For example, the factored load capacity of the standard connections that were illustrated previously was based on a 0.6 reduction of the lowest test value for initial failure. A value of $R_o = 1.4$ would be a conservative, but appropriate assumption. If the design is based on the requirements for Limited Ductility, the value of R_o should be reduced to 1.3 to be consistent. The studded connections (EM2, EM3 and EM4) exhibited very little ductility during the testing program (ref 6) and should be assigned a value of $R_d = 1.0$ for the 100mm (4" stud length). No testing was performed on the longer 150mm (6") studs during the research program, but $R_d = 1.0$ is also recommended. The EM1 and EM5, on the other hand, had good ductile shear performance and could be assigned a minimum $R_d = 1.5$.

NBCC Clause 4.1.8.18(7) for connections of elements of structures, minimum design forces are to be based on:

$$V_p = 0.3 \, F_a \, S_a(0.2) \, I_E \, S_p \, W_p$$

where

$$S_p = \frac{C_p \, A_r \, A_x}{R_p}$$

and

C_p	=	Element or component factor. (see 4.1.8.18(7)e)
	=	1.0 for ductile connections.
	=	2.0 for non-ductile connections.
A_r	=	Element or component force amplification factor, that depends on the flexibility of the component being connected
	=	1.0 for rigid elements
	=	2.5 for flexible elements
A_x	=	Height factor $= 1 + 2 \dfrac{h_x}{h_n}$
R_p	=	Component response factor
	=	1.0 for non-ductile components or materials
	=	2.5 for ductile connections or materials

For an example, assuming the same location as in Section 13.4.3, the out-of-plane connection force between the roof and panel of a single storey building is:
Site location, Vancouver, Site Class D soils

$$F_a = 0.98$$

$$S_a(0.2) = 0.848$$

$$C_p = 2.0 \quad \text{(non-ductile connection)}$$

$$A_r = 2.5 \quad \text{(flexible tilt-up panel)}$$

$$R_p = 1.0 \quad \text{(non-ductile connection)}$$

$$h_x = 0.5\,h_n$$

$$A_x = 1.0 + 2\left(\frac{0.5}{1.0}\right) = 2.0$$

$$S_p = \frac{2.0 \times 2.5 \times 2.0}{1.0} = 10.0 > 4.0 \rightarrow S_p = 4.0$$

$$V_p = 0.3 \times 0.98 \times 0.848 \times 1.0 \times 4.0\,W_p = 1.0\,W_p$$

Thus, the connection between the roof and the panel must be designed for a minimum out-of-plane design force of 1.0 times the tributary weight of the panel. This is five times the out-of-plane design force used for the panel. Where ductile connections are used, this force could be reduced.

13.13 Construction Requirements

13.13.1. Forming and Construction Tolerances

Chapter 23 does not provide specific requirements for tolerances in tilt-up construction. Instead, it refers to the CSA A23.4 standard for precast concrete with a precautionary note that adequate quality control procedures must be carried out. Otherwise, the tolerances are to comply with CSA A23.1.

Quality control of panel forming and reinforcing steel placing for site cast tilt-up concrete panels is usually better than for standard cast-in-place concrete work, but cannot compare with the controlled conditions of a precast concrete plant. Tolerance requirements should therefore be somewhere in between.

The tilt-up industry in North America has developed tolerance guidelines that have been used succesfully over the past 40 years:

Length and Height:
Up to 3 m +0 to – 13 mm
3 m to 6 m + 0 to – 13 mm
Over 6 m   +0 to – 16 mm

Straightness or Skewness:
Up to 3 m   ± 13 mm
3 m to 6 m   ± 16 mm
6 m to 12 m   ± 20 mm

Thickness:
Overall   ± 6 mm

Clear concrete cover over reinforcement in tilt-up panels should be greater than that required by CSA A23.4 for plant cast precast concrete. In general, the following covers have been adequate for tilt-up panels above grade:

Main Reinforcing
Outside face of panel 25 mm
Inside face of panel   20 mm
Edge of panel   50 mm

Ties and Stirrups
Inside or outside face   20 mm
Edge of panel   40 mm

Some contractors have found that concrete covers of less than 20 mm on the inside can make it difficult to finish the panel surface. On the outside face, insufficient cover tends to result in "mirroring" of

13

Tilt-up

the bars through the finished concrete. Concrete cover may also have to be adjusted for fire rating requirements, or where reveal strips are installed on the outside face of the panel.

13.13.2. Concrete Requirements

Concrete used for tilt-up panels should provide adequate strength for both the in-place condition and for erection requirements. A minimum compressive strength of 25 MPa should be provided. Often, the concrete mix is proportioned for flexural strength requirements as defined by the modulus of rupture. This property is important for resisting flexural cracking, particularly during the lifting operation. Depending on what is specified, the actual compressive strength may be greater than 25 MPa. There has been a trend in recent years to use 28 to 30 MPa concrete for panels.

Entrained air for freeze/thaw resistance is not normally required where exposed surfaces are primarily vertical and protected with a paint or sealer. Air entrainment has a negative effect on the modulus of rupture and will increase the potential for cracking at the time of lifting. Local experience in the performance of non-air entrained concrete should be investigated.

In summary, the following concrete specifications are suggested:

28 Day Compressive Strength	30 MPa
28 Day Flexural Strength	4.0 MPa
Maximum Size Aggregate	20 mm
Exposure Class	F2 unless adequately sealed
Entrained Air	4–7% unless adequately sealed

13.13.3. Reinforcing Steel

Standard grade 400 MPa reinforcing steel should be specified for tilt-up panels. Intermediate grade 300 MPa or less should be avoided. The main vertical bars should be 15M or 20M, with 10M bars used for horizontal distributed reinforcement or ties. Bars larger than 20M are not recommended for tilt-up panels with a thickness of 200mm or less.

The following are the minimum requirements in Clause14.1.8 for distributed reinforcement in walls:

Maximum bar diameter	0.10 x wall thickness
Number of layers	1 layer for wall thickness not exceeding 210mm
	2 layers for wall thickness of 160mm or greater recommended
Maximum spacing (see note)	3 x wall thickness or 500 mm
Minimum vertical reinforcement	$0.0015\,A_g$
Minimum horizontal reinforcement	$0.0020\,A_g$
Concentrated reinforcement	2 – 15M at perimeter
	1 – 15M bar in each layer around openings

Note: Where the reinforcement is placed in 2 layers and the wall thickness is 210mm or less, the horizontal distributed reinforcement can be on alternating faces and the spacing restrictions apply to the distance between alternate bars rather than to the bars in each individual layer. See the following diagrams.

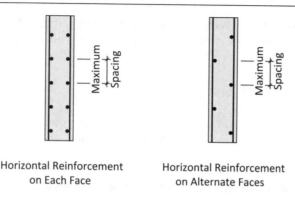

Horizontal Reinforcement
on Each Face

Horizontal Reinforcement
on Alternate Faces

Clearances between bars should comply with the requirements of CSA A23.1. The requirements for walls are overly restrictive for tilt-up panels since these elements are formed and poured as flat, open-faced slabs. Closer bar spacing can usually be tolerated, particularly where the reinforcement is run the full height or width without lap splices. See 13.13.1.

13.14 Design for Lifting Stresses

It has been common practice for the panel lift analysis and pick up point locations to be carried out by a separate designer. This is often the supplier of embedded lift inserts or other specialist engineers. Although there is no direct conflict with this split in responsibility, it is important for the building designer to have some basic knowledge of the requirements and potential limitations.

Panel lift design takes into account the following considerations:
- Bending stress should be kept low enough to avoid flexural cracking.
- The lift insert capacity should have a safety factor of at least 2.0 at the time of lift, including an allowance for adhesion and impact. Some Canadian jurisdictions require a safety factor of 2.5.
- The panel should tilt with about 10% of the weight at the bottom. It should be balanced to hang level when lifted off the casting bed.

A minimum concrete compressive strength of 17 MPa (2500 psi) is often specified for full lift insert capacity. Concrete flexural strengths of 2.9 MPa (420 psi) are sufficient to prevent panel cracking where computed bending stresses are less than 1.7 MPa (250 psi). Beyond this, reinforcing steel should be provided on the tension face to carry the entire load. Since the panel is often lifted before the full 28 day concrete strength is achieved, higher specified strengths are usually required. Many contractors will boost the specified concrete strength to ensure that there will be adequate strength for lifting in only a few days after pouring the panels.

Reinforcement in the middle of the panel section will only be effective after the concrete has cracked. It is also less efficient in resisting bending moments. Where two layers of reinforcement are specified for the panel design, it will often provide a net savings in the overall quantity of reinforcement since it is more efficient, and generally eliminates the need for additional reinforcement for lifting purposes. It is now standard practice to go with 2 layers of reinforcement in almost all tilt-up panels. As a result, there has been a significant decrease in the panel cracking associated with lifting.

The following are a few simple tips for panel layout that will make panel lifting easier and more cost effective:
- Avoid large panels, and try to limit the maximum weight to about 30 Tonnes (66,000 lbs).
- Panel size and weight should be consistent. This will avoid multiple rigging changes.
- Keep panel widths to about 6.5m or less, particularly when the height is greater than 9m.

13

Tilt-up

- Avoid spandrel panels, or panels with only one supporting leg. These will often require strongbacks for lifting, and can significantly increase erection time. These situations can usually be avoided by proper panel layout design.

13.15 Temporary Panel Bracing

The brace supplier usually provides design requirements for temporary bracing of tilt-up panels. It is recommended that this bracing comply with the guidelines outlined in the publication by the Tilt-up Concrete Association (ref. 8).

The building designer should be aware of some of the requirements for panel bracing, and make provisions in the building design to accommodate this. The following guidelines are suggested:
- Provide a minimum floor slab thickness of 140mm (5½") for bracing. Bracing connections to the floor require this minimum requirement in order to develop the capacity of the connecting bolt.
- Additional floor slab thickenings may be required to provide sufficient weight for anchoring the braces for panel heights in excess of 10m above the floor slab. Floor slab reinforcement is also helpful for brace anchorage by increasing the area of slab that can be used for uplift.

13.16 References

(1) Recommended Tilt-up Wall Panel Design, Structural Engineers Association of Southern California, 1979

(2) Test Report on Slender Walls, Southern California Chapter, American Concrete Association and Structural Engineers Association of Southern California, 1982.

(3) Approximate Methods for Analysis of Tilt-up Concrete Wall Panels, G. Weiler, ACI International, November, 1982.

(4) Earthquake Resistant Connections for Low Rise Concrete Buildings, R.A. Spencer., U.S./Japan Seminar on Precast Concrete Construction in Seismic Zones, October 1986, pp 61-81

(5) Connections for Tilt-up Construction, G.J. Weiler, Concrete International, June 1986.

(6) Behavior of Embedded Steel Connectors in Concrete Tilt-up Panels, Kevin Lemieux, Robert Sexsmith, Gerry Weiler, ACI Structural Journal, July-August 1998.

(7) Effect of Hinge Zone Tie Spacing on Ductility of Concrete Tilt-up Frame Panels, Michael Dew, Robert Sexsmith, Gerry Weiler, ACI Structural Journal, November, 2001.

(8) Guideline for Temporary Wind Bracing of Tilt-up Concrete Panels During Construction, Tilt-up Concrete Association, January 2005.

(9) Design Guide for Tilt-Up Concrete Panels, ACI 551.2R-10, March 2010.

(10) Guide to Tilt-Up Construction, ACI 551.1R-14, November 2014.

13.17 Design Examples

The purpose of these examples is to illustrate the CSA A23.3-14 requirements for design of tilt-up panels. Not all of the necessary checks are included in each example. Design engineers are encouraged to set up a spreadsheet analysis program that will routinely check the appropriate clauses of the code.

Material properties:
For the purposes of these examples the following material properties have been assumed:

ϕ_c = 0.65, ϕ_s = 0.85, ϕ_m = 0.75, unit weight of concrete γ = 24 kN/m³
f'_c = 30 MPa; E_c = 4500 $\sqrt{30}$ = 24,650 MPa
α_1 = 0.85 – 0.0015 x 30 = 0.805
β_1 = 0.97 – 0.0025 x 30 = 0.895
f_y = 400 MPa; E_s = 200,000 MPa

Example 13.1 - Plain Wall Panel

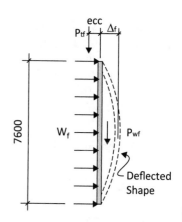

Panel properties: ℓ = 7600 mm, t = 140 mm, Δ_0 = 25 mm
Self-weight w_c = 0.140 x 24 = 3.36 kPa
Check ℓ / t:
$\dfrac{7600}{140}$ = 54 < 65   ∴ OK for 2 layers of reinforcement

Assumed loading:
Roof dead load = 1.0 kPa; snow load = 3.0 kPa
ecc = 140 / 2 = 70 mm; joist span = 10.9 m
Wind load w = 1.07 kPa

Strength Calculations:

Load case (4): 1.25**D** + 1.4**W** + 0.5**S**

P_{tf} = (1.25 x 1.0 + 0.5 x 3.0) 10.9 / 2 = 15.0 kN/m; P_{wf} = 1.25 x 3.36 x 7.6 / 2 = 16.0 kN/m
Axial load at mid-height: P_f = 15.0 + 16.0 = 31.0 kN/m; w_f = 1.4 x 1.07 = 1.5 kPa

Check axial load limit: $\dfrac{P_f}{A_g} = \dfrac{31.0}{0.140 \times 1000}$ = 0.22 MPa < 0.09 x 0.65 x 30 = 1.76 MPa   OK

Assume reinforcing on each face (EF):
A_s = 15M @ 400 EF   or   500 mm²/m EF;   d = 100 mm;   b = 1000 mm

$A_{s,eff}$= 500 + $\dfrac{31.0 \times 1000}{0.85 \times 400}\left(\dfrac{140}{2 \times 100}\right)$ = 564 mm²/m;   a = $\dfrac{564 \times 0.85 \times 400}{0.805 \times 0.65 \times 30 \times 1000}$ = 12.2 mm

Resisting Moment: M_r = $\dfrac{0.85 \times 564 \times 400 (100 - 12.2 / 2)}{10^6}$ = 18.0 kN-m/m

Bending stiffness (based on $A_{s,eff}$):

c = $\dfrac{12.2}{0.895}$ = 13.6 mm

I_{cr} = $\dfrac{bc^3}{3} + \dfrac{Es}{Ec} A_{s,eff}(d - c)^2 = \dfrac{1000 \times 13.6^3}{3} + \dfrac{200,000}{24,650} \times 564 (100 - 13.6)^2$ = 35.0 x 10⁶ mm⁴/m

K_{bf} = $\dfrac{48 \times 24,650 \times 35.0 \times 10^6}{5 \times 7600^2 \times 1000}$ = 143.4 kN-m/m; $\delta_b = \dfrac{1}{1 - \dfrac{P_f}{\phi_m K_{bf}}} = \dfrac{1}{1 - \dfrac{31.0}{0.75 \times 143.4}}$ = 1.40

Primary Bending Moment: M_b = $1.5 \times 7.6^2 / 8 + 15 \times 0.07 / 2 + 31.0 \times 0.025 = 12.1$ kN-m/m

Total Moment: M_f = $12.1 \times 1.40 = 16.9 < M_r = 18.0$ kN-m/m   OK

Total factored deflection: Δ_f = $\dfrac{M_f}{\phi_m K_{bf}} = \dfrac{16.9 \times 1000}{0.75 \times 143.4} = 157$ mm

Load case (3): $1.25D + 1.5S + 0.4W$

P_{tf} = $(1.25 \times 1.0 + 1.5 \times 3.0)\ 10.9 / 2 = 31.3$ kN/m; $P_{wf} = 1.25 \times 3.36 \times 7.6 / 2 = 16.0$ kN/m

P_f = $31.3 + 16.0 = 47.3$ kN/m; $w_f = 0.4 \times 1.07 = 0.43$ kPa

A_s = 500 mm²/m EF; $A_{s,eff} = 597$ mm²/m;   a = 12.9 mm; $M_r = 19.0$ kN-m/m

c = 14.4 mm; $I_{cr} = 36.5 \times 10^6$ mm⁴/m; $K_{bf} = 149.5$ kN-m/m; $\delta_b = 1.73$;

M_b = $0.43 \times 7.6^2 / 8 + 31.3 \times 0.07 / 2 + 47.3 \times 0.025 = 5.38$ kN-m/m

M_f = $5.38 \times 1.73 = 9.3$ kN-m/m < $M_r = 19.0$ OK

Deflections at service loads:

Load case: $1.0D + 1.0W + 0.5S$ ($I_w = 0.75, I_s = 0.9$)

w_c = 3.36 kPa; $P_{ws} = 3.36 \times 7.6 / 2 = 12.8$ kN/m

P_{ts} = $(1.0 + 0.5 \times 0.9 \times 3.0)\ 10.9 / 2 = 12.8$ kN/m;   ecc = 70mm

P_s = $12.8 + 12.8 = 25.6$ kN/m; $w_s = 0.75 \times 1.07 = 0.80$ kPa

I_g = $1000 \times 140^3 / 12 = 229 \times 10^6$ mm⁴/m

Cracking moment: $M_{cr} = \dfrac{f_r I_g}{y_t} = \dfrac{0.3 \sqrt{30} \times 229}{140 / 2} = 5.38$ kN-m/m

M_{bs} = $\dfrac{0.80 \times 7.6^2}{8} + \dfrac{12.8 \times 0.070}{2} + 25.6 \times 0.025 = 6.86 > M_{cr} = 5.38$ kN-m/m $\therefore I_{cr} < I_e < I_g$

A_s = 500 mm²/m;

Using a triangular concrete stress distribution:

n = $\dfrac{E_s}{E_c} = 8.11$; $kd = \dfrac{-n A_s + \sqrt{(n A_s)^2 + 2 b n A_s d}}{b}$

kd = $\dfrac{-8.11 \times 500 + \sqrt{(8.11 \times 500)^2 + 2 \times 1000 \times 8.11 \times 500 \times 100}}{1000} = 24.7$ mm

I_{cr} = $\dfrac{b (kd)^3}{3} + \dfrac{E_s A_s (d - kd)^2}{E_c}$

= $\dfrac{1000 \times 24.7^3}{3} + \dfrac{200,000 \times 500 (100 - 24.7)^2}{24,650} = 28.0 \times 10^6$ mm⁴/m

Initially assume $\Delta_s = \dfrac{\ell}{100} = \dfrac{7600}{100} = 76$ mm;

M_s = $M_{bs} + P_s \Delta_s = 6.86 + 25.6 \times 0.076 = 8.81$ kN-m/m

I_e = $I_{cr} + (I_g - I_{cr}) \left(\dfrac{M_{cr}}{M_s}\right)^3 = 28.0 + (229 - 28.0) \left(\dfrac{5.38}{8.81}\right)^3 = 73.8 \times 10^6$ mm⁴/m

K_{bs} = $\dfrac{48 E_c I_e}{5 \ell^2} = \dfrac{48 \times 24,650 \times 73.8 \times 10^6}{5 \times 7600^2 \times 1000} = 302$ kN-m/m; $\delta_{bs} = \dfrac{1}{1 - \dfrac{P_s}{K_{bs}}} = \dfrac{1}{1 - \dfrac{25.6}{302}} = 1.09$

M_s = 6.86 x 1.09 = 7.48 < 8.81 kN-m/m   OK

Δ_s = $\dfrac{M_s}{K_{bs}}$ = $\dfrac{7.48 \times 1000}{302}$ = 24.7 mm < 76 mm   OK

Panel design summary: (Load case (4) controls the design)
t = 140 mm
Vertical reinforcing: 15M @ 400 EF   (each face)
Horizontal reinforcing: 10M @ 350 AF   (alternating faces)

Reinforcement weight per m² = $\left(\dfrac{2 \times 200}{400} + \dfrac{100}{350} \right)$ 7.85 kg = 10.1 kg/m²

Compare to a design with reinforcing in the center of the panel section:

Maximum $\dfrac{\ell}{t}$ = 50 for 1 layer of reinforcement

Minimum t = $\dfrac{7600}{50}$ = 152 mm → ∴ assume t = 160mm   (formed with 2x6 plus 1x2)

Load case (4): 1.25**D** + 1.4**W** + 0.5**S**
Self weight w_c = 0.160 x 24 = 3.84 kPa; P_{wf} = 1.25 x 3.84 x 7.6 / 2 = 18.2 kN/m
P_{tf} =   (1.25 x 1.0 + 0.5 x 3.0) 10.9 / 2 = 15.0 kN/m;   ecc = 160 / 2 = 80 mm
Axial load at mid height: P_f = 15.0 + 18.2 = 33.2 kN/m; w_f = 1.4 x 1.07 = 1.5 kPa

Assume reinforcing in center of section:
A_s =   15M @ 250 = 800 mm²/m ;   d = 160 / 2 = 80 mm;   b = 1000 mm
$A_{s,eff}$ =   800 + $\dfrac{33.2 \times 1000}{0.85 \times 400} \left(\dfrac{160}{2 \times 80} \right)$ = 898 mm²/m;   a = $\dfrac{898 \times 0.85 \times 400}{0.805 \times 0.65 \times 30 \times 1000}$ = 19.45 mm
M_r =   0.85 x 898 x 400 (80 – 19.45 / 2) / 10⁶ = 21.5 kN-m/m

Bending stiffness (based on $A_{s,eff}$):
c   = $\dfrac{19.45}{0.895}$ = 21.7 mm

I_{cr} = $\dfrac{bc^3}{3} + \dfrac{E_s}{E_c} A_{s,eff} (d - c)^2$ = $\dfrac{1000 \times 21.7^3}{3} + \dfrac{200{,}000}{24{,}650}$ x 898 (80 - 21.7)² = 28.2 x 10⁶ mm⁴/m

K_{bf} = $\dfrac{48 \times 24{,}650 \times 28.2 \times 10^6}{5 \times 7600^2 \times 1000}$ = 115.5 kN-m/m; δ_b = $\dfrac{1}{1 - \dfrac{33.2}{0.75 \times 115.5}}$ = 1.62

M_b =   1.5 x 7.6² / 8 + 15.0 x 0.08 / 2 + 33.2 x 0.025 = 12.3 kN-m/m

M_f =   12.3 x 1.62 = 19.9 < M_r = 21.5 kN-m/m   OK

Total factored load deflection: Δ_f = $\dfrac{M_f}{\phi_m K_{bf}}$ = $\dfrac{19.9 \times 1000}{0.75 \times 115.5}$ = 230 mm

13

Tilt-up

Deflections at service loads

Load case   (1.0D + 1.0W + 0.5S)   ($I_w = 0.75$, $I_s = 0.9$)

w_c =   3.84 kPa; P_{ws} = 3.84 x 7.6 / 2 = 14.6 kN/m

P_{ts} =   (1.0 + 0.5 x 0.9 x 3.0) 10.9 / 2 = 12.8 kN/m;   ecc = 80 mm

P_s =   12.8 + 14.6 = 27.4 kN/m; w_s =0.75 x 1.07 = 0.80 kPa

I_g =   1000 x 160^3 / 12 = 341 x 10^6 mm^4/m

Cracking moment: $M_{cr} = \dfrac{0.3 \sqrt{30} \times 341}{160 / 2} = 7.00$ kN-m/m

M_{bs} = $\dfrac{0.80 \times 7.6^2}{8} + \dfrac{12.8 \times 0.080}{2} + 27.4 \times 0.025 = 6.97$ kN-m/m

Initially assume $\Delta_s = \dfrac{\ell}{100} = \dfrac{7600}{100} = 76$ mm

M_s =   6.97 + 27.4 x 0.076 = 9.05 > 7.00 kN-m/m;   ∴ $I_{cr} < I_e < I_g$

A_s =   800 mm^2/m;

Using a triangular concrete stress distribution:

n = $\dfrac{E_s}{E_c} = 8.11$; $kd = \dfrac{-n A_s + \sqrt{(n A_s)^2 + 2 b n A_s d}}{b}$

kd = $\dfrac{-8.11 \times 800 + \sqrt{(8.11 \times 800)^2 + 2 \times 1000 \times 8.11 \times 800 \times 80}}{1000} = 26.4$ mm

I_{cr} = $\dfrac{b (kd)^3}{3} + \dfrac{E_s A_s (d - kd)^2}{E_c}$

= $\dfrac{1000 \times 26.4^3}{3} + \dfrac{200,000 \times 800 (80 - 26.4)^2}{24,650} = 24.8 \times 10^6$ mm^4/m

I_e = $I_{cr} + (I_g - I_{cr}) \left(\dfrac{M_{cr}}{M_s} \right)^3 = 24.8 + (341 - 24.8) \left(\dfrac{7.00}{9.05} \right)^3 = 171.1 \times 10^6$ mm^4/m

K_{bs} = $\dfrac{48 E_c I_e}{5 \ell^2} = \dfrac{48 \times 24,650 \times 171.1 \times 10^6}{5 \times 7600^2 \times 1000} = 701$ kN-m/m; $\delta_{bs} = \dfrac{1}{1 - \dfrac{P_s}{K_{bs}}} = \dfrac{1}{1 - \dfrac{27.4}{701}} = 1.04$

M_s =   6.97 x 1.04 = 7.25 < 9.05 kN-m/m   OK

Δ_s = $\dfrac{M_s}{K_{bs}} = \dfrac{7.25 \times 1000}{701} = 10.34$ mm < 76 mm   OK

Panel design summary   (Load case (4) controls)

t = 160 mm

Vertical reinforcing: 15M @ 250 centered

Horizontal reinforcing: 10M @ 350

Reinforcement weight per m^2 = $\left(\dfrac{200}{250} + \dfrac{100}{350} \right)$ 7.85 kg = 8.52 kg/m^2

∴ A thicker panel is required for 1 layer of reinforcement, but the total weight of reinforcement is about 15% less.

Example 13.2 – Panel Continuous over Support

Assumed loading: Roof dead load = 1.0 kPa;
snow load = 3.0 kPa ;   ecc = 140 / 2 = 70 mm;
joist span = 18 m;   wind load w = 1.07 kPa
Panel properties: ℓ = 9000 mm;   t = 140 mm; Δ_0 = 25 mm
Self weight w_c = 0.140 x 24 = 3.36 kPa

Check ℓ /t:: $\dfrac{9000}{140}$ = 64.3 < 65

$\therefore$ OK for 2 layers of reinforcement
Effective height   k ℓ = 0.9 x 9000 = 8100 mm

Image shows panel with dimensions 9800, kℓ = 8100, loads P_{tf}, ecc, Δ_f, W_f, P_{wf}, Deflected Shape.

Load case (4): 1.25D + 1.4W + 0.5S

P_{tf} =   (1.25 x 1.0 + 0.5 x 3.0) 18 / 2 = 24.75 kN/m
P_{wf} =   1.25 x 3.36 x 8.1 / 2 = 17.0 kN/m
P_f =   24.75 + 17.0 = 41.75 kN/m
w_f =   1.4 x 1.07 = 1.5 kPa

Assume reinforcing on each face (EF):

A_s =   15M @ 300 EF   or   667 mm²/m EF;   d = 100 mm; b = 1000 mm

$A_{s,eff}$ = $667 + \dfrac{41.75 \times 1000}{0.85 \times 400}\left(\dfrac{140}{2 \times 100}\right)$ = 753 mm²/m;   a = $\dfrac{753 \times 0.85 \times 400}{0.805 \times 0.65 \times 30 \times 1000}$ = 16.3 mm

M_r = $\dfrac{0.85 \times 753 \times 400\ (100 - 16.3 / 2)}{10^6}$ = 23.5 kN-m/m

M_b =   1.5 x 8.1² / 8 + 24.75 x 0.07 / 2 + 41.75 x 0.025 = 14.21 kN-m/m
c   =   18.2 mm; I_{cr} = 42.9 x 10⁶ mm⁴; K_{bf} = 154.7 kN-m/m; δ_b = 1.56
M_f =   14.21 x 1.56 = 22.2 < M_r = 23.5 kN-m/m   OK

Load case (3): 1.25D + 1.5S + 0.4W

P_{tf} =   (1.25 x 1.0 + 1.5 x 3.0) 18 / 2 = 51.75 kN/m; P_{wf} = 1.25 x 3.36 x 8.1 / 2 = 17.0 kN/m
P_f =   51.75 + 17.0 = 68.75 kN/m; w_f = 0.4 x 1.07 = 0.43 kPa
A_s =   15M @ 300 EF or 667 mm²/m EF; $A_{s,eff}$ = 808 mm²/m;   a = 17.5 mm
M_r =   25.1 kN-m/m
M_b =   0.43 x 8.1² / 8 + 51.75 x 0.07 / 2 + 68.75 x 0.025 = 7.06 kN-m/m
c   =   19.5 mm; I_{cr} = 45.0 x 10⁶ mm⁴; K_{bf} = 162.3 kN-m/m; δ_b = 2.29
M_f =   7.06 x 2.29 = 16.2 kN-m/m < M_r = 25.1   OK

Panel design summary   (Load case (4) controls)
t = 140 mm
Vertical reinforcing: 15M @ 300 EF
Horizontal reinforcing: 10M @ 350 AF

Reinforcement weight per m² = $\left(\dfrac{200}{300} + \dfrac{100}{350}\right)$ x 7.85 kg = 7.48 kg/m²

13

Tilt-up

Example 13.3 – Panel with Openings

Panel properties:

ℓ = 7600 mm;   t = 160 mm;

Δ_0 = 25 mm

Self weight w_c = 0.160 x 24 = 3.84 kPa

Reinforcement on each face (EF);

d = 120 mm

Assumed loading:

Roof dead load = 1.0 kPa

snow load = 3.0 kPa

ecc = 160 / 2 = 80 mm

joist span = 10.9 m

wind load w = 1.07 kPa

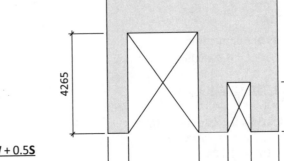

Assume load case (4): 1.25**D** + 1.4**W** + 0.5**S**

Left leg:

b = 900 mm;

Tributary area = $900 + \dfrac{3050}{2}$ = 2425 mm

P_{tf} = 2.425 (1.25 x 1.0 + 0.5 x 3.0) 10.9 / 2 = 36.3 kN

P_{wf} = 2.425 (1.25 x 3.84) 7.6 / 2 = 44.2 kN

P_f = 36.3 + 44.2 = 80.5 kN; w_f = 2.425 (1.4 x 1.07) = 3.63 kN/m

A_s = 5–15M = 1000 mm² EF; $A_{s,eff} = 1000 + \dfrac{80.5 \times 1000}{0.85 \times 400}\left(\dfrac{160}{2 \times 120}\right)$ = 1157 mm²;   a = 27.9 mm

M_r = 41.8 kN-m

M_b = 3.63 x 7.6² / 8 + 36.3 x 0.08 / 2 + 80.5 x 0.025 = 29.7 kN-m

c = 31.2 mm; I_{cr} = 83.1 x 10⁶ mm⁴; K_{bf} = 341 kN-m/m; δ_b = 1.46

M_f = 29.7 x 1.46 = 43.3 ≈ M_r = 41.8 kN-m   OK

Middle leg:

b = 1250 mm;   Tributary panel area $= 1250 + \dfrac{(3050 + 1000)}{2}$ = 3275 mm

P_{tf} = 3.275 (1.25 x 1.0 + 0.5 x 3.0) 10.9 / 2 = 49.1 kN

P_{wf} = 3.275 (1.25 x 3.84) 7.6 / 2 = 59.7 kN

P_f = 49.1 + 59.7 = 108.8 kN; w_f = 3.275 (1.4 x 1.07) = 4.91 kN/m

A_s = 7–15M = 1400 mm² EF; $A_{s,eff} = 1400 + \dfrac{108.8 \times 1000}{0.85 \times 400}\left(\dfrac{160}{2 \times 120}\right)$ = 1613 mm²; a = 27.9 mm

M_r = 58.1 kN-m

M_b = 4.91 x 7.6² / 8 + 49.1 x 0.08 / 2 + 108.8 x 0.025 = 40.1 kN-m

c = 31.1 mm; I_{cr} = 116.0 x 10⁶ mm⁴; K_{bf} = 475.2 kN–m/m; δ_b = 1.44

M_f = 40.1 x 1.44 = 57.7 < M_r = 58.1 kN-m   OK

Check for maximum reinforcement:

$\dfrac{A_s}{bd} \leq \dfrac{\alpha_1 \beta_1 \phi_c f'_c}{\phi_s f_y}\left(\dfrac{700}{700 + f_y}\right)$ = 0.0263

max A_s = 0.0263 x 120 x 1250 = 3945 > 1400 mm²   OK

Right leg:

b = 1200 mm;   Tributary panel area = $1200 + \dfrac{1000}{2} = 1700$ mm

P_{tf} = 1.700 (1.25 x 1.0 + 0.5 x 3.0) 10.9 / 2 = 25.5 kN
P_{wf} = 1.700 (1.25 x 3.84) 7.6 / 2 = 31.0 kN
P_f = 25.5 + 31.0 = 56.5 kN; w_f = 1.700 (1.4 x 1.07) = 2.55 kN/m

A_s = 4–15M = 800 mm^2 EF; $A_{s,eff}$ = $800 + \dfrac{56.5 \times 1000}{0.85 \times 400}\left(\dfrac{160}{2 \times 120}\right)$ = 911 mm^2; a = 16.4 mm

M_r = 34.6 kN-m
M_b = 2.55 x 7.6^2 / 8 + 25.5 x 0.08 / 2 + 56.5 x 0.025 = 20.8 kN-m
c = 18.3 mm; I_{cr} = 78.9 x 10^6 mm^4; K_{bf} = 323.3 kN-m/m; δ_b = 1.30
M_f = 20.8 x 1.30 = 27.0 < M_r = 34.6 kN-m   OK

Check service load deflection on the middle leg:

Tributary width = 3275 mm
Leg width b = 1250 mm
A_s = 7–15M EF = 1400 mm^2
w = 0.75 x 1.07 = 0.8 kPa;
w_c = 3.84 kPa
<u>Assume load case: 1.0**D** + 1.0**W** + 0.5**S**</u>
P_{ts} = 3.275 (1.0 + 0.5 x 0.9 x 3.0) 10.9 / 2
 = 41.9 kN
P_{ws} = 3.275 (3.84 x 7.6 / 2) = 47.8 kN
P_s = 41.9 + 47.8 = 89.7 kN
I_g = 1250 x 160^3 / 12
 = 427 x 10^6 mm^4

M_{cr} = $\dfrac{f_r I_g}{y_t} = \dfrac{0.3 \sqrt{30} \times 427}{160 / 2}$ = 8.77 kN-m

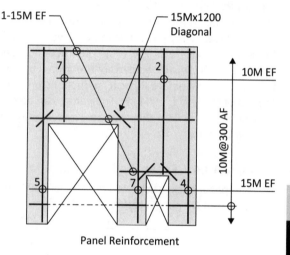

Panel Reinforcement

M_{bs} = 3.275 x 0.80 x 7.6^2 / 8 + 41.9 x 0.08 / 2 + 89.7 x 0.025 = 22.8 > M_{cr} = 8.77 kN-m $\therefore I_{cr} < I_e < I_g$
A_s = 1400 mm^2;

Using a triangular concrete stress distribution:

n = $\dfrac{E_s}{E_c}$ = 8.11; $kd = \dfrac{-n A_s + \sqrt{(n A_s)^2 + 2 b n A_s d}}{b}$

kd = $\dfrac{-8.11 \times 1400 + \sqrt{(8.11 \times 1400)^2 + 2 \times 1250 \times 8.11 \times 1400 \times 120}}{1250}$ = 38.5 mm

I_{cr} = $\dfrac{b (kd)^3}{3} + \dfrac{E_s A_s (d - kd)^2}{E_c} = \dfrac{1250 \times 38.5^3}{3} + \dfrac{200{,}000 \times 1400 (120 - 38.5)^2}{24{,}650}$

 = 99.2 x 10^6 mm^4

Initially assume $\Delta_s = \dfrac{\ell}{100} = \dfrac{7600}{100} = 76$ mm

M_s = $M_{bs} + P_s \Delta_s = 22.8 + 89.7 \times 0.076 = 29.6$ kN-m

I_e = $I_{cr} + (I_g - I_{cr})\left(\dfrac{M_{cr}}{M_s}\right)^3 = 99.2 + (427 - 99.2)\left(\dfrac{8.77}{29.6}\right)^3 = 107 \times 10^6$ mm^4

K_{bs} = $\dfrac{48 \times 24{,}650 \times 107 \times 10^6}{5 \times 7600^2 \times 1000} = 438$ kN-m/m; $\quad \delta_b = \dfrac{1}{1 - \dfrac{P_s}{K_{bs}}} = \dfrac{1}{1 - \dfrac{89.7}{438}} = 1.26$

M_s = $22.8 \times 1.26 = 28.7 < 29.6$ kN-m   OK

Δ_s = $\dfrac{M_s}{K_{bs}} = \dfrac{28.7 \times 1000}{438} = 65$ mm $< \Delta_{max} = 76$ mm   OK   (no need for further iterations)

Tilt-up Panel Shear Walls

The following examples illustrate the design of simple tilt-up concrete shear walls subjected to in-plane seismic forces. They represent the end wall of a 66.4 m x 27.4 m x 7.6 m high single storey building located in Langley B.C. The roof construction is assumed to be structural framing with a steel deck diaphragm. The seismic analysis of the overall building is not part of this example. The specified seismic force is 0.777 W before R_d or R_o reductions are applied. The shear force from the roof diaphragm to the top of the wall is 1904 kN. The panels can be designed for $R_d = 1.5$ and $R_o = 1.3$ as limited ductility. Specific components within the panel system may have to be designed for reduced R-values depending on their ductility.

Example 13.4   Shear Wall with Solid Panels

Given: panel thickness t = 140 mm; f'_c = 30 MPa;   unit weight γ = 24 kN/m3
Tributary roof weight = 3 kN/m;   maximum corner hold down weight = 100 kN

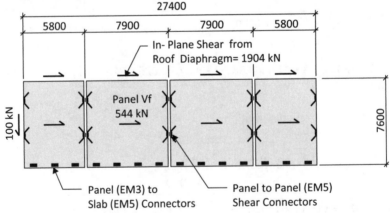

Roof weight   = 17 + 24 + 24 + 17 = 82 kN
Panel weight = 148 + 202 + 202 + 148 = 700 kN
                              Total = 782 kN

Panel seismic   115 + 157 + 157 + 115 = 544 kN
(at $R_d R_o$ = 1.0)

Base shear: ($R_d R_o = 1.3$)

Roof diaphragm $\quad V_f = \dfrac{1904}{1.0 \times 1.3} = \quad$ 1464 kN

Panel seismic shear $\quad V_f = \dfrac{544}{1.0 \times 1.3} = \quad$ <u>419 kN</u>

Total $\qquad\qquad V_f \qquad = \quad$ 1883 kN

Check maximum concrete shear: ($R_d R_o = 1.3$)

$V_f \quad \le \quad 0.25\, \phi_c\, f'_c\, t\, d_v\,; \quad d_v = 0.8 \times 27.4 = 21.92$ m

$V_f \quad = \quad 1883 < 0.25 \times 0.65 \times 30 \times 140 \times 21.92 = 14{,}960$ kN $\quad$ OK

Panel shear resistance: ($R_d R_o = 1.3$)

$v_c \quad = \quad \phi_c \lambda\, \beta\, \sqrt{f'_c} = 0.65 \times 1.0 \times 0.18 \sqrt{30} = 0.64$ MPa

$V_c \quad = \quad v_c\, b_w\, d_v = 0.64 \times 140 \times 21.92 = 1964$ kN

$V_s \quad = \quad \dfrac{\phi_s A_v f_y d_v \cot\theta}{s} = \dfrac{0.486\, A_v\, d_v}{s}$

Distributed reinforcement $\quad A_v = 10M @ 350 AF; \quad \rho = \dfrac{100}{350 \times 140} = 0.00204 > 0.002 \quad$ OK

$V_s \quad = \dfrac{0.486 \times 100 \times 21{,}920}{350} = 3044$ kN

Total $\qquad V_r \quad = 1964 + 3044 = 5008$ kN > 1883 kN $\quad$ OK

Average $\quad V_r \quad = 5008 / 27.4 = 183$ kN/m

Base connections: Assume welded connections with studded embeds ($R_d = 1.0$, $R_o = 1.3$)
EM5 in floor slab, $V_r = 125$ kN; $\quad$ EM3 in panel, $V_r = 110$ kN $\leftarrow$ EM 3 controls
Req'd $\quad V_f = 1883$ kN, less sliding friction $= 0.65 \times 0.75 \times 782 = 381$ kN; $\quad$ net $V_f = 1502$ kN
No. of connectors req'd $= \dfrac{1502}{110} = 13.7 \rightarrow$ use $14 - $ EM3 / EM5

Alternate: 15M dowels $\quad$ ($R_d = 1.5$, $R_o = 1.3$)

$V_r \quad = \phi_c\, \mu\, A_v\, f_y = \dfrac{0.65 \times 0.6 \times 200 \times 400}{1000} = 31$ kN, each dowel

Req'd $V_f = \dfrac{1883}{1.5} - 381 = 874$ kN; $\quad$ No. req'd $= \dfrac{874}{31} = 28.2 \rightarrow 29 - $ 15M dowels @ 1000mm

Panel overturning: ($R_d = 1.5$, $R_o = 1.3$)

Roof $V_f \quad = \dfrac{1904}{1.5 \times 1.3} = 976$ kN; $\quad$ Panel $V_f = \dfrac{544}{1.5 \times 1.3} = 279$ kN

Overturning moment: $\quad M_{of} = 976 \times 7.6 + 279 \times 7.6 / 2 = 8480$ kN-m
Resisting moments:

Panel $M_r = \dfrac{2 \times 148 \times 5.8}{2} + \dfrac{2 \times 202 \times 7.9}{2} \quad = 2454$ kN-m

Roof $M_r \quad = \dfrac{2 \times 17 \times 5.8}{2} + \dfrac{2 \times 24 \times 7.9}{2} \quad = 288$ kN-m

End Conn. $= 100 \times 5.8 \qquad\qquad\qquad = $ <u>580 kN-m</u>

$\qquad\qquad\qquad\qquad\qquad$ Total $\quad = 3322 \; < \; 8480$ kN-m

13

Tilt-up

Difference = 8480 – 3322 = 5158 kN-m

Try 2- EM5 edge connections per panel, V_r = 125 kN   each

Required connection resistance = $\dfrac{5158}{2\,(\,7.9 + 7.9 + 5.8\,)}$ = 119.5 kN or 239 kN each panel

Resolution of forces: (R_d = 1.5, R_o = 1.3)

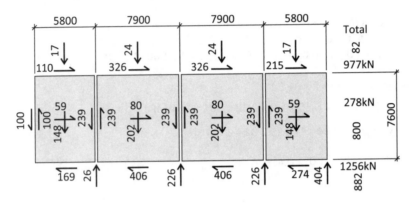

Panel M_r = 1059 + 2780 + 2780 + 1865 = 8484 kN-m

Maximum shear force in the panels = 404 / 7.6 = 53 < 183 kN/m

Maximum foundation load = 404 kN based on R_d = 1.5 and R_o = 1.3. Foundation loads indicated may not be point loads, depending on the type of foundations selected.

The distribution of roof shears forces to the top of the panel is controlled by the overturning capacity and are not necessarily in proportion to the panel width. A drag strut, such as a steel angle is needed to provide the redistribution of shear force.

Example 13.5   Shear Wall with Frame Panels

Given: Panel thickness   t   = 240 mm; f'_c = 30 MPa
         Tributary roof weight   = 3 kN/m;   Maximum corner hold down weight = 100 kN

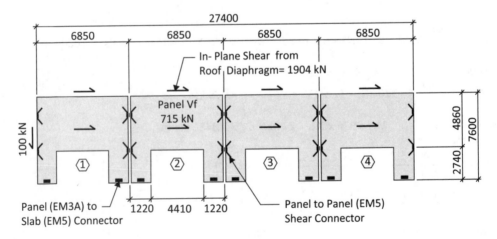

Roof weight   = 3 x 6.85 = 21 kN on each panel
Panel weight   = 24 (6.85 x 7.6 – 4.41 x 2.74) 0.240 = 230 kN each

Panel C of G $= \dfrac{24 \, (6.85 \times 7.6^2 \, / \, 2 - 4.41 \times 2.74^2 \, / \, 2) \, 0.240}{230} = 4.54$ m (from bottom)

Base shear: ($R_d \, R_o = 1.3$)

Roof diaphragm $V_f = \dfrac{1904}{1.0 \times 1.3}$ = 1465 kN

Panel shear $V_f = \dfrac{0.777 \times 4 \times 230}{1.0 \times 1.3}$ = <u>550 kN</u>

Total V_f = 2015 kN

Check concrete shear in legs:

  V_f = 2015 / 8 = 252 kN, each leg

  h   = 1220mm;   d = 1220 – 75 = 1145mm; d_v = 0.9 x 1145 = 1030 mm

Check min leg width = 1220 mm > 600   OK

  Max V_r = 0.25 x 0.65 x 30 x 240 x 1.030 = 1205 > 252 kN   OK

Panel leg shear resistance:

  V_c = 0.64 x 240 x 1.030 = 158 kN

  A_v = 10M ties @ 300; V_s $= \dfrac{0.486 \times 200 \times 1030}{300} = 334$ kN

  Tot. V_r = 158 + 334 = 492 kN > 252 kN   OK

Base connections:

Assume welded connections with studded embedments   ($R_d = 1.0$, $R_o = 1.3$)

  V_f = 2015 kN

    8–EM3A connections; V_r = 130 kN each; V_r = 8 x 130 = 1040 kN

Check concrete bearing where slab (25 MPa concrete, 200 mm thick) is locked into the panels:

  V_r = 0.85 ϕ_c f$'_c$ A_g = 0.85 x 0.65 x 25 x 240 x 200 / 1000 = 663 kN

Friction V_r = 0.65 x 0.75 x (21 + 230) x 4 = 490 kN

Total V_r = 1040 + 663 + 490 = 2193 > 2015 kN   OK

In-plane leg bending: ($R_d = 1.5$, $R_o = 1.3$)

  V_f $= \dfrac{252}{1.5} = 168$ kN, each leg

  M_f = 168 x 2.74 = 460 kN-m
  h   = 1220 mm, d = 1145 mm, t = 240 mm
  A_s = 3 – 25M = 1500 mm^2 ; a = 136 mm
  M_r $= \dfrac{0.85 \times 400 \times 1500}{10^6} (1145 - 68)$

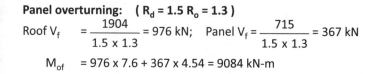

1220

3-25M each end
3-20M EF

240

10M ties @ 200

Section through panel leg

     = 550 > 460 kN-m   OK

Tie spacing in hinge region = 12 db = 12 x 20 = 240mm;   ∴ use 10M ties @ 200

Panel overturning: ($R_d = 1.5$ $R_o = 1.3$)

Roof V_f $= \dfrac{1904}{1.5 \times 1.3} = 976$ kN;   Panel $V_f = \dfrac{715}{1.5 \times 1.3} = 367$ kN

  M_{of} = 976 x 7.6 + 367 x 4.54 = 9084 kN-m

13

Tilt-up

Resisting moments:

Panel M_r $= \dfrac{4 \times 230 \times 6.85}{2}$ $= 3151$ kN-m;

Roof M_r $= \dfrac{4 \times 21 \times 6.85}{2}$ $= 288$ kN-m

End Conn. $= 100 \times 6.85$ $= \underline{685}$
$ 4124 < 9084$ kN-m

Difference $= 9084 - 4124 = 4960$ kN-m

Try 2- EM5 Connections per panel $V_r = 125$ kN each ($R_d = 1.5$, $R_o = 1.3$)

Required connection force $= \dfrac{4960}{2 \times 3 \times 6.85} = 121$ kN < 125 kN OK

Resolution of forces: ($R_d = 1.5$ $R_o = 1.3$)

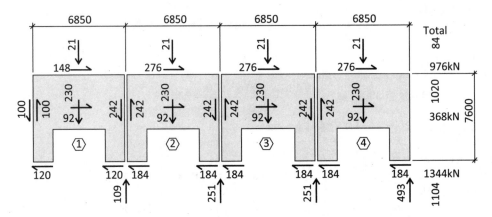

Check beam header in panel #3 for bending and shear (see free body diagram):

From overturning analysis at $R_d = 1.5$, $R_o = 1.3$:

max V_f $= 242 + 21 / 2 + 230 / 2 = 367.5$ kN

M_f $= 367.5 \times 3.425 + 10.5 \times 1.738 + 115 \times 1.53 - 138 \times 7.6 - 46 \times 4.54 = 195$ kN-m

h $= 4860$ mm; d $= 4860 - 75 = 4785$m

Assume $A_s = 2$–15M $= 400$ mm^2 ; a $= 36$ mm

M_r $= \dfrac{0.85 \times 400 \times 400}{10^6} (4785 - 18) = 648 > 195$ kN-m

Check for potential yielding of longitudinal reinforcement:

Multiply moment by $R_d = 1.5$, $R_o = 1.3$:

M_f $= 195 \times 1.5 \times 1.3 = 380$ kN-m < 648 kN-m

∴ reinforcement will not yield and anti-buckling ties not required in header

use 10M @ 400 EW $A_s = 500$ mm^2 /m ; $\rho = 0.0021 > 0.002$

Check shear in header ($R_d R_o = 1.3$)

V_f $= 367.5 \times 1.5 = 551$ kN

d_v $= 0.9 \times 4785 = 4300$ mm

V_c $= \dfrac{0.64 \times 240 \times 4300}{1000} = 661$ kN

V_s $= \dfrac{0.486 \times 200 \times 4300}{400} = 1045$ kN

V_r $= 661 + 1045 = 1706$ kN > 551 kN OK

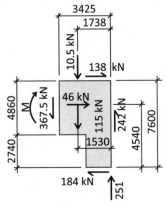

Free body diagram

Notes

Notes